MW00605341

History of Creativity

in the Arts, Science, & Technology

1500-PRESENT

SECOND EDITION

BRENT STRONG ■ MARK DAVIS

BRIGHAM YOUNG UNIVERSITY

Kendall Hunt
publishing company

Copyright © 2006, 2011 by Brent Strong

ISBN 978-0-7575-8621-7

Kendall Hunt Publishing Company has the exclusive rights to reproduce this work,
to prepare derivative works from this work, to publicly distribute this work,
to publicly perform this work and to publicly display this work.

All rights reserved. No part of this publication may be reproduced,
stored in a retrieval system, or transmitted, in any form or by any
means, electronic, mechanical, photocopying, recording, or otherwise,
without the prior written permission of Kendall Hunt Publishing Company.

Printed in the United States of America
10 9 8 7 6 5 4 3 2 1

Contents

Preface to the Second Edition   xv

Chapter 26 ■ Intent and Continuance: Centuries of Creativity   1

A New Look at Creativity 1
Periods of Dominance 3
The Joy of Creativity 5

Chapter 27 ■ Early Renaissance: Creativity Reborn   9

The Past Remembered 9
Causes of the Renaissance and the Rise of Humanism 10
The Importance of Sponsors 13
Early Renaissance Art and Sculpture 18
The Medici Family 22
Machiavelli: New Politics for a New Era 25
Creativity and the Early Renaissance 26
Machiavelli: The Prince 29
Article 1: Niccolò Machiavelli: The Prince 31

Chapter 28 ■ High Renaissance: Creatively Putting It All Together   35

Florence and Beyond 35
Leonardo da Vinci 36

Michelangelo Buonarroti 41

Raphael 43

Titian and the Venetian School 45

Renaissance Music 45

The Renaissance Man 47

Creative Ideas and the Renaissance 48

Chapter 29 ■ Protestant Reformation: Courageous Creativity   51

Background of the Reformation 51

Martin Luther 52

The Counter Reformation 57

German-Speaking Switzerland and Zwingli 58

French-Speaking Switzerland and Calvin 59

France 59

England 60

Creativity and the Reformation 63

Martin Luther: Salvation Through Faith Alone, 95 Theses, To the Christian
     Nobility of the German Nation, Address at the Diet of Worms 65

Article 2: Martin Luther: Salvation Through Faith Alone 67

Article 3: Martin Luther: 95 Theses *or* Disputation on the Power
     and Efficacy of Indulgences 69

Article 4: Martin Luther: To the Christian Nobility of the German Nation
     Concerning the Reform of the Christian Estate 71

Article 5: Martin Luther: The Speech of Dr. Martin Luther before the Emperor
     Charles and Princes at Worms on the Fifth Day After Misericordias
     Domini [April 18] in the Name of Jesus 75

John Calvin: Institutes of the Christian Religion 77

Article 6: John Calvin: Institutes of the Christian Religion: Predestination 79

Thomas More: Utopia 81

Article 7: Thomas More: Utopia 83

Chapter 30 ■ Northern Renaissance: Common Creativity   93

Migration Northward 93

Erasmus 94

Michel de Montaigne 97

Northern Renaissance Visual Art 97

Music of the Northern Renaissance 101

Creativity in the Northern Renaissance 101

Erasmus: A Discussion of Free Will; Hyperaspistes 103

Article 8: Erasmus: A Discussion of Free Will; Hyperaspistes 105

Montaigne: Essays 109

Article 9: Montaigne: Essays from The Complete Works 111

Chapter 31 ■ Elizabethan England: Acting Creatively

115

England: Separate and Different 115

Elizabeth's Ascension to the Throne 118

Solving the Problem of Personal Acceptance 119

Solving the Problem of Money 122

Solving the Problem of Religion 122

Solving the Problem of France 123

Solving the Problem of Scotland 123

Solving the Problem of Spain 124

Good Queen Bess 126

English Drama 127

William Shakespeare 127

Shakespeare's Use of Language 130

Shakespeare's Comedies 134

Shakespeare's Historical Plays 135

Shakespeare's Tragedies 135

Shakespeare's Sonnets 138

The English Bible 138

Summary 139

William Shakespeare: Hamlet Romeo and Juliet, The Sonnets 141

Article 10: William Shakespeare: Hamlet 143

Article 11: William Shakespeare: Romeo and Juliet 203

Article 12: William Shakespeare: The Sonnets 215

Chapter 32 ■ Absolute Monarchs: Creative Visions 217

The Seventeenth Century 217

Germany and the Thirty Years War 220

France 222

Spain 229

The Netherlands 231

England 235

Austria 239

Russia 240

Summary 243

Chapter 33 ■ Baroque: Impressive Creativity 247

Origins of the Baroque Movement 247

Specific Characteristics of the Baroque 248

Baroque Architecture and Sculpture 251

Baroque Painting 254

Baroque Music 259

Baroque Literature 267

Summary 270

Cervantes: The Adventures of Don Quixote de la Mancha 275

Article 13: The Adventures of Don Quixote de la Mancha 277

John Milton: Paradise Lost 285

Article 14: John Milton: Paradise Lost 287

Chapter 34 ■ Scientific Awakening: Creative Method 299

Thinking Directionally 299

When Science Went to Sleep: Classical and Medieval Science 301

Science, Technology, and Theory 303

Nicolas Copernicus 305

Galileo Galilei 308

Francis Bacon 312

René Descartes 314

Isaac Newton 316

Antoine Lavoisier 322

Summary 323

Francis Bacon: The New Organon 327

Article 15: Francis Bacon: The New Organon 329

René Descartes: Discourse on Method 333

Article 16: René Descartes: Discourse on Method 335

Isaac Newton: The Mathematical Principles of Natural Philosophy
     (Philosophiae Naturalis Principia Mathematica) 339

Article 17: Sir Isaac Newton: The Mathematical Principles
     of Natural Philosophy (Principia) 341

Blaise Pascal: Pensées 347

Article 18: Blaise Pascal: Pensées 349

Chapter 35 ■ Enlightenment: Creative Societies 353

The Scientific Method and Social Problems 353

The Nature of the Enlightenment 354

Foundations of Enlightenment: England 355

Popular Writing in the English Enlightenment 360

The Enlightenment in France 367

The Enlightenment in Germany 372

Reviewing the Enlightenment 373

Thomas Hobbes: Leviathan 375

Article 19: Thomas Hobbes: Leviathan 377

John Locke: An Essay Concerning Human Understanding, Two Treatises of Government. 381

Article 20: John Locke: An Essay Concerning Human Understanding 383

Article 21: John Locke: Two Treatises of Government 385

Alexander Pope: Essay on Man 389

Article 22: Alexander Pope: Essay on Man 391

Jonathan Swift: Gulliver's Travels, A Modest Proposal 395

Article 23: Jonathan Swift: Gulliver's Travels 397

Article 24: Jonathan Swift: A Modest Proposal 403

Voltaire: Treatise on Tolerance, "If God Did Not Exist He Would Have
     to Be Invented," Letters on England 409

Article 25: Voltaire: Treatise on Tolerance 411

Article 26: Voltaire: "If God Did Not Exist, He Would Have to Be Invented" 415

Article 27: Voltaire: Letters on England. 417

Jean-Jacques Rousseau: The Social Contract. 419

Article 28: Rousseau: The Social Contract 421

Chapter 36 ▪ Enlightened Despots: Conscience and Reality   425

Who Cares about the Enlightenment?. 425

Frederick II of Prussia 426

Catherine the Great of Russia 429

Gustavus III of Sweden 434

Charles III of Spain 434

Maria Theresa and Joseph II of Austria 435

George II and George III of England 437

Royal Dilemmas and Creativity 439

Chapter 37 ▪ Classical and Rococo: Creativity Rules   443

Rational Art and Music 443

Rococo Art and Architecture 444

Neoclassical Art 447

Classical Music 449

Creativity and Rules. 458

Chapter 38 ▪ American Revolution: Creative Implementation   461

A Novel Idea: The Better Life 461

Value: The Enlightenment Made Real 462

Causes of Revolution in America. 462

Novelty: A New Way to Fight 465

Intent: Independence 466

Excellence: Leadership and Government. 468

What Was Creative? 471

Tocqueville: Democracy in America 475

Article 29: Alexis de Tocqueville: Democracy in America 477

Chapter 39 ■ French Revolution and Napoleon: Extremely Creative 483

The Enlightenment and Revolutions 483
Causes of the French Revolution 484
The First Stage of the Revolution: Control by the Moderates 487
The Second Stage of the Revolution: Control by the Radicals 489
The Third Stage of Revolution: Return to Moderate Control 491
Napoleon's Rise to Power 492
Napoleon as First Consul 494
Napoleon as Emperor 495
The Demise of Napoleon 497
The Congress of Vienna 498
Comparing the French and American Revolutions 499

Chapter 40 ■ Romanticism: Feeling Creative 501

Revolutionary Literature, Music, and Painting 501
Romanticism 502
Romantic Literature 503
Romantic Music 506
Romantic Painting 512
Feelings about the Romantic Period 515
Sir Walter Scott: Ivanhoe 519
Article 30: Sir Walter Scott: Ivanhoe 521
Alexandre Dumas: The Three Musketeers 525
Article 31: Alexandre Dumas: The Three Musketeers 527

Chapter 41 ■ Industrial Revolution: Creativity Accelerated 531

The Scientific Revolution and Technology 531
A Unique Background for Growth 532
The Situation and the Concept 536
Textiles 537
General Manufacturing 541
Power 541
Transportation 542

The Spread of the Industrial Revolution 543

Effects of the Industrial Revolution 545

New Industrial Revolutions 546

Chapter 42 ■ Liberalism and Conservatism: Social Creativity   549

Tension 549

Personal Consequences of the Industrial Revolution 550

Universal Rights 552

The Rise of Class Conflicts 553

Conservatives and Liberals 554

Influence of Artists 555

Influence of Writers 555

Social Reformers: Utilitarianism 556

Social Reformers: Marxism 557

Social Reformers: Labor Unions 560

Social Change 560

John Stuart Mill: Utilitarianism 563

Article 32: John Stuart Mill: Utilitarianism 565

Karl Marx: Communist Manifesto 569

Article 33: Karl Marx: Communist Manifesto 571

Charles Dickens: Oliver Twist 575

Article 34: Charles Dickens: Oliver Twist 577

Chapter 43 ■ Empires and Inventions: Expanding Frontiers of Creativity   585

The British Empire 586

Post-Napoleonic France 589

Spain 589

Belgium 591

Russia 591

Germany 592

Italy 593

United States 593

Alfred, Lord Tennyson: The Charge of the Light Brigade 605

Article 35: Alfred, Lord Tennyson: The Charge of the Light Brigade 607

Ralph Waldo Emerson: Self-Reliance 609

Article 36: Ralph Waldo Emerson: Self-Reliance 611

Henry David Thoreau: Walden 613

Article 37: Henry David Thoreau: Walden 615

Walt Whitman: Leaves of Grass 617

Article 38: Walt Whitman: Leaves of Grass 619

Upton Sinclair: The Jungle 623

Article 39: Upton Sinclair: The Jungle 625

Chapter 44 ■ Determinism and Uncertainty: What Is, Isn't 629

Scientific Progress 629

Scientific Lighthouses 631

Louis Pasteur 631

Charles Darwin 633

Twentieth-Century Science 635

Challenges to Traditional Science Itself 637

Where Is Science in the Twenty-First Century? 640

Charles Darwin: The Origin of Species by Means of Natural Selection,
The Descent of Man 645

Article 40: Charles Darwin: The Origin of Species by Means of Natural Selection 647

Article 41: Charles Darwin: The Descent of Man 653

Thomas Kuhn: The Structure of Scientific Revolutions 655

Article 42: Thomas S. Kuhn: The Structure of Scientific Revolutions 657

Chapter 45 ■ Impressionism to Cubism: Creative Techniques 663

Art and Technology 663

Impressionism 667

Post-Impressionism 670

Cubism 674

Sculpture 675

Impressionism in Music 676

Literature 676

Technique 677

Henrik Ibsen: A Doll's House. 679

Article 43: Henrik Ibsen: A Doll's House 681

Chapter 46 ■ World War I: Creativity Gone Awry   687

Optimism and Pessimism. 687

The Causes of World War I 688

Alliances. 689

World War I 692

Russian Revolution. 697

Ending the War. 698

The Treaty of Versailles 699

Creativity and the War 701

Chapter 47 ■ Between the Wars: Good and Bad Creativity   703

Effects of World War I 703

Political Changes 704

Roaring Twenties and the Great Depression. 712

Modern Art. 714

Architecture 715

Literary Modernism 717

Modern Music 718

Disillusionment and Values 718

Aldous Huxley: Brave New World. 721

Article 44: Aldous Huxley: Brave New World 723

Chapter 48 ■ World War II: Linear and Lateral Creativity   733

Right-Brain and Left-Brain Thinking about War 733

German Supremacy 734

The Battle of Britain. 736

The Great Mistake in Russia 738

Japan Attacks 739

Some Allied Victories. 740

The Unexpected Strategy 745

The Atomic Bomb 746

Creativity Saved the Free World. 746

Viktor Frankl: Man's Search for Meaning 749

Article 45: Viktor Frankl: Man's Search for Meaning 751

Chapter 49 ■ The Contemporary World: Creativity and Value   755

Changing Values. 755

The Cold War 756

European Union 759

The Middle East 760

The United States of America 761

Literature in the Modern Era 763

Values 765

Chapter 50 ■ Epilogue: Personal Creativity   767

What Has Been Learned?. 767

Creative People in History 768

Creativity in the Arts 771

Creativity in Science 772

Creativity and Technology 772

Creativity and You 773

Improving Linear Thinking 774

Improving Lateral Thinking 775

Putting the Thinking Processes Together 776

The Benefits of Being Creative 777

Index   779

Preface to the Second Edition

This is the second volume of a highly unique textbook for Civilization and World History courses and an exciting history book for the general-interest reader. We know of no other book that maintains the chronological sequence of history, thus allowing the various periods of art and politics to be viewed in their natural order, and yet explores the interconnections and contrasts between these periods so that understanding can be fostered beyond just memorization of historical facts. This broad analysis is facilitated because of the unique focus of the book—creativity, an essential quality of human progress that permeates all phases of civilization from art to science to technology.

By looking at civilizations through the lens of creativity, we can see historical trends, differences between cultures, technological advances, great works of art and literature, and other elements of civilization with fresh perspectives. With creativity as a guide, we can gain unique insights by, for example, exploring the forces within society that came together to allow the creative burst that we know as the Renaissance, or looking at how creative technology influenced the direction of art in the Impressionist period. We can, of course, also look at the nature of creativity itself, although this is usually done within the context of historical events. For example, we can compare the inspirational creativity of Newton (after he had mastered previous science) with the inspirational creativity of Picasso (after he had mastered previous art).

The refreshing point of view of the book is further explained by the uniqueness of the authorship. One author, Dr. Strong, was trained as a chemist and teaches in the College of Engineering and Technology as well as General Education courses, including Civilization. He contributes, therefore, an understanding of technology and science that few other writers of history can equal. This viewpoint is especially important in light of the overwhelming influence of science and technology since the Scientific Awakening. The other author, Mark Davis, is a historian.

The intent of the book is always to integrate knowledge between periods, disciplines, and cultures, thus promoting understanding by contrast and comparison. This integration of knowledge is critically important in this modern world, where so much effort is spent in isolated silos of learning with little attempt to relate or explain that knowledge in a broad perspective. Yet, modern problems are so complex that their solutions increasingly require understanding in the broadest possible terms. Leadership in the modern world is, therefore, dependent on integration rather than the more commonly taught isolation of most majors and professions.

This book forms bridges of understanding between the diverse silos of science, technology, arts, politics, history, and economics. It is a reflection of the authors' personal interests and careers.

One of the advantages of this new edition is that it offers selected readings within each chapter.

These readings give a taste of primary sources and, therefore, allow the reader to sample directly the creativity of some of the people who molded civilization.

Another unique benefit of the book is the understanding that it gives to personal creativity. Students report that they are able to be more creative and, therefore, their personal fulfillment from the book is high. We need to be more creative as a society. Perhaps this book will help.

Intent and Continuance
Centuries of Creativity

> Definitions of creativity usually recognize at least two criteria: novelty and value. The creative product must be new and it must be judged to have some value according to external criteria. Gruber added a third criterion, intent: creative products are the result of purposeful behavior; and a fourth, continuance. Creative work takes time. . . . The criterion of continuance gives special meaning to that of intent or purpose, extending creativity over time and capturing the notion of a creative life. To live a creative life is one of the intentions of a creative person.
>
> —*Doris B. Wallace and Howard E. Gruber,* Creative People at Work, *Oxford University Press, 1989, pp. 28–29 (World renowned experts in creativity)*

■ A New Look at Creativity

In the first volume of this two-volume work on the History of Creativity, we laid the foundation for our study by exploring the fundamental nature of creativity as has been done by experts in the field of creativity, often psychologists but also natural scientists, artists, and many others who have made significant contributions to the discipline. We then examined the various cultures of the ancient and medieval world, to assess their creativity and to understand the forces within each society that enhanced or diminished the ability of the society to be creative. At the end of that first volume we concluded that creativity was often enhanced by interactions between societies, sometimes through peaceful trade, but also through war and conquest. We saw that the fruits of creativity, that is, the changes that were brought about, might be quite different in peaceful versus warlike periods. We also found that when warfare becomes so chaotic that the basic norms of society, such as individual safety and the ability to conduct commerce, are destroyed, creativity diminishes greatly, such as it did in the Early Medieval Period.

We discovered that creativity is rarely so original that it does not spring from some prior knowledge and so, in the broad picture, creativity can be shown through implementation and enhancement even if not in a totally new idea. Such enhancements were demonstrated when the Romans improved upon

Greek culture, but it should be remembered that the Greeks themselves based much of their culture on the Mesopotamians and the Egyptians. There were, to be sure, new and original ideas, but foundations were laid by others. A similar argument applies to creativity where the origin of the idea might be divine inspiration. We saw change in society and religion that was quite creative even though the religious groups, like the Muslims and the early Christians, believed the core concepts for the change came directly from God.

We also saw how environmental conditions can affect creativity. Cold weather and natural catastrophes adversely affected creativity during several periods, especially when people lost the ability to dedicate some of their time to pursuits other than merely feeding themselves and their family. People seem to need some leisure time to be creative.

Finally, strong forces for conservatism within a society can stifle creativity, as happened with the Egyptians, the Chinese, and the medieval Europeans. This constraint raises a dichotomy in creativity: The past should be valued as a resource for knowledge but should not become so controlling over current society that change is forbidden.

In the second volume of this work, we begin our study of the History of Creativity just before the year 1500 A.D., when Italy was attempting to recapture the glories and knowledge of the ancient past and move into a new period of progress. But before we begin that examination, let us again discuss the definitions of creativity, so that we can evaluate the various changes we see in societies and decide if they are creative. A working definition of creativity is: **creativity is thinking and doing (innovation) that brings unexpected, original, and valuable ideas to fruition.**

The quotation at the beginning of this chapter identifies four elements that constitute creativity: **value, intent, novelty,** and **excellence.** Novelty or uniqueness is commonly thought to be the essence of creativity. It is, of course, critically important, but it is not the entire story. In addition to novelty and uniqueness, the creative work must have value. Without this element it generally dies and has no chance to affect the society. It cannot, therefore, rise to the level of importance that

The VINE* of Creativity

- ■ **V**aluable—It is perceived as having worth and genuinely contributing to society.
- ■ **I**ntentional—It is the result of a deliberate effort. Can't be from stumbling blindly.
- ■ **N**ovel—It is new or has at least some element of originality.
- ■ **E**xcellent—Significant effort expended to make it the best it can be. Well executed.

*Creativity comes from the Latin *creatus*, literally "to have grown."

Figure 26.1 ■ Creativity elements.

would warrant our study of it in this course or, indeed, in any other course on the nature of civilization. These elements of creativity were critically important to our understanding of creativity up through the Medieval Period.

The other two elements of creativity, while present in ancient and Medieval creativity, become more important in the later times that we will now begin to study. With ever-increasing frequency, we will examine the creativity of individuals rather than entire societies, and in the examination of individuals, we will try to understand their *intent* in doing the creative work; we will also be able to gauge their contributions over a long period of time—their *excellence.* This study of creative individuals is fitting, not only because we can explore the nature of their personal creativity, but also because their works reflect and often define the creativity of a society in general.

Dean Keith Simonton, studying the influence of some creative individuals on the course of history, said, "So obvious is the debt civilizations owe these exceptional individuals that the appearance of such geniuses is often considered an indication of the creative health of a civilized culture."[1] He then reports a study conducted by Alfred Kroeber, an eminent cultural anthropologist, who suggested that there was no better method to gauge the emergence, growth, and stagnation of civilizations than by assessing the appearance of famous creators across a culture's history. As reported by Simonton, Kroeber said, "A civilization enjoyed a golden age when it overflowed with first-rate creative minds, experienced a silver age when the creative activity descended to a less notable level, and suffered a dark age when creators became few and far between."[2]

The distinction between the creativity of geniuses and of ordinary people brings to the fore a concept that helps us assess our own creativity and that of the people we will study. Creative works that change an area of expertise (usually called a **domain of knowledge**) are those that might affect all of society. We can refer to these works as having (big "C") **Creativity.** These might be defined as **esteemed creativity,** meaning that the creative work has value to society beyond just the immediate family and friends of the creator.

We can also understand that every individual creates things unique to that individual. In this sense, that element of creativity is satisfied. However, most of these works do not change a domain, and therefore receive little acclaim. These we can term (small "c") **creativity.** One of the purposes of this book is to study the nature of the big "C" creativity we see throughout history and thus improve our personal abilities to create big "C" works. Big "C" creativity can also be accomplished by individuals when their creativity receives praise and acceptance by society. This praise might come from professionals in the field, critics, or teachers. Usually, the praise that comes from family and friends is appreciated by the individual but is not sufficiently independent to raise the creativity to the level of big "C".

One clue to the work traits of these creative geniuses has been given by Benjamin Franklin as the following: "Genius is the ability to hold one's vision steady until it becomes a reality."[3] This quotation shows the importance of the third and fourth elements of creativity—intent and continuance—and, of course, suggests that we must develop that same kind of steady vision if we are to be esteemed creators.

■ Periods of Dominance

With the risk of oversimplifying history, we will give some broad generalizations that might be useful in relating the history of the ancient and Medieval world to the history that followed. The history of the ancient world was examined culture by culture, beginning first with the ancient river societies—Mesopotamians, Egyptians, Indians, and Chinese. We then examined the Greeks, a society that lived by trade, and then the Romans, a society that depended on trade and enforced their position by law backed by power. After the fall of the Western Roman Empire, we saw the continuation of the Byzantine Empire, the rise of the Islamic Empire and the collapse of Europe during the Early Medieval Period. Over several centuries the dominance of these three societies reversed; the Byzantine Empire collapsed and the Islamic Empire diminished, while Europe rose in power.

The change in Europe was studied in great detail because it is the origin of the civilization that is currently dominant in the world, especially in Europe and the Americas, but increasingly so in all parts of the world. We saw that throughout the Medieval period European society consisted of three groups that defined the society by their varying roles. The first of these groups, called the First Estate, was the clergy and all those associated with the church. During the early Middle Ages, the church was the primary basis on which European society was built and, for much of that period, the only coherent and lasting organization in Europe. The major functions of the First Estate were to pray and to help others find salvation. Gradually another group gained power and influence: the Second Estate or the nobility. The rise of this group coincided with the rise of nations. This group's purposes were to govern the secular life of Europe and to protect those who were in these developing nations, and also to enhance the power of the rulers through wars of conquest. The last group—the Third Estate—was composed of the commoners, usually peasant farmers. This group had little power or influence, especially at the beginning of the Medieval period.

As the Medieval period drew to a close, European society was changing radically. Because of corruption, internal disputes, and the rise of nations, the church was becoming less influential in people's lives. The ruling class was also changing, because kings were becoming increasingly more powerful at the expense of local leaders (barons and lords). Finally, commoners were becoming more powerful, with the rise of cities and the emergence of a wealthy merchant class.

As we now enter the period following the Middle Ages, we see that the changes in the Three Estates will continue throughout the period we will be discussing in this book. Interestingly, we can divide the history from 1500 to the present into three periods, each of which was focused on a re-examination and modification of each estate. The following summary might be useful as an outline:

■ 1500 to 1648—Dominated by the issue of what to believe in religion (Redefinition of the First Estate)

■ 1649 to 1789—Dominated by the issue of the mode of government (Redefinition of the Second Estate)

■ 1790 to present—Dominated by the issue of social and economic equality (Redefinition of the Third Estate)[4]

While these dates are open to discussion, the concepts that are the center of focus in each of the periods are certainly true. The first period encompassed debates on the role of the church versus the ancient past (paganism and humanism), and then flowed into the period of the Protestant Reformation, which ended as a major period with the Peace of Westphalia, concluding the Thirty Years War. The second period began with the execution of Charles I by the English Parliament, and concluded with the launching of the French Revolution. The third period began with the debates in France over the rights of the citizens, and has not yet concluded. Contemporary society is still highly energized over discussions of individual versus group rights, the role of the government in monitoring and regulating individual behavior, and the need for and advisability of economic reforms to equalize the distribution of property.

However, a quite different summary of the period we will be studying is, perhaps, equally en-lightening. This summary notes the cultural, economic, political, and military dominance of a specific country during each of the centuries since the fifteenth century. As with the previous list, the dates are highly approximate (perhaps more so in this list than in the former), but the general concepts are reasonable, and give us some thoughts that might be particularly applicable to the nature of creativity within these various nations.

■ Fifteenth century (1400s)—Domination by Italy

■ Sixteenth century (1500s)—Domination by Spain

■ Seventeenth century (1600s)—Domination by France

■ Eighteenth century (1700s)—Domination by England

■ Nineteenth century (1800s)—Domination by Germany

■ Twentieth century (1900s)—Domination by the United States

The Italian period was characterized by a rise in the power of the Italian city-states, the rebirth of ancient culture in the Renaissance, and then the decline of Italy's importance with the discovery of the Americas and the shift in trade from the Mediterranean to the Atlantic. The Spanish period began with the conquest of the Americas and the political control over most of Europe by the Spanish Hapsburg family. Inflation and corruption of Spanish money, wars of attrition, and the Protestant Reformation led to the demise of Spanish power in Europe. The power of France rose with the reasserted power of the Catholic Church and the clever manipulation of European powers by the French crown. French power began to decline with the death of Louis XIV, the most powerful of European monarchs. English power rose from their assertion of trading power (on the sea), first over the Dutch and then over everyone else. This power of mercantilism was enhanced by the Industrial Revolution, which flourished first in England and lasted well into the next century. However, in the nineteenth century the rise of

Germany as a nation was spectacular, and resulted in tremendous gains in military and economic might. Germany was also a cultural leader, especially in music, philosophy, and literature. The decline in Germany's power resulted from their defeat in World War I. America's rise was based on the incredible technological output of American inventors during the nineteenth and twentieth centuries, and the industrialization that capitalized on these inventions in the beginning of the twentieth century. America's involvement as a supplier during World War I spurred even further manufacturing capability, which received another boost during World War II.

The loss of dominance (and creativity) by the Spanish in the sixteenth century was explained by Jacques Barzun in his book *From Dawn to Decadence*, and might serve as a tool for understanding, at least in part, the declines in the other centuries.

Part of the ethos of this class [Spanish grandees] was to despise work and practicality; one could choose only between two careers: soldier or priest, the red and the black or their variants—explorer or civil servant, the one being a kind of soldier, the other a kind of "cleric," that is, able to read and write. This mighty aloofness from worldly goals offers the spectacle, unique in the west, of a society at least partly "anti-materialistic." Again like old Russia ("Muscovy" in the sixteenth century), it lacked a bustling middle class and was thus bound to resist new ideas, since these often travel as by-products of trade and are put forward as advantageous. Denouncers of "bourgeois values" meditate on Spain and its long isolation from mainstream European developments. Not until the turn of the nineteenth century, when the Spanish-American War put an end to the pride of empire, did Spain begin to prosper again and seek modernity.[5]

A modern scientific author, Fritjof Capra, has identified another feature of societies that are declining.

After civilizations have reached a peak of vitality, they tend to lose their cultural steam and decline. An essential element in this cultural breakdown is a loss of flexibility. . . . Whereas growing civilizations display endless variety and versatility, those in the process of disintegration show uniformity and lack of inventiveness. The loss of flexibility in a disintegrating society is accompanied by a general loss of harmony among its elements, which inevitably leads to the outbreak of social discord and disruption.[6]

In light of the list of domination by each country, a question logically comes to mind: "Is the United States going to break the pattern and continue its dominance long into the twenty-first century or will some other country rise to take its place?" Signs of cultural stagnation and loss of energy are already creeping into American culture. Part of the problem is the same as we saw from even ancient times—a satisfaction and reverence for the past but an inability to solve the dichotomy of using that reverence as a basis for progress rather than a retreat from change. The lack of change inevitably brings cultural lethargy. Change is the key to progress, and creativity is the key to change. To continue to lead in the world economy and politic, we must maintain and improve our creativity. As futurist Alvin Toffler said, "The illiterate of the twenty-first century will not be those who cannot read and write, but those who cannot learn, unlearn, and relearn."

■ The Joy of Creativity

We should, therefore, focus on "how to learn" as the primary activity during this analysis of the world's civilizations. Too often history is approached as an accumulation of facts and dates, with little attention to the questions of *why* something happened. The view taken in this book is different. We will attempt to look at motivations and consequences of major political events. We will keep in mind Robert Leamnson's statement about knowledge and learning: "Knowledge is not something that is the answer to a question; it is what is used to get the answer to the question."[7]

To answer the more complex questions about events, we will need a broad understanding of the environment of the moment and the backgrounds of the people who make the events occur. That will generally require that we have two kinds of knowledge: deep knowledge about the specifics of the moment, and broad knowledge about the environment that has led to the moment. This combination of depth and breadth is also critical for gaining the insights that give true understanding. As we discussed in the Prologue to the first volume of this work, the combination of depth (linear thinking) and breadth (lateral thinking) is also critical for developing personal creativity. We will see these traits in most of the individual creative geniuses we discuss.

Finally, we will try to keep in mind the wonderful analogy that expresses well the nature of creativity and, hopefully, will encourage the readers of this book to find the same motivation in both this study and in their own creativity.

Creativity is like cooking a great meal. The first essentials are the basic ingredients (such as the meat and the potatoes) which must be of the finest quality. This is the depth and for creativity it is the experience and study within the domain. The second important part involves the spices. These lift the taste to new areas. These are like the lateral thoughts and creative thinking skills. They excite the mind to new things. Finally, the chef must have passion for the meal. This is not easily explained but is clearly understood when it is present. It is the presentation, the choices, the verve when everything is put together. In creativity, it is the desire, persistence, and implementation.[8]

Good cooking! Good eating!

Notes

1. Simonton, Dean Keith, *Origins of Genius* (Oxford: Oxford University Press, 1999), 1.
2. Ibid.
3. Franklin, Benjamin, quoted in Thorpe, Scott, *How to Think Like Einstein* (New York: Barnes & Noble Books, Inc., 2000), 137.
4. Barzun, Jacques, *From Dawn to Decadence* (New York: Perennial, 2000), xxi (modified).
5. Barzun, Jacques, *From Dawn to Decadence* (New York: Perennial, 2000), 106.
6. Capra, Fritjof, *The Turning Point* (New York: Bantam Books 1982), 28.
7. Leamnson, Robert, *Thinking About Teaching and Learning* (Sterling, VA: Stylus Publishing, 1999), 110.
8. Goleman, Daniel, et al, *The Creative Spirit* (New York: Plume, 1992, 29–30).

Suggested Readings

Adams, James L., *Conceptual Blockbusting,* Addison-Wesley, 1986.

Capra, Fritjof, *Turning Point,* Bantam, 1982.

Csikszentmihalyi, Mihaly, *Creativity,* HarperPerennial, 1997.

De Bono, Edward, *Lateral Thinking,* Harper and Row, 1970.

De Bono, Edward, *Six Thinking Hats,* Back Bay, 1999.

De Bono, Edward, *The Mechanism of Mind,* Penguin, 1969.

Gardner, Howard, *Creating Minds,* BasicBooks, 1993.

Gardner, Howard, *Extraordinary Minds,* BasicBooks, 1994.

Ghiselin, Brewster, *The Creative Process,* University of California Press, 1952.

Goleman, Daniel, Paul Kaufman, and Michael Ray, *The Creative Spirit,* Plume, 1993.

Hofstadter, Douglas R., *Gödel, Escher, Bach,* Vintage, 1989.

Koestler, Arthur, *The Act of Creation,* Penguin, 1964.

Robert, Royston M., *Serendipity,* John Wiley & Sons, Inc., 1989.

Simonton, Dean Keith, *Genius, Creativity and Leadership,* Harvard University Press, 1984.

Simonton, Dean Keith, *Origins of Genius,* Oxford University Press, 1999.

Sternberg, Robert J. (ed.), *Handbook of Creativity,* Cambridge University Press, 1999.

Thorpe, Scott, *How to Think Like Einstein,* Barnes & Noble, 2000.

Wallace, Doris B. and Howard E. Gruber, *Creative People at Work,* Oxford University Press, 1989.

Weiner, Robert Paul, *Creativity and Beyond,* State University of New York Press, 2000.

Early Renaissance
Creativity Reborn

> When a mural or altarpiece came to be judged not for its pious effulgence and fitness for the spot in need of decoration, but instead for what we now call its aesthetic merit, art for art's sake was just below the horizon. Aesthetic appreciation is something more than spontaneous liking; a good eye for accurate representation is not enough; one must be able to judge and talk about style, technique, and originality.
>
> —*Jacques Barzun* From Dawn to Decadence, p. 70

■ The Past Remembered

When the Roman Empire finally collapsed in the West with the abdication of Emperor Romulus Augustulus in 476 A.D., the ancient world ended and a new era dawned. At the time, however, most Romans probably believed that the barbarians' victory would be short-lived. After all, the eastern half of the empire was still alive and strong. Creative civilization still flourished in Constantinople, and no loosely organized barbarians, regardless of their savagery, could long hold off the might and order of the Eastern Roman Empire. Very few people would have predicted that Western Europe would fall into nearly a millennium of darkness, disorder, and oppression where life was a daily grind just to survive. Yet, that was exactly what happened.

The Emperor Justinian did, in fact, reconquer major areas in Western Europe, but after his death the Eastern Empire (which we now call the Byzantine Empire) was forced to withdraw from the West because of its own problems. In later years, a growing rift in Christian theology between the East and West made the Byzantines reluctant to give aid to their fallen cousins.

Political chaos in the West, a cooling of the weather, population-destroying plagues, and general fear forced people to abandon the cities for small, isolated survival farms. The vibrancy of city life that was so important for the founding of civilization in the far ancient past had largely disappeared, and with it a period called the Dark Ages fell over Europe. Only around the year 1000 did Europe finally break free of the deep doldrums of this difficult existence and begin the slow and laborious climb back toward a highly creative civilization.

By the start of the 1300s, life in Europe had finally regained some semblance of order and normalcy, although daily life in Europe still lagged far behind life in Byzantium, the great empires of Asia, much of the Muslim world, and even some of the yet unknown civilizations of the Americas. Europe's hard-earned progress then faced a major challenge as the fourteenth century was torn apart by serious difficulties in all three of the basic social strata (called *estates*) on which civilization was based—the church, the nobility, and the commoners.

The Catholic Church, which had always been the one stable institution in Europe, was torn apart by the great schism that forced Christians to choose between multiple people claiming to be the pope. Even after the schism was healed, corruption in the church was rampant, thus leading to a dramatic decline in the church's influence in people's lives.

The second fundamental part of society, the nobility, was changed greatly by the near continuous, and largely fruitless, warfare of the fourteenth century with accompanying decline of the role of knights and their lords in relation to the rising power of national kings. This trend, coupled with other changes in society such as a return of population into cities, brought to an end the feudal system under which society had been politically and economically governed for hundreds of years.

For the commoners, the problems of war were further complicated by the onset of Black Death, or Bubonic Plague, which killed between 30 percent and 50 percent of the population of Europe, thus drastically changing the lives of most of the people who survived. Moreover, the demise of the feudal system meant an end to a known way of life, where families farmed the same ground for generations. Yet, amidst all of this turmoil, Europe took a much different route than it had when the Western Roman Empire collapsed at the start of the Middle Ages. This time, now at the end of the Middle Ages, the seeds of creativity were able to grow so that European society reacted to the changes with renewed energy and progress. The

church remained in chaotic corruption and the feudal system had largely disappeared, but the power of the kings gave strength and stability to society. The increase in royal power meant that commoners were used in the king's armies and, therefore, commoners had more money. Furthermore, as commoners left the farms for the cities, they were able to improve their status in life and begin to make additional money as artisans and traders. In addition, even though the plague obviously destroyed families throughout Europe, it also gave power and increased importance to those commoners who were left to carry on. A city-dwelling middle class arose as a new power in European society.

The strength of rulers and commoners was most immediately evident in the city-states of Italy, where trade and manufacturing had given great wealth to both the rulers and the middle class. Based on the new economics and methods of governance, a new ideology and perspective arose in several of these Italian city-states, but it became evident, first and foremost, in Florence. This period is known to history as the **Renaissance** (from the French word for rebirth). It lasted in Italy and southern Europe until the mid-1500s, and continued in northern Europe (where it got a later start) until the early 1600s. The name *Renaissance* is especially apt, for this era was indeed a time of rebirth for Europe, as the people sought to return to or recreate the glories and virtues of the Roman Empire. However, in striving to recreate Rome, Europe had to recreate itself, and the Renaissance also became a rebirth of creativity, technology, and artistic virtuosity. Indeed, the creative explosion that marked the Renaissance had no equal until the Industrial Revolution in the late eighteenth century, and some would argue not even then.

■ Causes of the Renaissance and the Rise of Humanism

The position of Florence as the birthplace of the Renaissance is due, in part, to the foundation laid by two great Florentine writers of the latter Middle

Ages—**Dante Alighieri** and **Francesco Petrarch.** Dante, of course, was most famous for his book *Divine Comedy,* which was written in the early fourteenth century. His choice to write it in Italian (in the Florentine dialect) rather than Latin was unusual for a medieval writer and showed that he understood how many people, including the middle class, could benefit from his work. Even though his book was clearly religious and quite medieval in outlook, Dante revered ancient Roman values as taught by Virgil and Cato and incorporated these men (as characters) and their teachings into his writings, along with numerous references to the classical culture of ancient Rome and Greece.

Francesco Petrarch, a Florentine who revered Dante and lived just a generation later, is often considered to be the link between the Middle Ages and the Renaissance. Petrarch was pivotal in shaping the minds of the people to believe a new age was dawning in Italy. He felt that the Germanic invasions that ended the western Roman Empire had caused a sharp and terrible cultural break. Petrarch yearned to reestablish the glories of the Roman past and hated the period of Germanic dominance, which he called the *Dark Ages.* He wanted the people of Italy to think of the immediate past as a middle time between two greater periods—the classical Roman past and the beginning Italian rebirth.

Petrarch was able to read Greek and Latin, and he studied classical writings. Using this knowledge he wrote his own set of ethical treatises and poems using the classical style and quoting classical phrases, but teaching principles that were Christian. Petrarch followed Dante's example and wrote in Italian so that more people could read his works. He also believed that a well-rounded education was critical to the success of the old Roman Empire. Thus, he was instrumental in reintroducing to Europe the idea of a liberal education that included history and art. Petrarch was asked by both Rome and France to serve as their poet laureate (officially recognized as the leading poet in the land); he accepted Rome's offer. During the laureate ceremony, Petrarch placed his laurel crown on St. Peter's tomb to show that he could be both a lover of the classics and a good Christian.

Petrarch's teachings are known as **humanism,** which became the basic ideology of the Renaissance. Although humanism would later take on broader meanings, it is understood most clearly in the days of the early Renaissance as a contrast to the thinking of medieval times. The contrast was explained by Alister McGrath as follows:

The Renaissance gave birth to the modern era, in that it was in this era that human beings first began to think of themselves as individuals. In the early Middle Ages, people had been happy to see themselves simply as parts of a greater whole—for example, as members of a great family, trade guild, nation, or church. This communal consciousness of the Middle Ages gradually gave way to the individual consciousness of the Renaissance.[1]

Humanism's focus on the individual led to Petrarch's insistence on improved education and, in particular, an education that emphasized values of individual existence, as did those of ancient Greece and Rome. Hence, analyzing and appreciating classical culture—including philosophy, literature, and art—were important to humanist education. All of these cultural aspects of the ancient world were reborn as part of the Renaissance. We should note here that some aspects of classical culture were pagan, such as the myths of the gods, temples, dramas, and much of the philosophy. Some of that philosophy had been incorporated into Christian thinking by St. Augustine in the fifth century and by St. Thomas Aquinas in the thirteenth century, but most of the other aspects of classical learning remained clearly pagan and, therefore, highly suspect in the strongly monolithic Christian world of fifteenth-century Italy. For this reason, Petrarch paid special attention to demonstrating that a person could be both a devout Christian and a humanist.

As important as men like Dante and Petrarch were in reintroducing Europe to some of the ideas of ancient Greece and Rome, it is likely that the Renaissance could not have occurred without a far greater availability of classical writings. About a generation after Petrarch was encouraging Italians to look back to the glories of Rome as a model for their society, there were several factors occurring in Italy (and, to a lesser extent, Europe as a whole) that allowed for a virtual flood of classical books, poems, treatises, art, and general knowledge to be introduced or reintroduced to Europe.

The largest factor to contribute to this new wave of classical knowledge was the collapse of the Byzantine Empire in the East. Byzantium had carried on as the inheritor of the Roman legacy throughout the period between the fall of the Western Roman Empire in the fifth century to the days of Petrarch. The Byzantine Empire was a center for trade, military power, Christianity, and the culture of the ancient Roman and Greek past, which were preserved in the libraries of Byzantium and taught by Byzantine scholars in (mostly) Greek. But the influence of the scholars decreased as the Muslims gained more and more territory from Byzantium, until by 1400, all that remained of the Byzantine Empire was the capital of Constantinople and a small area surrounding the city. Constantinople held out for a few decades, but in 1453 an army of 70,000 Ottoman Turks attacked the city's walls and its 7,000 defenders. The city fell, and Constantinople was renamed Istanbul, becoming the center of the Ottoman Empire. In the decades before the city fell, however, many of the Byzantine scholars had fled west to other Christian lands, taking their knowledge and their books with them to Europe.

A large number of these displaced Byzantine scholars and teachers went to Italy and thus helped to spur the Renaissance. Italy had several factors that made it an inviting home for the scholars. First, it was the center of Christianity in Western Europe, and despite the split that had occurred between the Western Catholic and the Eastern Orthodox churches, these scholars were, first and foremost, Christian teachers who would not be well regarded in a Muslim society. Second, Italy was more wealthy than most of Europe due to the wealthy banking and merchant families in the various city-states. Therefore, the Byzantine scholars could find paid positions as teachers or advisers in the courts and homes of the merchant elite. Third, the Italian peninsula was close and did not require a long and dangerous journey to get there. The importance of the documents brought by the Byzantines is revealed in the following quotation:

> *In 1423 . . . a Sicilian adventurer named Giovanni Aurispa returned from Constantinople with a hoard of 238 manuscripts written in Greek, a language that scholars in Italy had learned only in the previous few decades. Among these treasures were six lost plays by Aeschylus and seven by Sophocles. . . . But there was also a complete copy of the works of the geometer Proclus of Alexandria and, even more important for engineers, a treatise on ancient lifting devices, the Mathematical Collection of Pappus of Alexandria. In the decades that followed, so many manuscripts on Greek mathematics and engineering emerged that it is possible to speak of a "renaissance of mathematics" in fifteenth-century Italy.*[2]

Although the influx of Byzantine scholars may have been the most vital key to the start of the Renaissance, it was not the only important factor. Another vital key was the invention of movable printing type by **Johannes Gutenberg** in the early 1450s. A count of the printing businesses established in the first 30 years following Gutenberg's invention reveals that about 50 percent were in Italy. Undoubtedly, the money of the large middle class, the progressive atmosphere, and the newly awakened desire for classical literature played a part in fostering these businesses.

The demand for classical textbooks was also fueled by the growth of universities. From modest beginnings in the early thirteenth century, or even earlier for a few, the number and size of universities had grown rapidly, due in part to the desire of the new middle class to educate their children so that their ability to conduct business would be enhanced in the rapidly changing world. Moreover, literacy among all segments of the population had grown, in part because of the renewed emphasis on liberal education from people like Petrarch.

Europeans also began to travel more, both for trade and for pleasure. This travel brought interactions between cities that improved creativity and enhanced education, a willingness to try new concepts, and an awareness of other cities. The major city-states of Italy and the wealthy families who ran them felt a real sense of competition with one another. Each wanted their city to be the greatest, richest, most important, and most beautiful. This caused a virtual explosion of great artistic talent in Florence, Milan, Venice, Naples, and Rome as each city tried to outdo its rivals. Great art and beautiful buildings can be found in all of these cities, but Florence was probably the most successful.

The increased travel and trade in Europe also led to another factor that contributed to the Renaissance—wealth. It was a new kind of wealth, for the new merchant rich were not wealthy because of land ownership (which was the medieval model), but because they had goods to trade. The Italian city-states were especially successful because Italy was not yet unified into a nation-state, as was much of Europe. This was beneficial for the Italian merchant families because they didn't have to pay heavy taxes to the crown, which meant more profit for them.

The new merchant rich were especially important to the Renaissance for a variety of reasons. First, because their wealth was not tied up in land ownership, they had available cash and could spend money more easily. Second, the merchant rich were still not well respected by the traditional landed aristocracy, so to improve their reputations and soothe their egos, they did what they could to imitate the lifestyle of the nobility. They used their money to have large and elaborate palaces built and commissioned talented artists to paint and sculpt items to be placed in their homes. Third, they had a good deal of free time and used that time to study the newly reintroduced classical writings. They also spent time and money in civic service and paid artists to create art to beautify the city, often making sure that their names were listed as benefactors. A well-rounded education also became popular, and these citizens became knowledgeable in a vast array of subjects: speech, civics, math, poetry, painting, sculpture, engineering, architecture, theology, and so on, thus contributing to disciplines beyond just art and architecture.

These wealthy merchants (the Medici family in Florence, the Borghese family in Rome, the Sforza family in Milan, and others) along with the Catholic Church were the patrons of the great Renaissance artists. Artists were paid enough to be able to live and support themselves and their families. The very best even became wealthy. Also, because these merchants were enamored of the classics, they allowed artistic freedom beyond the set themes of the Middle Ages. Artists were often allowed to sign their work and thus gain a reputation. These conditions would not have existed even a century earlier. Eventually, in order to get the best artists, even the church had to change its means of operation and pay the artists handsomely and give them credit for their work. The desire to sponsor art was strongest in Florence, and that is where we begin our in-depth study of the Renaissance.

■ The Importance of Sponsors

In the year 1400, Florence was beset by another terrible plague, just as had occurred about every 10 years since the great plague of 1348 to 1350. In a typical medieval response, the Guild of Cloth Merchants decided to appease a possibly angry God by some act of good works. They saw that the baptistery of Saint John the Baptist located next to the cathedral was in poor repair. This neglect was made even more serious because John the Baptist was the patron saint of the city of Florence. Hence, they decided to pay for the construction of new doors for the baptistery in hopes that God would be pleased and take action to rid Florence of the plague.

However, the implementation of the project was not typical of medieval thinking. The guild decided to sponsor a contest for the right to build the doors. Such an artistic contest may have been the first since the days of competition in drama in ancient Athens. The rules of the competition required that the candidates make a door panel, about 17 inches by 13 inches and cast in bronze, of a scene of their own design representing Abraham's sacrifice of Isaac as described in Genesis 22:2–13.

The winning artist would not only receive a lucrative commission for the doors, but the potential for enhancing his reputation. Perhaps even more important, the competition meant that the nature of the art itself would be important in deciding the winner. Even though the original concept of the doors was more about heavenly appeasement than art, the competition guaranteed that the artistic nature of the work would be important in the final judgment, just as discussed in the quotation given at the beginning of this chapter. When the artistic component became important, the creativity of the work was improved and the individual artist was honored.

After the stipulated one-year period, the competitors submitted their panels. Two were judged to be superior. One was made by Filippo Brunelleschi, a young member of the Florentine goldsmith's guild with a few years of successful goldsmithing. The other was made by **Lorenzo Ghiberti,** a young apprentice whose previous work was little more than fancy earrings, but who had some new and creative ideas.

Two stories survive about the details of the final decision of the competition. Ghiberti's diary says that he won the contest with a unanimous vote of the evaluation committee. Brunelleschi, ever secret, kept no diary, but a biographer who lived only a generation later revealed that the vote of the committee was tied and that the committee suggested that the two artists work together to provide the doors. Brunelleschi stated that such a plan would be impossible and he withdrew from the competition, at which point the committee unanimously gave the award to Ghiberti. The two works are shown in Figures 27.1A and B.

Ghiberti's new ideas were immediately apparent. His panel was cast as a single piece, lending a flow and unity to the Ghiberti panel that is lacking in Brunelleschi's, which was cast in pieces and then mounted on the panel backing. Furthermore, the Ghiberti piece was more forward looking, using perspective and foreshortening to add depth to his panel and make it appear as if his characters are actually coming out of the background. The arrangement of the Ghiberti piece also used a triangular

Figure 27.1 ■ **A)** *Panel submitted for the competition of the doors of the baptistery by Ghiberti.* **B)** *Panel submitted for the competition of the doors of the baptistery by Brunelleschi.* A) © Arte & Immagini srl/CORBIS. B) © Arte & Immagini srl/CORBIS.

arrangement that makes it more pleasing to the eye. Finally, there is some obvious classical influence, as Ghiberti's Isaac is a nude. Brunelleschi's panel is not without merit, but it is certainly more medieval in feel. The Brunelleschi panel is more cluttered and lacks the perspective and motion that can be seen in Ghiberti's work.

The Ghiberti panels were installed on the east doors of the baptistery—the doors facing the cathedral itself.

After several years, the city decided to move Ghiberti's doors to the north side of the baptistery and to have another competition for new east doors. These doors were to be even more glorious than the previous winning doors. Ghiberti was again awarded the prize. He then spent the next seven years casting and sculpting the ten gilt bronze panels. The new doors had a much stronger Renaissance-inspired classical feel than the earlier panels. Rather than having the panels shaped as medieval style quatrefoils, these panels were simple, clean squares. One of the panels from the new doors is shown in Figure 27.2. Then, to highlight

the classical feel, the completed set of panels was framed by a series of Roman-styled busts of various prophets and other important church figures. The new east doors were so impressive that later when Michelangelo saw them he said that they were splendid enough to be the "gates of paradise." The doors are still called by that name today.

While Ghiberti was working on the doors to the baptistery, Brunelleschi left Florence and traveled to Rome, where he began to study art and architecture while supporting himself doing minor goldsmith work and, interestingly, making clocks. Brunelleschi's foresight was ingenious. He knew that Florence had a problem that was even greater than the neglect of the baptistery and, evidently, he was determined to prepare himself to solve that problem. The central cathedral of Florence had been under construction for more than a century but could not be finished because no one knew how to make a dome large enough to span the enormous vault of the altar area.

The city fathers in charge of the construction of the cathedral had gotten themselves into the

Figure 27.2 ■ One of the panels of the second Ghiberti's doors (part of the "Gates of Paradise".) © 2010 by Coia Hubert. Used under license of Shutterstock, Inc.

predicament because they wanted to build the largest and most original cathedral in all Christendom. They had torn down two previous churches to make way for the new cathedral and had employed several architects and master contractors over the many decades of construction, but no one had been able to propose a plan for the dome that satisfied the construction committee. The vault to be covered was wider (at 143 feet) than even the great Byzantine church, *Hagia Sophia,* which was the largest church and the widest span ever constructed up to that time. One previous architect built a model using a traditional wooden support structure that would be removed after the mortar of the bricks in the dome had cured (usually taking about 15 months in those days). However, this model collapsed under its own weight after a few weeks and was, therefore, rejected. Another architect proposed supporting the walls with flying buttresses in the typical gothic manner, but the committee felt that the gothic style was too much like the style of their French rivals. Besides, the city of Milan was building a gothic cathedral, and Florence did not want to appear to copy Milan.

It was in this environment of near desperation that the committee announced a new competition for the building of the dome in 1418, almost two decades after the competition on the baptistery doors. Several models were received from competitors, but all were rejected except two. One of the final models was made by Filippo Brunelleschi and the other was by, of course, Lorenzo Ghiberti. Each of the finalists was invited to explain their model and plan of construction to the committee. Brunelleschi gave few details but astounded the committee with the brashness of his proposal. He did, however, reveal his tremendous preparation for this project and the creative methods he would use rather then the traditional construction methods which he asserted would not work in the Florence cathedral.

He would not use a removable support structure, as was the prevailing technological standard but, rather, build the support structure into the dome itself, thus creating a wooden dome within the outer brick dome. Brunelleschi decided to use eight major ribs to support the structure. This would serve like an eight-sided gothic rib vault. The major ribs would be given added support by connecting them with 24 minor ribs. He then built two shells covering the ribs that interlocked to reinforce each other, in essence building a smaller dome over the ribs that supported a larger dome. See Figure 27.3. He would angle the bricks of the outer dome at steep angles, thus forcing the bricks to be somewhat self-supporting. This technique allowed Brunelleschi to successfully cover the large expanse while leaving the space below the dome in the cathedral open and free of supports. The technique was a success and has been copied repeatedly in famous buildings such as St. Peter's in Rome, St. Paul's in London, and the U.S. Capitol in Washington, D.C.

He would also construct special winches, lifting devices, and innovative scaffolding that would ensure safe and secure transport of the materials to the working areas above. (His sketches for these devices indicate that the concepts came from his clock-making experience.) This ability to think laterally to clock making was highly creative

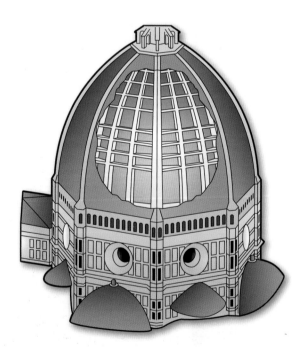

Figure 27.3 ■ Internal structure of the Florence cathedral dome. © *Kendall Hunt Publishing Company.*

and, when coupled with the linear thinking he had developed from his Roman studies, his presentation was very impressive. Brunelleschi discussed with the committee details of the merits and nuances of domes and other buildings that he had studied in Rome. He told the committee of the consulting work he had done on the cathedral dome in a neighboring city that was now successfully completed.

Brunelleschi also demonstrated his understanding of linear perspective through a remarkable painting that he had done. The painting was a scene looking from inside the cathedral toward the baptistery. To demonstrate perspective, he made a peephole in the center of the painting. The viewer stood at the point in the cathedral from which the scene was painted but turned the painting away from his or her face and peered through the peephole from the backside. A mirror was set up reflecting the painting to the viewer. The viewer looked at either the actual scene depicted by the painting or at a mirror reflecting back to the front of the painting. Brunelleschi's skill in perspective was so good that the painting and the scene looked the same.

Ghiberti, who had spent the last two decades making the doors of the baptistery and other similar works, was unable to match the architectural, mechanical, and dimensional expertise of Brunelleschi, and so the award for the dome went to Brunelleschi.

The work of the dome was completed in 1436, 18 years after the contract for the dome was given to Brunelleschi and 140 years after the original cathedral construction had commenced. The dome construction was not without problems, including some additional rivalry with Ghiberti, but overall the work proceeded as Brunelleschi planned. Only one person died in an accident working on the dome—a testament to the soundness of the support structures and lifting devices designed by Brunelleschi. Today, the dome of the cathedral is a wonder of Renaissance capability and a great tribute to Brunelleschi's creative genius. It is shown in Figure 27.4.

During the construction period, Brunelleschi modified some of those mechanical devices so that they could be used to lift cargo off ships on the Arno River, which flows through Florence. For those designs he was awarded the first patent ever

Figure 27.4 ■ The cathedral Santa Maria del Fiore in Florence is topped by Brunelleschi's dome. © 2010 by Blaz Kure. Used under license of Shutterstock, Inc.

issued, thus legally protecting his design from others who would want to copy it. He was ever secretive and afraid of rivals, and this secretiveness may have forced the city to grant the patent. The concept of patents has proven to be highly motivating to technologists who would make new devices. The patent is much like the lucrative commissions and name recognition that artists were beginning to receive at about the same time.

We should pause to consider the elements of creativity that Brunelleschi exhibited in the great cathedral dome. The acronym we developed in a previous chapter to characterize creativity is: VINE. This is shown by Brunelleschi as follows:

1. The value of this idea was seen in the acceptance of his idea by the committee and the praise and acceptance by the public over these many years since he finished his work.
2. His intent was reflected in the dogged determination of his preparation.
3. The novelty and uniqueness were shown in his refusal to use the traditional removable support scaffolding but, rather, to employ an internal and permanent support structure.
4. The excellence and continuance was reflected in the two decades of work that he used to prepare for the crowning achievement of his life and the excellence of execution of the actual project.

Brunelleschi was a model of creativity, and his cathedral dome invites us to visit and admire his accomplishment.

After the triumph of the cathedral dome, Brunelleschi was given other commissions. One of these, the Pazzi Chapel in Florence, has become the prototype of the Renaissance style. The whole structure was designed to look like a building from ancient Rome and was built on the concept of simple circles and rectangles—perfectly consistent with the ancient Greeks' love of simple mathematical shapes. Geometrical arrangement is everywhere. The small circles defining the entrances and the large circle defining the main vault of the building are built to a 1:2 ratio, while the squares enclosing the small circles are 1/8 the area of the square enclosing the larger circle. The

Figure 27.5 ■ A) The Expulsion from Paradise *(portion) by Masaccio.* © *Alinari Archives/CORBIS*

building has a very clean feel due to the plastered walls and lightly contrasting colors on the structural units. Finally, Brunelleschi used arches and Corinthian columns to enhance the Roman feel of the structure. It shows simple and beautiful lines that are classic in their form with beautiful symmetry and balance.

■ Early Renaissance Art and Sculpture

At the same time that Brunelleschi was building the dome of the cathedral in Florence, a young artist, Tomasso Guidi, known as **Masaccio,** was decorating the Brancacci Chapel of Santa Maria del Carmine, a church on the other side of the Arno River. Masaccio built on the work of Giotto (who was discussed in the previous volume of this work) to give realism to his figures rather than just the static symbolism that had been the norm throughout the Middle Ages. The fresco *The Expulsion from Paradise* from the Brancacci Chapel shows a distraught Adam and Eve fleeing from the Garden of Eden, as shown in Figure 27.5A. This focus on realism is typical of humanism and its emphasis on the individual, and became a charac-

Figure 27.5 ■ **B)** The Tribute Money, *also by Masaccio. B) © Sandro Vannini/CORBIS.*

teristic of the Renaissance style.

The Brancacci Chapel has another large fresco panel by Masaccio that is less dramatic than the Adam and Eve but is equally realistic and shows much greater complexity in both execution of the scene and in the way the subject is treated. This fresco, called *The Tribute Money,* depicts the events described in Matthew 17:24–27, when Jesus was asked whether he paid temple tribute. This is shown in Figure 27.5B. Jesus instructed Peter to go to the nearby Sea of Galilee, where he would find a fish that had a coin in its mouth. Then Peter was to take the coin and give it as tribute. The central part of the fresco shows a group of men surrounding Jesus. Although some symbolically have halos, the sizes of the men are all realistic (that is, Jesus is not larger because he is more important, as might have been the case in a medieval painting). Masaccio's painting shows Peter getting the fish out of the water on the left of the central group of people and then, on the right side of the fresco, Peter is shown giving the tribute money to the official. The simultaneous representation of the three parts of the story in a single fresco was highly creative, but the realistic representation of the story and, even more, the overall scene was even more impressive. The background of mountains and sky and buildings is highly realistic, perhaps as well done as any background landscape for decades to come. Even the clothes

are draped and shadowed to convey a feeling of three-dimensionality and, therefore, realism. The building in the fresco is realistically rendered in perspective, but not as dramatically as work Masaccio does later in his life.

The most dramatic use of perspective in the early Renaissance was displayed about a year later by Masaccio in yet another Florentine church—Santa Maria Novella. We don't know if Masaccio was aware of the perspective painting done by Brunelleschi to illustrate his skills to the committee evaluating dome proposals, but we do know that the entire Florentine art community was struggling to learn and demonstrate the rules of linear perspective at just this time. Masaccio's *The Holy Trinity,* shown in Figure 27.6, depicts Jesus on the cross with Mary and John at the foot of the cross and God the Father hovering to the rear and above Jesus. The entire scene is encased in an arched tunnel that is framed by classical pillars and the kneeling figures of the donors on the right and left. The tunnel roof and walls are depicted with astoundingly good linear perspective, so that the entire scene appears to be a vaulted recess in the walls of the church. The effect of the painting is dramatic and instantly involves the viewer in both the illusion of the apparently recessed vault and an admiration of the artist for the superior execution of the craft of linear perspective. The ability to execute linear perspective was

Figure 27.6 ■ The Holy Trinity *by Masaccio shows dramatic linear perspective.* Nimatallah/Art Resource, NY.

not easily learned, and several textbooks were written in the Renaissance to teach the highly mathematical skill.

The **concepts of perspective** are illustrated in Figure 27.7. They can be described as follows:

- **Overlapping.** Done by simply placing one object behind another to create an impression that the rear object is further away. This method has been used extensively since ancient times and is a normal method to depict a background such as a landscape scene, but can obviously be used to depict the spatial relationship of people or objects.
- **Diminution.** The objects that are further away are made smaller. This method is powerful because it is intuitive.
- **Vertical perspective.** The object to be represented as distant is placed above the nearer object. This method is not intuitive or dramatic in its effect.
- **Diagonal perspective.** The distant object is placed diagonally above the nearer object. This is similar to vertical but slightly more intuitive.

- **Atmospheric or aerial perspective.** This method simply makes the distant object fainter than the closer object. Colors are often employed to enhance this effect. The distant object is often painted in blues and grays to give the feeling of intervening atmosphere. This method is not only powerful and intuitive; it also has the advantage that entire landscapes can be represented as distant using this device.
- **Divergent perspective.** This method attempts to represent perspective using geometry. Then angles of the object are drawn so that the rear portions diverge from the front. This method is neither intuitive nor powerful.
- **Intuitive perspective.** This method is better than divergent in realistically representing perspective, but it does not give true perspective.
- **Linear perspective.** This method uses geometry to correctly form the angles of the object so that it appears to recede from the viewer. The geometrical lines can converge at either a single point or two points—these are called the *vanishing points* and must occur on the horizon. This is the most powerful and intuitively correct of all the methods of showing perspective.

As indicated in the following quotation, linear perspective became a hallmark of Renaissance art.

The grand innovation that made Renaissance painters certain that theirs was the only right path for art was the laws of perspective. . . . For some, Nature had been rediscovered; for the others, civilization had been restored. Perspective is based on the fact that we have two eyes. We therefore see objects as defined by two lines of sight that converge at a distance, the painter's "vanishing point" on the horizon. Since those two lines form an acute angle, plane geometry can show the size and place that an object at any distance must be given to the painting to make it appear as it looks in life . . . Hence the statement in an early

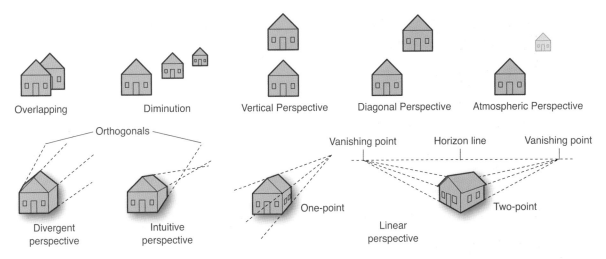

Figure 27.7 ■ Types of perspective.

Renaissance treatise that painting consists of three parts: drawing, measurement, and color. One of the uses of color is to create "aerial perspective" [atmospheric perspective]. A light blue-gray makes distant objects in the painting look hazy, as they appear to the eye owing to the thickness of the atmosphere. Combined, the two perspectives create the illusion of depth, the three-dimensional "reality" on a flat surface.[3]

Note the use of various types of perspective in both of the Masaccio paintings shown. In *The Tribute Money* the figures are placed in overlapping perspective, clearly giving the feeling that some in the crowd are behind others. The barren trees in the background are represented with diminution to give the feeling that the smaller trees are more distant. Peter at the water is also shown further away using diminution. The mountains in the background are painted with gray colors and with less distinct lines which are a use of atmospheric perspective. The building on the right uses a geometrical perspective that appears to be either intuitive or linear. Masaccio's *The Holy Trinity* uses linear perspective to create the vault effect. Although we will see many types of perspective in later paintings, some even more dra-

matic than these, Masaccio's works were important examples of the use of perspective and were especially creative at the time they were painted.

At the same time that Brunelleschi and Masaccio were working, another young artist was also demonstrating some creative ideas in Florence. This artist was a sculptor named **Donatello.**

The classical influence of ancient Greece and Rome that influenced much of the Renaissance also seems to have had an impact on Donatello, especially in his early work. Donatello's *St. George,* sculpted between 1415 and 1417 is well done, but could almost be a replica of an ancient Roman statue. The *Saint George* stands in a classical pose and has the severe look and classical proportions of a Roman work. This work is shown in Figure 27.8A.

Of greater fame and originality is Donatello's *David,* completed between 1428 and 1432 and also shown in Figure 27.8B. The biblical theme of David, who slew Goliath, is obviously religious in nature but has strong elements of classical influence. *David* is the first freestanding nude figure sculpted since Roman times nearly a thousand years earlier. Furthermore, the attention Donatello paid to *David's* form and musculature is also indebted to classical Greece and Rome. The overall feel of the statue is not religious, but pagan.

Figure 27.8 ■ **A)** Saint George *by Donatello.* **B)** David *by Donatello.* **C)** *Donatello's* Saint Mary Magdalene. *A) © Arte & Immagini srl/CORBIS. B) © Arte & Immagini srl/CORBIS. C) Erich Lessing/Art Resource, NY.*

Donatello's *David* is lithe and fairylike, with obvious attention given to the beauty of *David's* early adolescence. This David looks and feels as if he belongs in a Greek myth, not in an Old Testament battle or even in a Roman forum.

Finally, Donatello's *Saint Mary Magdalene,* completed between 1454 and 1455, is an impressive tribute to emotion being used in art. Donatello's *Mary Magdalene,* shown in Figure 27.8C, is haggard and weary from a life spent in penance for earlier sin—a medieval tradition attached to Mary Magdalene. The viewer is forced to compare Donatello's stark view of Mary Magdalene with the penitent young sinner the Bible portrays, thus forcing the viewer to become involved with the work and realize that repentance is a difficult road and lifelong endeavor. Both the realistic emotion of the piece and the attempt to involve the viewer are characteristics of the Renaissance period.

Art during the Renaissance developed the use of geometric arrangement. The reintroduction of ancient Greek and Roman mathematical texts allowed artists to develop a better understanding of geometric arrangement and refined what was pleasant for the eye. Thus, Renaissance painting seems less cluttered than medieval art. The use of

a triangular, or pyramid, shape became especially popular as it is both pleasant to behold and is a useful tool for directing the viewer's attention to a particular part of the painting.

One artist who used both triangular arrangements and the strong classical themes that were so typical of the Renaissance was **Alessandro (Sandro) Botticelli,** who lived from 1445 to 1510. A good example of this is Botticelli's masterpiece *Birth of Venus* which is presented in Figure 27.9A. Note that the pose of Venus in Botticelli's work is nearly identical to that of the ancient Venus sculpture, shown in Figure 27.9B, again attesting to the strong classical influence typically shown in his works.

■ The Medici Family

As we have already seen art and architecture in Florence in the early fifteenth century was primarily sponsored by the guilds and other citizen committees formed from the newly emerging wealthy middle class. In 1434 this somewhat haphazard sponsorship arrangement was organized and expanded when Cosimo de Medici, the leader of the richest family in Florence and, perhaps, the

Figure 27.9 ■ **A)** *Botticelli's* The Birth of Venus. *Notice the similarity to Figure 27.7B.* **B)** *An ancient Venus sculpture. A) © Corel. B) Alinari/Art Resource, NY.*

richest family in all of Europe, emerged as the popular leader of Florence. For the next six decades, the Medici family ruled Florence and directed the sponsorship of art and architecture, often using personal funds. There was a brief period of chaos and insurrection against their rule following the death of Lorenzo de Medici. When they returned again to rule, much of the vigor of the early days had gone. Their influence, however, continued for several decades more in Florence, as church leaders, and as queens and government officials throughout Europe.

Originally gaining fame as physicians (hence the name), the Medici family shifted its emphasis to banking in the early fourteenth century, becoming the financial backers for the tremendously successful wool trade between Flanders and Florence, as well as the personal investors and tax collectors for the pope. The Medicis were well educated, fiercely loyal to their city-state, highly skilled in politics, and personally involved in art and other activities that would improve their community. In all these activities, and more, they sought to imitate Pericles of ancient Athens.

Cosimo de Medici ruled Florence from 1434 to 1464 and was primarily responsible for the strong promotion of classical values and Renaissance

thinking in Florence. Cosimo spent vast sums of money collecting and copying various ancient manuscripts, paid for the establishment of a school in Florence for the study of Plato (which he appropriately named *The Academy*), and lavished money on the art of Florence, supporting early Renaissance artists such as Donatello. Cosimo was also an author, and he wrote his own compendium of the writings of Plato. Surely the Greek-speaking scholars fleeing the collapsing Byzantine Empire were employed by Cosimo in The Academy and in other functions of his court, but clearly the guiding hand that directed the activities of the city-state in politics and in art was Cosimo himself.

Upon the death of Cosimo, his son, Piero, became the ruler of the family and of the city-state. Although he ruled for only five years, Piero's desire to continue the policies of his father was evident in his support of artists such as Botticelli. As gratitude, Botticelli painted portraits of several of the Medici family in his great painting *The Adoration of the Magi.*

Florence reached its zenith under the rule of Cosimo's grandson, **Lorenzo de Medici,** also known as Lorenzo the Magnificent. Lorenzo, an accomplished poet himself, continued in the tradition of his grandfather and father and was an elaborate supporter of the arts within the city of Florence. He continued to support Botticelli and was a personal friend and sponsor of Michelangelo (see Chapter 28), who even lived in the Medici home for some time.

Lorenzo continued to promote classical and humanist viewpoints. He invited Greek scholars (mostly from Byzantium) to live and work in Florence and paid to rebuild the University of Pisa, where Galileo would work a century later. He also supported native Florentine scholars, who further expanded the concepts of humanism.

Chief among these native scholars was **Pico della Mirandola,** a close friend of Lorenzo. Pico was precociously brilliant and well-educated. He claimed to have read every book in Italy, and doesn't seem to have been seriously challenged in this assertion. He wrote a set of 900 theses (statements of truth) covering what he believed was the entire spectrum of human learning. He then offered to debate all comers on any or all of the theses. This kind of flamboyant arrogance caught the attention of church officials, who read his theses and identified 12 of them (mostly dealing with mysticism) as heretical. A trial was held and, although Pico retracted the offending theses, it was too late and he was sentenced to a brief term in prison. When released, he returned to Florence and continued writing.

His book *Oration on the Dignity of Man* is a strongly humanistic work proclaiming that all of the divine features of the universe can be expressed in each individual being. He said that a person can become like God, at least in understanding, through education and proper thinking. In this work he cited biblical references plus used Jewish, Arabic, and Platonic sources to support his arguments. Pico's story showed the continuing influence of the Catholic Church on life in the Renaissance period but also showed an increasing willingness to find God by means other than through the church itself.

Under Lorenzo the Magnificent, Florence became the dominant commercial and military power in Europe, with the prestige and wealth of the Medici family rising so high that one of Lorenzo's sons became Pope Leo X and his nephew became Pope Clement VII.

Upon the death of Lorenzo de Medici in 1492, his son Piero II became ruler of Florence. However, this Piero was a self-indulgent and weak ruler. He was highly unpopular, in part because of the preaching of **Savonarola,** a reform-minded Catholic priest who moved to Florence because of his strong beliefs about the problems he observed in the changes occurring there. Savonarola was a Dominican friar who was adamantly against the worldly life of many people in Florence, especially the Medici family, and the blatantly pagan themes of the new art. Just two years after Piero II became the leader of Florence, the political situation in the city-state became unstable. The French invaded Florence and, in the midst of that turmoil, the people overthrew Piero and expelled him from the city. Savonarola, who preached that the French were being used by God as an instrument for cleansing Florence, was named by the French king as the ruler of the city-state. Savonarola established a theocratic republic in which an assembly ran the day-to-day operation of the city but was directed in general policies by Savonarola, who administered what he believed were the dictates of a Christian state.

The atmosphere in Florence quickly became stridently anti-progress and anti-worldliness. (We are reminded of the strident priests of ancient Egypt who, like Savonarola, were against any change.) Citizens were asked to rid their households of pagan or worldly elements (especially things that promoted pride and vanity, such as cosmetics). Squads of Savonarola's supporters roamed the city looking for elements of evil and gathered them into the square in front of the Dominican church, where they were burned. Some artists, including Botticelli, submitted their artworks for destruction. This event has been called the **Bonfire of the Vanities.**

Soon, Savonarola began to preach against the corruption and evils he saw within the Catholic Church. He even urged the French king to march on Rome and restore a pure and holy papacy. When the French king threatened to convene a council to expel the current pope and install one who was more "righteous," the pope reacted by warning both Savonarola and the king. When the warnings were unheeded, the pope excommunicated Savonarola. By 1498 the majority of Florentines, including many from rival church groups like the Franciscans, were upset at his continuous harangue, and they seized Savonarola and held a trial, wherein he was declared guilty and then hung and burned in the main square of Florence.

The Florentine Republic continued following the death of Savonarola. While it was a reasonably efficient government, much of the luster and glory of the days of the Medici rule were missing. Over the next few years Piero de Medici made several attempts to regain control of city but was unsuccessful and ultimately died of drowning in 1503 while under the employ of the French army. However, in 1512 the Medici family regained control of Florence under Lorenzo's grandson. The Medici were again expelled in 1527 and the republic reformed, but then, in 1530, a siege by the Holy Roman Emperor Charles V brought down the republic and, at the nomination of Charles V, a Medici was again made ruler of the city-state. Despite several assassinations and revolts, the Medici continued to rule Florence, sometimes as mere figureheads, until the eighteenth century.

■ Machiavelli: New Politics for a New Era

The Renaissance was not just a new era for the arts and science, but also saw new ideas for governing people. Men like Pico della Mirandola, friend and supporter of the Medici family, believed that people were best governed by educated, classically trained men who had ties to the local community. Others, like the radical priest Savonarola, believed that the common people should rule under the strict authority of Christ's doctrines. However, the most important political thinker of the Renaissance was **Niccolò Machiavelli.** He was the legitimizer of a philosophy of government that has continued in several forms until the present day— absolute rule by one authority.

Machiavelli was a native Florentine and was involved in its governance in a variety of ways even as a young man. He was a diplomat for Lorenzo de Medici and then continued to serve the government as part of the ruling council after the brief reign of Savanarola. Machiavelli's office was in the city hall, and he could open a small interior window overlooking the large assembly room and hear the proceedings of the elected people's representatives. He reported the proceedings to the council, and that helped them rule and dominate the elected representatives, thus keeping the real power in the hands of a select few.

During this time Machiavelli fell out of favor with the Medici because of his support of the Florentine Republic, which prevented the Medici from returning to power in the city. However, the Florentine Republic was short-lived, and soon the Medici family was back in power. Machiavelli was sent to prison for a short time, after which the ruling family exiled him from the city. Machiavelli then spent the next few years trying to get back into favor with the Medici rulers so that he could return to Florence. Ironically, the Florentine Republic was briefly reestablished in 1527, but these new republican rulers refused to allow Machiavelli to return to Florence because they now viewed him as a Medici sympathizer because of his efforts to return to Medici favor. This rejection seriously affected Machiavelli, who died within a few months of the restoration of the republic.

The vehicle Machiavelli chose to win favor from the Medici rulers was a book he titled *Il Principe (The Prince). The Prince* was designed to outline how a prince (or ruler) could both govern effectively and retain his power. By writing *The Prince* Machiavelli hoped to show the Medici how to consolidate and strengthen their power in Florence in this time of political upheaval, and in doing so convince them he was once again their friend and supporter.

Machiavelli used Cesare Borgia as his model for a prince and the basis for his new ideas on governance. Cesare was the illegitimate son of a pope, and himself a cardinal of the church. However, that holy position did nothing to persuade

Cesare to do good. In an attempt to gain power for himself, Cesare Borgia conquered several cities in central Italy, including Urbino, and was suspected of murdering his brother to advance his own position. It was clear to Machiavelli that Cesare was successful in his attempts to gain and hold power and that the supposed "morals" or "ethics" of his position as cardinal did little to restrain him.

Thus, in *The Prince,* Machiavelli argued against the medieval concept that a Christian society should be run by a prince who is answerable to God and that the prince should govern according to Christian principles. The basic concept of *The Prince* is that the most pressing need of the prince is to retain power since the loss of power leads to warfare, murder, rape, loss of property, and a whole range of other social ills. Therefore, all decisions and considerations—moral, ethical, and religious—are secondary to the goal of stable government. In essence, when it comes to the retention of political power, *the end justifies the means.*

However, Machiavelli's political view is not quite as stark as it may first appear. Machiavelli argued that the successful prince should act according to moral and theological principles as much as possible, but only if such behavior is conducive to obtaining and maintaining political power. In other words, those in power should try to maintain Christian values but may violate them if the ruler feels that the stability of his position would be compromised by the Christian behavior. According to Machiavelli, reality, not idealism, must be the controlling paradigm of government. As Machiavelli said, "Therefore he must have a mind ready to turn in any direction as Fortune's winds and the variability of affairs require, yet, as I said above, he holds to what is right when he can but knows how to do wrong when he must."

Machiavelli's *The Prince* not only deals with the underlying principle that the prince's greatest responsibility to his people is to stay in power, but also gives practical advice about how to do so. For example, Machiavelli teaches that it is desirable for a prince to have both the people's fear and their love; however, if one must choose between the two emotions, creating fear is better because it is in the ruler's hands.

The Prince also teaches that a prince should be liberal in treating people well, but should not be perceived as liberal or overly generous: otherwise, the people will expect too much and become dissatisfied. In other words, a prince should speak kindly to people, as words cost little, but should be stingy with money and privilege because they are hard to recover. Machiavelli also said to kill if you must to retain power, but don't take away the dead person's inheritance, confiscate his property, or violate his women, or you will make enemies of his heirs, and that hatred will last for a long time. Finally, Machiavelli said that a prince must be strong like a lion and clever like a fox.

Machiavelli's *The Prince* was very creative in its separation of moral and secular authority, but it is also firmly rooted in the ideas of the Renaissance. For many of his conclusions, Machiavelli drew upon the writings of classical Greek and Roman authors. Furthermore, Machiavelli was simply arguing that the prince should return to the ideas of ancient Rome. The Roman emperors acted very similar to the manner Machiavelli outlined in *The Prince*—not allowing their power to be threatened by moral considerations. For the early pagan emperors of Rome, ethics was not a problem because they were viewed as gods, and thus *were* the moral authority. For the later Christian Roman emperors this dilemma was a little more tricky, but they eventually came to the same basic conclusion as Machiavelli: Their retention of power was for the good of the empire and therefore a violation of Christian doctrine was permissible if it was for the benefit of the people.

■ Creativity and the Early Renaissance

The introduction of humanism brought a new way of thinking about humans. Although the doctrines of the Catholic Church indicated that people were steeped in sinfulness, the new thinking suggested that human potential was also divine. To fulfill that potential, people sought learning and then creatively applied their learning to art, architecture, literature, politics, and many other fields.

This process was enhanced immeasurably by sponsors who, likewise, sought the very best of creative works. Sometimes the motives of the sponsors were civic pride and sometimes personal glory, but increasingly in the Renaissance, the sponsors recognized and supported artistic merit as an independent end.

Humanism promoted realism over symbolism. This was shown in art and in thinking. When scenes or concepts are presented realistically, people seem to be able to grasp them and attempt to control them, whereas, when only symbolic, there is a distance between the perceiver and the creative work. The humanist emphasis of art became, therefore, realistic. Some of the major creative concepts that contributed to this realism are the following: facial and body expressions that reflect true emotions, clothes that show three-dimensionality, arrangements of people that do not distort true sizes and proportions, and linear perspective. Classical themes such as mythology and simple geometric forms and symmetry were also reintroduced in Renaissance art.

The progress of technology and other recent developments in society enhanced many aspects of creative endeavor over what had been possible in the ancient classical past. Perhaps architecture was the most obvious example. Brunelleschi's brilliant solution to the problem of the cathedral dome shows that he was able to combine concepts from the classical past with new ideas of mechanics that came from recent advances conceived for clock making. This truly shows the combination of linear and lateral thinking, which he combined with some original ideas to create a wholly new concept. Machiavelli, too, combined the expertise of the classical past with current political examples to create a new and astonishingly compelling scenario on political control. With Machiavelli we are reminded, of course, that all creativity is not necessarily beneficial to mankind.

The Renaissance began a balancing act between religious concepts and secular ideas that continues in some forms even until today. Having just emerged from the Middle Ages when religion was the unifying force and ultimate authority in western civilization, the people of the Renaissance struggled to find ways to embrace ancient classical culture, which was sometimes pagan in both orientation and values, while maintaining their Christian ideals. Some people, following the lead of St. Augustine and St. Aquinas, creatively integrated these disparate values by adapting the culture of the pagan past to Christian concepts, essentially dismissing the wholly pagan concepts as being mistakes of ignorance.

Others, like Botticelli and Pico della Mirandola, accepted the pagan culture completely and then rejected it when the conflicts with Christian values were illuminated. Still others, like Machiavelli, accepted Christian concepts as far as possible, but rejected them when secular values were threatened. Most people, however, seemed to accept what was good (in their minds) of the pagan culture and also accept the Christian culture (perhaps without all the restrictions of the church) and to simply ignore the areas of conflict.

While all of these points of view required creative thinking, this last position broadened the thinking of the people and encouraged them to learn from whatever source they might encounter. In the end, creativity was enhanced, although some drift in personal ethics and morals also seems to have occurred because the anchor of the church was sometimes missing. Many creative ways to find personal anchors and to reaffirm personal beliefs became very important and are the subject of several ensuing chapters, but first we must see what happens when all of the techniques of the Renaissance are brought to their optimum best in the hands of creative geniuses. We examine those geniuses in the next chapter, "The High Renaissance."

■ Timeline—Important Dates

Date	Event
1401A.D.	*Competition for the baptistery doors in Florence*
1417–1436	*Brunelleschi built the dome of the Florentine cathedral*
1425–1428	*Masaccio painted the Brancacci Chapel and* Holy Trinity

1428–1432	*Donatello sculpts his* David
1434–1464	*Cosimo de Medici is ruler of Florence*
1453	*Fall of the Byzantine Empire*
About 1455	*Gutenberg establishes a printing house*
1462	*Founding of Platonic Academy in Florence*
1464–1469	*Piero de Medici rules in Florence*
1469–1492	*Lorenzo de Medici rules in Florence*
1475–1482	*Botticelli paints several pieces of art with pagan themes*
1486	*Pico della Mirandola writes* Oration on the Dignity of Man
1494	*Rise of Savonarola, Medici family in exile*
1498	*Savonarola executed*
1498	*Florentine Republic employs Machiavelli*
1512	*Medici power restored and Machiavelli exiled*
1513	*Machiavelli writes* The Prince
1527	*Florentine Republic restored and Machiavelli dies*
1530	*Medici power restored by Charles V*

■ Notes

1. McGrath, Alister, *In the Beginning* (New York: Anchor Books, 2001), 38.
2. King, Ross, *Brunelleschi's Dome* (New York: Penguin Books, 2000), 63.
3. Barzun, Jacques, *From Dawn to Decadence* (New York: Perennial, 2000), 73.

■ Suggested Readings

Barzun, Jacques, *From Dawn to Decadence,* Perennial, 2000.

Caldwell, Ian and Dustin Thomason, *The Rule of Four,* The Dia Press, 2004.

Cunningham, Lawrence S. and John J. Reich, *Culture and Values,* Volume II, 5th ed., Harcourt College Publishers, 2002.

King, Ross, *Brunelleschi's Dome,* Penguin Books, 2000.

Martines, Lauro, *April Blood,* Oxford University Press, 2003.

Machiavelli: The Prince

Niccolò Machiavelli (1469–1527) was the first great political philosopher of the Renaissance, but his later life was constantly a search for acceptance. He was born in Florence during the Medici rule and grew up in their city-state court. He served as a bureaucrat and diplomat under Lorenzo de Medici. This was a time of political upheaval for Italy, and a reform movement deposed the Medici government and replaced it with the Florentine Republic. The Republic's leaders recognized Machiavelli's governmental skills and gave him a position in the ruling council. He served well, but when the Medici family returned to power in 1512, he was imprisoned, tortured, and exiled because of his involvement in the Republic. In his years of banishment, he devoted himself to writing on politics, history, and even plays in an attempt to find favor again with the Medicis, but he never really succeeded. The Medici family was again briefly deposed from power and the Republic reinstated for a few years, but by then Machiavelli was considered pro-Medici for his attempts to win favor from the Medici family and so he was rejected by the new Republic. The reputation he gained for lacking principles put him out of favor with both sides. It is a lesson we can learn from his life, if not from his writings.

The Prince, his principle work, was written during the time he was exiled by the Medici family. It was an attempt to prove his abilities to the Medicis and regain a position in their court. It was to be a handbook on how to rule effectively but was highly controversial and quickly condemned by Pope Clement VIII. The book was largely based on, and contained praise of, the ruling methods of Cesare Borgia—a notorious tyrant who ruled in north-central Italy. Borgia held his power through his subjects' fear and through intrigues. Machiavelli suggested this was the most efficient way to rule. According to Machiavelli, the greatest evil in the state comes from chaos because in that horrid condition, nothing good can be accomplished. Therefore, stability is advocated as the ultimate goal of government and all other decisions are secondary to that premise. Christian virtues and being loved by one's subjects should only be valued as methods of maintaining stability which is, of course, achieved when the ruler remains in power. Deceit and exploitation are tools that are sometimes necessary to use to maintain stability. Interestingly, many people initially thought (and some still think) of *The Prince* as a satire of Borgia's rule, but Machiavelli's letters later proved that the concepts in *The Prince* were indeed his genuine beliefs.

Machiavelli's work has been the subject of many essays, both for and against. Those who condemn Machiavelli view his position as inherently evil. Many have suggested that his concepts, which have been summarized as "The end justifies the means," are among the most evil ever proposed. The vehemence of those who condemn him may come from the carefully reasoned way in which he presents his arguments and the obvious acceptance of his views by many leaders throughout history. Those who support his view may not openly say so, but they may practice what Machiavelli teaches as a way to succeed in their own realm. The following selections from *The Prince* are included to illustrate this controversial political philosophy. They discuss the importance of appearance over true character and being feared over being loved.

Article 1
Niccolò Machiavelli: The Prince

◼ Of the Qualities in Respect of Which Men, and Most of All Princes, Are Praised or Blamed

It now remains for us to consider what ought to be the conduct and bearing of a Prince in relation to his subjects and friends. And since I know that many have written on this subject, I fear it may be thought presumptuous in me to write of it also; the more so, because in my treatment of it I depart from the views that others have taken.

But since it is my object to write what shall be useful to whosoever understands it, it seems to me better to follow the real truth of things than an imaginary view of them. For many Republics and Princedoms have been imagined that were never seen or known to exist in reality. And the manner in which we live, and that in which we ought to live, are things so wide asunder, that he who quits to betake himself to the other is more likely to destroy than to save himself; since any one who would act up to a perfect standard of goodness in everything, must be ruined among so many who are not good. It is essential, therefore, for a Prince who desires to maintain his position, to have learned how to be other than good, and to use or not to use his goodness as necessity requires.

Laying aside, therefore, all fanciful notions concerning a Prince, and considering those only that are true, I say that all men when they are spoken of, and Princes more than others from their being set so high, are characterized by some one of those qualities which attach either praise or blame. Thus one is accounted liberal, another miserly (which word I use, rather than *avaricious,* to denote the man who is too sparing of what is his own *avarice* being the disposition to take wrongfully what is another's); one is generous, another greedy; one cruel, another tenderhearted; one is faithless, another true to his word; one effeminate and cowardly, another high-spirited and courageous; one is courteous, another haughty; one impure, another chaste; one simple, another crafty; one firm, another facile; one grave, another frivolous; one devout, another unbelieving; and the like. Every one, I know, will admit that it would be most laudable for a Prince to be endowed with all of the above qualities that are reckoned good; but since it is impossible for him to possess or constantly practise them all, the conditions of human nature not allowing it, he must be discreet enough to know how to avoid the infamy of those vices that would deprive him of his government, and, if possible, be on his guard also against those which might not deprive him of it; though if he cannot wholly restrain himself, he may with less scruple indulge in the latter. He need never hesitate, however, to incur the reproach of those vices without which his authority can hardly be preserved; for if he well consider the whole matter, he will find that there may be a

---

Source: "The Prince" by Niccolo Machiavelli, translated by N. H. Thomson, from *The Harvard Classics,* Volume 36 (New York: P. F. Collier & Son Co., 1910).

line of conduct having the appearance of virtue, to follow which would be his ruin, and that there may be another course having the appearance of vice, by following which his safety and well-being are secured.

■ Of Liberality and Miserliness

. . . A Prince, therefore, since he cannot without injury to himself practise the virtue of liberality so that it may be known, will not, if he be wise, greatly concern himself though he be called miserly. Because in time he will come to be regarded as more and more liberal, when it is seen that through his parsimony his revenues are sufficient; that he is able to defend himself against any who make war on him; that he can engage in enterprises against others without burdening his subjects; and thus exercise liberality towards all from whom he does not take, whose number is infinite, while he is miserly in respect of those only to whom he does not give, whose number is few. . . .

■ Of Cruelty and Clemency, and Whether It Is Better to Be Loved or Feared

. . . And here comes in the question whether it is better to be loved rather than feared, or feared rather than loved. It might perhaps be answered that we should wish to be both; but since love and fear can hardly exist together, if we must choose between them, it is far safer to be feared than loved. For of men it may generally be affirmed that they are thankless, fickle, false, studious to avoid danger, greedy of gain, devoted to you while you are able to confer benefits upon them, and ready, as I said before, while danger is distant, to shed their blood, and sacrifice their property, their lives, and their children for you; but in the hour of need they turn against you. The Prince, therefore, who without otherwise securing himself builds wholly on their professions is undone. For the friendships which we buy with a price, and do not gain by greatness and nobility of character,

though they be fairly earned are not made good, but fail us when we have occasion to use them.

Moreover, men are less careful how they offend him who makes himself loved than him who makes himself feared. For love is held by the tie of obligation, which, because men are a sorry breed, is broken on every whisper of private interest; but fear is bound by the apprehension of punishment which never relaxes its grasp.

Nevertheless a Prince should inspire fear in such a fashion that if he does not win love he may escape hate. For a man may very well be feared and yet not hated, and this will be the case so long as he does not meddle with the property or with the women of his citizens and subjects. And if constrained to put any to death, he should do so only when there is manifest cause or reasonable justification. But, above all, he must abstain from the property of others. For men will sooner forget the death of their father than the loss of their patrimony. . . .

■ How Princes Should Keep Faith

Every one understands how praiseworthy it is in a Prince to keep faith, and to live uprightly and not craftily. Nevertheless, we see from what has taken place in our own days that Princes who have set little store by their word, but have known how to overreach men by their cunning, have accomplished great things, and in the end got the better of those who trusted to honest dealing.

Be it known, then, that there are two ways of contending, one in accordance with the laws, the other by force; the first of which is proper to men, the second to beasts. But since the first method is often ineffectual, it becomes necessary to resort to the second. A Prince should, therefore, understand how to use well both the man and the beast. . . .

It is not essential, then, that a Prince should have all the good qualities which I have enumerated above, but it is most essential that he should seem to have them; I will even venture to affirm that if he has and invariably practises them all, they are hurtful, whereas the appearance of having them is useful. Thus, it is well to seem merciful, faithful, humane, religious, and upright, and also to be so; but the mind should remain so balanced that were it needful not to be so, you should be able and know how to change to the contrary.

And you are to understand that a Prince, and most of all a new Prince, cannot observe all those rules of conduct in respect whereof men are accounted good, being often forced, in order to preserve his Princedom, to act in opposition to good faith, charity, humanity, and religion. He must therefore keep his mind ready to shift as the winds and tides of Fortune turn, and, as I have already said, he ought not to quit good courses if he can help it, but should know how to follow evil courses if he must.

A Prince should therefore be very careful that nothing ever escapes his lips which is not replete with the five qualities above named, so that to see and hear him, one would think him the embodi-

ment of mercy, good faith, integrity, humanity, and religion. And there is no virtue which it is more necessary for him to seem to possess than this last; because men in general judge rather by the eye than by the hand, for every one can see but few can touch. Every one sees what you seem, but few know what you are, and these few dare not oppose themselves to the opinion of the many who have the majesty of the State to back them up.

Moreover, in the actions of all men, and most of all of Princes, where there is no tribunal to which we can appeal, we look to results. Wherefore if a Prince succeeds in establishing and maintaining his authority, the means will always be judged honourable and be approved by every one. . . .

*   *   *

High Renaissance
Creatively Putting It All Together

> The most heavenly gifts seem to be showered on certain human beings. Sometimes supernaturally, marvelously, they all congregate in one individual.... His [Leonardo's] talent was so rare that he mastered any subject to which he turned his attention.... His gifts were such that his celebrity was world-wide, not only in his day, but even more after his death, and so will continue until the end of time....
>
> The Almighty resolved to send to earth a spirit capable of supreme expression in all the arts, one able to give form to painting, perfection to sculpture, and grandeur to architecture. The Almighty Creator also graciously endowed this chosen one [Michelangelo] with an understanding of philosophy and with the grace of poetry ... so that everyone might admire and follow him as their perfect exemplar in life, work, and behavior, and he would be acclaimed as divine.
>
> —*Giorgio Vasari, 1550 (quoted by Robert Paul Weiner,* Creativity and Beyond, *State University of New York Press, 2000, p. 59)*

■ Florence and Beyond

The Renaissance originally took root in the mid-fifteenth century because of the favorable cultural conditions that existed in the Italian city-states. As we discussed in the previous chapter, those conditions included the following: an increase in education and literacy; an understanding of and desire to emulate the ancient Roman and Greek classical culture; an adoption of the liberating concepts of humanism; a steady flow of cash to the wealthy middle class and the ruling elite; an appreciation of art and a willingness to support it; a desire for excellence; and a vigorous creativity.

The conditions not only fostered the germination of the Renaissance, but they promoted the expansion of Renaissance ideas throughout all strata of Italian society. This occurred, in part, because Italian society provided nearly every man a pathway to improve or change his occupation if he desired to do so (women were still largely excluded). The pathway to personal change in status was to become a craftsman and then to branch into other pursuits. This process began with an apprenticeship in some appropriate field and then, after a few years learning the trade, the man would be accepted into a guild as a journeyman craftsman and then, with increased skill, become a master craftsman. A master craftsman then had several options available. He could practice his craft and make a reasonable living, or he could become a merchant by buying and selling goods made by others as well as his own, or he could focus on the imaginative side of the craft and become recognized as an artist (that is, an artisan). In Renaissance Italy, the last two options—merchant and artist—had the potential for great wealth and recognition. Two of those who began with humble circumstances and moved through the steps to become craftsmen and then highly rewarded artists were Leonardo and Michelangelo.

Although Florence was the first place to see a blossoming of the flower of the Renaissance, other major Italian city-states were quickly following the Florentine lead. This occurred because essentially the same conditions existed throughout Italy, so the methods of Florence could be readily copied. Also, the political turmoil at the end of the fifteenth century in Florence (the rise of Savonarola and the displacement of the Medici family) caused many Florentine artists to flee the city and look for work elsewhere. The beneficiaries of this flight were, especially, Rome and Milan. Venice, too, developed a strong artistic movement, although it seems to have arisen from native sons rather than displaced Florentines, some of whom were trained in Florence during the times of the Medici rule.

We see, therefore, an interesting pattern. Artists throughout Italy were nurtured by the creative and dynamic environment of Florence and then invigorated even further by the diversity and opportunities in the other cities. The result of this synergistic nurturing and invigorating was an elevation of creative talent to a height that may never have been reached in any other period of history. The heights of creativity were especially evident in a few individuals—the masters of the Renaissance. We will discuss these masters in some detail in this chapter.

■ Leonardo da Vinci

The artisans that we discussed in the previous chapter—Ghiberti, Brunelleschi, Masaccio, Donatello, and Botticelli—were great and talented artists, but the great master of the early Renaissance, and the bridge between the early and the high Renaissance, was **Leonardo da Vinci.** Leonardo was a **Renaissance man** in every sense of the term; he was highly creative, inquisitive about the entire world around him, talented in multiple areas, and master of many crafts. During his life he was a painter, musician, architect, engineer, scientist, teacher, historian, optician, cartographer, and adviser to nobles and kings. Leonardo da Vinci embodied the spirit of the Renaissance because he was so talented and well rounded, both artistically and technically. In fact, he saw little difference between art and technology—seeking excellence and fame by doing both together.

Leonardo was born in 1452 near Vinci, a small village just outside Florence. The illegitimate son of a local public notary and a peasant girl, Leonardo was raised in the home of his father (his mother was married to another man shortly after his birth). Leonardo's wide array of interests and talents became apparent early in his life. He had a passion for horses and would study them at length, in time becoming an excellent horse trainer. He was also fascinated by birds and studied them and their flight from an early age and throughout his life. Leonardo was also an excellent singer and could accompany himself on the lyre.

He showed early promise as an artist and was apprenticed at age 14 to a Florentine artist of renown, Andrea Verrocchio, from whom Leonardo learned art and engineering. Leonardo's habit of studying a subject extensively also applied to painting. For instance, before painting a plant, he would study botany; in order to paint humans, he studied anatomy. (After his reputation grew, he was able to convince the authorities of the city to let him dissect bodies of executed criminals, a privilege that was normally forbidden for religious reasons.) Leonardo was accepted into the Florentine Artists Guild at age 20, and, shortly thereafter, Verrocchio allowed him to take an important role in creating several commissioned paintings. Not long afterward, Leonardo opened his own studio in Florence and was soon a highly recognized and sought-after artist. Leonardo may have been the first artist to be able to create works of art on his own volition (without a sponsor) and then hold them for later sale. This practice illustrates the high demand for his artistic works.

Leonardo was an important figure in solidifying the characteristics of Renaissance painting by using (improving) the techniques developed as part of Renaissance art (which we discussed in the previous chapter) and by adding techniques that were uniquely his own. His painting, *Madonna of the Rocks,* which is shown in Figure 28.1, illustrates many of these techniques. Note, for instance, the triangular arrangement of the figures in the painting that draws attention to the important figures of Mary and the baby Jesus. He was praised for this arrangement, and others copied it widely throughout the Renaissance. We can also see the use of atmospheric perspective in the bluish-gray and lightly-defined mountains in the far background. We also see the use of a sophisticated type of diminution perspective in Mary's arm, which appears to be thrust toward the viewer. This method of diminution perspective is called **foreshortening.** This painting also demonstrates a technique of contrasting color and lighting that is called *chiaroscuro* (which means "light and dark"). In this technique, the lighting of the scene comes from a particular direction to highlight strongly some elements of the painting and to create dark shadows in other areas. The effect of this technique is to create increased three-dimensionality, and also drama. By the orientation of the figures in the scene, the faces and other features of the people can be emphasized, as is done in *Madonna of the Rocks.*

Leonardo's best use of linear perspective is demonstrated in *The Last Supper,* a fresco he created while in Milan. He went there shortly after the decline of the Medici rule and rise of Savonarola in Florence. He received a commission to paint the wall of the refectory (dining hall)

Figure 28.1 ■ Madonna of the Rocks *by Leonardo da Vinci.* © National Gallery, London/Art Resource, NY.

of a monastery. The supper of the apostles and Christ was deemed to be an ideal subject for such a place. The fresco is on the end wall of the room and gives the impression that Christ and the apostles are literally within the room with the monks (Figure 28.2A).

The strong linear perspective seems to suggest that the room goes on beyond the table where the last supper is served, thus bringing the apostles into the room with the monks. Note also, as is shown in the diagram in Figure 28.2B, that the vanishing point or focal point of the perspective is in the middle of Christ's forehead, thus giving him the central focus of the painting. It is also interesting to note that the right wall of the painted room in which Christ and the apostles are sitting is lighted, whereas the left wall is in shadow. This lighting is consistent with the window arrangement of the refractory in which the fresco is painted, thus adding even more realism to the scene.

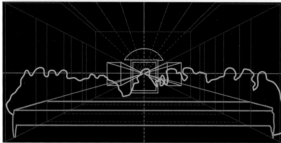

Figure 28.2 ■ **A)** The Last Supper *by Leonardo da Vinci.* **B)** *Diagram of the perspective in da Vinci's* Last Supper. *A) © Ted Spiegel/CORBIS.*

The poor quality of the fresco surface is due to an experiment in fresco materials that Leonardo conducted when he painted the scene. The experiment did not work well, but by the time the problem was discovered, the work had progressed too far to start over. Sadly, this poor condition means that the number of people who can visit the fresco is highly limited and great care must be taken to preserve the fresco from further decay. It is interesting to note, however, that during World War II the building in which the fresco is located was bombed, but the fresco itself suffered no damage.

Leonardo's principal position while in Milan was in the court of Duke Sforza as an architect and military engineer. It seems that the duke granted Leonardo the position for which he had no real training or experience, due in large part to Leonardo's having written the duke an astonishing letter in which he stated that he could build portable bridges, that he knew the techniques of constructing bombardments and of making cannons, and that he could build ships as well as armored vehicles, catapults, and other war machines. Some examples of Leonardo's inventions are shown in Figure 28.3.

While serving in this position, Leonardo was able to explore the more technical side of his genius. He designed a revolving stage and sets for plays, as well as a device that allowed the viewing of an eclipse without hurting the eyes. He also began a never-completed book on hydraulic works. Leonardo spent time teaching the Sforza family a wide array of subjects including mechanics, biology, math, physics, and art.

Although Leonardo's primary focus while under the patronage of Duke Sforza was more technological than artistic, the duke did not let Leonardo's artistic talent go unused. Leonardo was commissioned to sculpt a gigantic bronze equestrian statue of the duke. The sculpture was to

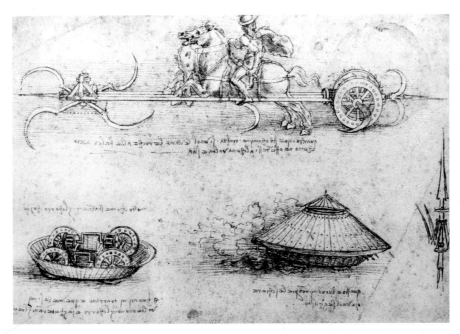

Figure 28.3 ■ Inventions of Leonardo da Vinci. **A)** War machine **B)** Bicycle **C)** Tank. © *2010 by Janaka Dharmasena. Used under license of Shutterstock, Inc.*

be so immense that Leonardo had to invent a new method for its casting. Leonardo returned to his boyhood love of horses and sketched the horse in great detail. He then made a full-size model from which to work. However, the final work was never completed, as the bronze that was to be used for the massive statue ended up as cannons because of an anticipated war with France.

Leonardo da Vinci stayed in Milan until the French armies invaded the city and killed the duke. Leonardo then left Milan and spent time in Mantua and Urbino before returning to Florence. During this second stay in Florence, Leonardo was in high demand as a portrait painter. It was during this time that he drew the initial sketches of what was to become his most famous painting, the *Mona Lisa,* which was completed sometime later. The subject of the Mona Lisa was the wife of a local official. She was so morose during the sittings that Leonardo hired jesters to try and make her smile. Eventually, he was able to capture her famous smile and it has, of course, become an intriguing psychological fascination (Figure 28.4).

Figure 28.4 ■ The Mona Lisa *by Leonardo da Vinci.* © *Corel.*

The *Mona Lisa* was an early use of another painting technique pioneered by Leonardo. This technique, called **sfumato** (which means "smoky"), is a technique used to smooth the outlines of elements in the painting to heighten their three-dimensionality and to give them a sensuous softness. The effect is seen in many parts of the *Mona Lisa,* including her famous smile and her hands. The light and shading technique in the Mona Lisa is exceptionally good and reflects a careful investigation made by Leonardo of angles of light and the corresponding highlights that the light creates. Note, in particular, that the forehead and bosom of the woman are lighted the same, suggesting a light coming from her upper right.

During this time, Leonardo increased his study of anatomy and even dug up the bodies of criminals in order to dissect and study them. From this information he wrote an anatomy text that was used in medical schools for many years. Leonardo was also commissioned to paint a wall in Florence's city hall. Working on another wall in the same room at the same time was Michelangelo. An intense rivalry arose between the two. Eventually, Leonardo quit without finishing the work, although historians disagree on the reason. Some argue that the intense pressure in competing with Michelangelo proved too much (Michelangelo did not finish his wall, either), while the more common view is that Leonardo simply gave up because the new technique he was trying did not work and the painting was deteriorating as he was creating it. Neither Leonardo's nor Michelangelo's frescos survive, although we do have some sketches that show what they might have looked like had they been finished.

It was also during this stay in Florence that the city of Florence went to war with its neighboring rival, Pisa. During this conflict an interesting collaboration occurred. In an effort to gain the upper hand against Pisa, the strategy of Florence was to divert the Arno River, the primary water source for both Florence and Pisa, so that it would no longer run its normal course to Pisa, thus depriving that city of its water supply. The men overseeing the project were Machiavelli, the civic leader, and da Vinci, the engineer.[1] The diversion project was never fully implemented, but in the end it did not matter as Florence eventually won the war.

Leonardo's notebooks, in which most of his technical notes were recorded, contain a wealth of information about scientific experiments he conducted, observations he made, questions he noted for future investigation, and comments about life as he saw it. Some of the comments are worth repeating here:

■ "He who neglects to punish evil sanctions the doing thereof."

■ "It is easier to resist at the beginning than at the end."

■ "Think well to the end, consider the end first."

■ "Poor is the pupil who does not surpass his master."

■ "He who wishes to become rich in a day is hanged in a year."[2]

In 1507, the French king, Louis XII, asked Leonardo to be his court painter and engineer. Leonardo accepted the position, although he regularly traveled back and forth between Italy and France until 1516, when he finally settled down permanently in France. He continued art and engineering—designing several palaces for the new king, Francis I. Three years later, Leonardo da Vinci, a true Renaissance man with one of the most expansive minds of all time, died in Cloux, France, near the city of Amboise where he lived. Today, a nice museum in Leonardo's home can be visited there. While respected during his life as a great artist and intelligent man, after his death Leonardo's reputation became even greater as others studied his extensive notebooks. Only then did the world realize how creative and extraordinary he was. Besides fabulous works of art such as the *Last Supper,* the *Mona Lisa,* and the *Madonna of the Rocks,* Leonardo's notebooks revealed endless notes and sketches dealing with science and mathematics, as well as blueprints and outlines for all types of technological devices such as armored tanks, pontoon bridges, multiple-fire weapons, helicopters, machine tools, wind-powered machines, bicycles, gear-driven cars, submarines, double-hulled ships, diving suits, and hundreds of other practical and creative inventions. He may have been the most creative man to ever live.

■ Michelangelo Buonarroti

One of these great artists, possibly the greatest of the entire Renaissance, was **Michelangelo Buonarroti.** He was born in a small village outside of Florence in 1475, the son of a stone cutter. He was apprenticed to the studio of Domenico and David Ghirlandaio, where his talent was so obvious that rather than paying an apprenticeship fee to the studio masters, they paid him a small salary. After a few years there, Michelangelo enrolled in the sculpture studio of Bertoldo di Giovanni. Normally a three-year apprenticeship, Michelangelo stayed for only one, since the master said he could teach Michelangelo no more because Michelangelo already knew more than he did. Therefore, undoubtedly because of his early successes, at age 15 Michelangelo was invited to live and work in the home of Florence's civil leader, Lorenzo de Medici, where he was treated like a son.

Upon the death of Lorenzo de Medici, Michelangelo fell out of favor with the Medici family when he became a follower of the crusading priest Savonarola. Because of the teachings of Savonarola, Michelangelo resolved to never again use pagan themes in his work.

The political situation in Florence under Savonarola was very delicate, so Michelangelo left for Rome. While in Rome, Michelangelo received a commission from one of the cardinals to sculpt a *Pietà,* a statue of Mary holding the body of her dead son, Jesus. Upon completion of the work, the *Pietà* received much acclaim and is generally still held to be the greatest *Pietà* ever sculpted. Michelangelo was very proud of the work and became enraged one evening when he overheard an admirer give credit for the work to another sculptor. To ensure that this mistake would not happen again, Michelangelo returned that night with his tools and carved his name on the sash across Mary's chest—the only piece he ever signed. The *Pietà* is shown in Figure 28.5.

Michelangelo then returned again to Florence to work on a commission to do the *David.* Originally designed to be placed high on the exterior of the cathedral, Michelangelo's *David* is huge and powerful. Tradition says that the block of marble he carved it from was so massive that it could not be brought down the mountain because of the steep grade and sharp curves. Thus Michelangelo

Figure 28.5 ■ The Pietà by Michelangelo. © *2010 by Hal_P. Used under license of Shutterstock, Inc.*

had to design and oversee the building of a new road from the marble quarry down the mountain. The city fathers were so impressed with the completed statue that they decided to place it in the town plaza instead of on top of the cathedral. It was also at this time that Michelangelo was commissioned to paint a wall in the city hall in a competition with Leonardo da Vinci. As has been mentioned, for one reason or another, neither artist completed his work. The original *David* is now located in a special building in Florence, called the Academy, and a duplicate stands in the town square.

Michelangelo returned to Rome to work on the tomb of Pope Julius II. Michelangelo's famous statue of *Moses* was one of the pieces carved for the tomb. The *Moses* is so lifelike that, upon its completion, Michelangelo reputedly tapped it with his hammer and commanded it to speak. The *Moses* is certainly realistic, as shown in Figure 28.6, but he does have one peculiarity—horns. Michelangelo gave his *Moses* horns because the Bible used in his day contained a mistranslation. The Old Testament, written in the original Hebrew, lacked vowels. Because of this, the priests and

scholars who translated the Bible from Hebrew into Latin often were required to decide between two or more words that could be represented by the same Hebrew consonants. Such a case occurred in the account of Moses descending from Mount Sinai, where the Bible says that Moses had "something" extending from his head. The translator, Jerome, saw the Hebrew letters that we render in English as "KRN" and had to decide which word was intended, since those letters could reasonably stand for *karnaim* (horns) or *koren* (light), both of which have the letters "KRN" with different vowels. Jerome chose horns and Michelangelo, faithful to the biblical text, sculpted Moses accordingly.

The *Moses* was only one of several pieces Michelangelo carved for Pope Julius' tomb. The tomb, however, was to be so elaborate and have so much statuary that it took 34 carts of marble. Michelangelo was forced to pay for all of this marble in advance out of his own pocket, and was then to be reimbursed by the church. However, the church was very slow in paying him back (in fact, he was never fully reimbursed for his expenses), and this made him a virtual prisoner in Rome, as he dared not leave for very long for fear he would never get his money.

Although being trapped in Rome was not good for Michelangelo, for the Catholic Church and art lovers throughout the world, it was a very good thing. Still waiting for the church to pay him back for his expenses on Julius' tomb, and with debts that needed to be paid, Michelangelo accepted another commission from the church. This time he was to fresco the ceiling of the Sistine Chapel. Michelangelo worked feverishly, often sleeping on the scaffolding at night and rarely coming down to bathe or care for himself. Supposedly, when he finally took off his boots, pieces of skin came off, too. Amazingly, in spite of the size of the ceiling, great detail of the work, and difficulty of painting on his back, Michelangelo completed the Sistine Chapel in just four short years, finishing in 1512. The completed work overwhelmed the pope and all those who saw it. It was then, and by many today, considered the greatest art work ever completed.

Upon completion of the Sistine Chapel, Michelangelo remained in Rome four more years

Figure 28.6 ■ Moses by Michelangelo. © *2010 by imagestalk. Used under license of Shutterstock, Inc.*

continuing work on Pope Julius' tomb (and trying to collect his money). Michelangelo finally left Rome (temporarily giving up on Julius' tomb and his money) and traveled around Italy for the next 16 years, working in several cities for different patrons. During this time he worked on various projects, including the Medici Chapel in Florence. In 1532, he finally returned to Rome to continue work on Julius' tomb and to renegotiate the contract once again.

However, after only two years of work, the new pope, Paul III, ordered Michelangelo to stop work on the tomb and begin the *Last Judgment* altarpiece in the Sistine Chapel. It took him seven years to paint the fabulous *Last Judgment.* After its completion, Michelangelo recommenced work on Pope Julius' tomb, as well as a series of frescos for Pope Paul III.

The mood of the time had begun to shift somewhat and Michelangelo's use of nudes in the *Last Judgment* brought some serious criticism. So, to avoid future criticism, Michelangelo focused his efforts on architecture and poetry. His most important architectural commission was for the massive St. Peter's cathedral in Rome. Although work had already begun on this massive structure, Michelangelo redesigned the cathedral's massive dome. During this last decade of his life, he also designed his own tomb and sculpted a few pieces for it. Michelangelo was, however, displeased with many of his works from this period, and was only prevented from destroying them because of the pleas of his students. He died in 1564 of old age, telling his pupils: "I regret that I am dying just as I am beginning to learn the alphabet of my profession."

Although Leonardo was probably the ultimate Renaissance man, Michelangelo is the likely choice for greatest Renaissance artist. A master of painting, sculpture, and architecture, he thought of himself first and foremost as a sculptor. He said that he could see the figures in the stones and that his job was merely to cut away the excess material to free the figures. It is a fitting tribute to his amazing talent that his greatest work is probably a fresco, the ceiling of the Sistine Chapel, yet he is still known as possibly the world's greatest sculptor.

■ Raphael

Another master of the high Renaissance period was the artist Raffaello Sanzio, commonly known as **Raphael.** Born in 1483 in the city of Urbino, Raphael was exposed to the world of Renaissance art early in life as his father was a court painter in Urbino. At age 16, Raphael was sent to the city of Perugia and was apprenticed to the painter Perugino. While working there Raphael imitated the style of his master so closely that modern art historians often have trouble distinguishing which artist painted many of the paintings that came from Perugino's studio at this time.

This skill of observing another artist's technique and then reproducing it proved quite beneficial to Raphael as he followed in the footsteps of several Renaissance masters. By studying the works of Leonardo, Raphael was able to learn geometric arrangement, accurate perspective, and the use of light and shadow. Similarly, Raphael learned to paint the human figure by studying the works of Michelangelo. Like the other masters, Raphael's abilities were not solely in art. For instance, he became skilled in archeology because of his efforts to learn about ancient Roman culture.

Upon completing his apprenticeship, Raphael went to Florence to participate in the nurturing atmosphere of that city. While there, he painted many of the madonnas for which he is famous. Raphael's madonnas are especially sweet and loving in appearance, which some critics believe came from Raphael's habit of carrying a sketch pad with him so that when he saw a woman or child on the street who conveyed maternal love and beauty, he could capture their likeness at the moment he observed it.

In 1508, Pope Julius II summoned Raphael to Rome to fulfill a commission to decorate the staterooms in the Vatican. This is when Raphael painted his famous fresco *The School of Athens,* which is shown in Figure 28.7. Raphael's *School of Athens* may be the ultimate example of Renaissance painting techniques—realism, perspective, geometric arrangement, *chiaroscuro,* and a classical setting. The fresco depicts a school, possibly the ancient Greek Academy, where Plato and Aristotle are teaching the great thinkers of the ages. Besides

Figure 28.7 ■ The School of Athens *by Raphael.* © *Ted Spiegel/CORBIS*

Plato and Aristotle, the *School of Athens* also depicts Socrates, Pythagoras, Euclid, Ptolemy, Zoroaster, Heraclitus, and Averroes, among many others. Raphael paid tribute to the Renaissance masters that came before him by depicting Leonardo da Vinci as Plato, the architect Bramante as Euclid, and Michelangelo as Heraclitus. Raphael also painted himself into the painting, but not as a great thinker of the past. The presence of this non-Christian scene in the Vatican, mere feet from the Sistine Chapel where new popes are elected, shows the extent to which the classical influence permeated even the Catholic Church, the most conservative institution of the Renaissance.

Raphael was painting the Vatican staterooms at the same time that Michelangelo was working on the Sistine Chapel. The close proximity of these two artists offers us an interesting insight into the personalities of two very talented, but different men. Raphael was good-looking, well-mannered,

fashionable and popular, while Michelangelo was surly and reclusive. Raphael always used assistants when he worked, whereas Michelangelo almost always worked alone, at least in his early and middle years. There is a noted occasion where once the two men passed on the street and Michelangelo, upon seeing the stylish and popular younger painter, commented that Raphael looked more like a prince than a painter. Raphael then replied that Michelangelo looked more like an executioner.

Raphael was also a noted architect, and was given the commission to be the architect for St. Peter's Cathedral when the original architect, Bramante, died. Raphael changed the design from the Greek cross shape (in which the legs of the cross have equal length) envisioned by Bramante to the Latin cross (one elongated leg). Many other design changes made by Raphael were changed by subsequent architects. (Michelangelo's commission to work on the cathedral followed Raphael's death.) Raphael died from a fever caught while on a dig serving as Rome's first director of antiquities. He was only 37 years old. Fittingly, Raphael was buried in the Pantheon, the ancient Roman temple to all of the gods.

■ Titian and the Venetian School

Florence was the birthplace of the Renaissance and the place where the greatest of Renaissance artists—Leonardo, Michelangelo, and Raphael—all received important training. The sponsorship of the Medici family and other civic and professional groups created both the desire and the means to develop a highly refined artistic culture. However, the political chaos that followed the death of Lorenzo de Medici led to the exodus of many great artists, including all three of the great masters. Other Italian cities therefore benefited directly from these great artists. That was especially true in Rome, where the popes were attempting to rebuild the city after the 72-year-move of the center of the church to Avignon, France, in the fourteenth century. While the papacy was centered in France, Rome became a forgotten and decrepit city. Churches were used to stable animals, and many of the ancient sites were destroyed as citizens used the ancient stones for building their houses and outbuildings. This was when the ancient Roman Forum was called "the camp of cows" because animals were allowed to graze there. All three of the great masters of the Renaissance were part of the effort to reconstruct Rome.

Other Italian city-states saw and envied the cultural progress of Florence and Rome. Venice, in particular, was anxious to create a vibrant new culture based on humanistic concepts, but, as was always the case with Venice, it did not want to merely mimic the other Italian cities. Because Venice was founded by the Byzantines and used by them as their primary port of entry to Europe throughout much of the Middle Ages, Venice had always considered itself separate from the rest of Italy in both culture and politics. The Venetian cathedral, for instance, was built in the Byzantine

style. Political treaties and trade were contracted separately from the rest of Italy, occasionally even favoring enemies of the other Italian city-states. Therefore, it is not surprising that Venetians established their own academy of learning and their own school of art. The foremost of the artists in the Venetian school was Vecellio Tiziano, known to us as **Titian.** We know of a fresco he assisted with in 1508, thus dating him to exactly the same period of time as Leonardo, Michelangelo, and Raphael.

Much of Titian's work was commissioned by the churches, civic institutes (such as the art academy), and wealthy patrons of Venice. We can see the same classical influences in his art and many of the same techniques that were demonstrated by the artists of the Florentine Renaissance, but some aspects of his art seem to be different from other artists of his day. Those characteristics were continued by other Venetian painters, thus establishing a unique Venetian school. The most obvious of these differences are seen in Titian's painting of *Bacchus and Ariadne,* which is shown in Figure 28.8. We see, in particular, a greater use of vibrant colors and considerably more dynamic and dramatic action in Titian's work. This work also suggests more sensuality (sexual) than in Florentine paintings, and that tendency became even more pronounced in later works and is consistent with the reputation of Venice as a worldly and sensual city (typical of cities with many sailors and port activities).

■ Renaissance Music

Music was slower to change during the Renaissance than other forms of art because it was dominated by the traditions of the Catholic Church. Because music was primarily used for the mass, it was kept simple and monophonic[a] so that the words of the mass could be easily heard and understood. In fact, during the early Renaissance,

---

[a]A single line or melody without accompaniment.

Figure 28.8 ■ Bacchus and Ariadne *by Titian.* © *National Gallery, London/Art Resource, NY.*

polyphony[b] was still thought of by the church as "devil music." However, changes were to come to music as well during the Renaissance. Those advances included the refinement of musical notation, the use of homophony,[c] and the invention of several new instruments such as the harpsichord, trumpet, trombone, and an early organ.

The most important composer of the 1400s was **Guillaume Dufay.** Dufay wrote both religious and secular music, but was most important for his blending of the two, which helped loosen the grip of the Catholic Church over musical forms. One of the most important changes introduced by Dufay was the secularization of the *motet.* The motet was a choral work that had originally been used in religious settings. However, Dufay wrote motets for coronations, noble marriages, and the signings of peace treaties. Secular motets caught on quickly with Renaissance nobility and wealthy merchants. Thus, composers who could write secular motets on short notice found work in the courts of the various Italian city-states.

Dufay was also among the first to take secular music and turn it into a religious piece. Dufay's best-known example of this is the *"L'homme armé"* mass, in which he blended the music of a French folk tune, *"L'homme armé" ("The Armored Man"),* with the form of a mass. Other composers soon followed his example, and these **chanson masses** were composed and used for the next 200 years. This blending of things secular and religious is, of course, very characteristic of the Renaissance.

The most important Renaissance composer was **Giovanni Palestrina.** Palestrina spent most of his life in Rome and held various important po-

---

[b]Two or more melodic lines of equal importance combined into a multi-voiced texture.

[c]A principal melody with accompanying harmony chords or melodies. The accompanying melodies are less important than the principal melody.

sitions including director of music for the Vatican, singer in the chorus of the Sistine Chapel, and choirmaster of St. Peter's Cathedral (although he was moved in and out of this position, depending on whether the current pope allowed a married man to hold it). Palestrina composed in the late sixteenth century, after the deaths of Raphael and Leonardo and when Michelangelo was an old man. The church during this time had become more conservative in music because of its desire to make the mass more meaningful for the members of the church. Many of the changes introduced in the previous century by Dufay and his followers were deemed by the church to be distracting from the words of the mass and thus were being suppressed. The church was discouraging the use of polyphony because, with many different melodies, it was complicated, and it usually obscured the words of the mass.

Palestrina worked under these strict conditions and wrote very conservative masses. However, Palestrina continued to use polyphony and was able to demonstrate that polyphony could be used without being distractive. Palestrina's genius came from his idea to use medieval Gregorian chants as the basis for his polyphonic renditions and then to limit the other voices to clear and simple melodies that blended beautifully with the basic chant. Palestrina's most famous work is the *Mass in Honor of Pope Marcellus,* but he wrote over a hundred masses, many of which used polyphony, achieving purity and beauty of both instrumental and vocal voices. Palestrina is credited with saving polyphony (which is the basis for many important forms of later music) and was buried in St. Peter's Cathedral with the epitaph, "The Prince of Music." Several later composers, such as Verdi and Wagner, attributed much of their musical heritage directly to Palestrina.

The Renaissance was also a time that saw a rise in secular music, especially encouraged by the introduction of new instruments. Although there were different styles of secular songs, the most popular in the courts were the **chansons.** Chansons were usually written for three voices and were usually about courtly love. **Madrigals,** also important in the Renaissance, were a form of poetry set to music and usually sung with great emotion. They were often polyphonic. The subject of a madrigal usually was humorous or satirical and often poked fun at the upper class or told about current events, making madrigals especially popular among the common people.

■ The Renaissance Man

In our modern culture, a person who is highly competent in many areas is called a *Renaissance man.* (That person might also be a woman, but in the days of the Renaissance the males dominated public creative works and so the "man" title has remained.) Naming such a person a Renaissance man clearly came from recognition of the capabilities of the great Renaissance masters like Leonardo, Michelangelo, and Raphael. We see their superb artistic talents but also see incredible talents in engineering, anatomy, architecture, and a host of other fields. We might ask, therefore, what level of expertise is required, and over how many areas, to qualify someone as a Renaissance man and, perhaps more appropriate for the subject of this book, what is the relationship between being creative and being a Renaissance man?

The first qualification for being a Renaissance man is familiarity with and perhaps expertise in many different areas of knowledge. Such a broad capability was shown by Plato and Aristotle, who surely served as models for their students. They wrote about philosophy, physics, politics, drama, biology, and many other topics. Alexander, a student of Aristotle, showed the diversity of his interests by taking scientists with him on his war campaigns, just as Napoleon did two millennia later. We can see many other examples in the ancient world, in the Renaissance, and in modern times.

We must be careful, however, that we are not led into too narrow a view of diversity. The explosion of information in modern times has led to a narrowing of fields of inquiry just to be able to understand the wealth of knowledge available. For instance, in the ancient world, the study of alchemy included all changes in all materials that were brought about by chemical reactions. Today, the field of chemistry is divided into areas such as organic, inorganic, analytical, physical, and biochemical. Under such narrowing of fields, a chemist might think that diversity means capability in more than one branch of chemistry. Such a definition would not, in general, qualify that chemist as a Renaissance man. To be truly diverse, in the Renaissance sense, means to be capable in fields that encompass the entire spectrum of human knowledge. We might consider the extremes of this knowledge as extending from the humanities to the sciences. Plato, Aristotle, Leonardo, Michelangelo, and Raphael certainly qualified as capable in areas from the humanities to the sciences and there have been many others. Some prominent examples are Francis Bacon, Isaac Newton, Benjamin Franklin, Thomas Jefferson, Theodore Roosevelt, and Albert Einstein.

Each Renaissance man was not only capable across a broad range of disciplines but also was at the forefront of knowledge and accomplishment in at least one particular area. The Renaissance men made significant contributions to their particular domain and would have probably been famous just for the accomplishments in the particular field. In fact, merely having a broad knowledge, without an expertise in some particular area, is probably not sufficient to qualify a person as a Renaissance man. The depth seems to bring an understanding of the nature of knowledge and a context for arranging that knowledge that cannot be gained simply by breadth alone. It is as if a person cannot tell the significance of his or her knowledge in any area until there is depth in some specific area. Both breadth and depth are required.

The combination of breadth and depth leads directly to the concept of creativity. Most experts in the study of creativity agree that the combination of breadth and depth is critically important. The depth in one field allows a person to understand what is required to be at or near the forefront of knowledge in some area of inquiry. That understanding allows the person to gauge knowledge in other fields so that he or she has a feeling for when enough is known to have a moderate mastery of the field. The breadth of knowledge gives the Renaissance man a capability to interrelate knowledge from diverse fields so that knowledge is given new application.

The field of creativity speaks of both depth and breadth in terms of linear and lateral thinking. Creativity is best done by employing both of these thinking methods. They naturally are connected with thinking in the left and right sides of the brain. The most creative people are those who can effectively use all their brain.

We need more people to become Renaissance men. By this, we do not denigrate those who are strictly specialists, but we believe that some types of creativity are most enhanced by making analogies and other connections between different and diverse fields, and that can best be done by people who are skilled in multiple areas. The secret to becoming a Renaissance man is curiosity about the entire world around us and a desire, coupled with determination, to explore and become competent wherever that curiosity leads.

▪ Creative Ideas and the Renaissance

The Renaissance was a time of great change. With the coming of the Renaissance and the new blending of things religious and secular, Europe was finally able to leave behind the long period of creative stagnation that was brought on by the fall of the Roman Empire one thousand years before. The reintroduction of classical thinking and a desire to return to the glories of ancient Rome encouraged people to be more open and creative. Although religion was still very important, there was also a new emphasis on the abilities and glories of humans. Those abilities were appreciated in the past and rewarded in the present. Creativity and education were encouraged, and the newfound wealth of the rising merchant class gave rise to an explosion of knowledge of all varieties— art, architecture, music, political thought, science, and technology. Culture made great leaps forward, and daily life became better and richer for everyone.

Some highly skilled and creative individuals became cultural icons, even in their own days.

Some of the most important of these people were Leonardo, Michelangelo, Raphael, and Palestrina. These great individuals represented ideals of Renaissance behavior. They were masters of a few areas and competently familiar with many, many more. They viewed life in terms of completeness rather than narrow specialization. Even Michelangelo, who viewed himself as a sculptor, was comfortable with painting, architecture, engineering, and poetry. Leonardo was, of course, more than comfortable in most of those same areas and many others. They all had insatiable curiosity and the will to pursue learning wherever it might be found. Leonardo said, "Iron rusts from disuse, stagnant water loses its purity and in cold weather becomes frozen; even so does inaction sap the vigor of the mind. . . . The natural desire of good men is knowledge." These great masters, Renaissance men, were examples of learning and creativity for all others over all subsequent times.

A summary of the creative developments of Renaissance art is probably appropriate at this stage of our discussion. These artistic characteristics began with the earliest Renaissance artists, like Masaccio, Brunelleschi, Donatello, and Botticelli, and then were expanded and improved by Leonardo, Michelangelo, and Raphael. The **principal characteristics of Renaissance art** include the following:

- **Realism.** People are represented as they really were or could have been, rather than just symbolic representations, and depicting appropriate emotion.
- **Diverse subject matter.** Pagan themes are included, in addition to religious themes.
- **Simple and clean lines and designs.** Designs reflect a desire to return to the geometric and symmetric standards of the ancient Greeks.
- **Perspective.** Many techniques are used to give three-dimensionality to the picture—especially the technique of linear perspective.
- **Geometric arrangement of figures.** To emphasize some figures in the painting over others of less importance, figures are placed geometrically, especially in triangular arrangements.

- **Chiaroscuro.** Light and dark shading enhanced three-dimensionality and also added to realism.
- **Sfumato.** Multiple layers of paint are applied to achieve a kind of smokiness that softened edges of figures in the painting to make them appear natural.

■ Timeline—Important Dates

Date	Event
1452 A.D.	Birth of Leonardo da Vinci
1467–1483	Leonardo in Florence
1475	Michelangelo born
1483	Birth of Raphael
1489	Decline of Medici power and migration of artists
1495–1498	The Last Supper painted by Leonardo in Milan
1498–1499	Pietà sculpted in Rome by Michelangelo
1501–1504	David sculpted in Florence by Michelangelo
1504	Bramante begins work on St. Peter's cathedral
1505–1512	Michelangelo in Rome—Julius' tomb/Sistine Chapel
1507	Leonardo to France (intermittent to 1516)
1508	Raphael in Rome—School of Athens
1514	Death of Bramante, Raphael architect for St. Peter's
1516	Titian becomes court painter in Venice
1519	Death of Leonardo
1522	Death of Raphael
1534–1541	Michelangelo paints Last Judgment in the Sistine Chapel
1534	Michelangelo appointed architect for St. Peter's
1564	Death of Michelangelo
1567	Palestrina composes Pope Marcellus Mass
1576	Titian dies of plague

■ Notes

1. Masters, Roger, *Machiavelli, Leonardo, and the Science of Power* (South Bend: University of Notre Dame Press, 1996), 15–16.

2. Da Vinci, Leonardo, *The Notebooks of Leonardo Da Vinci* (Old Saybrook, CT: Konecky & Konecky, 2003), 90–92.

■ Suggested Readings

Da Vinci, Leonardo, *The Notebooks of Leonardo Da Vinci,* Konecky & Konecky.

King, Ross, *Michelangelo and the Pope's Ceiling,* Walker and Co., 2003.

Snow, C. P., *The Two Cultures,* Cambridge University Press, 1998.

Van Doren, Charles, *A History of Knowledge,* Ballantine Books, 1991.

Protestant Reformation
Courageous Creativity

> Unless I am proved wrong by scriptures or by evident reason, then I am a prisoner in conscience to the word of God. I cannot retract and I will not retract. To go against the conscience is neither safe nor right. God help me. Amen.
>
> —*Luther (at the Diet of Worms)*

■ Background of the Reformation

The Italian Renaissance's emphasis on humanism—a focus on the value of the individual—naturally diminished the importance of institutions and organizations in people's lives. This diminishing of institutional importance was especially true in the case of the Catholic Church—the dominant institution of the Middle Ages—not only because of the rise of humanism, but also because of an ever-expanding recognition of the corruption of the church. As the Renaissance was dawning, the church was striving to rebuild Rome after the debacle of the seven-decade-long transfer of church headquarters to Avignon, France, in the late thirteenth and early fourteenth centuries. This rebuilding effort required great sums of money, and the church sought to find the funds through sources of income that many believed were, at a minimum, inappropriate. For many, they were blatantly evil.

These funding efforts included such questionable practices as **indulgences** (paying to diminish time in purgatory through forgiveness of sins, sometimes even before the sins were committed); **simony** (selling of church positions); **dispensations** (selling of papal exceptions to normal church rules such as ending a marriage, marrying someone closer than the laws of sanguinity would allow, taking a position in the church before the proper age, and holding of multiple church positions that conflicted in time and location); and conquest through war (wherein some of the popes became military leaders who fought against the kings and emperors of Europe to increase the territory and power of the Papal States).

The result of this highly objectionable situation (at least for many people) eventually led to a revolt against the church, principally led by **Martin Luther,** a German monk, but soon joined by many other people in many other locations. This movement came to be called the **Protestant Reformation,** and it changed the religious situation in Europe more profoundly than any other event or series of events since the conversion of the Roman Emperor Constantine in the fourth century. The history of Europe would be profoundly affected by the forces of the Protestant Reformation for centuries afterward. However, Martin Luther did not initially envision changes of the magnitude that he unleashed. How the situation grew to the intensity that it did is critical in understanding not only the history of the Protestant Reformation but also the fascinating creative thoughts and actions that led to the changes that we will examine. First, however, we should look back at other people, prior to Luther, who attempted to reform the Catholic Church.

The most important of the early reformers, especially for those who speak English, was **John Wycliffe,** who lived in the fourteenth century. He was a scholar who gained a Doctor of Theology degree and taught at Oxford. From that position he spoke out against certain doctrines of the church with which he disagreed, such as transubstantiation (the literal turning of the bread and wine of the Eucharist into the flesh and blood of Christ). He also criticized some practices of the church, such as the excessive use of excommunication as a method to enforce church loyalty, even though the excommunicant had committed no sin worthy of the punishment; the requirement of celibacy for priests; the holding of vast land tracts by the church; and the worshiping of "dumb wooden idols." Wycliffe even headed an English contingent to a conference of clerics and scholars in Ghent (now part of Belgium) to consider papal excesses. The conference failed to rally support for any reforms.

Wycliffe's criticisms soon brought him into conflict with the church hierarchy, and a trial was held for his excommunication. During the trial, Wycliffe's supporters protested so vigorously that the trial ended without a verdict. That outcome may also have been influenced by the strong support of Wycliffe by John of Gaunt, the son of the English king. Later, those supporters, who were called **Lollards,** staged an unsuccessful revolt against the church.

Wycliffe's most enduring contribution is his translation of the Bible into English. This act defied church policy that required the Bible to be written only in the approved Latin version of Jerome (which was made in the fifth century). This had effectively limited the reading of the Bible to scholars and clerics. Wycliffe believed that the Bible should be read by all people—a position that anticipated the humanist movement. Wycliffe's translation was well received among scholars. Later, when the King James Version of the Bible was created in the early seventeenth century, it would use the Wycliffe version as an important reference.

Wycliffe died in 1384 of natural causes. However, the continuing antipathy of the church toward him was demonstrated when, 40 years after Wycliffe's death, the pope ordered that his bones be exhumed and burned to ashes, likely to prevent Wycliffe's followers from treating him as a saint and using his bones as relics.

Another important reformer was **Jan Hus of Bohemia,** who lived a generation after Wycliffe. Hus was a supporter of the reforms suggested by Wycliffe, and he published tracts indicating this support. He also criticized other church practices and, in particular, denied papal infallibility. These actions would normally have resulted in an inquisition and conviction of Hus as a heretic, but he was protected by Wenceslas, the Holy Roman Emperor. When Wenceslas died in 1414, the church hierarchy requested that Hus be sent to a church council in Constance, Germany, to discuss the various points of dispute. The new emperor, Sigismund, wanted to settle the issue and gave Hus a promise of safe conduct (protection from harm) if Hus would go to the council. Hus agreed to go under those circumstances, but when he arrived, a trial was convened. Hus was found guilty and sentenced to death. Sigismund refused to honor his promise of safety, and so Hus was burned at the stake.

■ Martin Luther

Born in 1483 (only eight years after the birth of Michelangelo) to peasants in central Germany, Luther came from a common heritage and was proud of it throughout his life. He was a bright young man who studied at the University in nearby Erfurt and obtained both a bachelor's degree in liberal arts and a master's degree in law. He anticipated pursuing a doctorate in law, but shortly after receiving his master's degree, Luther's life changed because of a traumatic event that occurred while he was traveling. Luther was caught in a fierce rain and lightning storm that was so violent Luther believed he might die. In the midst of this personal turmoil, Luther prayed for God's protection and promised that if God would spare him, Luther would dedicate the remainder of his life to God's service. The storm abated and Luther lived. He then kept his promise and joined the Order of Austin just three months after graduating with his master's degree. He was ordained in 1505. Because of his obvious intelligence, Luther was able to enter Wittenburg University, where he studied theology and graduated with a doctorate in 1512. He then became a professor of theology at Wittenburg.

While teaching theology, Luther became depressed about his own laxness in keeping the strict rules of the church. For instance, his busy study and teaching schedule sometimes resulted in his neglecting to say the proper number of prayers that were required of all monks in his order. He therefore kept a record of the missed prayers and then, when he had time, such as on a Saturday, he would dedicate long hours to saying the prayers so that he could "catch up." Under these conditions, the prayers became rote and meaningless, and Luther increasingly questioned the value of complying with such seemingly meaningless church rules. He felt that his religious actions had shifted from devotion to Christ to mere compliance with the church. He became confused and depressed because of this conflict in his mind between the requirements of the church and his faith in Christ.

Adding to his depression was the doctrine of the church that all mankind was conceived in sin. He felt this sinfulness strongly, and sought help through the church sacraments. However, his own administration of those sacraments had become quite unfulfilling, and he sensed even less devotion to the rites among many of his fellow priests. This conflicted with the doctrine of the church that required the sacraments for all who would be saved.

Perhaps to help Luther with his depression and also to give him training in church doctrine, the local abbot of Luther's order sent Luther to Rome on a mission. The abbot may have thought that the change in scenery and some immersion in the affairs of the central workings of the church would help Luther find himself again. When Luther arrived at Rome, he was shocked by the open corruption and worldliness of the church hierarchy. He could see the incredible wealth of church officials, rampant immorality of high church officials, disregard for church rules by common priests and nuns, moonlighting of priests to increase their income, commission of civil wrongs that went unpunished because the clergy were exempt from civil laws and taxes, and many of the other abuses characteristic of the Roman church that were mentioned previously in this chapter. When Luther returned to Wittenburg, his depression had deepened rather than lifted.

To resolve this depression, Luther plunged into a study of the scriptures. While reading the book of Romans, Luther read that "a man is justified by faith without the deeds of the law" (Romans 3:28), and he believed that this empowered an individual to find justification from sin (salvation) directly through faith in Christ and without requiring the sacraments of the church.

The logical consequences of his new belief were quite far reaching. For instance, he concluded that the Bible should be available in common languages so that individuals could build their personal faith in Christ. He also felt that the corruption and abuses of the Catholic Church that he had observed in Rome diminished the importance and relevance of the church in people's lives. However, the most important and immediate conflict in Luther's mind was between his new belief and the concept of indulgences. He could not justify the payment of money to receive a forgiveness of sins by the church when he didn't even believe that the church had the *power* to remit sins.

The selling of indulgences arose from several interlocking concepts within the medieval church.

One concept was that punishments could be converted into a monetary value, as was done for civil wrongs under Moses. (If a person caused an injury to someone else, a just compensation could be the payment of monetary damages.) Another concept supporting the practice of selling indulgences was that over many years, the church had accumulated a treasury of grace because of its own good works and the good works and sufferings of the saints. A further related concept was that the church could forgive sins (which was obviously so because of the sacrament of confession), and that the extension of forgiveness of sins to the future was merely an implementation of the reality that forgiveness of sins only had value in the future, anyway.

At the very time Luther was wrestling with his new beliefs, Archbishop Albert of Mainz, Germany needed money to get a papal dispensation because he was underage to be a bishop and he held too many ecclesiastical posts at the same time. He decided on a scheme to raise the money. He would hire an expert salesman, Bishop Tetzel, to sell indulgences in Germany. Some of the money would go to the building of the new St. Peter's cathedral, and a portion would go to Albert for his own purposes. The Holy Roman Emperor, Charles V, supported the scheme as a way to ensure support of the pope for his reign (which was just then commencing).

Luther heard about the campaign to sell indulgences and was deeply troubled over both the concept of indulgences and the obvious monetary motives of the pope and the bishops. In keeping with good academic tradition, Luther expressed his disagreement with the practice by posting a list of **95 theses** (statements of truth) on the door of the chapel of Wittenburg University. He chose to post the theses on October 31, 1517, the day before All Saints' Day, so that the large crowds coming to the church would be sure to see the document. Although most of the theses were doctrinal, such as, "Every truly repentant Christian has a right to full remission of penalty and guilt, even without letters of pardon," and "Hell, purgatory, and heaven seem to differ as do despair, almost-despair, and the assurance of safety," some were clearly emotional

such as, "Why doesn't the pope, a very wealthy man, build St. Peter's cathedral out of his own pocket and not tax the poor Christians?"

Luther prepared a German-language translation of the theses and distributed it widely. Many read the document, agreed with Luther, and further distributed the document. The support for Luther was strong and widespread. Tetzel's ability to sell indulgences in this climate vanished, and so he complained to Bishop Albert, who then complained to the pope. The pope initially believed that the dispute was trivial and of academic interest only, and simply asked the head of Luther's order to silence Luther.

When Luther continued his inflammatory preaching, the Vatican sent a renowned debater, **Bishop Eck,** to confront Luther and embarrass him. The debate between Luther and Eck was spirited but largely academic until Eck asked Luther a critical question: "Do you personally believe that Jan Hus (the man we discussed previously in this chapter who was burned at the stake for heresy) should have been convicted of heresy and executed?" If Luther answered that he believed Hus was falsely convicted, Luther would, in essence, state his opposition to the pope's power and position. If Luther said that Hus was wrongfully convicted, Luther would destroy his credibility with the people. Luther stated that Hus was wrongfully convicted. Shortly thereafter, the pope sent an open letter of reprimand and a warning to Luther in which Luther was prohibited from any further public communication on this matter or risk excommunication. Luther publicly burned the pope's letter and was, therefore, excommunicated.

At this point, Emperor Charles V decided he would become involved. Charles believed that he could prevail upon Luther to accept the authority of the pope and, with some minor penance, return to full fellowship in the church. The emperor hoped that by healing the rift, he could gain the support of the German people who, up to that time, had not supported him as their emperor. Since he was a Belgian who was raised in Spain and had become emperor largely through clever intermarriages and political maneuvering, the Germans viewed him as a foreigner and an interloper. Charles therefore indicated that he would convene a **diet** in the city of Worms to hear the dispute. (A diet is a trial or convocation at which a member of the royalty presides.) Luther agreed to attend, and in 1521 at the Diet of Worms, Charles admonished Luther to stop criticizing the pope and the church. The basic issue of the diet was Luther's acceptance or not of the pope's ultimate authority. After hearing the emperor's statement, Luther gave the famous statement that was used as the quotation beginning this chapter. In essence, Luther stated that the authority of the scriptures and of logic were higher than the authority of the pope. To say otherwise would be against his personal conscience and against the will of God.

Luther left the Diet of Worms a renegade from the church and a candidate for execution by either the church or the emperor. To protect him from that fate, the friendly Frederick the Wise, Duke of Saxony, "kidnapped" Luther and placed him in Wartburg Castle, initially incognito but then openly. By doing this, the duke was able to demonstrate some German political independence from emperor Charles, reduce the power of the pope (which meant that the duke's power over the local clergy was enhanced), and support a person who was immensely popular with the German people. Besides, Luther might just be right.

The duke's actions should be viewed in light of medieval history. Throughout the early Middle Ages, the Catholic Church was the only viable organization in European society. The pope was, therefore, more powerful than any king. This power was tested repeatedly by many kings such as Henry IV of Germany and by Henry II and John of England. However, with the rise of nations and power of the kings in the High Middle Ages, the balance of power shifted to the kings and, as the ultimate example of that, Phillip IV of France briefly arrested the pope and, when that pope soon died, was successful in naming a French pope who transferred the headquarters of the church from Rome to Avignon, where it resided for most of the fourteenth century. The actions of Duke Frederick were merely a continuation of that same dispute, with the addition of the dispute between the local duke and the foreign emperor, also typical of disputes during the Middle Ages. The disputes between popes and kings continued for much of the next century and were only partially resolved in the church's Council of Trent wherein the church agreed that the king would have authority to dictate the religion of all the people in the nation (but more about that later in this chapter).

Luther used the enforced isolation of this "captivity" to formulate his ideas in depth and to write pamphlets explaining his positions on a wide range of religious and political topics. These pamphlets were widely circulated and, about two generations after Gutenberg's invention of the printing press, found a ready readership among the mostly literate German and Scandinavian population. Other writers also contributed to the more than 10,000 pamphlets published between 1500 and 1550, with more than 80 percent of them about religion. The Catholic Church's response was also in pamphlets, but theirs were mostly in Latin and, therefore, did not reach the people.

Luther also translated the Bible into German during this period. His translation has been widely acclaimed and is still used. This translation helped define modern German (along with the writings of Goethe), much as the King James Version of the Bible helped define modern English (along with Shakespeare). Luther wrote prefaces to many books of the Bible to assist the readers in understanding the text and Luther's position on the doctrine taught. For instance, in the preface to Romans Luther wrote,

This letter is truly the most important piece in the New Testament. It is purest Gospel. It is well worth a Christian's while not only to memorize it word for word but also to occupy himself with it daily, as though it were the daily bread of the soul. It is impossible to read or to meditate on this letter too much or too well. The more one deals with it, the more precious it becomes and the better it tastes. . . . You must not understand the word law here in human fashion, i.e., a regulation about what sort of works must be done or must not be done. That's the way it is with human laws: you satisfy the demands of the law with works, whether your heart is in it or not. God judges what is in the depths of the heart. Therefore his law also makes demands on the depths of the heart and doesn't let the heart rest content in works; rather it punishes as hypocrisy and lies all works done apart from the depths of the heart. . . . That is why faith alone makes someone just and fulfills the law; faith it is that brings the Holy Spirit through the merits of Christ. The Spirit, in turn, renders the heart glad and free, as the law demands. Then good works proceed from faith itself.[1]

Luther commented that the Epistle of James, with which he did not agree, was merely an "epistle of straw" because it taught that faith without works was dead. Luther did not actually reject the Epistle of James but, rather, placed it in a subordinate place in the scriptures along with the books of Hebrews, Jude, and Revelation.

Luther eventually emerged from the castle and began to openly preach and gather supporters. In 1542 he established a church, which his supporters insisted on naming the Lutheran Church. Luther decided that he should set an example of his belief that clergy should be married, and therefore he married a former nun with whom he lived contentedly for many years. Luther also became a cultural leader and general father figure for the German people.

He encouraged cultural creations by commenting that humankind is a creation of God and, therefore, any work of art or culture that raises the spirit of humankind is a testament to God's glory and a way to gain the spirit of Christ. These sentiments were the basis for a tremendous acceleration of music and science in northern Europe, beginning with Luther and continuing as a model for others for more than four centuries.

We see a very interesting pattern of creative thinking in Luther. During the early part of his life, he thought linearly. He was an academic with training in law and theology. There was nothing to suggest that he would exhibit the diversity of creativity that he eventually demonstrated. He could have been narrowly creative in an academic sense,

but probably not much more. Then, with some exposure to the wider world, he began an interesting path to wider creativity.

That process probably started with his trip to Rome, where he was exposed to a side of the church and the world that were new to him. The journey of change continued as he immersed himself in the scriptures, this time reading them in the light of his own depression and newly acquired awareness of the foibles of the Catholic Church. He then realized that his personal problem, and that of all Christians, could be resolved on the basis of personal faith. This concept focuses on the importance of the individual—it is a statement of religious humanism. We wonder whether his trip to Rome also exposed Luther to the teachings of Petrarch, Pico della Mirandola, and the other founders of Italian Renaissance thought. Certainly, at the core, his religious teachings about individualism mirrored their secular teachings.

In his 95 theses, we see even broader creative thinking in his direct criticisms of the pope and his appeal to the feelings of the common man, although we would generally consider most of the 95 theses as logical and, therefore, linear extensions of his studies of theology and the scriptures at that time. Then, in his confrontation with Eck and again at the Diet of Worms, he was forced to make a commitment either for or against the pope and to state the rationale for his position. He gave a heretofore unstated position that scriptures and logical reasoning were more important in his life than was the position of the pope. This statement broke with the Catholic Church and established the principal foundation of Protestant thinking. The crises of his confrontations seemed to have forced him to think more laterally, because the logical position he had kept for most of his life was cut off by the actions of the pope and emperor. We might suggest that encountering a crisis might be a way to stimulate lateral thinking and, with it, a new kind of creativity.

Up to the moment of decision at the Diet of Worms, Luther did not intend to break with the Catholic Church. He was merely a reformer. But, with his excommunication and fugitive status, the break was complete and he then entered a new world. He began to entertain a wide variety of thoughts concerning the position of all true Christian believers, the methods of enhancing their spiritual lives and enriching their cultural lives. He wrote extensively, and that appeared to encourage his lateral creative thinking. (We have found that also to be the case.) Writing seems to be a type of commitment to some thinking (if only until the delete key is hit), but still it forces the mind to solidify thoughts and to cut off others, and often that process forces lateral thinking. Luther's pamphlets clearly show his high level of creativity.

We might say, therefore, that the early part of Luther's protest had the intent of reform and was largely linear. Then, after he was faced with a crisis moment, he began to think laterally and the result was a rupture—surely a stronger position than mere reform.

While we are talking about Luther's creativity, we should mention one other aspect of personal creativity that Luther exhibited so well and which most of us who wish to be creative will also have to exhibit. That aspect of creativity is **courage.** Luther's creativity literally put his life in danger, as did the creativity of Wycliffe and Hus before him. Today, few of us must risk our lives for creativity, but we surely risk criticism and embarrassment. We must be confident and able to withstand or ignore those who would criticize us. Einstein was an example of the ability to ignore such criticism. "Once, one hundred Nazi professors wrote a book attacking Einstein's theories. Einstein just shrugged it off, saying, 'If I were wrong, one professor would have been enough.'"[2] The radical nature and, therefore, the required courage of Luther might be judged by analogy. When he spoke against papal authority and said that it was not binding on him or any other person, but every person had authority from the scriptures, it was like a person in the United States stating that the Supreme Court did not have the authority to interpret the U.S. Constitution but, rather, all people could interpret the Constitution for themselves. The potential for chaos was great, and Luther's personality helped to control the situation.

The political changes that resulted from Luther's actions were significant. Initially, individ-ual cities and principalities proclaimed that the local church could preach according to Luther's teachings. Local militancy eroded support for the Holy Roman Emperor, especially in Northern Europe, causing Charles V to abdicate the German/Austrian/Bohemian part of his realm to his brother who was residing in Vienna. A long war eventually began over religion (the Thirty Years War), which we will discuss in a later chapter, and that led to a division of Germany into the Protestant north and the Catholic south. Scandinavia also became Protestant.

■ The Counter Reformation

The Catholic Church did not sit idly by and watch large portions of Europe move into Protestantism. It began a movement to resist the Protestant Reformation and to make changes in the Catholic Church. Some of the changes were militant, some were educational, some were political, and some were internal reforms.

One of the first changes made by the church was the founding of the Society of Jesus (commonly called the **Jesuits**) by Ignacio Loyola in 1534. This society of dedicated priests was to strengthen the church by being both intellectual and moral warriors against those who would harm the church. One of the first duties of the Jesuits was to accompany the explorers of new territories in the Americas and in Asia to ensure that the native people were converted to the Catholic faith. Famous Jesuit missionaries of this period were Francis Xavier in Asia and Marquette in America. The Jesuits' fanatical support of their agenda and willingness to take action against leaders they believed to be against them or their cause led to problems in some countries. The Jesuits were actually suspended in Portugal and France in the mid-1700s and were even suspended by the pope from 1773 to 1814.

The **Inquisition** was another method employed by the church to ensure fidelity of those under their control. The Inquisition existed prior to the time of the Protestant Reformation, but was re-activated to ensure that members in Catholic regions would not adopt Protestant beliefs. The Inquisition was strongest in Catholic Spain, especially under Ferdinand and Isabella, but Charles V also used it to quell dissent, as did several kings and popes throughout the Protestant reformation period. The Inquisition attempted to control what people read, what they thought, and how they acted.

In an effort to reform itself and deal with the many issues raised by the Protestant Reformation, a series of church councils was convened in the city of Trent between 1545 and 1560. These Catholic Church councils ranged across many issues including the following: a redefinition of Catholic doctrine in light of the Protestant position, suggested reforms to the Catholic Church, a granting of greater freedom of individual thinking (especially to Catholics living near Protestant areas), and a proclamation that the king of each country could define the official church of the country and insist that all people belong to the same church. You might think that this last item would guarantee that those countries would forever be Protestant—exactly opposite to what the Catholics wanted. However, by the time the proclamation was issued, many states had already declared themselves to be Protestant, largely on the basis of belief of the people in those states. The church felt that, in general, the states that remained Catholic would not deviate. The Catholic Church realized the near impossibility of converting all those people back to Catholicism, but they hoped to be able to change the beliefs of the kings and therefore bring the people back by royal decree. We will examine some of the most important states in Europe to assess the state of their religion and see how successful the Catholic Church was in this hope.

◾ German-Speaking Switzerland and Zwingli

Switzerland in the sixteenth century was not a single, unified country but, rather, a group of independent regions, called **cantons.** The most powerful of these in the German-speaking portion of Switzerland was Zurich, and it is here that **Ulrich**

Zwingli led the people in a Protestant revolt. Zwingli was born in 1484, just one year after Luther, and like Luther became a priest. Zwingli was very popular with his parishioners and was appointed "people's priest" in Zurich, a position of leadership and trust. Luther's teachings quickly spread from Germany to northern Switzerland, where Zwingli soon adopted many of Luther's doctrines as his own. He was, for instance, a vocal critic of indulgences. Zwingli was also actively involved in Swiss politics, speaking out against military service of Swiss men in mercenary armies of foreign kings. Chiefly because of Zwingli's influence, the city-state of Zurich became a strong Protestant center.

Zwingli developed some religious thinking that was uniquely his own. The most important of these ideas was the belief that the Bible, Old and New Testament, should be interpreted literally. If a practice is not mentioned in the Bible, it should not be done. This was his basis for rejecting indulgences. Likewise, if a practice was outlined in the Bible, it should be adhered to faithfully. Zwingli's unwavering literal reading of the scriptures soon caused a split between himself and Luther. Attempts by local political leaders in both Switzerland and Germany to reconcile the differences between Luther and Zwingli were unsuccessful so long as they both remained alive. This began a fracturing of the Protestant movement that would continue until the present day. Even during Zwingli's life, a group of Protestants in Zurich believed that Zwingli did not go far enough in his reforms. They separated from the main Protestant body and called themselves the **Anabaptists** (baptized again). These people were expelled from Zurich. They fled to southern Germany, where they established a communal society in Münster. The Mennonites, Amish, and Hutterites are related groups arising from the Anabaptists.

Zwingli continued as the leader of the Zurich Protestants. In that position, he determined to lead the Protestant army in a war that broke out in 1531 against the Catholic cantons over control of all Switzerland. Zwingli died in the battle. The war ended with a resolution that the cantons could decide independently on their religion. The church building in which Zwingli taught is, today, a national treasure in Zurich, and Zwingli is respected as a leader of the Protestant movement.

■ French-Speaking Switzerland and Calvin

John Calvin was born in France in 1509 to a middle-class family. He studied for the priesthood as a youth but was later trained as a lawyer. He became a writer who worked for the Catholic Church as a specialist in canon (church) law in Paris. While there, he heard the teachings of Luther and became an ardent convert. He preached a public sermon critical of the Catholic Church and supporting Luther in 1533. The speech caused an uproar in strongly Catholic France, and Calvin had to flee. He was forced to seek refuge in several cities, among them Geneva, Switzerland, where an acquaintance requested that he stay and help the effort to make Geneva a Protestant city. Calvin agreed, and in 1541 pro-Protestant forces seized control of the city. Calvin became a major influence in both the politics and religion of the city. He attempted to establish the perfect Christian community in which a body of 200 elders governed the city. He called it a Presbyterian (elders) government. Catholics in the city were forced to convert or were expelled.

Calvin's doctrine was carefully reasoned and quite strict. He taught that God governs all things and is all powerful. The Bible is the sole source of the will of God, and no pope or any other person or tradition can overturn it. Therefore, the elders were to be God-fearing men who sought the will of God through the scriptures. However, because mankind was inherently evil, each person can only be saved through the grace of God. Since God is all powerful and all knowing, the identity of all those who will be saved is already known to God and, therefore, is predestined. Those who have been elected by God will be identified because they will profess their faith and follow God's commands.

Calvin attempted to control the details of each individual's life. He banned liquor, singing, and pleasure seeking except when the purpose of those was to seek Christian fellowship. Curfews were established, and some people were executed for not obeying Calvin's teachings. Even the names of babies were controlled to prevent giving a Catholic name.

Eventually, the city fathers grew weary of Calvin's harsh living conditions and his dictates to them. They asked Calvin to leave the city, and he moved to Strasbourg. However, after only a few years, a new city council was installed, and it asked Calvin to return to the city, which he did on his terms. He continued as a major force in the city until his death in 1564.

Calvin wrote extensively about Christian doctrine and organized a school for teaching Christian principles. People from all over Europe attended his school and then, as with John Knox from Scotland, returned to their country of origin to establish Calvinist churches. By this method, the concepts of Calvin became some of the strongest influences in Protestantism. Some countries, like Scotland and the Netherlands, adopted Calvinist Protestantism as their state religion.

■ France

The religious story of France during the sixteenth century reflects the strength and religiosity of the current leader of the country. An early ruler of the century, Francis I, a member of the Valois dynasty, was a strong supporter of the arts in the tradition of the Renaissance leaders of the Italian city-states. Leonardo da Vinci, who had moved to France, was active in the court of Francis I, who established a home for Leonardo not far from one of his major palaces. Francis constructed many beautiful chateaus in the Loire Valley of Central France and asked Leonardo to help design some of them. Today, the palace at Chambord shows the creative brilliance of Leonardo in, among other things, a double-helix staircase in the center of the chateau in which people can go up the two staircases and see each other but not meet. The entire region is full of beautiful palaces that are a tribute to Francis.

The religious issues of Protestantism did not arise in France because of the firm control of the king. He actively squelched Protestant thinking, forcing Calvin to flee France. Francis sought the support of the pope against his powerful neighbor, Charles V, who controlled Spain, the Netherlands, and the Holy Roman Empire. France was surrounded by Charles's territories. As Charles's influence with the pope declined, even reaching the point where Charles invaded and sacked Rome, Francis exerted pressure on the pope and gained the right to name French bishops, although the pope theoretically retained veto power.

When Francis I died in 1547, his son, Henry II became king. Henry was married to **Catherine de Medici,** one of the most powerful women in Europe from, obviously, one of Europe's most powerful families. When Henry died in 1559, he was succeeded by his young son, Francis II. Francis married Mary, Queen of Scotland. Francis was an ineffective ruler and was dominated by his mother. When Francis II died without a male heir, he was succeeded by his next younger brother, Charles IX. Again, Charles was ineffective and was dominated by his mother, Catherine de Medici. Charles also died after a short time as king and was succeeded by the youngest of Catherine's sons, Henry III. During the reign of Charles IX, Catherine felt that the French Protestants (who were called **Huguenots,** after a group of Swiss patriots) were gaining too much strength in the country. Therefore, on St. Bartholomew's Day in 1572, she authorized the ambush and murder of Huguenot leaders who had come to Paris to attend the wedding of Henry of Navarre, a Protestant who was the designated successor of Henry III. The killing of the Protestant leaders quickly spread across France, and thousands of Protestants were killed. It is said that the Seine River was clogged with bodies. Scores of bodies were hung as warnings to others who may want to convert to Protestantism. The event is called the **St. Bartholomew's Day Massacre.**

When Henry III died, there were no more male heirs in the Valois line. As previously indicated, Henry III had designated the king of Navarre, a region in the mountains between southern France and Spain, as his heir. Henry of Navarre was a member of the Bourbon family, and his family had converted to Protestantism years earlier. The French government faced a dilemma. Surely the Catholic Church and the French nobility would not allow this Protestant to become the king. However, to refuse him the title, after the previous king had clearly made him the heir, would certainly result in a civil war. Therefore, representatives of the church and nobility met with Henry of Navarre and struck a compromise. He would be allowed to peacefully claim the throne, but first he must convert to Catholicism. Henry agreed and became Henry IV, the first of the Bourbon rulers of France. Henry remained a Catholic his whole life but, shortly after becoming king, he issued the Edict of Nantes, in which the right of the Huguenots to practice their religion was guaranteed. France has remained a largely Catholic country to the present day.

■ England

Many in England believe that the Christian church of England is unique in all the world. They believe that Joseph of Arimathea, Mary the mother of Jesus, Mary Magdalene, and other disciples of Christ left Jerusalem in the early first century and traveled to England. There they settled on an island called Avalon, built a Christian church, and lived according to Christian principles. They converted many of the surrounding Celtic nobility in the first and second centuries and grew to become a major force in early England. King Arthur, they believe, was descended from one of these early Celtic Christian rulers. Those who believe these legends also believe that the Christians of England were active in helping the Christian church in Rome during the difficult days of Nero and that one of the English Christians (Linus) went to Rome where he became a Bishop of Rome, ordained by Peter. Therefore, according to the legend, the English church predates the Catholic Church in Rome and provided the person who became the second pope (succeeding Peter).

In 506 A.D. the Catholic Church's Pope Gregory I sent St. Augustine of Canterbury to England as an emissary to the Celtic Christian church. Augustine had great success in establishing the presence of the Catholic Church in England. Gradually, the Celtic and Catholic Churches reached an agreement, and the Catholic Church took precedence over the Celtic church. Therefore, through the latter Middle Ages, the church in England had become a part of the Roman Catholic Church.

At the time of Luther, some people in England converted to Protestantism. This conversion was promoted by the presence of the Wycliffe Bible and the later translation by **William Tyndale,** who was a contemporary of Luther. At this time, **King Henry VIII** was a staunch supporter of the pope against Luther, and so all English translations of the Bible were forbidden. Nevertheless, Tyndale published his Bible in the Netherlands and successfully smuggled the Bible into England.

A story is told of an English Catholic Bishop who went to the Netherlands to destroy all of Tyndale's Bibles. The bishop met with the printer, found out how many Bibles had been printed, and asked to buy all of them. The printer agreed, but indicated that the Bibles had already been moved to another location. He would, however, go and get them and give them to the bishop in a few days. After the bishop had left the print shop, the printer went to Tyndale, to whom the Bibles had been delivered, and told him the story. The printer suggested that Tyndale could give the Bibles to the printer, who would then sell them to the Bishop, thus making a nice profit. Tyndale could then use the money to print even more Bibles. That is just what happened.[3] Tyndale gave us many beautiful phrases and passages that were copied by those who created the King James Version, thus preserving a legacy from this important reformer. Eventually, under pressure of the English government, Tyndale was captured in Europe, tried in Belgium, and executed. His crime was giving a Bible to the English people.

King Henry VIII's support of the Catholic Church at this time was influenced by the thinking of **Thomas More,** who would become the king's chief legal counselor. More is the likely author of a treatise, which he ghost-wrote for the king, in which Luther and his teachings were strongly criticized. The treatise was so well done and so influential that the pope bestowed a new title on Henry— Defender of the Faith. In light of subsequent events, this title, still used by the king or queen of England,

is highly ironic. More was also the driving force behind the arrest and execution of Tyndale.

More was a leading intellectual who wrote, besides the treatise against Luther, the book *Utopia,* which describes his ideas of a perfect society and from which we derive the phrase **utopian society.** Literally, Utopia means "nowhere," which shows More's humor as well as his cleverness. The book was written as a conversation in which Raphael Hythloday, who had journeyed to Utopia, tells his friends, More and Giles, about what he saw during his journey. Raphael reported that in Utopia, the people were largely an agricultural society. The people of Utopia adopted a classless society in which all property was held in common. Raphael likes the Utopian system, but receives some doubt from More:

> *RAPHAEL: I'm convinced that you'll never get a fair distribution of goods, or a satisfactory organization of human life, until you abolish private property altogether. So long as it exists, the vast majority of the human race, and the vastly superior part of it, will inevitably go on labouring under a burden of poverty, hardship, and worry. MORE: I disagree. I don't believe you'd ever have a reasonable standard of living under a communist system. There'd always tend to be shortages, because nobody would work hard enough. In the absence of a profit motive, everyone would become lazy, and rely on everyone else to do the work for him. Then, when things really got short, the inevitable result would be a series of murders and riots, since nobody would have any legal method of protecting the products of his own labour—especially as there wouldn't be any respect for authority, or I don't see how there could be, in a classless society.[4]*

The insights of More to the problems of a communist society, about 300 years before Karl Marx, were astonishingly accurate. More's insights on the legal system of Utopia are equally interesting, as shown in the following quotation:

> *They [the Utopians] have very few laws, because, with their social system, very few laws*

are required. Indeed, one of their great complaints against other countries is that, although they've already got books and books of laws and interpretations of laws, they never seem to have enough. For, according to the Utopians, it's quite unjust for anyone to be bound by a legal code which is too long for an ordinary person to read right through, or too difficult for him to understand. What's more, they have no barristers [lawyers] to be over-ingenious about individual cases and points of law. They think it better for each man to plead his own cause, and tell the judge the same story as he'd otherwise tell his lawyer. Under such conditions, the point at issue is less likely to be obscured, and it's easier to get at the truth—for, if nobody's telling the sort of lies that one learns from lawyers, the judge can apply all his shrewdness to weighing the facts of the case, and protecting simple-minded characters against the unscrupulous attacks of clever ones.[5]

More makes equally insightful comments about how and why wars should be fought, how laws should be enacted, and the behavior of people in accepting each other and adopting Christian values. In this last respect, he sarcastically comments that some people believe that since we will not be able to get human behavior in line with Christian ethics, we should adapt Christian ethics to human behavior so that, at least, there will be some connection between the two.

The question of Christian ethics came directly into focus in More's personal life when King Henry VIII wanted to break with the Catholic Church over the issue of his divorce. The king sought acceptance of his actions from More because of More's high position in the government and his influence among the people. More did not agree with the king's actions but did not want to defy the king, and so he simply elected to remain silent. This frustrated the king, who placed incredible pressure on More to give support, even suggesting that More give public support of some minimal sort. More did not feel that he could give any support and be true to his Christian ethics.

Eventually, More was tried for treason, convicted, and executed. These events are described in the superb play, "A Man for All Seasons."

King Henry VIII's desire to separate from the Catholic Church was a complicated problem that began before Henry became king. He was actually the second son of Henry VII, the prior king of England. Henry VII wanted to cement a relationship between England and the most powerful country at the time, Spain. He did this by marrying his oldest son, Arthur, to Catherine of Aragon, the daughter of King Ferdinand and Isabella and aunt to Charles V. Prince Arthur died before his father, and so that meant that his next son, Henry, was the heir apparent. The king wanted to continue the bond with Spain, however, so he insisted that young Henry marry Catherine, the widow of his older brother. This type of marriage was against canon law because of a restriction in Leviticus 20:21, which reads, "And if a man shall take his brother's wife, it is an unclean thing: he hath uncovered his brother's nakedness; they shall be childless." However, at Henry VII's insistence, the pope gave a dispensation and the two were wed.

Henry VIII became king upon the death of his father and had a baby by Catherine, but, to Henry's great disappointment, the baby was a girl. After repeated miscarriages, some of which were males, Henry became convinced that his marriage with Catherine was cursed, just as the Bible had said. Catherine was 42 and was not likely to have additional children. Henry was convinced that he was not medically at fault, because he had fathered an illegitimate son. He therefore sought to annul the marriage with Catherine, claiming that the marriage should never have been allowed. However, the pope at this time was under the influence of Charles V of Spain, who supported his aunt Catherine. Francis I of France also urged the pope to not annul the marriage. The child of Henry and Catherine, Mary, was betrothed to the dauphin of France and therefore, should Mary inherit the English throne, the French would have a claim to the English throne after her death. (The dauphin died before he and Mary could be married.) Therefore, under the Spanish and French pressure, the pope refused to grant the annulment.

Henry proceeded to act on his own to grant himself the divorce and to marry another. When Henry took this step, he was excommunicated from the Catholic Church. Henry then declared himself the head of a new church—the Church of England. It was, in most respects, similar to the Catholic Church except that services were conducted in English and the leader of the church was the king rather than the pope. Henry took over the properties of the Catholic Church, including the vast holdings of the many monasteries, and either sold them or kept them as a long-term revenue source. Eventually, of course, the English church drew apart from the Catholic Church; it remains somewhat distant today. Later, some would arise in England and seek to move the church even further from Catholicism, but that is a story for a later chapter.

Henry had a reason for desiring a hasty divorce. While still married to Catherine, Henry fell in love with a young woman in the court, Anne Boleyn. Henry wanted to marry Anne and became convinced that if she had a child it would be a boy but Anne reportedly refused to submit to Henry's sexual advances until they were married. This urgency forced Henry into the divorce of Catherine. He married Anne Boleyn and she became pregnant shortly thereafter, but the child born to Anne was a girl, who they named Elizabeth. Not long afterward, Henry became convinced that Anne was unfaithful, and had her beheaded in the Tower of London.

He then married yet another young woman of the court, Jane Seymour. She also became pregnant and, to Henry's great delight, bore a son, who they named Edward. However, Jane Seymour died of birth complications only a few days later. Henry then married (by proxy) Anne of Cleves, a German princess. After seeing her in person, however, he refused to have her around him, put her in a distant castle, and annulled the marriage. He then married Catherine Howard, who was convicted of adultery and executed. The sixth wife of Henry VIII was Catherine Parr, a clever woman of strong protestant beliefs who tended Henry during his failing years. She outlived him.

Upon Henry's death, his son succeeded to the throne as Edward VI. He was a young man who was sickly throughout his short reign of only six years. When Edward died, the chief counselor of the court attempted to place his daughter-in-law, a cousin to Edward VI, on the throne. She was Lady Jane Grey and was actually crowned queen by certain counselors, but was ousted by Parliament after only nine days. She and her husband were convicted of treason and executed. Then, with the approval of Parliament, Mary, oldest child of Henry was declared queen Mary I.

Mary was a Catholic, being the child of Catherine of Aragon, and held to the position of the pope that the original marriage was properly made. She tried to crush the new Protestant faith in England and reestablish Catholicism. Many refused to convert and she killed them, thus earning the title **Bloody Mary.** She also married the Spanish king, a very unpopular move with the English people, who saw the powerful Spanish king, Philip II, as a dominating force over Mary and therefore the *de facto* ruler of England. This seemed to be proven out when Mary declared war on France simply because Philip asked her to do it. Mary and Philip were unable to have children, and, after only five years as queen, Mary died. She was succeeded by Elizabeth, her half-sister and the daughter of Henry and Anne Boleyn. We will discuss Elizabeth's reign in a later chapter.

■ Creativity and the Reformation

Protests against the Catholic Church in the sixteenth century required great courage. Some people had previously died for their protests. However, the decline of papal power meant that some local rulers were able to protect protestors, and this is what allowed Luther to continue his movement against the Catholic Church until it achieved a complete rupture and could stand on its own. Other reformers in other countries continued to require courage, but their path was less trying than Luther's because of the precedent that had been set.

The nature of creativity in religion during this era was interesting. Because of the basically conservative nature of religion, as has been evident since the ancient Egyptians, religious creativity is rare.

Even Luther did not seek radical breaks but only minor revisions. These revisions were generally logical and, in creativity terms, were due to linear thinking. However, as the pressure on him from the church and the emperor increased, Luther's logical pattern was disrupted and he was forced to think laterally. It was under these conditions that he began to see a much wider picture that included a complete break from the Catholic Church and the creation of a new faith—Lutheranism.

Similarly, the threat against the life of John Calvin caused him to flee France and begin a radical and new Christian society in Geneva. He strove to establish a perfect society along lines that he believed were correct. He did not pretend to give freedom of choice to those who lived in his city, but, rather, sought religious rigor and uniformity. While these conditions may have been onerous for some, others thrived. As a result, Calvinism was spread widely across Europe.

Henry VIII was also forced into lateral thinking by a crisis. This time the crisis was one of succession to the throne. He wanted a son and needed to find a way to rid himself of a marriage that he believed was cursed. He did so by divorcing his wife and separating from the Catholic Church. He then creatively used the opportunity to establish a new church and to expropriate the property of the Catholic Church to finance his reign.

Along the way, others also demonstrated both courage and creativity. Some, like Thomas More and Ulrich Zwingli gave their lives for their convictions. Still others, like Mary I, defended their faith but died of natural causes. Most people in this time were convinced of the rightfulness of their faith. It seems that few were passive. They made decisions as individuals and, surely, that was in keeping with the humanistic concepts that were typical of the time.

■ Timeline—Important Dates

Date	Event
1330–1384	Wycliffe protests in England
1415	Jan Hus executed for his protests
1483	Birth of Martin Luther
1517	Martin Luther posts 95 theses
1521	Diet of Worms
1529	Thomas More executed
1531	Zwingli dies in battle
1533	Henry VIII's divorce occurs
1534	Henry VIII recognized as head of English church
1534	Society of Jesus (Jesuits) formed
1536	Calvin in Geneva
1542	Lutheran Church formed
1545–1560	Council of Trent
1546	Death of Martin Luther
1564	Death of John Calvin
1572	St. Bartholomew's Day Massacre

■ Notes

1. Martin Luther, *Preface to the Letter of St. Paul to the Romans* (translated by Brother Andrew Thornton, OSB), http://www.ccel.org/l/luther/romans/pref_romans.html.
2. Scott Thorpe, *How to Think Like Einstein* (New York: Barnes & Noble, 2000), 142.
3. Alister McGrath, *In the Beginning* (New York: Anchor Books, 2001), 84–86.
4. Sir Thomas More, *Utopia* (New York: Penguin Books, 1961), 60.
5. Sir Thomas More, *Utopia* (New York: Penguin Books, 1961), 106.

■ Suggested Readings

Goldstone, Lawrence and Nancy Goldstone, *Out of the Flames,* Broadway Books, 2002.

McGrath, Alister, *In The Beginning,* Anchor Books, 2001.

More, Thomas, *Utopia,* Penguin Classics, 1965.

Thorpe, Scott, *How to Think Like Einstein,* Barnes & Noble, 2000.

White, Michael, *The Pope and the Heretic,* Perennial, 2002.

Martin Luther: Salvation Through Faith Alone, 95 Theses, To the Christian Nobility of the German Nation, Address at the Diet of Worms

Martin Luther (1483–1546), born of German, peasant stock, is considered to be one of the most pivotal men in western civilization. While studying at a university, he had a startling religious experience during which he committed to live his life for God. In the selection, *Salvation Through Faith Alone,* Martin Luther tells the story of his enlightenment or spiritual awakening.

He then became a monk, received a Ph. D. in theology at the University of Wittenberg, and began to teach theology there. He developed deep feelings of agony for the effects of original sin and his own sins, causing him to submerge himself in a study of the scriptures in hopes of finding the path to personal purification. Through this scripture study, he came to a key belief that was outside Catholic dogma. He believed that mankind could be saved through faith. This undermined the Catholic Church's reason for existence, as they taught that salvation came through works, such as the sacraments, which were only available through the church's priesthood. Luther's break with Catholic doctrine was especially pertinent at that time because of the strong campaign that the Catholic Church was conducting to sell indulgences (forgiveness of sins) as a method of getting money to pay for the erection of the new St. Peter's Basilica in Rome. According to Luther's belief, these indulgences were doctrinally improper and also offensive because they took money away from the German people and sent it to what he believed was a corrupt Rome. Luther wrote his ob-

jections to the indulgences and outlined his beliefs in a set of ninety-five statements (called theses), which he posted on the door of the church at the University of Wittenberg on October 31, 1517.

Shortly thereafter, Pope Leo X complained to the nobles around Luther, as well as the head of his monastic order, to try and silence him. Luther responded by publishing the *95 Theses* (using the newly invented printing press) in a work entitled *To the Christian Nobility of the German Nation Concerning the Reform of the Christian Estate,* which was spread throughout northern Europe. This work, addressed to the rulers and landowners of his kinsmen, further discussed the foundation of his differences with Catholicism. The Pope's response to this work was to condemn Luther (1520) and order him to burn all documents critical of the Church. Luther's response to this was to publicly burn the order, for which he was excommunicated.

Soon after, the Holy Roman Emperor, Charles V, summoned Luther to appear before a diet (assembly) of officials of the Empire in the city of Worms. Charles hoped to solve the problem there and have Luther recant his criticism so that he could be reinstated in the Catholic Church. The entire countryside of Germany was in upheaval because of Luther's stand, and Charles desperately wanted to restore the peace. With safe passage guaranteed by the Emperor, Luther appeared before the diet on April 17, 1521. When asked whether he wished to continue in his stand against the Pope or rescind some of his statements, Luther gave the famous *Address at the Diet of Worms.* Charles then placed Luther under an imperial ban as an outlaw, but Luther escaped on April 23 and was hidden by friends in Wartburg Castle. Luther's story had become both a protest against the Catholic Church and a political statement of independence from foreign dominance of the Habsburg dynasty of Charles V. The environment was ripe for revolution and that is what occurred. Wars were fought for nearly a century over religion and political independence. Eventually, the northern parts of Europe became religiously Protestant and gained some political independence.

Originally, Luther hoped that his convictions would change the Church from within. However, the Catholic Church's threats only made Luther bolder and more belligerent until he had completely severed his ties with Rome. His vast numbers of adherents followed him along this path, causing a great rift in the religious structure of the Western World. The reformed church of Lutheranism would split countless times itself into the myriad of Protestant sects that we know today. The Protestant movement is the legacy of Luther's doctrine of personal salvation and the accompanying doctrine of personal interpretation of scripture.

Article 2
Martin Luther: Salvation Through Faith Alone

[In this selection Martin Luther tells his own story.]

I, Martin Luther, entered the monastery against the will of my father and lost favor with him, for he saw through the knavery of the monks very well. On the day on which I sang my first mass he said to me, "Son, don't you know that you ought to honor your father?" . . . Later when I stood there during the mass and began the canon, I was so frightened that I would have fled if I hadn't been admonished by the prior. . . .

When I was a monk I was unwilling to omit any of the prayers, but when I was busy with public lecturing and writing I often accumulated my appointed prayers for a whole week, or even two or three weeks. Then I would take a Saturday off, or shut myself in for as long as three days without food and drink, until I had said the prescribed prayers. This made my head split, and as a consequence I couldn't close my eyes for five nights, lay sick unto death, and went out of my senses. Even after I had quickly recovered and I tried again to read, my head went 'round and 'round. Thus our Lord God drew me, as if by force, from that torment of prayers. . . .

The words "righteous" and "righteousness of God" struck my conscience like lightning. When I heard them I was exceedingly terrified. If God is righteous [I thought], he must punish. But when by God's grace I pondered, in the tower and heated room of this building, over the words, "He who through faith is righteous shall live" [Rom. 1:17] and "the righteousness of God" [Rom. 3:21], I soon came to the conclusion that if we, as righteous men, ought to live from faith and if the righteousness of God should contribute to the salvation of all who believe, then salvation won't be our merit but God's mercy. My spirit was thereby cheered. For it's by the righteousness of God that we're justified and saved through Christ. These words [which had before terrified me] now became more pleasing to me. The Holy Spirit unveiled the Scriptures for me in this tower.

God led us away from all this in a wonderful way; without my quite being aware of it he took me away from that game more than twenty years ago. How difficult it was at first when we journeyed toward Kemberg after All Saints' Day in the year 1517, when I first made up my mind to write against the crass errors of indulgences! Jerome Schurff advised against this: "You wish to write against the pope? What are you trying to do? It won't be tolerated!" I replied, "And if they have to tolerate it?" Presently Sylvester, master of the sacred palace, entered the arena, fulminating against me with this syllogism: "Whoever questions what the Roman church says and does is heretical. Luther questions what the Roman church says and does, and therefore [he is a heretic]." So it all began.

Source: Reprinted from *Luther's Works,* Vol. 54 edited by Theodore G. Tappert, © 1967 Fortress Press.

Article 3

Martin Luther: 95 Theses *or* Disputation on the Power and Efficacy of Indulgences

Out of love and zeal for truth and the desire to bring it to light, the following theses will be publicly discussed at Wittenberg under the chairmanship of the reverend father Martin Luther, master of Arts and Sacred Theology and regularly appointed Lecturer on these subjects at that place. He requests that those who cannot be present to debate orally with us will do so by letter.

In the Name of Our Lord Jesus Christ.

Amen. . . .

5. The pope neither desires nor is able to remit any penalties, except those imposed by his own authority or that of the canons.

6. The pope cannot remit any guilt, except by declaring and showing that it has been remitted by God; or, to be sure, by remitting guilt in cases reserved to his judgment. If his right to grant remission in these cases were disregarded, the guilt would certainly remain unforgiven. . . .

20. Therefore the pope, when he uses the words "plenary remission of all penalties," does not actually mean "all penalties," but only those imposed by himself.

21. Thus those indulgence preachers are in error who say that a man is absolved from every penalty and saved by papal indulgences.

22. As a matter of fact, the pope remits to souls in purgatory no penalty which, according to canon law, they should have paid in this life.

23. If remission of all penalties whatsoever could be granted to anyone at all, certainly it would be granted only to the most perfect, that is, to very few.

24. For this reason most people are necessarily deceived by that indiscriminate and high-sounding promise of release from penalty.

25. That power which the pope has in general over purgatory corresponds to the power which any bishop or curate has in a particular way in his own diocese or parish.

26. The pope does very well when he grants remission to souls in purgatory, not by the power of the keys, which he does not have, but by way of intercession for them.

27. They preach only human doctrines who say that as soon as the money clinks into the money chest, the soul flies out of purgatory.

28. It is certain that when money clinks in the money chest, greed and avarice can be increased; but when the church intercedes, the result is in the hands of God alone. . . .

32. Those who believe that they can be certain of their salvation because they have indulgence letters will be eternally damned, together with their teachers.

Source: From *Luther's Works,* Vol. 32, edited by George W. Forell & Helmut T. Lehman (Philadelphia: Muhlenberg Press, 1958).

33. Men must especially be on their guard against those who say that the pope's pardons are that inestimable gift of God by which man is reconciled to him. . . .

35. They who teach that contrition is not necessary on the part of those who intend to buy souls out of purgatory or to buy confessional privileges preach unchristian doctrine.

36. Any truly repentant Christian has a right to full remission of penalty and guilt, even without indulgence letters.

37. Any true Christian, whether living or dead, participates in all the blessings of Christ and the church; and this is granted him by God, even without indulgence letters. . . .

42. Christians are to be taught that the pope does not intend that the buying of indulgences should in any way be compared with works of mercy.

43. Christians are to be taught that he who gives to the poor or lends to the needy does a better deed than he who buys indulgences. . . .

45. Christians are to be taught that he who sees a needy man and passes him by, yet gives his money for indulgences, does not buy papal indulgences but God's wrath. . . .

50. Christians are to be taught that if the pope knew the exactions of the indulgence preachers, he would rather that the basilica of St. Peter were burned to ashes than built up with the skin, flesh, and bones of his sheep. . . .

62. The true treasure of the church is the most holy gospel of the glory and grace of God. . . .

66. The treasures of indulgences are nets with which one now fishes for the wealth of men. . . .

86. Again, "Why does not the pope, whose wealth is today greater than the wealth of the richest Crassus, build this one basilica of St. Peter with his own money rather than with the money of poor believers?" . . .

94. Christians should be exhorted to be diligent in following Christ, their head, through penalties, death, and hell;

95. And thus be confident of entering into heaven through many tribulations rather than through the false security of peace.

Martin Luther: To the Christian Nobility of the German Nation Concerning the Reform of the Christian Estate

■ Jesus

To the Esteemed and Reverend Master, Nicholas von Amsdorf, Licentiate of Holy Scripture, and Canon of Wittenberg, my special and kind friend, from Doctor Martin Luther.

The grace and peace of God be with you, esteemed, reverend, and dear sir and friend.

The time for silence is past, and the time to speak has come, as Ecclesiastes says [3:7]. I am carrying out our intention to put together a few points on the matter of the reform of the Christian estate, to be laid before the Christian nobility of the German nation, in the hope that God may help his church through the laity, since the clergy, to whom this task more properly belongs, have grown quite indifferent. I am sending the whole thing to you, reverend sir, [that you may give] an opinion on it and, where necessary, improve it.

I know full well that I shall not escape the charge of presumption because I, a despised, inferior person, venture to address such high and great estates on such weighty matters, as if there were nobody else in the world except Doctor Luther to take up the cause of the Christian estate and give advice to such high-ranking people. I make no apologies no matter who demands them. Perhaps I owe my God and the World another work of folly. I intend to pay my debt honestly. And if I succeed, I shall for the time being become a court jester. And if I fail, I still have one advantage—no one need buy me a cap or put scissors to my head.[1]

*   *   *

The Romanists have very cleverly built three walls around themselves. Hitherto they have protected themselves by these walls in such a way that no one has been able to reform them. As a result, the whole of Christendom has fallen abominably.

In the first place, when pressed by the temporal power they have made decrees and declared that the temporal power had no jurisdiction over them, but that, on the contrary, the spiritual power is above the temporal. In the second place, when the attempt is made to reprove them with the Scriptures, they raise the objection that only the pope may interpret the Scriptures. In the third place, if threatened with a council, their story is that no one may summon a council but the pope.

---

[1]A jocular comparison of the monk's cowl and tonsure with the jester's cap and bells.

Source: From *Luther's Works,* Vol. 54, edited by Theodore G. Tappert (Philadelphia: Fortress Press, 1967).

In this way they have cunningly stolen our three rods from us, that they may go unpunished. They have ensconced themselves within the safe stronghold of these three walls so that they can practice all the knavery and wickedness which we see today. Even when they have been compelled to hold a council they have weakened its power in advance by putting the princes under oath to let them remain as they were. In addition, they have given the pope full authority over all decisions of a council, so that it is all the same whether there are many councils or no councils. They only deceive us with puppet shows and sham fights. They fear terribly for their skin in a really free council! They have so intimidated kings and princes with this technique that they believe it would be an offense against God not to be obedient to the Romanists in all their knavish and ghoulish deceits.

May God help us, and give us just one of those trumpets with which the walls of Jericho were overthrown to blast down these walls of straw and paper in the same way and set free the Christian rods for the punishment of sin, [and] bring to light the craft and deceit of the devil, to the end that through punishment we may reform ourselves and once more attain God's favor.

Let us begin by attacking the first wall. It is pure invention that pope, bishop, priests, and monks are called the spiritual estate while princes, lords, artisans, and farmers are called the temporal estate. This is indeed a piece of deceit and hypocrisy. Yet no one need be intimidated by it, and for this reason: all Christians are truly of the spiritual estate, and there is no difference among them except that of office. Paul says in I Corinthians 12 [:12–13] that we are all one body, yet every member has its own work by which it serves the others. This is because we all have one baptism, one gospel, one faith, and are all Christians alike; for baptism, gospel, and faith alone make us spiritual and a Christian people.

*   *   *

Therefore, just as those who are now called "spiritual," that is, priests, bishops, or popes, are nei-

ther different from other Christians nor superior to them, except that they are charged with the administration of the word of God and the sacraments, which is their work and office, so it is with the temporal authorities. They bear the sword and rod in their hand to punish the wicked and protect the good. A cobbler, a smith, a peasant—each has the work and office of his trade, and yet they are all alike consecrated priests and bishops. Further, everyone must benefit and serve every other by means of his own work or office so that in this way many kinds of work may be done for the bodily and spiritual welfare of the community, just as all the members of the body serve one another.

*   *   *

For these reasons the temporal Christian authority ought to exercise its office without hindrance, regardless of whether it is pope, bishop, or priest whom it affects. Whoever is guilty, let him suffer. All that canon law has said to the contrary is the invention of Romanist presumption. For thus St. Paul says to all Christians, "Let every soul (I take that to means the pope's soul also) be subject to the temporal authority; for it does not bear the sword in vain, but serves God by punishing the wicked and benefiting the good" [Rom. 13:1, 4]. St. Peter, too, says, "Be subject to all human ordinances for the sake of the Lord, who so wills it" [I Pet. 2:13, 15]. He has also prophesied in II Peter 2 [:1] that such men would arise and despise the temporal authority. This is exactly what has happened through the canon law.

So, then, I think this first paper wall is overthrown. Inasmuch as the temporal power has become a member of the Christian body it is a spiritual estate, even though its work is physical. Therefore, its work should extend without hindrance to all the members of the whole body to punish and use force whenever guilt deserves or necessity demands, without regard to whether the culprit is pope, bishop, or priest. Let the Romanists hurl threats and bans about as they like. That is why guilty priests, when they are handed over to secular law, are first deprived of their priestly dignities. This would not be right unless the secular sword previously had had authority over these priests by divine right.

*   *   *

Where sin is, there is no longer any shielding from punishment. St. Gregory writes that we are indeed all equal, but guilt makes a man inferior to others. Now we see how the Romanists treat Christendom. They take away its freedom without any proof from Scripture, at their own whim. But God, as well as the apostles, made them subject to the temporal sword. It is to be feared that this is a game of the Antichrist, or at any rate that his forerunner has appeared.

The second wall is still more loosely built and less substantial. The Romanists want to be the only masters of Holy Scripture, although they never learn a thing from the Bible all their life long. They assume the sole authority for themselves, and, quite unashamed, they play about with words before our very eyes, trying to persuade us that the pope cannot err in matters of faith, regardless of whether he is righteous or wicked. Yet they cannot point to a single letter. This is why so many heretical and un-Christian, even unnatural, ordinances stand in the canon law. But there is not need to talk about these ordinances at present. Since these Romanists think the Holy Spirit never leaves them, no matter how ignorant and wicked they are, they become bold and decree only what they want. And if what they claim were true, why have Holy Scripture at all? Of what use is Scripture? Let us burn the Scripture and be satisfied with the unlearned gentlemen at Rome who possess the Holy Spirit! And yet the Holy Spirit can be possessed only by pious hearts. If I had not read the words with my own eyes, I would not have believed it possible for the devil to have made such stupid claims at Rome, and to have won supporters for them.

*   *   *

Therefore, their claim that only the pope may interpret Scripture is an outrageous fancied fable.

They cannot produce a single letter [of Scripture] to maintain that the interpretation of Scripture or the confirmation of its interpretation belongs to the pope alone. They themselves have usurped this power. And although they allege that this power was given to St. Peter when the keys were given him, it is clear enough that the keys were not given to Peter alone but to the whole community. Further, the keys were not ordained for doctrine or government, but only for the binding or loosing of sin. Whatever else or whatever more they arrogate to themselves on the basis of the keys is a mere fabrication. But Christ's words to Peter, "I have prayed for you that your faith fail not" [Luke 22:32], cannot be applied to the pope, since the majority of the popes have been without faith, as they must themselves confess. Besides, it is not only for Peter that Christ prayed, but also for all apostles and Christians, as he says in John 17 [:9, 20], "Father, I pray for those whom thou hast given me, and not for these only, but for all who believe on me through their word." Is that not clear enough?

*   *   *

The third wall falls of itself when the first two are down. When the pope acts contrary to the Scriptures, it is our duty to stand by the Scriptures, to reprove him and to constrain him, according to the word of Christ, Matthew 18 [:15–17], "If your brother sins against you, go and tell it to him, between you and him alone; if he does not listen to you, then take one or two others with you; if he does not listen to them, tell it to the church; if he does not listen to the church, consider him a heathen." Here every member is commanded to care for every other. How much more should we do this when the member that does evil is responsible for the government of the church, and by his evildoing is the cause of much harm and offense to the rest! But if I am to accuse him before the church, I must naturally call the church together.

The Romanists have no basis in Scripture for their claim that the pope alone has the right to call or confirm a council. This is just their own ruling, and it is only valid as long as it is not harmful to Christendom or contrary to the laws of God. Now when the pope deserves punishment, this ruling no longer obtains, for not to punish him by authority of a council is harmful to Christendom.

*   *   *

Therefore, when necessity demands it, and the pope is an offense to Christendom, the first man who is able should, as a true member of the whole body, do what he can to bring about a truly free council. No one can do this so well as the temporal authorities, especially since they are also fellow-Christians, fellow-priests, fellow-members of the spiritual estate, fellow-lords over all things. Whenever it is necessary or profitable they ought to exercise the office and work which they have received from God over everyone. Would it not be unnatural if a fire broke out in a city and everybody were to stand by and let it burn on and on and consume everything that could burn because nobody had the authority of the mayor, or because, perhaps, the fire broke out in the mayor's house? In such a situation is it not the duty of every citizen to arouse and summon the rest? How much more should this be done in the spiritual city of Christ if a fire of offense breaks out, whether in the papal government, or anywhere else! The same argument holds if an enemy were to attack a city. The man who first roused the others deserves honor and gratitude. Why, then, should he not deserve honor who makes known the presence of the enemy from hell and rouses Christian people and calls them together?

*   *   *

With this I hope that all this wicked and lying terror with which the Romanists have long intimidated and dulled our conscience has been overcome, and that they, just like all of us, shall be made subject to the sword. They have no right to interpret Scripture merely by authority and without learning. They have no authority to prevent a council, or even worse yet at their mere whim to pledge it, impose conditions on it, or deprive it of its freedom. When they do that they are truly in the fellowship of Antichrist and the devil. They have nothing at all of Christ except the name.

Martin Luther: The Speech of Dr. Martin Luther before the Emperor Charles and Princes at Worms on the Fifth Day After Misericordias Domini [April 18] in the Name of Jesus

"Most serene emperor, most illustrious princes, most clement lords, obedient to the time set for me yesterday evening, I appear before you, beseeching you, by the mercy of God, that your most serene majesty and your most illustrious lordships may deign to listen graciously to this my cause—which is, as I hope, a cause of justice and of truth. If through my inexperience I have either not given the proper titles to some, or have offended in some manner against court customs and etiquette, I beseech you to kindly pardon me, as a man accustomed not to courts but to the cells of monks. I can bear no other witness about myself but that I have taught and written up to this time with simplicity of heart, as I had in view only the glory of God and the sound instruction of Christ's faithful. . . .

"[A] group of my books attacks the papacy and the affairs of the papists as those who both by their doctrines and very wicked examples have laid waste the Christian world with evil that affects the spirit and the body. . . .

"However, because I am a man and not God, I am not able to shield my books with any other protection than that which my Lord Jesus Christ himself offered for his teaching. When questioned before Annas about his teaching and struck by a servant, he said: 'If I have spoken wrongly, bear witness to the wrong' [John 18:19–23]. If the Lord himself, who knew that he could not err, did not refuse to hear testimony against his teaching, even from the lowliest servant, how much more ought I, who am the lowest scum and able to do nothing except err, desire and expect that somebody should want to offer testimony against my teaching! Therefore, I ask by the mercy of God, may your most serene majesty, most illustrious lordships, or anyone at all who is able, either high or low, bear witness, expose my errors, overthrowing them by the writings of the prophets and the evangelists. Once I have been taught I shall be quite ready to renounce every error, and I shall be the first to cast my books into the fire.

"From these remarks I think it is clear that I have sufficiently considered and weighed the hazards and dangers, as well as the excitement and dissensions aroused in the world as a result of my

---

Source: From *Selected Writings of Martin Luther,* edited by Theodore G. Tappert (Philadelphia: Fortress Press, 1967).

teachings, things about which I was gravely and forcefully warned yesterday. To see excitement and dissension arise because of the Word of God is to me clearly the most joyful aspect of all in these matters. For this is the way, the opportunity, and the result of the Word of God, just as He [Christ] said, 'I have not come to bring peace, but a sword. For I have come to set a man against his father, etc.' [Matt. 10:34–35]. . . .

Therefore we must fear God. I do not say these things because there is a need of either my teachings or my warnings for such leaders as you, but because I must not withhold the allegiance which I owe my Germany. With these words I commend myself to your most serene majesty and to your lordships, humbly asking that I not be allowed through the agitation of my enemies, without cause, to be made hateful to you. I have finished."

When I had finished, the speaker for the emperor said, as if in reproach, that I had not answered the question, that I ought not call into question those things which had been condemned and defined in councils; therefore what was sought from me was not a horned response, but a simple one, whether or not I wished to retract.

Here I answered:

"Since then your serene majesty and your lordships seek a simple answer, I will give it in this manner, neither horned nor toothed: Unless I am convinced by the testimony of the Scriptures or by clear reason (for I do not trust either in the pope or in councils alone, since it is well known that they have often erred and contradicted themselves), I am bound by the Scriptures I have quoted and my conscience is captive to the Word of God. I cannot and I will not retract anything, since it is neither safe nor right to go against conscience.

"I cannot do otherwise, here I stand, may God help me, Amen."

John Calvin: Institutes of the Christian Religion

John Calvin (1509–1564) was a religious reformer and theologian who, along with Luther, established the doctrinal basis of Protestantism. Like Luther, Calvin also led his followers into a new church that has been influential in giving direction and an ethical basis for living. However, Calvin's view of Christianity differed from Luther's in some fundamental beliefs and practices, and these differences ultimately resulted in divergence between their followers. Nevertheless, these two reformers served as the two most important fountains of knowledge within early Protestant thought.

Calvin was born to an upper-middle-class family in France. He initially received some training in theology, Greek, and Hebrew, but, at his father's urging, decided also to study law. During his law studies, Calvin was introduced to the teachings of Luther. Calvin became a strong and vigorous convert to Luther's basic ideas and began to write and give speeches calling for reforms in the Catholic Church. His preaching gained some adherents but also marked him as a reformer and forced him to flee the area to escape the anti-reformation actions of King Francis I. Calvin was invited to live in Geneva after Protestant forces took over the city government. There he established a protestant school where he taught and wrote extensively. He strongly influenced the government of Geneva and, for a time, was not welcome in the city under a new governmental council because of his strident views on how the people in the city should behave, even assenting to the expulsion and execution of dissidents from his Protestant views. Calvin left for a time, living in Strasbourg, but was eventually asked to return to Geneva to resume his work. He remained in Geneva for the remainder of his life.

Calvin will be most remembered for his contributions to the Protestant theology that were adopted by many Protestant denominations. He took Luther's concept of salvation through grace one step further. If humans are not inherently capable of affecting their own salvation, and it only is achieved through the grace of God, then God must already know who has been foreordained to achieve that salvation. Those people who have been determined to receive salvation by God manifest their election by living good lives. This concept, termed predestination, has been a tenet of many Protestant sects, especially those in the Netherlands and Scotland, and is a foundation of the English Puritan sects.

Calvin's greatest creative contribution was his massive work, *Institutes of the Christian Religion*. He spent most of three decades of his stay in Switzerland working tirelessly on this work. The work outlines the doctrines of Calvin's unique view of Christian doctrine: the justification for reform, the scriptures as the primary authority, predestination, and salvation through grace and not by works. The following passage from *Institutes* presents part of Calvin's explanation of the doctrine of predestination.

The covenant of life is not preached equally to all, and among those to whom it is preached, does not always meet with the same reception. This diversity displays the unsearchable depth of the divine judgment, and is without doubt subordinate to God's purpose of eternal election. But if it is plainly owing to the mere pleasure of God that salvation is spontaneously offered to some, while others have no access to it, great and difficult questions immediately arise, questions which are inexplicable, when just views are not entertained concerning election and predestination.

. . . By predestination we mean the eternal decree of God, by which he determined with himself whatever he wished to happen with regard to every man. All are not created on equal terms, but some are preordained to eternal life, others to eternal damnation; and, accordingly, as each has been created for one or other of these ends, we say that he has been predestinated to life or to death. . . .

We say, then, that Scripture clearly proves this much, that God by his eternal and immutable counsel determined once for all those whom it was his pleasure one day to admit to salvation, and those whom, on the other hand, it was his pleasure to doom to destruction. We maintain that this counsel, as regards the elect, is founded on his free mercy, without any respect to human worth, while those whom he dooms to destruction are excluded from access to life by a just and blameless, but at the same time incomprehensible judgment. In regard to the elect, we regard calling as the evidence of election, and justification as another symbol of its manifestation, until it is fully accomplished by the attainment of glory. But as the Lord seals his elect by calling and justification, so by excluding the reprobate either from the knowledge of his name or the sanctification of his Spirit, he by these marks in a manner discloses the judgment which awaits them. I will here omit many of the fictions which foolish men have devised to overthrow predestination. There is no need of refuting objections which the moment they are produced abundantly betray their hollowness. I will dwell only on those points which either form the subject of dispute among the learned, or may occasion any difficulty to the simple, or may be employed by impiety as specious pretexts for assailing the justice of God.

Source: From Institutes of the Christian Religion by John Calvin, translated by Henry Beveridge (Grand Rapids: Wm. B. Eerdmans Publishing Co., 1957).

Thomas More: Utopia

Thomas More (1478–1535) was the greatest of the English humanists. He studied Greek and Latin and even wrote comedies at Oxford. His love of the principles of humanism was deepened through his great friendship with Erasmus, the great Dutch humanist. Although clearly a scholar, More decided that he could best serve the people in law. His attention to the poor and impartiality in judgment achieved legendary status in England, thus attracting the attention of King Henry VIII. More was successful in every post and assignment given him by the King and was eventually appointed Lord Chancellor of England, being the first layman ever appointed as such. But he fell out of favor with Henry over Henry's desire to divorce Catherine of Aragon. More's struggles with Henry are dramatized in *A Man for All Seasons.*

More's humanism is readily revealed in his most famous work, *Utopia,* from which we get our term "utopian." Like Plato's *Republic,* More's *Utopia* is a model for an ideal society. More presents his description of this society by relating a supposed conversation with a visitor who has returned from the fictional land. Like a Platonic Form however, More's ideal society never would exist in real life, but could be imagined and described. In fact, the term "utopia" means "no place." The dialogue in *Utopia* constantly contrasts the utopian ideal with the contemporary society in England, demonstrating More's dislike for many parts of the way of life in his homeland. Much of the criticism is aimed at the legal and legislative system in which More spent most of his working life.

The following excerpts from *Utopia* were chosen to illustrate More's most important suggestions for the ideal society. The work has sometimes been labeled Communist, as it declares private property to be a bane to happiness and justice. But More uses his own character in the discussion to decry the potential problems of Communism—ideas which seem prophetic in hindsight following the failure of Communism in the twentieth century. These and other comments show More's intellectual foresight and deep concern for the common man.

The principal characters in *Utopia* are:

Sir Thomas More—diplomat for King Henry VIII

Peter Giles—More's friend and the person for whom More records the book

Raphael Hythloday—the traveler who supposedly has been to Utopia and describes it

Thus the days, the months, the years slip by. You may ask, when *do* I write then? Well, so far I haven't mentioned sleep, or meals—which many people allow to consume as much time as sleep itself—and in fact the only time I ever get to myself is what I steal from sleep and meals. There isn't very much of it, so my progress has been slow—but there has at least been some, so I've finally finished *Utopia,* and I'm sending it to you, my dear Peter, in the hope that you will read it, and tell me if I've left anything out. I feel fairly confident on that score—for I only wish my scholarship and intelligence were up to the standard of my memory—but not quite confident enough to assume that nothing could have slipped my mind.

As you know, my young assistant, John Clement, was with us at the time. I never let him miss any conversation that might have some educational value, for he has already begun to show such promise in Latin and Greek that I expect great things of him one day. Well, he has made me feel very doubtful about one point. As far as I can recall, Raphael told us that the bridge across the river Nowater at Aircastle was five hundred yards long, but John wants me to reduce this number by two hundred, for he says the river wasn't more than three hundred yards wide at that point. Will you please search your memory for the correct figure? If you agree with him, I'll take your word for it, and assume that I've made a mistake. But if you've completely forgotten, I'll let my figure stand, for that's how I seem to remember it. You see, I'm extremely anxious to get my facts right, and, when in doubt, any lies that I tell will be quite unintentional, for I'd much rather be thought honest than clever.

However, the simplest solution would be for you to ask Raphael himself, either by word of mouth or by letter—in fact you must do that anyway, because of another little problem which has cropped up. I don't know whose fault it was, mine, yours, or Raphael's, but we never thought of asking, and he never thought of telling us whereabouts in the New World Utopia is. I'd gladly give what little money I possess to repair the omission. For one thing, it makes me feel rather a fool, after all I've written about the island, not to know what sea it's in. . . .

So, Peter, will you please arrange to see Raphael, if you conveniently can, or else write to him, and make sure that my work contains the whole truth and nothing but the truth? Perhaps it would be best for you to show him the book itself, for he's the person best qualified to correct any mistakes, and he can't very well do so, unless he reads the thing right through. Besides, in that way you'll be able to find out how he reacts to the idea of my writing up the results of his researches. For if he's planning to write them up himself, he'd probably rather I didn't—and I certainly shouldn't want to give Utopia premature publicity, so that his story lost the charm of novelty. . . .

*　　*　　*

Source: From *Utopia* by Thomas More, translated by Paul Turner. (Penguin Classics, 1961). Copyright © Paul Turner, 1961. Reprinted by permission of Penguin Group, UK.

[More comments on the basis of some wars by citing an incident in Nolandia.]

I then refer to an incident in the history of Nolandia, a country just south-east of Utopia. On the strength of some ancient marriage, the King of Nolandia thought he had a hereditary claim to another kingdom, so his people started a war to get it for him. Eventually they won, only to find that the kingdom in question was quite as much trouble to keep as it had been to acquire. There were constant threats of internal rebellion and external aggression. They were always having to fight either for their new subjects or against them. They never got a chance to demobilize, and in the meantime they were being ruined. All their money was going out of the country, and men were losing their lives to pay for someone else's petty ambition. Conditions at home were no safer than they'd been during the war, which had lowered moral standards, by encouraging people to kill and steal. There was no respect whatever for the law, because the king's attention was divided between the two kingdoms, so that he couldn't concentrate properly on either.

Seeing that this hopeless situation would continue indefinitely, if they didn't do something about it, the Nolandians finally decided on a course of action, which was to ask the king, quite politely, which kingdom he wanted to keep.

'You can't keep them both,' they explained, 'because there are too many of us to be governed by half a king. Why, even if we were a lot of mules, it would be a full-time job looking after us!'

So that exemplary monarch was forced to hand over the new kingdom to a friend of his—who was very soon thrown out—and make do with the old one. . . .

*   *   *

[On politics and communal property.]

. . . I don't know whether it's right for a philosopher to tell lies, but it's certainly not my way. Besides, though they might be annoyed by what I said, I don't see why it should be thought so fantastically out of the ordinary. It's not as if I'd recommended the system operated in Plato's imaginary *Republic,* or in Utopia today. Now that, while undoubtedly better than ours, might well strike them as rather odd, because it's based on communal ownership instead of private property.

Of course they wouldn't like my proposals. Having set their hearts on a certain course of action, they'd naturally resent being shown the dangers that lay ahead, and told to give the whole thing up. But apart from that, what did I say that couldn't or shouldn't be said in any company? If we're never to say anything that might be thought unconventional, for fear of its sounding ridiculous, we'll have to hush up, even in a Christian country, practically everything that Christ taught. But that was the last thing He wanted. Didn't He tell His disciples that everything He had whispered in their ears should be proclaimed on the housetops? And most of His teaching is far more at variance with modern conventions than anything I suggested, except in so far as His doctrines have been modified by ingenious preachers—doubtless on your recommendation!

'We'll never get human behaviour in line with Christian ethics,' these gentlemen must have argued, 'so let's adapt Christian ethics to human behaviour. Then at least there'll be some connexion between them.'

But I can't see what good they've done. They've merely enabled people to sin with a clear conscience—and that's about all I could do at a Cabinet meeting. For I'd either have to vote against my colleagues, which would be equivalent to not voting at all, or else I'd have to vote with them, in which case, like Micio in Terence, I'd be 'aiding and abetting insanity'. . . .

There's a delightful image in Plato, which explains why a sensible person is right to steer clear of politics. He sees everyone else rushing into the street and getting soaked in the pouring rain. He can't persuade them to go indoors and keep dry. He knows if he went out too, he'd merely get equally wet. So he just stays indoors himself, and, as he can't do anything about other people's stupidity, comforts himself with the thought: 'Well, I'm all right, anyway.'

Though, to tell you the truth, my dear More, I don't see how you can ever get any real justice or prosperity, so long as there's private property, and everything's judged in terms of money—unless you consider it just for the worst sort of people to have the best living conditions, or unless you're prepared to call a country prosperous, in which all the wealth is owned by a tiny minority—who aren't entirely happy even so, while everyone else is simply miserable.

In fact, when I think of the fair and sensible arrangements in Utopia, where things are run so efficiently with so few laws, and recognition of individual merit is combined with equal prosperity for all—when I compare Utopia with a great many capitalist countries which are always making new regulations, but could never be called well-regulated, where dozens of laws are passed every day, and yet there are still not enough to ensure that one can either earn, or keep, or safely identify one's so-called private property—or why such an endless succession of never-ending lawsuits?—when I consider all this, I feel much more sympathy with Plato, and much less surprise at his refusal to legislate for a city that rejected egalitarian principles. It was evidently quite obvious to a powerful intellect like his that the one essential condition for a healthy society was equal distribution of goods—which I suspect is impossible under capitalism. For, when everyone's entitled to get as much for himself as he can, all available property, however much there is of it, is bound to fall into the hands of a small minority, which means that everyone else is poor. And wealth will tend to vary in inverse proportion to merit. The rich will be greedy, unscrupulous, and totally useless characters, while the poor will be simple, unassuming people whose daily work is far more profitable to the community than it is to them.

In other words, I'm quite convinced that you'll never get a fair distribution of goods, or a satisfactory organization of human life, until you abolish private property altogether. So long as it exists, the vast majority of the human race, and the vastly superior part of it, will inevitably go on labouring under a burden of poverty, hardship, and worry. I don't say that the burden can't be reduced, but you'll never take it right off their shoulders. You might, of course, set a statutory limit to the amount of money or land that any one person is allowed to possess. You might, by suitable legislation, maintain a balance of power between the King and his subjects. You might make it illegal to buy, or even to apply for a public appointment, and unnecessary for a state official to spend any money of his own—otherwise he's liable to recoup his losses by fraud and extortion, and wealth, rather than wisdom, becomes the essential qualification for such posts. Laws of that type would certainly relieve the symptoms, just as a chronic invalid gets some benefit from constant medical attention. But there's no hope of a cure, so long as private property continues. If you try to treat an outbreak in one part of the body politic, you merely exacerbate the symptoms elsewhere. What's medicine for some people is poison for others—because you can never pay Paul without robbing Peter.

MORE: I disagree. I don't believe you'd ever have a reasonable standard of living under a communist system. There'd always tend to be shortages, because nobody would work hard enough. In the absence of a profit motive, everyone would become lazy, and rely on everyone else to do the work for him. Then, when things really got short, the inevitable result would be a series of murders and riots, since nobody would have any legal method of protecting the products of his own labour—especially as there wouldn't be any respect for authority, or I don't see how there could be, in a classless society.

RAPHAEL: You're bound to take that view, for you simply can't imagine what it would be like—not accurately, at any rate. But if you'd been with me in Utopia, and seen it all for yourself, as I did—I lived there for more than five years, you know, and the only reason why I ever left was that I wanted to tell people about the New World—you'd be the first to admit that you'd never seen a country so well organized.

PETER: I must say, I find it hard to believe that things are so much better organized in the New World than in the Old. I should think we're just as intelligent as they are, and our civilization is older. It therefore embodies the fruits of long experience, by which I mean all the schemes that we've worked out for making life more comfortable—not to mention several chance discoveries, which could never have been achieved by deliberate planning.

RAPHAEL: You'd be more qualified to judge the age of their civilization, if you'd read their history books. If these are to be trusted, there were towns in the New World before human life had even begun in the Old. As for what you say about intelligence and chance discoveries, there's no reason to suppose we have a monopoly of either. We may or may not be more intelligent than they are, but I'm quite sure they leave us far behind in their capacity for concentration and hard work. . . .

*   *   *

[A discussion of government.]

Now for their system of local government. The population is divided into groups of thirty households, each of which elects an official called a Styward every year. Styward is the Old Utopian title—the modern one is District Controller. For every ten Stywards and the households they represent there is a Bencheater, or Senior District Controller.

Each town has two hundred Stywards, who are responsible for electing the Mayor. They do it by secret ballot, after solemnly swearing to vote for the man that they consider best qualified. He has to be one of four candidates nominated by the whole electorate—for each quarter of the town chooses its own candidate and submits his name to the Council of Bencheaters. The Mayor remains in office for life, unless he's suspected of wanting to establish a dictatorship. Bencheaters are elected annually, but they're not normally changed. All other municipal appointments are for one year only.

Every three days, or more often if necessary, the Bencheaters have a meeting with the Mayor, at which they discuss public affairs, and promptly settle any private disputes—though these are very rare. They always invite two Stywards, a different pair each day, to attend their meetings, and there's a rule that no question affecting the general public may be finally decided until it has been debated for three days. It's a capital crime to discuss such questions anywhere except in the Council or the Assembly. Apparently this is to discourage the Mayor and Bencheaters from plotting to override the people's wishes and change the constitution.

For the same reason any major issue is referred to the Assembly of Stywards, who explain it to all their households, talk it over among themselves, and then report their views to the Council. Occasionally the matter is referred to Parliament.

There's also a rule in the Council that no resolution can be debated on the day that it's first proposed. All discussion is postponed until the next well-attended meeting. Otherwise someone's liable to say the first thing that comes into his head, and then start thinking up arguments to justify what he has said, instead of trying to decide what's best for the community. That type of person is quite prepared to sacrifice the public to his own prestige, just because, absurd as it may sound, he's ashamed to admit that his first idea might have been wrong—when his first idea *should* have been to think before he spoke.

And now for their working conditions. Well, there's one job they all do, irrespective of sex, and that's farming. It's part of every child's education. They learn the principles of agriculture at school, and they're taken for regular outings into the fields near the town, where they not only watch farmwork being done, but also do some themselves, as a form of exercise.

Besides farming which, as I say, is everybody's job, each person is taught a special trade of his own. He may be trained to process wool or flax, or he may become a stonemason, a blacksmith, or a carpenter. Those are the only trades that employ any considerable quantity of labour. They have no tailors or dressmakers, since everyone on the island wears the same sort of clothes—except that they vary slightly according to sex and marital status—and the fashion never changes. These clothes are quite pleasant to look at, they allow free movement of the limbs, they're equally suitable for hot and cold weather—and the great thing is, they're all home-made. So everybody learns one of the other trades I mentioned, and by everybody I mean the women as well as the men—though the weaker sex are given the lighter jobs, like spinning and weaving, while the men do the heavier ones.

Most children are brought up to do the same work as their parents, since they tend to have a natural feeling for it. But if a child fancies some other trade, he's adopted into a family that practises it. Of course, great care is taken, not only by the father, but also by the local authorities, to see that the foster-father is a decent, respectable type. When you've learned one trade properly, you can, if you like, get permission to learn another—and when you're an expert in both, you can practise whichever you prefer, unless the other one is more essential to the public.

The chief business of the Stywards—in fact, practically their only business—is to see that nobody sits around doing nothing, but that everyone gets on with his job. They don't wear people out, though, by keeping them hard at work from early morning till late at night, like cart-horses. That's just slavery—and yet that's what life is like for the working classes nearly everywhere else in the world. In Utopia they have a six-hour working day—three hours in the morning, then lunch—then a two-hour break—then three more hours in the afternoon, followed by supper. They go to bed at 8 p.m., and sleep for eight hours. All the rest of the twenty-four they're free to do what they like—not to waste their time in idleness or self-indulgence, but to make good use of it in some congenial activity. Most people spend these free periods on further education, for there are public lectures first thing every morning. Attendance is quite voluntary, except for those picked out for academic training, but men and women of all classes go crowding in to hear them—I mean, different people go to different lectures, just as the spirit moves them. However, there's nothing to stop you from spending this extra time on your trade, if you want to. Lots of people do, if they haven't the capacity for intellectual work, and are much admired for such public-spirited behaviour.

After supper they have an hour's recreation, either in the gardens or in the communal dining-halls, according to the time of year. Some people practise music, others just talk. They've never heard of anything so silly and demoralizing as dice, but they have two games rather like chess. The first is a sort of arithmetical contest, in which certain numbers 'take' others. The second is a pitched battle between virtues and vices, which illustrates most ingeniously how vices tend to conflict with one another, but to combine against virtues. It also shows which vices are opposed to which virtues, how much strength vices can muster for a direct assault, what indirect tactics they employ, what help virtues need to overcome vices, what are the best methods of evading their attacks, and what ultimately determines the victory of one side or the other.

But here's a point that requires special attention, or you're liable to get the wrong idea. Since they only work a six-hour day, you may think there must be a shortage of essential goods. On the contrary, those six hours are enough, and more than enough to produce plenty of everything that's needed for a comfortable life. And you'll understand why it is, if you reckon up how large a proportion of the population in other countries is totally unemployed. First you have practically all the women—that gives you nearly fifty per cent for a start. And in countries where the women *do* work, the men tend to lounge about instead. Then there are all the priests, and members of so-called religious orders—how much work do they do? Add all the rich, especially the landowners, popularly known as nobles and gentlemen. Include their domestic staffs—I mean those gangs of armed ruffians that I mentioned before. Finally, throw in all the beggars who are perfectly hale and hearty, but pretend to be ill as an excuse for being lazy. When you've counted them up, you'll be surprised to find how few people actually produce what the human race consumes.

And now just think how few of these few people are doing essential work—for where money is the only standard of value, there are bound to be dozens of unnecessary trades carried on, which merely supply luxury goods or entertainment. Why, even if the existing labour force were distributed among the few trades really needed to make life reasonably comfortable, there'd be so much over-production that prices would fall too low for the workers to earn a living. Whereas, if you took all those engaged in non-essential trades, and all who are too lazy to work—each of whom consumes twice as much of the products of other people's labour as any of the producers themselves—if you put the whole lot of them on to something useful, you'd soon see how few hours' work a day would be amply sufficient to supply all the necessities and comforts of life—to which you might add all real and natural forms of pleasure. . . .

*   *   *

[On Law.]

Most married couples are parted only by death, except in the case of adultery or intolerably bad behaviour, when the innocent party may get permission from the Council to marry someone else—the guilty party is disgraced, and condemned to celibacy for life. But in no circumstances can a man divorce his wife simply because, through no fault of her own, she has deteriorated physically. Quite apart from the cruelty of deserting a person at the very time when she most needs sympathy, they think that, if this sort of thing were allowed, there'd be no security whatever for old age, which not only brings many diseases with it, but is really a disease in itself.

Occasionally, though, divorce by mutual consent is allowed on grounds of incompatibility, when both husband and wife had found alternative partners that seem likely to make them happier. But this requires special permission, which can only be got after a thorough investigation by the Bencheaters and their wives. Even then they're rather reluctant to give it, for they think there's nothing less calculated to strengthen the marriage tie than the prospect of easy divorce.

Adulterers are sentenced to penal servitude of the most unpleasant type. If both offenders are married, their injured partners may, if they like, obtain a divorce and marry one another, or anyone else they choose. But if they continue to love their undeserving mates, they're allowed to stay married to them, provided they're willing to share their working conditions. In such cases the Mayor is sometimes so touched by the guilty party's remorse and the innocent party's loyalty that he lets them both go free. But a second conviction means capital punishment.

Otherwise there are no fixed penalties prescribed by law—the Council decides in each case what sentence is appropriate. Husbands are respon-

sible for punishing their wives, and parents for punishing their children, unless the offence is so serious that it has to be dealt with by the authorities, in the interests of public morality. The normal penalty for any major crime is slavery. They say it's just as unpleasant for the criminals as capital punishment, and more useful to society than getting rid of them right away, since live workers are more valuable than dead ones, and have a more prolonged deterrent effect. However, if convicts prove recalcitrant under this treatment, and don't respond to any sort of prison discipline, they're just slaughtered like wild beasts. But the prospects of those who accept the situation aren't absolutely hopeless. If, after being tamed by years of hardship, they show signs of feeling really sorry, not merely for themselves, but for what they've done, their sentence is either reduced or cancelled altogether, sometimes at the discretion of the Mayor, and sometimes by a general plebiscite.

Attempted seduction is punished no less severely than actual seduction. The same applies to every other type of offence—anyone who deliberately tries to commit a crime is legally assumed to have committed it. It's no fault of his, they argue, that he didn't bring it off, so why give him credit for his failure?

They're extremely fond of people who are mentally deficient and, though it's considered very bad form to insult them, it's quite in order to find their silly behaviour amusing. In fact, it's thought better for them that you should, for, if you haven't enough sense of humour to see anything funny about the things they say and do, you're obviously not the right person to look after them. I mean, if you don't value them even as a source of entertainment, which is the only thing they're good for, you won't treat them kindly enough.

But if you start laughing at anyone who's ugly or deformed everyone will start laughing at *you*. You'll have made an awful fool of yourself by implying that people are to blame for things they can't help—for, although one's thought very lazy if one doesn't try to preserve one's natural beauty, the Utopians strongly disapprove of make-up. Actually, they've found by experience that what husbands look for in their wives is not so much physical beauty, as modesty and a respectful attitude towards themselves. A pretty face may be enough to catch a man, but it takes character and good nature to hold him.

The Utopian system includes not only deterrents from crime, but also incentives to good behaviour in the form of public honours. For instance, they put up statutes in the market-place of people who've distinguished themselves by outstanding services to the community, partly to commemorate their achievements, and partly to spur on future generations to greater efforts, by reminding them of the glory of their ancestors. But anyone who deliberately tries to get himself elected to a public office is permanently disqualified from holding one. Social relations are uniformly friendly, for officials are never pompous or intimidating in their manner. They're normally addressed as 'Father', and that's how they behave. Everyone treats them with proper respect, but nobody's forced to do so. Even the Mayor himself wears perfectly ordinary clothes, without any special head-dress. His only badge of office is a bunch of corn that he carries—just as a Bishop carries a taper.

They have very few laws, because, with their social system, very few laws are required. Indeed, one of their great complaints against other countries is that, although they've already got books and books of laws and interpretations of laws, they never seem to have enough. For, according to the Utopians, it's quite unjust for anyone to be bound by a legal code which is too long for an ordinary person to read right through, or too difficult for him to understand. What's more, they have no barristers to be over-ingenious about individual cases and points of law. They think it better for each man to plead his own cause, and tell the judge the same story as he'd otherwise tell his lawyer. Under such conditions, the point at issue is less likely to be obscured, and it's easier to get at the truth—for, if nobody's telling the sort of lies that one learns from lawyers, the judge can apply all his shrewdness to weighing the facts of the case, and protecting simple-minded characters against the unscrupulous attacks of clever ones.

This arrangement wouldn't work very well in other countries, because there's such a mass of complicated legislation to deal with. But in Utopia everyone's a legal expert, for the simple reason that there are, as I said, very few laws, and the crudest interpretation is always assumed to be the right one. They say the only purpose of a law is to remind people what they ought to do, so the more ingenious the interpretation, the less effective the laws, since proportionately fewer people will understand it—whereas the simple and obvious meaning stares everyone in the face. From the point of view of the lower orders, who form the largest section of the community, and are most in need of such reminders, you might just as well not make a law at all, as make one and then interpret it in a sense that can only be established after a lot of clever argument—for the ordinary person who's busy earning his living hasn't either the time or the mental capacity for that type of research. . . .

But in their part of the world, which is diametrically opposed to ours, no less in a social and moral than in a geographical sense, you can't rely on treaties at all. The more solemnly they're made, the sooner they're violated, by the simple process of discovering some loophole in the wording. Indeed, such loopholes are often incorporated deliberately in the original text, so that, no matter how binding one's commitments appear to be, one can always wriggle out of them, thus breaking both treaty and faith simultaneously. The fact is, such diplomacy is downright dishonest. If the very people who pride themselves on suggesting such tricks to their rulers found the same sort of thing going on in connexion with a private contract, they'd be the first to denounce it, in shrill, self-righteous tones, as sacrilegious and criminal. The implication seems to be that honesty is a low plebeian virtue, far beneath the dignity of royalty—or at least that there are two kinds of honesty. One is suitable for ordinary people, a plodding hack which is kept securely tethered, so that it can't go leaping any fences. The other, reserved for kings, is a far nobler animal which enjoys far greater freedom—for it's allowed to do exactly what it likes.

Anyway, that's how kings behave out there, and that, as I was saying, is presumably why the Utopians make no treaties. Perhaps if they lived in Europe they'd change their minds—though actually they disapprove of treaties on principle, however scrupulously they're observed. They say treaties make people regard one another as natural enemies. The mere fact of living on different sides of a small hill or river is supposed to sever all ties of humanity, and justify two nations in trying to destroy each other, unless there's a special treaty to forbid it. And even if there is such a treaty, it still doesn't mean that they're friends, for they always retain the right to rob one another, in so far as the drafters of the treaty have carelessly failed to include enough provisions to the contrary. The Utopians take precisely the opposite view. They think no one should be regarded as an enemy who hasn't done you any harm. Human nature constitutes a treaty in itself, and human beings are far more effectively united by kindness than by contracts, by feelings than by words.

And that brings us to the subject of war. Well, fighting is a thing they absolutely loathe. They say it's a quite subhuman form of activity, although human beings are more addicted to it than any of the lower animals. In fact, the Utopians are practically the only people on earth who fail to see anything glorious in war. Of course, both sexes are given military training at regular intervals, so that they won't be incapable of fighting if they ever have to do it. But they hardly ever go to war, except in self-defence, to repel invaders from friendly territory, or to liberate the victims of dictatorship—which they do in a spirit of humanity, just because they feel sorry for them. However, they give military support to 'friendly powers', not only in defensive wars, but also in attempts to make reprisals for acts of aggression. This is always on condition that they're consulted well in advance, that they think the *casus belli* adequate, that compensation has been demanded and refused, and that the control of operations is left entirely to them. Their idea of an adequate *casus belli* includes more than robbery by force of arms. They take even stronger action to protect the rights of traders who are subjected to any kind of legal injustice in foreign countries, either as a result of unfair laws, or of fair ones deliberately misinterpreted.

That's how the war with Blindland started, a little before our time. The Utopians gave military aid to the Cloudians, because some Cloudian businessmen operating in Blindland had been the victims of some sort of legal fraud—or so the Utopians thought. Whether they were right or wrong, the result was a major war, for the bitterness of the original conflict was stepped up by the intervention of all the surrounding countries. By the time it was over, the strength of several great powers had been shattered, and others had sustained crippling losses. As for the Blindlanders, after a series of disasters they finally had to give in. The Utopians got nothing out of it—their motives were quite disinterested throughout—but the Blindlanders became the slaves of the Cloudians, who in the old days had been no match for them at all.

So you see how quick the Utopians are to avenge injuries done to their friends, even in money matters. But they're far more tolerant of injuries done to themselves. If a Utopian trader is cheated out of his goods, but suffers no physical injury, the strongest action they take is to suspend trade relations with the country concerned, until they receive compensation. Not that they care less about their own people—it's just that members of other nations are far more vulnerable to fraud, since it means the loss of their own private property, whereas a Utopian in similar circumstances loses nothing whatever. The loss is borne by the state. Besides, any goods lost are surplus to home requirements, or they'd never have been exported. So nobody feels any the worse for it—and they think it would be cruel to kill large numbers of people in revenge for something which hasn't made the slightest difference to the life or the livelihood of a single Utopian. But they take a very different line if one of their citizens is physically disabled or killed, either by a foreign government or by an individual foreigner. The moment they get news of such an incident through diplomatic channels, they immediately declare war. No form of appeasement has any effect, except the surrender of the people responsible—in which case they're sentenced to death or slavery.

They don't like bloody victories—in fact they feel ashamed of them, for they consider it stupid to pay too high a price for anything, however valuable it is. What they're really proud of is outwitting the enemy. They celebrate any success of this kind by a triumphal procession, and by putting up a trophy, as for some feat of heroism. You see, their idea of quitting themselves like men is to achieve victory by means of something which only man possesses, that is, by the power of the intellect. They say any animal can fight with its body—bears, lions, boars, wolves, dogs can all do it, and most of them are stronger and fiercer than we are—but what raises us above them is our reason and intelligence.

Their one aim in wartime is to get what they've previously failed to get by peaceful means—or, if that's out of the question, to punish the offenders so severely that nobody will ever dare to do such a thing again. They make for these objectives by the shortest possible route—but always on the principle of safety first, and national prestige second. So the moment war's declared they arrange through secret agents for lots of posters to go up simultaneously at all points on enemy territory where they're most likely to be seen. These posters carry the official seal of the Utopian government, and offer a huge reward for killing the enemy king. They also offer smaller, but still very considerable sums for killing certain individuals, whose names appear on a list, and who are presumed to be the chief supporters, after the king, of anti-Utopian policies. The reward for bringing such people in alive is twice as much as for killing them—and they themselves are offered the same amount of money, plus a free pardon, for turning against their own associates.

The immediate result is that everyone mentioned on the list becomes suspicious of everything in human shape. They all stop trusting one another, and stop being trustworthy. They live in a constant state of terror, which is perfectly justified—for it's often been known to happen that all of them, including the king himself, are betrayed by the very person that they pinned most faith on. The fact is, people will do anything for money, and there's no limit to the amount of

money that the Utopians are prepared to give. Bearing in mind the risks that they're inviting each traitor to run, they're very careful to offer him compensating advantages. So, in addition to vast quantities of gold, they also promise him the freehold of a valuable estate in safe and friendly territory—and such promises they invariably keep.

This system of making take-over bids for the enemy is generally considered mean and cruel, but the Utopians are very proud of it. They say it's extremely sensible to dispose of major wars like this without fighting a single battle, and also most humane to save thousands of innocent lives at the cost of a few guilty ones. They're thinking of all the soldiers who would have been killed in action, on one side or the other—for they feel almost as much sympathy for the mass of the enemy population as they do for their own. They realize that these people would never have started a war if they hadn't been forced into it by the insanity of their rulers.

If this method fails, they sow and foster the seeds of discord among their enemies, by encouraging the king's brother or some other member of the aristocracy to aspire to the throne. If internal dissension shows signs of flagging, they inflame hostility in some adjacent country by digging up one of those ancient claims that kings are always so well provided with. They promise to support the claimant's war effort, and do it by supplying plenty of money and very little manpower—for they're much too fond of one another to be willing to sacrifice a single Utopian citizen, even in exchange for the enemy king himself. But they're perfectly happy to hand out silver and gold, because that's all they keep it for, and they know it won't make any difference to their standard of living if they spend the whole lot. Besides, quite apart from their capital at home, they possess vast foreign assets, for, as I explained before, a great many countries owe them money.

Northern Renaissance
Common Creativity

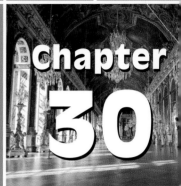

> But to speak of arts, what set men's wits on work to invent and transmit to posterity so many famous, as they conceive, pieces of learning but the thirst of glory?
>
> —*Erasmus*, In Praise of Folly

Migration Northward

The ideas and culture of the Renaissance began in Italy and then slowly spread northward throughout Europe. Humanism, with its focus on education and the arts, had a profound impact on northern countries such as Germany, England, and the Low Countries (present day Netherlands, Belgium, and Luxembourg), just as it had influenced Italy. However, the Northern Renaissance was different than Renaissance Italy, mostly because of major differences in lifestyle, traditions, and, increasingly, religion. The North, which had largely been outside the Roman Empire, was less interested in the Greek and Roman classics and certainly did not feel itself the inheritor of the Roman culture, as did Italy. Therefore, pagan themes were rare in northern art and literature. The religious nature of the North, and therefore the art, was more adherent to strictly biblical themes and less likely to be interested in traditions such as the stories of the saints or elaborations on the life of Mary. This biblical focus was further enhanced because of the Protestant Reformation, which was biblically based. The Reformation profoundly affected art and literature in the North after Martin Luther.

Consistent with the ideas of the Reformation, individualism became more important in the North than in Italy. This was seen in art subjects and methods of distributing art. Northern art and literature spoke to the emerging middle class and were also supported by that same group. Since the funds of these merchants and artisans were more limited than those of the elite sponsors in Italy, like the Medici family and the Catholic Church, the artists of the North needed to find ways to make their art more widely accessible. Therefore, we see great creativity employed in tailoring art for the common people. We observe a similarity to Italian art and literature, but with a definite orientation toward common people and straightforward religious experience.

The spread of the Renaissance to the North generally began with students who traveled to Italy and attended universities there. The universities in both Padua and Bologna were among Europe's best and attracted students from all over Europe. Even in the early Renaissance, the Italian universities focused less on the traditional medieval curriculum and more on humanism and the arts, thus giving their students grounding in humanism. Students from the northern countries would also be exposed to the great art sponsored by the Italian city-states and the Catholic Church when visiting cities such as Florence, Milan, or Rome. Thus, when they graduated and returned home, these young scholars had both learned about the world from a new humanistic perspective and seen the results of living that Renaissance lifestyle.

These returning scholars spread the news of the Renaissance and the wonders of the new art style. Soon, aspiring artists in the North joined the migration to Italy, where they were taught the techniques of Renaissance art. These artists returned to the North, where they adapted their new knowledge to the culture and conditions of their homelands. However, the overall adoption of the Renaissance proceeded slowly in the North because conflicts over religion distracted potential sponsors and artists alike. Furthermore, in Northern Europe political power was coalescing around princedoms or nations rather than cities. The larger political entities took longer to develop into a politically stable and financially sound entity, and it simply took more time for ideas to spread across Germany than it did for them to circulate around a city like Florence or Rome. These factors caused the Northern Renaissance to lag behind Italy by roughly a century.

Yet another factor slowing the adoption of the Renaissance in the North was the restrictive nature of the occupational trade guilds of Northern Europe. These trade guilds governed the teaching of occupational skills such as blacksmithing, goldsmithing, construction, glassmaking, masonry, and so on. Many of these guilds taught the same or similar skills used by artists such as Brunelleschi, Michelangelo, Ghiberti, and Leonardo, but the Italian artists were able to break away from the restrictions of the guilds and create new and unique art pieces. In the North, the lack of sponsors inhibited this freedom, as did the great strength of the Northern guilds. These guilds were active is determining what projects were to be done, so individual workers had less say in how they would use their talents and probably less individual recognition for their achievements. The guild restrictions of the North took time to overcome.

In spite of all the differences between the Italian and the Northern Renaissance, there was a shared theme of humanism. Humankind once again viewed itself as the greatest of God's creations and, therefore, worthy of study and praise. There was also a renewed interest in discovering and displaying human talents and abilities. We will look at great humanistic scholars, inventors of new literary genres, and artists who adapted Renaissance art to Northern subjects, and others who contributed the growth of Renaissance ideas across the North. In this chapter we will examine the Renaissance in the Low Countries, France, and Germany. The Renaissance in England is the subject of the next chapter.

▪ Erasmus

The first and greatest of the Northern Renaissance humanists was Desiderius Erasmus. Born in Rotterdam, Holland, in 1466, **Erasmus** was the illegitimate son of a Catholic priest and a local peasant woman. Both his parents died while Erasmus was still in his early teens, and Erasmus was forced to join the local monastery by his new guardians. Although highly religious by nature, Erasmus felt no passion for the calling of a monk and spent most of his time in the local monastery library studying the Classics. A nearby bishop noticed Erasmus and was impressed with his studious nature and obvious intellectual skills. The bishop offered Erasmus a position as his personal secretary and traveling companion. The bishop later ordained Erasmus to the priesthood, and Erasmus became the Bishop's personal priest (confessor). This bishop helped Erasmus enter the University of Paris, where Erasmus focused on ancient languages, becoming an expert in both Greek and Latin. Using his knowledge of those languages, Erasmus studied the ancient classical texts and translated many of them into the vernacular. His accuracy and excellent writing style in these translations led to fame and widespread recognition as Europe's foremost authority on ancient texts and languages.

Over time, Erasmus began to doubt the reliability of St. Jerome's translation of the Bible (called the Vulgate version), which was completed in the fifth century A.D. and had been the version commonly accepted and used by the Catholic Church throughout Europe since that time. (We discussed in Chapter 28 an error in which Jerome misread the Hebrew account of Moses descending from Mt. Sinai and said that Moses' head had horns instead of a crown of light.) Erasmus decided to create a new Latin translation of the Bible in which many of the errors of the Vulgate would be corrected.

To gain access to more ancient manuscripts, Erasmus traveled to the British Isles, where many ancient manuscripts had been preserved in monasteries. (The preservation of these ancient manuscripts, initially in Ireland and then in Northern England, was critical to the minor awakening of civilization at the time of Charlemagne in roughly 800 A.D. and to the full flowering of the Renaissance at the time of Erasmus. The story is told in *How the Irish Saved Civilization* by Thomas Cahill, which is referenced in the Suggested Readings at the end of this chapter.) Using these early Greek manuscripts, and with the assistance of his friend Sir Thomas More (who we discussed in Chapter 29), Erasmus began to retranslate the New Testament and correct its errors. Erasmus' New Testament translation was finally published in 1516, together with a commentary. His New Testament was the first translation to use both the early Greek manuscripts and comparisons with later translations, such as the English translation done by Wycliffe over a century earlier.

Some of the changes made by Erasmus were criticized by the Catholic Church. For example, 1 John 5:7 reads as follows in the English King James Version, "For there are three that bear witness in Heaven, the Father, the Word, and the Holy Spirit: And these three are One." This verse was especially important in Catholic doctrine as it was the only verse in the Bible that seemed to specifically refer to the concept of the Trinity. However, the Greek texts which Erasmus used did not contain this verse. Therefore, Erasmus eliminated the verse entirely from his translation of the New Testament.

Erasmus' translation was written in Latin. This contrasts with Wycliffe, who translated into English, and with Luther, who translated into German. (Luther's translation followed Erasmus' version by about six years and may have used Erasmus as a reference.) Erasmus was not trying to disrupt the traditions of the Catholic Church, which still conducted services in Latin and believed that Latin was a more pure and elevated language for conducting religious rites. The differences between the biblical translations of Erasmus and Luther reflected their basic differences in how to address the fallacies and problems each saw in the Catholic Church. Initially, Erasmus' criticisms of the church were viewed with the same alarm as were Luther's and treated in much the same way. However, whereas Luther believed that a complete break with the Catholic Church was necessary (perhaps because of his own excommunication), Erasmus favored reform within the framework of the church. When he was forced to choose between rebellion and papal authority, Erasmus supported the pope.

Although their views were initially similar, this fundamental difference in approach led Luther and Erasmus to openly criticize each other's teachings and eventually led to personal attacks. For instance, Erasmus viewed Luther as hypocritical in advocating the importance of each person reading and following the Bible and then telling them what to believe. Luther saw Erasmus as hypocritical in not taking strong positions against what were obvious deficiencies in church practices.

Luther became the church's most influential critic and Erasmus its principal defender. Some believe that Erasmus helped Thomas More write the treatise signed by Henry VIII, which defended the Catholic Church against some of Luther's claims and for which Henry was named Defender of the Faith by the pope. Erasmus gave the Catholic Church a foundation from which it fought the challenges of Protestantism and became the leading intellectual of his age.

However, Erasmus' most lasting literary achievement was not his translation work, but an original discourse, written with many classical allusions, titled *In Praise of Folly*. This attempt at understanding the nature of mankind falls firmly within the humanist tradition and makes *In Praise of Folly* among the first humanistic writings of the Northern Renaissance. *In Praise of Folly*, published in 1509, is in a letter format from Erasmus to his friend Thomas More. Originally only meant for private circulation, at least in format, *In Praise of Folly* soon found a wider audience and went through seven editions in only a few months. In this treatise, Erasmus satirically attacked the follies of various social classes, including some vigorous attacks on the culture and practices of the church. The sarcasm and skepticism of *In Praise of Folly* was intended to point out the weaknesses in human nature and several of its institutions so that humans could better understand themselves and improve their institutions. Erasmus' criticism of indulgences, saints, and extreme worship of Mary are revealed in the following passage:

And now suppose some merchant, soldier, or judge, out of so many rapines, parts with some small piece of money. He straight conceives all that sink of his whole life quite cleansed; so many perjuries, so many lusts, so many debaucheries, so many contentions, so many murders, so many deceits, so many breaches of trusts, so many treacheries bought off, as it were by compact; and so bought off that they may begin upon a new score. But what is more foolish than those, or rather more happy, who daily reciting those seven verses of the Psalms promise to themselves more than the top of felicity? Which magical verses some devil or other, a merry one without doubt but more a blab of his tongue than crafty, is believed to have discovered to St. Bernard, but not without a trick. And these are so foolish that I am half ashamed of them myself, and yet they are approved, and that not only by the common people but even the professors of religion.

And what, are not they also almost the same where several countries avouch to themselves their peculiar saint, and as everyone of them has his particular gift, so also his particular form of worship? As, one is good for the toothache; another for groaning women; a third, for stolen goods; a fourth, for making a voyage prosperous; and a fifth, to cure sheep of the rot; and so of the rest, for it would be too tedious to run over all. And some there are that are good for more things than one; but chiefly, the Virgin Mother, to whom the common people do in a manner attribute more than to the Son.[1]

In spite of Erasmus' relatively harmless intentions to encourage reform from within, many felt that the attacks were too severe and, later, when the Protestant Reformation exploded across Europe, some within the Church pointed to *In Praise of Folly* as the Reformation's intellectual forerunner, in that it set a precedent for the open criticism of the church. The critical pressure on Erasmus built as Luther confronted the church, and eventually Erasmus was forced to publicly choose between Luther and the Pope.

As we have already noted, Erasmus spoke out against Luther and the Protestant Reformation, encouraging them to reconcile and seek for reform from within the Church. He became ever more critical as Luther took personal offense at what Erasmus wrote and vigorously defended himself by both intellectual argument and personal attack on Erasmus. In speaking out strongly against Luther, Erasmus silenced his critics and possibly avoided the fate of his friend, Sir Thomas More, who would soon face a similar choice between the Pope and King Henry VIII in England, as we discussed in Chapter 29.

Today, some see Erasmus as weak in his criticism of the church and basically a fence-sitter. Others see him as strong in his defense of the church and his resolution to reform from within. Whichever position is the correct view of Erasmus, he is generally accepted as an intellectual leader and disseminator of humanistic thought. He wrote with high intellectual rigor, but seemed to reflect the position of those common people who wished to see progress without disruption of society and basic institutions.

■ Michel de Montaigne

The great Renaissance literary figure in France was **Michel de Montaigne** (1533–1592), the inventor of the genre of the essay. The purpose of Montaigne's writings, of the essay, was to reveal the author's mind rather than to convince or motivate. It is a genre that seems very private and well suited to adoption by the common person. It is, therefore, humanistic in its basic affirmation of the individual's importance.

In Montaigne's hand, the essay strongly reflects a trait of the Renaissance—**classical allusions.** Montaigne, like the other writers of the Northern Renaissance, was familiar with the thinkers of the classical era and used classical allusions in his essays. These tended to elevate the genre above the common person, because knowledge of the classics was chiefly known to the well-educated and intellectual (although classical knowledge was more commonly known even by the commoners then than it is today). Therefore, in Northern Renaissance literature, there was a natural dichotomy—appeal to the common person and simultaneous use of classical allusions that are best understood by the intellectuals. Montaigne handled this dichotomy well, perhaps because his new style was so personal and accessible.

Montaigne tried to be very honest in his writing so that the reader would be able to evaluate the truth or falsity of his opinions based on what he understood Montaigne's mind to· be when he wrote the essay. Montaigne's style was easy and conversational. For instance, the preface to his collection of essays begins as follows:

This, reader, is an honest book. It warns you at the outset that my sole purpose in writing it has been a private and domestic one. I have had no thought of serving you or of my own fame; such a plan would be beyond my powers. I have intended it solely for the pleasure of my relatives and friends so that, when they have lost me—which they soon

must—they may recover some features of my character and disposition, and thus keep the memory they have of me more completely and vividly alive. . . . So, reader, I am myself the substance of my book, and there is no reason why you should waste your leisure on so frivolous and unrewarding a subject.[2]

Montaigne directed his various short writings to specific issues. For example, Montaigne wrote essays *On Repentance* and *Of Experience.* The easy style of the Preface continues in the essays themselves, as illustrated in this brief quotation from *On Repentance:*

Let me here excuse what I often say, that I rarely repent and that my conscience is content with itself—not as the conscience of an angel or a horse, but as the conscience of a man; always adding this refrain, not perfunctorily but in sincere and complete submission that I speak as an ignorant inquirer, referring the decision purely and simply to the common and authorized beliefs. I do not teach, I tell.

Herein you can see the continuing belief of Montaigne in the Catholic Church and its traditions, as opposed to Luther and even to Erasmus. The essay is Renaissance in tone because it puts the author (man) at the center of the issue.

A common theme of Montaigne's essays was morality, with an emphasis on individual morality rather than group or societal morality. This also shows the emphasis on man, as opposed to society or religion. Finally, Montaigne's essays also fall within the Renaissance tradition of self-help books, which were popular at the time and included classics such as Machiavelli's *The Prince,* a decidedly different point of view from Montaigne's.

■ Northern Renaissance Visual Art

An interesting and, perhaps, unexpected difference between the North and Italy was the relative unimportance of the visual arts in the North—especially religious art. That is not to say that the visual arts did not play a role in the Northern

Renaissance, because they did. However, the Northern Renaissance focused more on the written word and intellectual pursuits than it did the visual arts. This difference in emphasis existed for several reasons that we briefly touched on earlier. Let's look at them in more detail now.

One reason was likely the reduction in the amount of visual art in Protestant churches, where the concept of avoiding "graven images" was very important and churches tended to emphasize simplicity and plainness. In contrast, the Catholic Church commissioned great paintings, sculptures, and other decorations to help the people understand God's majesty and glory. The Protestant churches viewed grandiose and elaborate art as a possible distraction to the worshipper's communing with God.

A second limiting factor on the visual arts was that Northern Europeans were strongly conservative in their morals and, as a result, rarely portrayed fully undressed nudes. The North did not share the classical tradition of Italy, and thus found much of classical art repulsive. This reluctance to portray nudes inevitably led away from the visual arts.

Another reason may have been economic. The long periods required to create large visual art pieces, such as the ceiling of the Sistine Chapel or the massive *School of Athens,* required large sums of money to support the artists while they worked. The Catholic Church and major sponsors such as the Medici family could afford to do it, but there were fewer such sponsors in the North.

While the visual arts were not as important to the Northern Renaissance as they were in Italy, there was still a great deal of significant art being produced by some great masters of the Northern Renaissance. The earliest of these northern artists reflected their origins as craftsmen. The woodcarvers were some of the most talented of these early artisans, and they produced some art pieces that were well known in their own time and today rank as among the best woodcarvings ever to have been made.

Tilman Riemenschneider was the first of the well-known woodcarvers. He was born in Germany in 1460 and received most of his support from the churches of central Germany. He should be considered a transition artist who bridged the medieval and Renaissance styles. For instance, his carving of John the Baptist depicts John holding a lamb and pointing toward it while parting his lips as if to say, "Behold the lamb of God," a symbolic and medieval-like reference to John's comments when he saw Christ just prior to Christ's baptism. The Renaissance style is illustrated in that work in its high detail and the realism with which John was depicted.

Renaissance characteristics are even more clearly seen in the realism in expressions, gestures, clothing, and setting of the apostles in Riemenschneider's great *Last Supper* from the *Altarpiece of the Holy Blood,* which is in the St. Jakobskirche, Rothenburg ob der Tauber, Germany, shown in Figure 30.1. Note how each figure seems to be caught in its own moment of reflection. He also shows an interesting geometrical arrangement of the figures—not the triangular arrangement taught by Leonardo about the same time, but clearly an improvement over the strictly linear arrangement of medieval works and, perhaps, as interesting as Leonardo's.

Perhaps the most well known of the artisans of the Northern Renaissance was Germany's **Albrecht Dürer.** He was born in a large and poor German family in which two sons wished to become artists, Albrecht and Albert. According to tradition, the family was too poor to allow both brothers to attend the academy in Nuremberg where they would learn art, so the brothers decided that one would support the other and then, when the first became a well-known artist, they would reverse roles. Albrecht won the coin toss and his brother worked in a mine to support him. At the school, Albrecht achieved immediate success, where his etchings, woodcuts, and paintings were generally better than the works of his professors. Albrecht earned considerable fees from his works. After completing his studies, Albrecht returned home to allow his brother to leave and pursue his art career. Albrecht informed his brother of the situation, but his brother began to cry and mutter, "No, no, no." When asked why he was crying, the brother responded by holding up his bruised

Figure 30.1 ■ Last Supper *by Tilman Riemenschneider from the Altarpiece of the Holy Blood, St. Jakobskirche, Rothenburg ob der Tauber, Germany (Height of tallest figure is 39 inches).* © Wolfgang Kaehler/CORBIS.

and broken hands which were so damaged from working in the mine that he could hardly hold his mining tools, let alone the tools of an artist. Albrecht was dumbstruck. He then immortalized his brother's sacrifice with a series of drawings of hands. One of the drawings is shown in Figure 30.2.

Dürer was a very talented painter, as can be seen from the sketch of the hands, and was even more widely known for a series of excellent self-portraits done throughout his life. However, Dürer is most famous for his elaborate and detailed woodcarvings. An example of his woodcarvings is *St. Jerome in his Cell,* shown in Figure 30.3. He combines some medieval symbolism, such as the lion sleeping with the lamb, but also shows strong Renaissance influences in his use of perspective. Other famous Dürer woodcuts depict biblical scenes such as *Four Horsemen of the Apocalypse* and a classical scene of *The Knight, Death and the Devil* in Figure 30.4.

Some of these woodcarvings were created to make printed ink copies for books, often for Protestant translations of the Bible. Thus, readers of a Bible that contained an inked copy of Dürer's

Figure 30.2 ■ *Sketch of hands by Albrecht Dürer.* © Bettmann/CORBIS.

work could use the illustration to not only bring the story to life, but to place themselves as the story's hero. Due to the recent invention of the printing press, Dürer's woodcarvings were often copied as free-standing prints, and he became quite well

Figure 30.3 ▪ St. Jerome in his Cell *by Albrecht Dürer.* © *Historical Picture Archive/CORBIS.*

Figure 30.4 ▪ *Knight, Death and Devil by Albrecht Dürer.* Bridgeman-Giraudon/Art Resource, NY.

known during his lifetime. He likely became the most successful artist of the Northern Renaissance. Dürer was able to support himself from the commissions he received for his work and proved that artists in the North could live from their artistic talent even without the patronage of wealthy city-states and the Catholic Church. His high-volume production of art was creative in its methods and in the recognition of the common people as his most important sponsors.

The leaders of the Northern Renaissance painters were from the Low Countries. These Dutch and Flemish painters had more exposure to the ideas of the Italian Renaissance because Holland was a Spanish territory and therefore had more interaction with the Catholic South than did most of the other areas in the North. Much of the painting of the Low Countries focused on depicting the life of common people—again, because of the economic power of the middle class.

The first of the great Dutch painters was **Pieter Bruegel,** the Elder. Bruegel worked to adopt the techniques of Italy, where he studied,

and mastered many of the Renaissance's technical aspects. Paintings such as *Peasant Wedding Feast,* shown in Figure 30.5, captured the elements of daily life for the common man in Holland. The painting showed Renaissance techniques such as perspective; realism in gesture, expression, and clothes; and a thematic emphasis on common people. Bruegel set the precedent and tone for much of the Dutch art that was to follow with his use of commoners as the subjects of his paintings in common settings. He also showed great attention to detail—a trait that would also become characteristic of the Dutch School of artists.

Another important figure of the Dutch school was **Hieronymus Bosch.** His paintings were unique but had little of the Renaissance technique, except for realism. Bosch's main subject was human folly in its various forms, and his theme was the imminent punishment for sin in hell. Bosch created elaborate fantasy worlds where men and monsters are engaged in all variety of carnal sins. His triptych *The Garden of Earthly Delights* was an encapsulation of both his unique style and sub-

Figure 30.5 ■ Peasant Wedding Feast *by Pieter Bruegel, the Elder.*
© *Erich Lessing/Art Resource, NY.*

ject. The Spanish monarch Phillip II was reported to have favored this work in particular, and it is now in the great art museum of Spain—the Prado in Madrid.

■ Music of the Northern Renaissance

Although the music of the Italian Renaissance was mostly religious, with only a minor nod to the secular, music in the North was the opposite. Madrigals, which were readily available to the common people, were the principal music form in the North. These were not only the love ballads of earlier times; they were also adventure tales that encouraged the audience to imagine a world of adventures. They were often performed at fairs and markets, where the common people were the chief audience.

Some of the most important Northern music was based on folk tunes, which were not only well known to the common people, but were characteristic of the area in which the people lived. These folk tunes took the place of Gregorian chants as the basis of church music. Many hymns were based on folk tunes, some of which were written by Martin Luther himself. Luther applauded writing church music as a method of drawing close to Christ. He reasoned that any work that elevated the human spirit would help a person commune with God and, therefore, was worthy of being played in church. This attitude encouraged both vocal music (called *motets* in French and *anthems* in English) and also instrumental music. In this, the Northern Renaissance was very different from the Italian Renaissance, where instrumental music was not allowed in church because it did not express the words of the mass.

In the North, some music was even written for the stage, but that is a subject that becomes most important in the English Renaissance, which is the subject of the next chapter.

■ Creativity in the Northern Renaissance

The Renaissance in the North was different in its emphasis than its Italian parent. Whereas Italy emphasized visual arts such as painting, sculpture, and architecture, the North emphasized literature. Furthermore, the ideas of the Northern

Renaissance were shaped by both Protestant theology and the more conservative middle class of Northern Europe. However, the underlying principles were the same: a focus on the importance and abilities of humans, the religious and secular blurring of humanism, and a return to the ideas of Classical Greece and Rome. Using their creative ingenuity, scholars and artists across Northern Europe were able to observe the fabulous changes occurring in Italy and reshape them into something that possessed the same power, but better fit the culture and lifestyle of the North.

■ Timeline—Important Dates

Date	Event
1460–1531	*Tilman Riemenschneider*
1466–1536	*Erasmus*
1471–1528	*Albrecht Dürer*
1509	*Publication of Erasmus'* In Praise of Folly
1516	*Publication of Erasmus'* New Testament translation
1525–1569	*Pieter Bruegel, the Elder*
1533–1592	*Michel Montaigne*

■ Notes

1. Erasmus, *In Praise of Folly,* translated by John Wilson, 1688, http://www.ccel.org/e/erasmus/folly/folly.html.
2. Montaigne, *The Complete Works of Montaigne: Essays, Travel Journal, Letters,* Translated by Donald M. Frame (Palo Alto: Stanford University, 1957), preface.

■ Suggested Readings

Cahill, Thomas, *How the Irish Saved Civilization,* Anchor Books, 1995.

Erasmus, *The Praise of Folly and Other Writings,* Norton, 1989.

Erasmus: A Discussion of Free Will; Hyperaspistes

Desiderius Erasmus (1466–1536) will always be considered a prototypical Renaissance humanist and was widely regarded as one of the most intelligent men of his day. He was respected, but also criticized by some, for his slowness in taking sides during the Reformation. He was born an illegitimate child in Holland, became a Priest, then a Monk, and then a traveling scholar of Latin and Greek. His love for the ancient classics gave him an appreciation for the works of man, and he became an ardent Humanist. This desire to promote the works of mankind provoked in him a strong desire to justify the glory of mankind's efforts with the often condescending views of the church. He was particularly critical of the church's adoption of scholasticism and the hair-splitting atmosphere of philosophical debate it fostered. He published biting satire of church practices, which he felt were wrong and laid out the principles on which he based his views.

Many attribute the beginnings of the Reformation to the writings of Erasmus. He was clearly critical of the church, but he never advocated a split from Rome. His objective was to encourage reform from within the church. He was initially a friend and ally of Martin Luther, and when Luther was attacked by the Catholic Church, Erasmus was mentioned as a co-enemy of the church. Eventually, as Luther became increasingly separatist, Erasmus moved away from Luther but did not openly condemn him. It took many years for Erasmus to finally quit his "fence-sitting" and decide that he should remain loyal to Rome. In his eventual efforts to prove his loyalty to the church,

Erasmus began to publish works of reason and scriptural-based arguments to discredit Lutheran principles. What followed was a long, bitter, published dispute between the two—effectively making Erasmus one of Luther's most hated enemies. However, Erasmus was never considered a champion for the Catholic Church because of his earlier critical remarks against the church.

Erasmus greatly disliked the upheaval of the Lutheran movement and how its adherents were following their emotions rather than rational study. He traced this to Luther's denial of free will in *Diatribe de Libero Arbitrio* ("A Discussion of Free Will"). This was Erasmus' first real stand for one side or the other and was considered by Luther to be a direct attack. In response, Luther published *De Servo Arbitrio* ("On the Enslaved Will"), in which he declared the incompetence of man in his fallen state to act righteously on his own. It was specifically meant to be a blow to Erasmus' humanist ideals. *Hyperaspistes* was Erasmus' reply; an attack that Luther would not publicly acknowledge as having any effect, but which privately he admitted had caused much irritation.

The last passage in "A Discussion of Free Will" is presented here; it is the thesis of the entire work and illustrates Erasmus' cool, collective, and scholarly method of disputation. The passage from *Hyperaspistes* is Erasmus' attack on Luther's interpretation of scripture. Erasmus effectively asks why Luther should be able to interpret scripture better than others, thus undermining Luther's position as the leader of the reform movement.

▪ From *A Discussion of Free Will*

[Why we must attribute something to free will]
Why, you may ask, attribute anything at all to free will? To allow the ungodly, who have deliberately fallen short of the grace of God, to be deservedly condemned; to clear God of the false accusation of cruelty and injustice; to free us from despair, protect us from complacency, and spur us on to moral endeavour. For these reasons nearly everyone admits the existence of free will; but, lest we claim anything for ourselves, they assert that it can achieve nothing without the perpetual grace of God. 'What good is free will,' someone may ask, 'if it can achieve nothing?' What good is the whole man, I reply, if God works in him as the potter works with clay, and as he could have worked with stone? And now, it may be, this subject has been adequately proven to be such that it is not conducive to godliness to examine it in more detail than necessary, especially in front of the unlearned. I believe it has been shown that this doctrine is supported by more, and plainer, scriptural testimonies than the opposite doctrine. It seems clear that in many places Holy Scripture is obscured by figures of speech, or seems at first sight to contradict itself, so that whether we like it or not we must depart from its literal meaning and guide our judgment by interpretation. Finally, it seems obvious how many disagreeable, not to say absurd, consequences follow once free will is denied; and it appears that if we accept the opinion which I have expounded, it does not invalidate Luther's godly, Christian assertions that we must love God above all else, that we must remove our trust from our own merits, deeds, and powers and put it all in God and his promises. If all this is so, I should like the reader to consider whether he thinks it right to condemn the opinion of so many Doctors of the church, approved by the consensus of so many ages and nations, and to accept a number of paradoxes which are causing the present uproar in Christendom.

If these paradoxes are true, then I will frankly admit that I am too dull to follow them. I certainly do not knowingly oppose the truth; I wholeheartedly support true evangelical freedom, and I detest anything contrary to the gospel. I do not play the part of a judge here, but of a disputant, as I have said; and yet I can truly affirm that in disputing I have acted with the same scrupulousness once demanded of those sworn to judge capital cases. Nor, though an old man, will I be either ashamed or reluctant to learn from a young one, if there is anyone who can teach me more evident doctrines with evangelical mildness.

I know I shall hear the objection, 'Erasmus should come to know Christ and bid farewell to

---

Source: From *Collected Works of Erasmus* by Erasmus, translated by Peter Macardle and Clarence H. Miller. Copyright © 1999 by University of Toronto Press. Reprinted by permission.

human learning. No one understands these matters unless he has the spirit of God.' Well, if I still have no understanding of Christ, I have clearly been far off the mark till now! And yet I would be glad to learn what spirit all the Christian doctors and people (for it is likely that the people agreed with the bishops' teaching) have had these last thirteen hundred years, since they too lacked that understanding.

I have discussed the issue. Let others pass judgment.

*   *   *

■ From *Hyperaspistes*

[Who has the Spirit that understands Scripture?]
Well now, I come to those to whom you attribute the Spirit, which, as you write, they have drunk in from your books. Where do the quite significant disagreements in their writings come from? If they are all moved by the same Spirit and are dealing with the same Scripture, there cannot be such perspicuous clarity that linguistic skill and common sense are sufficient. But you will say that Zwingli and Oecolampadius lost the Spirit after they started writing against you. Does not Philippus Melanchthon sometimes speak hesitantly and suspend judgment in his brief commentaries? But you say it is wrong to do this in dealing with Holy Scripture, where the clear truth is to be boldly asserted. When Oecolampadius had not yet disagreed with you, he did not deny that there was nay obscurity in Isaiah, but he thought it sufficient if he could keep the pious and persistent reader from falling into despair, and in his preface he was so far from professing that there is nothing he has not explained that he confesses that his attempt would have been futile if he had not been aided by the Hebrew commentaries, at the same time speaking of Jerome with somewhat more reverence than you do when you make such a man out to be a sacrilegious blasphemer in this book of yours, so perfect as it is in all respects. Is not Bugenhagen, whom you praise so much, a Sceptic in some places in his commentary on the Psalms,

walking on eggshells, as you say, with hesitant steps?

But perhaps you will find a way to evade what others have said; I will press you with what you yourself have said, since you consider it an affront and blasphemy against Holy Scripture if someone attributes any obscurity to it. Note how this paradox agrees with your preface to the Psalms. There you say as follows: 'I am teaching the Psalter etc, but I teach it in such a way that I would not want anyone to presume to get from me what none of the most learned and holiest men has yet been able to furnish, that is, an understanding and explanation some of its meaning and that only partially. The Spirit keeps many things to himself, so that he may always have students; many things he displays only so as to lure us on, he hands down many things to move our feelings. And, as St Augustine has excellently said, "no one ever spoke so as to be understood by everyone on every point." Even more so the Holy Spirit himself is the only one who understands all his own words. Hence I must frankly confess that I do not know whether or not I have a proper understanding of the Psalms etc.' Again, somewhat further on: 'What, then, remains but that we help each other, forgiving those who make mistakes because we ourselves have erred or will err?' Again, in that place: 'I know that it would bespeak a most shameless recklessness if anyone should dare to profess that he understands any one book of Scripture in all respects. Indeed who would dare to presume that he understands one psalm entirely?' There is an enormous difference between your language here, Luther, and the paradox about the wonderful clarity of Scripture which you teach in this book with such earnest perseverance, asserting that unless this point is granted everything will be transformed into darkness and there will be no certainty in human affairs. Who would believe that it is the same man who wrote these things when he was about to comment on the Psalms and who now challenges all comers to bring forth even one place which is obscure to you?

But what good does it do now to pick out places from your commentary where you profess that you have been abandoned by the interpreters, who disagree with each other, and are following what your own mind has dreamed up, or again, where you confess you do not understand at all how a verse hangs together with the preceding verse and call your opinion mere folly. Thus on Psalm 17 you say, 'The doctrine of the church is beyond the grasp of human understanding,' and now skill in grammar is enough! On Psalm 19 you speak as follows: 'I have expounded this psalm as an example of the faith of some king or other, nor is it certain that I have reached the right meaning,' and then you put off onto your reader what judgment to make about your interpretation. Once more, on Psalm 20 you confess you are uncertain 'whether to understand it as concerning Christ or rather some king,' and you accuse me of a theology of Scepticism because I would not dare to make pronouncements on the intricate difficulties of scholastic questions! Where was that Stoic asserter then? Where was that know-it-all? You say to me, no one but a Lucian or an Epicurus speaks so hesitantly, and you forgive yourself for speaking the same way in a profoundly religious work. At the end of this book you say, 'I do not want anyone to have the right to judge, but I urge everyone to assent' and on the psalm you pass the judgment on to your reader. You make me into a Proteus, but in doing such things how are you consistent with yourself? Did you not have the Spirit at that time? I imagine you will say 'I did not.' But if you had only persevered in such modesty! There you call the ancient, orthodox writers consummately orthodox, holy, and learned; here you laugh at me for attributing holiness to them, while you charge them with blindness, ignorance, even blasphemy and sacrilege. And you can find no other excuse that would enable them to be saved except that they meant something different from what they wrote or repented of their error before they died. And since you require internal clarity from all Christians in such a way that without it you give them no hope of salvation, what can we think but that they all perished because concerning such a necessary article of the faith they were, I will not say ignorant, but recalcitrant, overthrowing necessity and professing free will. You call me blasphemous so often because I have

doubts about your teaching and argue about it, and do you imagine it is not clear what such a judgment would lead you to pronounce about them?

And here again is a new paradox: if someone has the Spirit, nothing is obscure to him; if he does not, he understands not even a single iota. There is nothing in between. Therefore if someone professes that he is in doubt about some places in Scripture, either he has the Spirit and is lying about a non-existent obscurity or he does not have it and does not understand a single iota. Tertullian, an outstanding Doctor of the church, later slipped over into the teachings of Montanus and left the communion of the church. When he lost the Spirit, did he not understand a single iota? But you take 'he did not understand' to mean 'he did not feel, he was not affected.' But we were dealing with the certainty of doctrine, not with a person's unknown feelings, about which you confess that no one can pronounce with certainty except God alone. For since, according to Paul, some only pretend to have the Spirit, and an angel of Satan 'transforms himself into an angel of light,' even someone who believes he is moved by a good spirit can be deceived. But if you attribute a total understanding of the Holy Scripture to the Holy Spirit, why do you make an exception only for ignorance of grammar? In a matter of such importance will the Spirit allow grammar to stand in the way of man's salvation? Since he did not hesitate to impart such riches of eternal wisdom, will he hesitate to impart grammar and common sense? Whoever attributes even the tiniest bit to free will blasphemes against God; and are you pious when you grant such importance to grammar that it alone darkens the supremely bright light of Scripture? Those who complain that there is darkness in Scripture hardly deny that it is perfectly clear to the Spirit who is the author of Scripture, but rather they impute this darkness to the weakness of human nature. Though you profess this most openly in the preface which I just cited, here you most boldly deny it, affirming that nothing is more capable of understanding Holy Scripture than human weakness. But, to press you to deal with the matter at hand, show us by what arguments we can be sure that you have the Spirit as your master and are not deceived in explaining Scripture, even though all the Doctors of the church were deluded about it. You confess that some obscurity arises from ignorance of languages. On this point, then, since many disagree with each other and each one of them claims to have skill in languages, how will I be certain who is blind about language and who is not? For on this, as you say, depends the certitude of interpretation. . . .

*   *   *

Montaigne: Essays

Michel de Montaigne (1533–1592) was the greatest of the French Renaissance writers. Montaigne was a prototypical Renaissance humanist; he viewed the world from a very human perspective, believed in a search for truth (as did Socrates), loved the classics, and frequently alluded to them in his writings. He urged tolerance and understanding of others and was critical whenever he encountered non-rational dogmatism. Living in a time of discovery and advancement, he had many new subjects to discuss, which he usually viewed from the viewpoint of man's relationship with his surroundings.

Montaigne was born to a wealthy French family and was given the best education possible in that day. He traveled extensively and then settled into the life of a country gentleman, where he continued to interact with his local society and was actively engaged in local government, serving for a time as the mayor of Bordeaux, France.

Perhaps Montaigne's greatest contribution was the invention of the genre of the essay—a short writing on a specific subject meant to reveal the author's mind rather than convince or motivate. Montaigne pioneered the use of the essay by collecting his thoughts on different subjects and publishing them in collections. He wrote in a lively conversational tone that both conveys his thinking and invites the reader to participate actively in the discourse. The essay has since always been an effective way of communicating personal opinions and insights of an author.

Montaigne's essays have been published in various collections. Even today, they are considered thought-provoking and pleasant reading. The account of his search for truth is almost like reading through his journal and can be a personal experience for the reader. The introduction to his *Essays* seems to instantly connect the reader with the author. Two essays are included here. They discuss intentions and then repentance.

That Intention Is Judge of Our Actions

Death, they say, acquits us of all our obligations. I know those who have taken this in a strange sense. Henry VII, king of England, made an agreement with Don Philip, son of Emperor Maximilian—or, to place him more honorably, father of Emperor Charles V—that the said Philip would deliver into his hands the duke of Suffolk of the White Rose, his enemy, who had escaped and withdrawn to the Low Countries, in exchange for which Henry promised to make no attempt on the life of the said duke. However, nearing death, Henry ordered in his will that his son should have the duke killed as soon as he, Henry, was dead.

Recently, in the tragedy that the duke of Alva showed us in Brussels involving the counts of Horn and Egmont, there were plenty of noteworthy events, among them that the said count of Egmont, on whose faith and assurance the count of Horn had come and given himself up to the duke of Alva, demanded most insistently that he should himself be killed the first, so that his death should free him from his obligation to the said count of Horn.

It seems to me that death did not discharge King Henry from his promise, and that the count of Egmont was quit of his even without dying. We cannot be bound beyond our powers and means.

For this reason—that we have no power to effect and accomplish, that there is nothing really in our power but will—all man's rules of duty are necessarily founded and established in our will. Thus the count of Egmont, considering his soul and will in debt to his promise, though the power to carry it out was not in his hands, was certainly absolved of his duty even had he survived the count of Horn. But the king of England, in intentionally breaking his word, cannot be excused merely on the ground that he delayed the execution of his dishonest plan until after his death; any more than Herodotus' mason, who, having loyally kept during his life the secret of the treasures of his master the king of Egypt, revealed it to his children as he died.

I have seen several in my time, convicted by their conscience of keeping other people's goods, plan to make restitution in their will after death. By delaying a thing so urgent and wishing to right a wrong with so little feeling and sacrifice, they do no good. They owe a part of what is most their own. And the more onerous and inconvenient their restitution, the more just and deserving it is. Penitence demands a burden.

They do still worse who save till their dying wish the revelation of some hateful intent against those near to them, which they have hidden during their life. They show they have small care for their own honor, by irritating the offended person against their memory, and less for their

Source: The Completed Works of Montaigne: Essays, Travel Journal, Letters by Frame, Donald M., translator. Copyright © 1943 by Donald M. Frame. 1948, 1957 by the Board of Trustees of the Leland Stanford Junior University. All rights reserved. Used under permission of Stanford University Press, www.sup.org.

conscience, by failing to kill their ill will, even out of respect for death, and by extending its life beyond their own. Unjust judges, who put off judging till they no longer know the case!

If I can, I shall keep my death from saying anything that my life has not already said.

■ Of Repentance

Others form man; I tell of him, and portray a particular one, very ill-formed, whom I should really make very different from what he is if I had to fashion him over again. But now it is done.

Now the lines of my painting do not go astray, though they change and vary. The world is but a perennial movement. All things in it are in constant motion—the earth, the rocks of the Caucasus, the pyramids of Egypt—both with the common motion and with their own. Stability itself is nothing but a more languid motion.

I cannot keep my subject still. It goes along befuddled and staggering, with a natural drunkenness. I take it in this condition, just as it is at the moment I give my attention to it. I do not portray being: I portray passing. Not the passing from one age to another, or, as the people say, from seven years to seven years, but from day to day, from minute to minute. My history needs to be adapted to the moment. I may presently change, not only by chance, but also by intention. This is a record of various and changeable occurrences and of irresolute and, when it so befalls, contradictory ideas; whether I am different myself, or whether I take hold of my subjects in different circumstances and aspects. So, all in all, I may indeed contradict myself now and then; but truth, as Demades said, I do not contradict. If my mind could gain a firm footing, I would not make essays, I would make decisions; but it is always in apprenticeship and on trial.

I set forth a humble and inglorious life; that does not matter. You can tie up all moral philosophy with a common and private life just as well as with a life of richer stuff. Each man bears the entire form of man's estate.

Authors communicate with the people by some special extrinsic mark; I am the first to do so by my entire being, as Michel de Montaigne, not as a grammarian or a poet or a jurist. If the world complains that I speak too much of myself, I complain that it does not even think of itself.

But is it reasonable that I, so fond of privacy in actual life, should aspire to publicity in the knowledge of me? Is it reasonable too that I should set forth to the world, where fashioning and art have so much credit and authority, some crude and simple products of nature, and of a very feeble nature at that? Is it not making a wall without stone, or something like that, to construct books without knowledge and without art? Musical fancies are guided by art, mine by chance.

At least I have one thing according to the rules: that no man ever treated a subject he knew and understood better than I do the subject I have undertaken; and that in this I am the most learned man alive. Secondly, that no man ever penetrated more deeply into his material, or plucked its limbs and consequences cleaner, or reached more accurately and fully the goal he had set for his work. To accomplish it, I need only bring it to fidelity; and that is in it, as sincere and pure as can be found. I speak the truth, not my fill of it, but as much as I dare speak; and I dare to do so a little more as I grow old, for it seems that custom allows old age more freedom to prate and more indiscretion in talking about oneself. It cannot happen here as I see it happening often, that the craftsman and his work contradict each other: "Has a man whose conversation is so good written such a stupid book?" or "Have such learned writings come from a man whose conversation is so feeble?"

If a man is commonplace in conversation and rare in writing, that means that his capacity is in the place from which he borrows it, and not in himself. A learned man is not learned in all matters; but the capable man is capable in all matters, even in ignorance.

In this case we go hand in hand and at the same pace, my book and I. In other cases one may commend or blame the work apart from the workman; not so here; he who touches the one, touches the other. He who judges it without knowing it will injure himself more than me; he who has known it will completely satisfy me.

Happy beyond my deserts if I have just this share of public approval, that I make men of understanding feel that I was capable of profiting by knowledge, if I had had any, and that I deserved better assistance from my memory.

Let me here excuse what I often say, that I rarely repent and that my conscience is content with itself—not as the conscience of an angel or a horse, but as the conscience of a man; always adding this refrain, not perfunctorily but in sincere and complete submission that I speak as an ignorant inquirer, referring the decision purely and simply to the common and authorized beliefs. I do not teach, I tell.

There is no vice truly a vice which is not offensive, and which a sound judgment does not condemn; for its ugliness and painfulness is so apparent that perhaps the people are right who say it is chiefly produced by stupidity and ignorance. So hard it is to imagine anyone knowing it without hating it.

Malice sucks up the greater part of its own venom, and poisons itself with it. Vice leaves repentance in the soul, like an ulcer in the flesh, which is always scratching itself and drawing blood. For reason effaces other griefs and sorrows; but it engenders that of repentance, which is all the more grievous because it springs from within, as the cold and heat of fevers is sharper than that which comes from outside. I consider as vices (but each one according to its measure) not only those that reason and nature condemn, but also those that man's opinion has created, even false and erroneous opinion, if it is authorized by laws and customs.

There is likewise no good deed that does not rejoice a wellborn nature. Indeed there is a sort of gratification in doing good which makes us rejoice in ourselves, and a generous pride that accompanies a good conscience. A boldly vicious soul may perhaps arm itself with security, but with this complacency and satisfaction it cannot provide itself. It is no slight pleasure to feel oneself preserved from the contagion of so depraved an age, and to say to oneself: "If anyone should see right into my soul, still he would not find me guilty either of anyone's affliction or ruin, or of vengeance or envy, or of public offense against the laws, or of innovation and disturbance, or of failing in my word; and in spite of what the license of the times allows and teaches each man, still I have not put my hand either upon the property or into the purse of any Frenchman, and have lived only on my own, both in war and in peace; nor have I used any man's work without paying his wages." These testimonies of conscience give us pleasure; and this natural rejoicing is a great boon for us, and the only payment that never fails us.

Elizabethan England
Acting Creatively

Chapter 31

> This royal throne of kings, this sceptered isle,
> This earth of majesty, this seat of Mars,
> This other Eden, demi-paradise,
> This fortress built by Nature for herself
> Against infection and the hand of war,
> This happy breed of men, this little world,
> This precious stone set in the silver sea,
> Which serves it in the office of a wall
> Or as the moat defensive to a house
> Against the envy of less happier lands—
> This blessed plot, this earth, this realm, this England.
>
> —*Shakespeare* (Richard II—Act 2, Scene 1, 43–53)

■ England: Separate and Different

We believe that the verse that opens this chapter accurately describes the thinking of the English people about their land and its monarchy; both in the days of Richard II (about 1400 A.D.) when the verse is set, and in the days of Shakespeare (about 1600 A.D.), when the verse was written. These English feelings of extreme love of country were unusual among Europeans and profoundly affected the ways in which the ideas of the Renaissance took root in the land of Shakespeare and Elizabeth I.

As background, we should remember that England, unique among European nations, had not been successfully invaded since 1066. Therefore, the English monarchy was stable and enduring. Shakespeare links the enduring nature of the monarchy to the physical characteristics of the land, which were, of course, also enduring and special. In his view, its island nature made England a fortress and its inherent beauty gave it a blessed status. The pagan god of war, Mars, chose it as his headquarters; the Christian God chose it as an Eden and a paradise. Nature built the island as a place for herself—apart from the ravages of war and plague. It was a precious jewel that engendered a breed of happy men. Whether England was better than other countries and whether the English people were happier are, of course, debatable issues. But, we can be reasonably sure that the people of England *felt* that they were better and happier. These feelings led to immediate acceptance of the concepts of the Renaissance that stressed the importance of individuals and their uniqueness in the plan of God. But the English did not just mimic the Italian Renaissance, nor did they copy the patterns of Renaissance adoption in Northern Europe. We will see that the cultural areas most affected by these humanistic ideals were those where the English were most unique—social structure, religion, and language.

The social structure of England in the time of Elizabeth was unique because of the presence and power of a merchant class. France, Germany, Spain, and Eastern Europe were all characterized by a three-tiered society—church, nobility, and peasants—that had existed throughout the Middle Ages. In England, another class existed—the merchants. In northern Italy and in Flanders (the Low Countries) mercantilism also created a class of rich merchants, but those merchant classes were different than in England. In the Low Countries, the merchants had little political power since they were still under the ruthless domination of Spain. (It would take a revolution in the 1600s before the Dutch and Flemish merchants could exert their political power.) The Italian merchants were politically powerful, as attested to by the Medici family, but they *became* the rulers—a move that changed their basic viewpoint and position into that of nobility rather than merchants. Only in England was the merchant class large, non-nobility, influential, and stable. In England, the merchant class created an environment that affected public policy. (It also created a unique market for artistic output.)

Throughout the Middle Ages, England, like the rest of Europe, was a feudal society in which the economy was based on agriculture done by peas-

ants. Then, in the latter years of the Middle Ages, England's growing population, combined with its limited land available for new agricultural development and its island status, forced the people to begin looking at trade as an important component of economic growth. Initially, that trade was within the British Isles but soon it spread to include Northern Europe. Later, as Portugal and Spain developed the lands surrounding the Atlantic Ocean as important trading areas, England capitalized on its Atlantic frontage to increase its trading territory to include the Americas.

As an island nation with limited tillable land, England was much like ancient Greece. The concept of economic development through trade became an important part of English public policy. Therefore, the social status of craftsmen/manufacturers and of trading merchants increased accordingly. This acceptance of the prestige of the merchant class took some time because the English nobility were French in outlook (remember that English nobility came from Normandy and spoke French until the 1400s). The medieval nobility saw land as the exclusive measure of wealth, but eventually the growth of the merchant class in numbers and wealth brought acceptance of a new way of thinking. Just as with ancient Greece, this acceptance then led to political power. (The development of democracy in Greece can be directly attributed to an acceptance of the merchant class and to recognition that if the economy was to thrive, this important segment of society needed to have political voice.)

The rise of political power within the merchant class in England also benefited from the long-held tradition within English society of a limitation of royal power by law. In 1215 A.D. the English king had been forced to accept many limitations of power, and these had been recorded in a document called *Magna Carta*. Although occasionally challenged by especially powerful kings, the general limitations of *Magna Carta* had endured into the times of the Renaissance, thus creating a mechanism whereby the power of the emerging merchant class could grow. Although the full power of the merchant class would not be seen until the 1600s when the merchants resisted efforts of a series of kings who tried to force absolute rule, even in the early 1500s the political power of the merchants was significant within the social structure of England.

Religion was also unique in England. As we discussed in Chapter 29, King Henry VIII initially resisted the changes to the Roman Catholic Church suggested by Martin Luther. In fact, Henry publicly denounced Luther and earned the gratitude of the pope, who named Henry "Defender of the Faith." However, because of Henry's desire to have a male heir, which was not possible with his wife, Catherine, and, perhaps, because of his infatuation with Anne Boleyn, Henry broke from the Catholic Church and formed the Church of England. In contrast to the other Protestant churches, the doctrines of the Church of England were not much different from the Catholic Church. The liturgy was also similar, except that Latin was abandoned and English was substituted in its place. However, the head of the Church of England was the English king, and the pope was viewed as an interfering and evil force.

Henry VIII used the break from the Catholic Church as an opportunity to enrich the crown. He seized the possessions of the Catholic Church, especially the lands of the monasteries, and then retained them for income or sold them for immediate profit. We see, therefore, that the creation of the English church was first and foremost political and economic rather than doctrinal, as had been the case with the other Protestant churches. Therefore, the incentive to create art for religious purposes, which generally supported and was driven by a desire to explain doctrine, was less important in England than in Catholic Italy or Protestant Germany—both of which were defending their religious positions. The principal art forms of the Italian Renaissance—painting, sculpture, and architecture—were largely religious in nature. Because of England's less doctrinaire nature, at least at this time, these art forms were less important. As we will see, other art forms emerged in England. The most important of these was drama, which relied on both visual effects and language.

As mentioned previously, *language* was another unique aspect in English society that affected the way Renaissance ideas were adopted. English was a language that went through three developmental stages—Old English, Middle English, and Modern English. Other European languages had also evolved, but not in the same way or for the same reasons as English. As a result, the basic concepts behind the other European languages were quite different from English. (The basic concepts of the other languages are still very different from English, even today.)

Old English was a German-based language. These Germanic languages (and also the Nordic and Slavic languages) had developed largely outside the influence of Latin (since these areas were not part of the Roman Empire) and were, therefore, largely unchanged from their origins prior to medieval times. Although England (Britain) was part of the Roman Empire, it was the last area conquered and the first abandoned. Latin therefore never really took root in England, as it did in other parts of the Roman Empire.

The Latin-based languages of Europe (called the Romance languages) were descended from Roman times with some foreign influences such as German (for French, and Italian) and Arabic (for Spanish). In general, after the fall of the Roman Empire, the barbarian rulers of these countries adopted the languages of the Latin-speaking peasantry quite early in the medieval period. Therefore, French, Italian, Spanish, and other Romance languages were solidified quite early in the medieval period, with both peasants and nobility speaking the same language.

Thus, all of the languages of Europe—German-based and Latin-based—had ancient origins with an underlying concept that new words should be based on ancient roots as a way to maintain the purity and unique characteristics of the language. Grammar, likewise, was to be maintained according to ancient rules. (These languages are inherently *conservative* in nature and continue with that concept today.)

If England had continued to be ruled by the Anglo-Saxons, its language (*Old English*) would have persisted largely intact with only minor modifications by Nordic and, perhaps, other foreign influences. In this it would have been like other

European languages and would have had the same conservative concept of maintaining ancient roots for vocabulary and grammar. Typically, new words in these languages would have been developed by combining existing words as multinoun substitutions for a single word in another language. These multinouns often had a **metaphoric tendency,** especially in poetic works. For example, Old English coined the phrase *hwael-weg,* or "whale-way," as a substitute for *sea.* In an Old English rendering of the Bible, *Pharisees* was given as *"sundor-halgan,"* or "apart-holies." These compound words are called **kennings.** (Old English is discussed in more detail in Volume 1 of this work.)

However, in 1060 England was successfully invaded by the French-speaking Normans. This brought a language conflict to Britain. The common people spoke Old English but the nobility spoke French. The shear weight of population numbers favored Old English as the language of England, but prestige favored French. In the end (over about three centuries), a compromise was reached in which French-based words were incorporated freely into English. The compromise was *de facto,* or naturally occurring, rather than *de jure,* or mandated by law. This compromise language became known as **Middle English.** (It is also discussed in more detail in Volume 1.) This concept of free incorporation of words changed the basis on which English operated and evolved. It was no longer a conservative language but became *acquisitive* in nature. In this, it was unique among major European languages.

The grammar of Middle English also needed attention. Should it be Germanlike or Frenchlike? In the end, it was neither. English grammarians of the time (whoever they were) simplified the grammar, thus making English different from any other language. This simplification was one of the most creative events in language history. The result was an adoption of Middle English as the language of both the people and the court, proclaimed as such by Henry V about the year 1420.

As Renaissance times approached, a further development of English began to occur. That change created **Modern English** and came about largely through the efforts of people like William Shakespeare and through important literary works like the King James Version of the Bible. Richness of vocabulary became a mark of the English language because words could not only be acquired from other languages but could also be invented by an author. The characteristics of rich vocabulary and simplified grammar led to great pride in language. Language became the foremost method of demonstrating art in England, with its principal expression through drama.

The features of Modern English are an important study of this chapter, but first we should look at the life and times of Elizabeth I. She set the climate for the changes in language and for much else that we find in Renaissance England. Truly, this time is **Elizabethan England.**

■ Elizabeth's Ascension to the Throne

As explained in Chapter 29, King Henry VIII of England's efforts to get a male heir did not end with his divorce of Catherine of Aragon. Henry and his second wife, Anne Boleyn, also had only a daughter, Elizabeth, before Henry had Anne executed for infidelity. Henry soon married a third wife, Jane Seymour, who finally gave birth to Edward, the son Henry had desired for so long. However, Jane Seymour died shortly after the birth of her son, and Henry eventually went on to marry three more women—Anne of Cleves, Catherine Howard, and Catherine Parr—none of whom bore Henry any children. Thus, at King Henry's death, he had three heirs: Edward, son of Jane Seymour and first in line to the throne because he was male; Mary, his daughter with his first wife, Catherine of Aragon; and Elizabeth Tudor, daughter of his second wife, Anne Boleyn. Henry's will specified these three as his heirs and stipulated their order of ascendancy: Edward, Mary, and then Elizabeth.

Therefore, upon the death of Henry VIII in 1547, his 10-year-old son, Edward, ascended to the throne, becoming England's King Edward VI. King Edward was a reasonable king and was generally beloved of the people but was, of course, often dominated by his counselors because of his youthful age. Wanting to end the religious disharmony that had divided England ever since his father had broken with the Catholic Church, Edward revoked all laws restricting religious freedom. This allowed the people of England to worship freely as either Protestants or Catholics. Edward also encouraged Parliament to approve the **Book of Common Prayer,** which contained both Catholic and Protestant prayers to be used in worship. Other aspects of Edward's reign were also especially kind and reasonable. In fact, King Edward's reasonableness caused some to wonder if, perhaps, an imposter had somehow obtained the throne. This was the inspiration for Mark Twain's classic novel *The Prince and the Pauper,* written three centuries later. Edward's reign was a healing time for England, but it was to be all too brief. Edward, who had always been quite sickly, died in 1553 after just a six-year reign.

Edward had no children to inherit the throne, so when his health began to fail, he named his cousin, Lady Jane Grey, as his heir (or so claimed the leader of Edward's privy council, Lady Jane Grey's father-in-law). Supposedly (and doubtfully), Edward took this action in an effort to keep his older sister Mary, daughter of Catherine of Aragon and a strong Catholic, from inheriting the throne. At Edward's death, Lady Jane Grey was declared queen of England by the privy council. Mary's backers, however, protested that Mary was the legitimate heir and, after several days of debate, Parliament recognized Mary's claim to the throne. Lady Jane Grey was then arrested, convicted of treason, and executed. She had been queen for nine days.

Mary, daughter of Henry and Catherine of Aragon, became queen Mary I (in 1553), but was immediately unpopular with the majority of the people. Not only was she a Catholic, but also she married King Phillip II of Spain, the enemy and chief rival of England. Furthermore, the English people feared that England would become a territory of Spain through marriage, much as had happened to Holland, Austria, and Naples. An ardent Catholic, Mary also reinstated the Catholic

Church as the only acceptable church in England. Both the people and Parliament resisted this action, and the transformation back to Catholicism did not go smoothly. Mary was not able to repossess the lands of the church, as she did not have the money to buy back the lands that had been sold by her father. Also, several actions by the pope during the time of Henry VIII and Edward VI were viewed with anger and suspicion by the English people, thus increasing their animosity toward the Catholic Church. This situation forced Queen Mary to take action against dissenters from Catholicism, sometimes resulting in massive executions. Over the course of her reign, Mary Tudor had more than 300 Protestants executed, earning her the nickname "Bloody Mary." Mary, like her brother Edward, had been sickly throughout much of her life, and died in 1558. She was queen for only five tumultuous years.

Mary's death meant that King Henry's third child, Elizabeth, would become queen, as Mary had no children. Elizabeth was politically astute and was able to lead England into an era of prosperity that has become known as the **Elizabethan Golden Age.** However, this could only be done by creatively solving some of the most perplexing and critical problems ever faced by a monarch. The succession in Tudor times and in early Stuart times and the relationships of the various monarchs and those with claims to the throne are shown in Figure 31.1.

▪ Solving the Problem of Personal Acceptance

The most immediate problem facing Elizabeth upon her coronation was the most basic problem that could be faced by any monarch—her right to ascend to the throne. Many in England, especially the Catholics, believed that the marriage of Henry VIII to Anne Boleyn, Elizabeth's mother, was illegal. That would, of course, make Elizabeth illegitimate and therefore ineligible to become the queen. Some even called her the *Bastard Queen.* Elizabeth countered these arguments by citing her father's will in which she was recognized as a

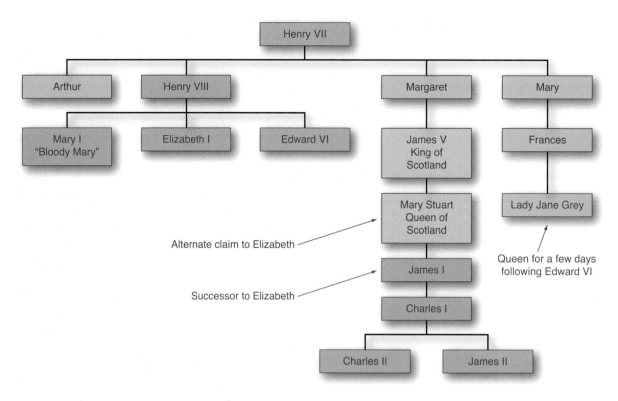

Figure 31.1 ■ English succession during Tudor and early Stuart times. © *Kendall Hunt Publishing Company.*

legitimate heir. She also sought for and obtained the backing of Parliament, legitimizing her rule. (Even those members of Parliament who were against Elizabeth were not anxious to precipitate a civil war over succession.)

Another problem she faced was a question about her age and experience. When she was crowned in 1558, Elizabeth was only 25. Furthermore, she had received practically no preparation to be queen. (Third heirs to the crown, especially daughters, almost never come to power.) Moreover, Elizabeth had astutely kept away from court throughout her sister's reign so that Mary would not be threatened by Elizabeth's presence and, perhaps, act against her. Therefore, Elizabeth was outside the power stream throughout Mary's reign and had little actual experience with politics, especially current issues. She solved the experience problem by selecting very strong advisers. But, in order to keep the advisers from gaining too much power, Elizabeth chose advisers from two

different and competing groups, thus forcing them to balance against each other. This proved to be a creative solution for the problem of experience and was retained throughout her reign as an effective method to balance the advice given to her.

Still another fundamental problem was her gender. Not only was there a general reluctance throughout all European countries to accept female leaders (England being one of only a few countries that would allow females to rule, and then only in the absence of direct male heirs), England had just suffered through a difficult period of female leadership under Bloody Mary. Moreover, the issue of male dominance in the royal family had become important during the reign of Mary I, as she readily complied with orders from her husband, Philip II of Spain, even though those orders were not necessarily in the best interests of England. (For instance, Mary declared war on France because Philip wanted

France to be forced to fight on a second front in his own war against France.)

Elizabeth was an insightful politician, however, and was able to turn her gender into an advantage by never marrying. This had two useful effects. First, being queen, Elizabeth had a never-ending parade of suitors before her, as nobles far and wide courted her with hopes of winning her heart and, with it, the wealth and power of the English crown. Elizabeth dangled these men along when she needed their support, wealth, or strength, and then let them go when they were no longer politically useful. She also would play rivals for her attention off of one another, thus keeping their attentions on each other rather than on efforts to steal her throne. Second, the English people embraced the idea and image of the "Virgin Queen"—the pure and guileless monarch who looked over the realm as if it were the child she never had. Although Queen Elizabeth was likely not a virgin, she played to the image, as it won her the adoration of the masses and was useful in keeping her power.

From her coronation day, Elizabeth understood the value of image. She arranged for a massive celebration of her coronation, including a parade in which she rode in an open carriage and went on a circuitous route so that she could get close to as many of her subjects as possible. Those leading the parade were instructed to divert the direction of the parade toward any collection of people that might be waiting to see the queen. The people were encouraged to carry placards of praise for England and the new queen. Some of the placards identified the guild whose members were gathered together along the parade route. Elizabeth would stop her carriage and greet the leader of each guild and talk about the nature of the craft. Of course this elevated the pride of the guilds and also gave Elizabeth an understanding of the diversity and capability of her subjects. She undoubtedly also realized the importance of these moneyed craftsmen to the economic well-being of her state.

Spontaneous (or planned) demonstrations were also promoted during the coronation parade. It is told, for instance, that at one point along the parade route a small girl was suspended over the middle of the street by a crane and pulley mechanism. When Elizabeth approached, she commanded that the royal carriage be stopped for what was surely a demonstration. The little girl, who was holding a present for the queen, was lowered, like an angel descending, until she was just above Elizabeth. The girl then gave the present to Elizabeth after which the queen kissed the little girl, who was then lifted again into the air. Elizabeth unwrapped the gift and, seeing that it was a Bible, held it aloft for all to see and then kissed it and clutched it tightly to her bosom while proclaiming that she would treasure it forever and keep it next to her bed. The crowd went wild!

Elizabeth also faced the traditional antagonism of the English lords. This competition was not unique to England, but was accentuated by the problems that we have already discussed— Elizabeth's right to the throne, age, lack of experience, and gender. Elizabeth devised a unique method that helped her combat the rivalry of the lords and to simultaneously build acceptance of her reign among the peasants and the increasingly important merchant class. The scheme also allowed her to keep a close watch on her lords and to bring all of England together in a common purpose. Still another advantage of the plan was saving money, and thus replenishing the sorely depleted financial reserves of the crown.

Elizabeth's ingenious idea was to go on long trips throughout the English countryside and visit her nobles. Elizabeth would announce to a lord that she and her court would be visiting for a fortnight or so. Of necessity, the lord would be required to agree to the visit. Thus, by staying at the manors and castles of her nobility rather than at court, she was able to save her wealth, as the lord was expected to provide food, lodging, and entertainment for the queen and her entourage.

On these trips, Elizabeth would stage parades in the towns and villages of the lord's area. She had seen the tremendous benefits of such parades from her coronation day. By these parades, she brought all of the people throughout the realm into a first-hand acquaintance with the queen and a feeling of involvement with her. This helped Elizabeth win the love and trust of the people, who were unaccustomed to attention from the nobility. She could, moreover, sense the feelings of the people on important issues (perhaps during separate private meetings in which leading local citizens were invited to visit with her). The overall upwelling of support naturally influenced the feelings (or at least the actions) of the lords. They were constrained by the opinions of the people to support Elizabeth. She knew that, ultimately, the people controlled the lords.

◼ Solving the Problem of Money

The financial situation when Elizabeth came into power was terrible. Henry VIII had spent lavishly and was required to use the money gained from the sale of expropriated Catholic properties to pay for old debts. When Bloody Mary became queen, she attempted to repurchase the former Catholic lands, but was not able to find sufficient money to do so. Moreover, when she embarked in a war with France, she began to incur enormous debt. Elizabeth unilaterally stopped this war with France, thus saving the money that was being expended on this unpopular and counterproductive war.

We have already discussed how Elizabeth saved money by visiting the lords of the realm and living on their money while she was there. We also discussed how she became acquainted with the many guilds and recognized the importance of the merchant and manufacturing class. She further promoted trade and manufacturing by organizing several **royal charters**—granting of privileges to certain manufacturers who showed especially good quality and technology. For instance, she would name a particular ceramics company as the vendor of dinnerware to the crown. The company could then use this prestige to promote their company. The naming of such a company inevitably was accompanied with some economic benefit for the crown in either lower prices or direct payments. Hence, merely by the act of naming a company as a royal charter, she increased her money reserves.

She encouraged the creation of a merchant fleet to improve trade and to provide the basis of a shipbuilding industry. One way she helped these merchant sailors was to give them immunity from prosecution for stealing another country's ships. While such captains and sailors would normally be considered pirates, when sanctioned by the crown they were called *privateers*. The privateers were required to share a percentage of their loot with the crown. When the offended country complained to her, Elizabeth generally feigned alarm and protested her ignorance of the situation. Some of the most important naval heroes in England, such as **Sir Francis Drake,** were privateers.

Elizabeth also encouraged exploration of the new world. She sent expeditions to America and also rewarded Drake's journey around the world (which he did to escape Spanish ships that were chasing him). Elizabeth granted charters for land in newly discovered territories and otherwise tried to increase shipping and trade.

◼ Solving the Problem of Religion

Among Elizabeth's first concerns was bringing an end to the religious turmoil that had plagued England throughout her sister's reign. However, she had to do this by unalterably affirming the preeminent position of the Church of England. You can imagine her difficulty if the Roman Catholic Church were to be the church of the state. Because the Catholic Church insisted that the marriage between Henry VIII and Catherine of Aragon had never been dissolved legally, the marriage between Henry and Anne Boleyn, Elizabeth's mother, would be illegal and, therefore, Elizabeth would not be legitimate. Hence, Elizabeth was required to be a Protestant herself and, furthermore, declared that the Church of England was once again the state religion of England. She allowed Parliament to dissolve all ties to Catholicism that were enacted during the reign of Mary I (Bloody Mary).

However, in contrast to her sister, Queen Elizabeth embraced religious toleration and allowed Catholics to worship within England. Some members of her privy council were Catholics. She steadfastly refused to give in to the demands of religious zealots in Parliament and maintained a religious peace, at least as far as that was possible in the time of religious conflict that existed throughout Europe at the time. Her moderate stance calmed most of the conflict between Catholicism and Anglicanism, at least during her reign.

■ Solving the Problem of France

Although Elizabeth did not support the war between England and France that was declared by her sister, there were problems in just withdrawing. One problem was the pride of the English people. France was the traditional enemy of England, especially during the latter part of the Middle Ages, when a series of battles between the countries lasted for about a hundred years. In the end of the **Hundred Years War,** the English had lost almost all territories in France, thus effectively losing the war. Now, to withdraw from this new French war would be another admission of defeat that might prove to be very unpopular with the English people.

Furthermore, some of the people, especially the war-hungry lords, might suspect that as a woman she would be naturally against war and, in the future, would not be able to lead the country in a situation where England's survival might be at stake. Whatever action she took, she must not demonstrate timidity or cowardice.

After careful consideration, she resolved that the best way to solve all these problems was to boldly and unilaterally declare England's withdrawal from the war. She hoped that such a bold move would not be perceived as weak, especially in light of the general unpopularity of the war. Then, to ensure that the French would not pursue the war, she agreed to renounce all English claims to French land that persisted from the Hundred Years War. To counteract the potential loss of prestige, she promoted English pride, especially in areas like commerce and the arts.

■ Solving the Problem of Scotland

France was not the only traditional rival of England. Another was Scotland. During Elizabeth's reign,

these rivalries were made much worse than normal because the queen of Scotland, Mary Stuart, was the next in line to the English throne. Mary of Scotland was a Catholic, so many English Catholics hoped for her ascension to the English throne. These Catholics considered Elizabeth to be illegitimate and therefore believed that Mary Stuart, as Henry VII's granddaughter and heir to the English throne after Henry VIII's children, should become the queen of England. To further complicate the situation, Mary was married to the king of France. Fortunately for Elizabeth, the marriage of Mary to the king of France lasted for only two years because of the king's early death; but even after the return of Mary to Scotland, Elizabeth was faced with a continuing challenge from Mary Stuart and those who supported her as a replacement for Elizabeth.

The life of **Mary Stuart, Queen of Scots,** was an interesting one, especially in light of the creativity that Elizabeth showed in dealing with her. Mary became queen of Scotland in 1542 when only six days old when her father, James V of Scotland, died with no other heirs. When Mary was two years old, Henry VIII of England attempted to force, by war, a marriage between the infant Mary and the boy prince Edward, only five years Mary's senior. The war has been called **the rough wooing.** To protect her, Mary's advisers sent her to France, where she was schooled. (A regent was named to rule Scotland while Mary was in France.) In 1558, when she was 16 and still in France, Mary, Queen of Scots, married the dauphin (heir to the throne) of France. Mary's husband became King Francis II of France when his father died. (It is said that the spelling of Mary's name changed from Stewart to Stuart at that time to fit conventional French spelling.) Mary's husband died (of an ear infection) just two years later and, since Mary's marriage to the king resulted in no children, the succeeding king of France was Francis's younger brother, Charles IX. Having no claim to the French throne and in danger as a potential rival of the new king, Mary returned home to Scotland.

During Mary's stay in France, the regency of Scotland had passed to Mary's mother, Mary of Guise, a French-born woman who was very unpopular with the Scottish people. This unpopularity led to a religious revolt under the leadership of **John Knox.** Knox was a former Catholic priest who turned against the church when the Catholic Bishop of Edinburgh killed Henry VIII's emissary while he was trying to arrange the marriage of Mary Stuart to the future Edward VI. This murder set off the war between England and Scotland (the rough wooing). Knox was forced to flee Scotland when the Catholics prevailed in the war. He lived for a time in Geneva, where he was trained by John Calvin, and in England under Edward VI.

When Mary I became ruler of England, Knox returned to Geneva but then, in 1559, returned to Scotland and began to organize the Protestants. The unpopularity of Mary of Guise worked to Knox's advantage, and he was able to begin an open rebellion against the queen regent. However, his revolt was collapsing and so he sought help from the newly installed Queen Elizabeth of England. Recognizing the advantages of a Protestant Scotland, Elizabeth sent money and military support to Knox, who was able to prevail over the queen regent and, in 1560, establish Calvinist Protestantism as the official state religion (known as the Church of Scotland, or sometimes called the **Presbyterian Church**).

Upon returning home later in 1560, Mary received a surprisingly strong welcome from the Scottish people, perhaps in hopes of improving the overall prosperity within the country. However, just five years after her return, young Mary foolishly married a weak and corrupt young man who was highly unpopular with the Scottish Parliament. He was Henry Lord Darnley, Mary's second cousin. Only a year later, Darnley participated in an attempted plot to overthrow the pregnant Mary, but the plot failed and Darnley was not punished. When her baby was born, relations between Mary and Darnley became even worse, perhaps because Darnley saw himself as a regent if Mary were to die or be overthrown, thus creating a subtle threat to Mary. Then, within a year Darnley was assassinated, probably by the Earl of Bothwell, whom Mary married only three months later. This proved to be too much for the largely Protestant Parliament. They forced Mary to abdicate in favor of

her son, who became James VI of Scotland. Parliament appointed a regent who ruled until the boy became of age and stipulated that the boy would be raised as a Protestant.

Mary was forced to leave Scotland and, surprisingly, was offered sanctuary by Elizabeth. Since she had few alternatives, Mary accepted the offer and went to England, where she was given a castle to live in—complete with a guard that assured that Mary would not leave the castle. Elizabeth wanted to appear to be kind and generous to her cousin, but also wanted to control the situation so that Mary would not directly threaten her. However, after nearly twenty years of captivity, Mary's involvement in a plot to overthrow Elizabeth led Elizabeth to sign a death warrant—but she intentionally did not issue it. Elizabeth's advisers found the death warrant (did Elizabeth lead them to it?), and they had Mary, Queen of Scots, executed. To the end, Elizabeth claimed that the execution was done without her consent. As a final ironic twist, Elizabeth chose Mary's son, King James of Scotland, to be her heir. As a devout Protestant and one of Elizabeth's closest blood relatives, James was an acceptable choice to the English people. Thus, James Stuart served as both King James VI of Scotland and became King James I of England when Elizabeth died in 1603. This led, after several decades, to the eventual unification of the two nations and the formation of the United Kingdom.

■ Solving the Problem of Spain

During Elizabeth's reign, Spain was the most powerful country on earth. The Spanish monarchs were reaping the benefits of the American colonies and exerting control over almost half of the European continent as rulers of Spain, Portugal, Naples, Sicily, the Netherlands, and through a related family, the Holy Roman Empire. Spain had gathered this vast territory through heredity, exploration, and strategic marriages. The desire of the Spanish throne to include England within Spain's sphere was seen as early as the marriages of Henry VIII's brother and then Henry himself to

Catherine of Aragon, a princess of Spain. Spain fought the later dissolution of Henry VIII's marriage with Catherine, but when faced with the accomplished fact, Spain simply sought another path to bring England into the Spanish realm.

After the deaths of Henry VIII and his son, Edward VI, Spain saw another golden opportunity to obtain England as a part of its empire. Mary I, the new queen, was half Spanish, Catholic, and eligible for marriage. In keeping with its long tradition of strategic marriages, the Spanish crown extended an invitation for Mary I to become the wife of King Philip II of Spain. This invitation was gratefully accepted, and the couple wed in 1554. Although Philip had a son by a previous marriage, that son was declared mentally incompetent, and so a male child from the marriage of Philip and Mary I would stand to inherit the crowns of both the Spanish empire and England, thus uniting the two.

The people of England were well aware of the potential of future union with Spain, and were adamantly opposed. This opposition became even more widespread and strident when Mary I, at her husband's urging, joined Spain in its war with France. The people of England felt that they were puppets of the Spanish king.

Following their marriage, Philip spent several months in England with Mary, but was forced to leave when problems in the Netherlands required his attention. He was to return to England to be with Mary only once more before Mary's death in 1558. Their marriage produced no children.

When Elizabeth became queen, her actions to restore Protestantism as the official church in England and to withdraw from the war with France naturally angered the Spanish government, but could not be unexpected since Spain surely knew what Elizabeth's position would be and also knew of the natural rivalries between England and Spain. The Spanish loathed English trade with the Low Countries because English money helped pay for the Low Countries' fight for independence from Spain. Add to that the animosity between Catholic and Protestant nations and Spain's perceived insult at Henry VIII's divorce of Catherine of Aragon a generation before, and it did not take

much for the old hatreds to resurface on both sides. Therefore, the formal alliance between England and Spain that had been reached during the time of Mary I's reign was formally cancelled upon Elizabeth's withdrawal from the French war.

After the cancellation of their treaty, the interactions between England and Spain grew more complex. Spain continued to desire a closer relationship with England, with the ultimate hope of uniting both countries under a Spanish king. To this end, a formal proposal was made to Elizabeth that she become the wife of King Philip II, replacing Mary I in that position. The English people were generally against such a marriage, the largely Protestant Parliament was against it, and Elizabeth's own personal inclinations were to avoid any permanent entanglements. Elizabeth, however, did not immediately reject the matrimonial proposal. She decided to wait as long as possible to give Philip her response.

Several factors favored Elizabeth's delaying tactics. First, of course, was the political situation. Spain could easily choose to invade England and, with the largest army, navy, and treasury of any country, would likely have succeeded. Were that invasion to occur, England would have few allies. France's position would be uncertain because of the long-held rivalries between England and France and because France was Catholic. Although many of the northern German states were Protestant, they were still nominally under the control of the Holy Roman Emperor, a member of the same royal family (Hapsburg) as Philip of Spain. Although the Low Countries would shortly revolt against Spain, at this time they were still possessions of Spain and might serve as ports from which Spanish attacks could be launched. Even Portugal, a potential ally for England, had come under strong Spanish influence and would be unlikely to join against Spain. Delays in Elizabeth's reply kept Spain at least somewhat friendly.

Elizabeth could also see that delays would work in England's favor because of the shifts that were occurring in world strengths. England was rising in power while Spain's power had crested. Elizabeth could sense the rising desires for independence in the Low Countries and probably realized that, by waiting, the strategic position of the Low Countries in any attack on England might be eliminated by a revolution in the Low Countries against Spain. (Such a revolution began only a few years later.)

Another factor that favored delaying a response was personal. Perhaps Philip really did want a marriage that was more than just a political union. If so, Elizabeth's greatest power over him was likely during the courting stage, and so delay kept her in control of the situation.

The people of England were also pleased with the delay as that meant that the hated union with Spain was still only a vague possibility, and probably less likely as time went on. Elizabeth quietly encouraged the people's animosity toward Spain, since she knew that when people directed their anger outward, they were less likely to be angry at the domestic problems she was still working on solving.

The delay also gave the Spanish a continuing hope for a resolution in Spain's favor. Because of that hope, the Spanish were reluctant to pursue strong sanctions against Elizabeth's privateers and the queen's continuing denial of any knowledge of these privateers' activities. During this time, of course, she was benefiting greatly from the booty that the privateers were bringing home.

While the delays and renewed rivalry were useful to Elizabeth, they were a nuisance to King Phillip and the Spanish. Feeling robbed of colonial wealth because of the privateers, as well as his dignity, King Phillip took steps to interfere in England's domestic affairs and weaken Elizabeth's power. Largely, however, these diplomatic and, at times, conspiratorial efforts proved unsuccessful. After nearly two years of waiting for Elizabeth's response, Philip abandoned his pursuit of Elizabeth and married a French princess as part of the settlement of Spain's war with France.

To continue his attempts to disrupt and therefore conquer England, Philip sent powerful ambassadors to the English court to try and pit one English courtier against another. They especially encouraged those who supported the claim of Mary, Queen of Scots. This plot also failed. Philip's attempts at peaceful and diplomatic dom-

ination over England came to an end when Mary, Queen of Scots, was executed.

Philip decided to intervene militarily and assembled an immense naval and army taskforce, the Spanish Armada. The armada set sail in 1588. However, through favorable weather conditions, superior maneuvering and some good luck, the smaller English fleet confronted and defeated the Spanish fleet in the English Channel. Spain lost about half its ships and about two-thirds of its army. Sir Francis Drake, the privateer, was in command of the English navy, thus heaping insult on top of the victory over Spain.

The English reaction to the victory over Spain was immediate and elaborate. Elizabeth honored the commanders of the English fleet, declared a season of celebration, and spread the word of the English triumph across all the courts of Europe. The English ambassadors made the victory seem to be a crippling defeat for the Spanish, which was undoubtedly an exaggeration. However, with constant telling of the story, it became true. The power of the Spanish navy declined from that date onward. The Spanish army was also adversely affected, and the enthusiasm of its enemies revived, especially in the Low Countries, where they saw the defeat of the Spanish Armada by little England as a direct analogy to their own situation. The era of Spanish supremacy was near its end, and England took credit for the situation. It was a David versus Goliath analogy. From that point in history onward, the confidence of the English navy soared.

■ Good Queen Bess

Queen Elizabeth came to the throne of England under a dark cloud of problems. Some problems were personal, such as whether the people and nobility of England would accept her and whether she could actually lead as a queen. Other problems were political, such as the problems of France, Scotland, and Spain. Through creativity, she was able to solve the problems and lead England into a Golden Age. She realized that creativity involved both thinking (to find the right solution) and acting properly (to carry out the solution). In fact, from the first day of her reign, she was a superb actress. She played the young and attractive virgin, the vigorous Protestant, the forgiving Christian, the naïve young queen, the wily and smart stateswoman, and, with time, the loving and compassionate mother of her people. She understood the value of image and created one for herself that was overwhelmingly popular among the English people. She was, perhaps, the most popular ruler England has ever had.

Her success and popularity were heightened by England's prosperity at the time of her reign. We have already discussed some of Elizabeth's schemes to get more money for her treasury. She was also a frugal leader who spent little on elaborate palaces and other symbols of royal privilege. Her efforts at mercantilism and trade brought increased revenues to all parts of her realm, thus raising the standard of living for the people in general. The increased prestige of the royal navy was accompanied by an increase in size of both the navy and the merchant fleet. In the decades following Elizabeth's reign, England was to become the greatest naval force in the world (although not without challenges by others such as the Dutch and French).

This prosperity, combined with an influx of Renaissance ideas of individual importance and improvement, allowed for increased leisure time and a general increase in the arts in England. Several famous English literary works were written at this time, including Edmund Spenser's *The Faerie Queen*. Renaissance architecture began to be seen in London. Painting, especially portrait paintings of the wealthy and aristocratic, became popular and the artists skilled. English secular and hymn music increased in quality and presence. However, the height of the English arts during the Elizabethan era was drama. This is somewhat surprising, since drama was still considered a lowly profession. Generally, only men could be dramatists, perhaps because women dramatists were considered to be promiscuous. With success, however, drama gained respectability and provided a reasonable living. Within this English drama we see many of the ideas of the Renaissance bloom fully.

The focus on individuals and their place in society was complex and meaningful. Some say that Elizabethan drama was the best ever produced.

■ English Drama

By the time of Elizabeth, there was already a tradition of traveling acting troupes in England and, as their popularity increased, many of these groups settled down in the large cities and built permanent theatres to showcase their talents. Initially these troupes performed the Classics of Greece and Rome: Aeschylus, Euripides, Sophocles, and Seneca. However, with time and the development of the English language, a generation of English playwrights began to compose their own plays. Many of these plays were strongly patriotic and combined English history with classical concepts, especially to justify English traditions that were generally seen as classically inspired, much as the Italians saw their traditions as coming from the ancient Romans.

The first of these great English playwrights was **Christopher Marlowe.** Born a few months before William Shakespeare, Marlowe had already created several monumental and extremely popular plays before Shakespeare became famous. Among these were the epic plays *Tamburlaine* and *Dr. Faustus*. Christopher Marlowe was killed in a duel over a tavern bill at age 29. Other playwrights were also active, and the London theater scene had several groups competing for public attention. However, one man and the company that performed his plays soon became the leaders of English drama, both in Elizabeth's time and into our own.

■ William Shakespeare

English drama, and perhaps all English literature is dwarfed by the creative genius of **William Shakespeare.** His works have been studied intensely (more in some ages than others, however) since just after they were published a few years after his death as a collection called *The First Folio*. Even in countries that do not speak English,

Figure 31.2 ■ Statue of Shakespeare (note the inscription on the statue). © *2010 by Mika Schick. Used under license of Shutterstock, Inc.*

Shakespeare's works are studied and his genius generally confirmed. A statue of William Shakespeare located in the theater district in London is shown in Figure 31.2. The inscription on the statue says, "There is no darkness but ignorance." This is a wonderful epitaph for such a creative and exploring mind.

The breadth of the themes of his stories is nearly unbelievable, as can be seen in the list of his plays given in Figure 31.3. He wrote 37 plays between 1588 and 1613—about 1.5 plays per year. This is an astounding number in light of their creativity and diversity. He not only wrote the plays, he starred in and directed many of them. He also wrote several major poems and 154 sonnets during this time.

He wrote about Greeks, Romans, medieval times, Renaissance concepts, English characters from all periods, and various other European settings, which added interest and depth. He wrote histories, comedies, and tragedies, but not like other plays that may have been defined by the usual characteristics of those genres. In Shakespeare we see the genre boundaries strained as when, for example, he begins a play *(Othello)* as a comedy with the usual conflict preventing two lovers from uniting, but then moves into a deep and very moving tragedy in which the lovers become entrapped in a wicked scheme in which they are ultimately estranged and killed. The tragedy at the end is heightened by the comedy at the beginning.

Many of Shakespeare's basic plots came from ideas he gleaned from existing sources, such as histories, other plays, and myths. His creativity is demonstrated, not necessarily in the originality of the basic idea, but in the unusual twists that he gives to the stories, the depth of understanding of life, and his beautiful wording.

For example, in Shakespeare's time there was a familiar story of a woman begging a judge for the life of her beloved (perhaps a husband, brother, or father) only to have the judge bargain that only if she slept with him (the judge) would the beloved go free. The woman usually complies and then the judge reneges on his bargain. In Shakespeare's telling of the story, *Measure for Measure,* the woman refuses to submit to the judge's demand. The story then revolves around the interaction of the woman and her beloved (in this case, her brother). He accepts her decision at first, especially because she is a novice nun and, of course, chastity is very important to her. Later, as he considers his execution, the brother becomes upset and accuses his sister of a lack of charity. Shakespeare then deals with the conflict between charity and chastity, a much more significant drama than the melodrama setting that was the norm.

His plays are panoramas of life. Shakespeare's characters have remarkable fullness and development; breadth and depth. For instance, we see the actions of kings in some of his plays, but these are not just thin portraits of kings, they are real men with real and very personal problems that are acted out on both the personal and kingly levels. Usually, we look through the king to see the person that is within, where the human drama is most poignant. We might say that Shakespeare's characters live out their private lives in public places.

1588–93	The Comedy of Errors	1599–1600	As You Like It
1588–92	Henry VI (three parts)	1600–02	Twelfth Night
1592–93	Richard III	1600–01	Hamlet
1592–94	Titus Andronicus	1597–1601	The Merry Wives of Windsor
1593–94	The Taming of the Shrew	1600–01	"The Phoenix and the Turtle"
1593–94	The Two Gentlemen of Verona	1601–02	Troilus and Cressida
1593–94	"The Rape of Lucrece"	1602–04	All's Well That Ends Well
1593–1600	"Sonnets"	1603–04	Othello
1588–95	Love's Labor's Lost	1604	Measure for Measure
1594–96	Romeo and Juliet	1604–09	Timon of Athens
1595	Richard II	1605–06	King Lear
1594–96	A Midsummer Night's Dream	1605–06	Macbeth
1590–97	King John	1606–07	Antony and Cleopatra
1592	"Venus and Adonis"	1607–09	Coriolanus
1596–97	The Merchant of Venice	1608–09	Pericles
1597	Henry IV (Part I)	1609–10	Cymbeline
1597–98	Henry IV (Part II)	1610–11	The Winter's Tale
1598–1600	Much Ado About Nothing	1611	The Tempest
1598–99	Henry V	1612–13	Henry VIII
1599	Julius Caesar	1613	The Two Noble Kinsmen

Figure 31.3 ■ *A list of Shakespeare's plays and major poems.*

We see a remarkable fullness of even relatively minor characters. Consider, for example, Polonius in *Hamlet,* the chamberlain of the king and father to Ophelia and Laertes. Shakespeare's treatment of Polonius is outlined by Jacques Barzun in his book *From Dawn to Decadence:*

How does Shakespeare create the roundness of character? By throwing light on new aspects of the person in successive relations. Polonius as a courtier is obsequious, as a royal adviser overconfident, as a father to his daughter callously blind, as a father to his son, endearingly wise. The grand result of this method, this multi-dimensional mapping, is that since Montaigne and Shakespeare, plays, novels, and biographies have filled the western mind with a galaxy of characters whom we know better than ourselves and our neighbors.

One of the creative tools that Shakespeare used to give depth to his characters was the soliloquy. In these moments in which the character reveals his thoughts only to the audience, we see how emotions, reason, personal traits, and other human characteristics interplay in the mind of the character. Using soliloquy expertly, Shakespeare seems to have invented the concept of the "self," that is, a person's awareness of a being within: that is, perhaps, the true being. The interactions between this self and the outer person are some of the most interesting features of Shakespeare's plays. In some plays, the self that is revealed through soliloquy is seen more clearly by the audience than by the character himself or herself.

You might think that with characters as deep and complex as these, Shakespeare would only have a few in each play. He could have used the method of the Greek plays in which no more than three actors were ever on the stage at the same time. Shakespeare, however, never used fewer than 15 characters and sometimes as many as 50. Not all, of course, were developed to the extent that we have suggested here, but a surprising number are well rounded and complex.

This character development is assisted by the complexity of the plots. Most plays have multiple plotlines. One, *A Mid-Summer Night's Dream,* has five. Shakespeare's ability to keep the plots separate and yet interwoven is a mastery of writing and staging. What fun it is to see how, often by Shakespeare's contrived coincidences, the various plots become resolved and unified.

For a man of such immense talent, popularity, and historical significance, surprisingly little is known about William Shakespeare. The general consensus is that William Shakespeare was born in 1564 in Stratford-on-Avon, England, to a middle-class family (his father was a glove maker). Shakespeare is believed to have led a normal childhood and is known to have attended a local primary school. He later married Anne Hathaway and the couple had three children.

At some point, Shakespeare became an actor, eventually moving to London where he was affiliated with a group known as the Chamberlain's Men (which means that they were sponsored by the Queen's Chamberlain, a high court official). Much later, after the ascension of King James I following Elizabeth's death, the group became known as the King's Men, presumably because King James took a special liking to them and became their sponsor. This may have reflected the group's prestige by the time of Elizabeth's death, no doubt due to Shakespeare's role.

Early in Shakespeare's career, he decided to become a co-owner of the newly constructed Globe Theatre. This was probably a great financial risk but proved to be a good one, and the Globe became one of London's most popular theaters. Possibly because he needed more plays to perform in his new theatre in order to make money, Shakespeare began writing plays.

The Globe Theatre, depicted in a sketch in Figure 31.4, was an open-air playhouse. The lack of lighting dictated that the performances be during the day, usually in the afternoon. Some of the patrons stood on the ground level surrounding the stage. More expensive admissions were in the tiers of boxes along the inner walls of the theatre. Everyone was within 50 feet of the center of the stage—a necessity in days without electronic voice amplification. The stage was large enough to portray a battle scene or a duel with all the courtiers looking on. It was also possible to believably have several groups on the stage at the same time and not be known to other groups also on stage. For instance, in *Troilus and Cressida,* one scene has three groups on stage simultaneously with two of the groups independently eavesdropping on the other. This could not be done believably on a small stage. Shakespeare took advantage of the tools he was given to enhance the total play-going experience.

■ Shakespeare's Use of Language

Of all the tools available to him, language was the most important—and the one that Shakespeare used to the most benefit. Imagine the setting on a warm summer afternoon in London at the Globe Theatre. How would Shakespeare capture the attention of the patrons? There were no lights for dramatic effect, there was little scenery to dazzle the customers, there were few props and costumes were simple. His most available tools were language and action. Of these, Shakespeare's use of language was without equal. (We presume he was also good at acting, but that is lost to us.)

We can see his creativity as we consider some of the language techniques he used to capture attention and dramatically tell his stories. We should first consider his vocabulary. Shakespeare used more than 27,000 words in his complete works. To give comparison, the King James Version of the Bible, written within the time of Shakespeare's life, used a total of 7,000 words. About 2,000 of the words that Shakespeare used were invented by him. Most of these invented words were readily understood by his audiences because these new words were clever expansions on existing words. For instance, he invented *majestic,* which was clearly an adjective that related to the existing word *majesty.* Other new words, most of which were similarly understood and logical in nature include the following: *accommodation, aggravate, assassination, castigate, countless, critical, dislocate, excellent, forefathers, fragment, frugal, guest,*

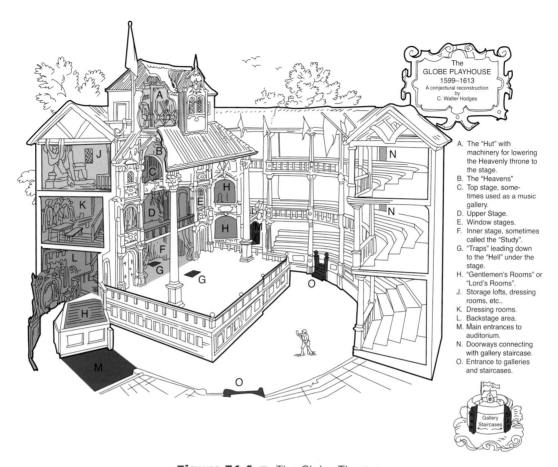

A. The "Hut" with machinery for lowering the Heavenly throne to the stage.
B. The "Heavens"
C. Top stage, sometimes used as a music gallery.
D. Upper Stage.
E. Window stages.
F. Inner stage, sometimes called the "Study".
G. "Traps" leading down to the "Hell" under the stage.
H. "Gentlemen's Rooms" or "Lord's Rooms".
J. Storage lofts, dressing rooms, etc..
K. Dressing rooms.
L. Backstage area.
M. Main entrances to auditorium.
N. Doorways connecting with gallery staircase.
O. Entrance to galleries and staircases.

Figure 31.4 ■ *The Globe Theatre.*

hint, homicide, hurry, lonely, monumental, obscene, premeditated, reliance, submerged, summit, and many others. What would we do without these words? He filled in the language.

Some of his new words have not been adopted as well as these but show his humor and creativity. For instance, when two people were walking and the second followed closely behind the first, Shakespeare has the first person (Anthony) comment that the second *spanielled me at heels*. What a delightful image that creates! Notice, also, how Shakespeare took one part of speech in the above example (the noun *spaniel* in this case) and turned it into a verb. The ability to make these transitions is common in English and rare in other languages (perhaps because Shakespeare was vital in the formation of Modern English).

Another powerful language technique Shakespeare used was the creation of many catchy phrases. Many of these phrases are highly metaphorical, thus demonstrating Shakespeare's lateral thinking and enhanced visualization. These phrases are so powerful in their effect that many have been adopted into common English usage, as revealed expertly in the following selection by Bernard Levin which was quoted in *The Story of English* by Robert McCrum, William Cran, and Robert MacNeil.

If you cannot understand my argument, and declare 'It's Greek to me,' you are quoting Shakespeare; if you claim to be more sinned against than sinning, you are quoting Shakespeare; if you recall your salad days, you are quoting Shakespeare; if you act more in sorrow than in anger, if your wish is farther to the thought, if your lost property has vanished into thin air, you are quoting Shakespeare; if you have ever refused to budge an inch or suffered from green-eyed jealousy, if you have played fast and loose, if you have been tongue-tied, a tower of strength, hoodwinked or in a pickle, if you have knitted your brows, made a virtue of necessity, insisted on fair play, slept not one wink, stood on ceremony, danced attendance (on your lord and master), laughed yourself into stitches, had short shrift, cold comfort or too much of a good thing, if you have seen better days or lived in a fool's paradise—why, be that as it may, the more fool you, for it is a foregone conclusion that you are (as good luck would have it) quoting Shakespeare; if you think it is early days and clear out bag and baggage, if you think it is high time and that that is the long and short of it, if you believe that the game is up and that truth will out even if it involves your own flesh and blood, if you lie low till the crack of doom because you suspect foul play, if you have your teeth set on edge (at one fell swoop) without rhyme or reason, then—to give the devil his due—if the truth were known (for surely you have a tongue in your head), you are quoting Shakespeare; even if you bid me good riddance and send me packing, if you wish I was dead as a door-nail, if you think I am an eyesore, a laughing stock, the devil incarnate, a stony-hearted villain, bloodyminded or blinking idiot, then—by Jove! it is all one to me, for you are quoting Shakespeare.

Still another technique to catch and hold the attention of the audience was his selected use of prose and several different types of poetry. In general, when Shakespeare wanted to impress the audience with the importance of a speech and help them remember it, he used iambic pentameter. This is a poetic form that has 10 syllables to the line with an emphasis on every other syllable beginning with the second. For instance, consider the following lines spoken by Cassius in the play *Julius Caesar*:

> *Why, man, he doth bestride the narrow world*
> *Like a Colossus, and we petty men*
> *Walk under his huge legs and peep about*
> *To find ourselves dishonourable graves.*

Notice that each line contains 10 syllables and that, generally, the emphasized syllables are those that would have the even numbers in the line. Shakespeare's cleverness in choosing words that fit the pattern of syllables and beats is evident in the way he sometimes chose multi-syllabic words (like *dishonourable*) and yet kept the pattern constant.

However, he seemed to occasionally deviate from the strict iambic pentameter pattern—often to add emphasis. For instance, in the famous speech by Mark Anthony, also from *Julius Caesar,* we see that the *first* word is emphasized, clearly to help the audience (both Roman and English) remember that Anthony wants the people to see themselves as his friends. Note also that the second line has an extra beat, perhaps to force the listener to consider the word *Caesar* as being special. The next lines return to the normal iambic pentameter pattern (especially if you pronounce *interred* as a three-syllable word—*in-ter'-red*—which is needed for the rhythm and why some Shakespearean language seems odd when we first hear it).

> *Friends, Romans, countrymen, lend me your*
> *   ears;*
> *I come to bury Caesar, not to praise him.*
> *The evil that men do lives after them;*
> *The good is oft interred with their bones;*

You might also review the quotation given at the beginning of this chapter for the same type of iambic pentameter that is broken only by the final word, *England,* which gives special emphasis to this key word.

Why does iambic pentameter hold our attention? Perhaps because it resonates with some internal pulse or natural pattern of our body. We have seen similar rhythmic schemes used in the ancient past as ways to help memory in, for example, Homer's *Iliad* and *Odyssey*. The specific rhythms of other works may have been different from iambic pentameter, but those rhythms may have fit better the Greek language rather than English.

Sometimes Shakespeare wants his characters to be funny or bawdy or relaxed. These situations are often written in prose. The mood of these lines is quite different from the formality of iambic pentameter. His ability to seamlessly and effectively move from verse to prose is one of Shakespeare's greatest gifts.

In still other places Shakespeare wants to fix our attention even more strongly than he can with iambic pentameter. He does this by rhyming the lines. (His iambic pentameter is usually not rhymed, but is a poetic scheme called blank verse.) An example of the use of rhymed verse is when Romeo and Juliet speak to each other just after meeting at the Capulet party. Juliet is envisioned in a statue near her supposed home in Verona, Italy, as seen in Figure 31.5. Romeo playfully expresses his desire to hold hands and then

to kiss. Juliet responds by calling him a pilgrim (the meaning of the name *Romeo*) and with a playful acceptance of touching hands, but with a denial of the kiss because, she says, saints kiss with their hands—palm to palm. (Here she is also using a pun on the word *palmer*, which means both a pilgrim and a person who uses a palm.) Romeo counters that saints have lips too, but Juliet suggests that the lips of saints are used for prayer. Romeo's gentle coaxing and clever arguments bid Juliet to hold still while he gives her a saintly kiss as a prayer. She allows it and then subtly invites another kiss, which Romeo is only too happy to give. He then breaks the rhyme and rhythm by requesting another kiss, and she responds with a short and nonrhymed statement—both of which are emphasized by their difference from the pattern of the verses before them.

Romeo. [To Juliet]
    If I profane with my unworthiest hand
    This holy shrine, the gentle fine is this,—
    My lips, two blushing pilgrims, ready stand
    To smooth that rough touch with a tender
        kiss.

Juliet.
    Good pilgrim, you do wrong your hand too
        much,
    Which mannerly devotion shows in this;
    For saints have hands that pilgrims' hands
        do touch,
    And palm to palm is holy palmers' kiss.

Romeo.
    Have not saints lips, and holy palmers too?

Juliet.
    Ay, pilgrim, lips that they must use in prayer.

Romeo.
    O, then, dear saint, let lips do what hands do;
    They pray, grant thou, lest faith turn to despair.

Juliet.
    Saints do not move, though grant for prayers'
        sake.

Figure 31.5 ■ Statue of Juliet near her home (supposed) in Verona, Italy. © *2010 by Sailorr. Used under license of Shutterstock, Inc.*

Romeo.
> *Then move not while my prayer's effect I take.*
> *Thus from my lips, by thine my sin is purg'd.*
> *[Kissing her.]*

Juliet.
> *Then have my lips the sin that they have took.*

Romeo.
> *Sin from my lips? O trespass sweetly urg'd!*
> *Give me my sin again.*

Juliet.
> *You kiss by the book.*

Shakespeare's language is obviously rich in many different ways. His writings helped to solidify Modern English, much like Dante did for Italian or Luther's Bible did for German or Chaucer did for Middle English two centuries earlier. Shakespeare's love of new words, his frequent conversions of words from one part of speech to another, his selective use of rhythms and rhymes, and his extensive vocabulary all fit exactly the characteristics of English, even before his time, but especially afterward—no doubt because of him.

Although this book is not intended to be a detailed analysis of Shakespeare, we can gain a greater appreciation for his creativity by briefly examining some of his specific works. *The First Folio* divided his plays into three groups—comedies, histories, and tragedies. We will look at each of these groups, especially in light of the time in which he lived—the Renaissance. We will then briefly look at his sonnets—works that are, perhaps, less well known but that reveal some interesting capabilities of Shakespeare that are often overlooked.

▪ Shakespeare's Comedies

Shakespeare's early career emphasized comedies. These, and the other comedies that he wrote throughout his career, are usually about lovers who are prevented from joining together because of some outside impediment. The plays then explore the ways in which the lovers overcome the impedi-

ment. The play ends in their union, usually a wedding. The mood of the comedies is light and the underlying theme is love. Shakespeare's creativity is exhibited in the ways that he uses the standard format for the story but cleverly deviates to add interest and variety. We will briefly examine two comedies that illustrate how these variations can occur.

Taming of the Shrew contains a subplot that fits the standard genre almost exactly. In this subplot, a younger sister, Bianca, is prevented from marrying because her father has decreed that Bianca cannot marry until her older sister, Katherine, a shrewish woman, marries first. Eventually this subplot is resolved with Bianca's marriage.

The main plot, also a comedy, does not fit the normal pattern. This plot concerns Katherine and her change from a shrew to a "loving" wife. Early in the play, Katherine is "roughly" wooed by Petruchio, a man who has heard of Katherine and her father's generous dowry to be given to anyone who would marry her. This rough wooing consists of his giving to her the same type of abuse that she gives to others. Petruchio and Katherine marry near the middle of the play and then leave for Petruchio's home. Petruchio continues his heaping of abuse on Katherine, which she initially continues to return, but, now that she is his wife, she finds that he now has power over her (in obtaining food, clothes, and so on) and she must, therefore, comply with his demands and accept his insults. (We are told, by the way, that the "abuse" given to Katherine was not considered abuse in Shakespeare's day and, therefore, would not have shocked the audience, although it would probably have been considered excessive—but that was part of the story.) Somehow, subtly, Katherine realizes that the insults and demands are a playful way to teach her not to be shrewish. Katherine and Petruchio discover a mutual respect and love, which is proven to all the others at the end of the play.

Another comedy that does not quite fit the usual pattern is *The Merchant of Venice*. The deviation in this play concerns a dark and tragic situation in which one of the principle characters is to be killed because he has not been able to pay his debt. The holder of the debt is a Jewish merchant, Shylock, who has stipulated that if the debt is not paid, he is due a pound of flesh from the breast of the defaulter, Antonio. Shylock's Jewishness gives motivation to his actions—not because he is a Jew, but because he is an outsider who has been treated badly by the rest of society and, therefore, seeks revenge against all. Antonio is completely without blame and further elicits our sympathy because he incurred the debt to help his friend, Bassanio, win his beloved, Portia. Shylock takes the stipulation of default literally and is on the verge of exacting the payment (and the death of Antonio). Antonio and all his friends plead for mercy, and it is decided that a trial will be held to validate Shylock's claim. The climax of the trial occurs when the defense attorney, Portia (in disguise), points out to Shylock that he must exact his payment but cannot take one ounce of blood, as that would be more than the contract literally allowed. Shylock, caught in the literalness of the agreement, behaves badly and is punished. After some continuing and playful plot complications, the lovers are united in matrimony at the end, as is common in comedies.

Shakespeare's Historical Plays

Shakespeare's historical plays must have been very popular in Renaissance England as they helped the public gain an appreciation for and love of their heritage. Just as the Italians studied the classical times of Greece and Rome because they gave them a sense of greatness, so too did the English want a noble history that reflected the values that their society had come to treasure. Shakespeare's history plays dealt with such glorious events.

However, just as he deviated from the norm in his comedies, his histories also provided his audience with insights that were quite different from their normal expectations. For instance, some of the English kings about whom Shakespeare wrote were not very noble. Examples would be Richard III (a wicked and knavish murderer) and Richard II (a weak and ineffective ruler). Shakespeare also showed the development of a prince/king (Henry V) from rowdy youth (Prince Hal) to national hero. The story of Henry V, youth and hero, is told through the plays *Henry IV, parts 1* and *2,* and *Henry V.*

Perhaps the crowning moment in this sequence of plays is Henry V's speech to his troops just prior to the Battle of Agincourt during the Hundred Years War between England and France. The English troops were vastly outnumbered and were very discouraged on the eve of the battle, as Henry was able to plainly see as he walked, disguised, among the troops. He therefore realized that something must be done, and gave them a talk that is considered to be one of the great works of English motivational literature. It is called the **St. Crispin's Day speech** because that was the saint's day on which it was given. The following is the conclusion of the speech.

> *This story shall the good man teach his son;*
> *And Crispin Crispian shall ne'er go by,*
> *From this day to the ending of the world,*
> *But we in it shall be remembered—*
> *We few, we happy few, we band of brothers;*
> *For he to-day that sheds his blood with me*
> *Shall be my brother; be he ne'er so vile,*
> *This day shall gentle his condition;*
> *And gentlemen in England now-a-bed*
> *Shall think themselves accurs'd they were not here,*
> *And hold their manhoods cheap whiles any speaks*
> *That fought with us upon Saint Crispin's day.*

In spite of the deviations from the normal pattern of historical plays, we should also note that Shakespeare was well aware of the political situation in which he lived. He did not criticize the current ruler, Elizabeth, nor did he represent her family, the Tudors, in any light but favorable. In fact, he painted members of rival families, such as Richard III, as, perhaps, worse than they really were.

Shakespeare's Tragedies

In standard tragedies, the hero is confronted with a situation that is very difficult for him because of a tragic flaw in the hero's personality. Eventually, this flaw leads to the hero's death or other disaster. This analysis of a tragedy was originally proposed by Aristotle, who used Sophocles' play, *Oedipus Rex,* as the prototype of a tragedy. Therefore, the character flaw in tragic heroes is sometimes called a **Sophoclean defect.**

Many consider *Hamlet* to be the best of Shakespeare's tragedies. Action packed and psychologically complex, *Hamlet* deals with the moral problems connected with revenge, nagging self-doubt, questions about death, and the issue of what is real. The play is given added drama by being set in a real location—Elsinore castle in Denmark (Figure 31.6). In the play, his father's ghost tells Hamlet that he, the father, was murdered by his brother, who has now become the king and the husband of Hamlet's mother, Queen Gertrude. The ghost commands Hamlet to avenge his death. However, Hamlet has doubts. He questions whether he truly saw a ghost or whether his mind merely made up the ghost appearance because he feels that his mother married the new king much too quickly. Even if the ghost were real, Hamlet questions whether this ghost was sent as a messenger from God or if it might not be a trick of the devil to claim his soul.

Hamlet must deal with the moral dilemma of revenge: Is revengeful murder wrong if it is done to right a wrong? Is murder wrong if God (or a spirit sent from God) commands it? We are brought into these moral dilemmas through action, soliloquy, dialogue, and narration. We share the evolution with Hamlet and feel the moment in which he decides to take strong and affirmative action. This sharing of feelings heightens our grief when, almost by accident but really out of justice, Hamlet dies. Only the accompanying deaths of all the villains give us some relief.

It is Shakespeare's genius that one underlying theme of *Hamlet*—medieval religious obedience versus humanistic inquiry and doubt—was meaningful for nearly every member of his Renaissance audience. The question of the secular versus the religious also has modern relevance, which has contributed to the continued success of *Hamlet.*

Another part of Shakespeare's genius in *Hamlet* is that nearly all of the characters are forced to deal with difficult and complex issues.

Figure 31.6 ▪ Hamlet's castle in Elsinore, Denmark. © *2010 by Andrei Nekrassov. Used under license of Shutterstock, Inc.*

For example, Hamlet's lover, Ophelia, must battle with her own inability to make decisions. Ophelia allows her life to be dictated to her by her father, brother, and lover. She molds herself to become what they want her to be and never learns to think for herself. Thus, when her father, brother, and lover come into conflict, and especially when her father, whom she has finally decided to follow, is killed, Ophelia can't handle the situation and she goes crazy. She then commits suicide. This tragic act has often served as inspiration for artists (see Figure 31.7).

Shakespeare's characterization of Ophelia as an indecisive pawn is so accurate that modern analysts (especially Professor Thomas G. Plummer at Brigham Young University) have labeled young people who have trouble thinking for themselves as having an **Ophelia Syndrome.** Plummer suggests that when Ophelia responded to her father's inquiry about Hamlet's intentions with the words, "I do not know, my lord, what I should think," she surrendered her ability to think for herself and has embarked on a doomed path. Her father doesn't help her at all when he responds, "I'll teach you. Think yourself a baby. . . ." Plummer then goes on to suggest our education system promotes this nonthinking attitude but that, eventually, people must learn to think for themselves. They must consider the value of the past and the advice from those with experience, but be prepared to make independent decisions.

Ophelia's difficulty is just one example of an instance where Shakespeare's insights have given the world examples that can be used in understanding basic problems of contemporary life. Sometimes the modern analyses are deeply moving and sometimes whimsical, as in the business-related book *Shakespeare in Charge,* where various characters from Shakespeare's plays are used as examples of how people in business should act.

Shakespeare demonstrated his ability to creatively deviate from the usual pattern in tragedies, thus giving emphasis and insights that might not be available through standard genre treatments of the same themes. One example is *Othello,* a tragedy that begins as a comedy. Two lovers, Othello and Desdemona, are prevented from marrying by Desdemona's father because, in his opinion, Othello is not a worthy husband and is seeking Desdemona for money or merely casual sex. However, Desdemona convinces her father that she really loves Othello and that Othello has acted properly and with great love as well. The father relents, and the two are married. This sounds standard for a comedy but, all this has occurred in the early part of the play. It is after the marriage that the tragedy begins. In this play, an evil character, Iago, cleverly and insidiously convinces Othello that Desdemona is unfaithful. Eventually convinced, Othello kills Desdemona and then, when the truth is revealed, commits suicide. The deep sadness of the situation has been enhanced by the happiness with which the play began.

Like *Othello,* the play *Romeo and Juliet* begins as a comedy (two lovers denied their union by forces beyond themselves), and their union occurs early in the play. However, in *Romeo and Juliet,* the unraveling of their joy occurs through a combination of youthful impetuosity (such as when Romeo kills Tybalt) and through simple misfortune (as when the priest sent to tell Romeo of Juliet's feigned death misses Romeo and cannot, therefore, tell him of the plan). The depth of sadness in the final scene is increased because of the nearness of the possibility that all could have been right.

Figure 31.7 ■ An artistic representation of Ophelia. © 2010 by Jose AS Reyes. Used under license of Shutterstock,Inc.

These examples are but representative of the many great tragedies with many different variations that Shakespeare presented to his audience and to us. His plays, of all three genres, were masterful and meaningful. It is no wonder that he is usually considered to be the best playwright in history.

■ Shakespeare's Sonnets

William Shakespeare was also an accomplished poet who demonstrated those skills in several long poems and in at least 154 sonnets. Most of the sonnets were written fairly early in Shakespeare's career, probably before 1600. The sonnets are traditionally divided into two sets addressed to two different persons. The first poems, sonnets 1 to 126, are addressed to a young man who is being urged to find a proper young woman and marry so that he can have children and a normal life. The remaining sonnets are addressed to a young woman, sometimes called the Dark Lady because she has dark hair and is otherwise unknown. The poems to her are more romantic, although both sets of sonnets deal with themes of love and fidelity.

As with the plays, Shakespeare's sonnets demonstrate his ability to strictly comply with a generic form or pattern and also to deviate from the pattern when necessary to give interest or emphasis. The strict pattern of the English sonnet is fourteen lines consisting of three quatrains plus a doublet. The rhyme scheme is ABAB, DCDC, EFEF, GG with each line given in rhymed iambic pentameter (that is, 10 syllables per line in a weak/strong emphasis) with 140 total syllables. The following is one of the most well known of the sonnets (Number 116) which is sometimes called the "Marriage Sonnet" today.

> *Let me not to the marriage of true minds*
> *Admit impediments. Love is not love*
> *Which alters when it alteration finds,*
> *Nor bends with the remover to remove.*
> *O no, it is an ever-fixed mark,*
> *That looks on tempests and is never shaken;*
> *It is the star to every wandering bark,*

> *Whose worth's unknown, although his height*
> *be taken.*
> *Love's not Time's fool, though rosy lips and*
> *cheeks*
> *Within his bending sickle's compass come;*
> *Love alters not with his brief hours and*
> *weeks,*
> *But bears it out even to the edge of doom.*
> *If this be error and upon me proved,*
> *I never writ, nor no man ever loved.*

In general, the lines obey the strict requirements of the sonnet pattern. However, in this sonnet Shakespeare has created interesting thought patterns in the way he has controlled the movement of the poem through the use of line-ending punctuation. For example, the first line and half of the second line run together to create a strong statement that is quickly followed by the remainder of the second line and the following two lines, which makes another strong statement. When we have read just that much, we clearly understand the thesis of the sonnet—true love is not susceptible to change. The next eight lines reinforce the theme with several examples. He then finishes the poem with a statement of confidence that is almost too strong but, thereby, seals his statements with finality. The power of the sonnet, and its beauty, are both evident.

Other sonnets are equally interesting. Some are very regular. Some have rhythm deviations for emphasis, while others have rhyme deviations. It is Shakespeare's genius that, in all his works, he has the capability to observe the strict pattern and the wisdom of when to deviate from it. As we have seen, an analysis of all Shakespeare's works seems to come to similar conclusions—the more closely it is examined, the better it becomes. Such is the stuff creative genius is made of!

■ The English Bible

With their love of language, you might expect that the English would have sought a Bible in their native tongue early in their history. There were, in fact, partial renderings (not real translations) of the

Bible in Old English before the eleventh century. In the fourteenth century John Wycliffe translated the Bible into English and was tried and convicted for his efforts. (He also disagreed with the pope about indulgences and church power—both subjects that Martin Luther was later to pursue.) Although he died a natural death after his trial, the pope declared that Wycliffe's body be exhumed, burned, and the ashes scattered so that his followers could not keep parts of his body as relics.

In the sixteenth century William Tyndale again translated the Bible into English, this time using the ancient Greek and Hebrew manuscripts as sources. (Wycliffe used the Latin Bible as his chief source.) Tyndale's work was very popular, especially because of the beautiful language it contained. Like Shakespeare after him, Tyndale composed phrases that were highly expressive, such as the following: *Let there be light; eat, drink and be merry: the powers that be; a prophet has no honor in his own country; ye of little faith; am I my brother's keeper; the spirit is willing; the salt of the earth; a law unto themselves;* and *signs of the times.* Many of these phrases were later included in the King James Version of the Bible. Tyndale, however, was convicted of violating the law that permitted only authorized versions of the Bible to be published in England. Tyndale was strangled and then burnt.

King James I succeeded Elizabeth I in 1603. James I was the son of Mary, Queen of Scots. He had been raised as a Protestant and, therefore, was religiously acceptable to Elizabeth as her successor. He was also the next in line to the throne and, therefore, the logical choice from a political standpoint. When he became king, he objected to all of the Bibles then available in English. Some were clearly Catholic (especially the Douay version), while others contained footnotes that were strongly Calvinist (such as the Geneva version).

He wanted a version that contained no footnotes and was doctrinally neutral. He also wanted a version that was beautifully written. Therefore, he assembled a team of scholars and charged them to take the best from all previous versions in English, German, French, and Latin and also to use the original Hebrew and Greek texts to ensure doctrinal and grammatical accuracy, as well as could be done in those days. (In general, every word in the original Hebrew and Greek texts was translated and then, when required for meaning, additional English words were added.) Some of the phrases came from Tyndale, as already indicated, but others were added and, in some cases, reflect the syntax of the ancient languages. Some examples of these latter phrases are: *To lick the dust; to fall flat on his face; to pour out one's heart; the land of the living; under the sun; sour grapes; from time to time; pride goes before a fall; the skin of my teeth; to put words in his mouth; like a lamb to the slaughter; rise and shine; to see the writing on the wall; a thorn in the flesh;* and *a fly in the ointment.*

The resulting translation, published in 1611 (which is while Shakespeare was still alive) was called the King James Version or the Authorized Version, and it became the only version allowed in the churches in England. Both the Church of England and the Calvinist Church of Scotland (and the later English Puritans) adopted it. It has become the most important version of the Bible in the English language. Along with Shakespeare, the King James Version helped to define and solidify Modern English.

■ Summary

The English Renaissance strongly reflected the atmosphere and qualities of two people—Elizabeth I and William Shakespeare. Both Shakespeare and Elizabeth understood human nature and the emerging individualism of the English public. Elizabeth, of course, directly and immediately affected life in England. Shakespeare's effect was felt immediately by a smaller group, but was realized more fully much later. He provided entertainment, both immediate and extended, and furthermore, helped define Modern English. Because language has so much influence on our thought processes and values, he helped shape the thinking of multiple generations.

Although Elizabeth was a traditional Tudor, with the strong will and authoritative behavior that were common to her family, she also realized that public acceptance of her policies and actions would greatly increase her power. She understood that acceptance would also lead to a unity of purpose in the country and, therefore, a progress that could not be obtained otherwise. To gain this acceptance she had to act well the part of a queen and, simultaneously, solve the difficult problems that greeted her, especially as she began her reign. She did both of these, and did them in a creative fashion. This creativity kept her enemies off balance and gave her the time to solidify her position. The result was a golden age.

Shakespeare's contribution was also in acting well the part. In his case, it was the part of an actor and author. His plays were complex and meaningful—often asking the audience to carefully examine their own basic values and attitudes. When the audience did so, often over many generations of commentary and analysis, they developed a sense of "self" that led to both a stronger country and a populace that was better able to cope with the difficult situations that life inevitably brought.

■ Timeline—Important Dates

Date	Event
1509–1547	*Reign of Henry VIII*
1516	*Birth of Mary I (Tudor) Catherine of Aragon*
1533	*Birth of Elizabeth I (Tudor)to Anne Boleyn*
1537	*Birth of Edward VI to Jane Seymour*
1542	*Mary Stuart becomes queen of Scotland at only six days old*
1547–1553	*Reign of Edward VI*
1553	*Brief reign of Lady Jane Grey*
1553–1558	*Reign of Mary I (Tudor)*
1564–1616	*Life of William Shakespeare*
1558–1603	*Reign of Elizabeth I*
1558–1560	*Mary, Queen of Scots, is Queen Consort of France*
1559	*John Knox returns to Scotland to found the Presbyterian church*
1587	*Mary, Queen of Scots, is executed in England*
1588	*Spanish Armada defeated in English Channel*
1588–1613	*Shakespeare pens 37 plays, plus many sonnets*
1603–1625	*Reign of James I of England*
1611	*King James Version of the Bible published*

■ Suggested Readings

Augustine, Norman and Kenneth Adelman, *Shakespeare in Charge,* Talk Miramax Books, 1999.

Barzun, Jacques, *From Dawn to Decadence,* Perennial, 2000.

Bryson, Bill, *The Mother Tongue,* Avon Books, 1990.

McCrum, Robert, William Cran, and Robert MacNeil, *The Story of English,* Penguin Books, 1992.

Plummer, Thomas G., "Diagnosing and Treating the Ophelia Syndrome," *BYU Today,* January 1991.

William Shakespeare: Hamlet, Romeo and Juliet, The Sonnets

Drama has been a popular diversion since the days of ancient Greece, but no civilization at any other period in the history of the world has identified itself so much with theater as did the English in the Elizabethan era. The people of England had great pride in their language, which they considered to be an elite selection of the best words and concepts of all other tongues. This pride translated into a love for the spoken word, which, they felt, powerfully conveyed emotions and important principles. The theater was the most powerful medium for showcasing these traits of the English language.

One English playwright stands head and shoulders above the rest and has become a recognized symbol of drama in our contemporary culture. William Shakespeare (1564–1616) grew up in a modest household in a small, rural village but left to join a theater company in London as both an actor and dramatist. His productions were instantly popular, allowing his theater to be recognized and supported by both Queen Elizabeth and King James I. His productions contain many familiar names, words, and phrases that have been immortalized in our culture. His impact on drama and the English language itself are testaments to Shakespeare's creative genius and qualify him as the greatest writer of the English language.

Perhaps the most brilliant of all of Shakespeare's works was *Hamlet*. It is thought that *Hamlet* may have been based upon a twelfth century story concerning an actual Danish prince whose uncle murdered the king, married the queen, and claimed the throne. The prince feigned lunacy to keep his uncle from knowing his designs and then killed the uncle. How Shakespeare took this unremarkable story and turned it into a psychological masterpiece is where his creativity is revealed. In the play, prince Hamlet becomes a philosophically troubled young man who is plagued with uncertainty in all that is most important—loyalty to his dead father's memory, loyalty to the new king, respect for his mother, love of a potential wife, trustworthiness of friends, and reliability of his own mind and senses. Not only Hamlet, but the entire audience is drawn into wondering if the ghost was real and honest, if Hamlet still loved Ophelia, whether Gertrude was guilty of sin, as well as countless other subjects of thoughtful discussion. Pondering human character was an underlying theme of the Renaissance; this is why *Hamlet* connected so strongly with the humanist culture of Europe around the year 1600.

Romeo and Juliet may have been Shakespeare's most emotionally powerful play. The tale of two lovers from feuding families is a treatise on the transcendent nature of love. This play has been so well accepted over the years that Romeo and Juliet are considered by our culture to be the quintessential lovers. His writing style emphasizes the special relationship of the lovers. Whereas they speak to each other in either strict rhymed meter or sonnet-like verse, other characters speak in the more relaxed iambic pentameter or prose. This contrast seems to freeze the lovers in time. When they are apart, they are caught in the rush towards disaster that seems inevitable within the surrounding world. By having this time-stopping love end in such a tragic manner, Shakespeare succeeds in touching our souls with a shock of grief.

In Shakespeare's early years, he devoted much of his energy to authoring sonnets. The English sonnet had a very strict form and rhyme scheme, which Shakespeare followed for 153 of the 157 sonnets he wrote. It is his use of language and imagery that make his sonnets so entertaining and memorable. While various themes are explored in the sonnets, some are among the most moving of all love poems, including the selection included herein.

■ PERSONS REPRESENTED.

Claudius, King of Denmark.
Hamlet, Son to the former, and Nephew
    to the present King.
Polonius, Lord Chamberlain.
Horatio, Friend to Hamlet.
Laertes, Son to Polonius.
Voltimand, Courtier.
Cornelius, Courtier.
Rosencrantz, Courtier.
Guildenstern, Courtier.
Osric, Courtier.
A Gentleman, Courtier.
A Priest.
Marcellus, Officer.
Bernardo, Officer.
Francisco, a Soldier.
Reynaldo, Servant to Polonius.
Players.
Two Clowns, Grave-diggers.
Fortinbras, Prince of Norway.
A Captain.
English Ambassadors.
Ghost of Hamlet's Father.
Gertrude, Queen of Denmark, and Mother
    of Hamlet.
Ophelia, Daughter to Polonius.
Lords, Ladies, Officers, Soldiers, Sailors,
    Messengers, and other Attendants.
SCENE. Elsinore.

■ Act I

**Scene I Elsinore. A Platform
before the Castle**

[*Francisco at his post. Enter to him Bernardo.*]

BER. Who's there?
FRAN. Nay, answer me: stand, and unfold[1]
    yourself.
BER. Long live the king!
FRAN. Bernardo?
BER. He.
FRAN. You come most carefully upon your hour.
BER. 'Tis now struck twelve. Get thee to bed,
    Francisco.
FRAN. For this relief much thanks: 'tis bitter cold,
    And I am sick at heart.
BER. Have you had quiet guard?
FRAN. Not a mouse stirring.
BER. Well, good night. If you do meet Horatio
    and Marcellus, The rivals[2] of my watch, bid
    them make haste.
FRAN. I think I hear them.—Stand, ho! Who is
    there?

(*Enter Horatio and Marcellus.*)

HOR. Friends to this ground.
MAR. And liegemen to the Dane.[3]
FRAN. Give you good-night.

---

[1]reveal

[2]partners

[3]Loyal subjects of the Danish King

Source: From *Hamlet* by William Shakespeare.

MAR. O, farewell, honest soldier; Who hath reliev'd you?

FRAN. Bernardo has my place. Give you good-night.

(*Exit.*)

MAR. Holla! Bernardo!

BER. Say. What, is Horatio there?

HOR. A piece of him.

BER. Welcome, Horatio:—Welcome, good Marcellus.

MAR. What, has this thing appear'd again to-night?

BER. I have seen nothing.

MAR. Horatio says 'tis but our fantasy, and will not let belief take hold of him touching this dreaded sight, twice seen of us: therefore I have entreated him along with us to watch the minutes of this night; that, if again this apparition come He may approve[4] our eyes and speak to it.

HOR. Tush, tush, 'twill not appear.

BER. Sit down awhile, and let us once again assail your ears, that are so fortified against our story, what we two nights have seen.

HOR. Well, sit we down, and let us hear Bernardo speak of this.

BER. Last night of all, when yond same star that's westward from the pole had made his course to illume that part of heaven where now it burns, Marcellus and myself, the bell then beating one,—

MAR. Peace, break thee off; look where it comes again!

(*Enter Ghost, armed.*)

BER. In the same figure, like the king that's dead.

MAR. Thou art a scholar; speak to it, Horatio.

BER. Looks it[5] not like the King? mark it, Horatio.

HOR. Most like:—it harrows me with fear and wonder.

BER. It would be spoke to.

MAR. Question it, Horatio.

HOR. What are thou, that usurp'st this time of night, together with that fair and warlike form In which the majesty of buried Denmark Did sometimes march? By heaven I charge thee, speak!

MAR. It is offended.

BER. See, it stalks away!

HOR. Stay! speak, speak! I charge thee speak!

(*Exit Ghost.*)

MAR. 'Tis gone, and will not answer.

BER. How now, Horatio! You tremble and look pale: Is not this something more than fantasy? What think you on't?

HOR. Before my God, I might not this believe Without the sensible and true avouch Of mine own eyes.

MAR. Is it not like the King?

HOR. As thou art to thyself: such was the very armour he had on when he the ambitious Norway[6] combated; so frown'd he once when, in an angry parle,[7] He smote the sledded Polacks on the ice. 'Tis strange.

MAR. Thus twice before, and jump[8] at this dead hour, with martial stalk hath he gone by our watch.

HOR. In what particular thought to work I know not; but, in the gross and scope of my opinion, this bodes some strange eruption to our state.

MAR. Good now, sit down, and tell me, he that knows, why this same strict and most observant watch so nightly toils the subject of the land; and why such daily cast of brazen cannon, and foreign mart for implements of war; why such impress of

---

[4]confirm

[5]he

---

[6]King of Norway

[7]parley

[8]just

shipwrights, whose sore task does not divide the Sunday from the week; what might be toward, that this sweaty haste doth make the night joint-labourer with the day: who is't that can inform me?

HOR. That can I; at least, the whisper goes so. Our last king, whose image even but now appear'd to us, was, as you know, by Fortinbras of Norway, thereto prick'd on by a most emulate pride, dar'd to the combat; in which our valiant Hamlet,—for so this side of our known world esteem'd him,—did slay this Fortinbras; who, by a seal'd compact, well ratified by law and heraldry, did forfeit, with his life, all those his lands, which he stood seiz'd of, to the conqueror: against the which, a moiety competent was gaged[9] by our king; which had return'd to the inheritance of Fortinbras, had he been vanquisher; as by the same cov'nant,[10] and carriage of the article design'd, his fell to Hamlet. Now, sir, young Fortinbras, of unimproved mettle hot and full, hath in the skirts[11] of Norway, here and there, shark'd up a list of lawless resolutes, for food and diet, to some enterprise that hath a stomach in't; which is no other,—as it doth well appear unto our state,—but to recover of us, by strong hand, and terms compulsatory, those foresaid lands so by his father lost: and this, I take it, is the main motive of our preparations, the source of this our watch, and the chief head of this post-haste and romage[12] in the land.

BER. I think it be no other but e'en so: well may it sort, that this portentous figure comes armed through our watch; so like the king that was and is the question of these wars.

HOR. A mote it is to trouble the mind's eye. In the most high and palmy state of Rome, a little ere the mightiest Julius fell, the graves stood tenantless, and the sheeted dead did squeak and gibber in the Roman streets; as, stars with trains of fire and dews of blood, disasters in the sun; and the moist star, upon whose influence Neptune's empire stands. Was sick almost to doomsday with eclipse: and even the like precurse of fierce events,—as harbingers preceding still the fates, and prologue to the omen coming on,—have heaven and earth together demonstrated unto our climature[13] and countrymen.—But, soft, behold! lo, where it comes again!

(*Re-enter Ghost.*)

I'll cross it, though it blast me.—Stay, illusion! If thou has any sound, or use of voice, Speak to me: if there be any good thing to be done, that may to thee do ease, and, race to me, speak to me: if thou are privy to thy country's fate, which, happily, foreknowing may avoid, O, speak! Or if thou hast uphoarded in thy life extorted treasure in the womb of earth, for which, they say, you spirits oft walk in death,

(*The cock crows.*)

Speak of it:—stay, and speak!—Stop it, Marcellus!

MAR. Shall I strike at it with my partisan?[14]

HOR. Do, if it will not stand.

BER. 'Tis here!

HOR. 'Tis here!

MAR. 'Tis gone!

(*Exit Ghost.*)

---

[9]pledged

[10]agreement

[11]borders

[12]bustle

---

[13]regions

[14]pike (a type of spear)

We do it wrong, being so majestical, to offer it the show of violence; for it is, as the air, invulnerable, and our vain blows malicious mockery.

BER. It was about to speak, when the cock crew.

HOR. And then it started, like a guilty thing upon a fearful summons. I have heard the cock, that is the trumpet to the morn, doth with his lofty and shrill-sounding throat awake the god of day; and at his warning, whether in sea or fire, in earth or air, the extravagant and erring spirit hies to his confine: and of the truth herein this present object made probation.

MAR. It faded on the crowing of the cock. Some say that ever 'gainst that season comes wherein our Saviour's birth is celebrated, the bird of dawning singeth all night long; and then, they say, no spirit dare stir abroad: the nights are wholesome; then no planets strike, no fairy takes, nor witch hath power to charm, so hallow'd and so gracious is the time.

HOR. So have I heard, and do in part believe it. But, look, the morn, in russet mantle clad, walks o'er the dew of yon high eastward hill: break we our watch up: and by my advice, let us impart what we have seen to-night unto young Hamlet; for, upon my life, this spirit, dumb to us, will speak to him; do you consent we shall acquaint him with it, as needful in our loves, fitting our duty?

MAR. Let's do't, I pray; and I this morning know where we shall find him most conveniently.

(*Exeunt.*)

Scene II Elsinore. A Room of State in the Castle

[*Enter the King, Queen, Hamlet, Polonius, Laertes, Voltimand, Cornelius, Lords, and Attendant.*]

KING. Though yet of Hamlet our dear brother's death the memory be green, and that it us befitted to bear our hearts in grief, and our whole kingdom to be contracted in one brow of woe; yet so far hath discretion fought with nature that we with wisest sorrow think on him, together with remembrance of ourselves. Therefore our sometime sister, now our queen, the imperial jointress[1] to this warlike state, have we, as 'twere with a defeated joy,—with an auspicious and one dropping eye, with mirth in funeral, and with dirge in marriage, in equal scale weighing delight and dole,—taken to wife; nor have we herein barr'd your better wisdoms, which have freely gone with this affair along:—or all, our thanks. Now follows, that you know, young Fortinbras, holding a weak supposal of our worth, or thinking by our late dear brother's death our state to be disjoint and out of frame, colleagued with this dream of his advantage, he hath not fail'd to pester us with message, importing the surrender of those lands lost by his father, with all bonds of law, to our most valiant brother. So much for him,—now for ourself and for this time of meeting: thus much the business is:—we have here writ to Norway, uncle of young Fortinbras,—who, impotent and bed-rid, scarcely hears of this his nephew's purpose,—to suppress his further gait herein; in that the levies, the lists, and full proportions[2] are all made out of his subject:—and we here dispatch you, good Cornelius, and you, Voltimand, for bearers of this greeting to old Norway; giving to you no further personal power to business with the king, more than the scope of these dilated articles[3] allow. Farewell; and let your haste commend your duty.

COR. AND VOLT. In that and all things will we show our duty.

KING. We doubt it nothing: heartily farewell.

(*Exeunt Voltimand and Cornelius.*)

---

[1]partner

[2]provisions

[3]detailed documents

And now, Laertes, what's the news with you? you told us of some suit; what is't, Laertes? You cannot speak of reason to the Dane, and lose your voice: what wouldst thou beg, Laertes, that shall not be my offer, not thy asking? The head is not more native to the heart, the hand more instrumental to the mouth, than is the throne of Denmark to thy father. What wouldst thou have, Laertes?

LAER. Dread my lord, your leave and favour to return to France; from whence though willingly I came to Denmark, to show my duty in your coronation; yet now, I must confess, that duty done, my thoughts and wishes bend again toward France, and bow them to your gracious leave and pardon.

KING. Have you your father's leave? What says Polonius?

POL. He hath, my lord, wrung from me my slow leave by laboursome petition; and at last upon his will I seal'd my hard consent: I do beseech you, give him leave to go.

KING. Take thy fair hour, Laertes; time be thine, and thy best graces spend it at thy will!—But now, my cousin Hamlet, and my son—

HAM. [Aside.] A little more than kin, and less than kind!

KING. How is it that the clouds still hang on you?

HAM. Not so, my lord; I am too much i' the sun.

QUEEN. Good Hamlet, cast thy nighted colour off, and let thine eye look like a friend on Denmark. Do not for ever with thy vailed[4] lids seek for thy noble father in the dust: thou know'st 'tis common,—all that lives must die, passing through nature to eternity.

HAM. Ay, madam, it is common.

QUEEN. If it be, why seems it so particular with thee?

HAM. Seems, madam! Nay, it is; I know not seems. 'Tis not alone my inky cloak, good mother, nor customary suits of solemn black, nor windy suspiration of forc'd breath, no,

nor the fruitful river in the eye, nor the dejected 'havior of the visage, together with all forms, moods, shows of grief, that can denote me truly: These, indeed, seem; for they are actions that a man might play; but I have that within which passeth show; these but the trappings and the suits of woe.

KING. 'Tis sweet and commendable in your nature, Hamlet, to give these mourning duties to your father; but, you must know, your father lost a father; that father lost, lost his; and the survivor bound, in filial obligation, for some term to do obsequious sorrow: but to persevere in obstinate condolement[5] is a course of impious stubbornness; 'tis unmanly grief; it shows a will most incorrect to heaven; a heart unfortified, a mind impatient; an understanding simple and unschool'd; for what we know must be, and is as common as any the most vulgar thing to sense, why should we, in our peevish opposition, take it to heart? Fie! 'tis a fault to heaven, a fault against the dead, a fault to nature, to reason most absurd; whose common theme is death of fathers, and who still hath cried, from the first[6]corse till he that died to-day, 'This must be so.' We pray you, throw to earth this unprevailing woe; and think of us as of a father: for let the world take note you are the most immediate to our throne; and with no less nobility of love than that which dearest father bears his son do I impart toward you. For your intent in going back to school in Wittenberg, it is most retrograde to our desire: and we beseech you bend you to remain here in the cheer and comfort of our eye, our chiefest courtier, cousin, and our son.

QUEEN. Let not thy mother lose her prayers, Hamlet: I pray thee stay with us; go not to Wittenberg.

HAM. I shall in all my best obey you, madam.

---

[4]lowered

[5]mourning

[6]corpse

KING. Why, 'tis a loving and a fair reply: be as ourself in Denmark.—Madam, come; this gentle and unforc'd accord of Hamlet sits smiling to my heart: in grace whereof, no jocund health that Denmark drinks to-day but the great cannon to the clouds shall tell; and the king's rouse the heaven shall bruit[7] again, re-speaking earthly thunder. Come away.

(*Exeunt all but Hamlet.*)

HAM. O that this too too solid flesh would melt, thaw, and resolve itself into a dew! Or that the Everlasting had not fix'd his canon[8] 'gainst self-slaughter! O God! O God! How weary, stale, flat, and unprofitable seem to me all the uses of this world! Fie on't! O fie! 'tis an unweeded garden, that grows to seed; things rank and gross in nature possess it merely. That it should come to this! But two months dead!—nay, not so much, not two: so excellent a king; that was, to this, hyperion[9] to a satyr; so loving to my mother, that he might not beteem[10] the winds of heaven visit her face too roughly. Heaven and earth! Must I remember? Why, she would hang on him as if increase of appetite had grown by what it fed on: and yet, within a month,—let me not think on't,—frailty, thy name is woman!—a little month; or ere those shoes were old with Which she followed my poor father's body like Niobe,[11] all tears;—why she, even she,—O God! a beast that wants discourse of reason, would have mourn'd longer,—married with mine uncle, my

father's brother; but no more like my father than I to Hercules: within a month; ere yet the salt of most unrighteous tears had left the flushing in her galled eyes, she married:—O, most wicked speed, to post[12] with such dexterity to incestuous sheets! It is not, nor it cannot come to good; but break my heart,—for I must hold my tongue!

(*Enter Horatio, Marcellus, and Bernardo.*)

HOR. Hail to your lordship!

HAM. I am glad to see you well: Horatio,—or I do forget myself.

HOR. The same, my lord, and your poor servant ever.

HAM. Sir, my good friend; I'll change that name with you: and what make you from Wittenberg, Horatio?—Marcellus?

MAR. My good lord,—

HAM. I am very glad to see you.—Good even, sir.—But what, in faith, make you from Wittenberg?

HOR. A truant disposition, good my lord.

HAM. I would not hear your enemy say so; nor shall you do my ear that violence, to make it truster of your own report against yourself: I know you are no truant. But what is your affair in Elsinore? We'll teach you to drink deep ere you depart.

HOR. My lord, I came to see your father's funeral.

HAM. I prithee do not mock me, fellow-student. I think it was to see my mother's wedding.

HOR. Indeed, my lord, it follow'd hard upon.

HAM. Thrift, thrift, Horatio! The funeral bak'd meats did coldly furnish forth the marriage tables. Would I had met my dearest foe in heaven or ever I had seen that day, Horatio!—My father,—methinks I see my father.

HOR. Where, my lord?

HAM. In my mind's eye, Horatio.

HOR. I saw him once; he was a goodly king.

---

[7]noisily proclaim

[8]law

[9]the Sun God, a symbol of ideal beauty

[10]allow

[11]a mother, who, according to Greek myth, wept so profusely at the death of her children that she was turned to stone by gods

[12]hasten

HAM. He was a man, take him for all in all, I shall not look upon his like again.

HOR. My lord, I think I saw him yesternight.

HAM. Saw who?

HOR. My lord, the king your father.

HAM. The King my father!

HOR. Season your admiration for awhile with an attent ear, till I may deliver, upon the witness of these gentlemen, this marvel to you.

HAM. For God's love let me hear.

HOR. Two nights together had these gentlemen, Marcellus and Bernardo, on their watch in the dead vast and middle of the night,been thus encounter'd. A figure like your father, armed at point exactly, cap-a-pe,[13] appears before them and with solemn march goes slow and stately by them: thrice he walk'd by their oppress'd and fear-surprised eyes, within his truncheon's length; whilst they, distill'd almost to jelly with the act of fear, stand dumb, and speak not to him. This to me in dreadful[14] secrecy impart they did; and I with them the third night kept the watch: where, as they had deliver'd, both in time, form of the thing, each word made true and good, the apparition comes: I knew your father; these hands are not more like.

HAM. But where was this?

MAR. My lord, upon the platform where we watch'd.

HAM. Did yo not speak to it?

HOR. My lord, I did; but answer made it none: yet once methought it lifted up it head, and did address itself to motion, like as it would speak: but even then the morning cock crew loud, and at the sound it shrunk in haste away, and vanish'd from our sight.

HAM. 'Tis very strange.

HOR. As I do live, my honour'd lord, 'tis true; and we did think it writ down in our duty to let you know of it.

HAM. Indeed, indeed, sirs, but his troubles me. Hold you the watch to-night?

MAR. AND BER. We do, my lord.

HAM. Arm'd, say you?

BOTH. Arm'd, my lord.

HAM. From top to toe?

BOTH. My lord, from head to foot.

HAM. Then saw you not his face?

HOR. O, yes, my lord: he wore his beaver[15] up.

HAM. What, look'd he frowningly?

HOR. A countenance more in sorrow than in anger.

HAM. Pale or red?

HOR. Nay, very pale.

HAM. And fix'd his eyes upon you?

HOR. Most constantly.

HAM. I would I had been there.

HOR. It would have much amaz'd you.

HAM. Very like, very like. Stay'd it long?

HOR. While one with moderate haste might tell a hundred.

MAR. AND BER. Longer, longer.

HOR. Not when I saw't.

HAM. His beard was grizzled,—no?

HOR. It was, as I have seen it in his life, a sable silver'd.

HAM. I will watch to-night; perchance 'twill walk again.

HOR. I warr'nt it will.

HAM. If it assume my noble father's person, I'll speak to it, though hell itself should gape and bid me hold my peace. I pray you all, if you have hitherto conceal'd this sight, let it be tenable in your silence still; and whatsoever else shall hap to-night, give it an understanding, but no tongue: I will requite your loves. So, fare ye well: Upon the platform, 'twixt eleven and twelve, I'll visit you.

ALL. Our duty to your honour.

HAM. Your loves, as mine to you: farewell.

(Exeunt Horatio, Marcellus, and Bernardo.)

---

[13]head to foot

[14]fearful

---

[15]visor, face guard

My father's spirit in arms! All is not well; I doubt some foul play: would the night were come! Till then sit still, my soul: foul deeds will rise, though all the earth o'erwhelm them, to men's eyes.

(*Exit.*)

Scene III. A Room in Polonius's House
[*Enter Laertes and Ophelia.*]

LAER. My necessaries are embark'd: farewell: and, sister, as the winds give benefit and convoy is assistant, do not sleep, but let me hear from you.

OPH. Do you doubt that?

LAER. For Hamlet, and the trifling of his favour, hold it a fashion, and a toy in blood: a violent in the youth of primy nature,[1] forward, not permanent, sweet, no lasting; the perfume and suppliance[2] of a minute; no more.

OPH. No more but so?

LAER. Think it no more: for nature, crescent,[3] does not grow alone in thews and bulk; but as this temple waxes, the inward service of the mind and soul grows wide withal. Perhaps he loves you now; and now no soil nor cautel[4] doth besmirch the virtue of his will: but you must fear, his greatness weigh'd, his will is not his own; for he himself is subject to his birth: he may not, as unvalu'd persons do, carve for himself; for on his choice depends the safety and health of this whole state; and therefore must his choice be circumscrib'd unto the voice and yielding of that body whereof he is the head. Then if he says he loves you, it fits your wisdom so far to believe it as he in his particular act and place

may give his saying deed; which is no further than the main voice of Denmark goes withal. Then weigh what loss your honour may sustain if with too credent ear you list his songs, or lose your heart, or your chaste treasure open to his unmaster'd importunity. Fear it, Ophelia, fear it, my dear sister; and keep you in the rear of your affection, out of the shot and danger of desire. The chariest maid is prodigal enough if she unmask her beauty to the moon: virtue itself scopes not caluminous strokes: the canker galls the infants of the spring too oft before their buttons[5] be disclos'd: and in the morn and liquid dew of youth contagious blastments are most imminent. Be wary then; best safety lies in fear: youth to itself rebels, though none else near.

OPH. I shall th' effect of this good lesson keep as watchman to my heart. But, good my brother, do not, as some ungracious pastors do, show me the steep and thorny way to heaven; whilst, like a puff'd and reckless libertine, himself the primrose path of dalliance treads and recks not his own read.[6]

LAER. O, fear me not. I stay too long:—but here my father comes.

(*Enter Polonius.*)

A double blessing is a double grace; occasion smiles upon a second leave.

POL. Yet here, Laertes! aboard, aboard, for shame! The wind sits in the shoulder of your sail, and you are stay'd for. There,—my blessing with thee!

(*Laying his hand on Laertes's head.*)

[1] springlike

[2] occupation

[3] growing

[4] deceit

[5] buds/buttons

[6] does not heed his own advice

And these few precepts in thy memory look thou character.[7] Give thy thoughts no tongue, nor any unproportion'd thought his act. Be thou familiar, but by no means vulgar. Those friends thou hast, and their adoption tried, grapple them unto thy soul with hoops of steel; but do not dull thy palm with entertainment of each new-hatch'd, unfledg'd comrade. Beware of entrance to a quarrel; but, being in, bear't that the opposed may beware of thee. Give every man thine ear, but few thy voice: take each man's censure, but reserve thy judgment. Costly thy habit as thy purse can buy, but not express'd in fancy; rich, not gaudy: for the apparel oft proclaims the man; and they in France of the best rank and station are most select and generous chief in that. Neither a borrower nor a lender be: for loan oft loses both itself and friend; and borrowing dulls the edge of husbandry. This above all,—to thine own self be true; and it must follow, as the night the day, thou canst not then be false to any man. Farewell: my blessing season this in thee!

LAER. Most humbly do I take my leave, my lord.

POL. The time invites you; go, your servants tend.

LAER. Farewell, Ophelia; and remember well what I have said to you.

OPH. 'Tis in my memory lock'd, and you yourself shall keep the key of it.

LAER. Farewell.

(*Exit.*)

POL. What is't, Ophelia, he hath said to you?

OPH. So please you, something touching the Lord Hamlet.

POL. Marry, well bethought: 'Tis told me he hath very oft of late given private time to you; and you yourself have of your audience been most free and bounteous; if it be so,—as so 'tis put on me, and that in way of caution,—I must tell you you do not understand yourself so clearly as it behooves my daughter and your honour. What is between you? give me up the truth.

OPH. He hath, my lord, of late made many tenders of his affection to me.

POL. Affection! pooh! you speak like a green girl, unsifted in such perilous circumstance. Do you believe his tenders, as you call them?

OPH. I do not know, my lord, what I should think.

POL. Marry, I'll teach you: think yourself a baby; that you have ta'en these tenders for true pay, which are not sterling. Tender yourself more dearly; or,—not to crack the wind of the poor phrase, wronging it thus,—you'll tender me a fool.

OPH. My lord, he hath importun'd me with love in honourable fashion.

POL. Ay, fashion you may call it; go to, go to.

OPH. And hath given countenance to his speech, my lord, with almost all the holy vows of heaven.

POL. Ay, springes to catch woodcocks.[8] I do know, when the blood burns, how prodigal the soul lends the tongue vows: these blazes, daughter, giving more light than heat,—extinct in both, even in their promise, as it is a-making,—you must not take for fire. From this time be something scanter of your maiden presence; set your entreatments at a higher rate than a command to parley. For Lord Hamlet, believe so much in him, that he is young; and with a larger tether may he walk than may be given you: in few, Ophelia, do not believe his vows; for they are brokers,—not of that dye which their investments show, but mere implorators of unholy suits, breathing like sanctified and pious bawds, the better to beguile. This is for all,—I would not, in plain terms, from this time forth have you so slander any moment leisure as to give words or talk with the Lord Hamlet. Look to't, I charge you; come your ways.

OPH. I shall obey, my Lord.

(*Exeunt.*)

---

[7]inscribe

[8]traps to catch stupid birds

Scene IV. The Platform

[*Enter Hamlet, Horatio, and Marcellus.*]

Ham. The air bites shrewdly; it is very cold.
Hor. It is a nipping and an eager air.
Ham. What hour now?
Hor. I think it lacks of twelve.
Mar. No, it is struck.
Hor. Indeed? I heard it not: then draws near the season wherein the spirit held his wont to walk.

(*A flourish of trumpets, and ordnance shot off within.*)

What does this mean, my lord?
Ham. The King doth wake to-night and takes his rouse, keeps wassail, and the swaggering up-spring reels; and, as he drains his draughts of Rhenish down, the kettle-drum and trumpet thus bray out the triumph of his pledge.
Hor. Is it a custom?
Ham. Ay, marry, is't; but to my mind,—though I am native here, and to the manner born,—it is a custom more honour'd in the breach than the observance. This heavy-headed revel east and west makes us traduc'd and tax'd of other nations: they clepé us drunkards, and with swinish phrase soil our addition;[2] and, indeed, it takes from our achievements, though perform'd at height, the pith and marrow of our attribute. So oft it chances in particular men that, for some vicious mole of nature in them, as in their birth,—wherein they are not guilty, since nature cannot choose his origin,—by the o'ergrowth of some complexion, oft breaking down the pales[3] and forts of reason; or by some habit, that too much o'er-leavens the form of plausive[4] manners;—that these

men,—carrying, I say, the stamp of one defect, being nature's livery, or fortune's star,—their virtues else,—be they as pure as grace, as infinite as man may undergo,—shall in the general censure take corruption from that particular fault: the dram of eale doth all the noble substance often doubt to his own scandal.
Hor. Look, my lord, it comes!

(*Enter Ghost.*)

Ham. Angels and ministers of grace defend us!—Be thou a spirit of health or goblin damn'd, bring with thee airs from heaven or blasts from hell, be thy intents wicked or charitable, thou com'st in such a questionable shape that I will speak to thee: I'll call thee Hamlet, King, father, royal Dane; O, answer me! Let me not burst in ignorance; but tell why thy canoniz'd bones, hearsed in death, have burst their cerements;[5] why the sepulchre, wherein we saw thee quietly in-urn'd, hath op'd his ponderous and marble jaws to cast thee up again! What may this mean, that thou, dead corse, again in complete steel, revisit'st thus the glimpses of the moon, making night hideous, and we fools of nature so horridly to shake our disposition with thoughts beyond the reaches of our souls? Say, why is this? wherefore? what should we do?

(*Ghost beckons Hamlet.*)

Hor. It beckons you to go away with it, as if it some impartment[6] did desire to you alone.
Mar. Look with what courteous action it waves you to a more removed ground: but do not go with it!

---

[1]call

[2]reputation

[3]enclosures

[4]pleasing

---

[5]shroud

[6]communication

HOR. No, by no means.

HAM. It will not speak; then will I follow it.

HOR. Do not, my lord.

HAM. Why, what should be the fear? I do not set my life at a pin's fee; and for my soul, what can it do to that, being a thing immortal as itself? It waves me forth again;—I'll follow it.

HOR. What if it tempt you toward the flood, my lord, or to the dreadful summit of the cliff that beetles o'er his base into the sea, and there assume some other horrible form which might deprive your sovereignty of reason, and draw you into madness? think of it: the very place puts toys of desperation, without more motive, into every brain that looks so many fadoms to the sea and hears it roar beneath.

HAM. It waves me still.—Go on; I'll follow thee.

MAR. You shall not go, my lord.

HAM. Hold off your hands.

HOR. Be rul'd; you shall not go.

HAM. My fate cries out, and makes each petty artery in this body as hard as the Nemean lion's[7] nerve.—

(*Ghost beckons.*)

Still am I call'd;—unhand me, gentlemen;—

(*Breaking free from them.*)

By heaven, I'll make a ghost of him that lets me!—I say, away!—Go on; I'll follow thee.

(*Exeunt Ghost and Hamlet.*)

HOR. He waxes desperate with imagination.

MAR. Let's follow; 'tis not fit thus to obey him.

HOR. Have after.—To what issue will this come?

MAR. Something is rotten in the state of Denmark.

HOR. Heaven will direct it.

MAR. Nay, let's follow him.

(*Exeunt.*)

Scene V. A More Remote Part of the Castle

[*Enter Ghost and Hamlet.*]

HAM. Whither wilt thou lead me? speak! I'll go no further.

GHOST. Mark me.

HAM. I will.

GHOST. My hour is almost come, when I to sulph'uous and tormenting flames must render up myself.

HAM. Alas, poor ghost!

GHOST. Pity me not, but lend thy serious hearing to what I shall unfold.

HAM. Speak; I am bound to hear.

GHOST. So art thou to revenge, when thou shalt hear.

HAM. What?

GHOST. I am thy father's spirit; doom'd for a certain term to walk the night, and for the day confin'd to wastein fires, till the foul crimes done in my days of nature are burnt and purg'd away. but that I am forbid to tell the secrets of my prison-house, I could a tale unfold whose lightest word would harrow up thy soul; freeze thy young blood; make thy two eyes, like stars, start from their spheres; thy knotted and combined locks to part, and each particular hair to stand on end like quills upon the fretful porcupine[1]: but this eternal blazon must not be to ears of flesh and blood.—List, list, O, list!—If thou didst ever thy dear father love—

HAM. O God!

GHOST. Revenge his foul and most unnatural murder.

HAM. Murder!

GHOST. Murder most foul, as in the best it is; but this most foul, strange, and unnatural.

HAM. Haste me to know't, that I, with wings as swift as meditation or the thoughts of love, My sweep to my revenge.

---

[7]mythical lion killed by the Greek Hero Hercules

[1]timid porcupine

GHOST. I find thee apt; and duller shouldst thou be than the fat weed that rots itself in ease on Lethe[2] wharf, wouldst thou not stir in this. Now, Hamlet, hear. 'Tis given out that, sleeping in my orchard, a serpent stung me; so the whole ear of Denmark is by a forged process of my death rankly abus'd; but know, thou noble youth, the serpent that did sting thy father's life now wears his crown.

HAM. O my prophetic soul! Mine uncle!

GHOST. Ay, that incestuous, that adulterate beast, with witchcraft of his wit, with traitorous gifts,—O wicked wit and gifts, that have the power so to seduce!—won to his shameful lust the will of my most seeming-virtuous queen: O Hamlet, what a falling-off was there! From me, whose love was of that dignity that it went hand in hand even with the vow I made to her in marriage; and to decline upon a wretch whose natural gifts were poor to those of mine! But virtue, as it never will be mov'd, thought lewdness court it in a shape of heaven; so lust, though to a radiant angel link'd, will sate itself in a celestial bed and prey on garbage. But soft! methinks I scent the morning air; brief let me be.—Sleeping within my orchard, my custom always of the afternoon, upon my secure hour thy uncle stole, and in the porches of my ears did pour the leperous distilment; whose effect holds such an enmity with blood of man that, swift as quicksilver, it courses through the natural gates and alleys of the body; and with a sudden vigour it doth posset[4] and curd, like eager[5] droppings into milk, the thin and wholesome blood; so did it mine; and a most instant tetter[6] bark'd about, most lazar-like,[7] with vile and loathsome crust all my smooth body. thus was I, sleeping, by a brother's hand, of life, of crown, of queen, at once dispatch'd: cut off even in the blossoms of my sin, unhous'led, disappointed, unanel'd;[8] no reckoning made, but sent to my account with all my imperfections on my head: O, horrible! O, horrible! most horrible! If thou has nature in thee, bear it not; let not the royal bed of Denmark be a couch for luxury and damned incest. But, howsoever thou pursu'st this act, taint not thy mind, nor let thy soul contrive against thy mother aught: leave her to heaven, and to those thorns that in her bosom lodge, to prick and sting her. Fare thee well at once! The glowworm shows the matin[9] to be near, and 'gins to pale his uneffectual fire: adieu, adieu! Hamlet, remember me.

(*Exit.*)

HAM. O all you host of heaven! O earth! what else? And shall I couple hell? O, fie!—Hold, my heart; and you, my sinews, grow not instant old, but bear me stiffly up.—Remember thee! Ay, thou poor ghost, while memory holds a seat in this distracted globe. Remember thee! Yea, from the table of my memory I'll wipe away all trivial fond records, all saws of books, all forms, all pressures past, that youth and observation copied there; and thy commandment all alone shall live within the book and volume of my brain, unmix'd with baser matter: yes, by heaven!—O most pernicious woman! O villain, villain, smiling, damned villain! My tables,—meet it is I set it down, that one may smile, and smile, and be a villain; at least, I am sure, it may be so in Denmark:

(*Writing.*)

---

[2]river of forgetfulness

([3]not in this version)

[4]curdle

[5]acid

[6]scab

[7]leper like

---

[8]without taking communion, unabsolved, without extreme unction

[9]morning

So, uncle, there you are. Now to my word; it is
   'Adieu, adieu! remember me:' I have sworn't.

HOR. [Within.] My lord, my lord,—

MAR. [Within.] Lord Hamlet,—

HOR. [Within.] Heaven secure him!

HAM. So be it!

MAR. [Within.] Illo, ho, ho, my lord!

HAM. Hillo, ho, ho, boy! Come, bird, come.

(*Enter Horatio and Marcellus.*)

MAR. How is't, my noble lord?

HOR. What news, my lord?

HAM. O, wonderful!

HOR. Good my lord, tell it.

HAM. No; you'll reveal it.

HOR. Not I, my lord, by heaven.

MAR. Nor I, my Lord.

HAM. How say you than; would heart of man
   once think it?—but you'll be secret?

HOR. AND MAR. Ay, by heaven, my lord.

HAM. There's ne'er a villain dwelling in all
   Denmark but he's an arrant knave.

HOR. There needs no ghost, my lord, come from
   the grave to tell us this.

HAM. Why, right; you are i' the right; and so,
   without more circumstance at all, I hold it fit
   that we shake hands and part: you, as your
   business and desires shall point you,—for
   every man hath business and desire, such as
   it is;—and for my own poor part, look you,
   I'll go pray.

HOR. These are but wild and whirling words, my
   lord.

HAM. I'm sorry they offend you, heartily; yes,
   faith, heartily.

HOR. There's no offence, my lord.

HAM. Yes, by Saint Patrick, but there is, Horatio,
   and much offence too. Touching this vision
   here,—it is an honest ghost, that let me tell
   you: for your desire to know what is between
   us, O'ermaster't as you may. And now, good
   friends, as you are friends, scholars, and
   soldiers, give me one poor request.

HOR. What is't, my lord? we will.

HAM. Never make known what you have seen
   to-night.

HOR. AND MAR. My lord, we will not.

HAM. Nay, but swear't.

HOR. In faith, my lord, not I.

MAR. Nor I, my lord, in faith.

HAM. Upon my sword.

MAR. We have sworn, my lord, already.

HAM. Indeed, upon my sword, indeed.

GHOST. [Beneath.] Swear.

HAM. Ha, ha boy! say'st thou so? art thou there,
   truepenny?[10]—Come on!—you hear this
   fellow in the cellarage,—consent to swear.

HOR. Propose the oath, my lord.

HAM. Never to speak of this that you have seen,
   swear by my sword.

GHOST. [Beneath.] Swear.

HAM. Hic et ubique?[11] then we'll shift our
   ground.—come hither, gentlemen, and lay
   your hands again upon my sword: never to
   speak of this that you have heard, swear by
   my sword.

GHOST. [Beneath.] Swear.

HAM. Well said, old mole! canst work i' the earth
   so fast? A worthy pioner![12]—Once more
   remove, good friends.

HOR. O day and night, but this is wondrous
   strange!

HAM. And therefore as a stranger give it
   welcome. There are more things in heaven
   and earth, Horatio, than are dreamt of in your
   philosophy. But come;—here, as before,
   never, so help you mercy, how strange or odd
   soe'er I bear myself,—as I, perchance,
   hereafter shall think meet to put an antic
   disposition on,—that you, at such times
   seeing me, never shall, with arms encumber'd
   thus, or this head-shake, or by pronouncing
   of some doubtful phrase, as 'Well, well, we
   know'; or 'We could, an if we would';—or 'If
   we list to speak'; or 'There be, an if they
   might';—or such ambiguous giving out, to
   note that you know aught of me:—this is not

---

[10]honest fellow

[11]here and everywhere

[12]miner

to do, so grace and mercy at your most need help you, swear.

GHOST. [Beneath.] Swear.

HAM. Rest, rest, perturbed spirit!—So, gentlemen, with all my love I do commend me to you: And what so poor a man as Hamlet is may do, to express his love and friending to you, God willing, shall not lack. Let us go in together; and still your fingers on your lips, I pray. The time is out of joint:—O cursed spite, that ever I was born to set it right!—Nay, come, let's go together.

(*Exeunt.*)

■ Act II

Scene I. A Room in Polonius's House

[*Enter Polonius and Reynaldo.*]

POL. Give him this money and these notes, Reynaldo.

REY. I will, my lord.

POL. You shall do marvellous wisely, good Reynaldo, before You visit him, to make inquiry of his behaviour.

REY. My lord, I did intend it.

POL. Marry, well said; very well said. Look you, sir, enquire me first what Danskers[1] are in Paris; and how, and who, what means, and where they keep, what company, at what expense; and finding, by this encompassment and drift of question, that they do know my son, come you more nearer than your particular demands will touch it: take you, as 'twere, some distant knowledge of him; as thus, 'I know his father and his friends, and in part him;—do you mark this, Reynaldo?

REY. Ay, very well, my lord.

POL. 'And in part him;—but,' you may say, 'not well: but if 't be he I mean, he's very wild; addicted so and so;' and there put on him

what forgeries you please; marry, none so rank as may dishonour him; take heed of that; but, sir, such wanton, wild, and usual slips as are companions noted and most known to youth and liberty.

REY. As gaming, my lord.

POL. Ay, or drinking, fencing, swearing, quarrelling, drabbing:[2]—you may go so far.

REY. My lord, that would dishonour him.

POL. Faith, no; as you may season it in the charge. You must not put another scandal on him, that he is open to incontinency; that's not my meaning: but breathe his faults so quaintly that they may seem the taints of liberty; the flash and outbreak of a fiery mind; a savageness in unreclaimed blood, of general assault.[3]

REY. But, my good lord,—

POL. Wherefore should you do this?

REY. Ay, my lord, I would know that.

POL. Marry, sir, here's my drift; and I believe it is a fetch of warrant: you laying these slight sullies on my son as 'twere a thing little soil'd i' the working, Mark you, your party in converse, him you would sound, having ever seen in the prenominate crimes the youth you breathe of guilty, be assur'd he closes with you in this consequence; 'Good sir,' or so; or 'friend,' or 'gentleman'—according to the phrase or the addition of man and country.

REY. Very good, my lord.

POL. And then, sir, does 'a[4] this,—he does—What was I about to say?—by the mass, I was about to say something:—Where did I leave?

REY. At 'closes in the consequence,' at 'friend or so,' and 'gentleman.'

POL. At—'closes in the consequence'—ay, marry! He closes with you thus:—'I know the gentleman; I saw him yesterday, or t'other day, or then, or then; with such, or such; and,

---

[1]Danes

[2]womanizing

[3]common to all

[4]he

as you say, there was he gaming; there o'ertook in's rouse; there falling out at tennis': or perchance, 'I saw him enter such a house of sale,'—videlicet,[5] a brothel,—or so forth.—see you now; your bait of falsehood takes this carp of truth: and thus do we of wisdom and of reach, with windlaces, and with assays of bias, by indirections find directions out:so, by my former lecture and advice, shall you my son. You have me, have you not?

REY. My lord, I have.

POL. God b' wi' you, fare you well.

REY. Good my lord!

POL. Observe his inclination in yourself.

REY. I shall, my lord.

POL. And let him play his music.

REY. Well, my lord.

POL. Farewell!

(*Exit Reynaldo.*)

(*Enter Ophelia.*)

How now, Ophelia! what's the matter?

OPH. Alas, my lord, I have been so affrighted!

POL. With what, i' the name of God?

OPH. My lord, as I was sewing in my chamber, Lord Hamlet,—with his doublet all unbrac'd;[6] no hat upon his head; his stockings foul'd, ungart'red, and down-gyved[7] to his ankle pale as his shirt; his knees knocking each other; and with a look so piteous in purport as if he had been loosed out of hell to speak of horrors,—he comes before me.

POL. Mad for thy love?

OPH. My lord, I do not know; but truly I do fear it.

POL. What said he?

OPH. He took me by the wrist, and held me hard; then goes he to the length of all his arm; and with his other hand thus o'er his brow, he falls to such perusal of my face as he would draw it. Long stay'd he so; at last,—a little shaking of mine arm, and thrice his head thus waving up and down,—he rais'd a sigh so piteous and profound as it did seem to shatter all his bulk and end his being: that done, he lets me go: and, with his head over his shoulder turn'd he seem'd to find his way without his eyes; for out o' doors he went without their help, and to the last bended their light on me.

POL. Come, go with me: I will go seek the king. This is the very ecstasy of love; whose violent property fordoes itself, and leads the will to desperate undertakings, as oft as any passion under heaven that does afflict our natures. I am sorry,—what, have you given him any hard words of late?

OPH. No, my good lord; but, as you did command, I did repel his letters and denied his access to me.

POL. That hath made him mad. I am sorry that with better heed and judgment I had not quoted him: I fear'd he did but trifle, and meant to wreck thee; but beshrew my jealousy! It seems it as proper to our age to cast beyond ourselves in our opinions as it is common for the younger sort to lack discretion. Come, go we to the king: this must be known; which, being kept close, might move more grief to hide than hate to utter love.

(*Exeunt.*)

Scene II. A Room in the Castle

[*Enter King, Rosencrantz, Guildenstern, and Attendants.*]

KING. Welcome, dear Rosencrantz and Guildenstern! Moreover that we much did long to see you, the need we have to use you did provoke our hasty sending. Something have you heard of Hamlet's transformation;

---

[5]namely

[6]jacket completely unfastened

[7]hanging down like fetters

so I call it, sith[1] nor the exterior nor the inward man resembles that it was. What it should be, more than his father's death, that thus hath put him so much from the understanding of himself, I cannot dream of: I entreat you both that, being of so young days brought up with him, and since so neighbour'd to his youth and humour,[2] that you vouchsafe your rest here in our court some little time: so by your companies to draw him on to pleasures, and to gather, so much as from occasion you may glean, whether aught, to us unknown, afflicts him thus, that, open'd, lies within our remedy.

QUEEN. Good gentlemen, he hath much talk'd of you, and sure I am two men there are not living to whom he more adheres. If it will please you to show us so much gentry[3] and good-will as to expend your time with us awhile, for the supply and profit of our hope, your visitation shall receive such thanks as fits a king's remembrance.

ROS. Both your majesties might, by the sovereign power you have of us, put your dread pleasures more into command than to entreaty.

GUIL. We both obey, and here give up ourselves, in the full bent, to lay our service freely at your feet, to be commanded.

KING. Thanks, Rosencrantz and gentle Guildenstern.

QUEEN. Thanks, Guildenstern and gentle Rosencrantz: and I beseech you instantly to visit my too-much-changed son.—Go, some of you, and bring these gentlemen where Hamlet is.

GUIL. Heavens make our presence and our practices pleasant and helpful to him!

QUEEN. Ay, amen!

(*Exeunt Rosencrantz, Guildenstern, and some Attendants.*)

(*Enter Polonius.*)

POL. Th' ambassadors from Norway, my good lord, are joyfully return'd.

KING. Thou still hast been the father of good news.

POL. Have I, my lord? Assure you, my good liege, I hold my duty, as I hold my soul, both to my God and to my gracious king: and I do think,—or else this brain of mine hunts not the trail of policy so sure as it hath us'd to do,—that I have found the very cause of Hamlet's lunacy.

KING. O, speak of that; that do I long to hear.

POL. Give first admittance to the ambassadors; my news shall be the fruit to that great feast.

KING. Thyself do grace to them, and bring them in.

(*Exit Polonius.*)

He tells me, my sweet queen, he hath found the head and source of all your son's distemper.

QUEEN. I doubt it is no other but the main,—his father's death and our o'erhasty marriage.

KING. Well, we shall sift him.

(*Enter Polonius, with Voltimand and Cornelius.*)

Welcome, my good friends! Say, Voltimand, what from our brother Norway?

VOLT. Most fair return of greetings and desires. Upon our first, he sent out to suppress his nephew's levies; which to him appear'd to be a preparation 'gainst the Polack; but, better look'd into, he truly found it was against your highness; whereat griev'd,—that so his sickness, age, and impotence was falsely borne in hand,—sends out arrests on Fortinbras; which he, in brief, obeys; receives rebuke from Norway; and, in fine,[4] makes vow before his uncle never more to give th'

---

[1]since

[2]behavior

[3]courtesy

[4]finally

assay of arms against your majesty. Whereon
old Norway, overcome with joy, gives him
three thousand crowns in annual fee; and his
commission to employ those soldiers, so
levied as before, against the Polack: with an
entreaty, herein further shown,

(*Gives a paper.*)

That it might please you to give quiet pass
through your dominions for this enterprise,
on such regards of safety and allowance as
therein are set down.
KING. It likes us well; and at our more consider'd
time we'll read, answer, and think upon this
business. Meantime we thank you for your
well-took labour: go to your rest; at night
we'll feast together: most welcome home!

(*Exeunt Voltimand and Cornelius.*)

POL. This business is well ended.—My liege, and
madam,—to expostulate what majesty should
be, what duty is, why day is day, night is
night, and time is time. Were nothing but to
waste night, day, and time. Therefore, since
brevity is the soul of wit, and tediousness the
limbs and outward flourishes, I will be
brief:—your noble son is mad: mad call I it;
for to define true madness, what is't but to be
nothing else but mad? But let that go.
QUEEN. More matter, with less art.
POL. Madam, I swear I use no art at all. That he
is mad, 'tis true: 'tis true 'tis pity; and pity 'tis
'tis true: a foolish figure;[5] but farewell it, for
I will use no art. Mad lest us grant him then:
and now remains that we find out the cause
of this effect; or rather say, the cause of this
defect, for this effect defective comes by
cause: thus it remains, and the remainder
thus. Perpend.[6] I have a daughter,—have

whilst she is mine,—who, in her duty and
obedience, mark, hath given me this: now
gather, and surmise.

(*Reads.*)

'To the celestial, and my soul's idol, the most
beautified Ophelia,'—that's an ill phrase, a
vile phrase; 'beautified' is a vile phrase: but
you shall hear. Thus:

(*Reads.*)

'In her excellent white bosom, these, &c.'
QUEEN. Came this from Hamlet to her?
POL. Good madam, stay awhile; I will be faithful.

(*Reads.*)

'Doubt thou the starts are fire;
   Doubt that the sun doth move;
Doubt truth to be a liar;
   But never doubt I love.
'O dear Ophelia, I am ill at these numbers; I have
not art to reckon my groans:
But that I love thee best, O most best, believe it.
Adieu.
'Thine evermore, most dear lady, whilst this
machine is to him, HAMLET.'
This, in obedience, hath my daughter show'd me;
and more above, hath his solicitings, as they
fell out by time, by means, and place. All
given to mine ear.
KING. But how hath she receiv'd his love?
POL. What do you think of me?
KING. As of a man faithful and honourable.
POL. I would fain prove so. But what might you
think, when I had seen this hot love on the
wing,—as I perceiv'd it, I must tell you that,
before my daughter told me,—what might
you, or my dear majesty your queen here,
think, if I had play'd the desk or table-book,[7]

---

[5]rhetorical device

[6]consider carefully

---

[7]had kept secrets

or given my heart a winking, mute and dumb; or look'd upon this love with idle sight;—what might you think? No, I went round to work, and my young mistress thus I did bespeak: 'Lord Hamlet is a prince, out of thy sphere;[8] this must not be:' and then I precepts gave her, that she should lock herself from his resort, admit no messengers, receive no tokens. Which done, she took the fruits of my advice; and he, repulsed,—a short tale to make,—fell into a sadness; then into a fast; thence to a watch; thence into a weakness; thence to a lightness; and, by this declension, into the madness wherein now he raves, and all we wail for.

KING. Do you think 'tis this?

QUEEN. It may be, very likely.

POL. Hath there been such a time,—I'd fain know that—that I have positively said "Tis so,' when it prov'd otherwise?

KING. Not that I know.

POL. Take this from this, if this be otherwise:

(*Points to his head and shoulder.*)

If circumstances lead me, I will find where truth is hid, though it were hid indeed within the centre.

KING. How may we try it further?

POL. You know sometimes he walks for hours together here in the lobby.

QUEEN. So he does indeed.

POL. At such a time I'll loose my daughter to him: be you and I behind an arras[9] then; mark the encounter: if he love her not, and he not from his reason fall'n thereon let me be no assistant for a state, but keep a farm and carters.

KING. We will try it.

QUEEN. But look where sadly the poor wretch comes reading.

POL. Away, I do beseech you, both away I'll board him presently:—O, give me leave.

(*Exeunt King, Queen, and Attendants.*)

(*Enter Hamlet, reading.*)

How does my good Lord Hamlet?

HAM. Well, God-a-mercy.

POL. Do you know me, my lord?

HAM. Excellent well; you're a fishmonger.[10]

POL. Not I, my lord.

HAM. Then I would you were so honest a man.

POL. Honest, my lord!

HAM. Ay, sir; to be honest, as this world goes, is to be one man picked out of ten thousand.

POL. That's very true, my lord.

HAM. For if the sun breed maggots in a dead dog, being a god-kissing carrion,—have you a daughter?

POL. I have, my lord.

HAM. Let her not walk i' the sun: conception is a blessing, but not as your daughter may conceive:—friend, look to't.

POL. How say you by that?—[Aside.] Still harping on my daughter:—yet he knew me not at first; he said I was a fishmonger: he is far gone, far gone: and truly in my youth I suffered much extremity for love; very near this. I'll speak to him again.—What do you read, my lord?

HAM. Words, words, words.

POL. What is the matter, my lord?

HAM. Between who?

POL. I mean, the matter that you read, my lord.

HAM. Slanders, sir: for the satirical slave says here that old men have grey beards; that their faces are wrinkled; their eyes purging thick amber and plum-tree gum; and that they have a plentiful lack of wit, together with most weak hams: all which, sir, though I most powerfully and potently believe, yet I hold it not honesty to have it thus set down; for you

_____

[8]sphere/star

[9]tapestry hanging in front of a wall

[10]dealer in fish (slang for a procurer)

yourself, sir, should be old as I am, if, like a crab, you could go backward.

Pol. [Aside.] Though this be madness, yet there is a method in't.—Will you walk out of the air, my lord?

Ham. Into my grave?

Pol. Indeed, that is out o' the air. [Aside.] How pregnant[11] sometimes his replies are! a happiness that often madness hits on, which reason and sanity could not so prosperously be delivered of. I will leave him and suddenly contrive the means meeting between him and my daughter.—My honourable lord, I will most humbly take my leave of you.

Ham. You cannot, sir, take from me anything that I will more willingly part withal,—except my life, except my life, except my life.

Pol. Fare you well, my lord.

Ham. These tedious old fools!

(*Enter Rosencrantz and Guildenstern.*)

Pol. You go to seek the Lord Hamlet; thee he is.

Pol. You go to seek the Lord Hamlet; there he is.

Ros. [To Polonius.] God save you, sir!

(*Exit Polonius.*)

Guil. My honoured lord!

Ros. My most dear lord!

Ham. My excellent good friends! How dost thou, Guildenstern? Ah, Rosencrantz! Good lads, how do ye both?

Ros. As the indifferent children of the earth.

Guil. Happy in that we are not over-happy; on fortune's cap we are not the very button.

Ham. Nor the soles of her shoe?

Ros. Neither, my lord.

Ham. Then you live about her waist, or in the middle of her favours?

Guil. Faith, her privates we.

Ham. In the secret parts of fortune? O, most true; she is a strumpet. What's the news?

Ros. None, my lord, but that the world's grown honest.

Ham. Then is doomsday near; but your news is not true. Let me question more in particular: what have you, my good friends, deserved at the hands of fortune, that she sends you to prison hither?

Guil. Prison, my lord!

Ham. Denmark's a prison.

Ros. Then is the world one.

Ham. A goodly one; in which there are many confines, wards,[12] and dungeons, Denmark being one o' the worst.

Ros. We think not so, my lord.

Ham. Why, then 'tis none to you; for there is nothing either good or bad but thinking makes it so: to me it is a prison.

Ros. Why, then, your ambition makes it one; 'tis too narrow for your mind.

Ham. O God, I could be bounded in a nutshell, and count myself a king of infinite space, were it not that I have bad dreams.

Guil. Which dreams, indeed, are ambition; for the very substance of the ambitious is merely the shadow of a dream.

Ham. A dream itself is but a shadow.

Ros. Truly, and I hold ambition of so airy and light a quality that it is but a shadow's shadow.

Ham. Then are our beggars bodies, and our monarchs and outstretch'd heroes the beggars' shadows. Shall we to the court? for, by my fay,[13] I cannot reason.

Ros. and Guild. We'll wait upon you.

Ham. No such matter: I will not sort you with the rest of my servants; for, to speak to you like an honest man, I am most dreadfully attended. But, in the beaten way of friendship, what make you at Elsinore?

Ros. To visit you, my lord; no other occasion.

Ham. Beggar that I am, I am even poor in thanks; but I thank you: and sure, dear friends, my

---

[11]meaningful

[12]cells

[13]faith

thanks are too dear a halfpenny. Were you not sent for? Is it your own inclining? Is it a free visitation? Come, deal justly with me: come, come; nay, speak.

GUIL. What should we say, my lord?

HAM. Why, anything—but to the purpose. You were sent for; and there is a kind of confession in your looks, which your modesties have not craft enough to colour:I know the good king and queen have sent for you.

ROS. To what end, my lord?

HAM. That you must teach me. But let me conjure you, by the rights of our fellowship, by the consonancy of our youth, by the obligation of our ever-preserved love, and by what more dear a better proposer could charge you withal, be even and direct with me, whether you were sent for or no.

ROS. [To Guildenstern.] What say you?

HAM. [Aside.] Nay, then, I have an eye of you.—If you love me, hold not off.

GUIL. My lord, we were sent for.

HAM. I will tell you why; so shall my anticipation prevent your discovery, and your secrecy to the king and queen moult no feather. I have of late,—but wherefore I know not,—lost all my mirth, forgone all custom of exercises; and indeed, it goes so heavily with my disposition that this goodly frame, the earth, seems to me a sterile promontory; this most excellent canopy, the air, look you, this brave o'erhanging firmament, this majestical roof fretted with golden fire,—why, it appears no other thing to me than a foul and pestilent congregation of vapours. What a piece of work is man! How noble in reason! how infinite in faculties! in form and moving, how express[14] and admirable! in action how like an angel! in apprehension, how like a god! the beauty of the world! the paragon of animals! And yet, to me, what is this quintessence of dust? Man delights not me;

no, nor woman neither, though by your smiling you seem to say so.

ROS. My lord, there was no such stuff in my thoughts.

HAM. Why did you laugh then, when I said 'Man delights not me'?

ROS. To think, my lord, if you delight not in man, what lenten[15] entertainment the players shall receive from you: we coted[16] them on the way; and hither are they coming to offer you service.

HAM. He that plays the king shall be welcome,—his majesty shall have tribute of me; the adventurous knight shall use his foil and target; the lover shall not sigh gratis; the humorous man shall end his part in peace; the clown shall make those laugh whose lungs are tickle o' the sere;[17] and the lady shall say her mind freely, or the blank verse shall halt for't. What players are they?

ROS. Even those you were wont to take such delight in,—the tragedians of the city.

HAM. How chances it they travel? their residence, both in reputation and profit, was better both ways.

ROS. I think their inhibition comes by the means of the late innovation.

HAM. Do they hold the same estimation they did when I was in the city? Are they so followed?

ROS. No, indeed, are they not.

HAM. How comes it? do they grow rusty?

ROS. Nay, their endeavour keeps in the wonted pace: but there is, sir, an aery[18] of children, little eyases, that cry out on the top of question, and are most tyrannically clapped for't: these are now the fashion; and so berattle the common stages,—so they call them,—that many wearing rapiers are afraid of goose-quills and dare scarce come thither.

---

[14]exact

[15]scanty

[16]overtook

[17]on hair trigger

[18]nest

HAM. What, are they children? who maintains 'em? How are they escoted?[19] Will they pursue the quality[20] no longer than they can sing? will they not say afterwards, if they should grow themselves to common players,—as it is most like, if their means are no better,—their writers do them wrong to make them exclaim against their own succession?

ROS. Faith, there has been much to do on both sides; and the nation holds it no sin to tarre[21] them to controversy: there was, for awhile, no money bid for argument unless the poet and the player went to cuffs in the question.

HAM. Is't possible?

GUIL. O, there has been much throwing about of brain.

HAM. Do the boys carry it away?

ROS. Ay, that they do, my lord; Hercules and his load too.

HAM. It is not very strange; for my uncle is king of Denmark, and those that would make mouths at him while my father lived, give twenty, forth, fifty, a hundred ducats a-piece for his picture in little. 'Sblood, there is something in this more than natural, if philosophy could find it out.

(Flourish of trumpets within.)

GUIL. There are the players.

HAM. Gentlemen, you are welcome to Elsinore. Your hands, come: The appurtenance of welcome is fashion and ceremony: let me comply with you in this garb; lest my extent[22] to the players, which I tell you must show fairly outward, should more appear like entertainment than your. You are welcome: but my uncle-father and aunt-mother are deceived.

GUIL. In what, my dear lord?

HAM. I am but mad north-north-west: when the wind is southerly I know a hawk from a handsaw.

(Enter Polonius.)

POL. Well be with you, gentlemen!

HAM. Hark you, Guildenstern;—and you too;—at each ear a hearer: that great baby you see there is not yet out of his swaddling clouts.

ROS. Happily he's the second time come to them; for they say an old man is twice a child.

HAM. I will prophesy he comes to tell me of the players; mark it.—You say right, sir: o' Monday morning; 'twas so indeed.

POL. My lord, I have news to tell you.

HAM. My lord, I have news to tell you. When Roscius[23] was an actor in Rome,—

POL. The actors are come hither, my lord.

HAM. Buzz, buzz!

POL. Upon my honour,—

HAM. Then came each actor on his ass,—

POL. The best actors in the world, either for tragedy, comedy, history, pastoral, pastoral-comical, historical-pastoral, tragical-historical, tragical-comical-historical-pastoral, scene individable, or poem unlimited: Seneca[24] cannot be too heavy nor Plautus[25] too light. For the law of writ and the liberty, these are the only men.

HAM. O Jephthah, judge of Israel, what a treasure hadst thou!

POL. What treasure had he, my lord?

HAM. Why—'One fair daughter, and no more, the which he loved passing well.'

POL. [Aside.] Still on my daughter.

HAM. Am I not i' the right, old Jephthah?

---

[19]financially supported

[20]acting profession

[21]incite

[22]behavior

[23]famous comic actor in ancient Rome

[24]roman tragic dramatist

[25]roman comic dramatist

Pol. If you call me Jephthah, my lord, I have a daughter that I love passing well.

Ham. Nay, that follows not.

Pol. What follows, then, my lord?

Ham. Why—'As by lot, God wot,' and then, you know, 'it came to pass, as most like it was—the first row of the pious chanson will show you more; for look where my abridgment comes.

(Enter four or five Players.)

You are welcome, master; welcome, all:—I am glad to see thee well.—welcome, good friends.—O, my old friend! Thy face is valanc'd[26] since I saw thee last; comest thou to beard me in Denmark?—What, my young lady and mistress! By'r lady, your ladyship is nearer to heaven than when I saw you last, by the altitude of a chopine.[27] Pray God, your voice, like a piece of uncurrent gold, be not cracked within the ring.—Masters, you are all welcome. We'll e'en to't like French falconers, fly at anything we see: we'll have a speech straight: come, give us a taste of your quality: come, a passionate speech.

I Play. What speech, my lord?

Ham. I heard thee speak me a speech once,—but it was never acted; or if it was, not above once; for the play, I remember, pleased not the million, 'twas caviare to the general; but it was,—as I received it, and others, whose judgments in such matters cried in the top of mine,—an excellent play, well digested in the scenes, set down with as much modesty as cunning. I remember, one said there were no sallets[28] in the lines to make the matter savoury, nor no matter in the phrase that might indite the author of affectation; but called it an honest method, as wholesome as sweet, and by very much more handsome than fine. One speech in it I chiefly loved:

'twas AEneas' tale to Dido, and thereabout of it especially where he speaks of Priam's slaughter: if it live in your memory, begin at this line;—let me see, let me see:—the rugged Pyrrhus, like th' Hyrcanian beast,[29]—it is not so:—it begins with Pyrrhus:—'The rugged Pyrrhus,—he whose sable arms, black as his purpose, did the night resemble when he lay couched in the ominous horse,—hath now this dread and black complexion smear'd with heraldry more dismal; head to foot now is be total gules; horridly trick'd[30] with blood of fathers, mothers, daughters, sons, bak'd and impasted with the parching streets, that lend a tyrannous and a damned light to their vile murders; Roasted in wrath and fire, and thus o'ersized with coagulate gore, with eyes like carbuncles, the hellish Pyrrhus old grandsire Priam seeks.' So, proceed you.

Pol. 'Fore God, my lord, well spoken, with good accent and good discretion.

I Play. Anon he finds him, striking too short at Greeks: his antique sword, rebellious to his arm, lies where it falls, repugnant to command: unequal match'd, Pyrrhus at Priam drives; in rage strikes wide; but with the whiff and wind of his fell sword the unnerved father falls. Then senseless Ilium, seeming to feel this blow, with flaming top stoops to his base; and with a hideous crash takes prisoner Pyrrhus' ear: for lo! his sword, which was declining on the milky head of reverend Priam, seem'd i' the air to stick: so, as a painted tyrant, Pyrrhus stood; and, like a neutral to his will and matter, did nothing. But as we often see, against some storm, a silence in the heavens, the rack[31] stand still, the bold winds speechless, and the orb below as hush as death, anon the dreadful thunder doth rend the region; so, after Pyrrhus' pause,

---

[26]fringed with a beard

[27]thick-soled shoe

[28]salads, spicy jest

[29]tiger (Hyrcania was in Asia and notorious for its wild animals)

[30]all red, horridly adorned

[31]clouds

a roused vengeance sets him new a-work; and
never did the Cyclops' hammers fall on
Mars's armour, forg'd for proof eterne, with
less remorse than Pyrrhus' bleeding sword
now falls on Priam.—Out, out, thou
strumpet, Fortune! All you gods, in general
synod,[32] Take away her power; break all the
spokes and fellies[33] from her wheel, and
bowl the round nave[34] down the hill of
heaven, as low as to the fiends!

POL. This is too long.

HAM. It shall to the barber's, with your
beard.—Pr'ythee say on.—He's for a jig or a
tale of bawdry, or he sleeps:—say on; come
to Hecuba.

I PLAY. But who, O who, had seen the mobled[35]
queen,—

HAM. 'The mobled queen'?

POL. That's good! 'Mobled queen' is good.

I PLAY. Run barefoot up and down, threatening
the flames with bisson rheum;[36] a clout[37]
upon that head where late the diadem stood,
and for a robe, about her lank and all
o'erteemed loins, a blanket, in the alarm of
fear caught up;—who this had seen, with
tongue in venom steep'd, 'gainst Fortune's
state would treason have pronounc'd: but if
the gods themselves did see her then, when
she saw Pyrrhus make malicious sport in
mincing with his sword her husband's limbs,
the instant burst of clamour that she
made,—unless things mortal move them not
at all,—would have made milch the burning
eyes of heaven, and passion in the gods.

POL. Look, whether he has not turn'd his colour,
and has tears in's eyes.—Pray you, no more!

HAM. 'Tis well, I'll have thee speak out the rest
of this soon.—Good my lord, will you see the

---

[32]council

[33]rims

[34]hub

[35]muffled

[36]blinding tears

[37]rag

players well bestowed?[38] Do you hear? Let
them be well used; for they are the abstracts
and brief chronicles of the time; after your
death you were better have a had epitaph than
their ill report while you live.

POL. My lord, I will use them according to their
desert.

HAM. Odd's bodikin, man, better: use every man
after his desert, and who should scape
whipping? Use them after your own honour
and dignity: the less they deserve, the more
merit is in your bounty. Take them in.

POL. Come, sirs.

HAM. Follow him, friends. we'll hear a play
to-morrow.

(*Exeunt Polonius with all the Players but the
First.*)

Dost thou hear me, old friend? Can you play 'The
Murder of Gonzago'?

I PLAY. Ay, my lord.

HAM. We'll ha't to-morrow night. You could, for
a need, study a speech of some dozen or
sixteen lines which I would set down and
insert in't? could you not?

I PLAY. Ay, my lord.

HAM. Very well.—Follow that lord; and look you
mock him not.

(*Exit First Player.*)

—My good friends [to Ros. and Guild.], I'll leave
you till night: you are welcome to Elsinore.

ROS. Good my lord!

(*Exeunt Rosencrantz and Guildenstern.*)

HAM. Ay, so, God b' wi' ye! Now I am alone. O,
what a rogue and peasant slave am I!

Is it not monstrous that this player here, but in a
fiction, in a dream of passion, could force his
soul so to his own conceit[39] that from her

---

[38]housed

[39]imagination

working all his visage wan'd; tears in his eyes, distraction in's aspect, a broken voice, and his whole function suiting with forms to his conceit? And all for nothing! For Hecuba? What's Hecuba to him, or he to Hecuba, that he should weep for her? What would he do, had he the motive and the cue for passion that I have? He would drown the stage with tears and cleave the general ear with horrid speech; make mad the guilty, and appal the free; confound the ignorant, and amaze, indeed, the very faculties of eyes and ears. Yet I, a dull and muddy-mettled rascal, peak, like John-a-dreams, unpregnant of my cause, and can say nothing; no, not for a king upon whose property and most dear life a damn'd defeat was made. Am I a coward? who calls me villain? breaks my pate across? Plucks off my beard and blows it in my face? Tweaks me by the nose? gives me the lie i' the throat as deep as to the lungs? who does me this, ha? 'Swounds, I should take it: for it cannot be but I am pigeon-liver'd, and lack gall to make oppression bitter; or ere this I should have fatted all the region kites[40] with this slave's offal: bloody, bawdy villain! Remorseless, treacherous, lecherous, kindless villain! O, vengeance! Why, what an ass am I! This is most brave, that I, the son of a dear father murder'd, prompted to my revenge by heaven and hell, must, like a whore, unpack my heart with words and fall a-cursing like a very drab,[41] a scullion! Fie upon't! foh!—About, my brain! I have heard that guilty creatures, sitting at a play, have by the very cunning of the scene been struck so to the soul that presently they have proclaim'd their malefactions; for murder, though it have no tongue, will speak with most miraculous organ, I'll have these players play something like the murder of my father before mine uncle: I'll observe his looks I'll tent[42] him to the quick: if he but blench, I know my course. The spirit that I have seen may be the devil: and the devil hath power to assume a pleasing shape; yea, and perhaps out of my weakness and my melancholy,—as he is very potent with such spirits,—abuses me to damn me: I'll have grounds more relative than this.—the play's the thing wherein I'll catch the conscience of the king.

(*Exit.*)

■ Act III

Scene I. A Room in the Castle

[*Enter King, Queen, Polonius, Ophelia, Rosencrantz, and Guildenstern.*]

KING. And can you, by no drift of circumstance, get from him why he puts on this confusion, grating so harshly all his days of quiet with turbulent and dangerous lunacy?

ROS. He does confess he feels himself distracted, but from what cause he will by no means speak.

GUIL. Nor do we find him forward to be sounded, but, with a crafty madness, keeps aloof when we would bring him on to some confession of his true state.

QUEEN. Did he receive you well?

ROS. Most like a gentleman.

GUIL. But with much forcing of his disposition.

ROS. Niggard of question; but, of our demands, most free in his reply.

QUEEN. Did you assay[1] him to any pastime?

ROS. Madam, it so fell out that certain players we o'er-raught[2] on the way: of these we told him, and there did seem in him a kind of joy to hear of it: they are about the court, and, as I think, they have already order this night to play before him.

---

[40]scavenger birds

[41]prostitute

[42]probe

---

[1]tempt

[2]overtook

POL. 'Tis most true; and he beseech'd me to entreat your majesties to hear and see the matter.

KING. With all my heart; and it doth much content me to hear him so inclin'd.—Good gentlemen, give him a further edge, and drive his purpose on to these delights.

ROS. We shall, my lord.

(*Exeunt Rosencrantz and Guildenstern.*)

KING. Sweet Gertrude, leave us too; for we have closely sent for Hamlet hither, that he, as 'twere by accident, may here affront Ophelia: her father and myself,—lawful espials,—will so bestow ourselves that, seeing, unseen, we may of their encounter frankly judge; and gather by him, as he is behav'd, if 't be the affliction of his love or no that thus he suffers for.

QUEEN. I shall obey you:—and for your part, Ophelia, I do wish that your good beauties be the happy cause of Hamlet's wildness: so shall I hope your virtues will bring him to his wonted way again, to both your honours.

OPH. Madam, I wish it may.

(*Exit Queen.*)

POL. Ophelia, walk you here.—Gracious, so please you, We will bestow ourselves.—[To Ophelia.] Read on this book; that show of such an exercise may colour your loneliness.—We are oft to blame in his,—'Tis too much prov'd,—that with devotion's visage and pious action we do sugar o'er the Devil himself.

KING. [Aside.] O, 'tis too true! How smart a lash that speech doth give my conscience! The harlot's cheek, beautied with plastering art, is not more ugly to the thing that helps it than is my deed to my most painted word: O heavy burden!

POL. I hear him coming: let's withdraw, my lord.

(*Exeunt King and Polonius.*)

(*Enter Hamlet.*)

HAM. To be, or not to be,—that is the question:—Whether 'tis nobler in the mind to suffer the slings and arrows of outrageous fortune or to take arms against a sea of troubles, and by opposing end them?—To die,—to sleep,—No more; and by a sleep to say we end the heartache, and the thousand natural shocks that flesh is heir to,—'tis a consummation devoutly to be wish'd. To die,—to sleep;—to sleep! perchance to dream:—ay, there's the rub; for in that sleep of death what dreams may come, when he have shuffled off this mortal coil, must give us pause: there's the respect that makes calamity of so long life; for who would bear the whips and scorns of time, the oppressor's wrong, the proud man's contumely, the pangs of despis'd love, the law's delay, the insolence of office, and the spurns that patient merit of the unworthy takes, when he himself might his quietus[3] make with a bare bodkin?[4] who would these fardels[5] bear, to grunt and sweat under a weary life, but that the dread of something after death,—the undiscover'd country, from whose bourn[6] no traveller returns,—puzzles the will, and makes us rather bear those ills we have than fly to others that we know not of? Thus conscience does make cowards of us all; and thus the native hue of resolution is sicklied o'er with the pale cast[7] of thought; and enterprises of great pitch[8] and moment, with this regard, their currents turn awry, and lose the name of action.—Soft you now! The fair Ophelia!—Nymph, in thy orisons[9] be all my sins remember'd.

---

[3]full discharge (a legal term)

[4]dagger

[5]burdens

[6]regions

[7]color

[8]height

[9]prayers

OPH. Good my lord, how does your honour for this many a day?

HAM. I humbly thank you; well, well, well.

OPH. My lord, I have remembrances of yours that I have longed long to re-deliver. I pray you, now receive them.

HAM. No, not I; I never gave you aught.

OPH. My honour'd lord, you know right well you did; and with them words of so sweet breath compos'd as made the things more rich; their perfume lost, take these again; for to the noble mind rich gifts wax poor when givers prove unkind. There, my lord.

HAM. Ha, ha! are you honest?

OPH. My lord?

HAM. Are you fair?

OPH. What means your lordship?

HAM. That if you be honest and fair, your honesty should admit no discourse to your beauty.

OPH. Could beauty, my lord, have better commerce than with honesty?

HAM. Ay, truly; for the power of beauty will sooner transform honesty from what it is to a bawd[10] than the force of honesty can translate beauty into his likeness: this was sometime a paradox, but now the time gives it proof. I did love you once.

OPH. Indeed, my lord, you made me believe so.

HAM. You should not have believ'd me; for virtue cannot so inoculate our old stock but we shall relish of it: I loved you not.

OPH. I was the more deceived.

HAM. Get thee to a nunnery: why wouldst thou be a breeder of sinners? I am myself indifferent honest; but yet I could accuse me of such things that it were better my mother had not borne me: I am very proud, revengeful, ambitious; with more offences at my beck than I have thoughts to put them in, imagination to give them shape, or time to act them in. What should such fellows as I do crawling between earth and heaven? We are arrant knaves, all; believe none of us. Go thy ways to a nunnery. Where's your father?

OPH. At home, my lord.

HAM. Let the doors be shut upon him, that he may play the fool nowhere but in's own house. Farewell.

OPH. O, help him, you sweet heavens!

HAM. If thou dost marry, I'll give thee this plague for thy dowry,—be thou as chaste as ice, as pure as snow, thou shalt not escape calumny. Get thee to a nunnery, go: farewell. Or, if thou wilt needs marry, marry a fool; for wise men know well enough what monsters you make of them. To a nunnery, go; and quickly too. Farewell.

OPH. O heavenly powers, restore him!

HAM. I have heard of your paintings too, well enough; God hath given you one face, and you make yourselves another: you jig, you amble, and you lisp, and nickname God's creatures, and make your wantonness your ignorance. Go to, I'll no more on't; it hath made me mad. I say, we will have no moe[11] marriage: those that are married already, all but one, shall live; the rest shall keep as they are. To a nunnery, go.

(*Exit.*)

OPH. O, what a noble mind is here o'erthrown! The courtier's, scholar's, soldier's, eye, tongue, sword, the expectancy and rose of the fair state, the glass of fashion and the mould of form, the observ'd of all observers,—quite, quite down! And I, of ladies most deject and wretched that suck'd the honey of his music vows, now see that noble and most sovereign reason, like sweet bells jangled, out of tune and harsh; that unmatch'd form and feature of blown youth blasted with ecstasy:[12] O, woe is me, to have seen what I have seen, see what I see!

(*Re-enter King and Polonius.*)

---

[10]procurer

[11]more

[12]madness

KING. Love! his affections do not that way tend;
nor what he spake, though it lack'd form a
little, was not like madness. There's
something in his soul o'er which his
melancholy sits on brood; and I do doubt the
hatch and the disclose will be some danger:
which for to prevent, I have in quick
determination thus set it down:—he shall
with speed to England for the demand of our
neglected tribute: haply the seas, and
countries different, with variable objects,
shall expel this something-settle matter in his
heart; whereon his brains still beating puts
him thus from fashion of himself. What think
you on't?

POL. It shall do well: but yet do I believe the
origin and commencement of his grief
sprung from neglected love.—How now,
Ophelia! You need not tell us what Lord
Hamlet said; we heard it all.—My lord, do as
you please; but if you hold it fit, after the
play, let his queen mother all alone entreat
him to show his grief: let her be round with
him; and I'll be plac'd, so please you, in the
ear of all their conference. If she find him
not, to England send him; or confine him
where your wisdom best shall think.

KING. I shall be so: madness in great ones must
not unwatch'd go.

(*Exeunt.*)

Scene II. A Hall in the Castle
[*Enter Hamlet and Players.*]

HAM. Speak the speech, I pray you, as I
pronounced it to you, trippingly on the
tongue: but if you mouth it, as many of your
players do, I had as lief the town crier spoke
my lines. Nor do not saw the air too much
with your hand, thus, but use all gently: for in
the very torrent, tempest, and, as I may say,
whirlwind of passion, you must acquire and
beget a temperance that may give it
smoothness. O, it offends me to the soul, to
hear a robustious periwig-pated fellow tear a
passion to tatters, to very rags, to split the
cars of the groundlings,[1] who, for the most
part, are capable of nothing but inexplicable
dumb shows and noise: I would have such a
fellow whipped for o'erdoing Termagant; it
out-herods Herod:[2] pray you avoid it.

I Player. I warrant your honour.

HAM. Be not too tame neither; but let your own
discretion be your tutor: suit the action to the
word, the word to the action, with this special
observance, that you o'erstep not the
modesty of nature: for anything so overdone
is from the purpose of playing, whose end,
both at the first and now, was and is, to hold,
as 'twere, the mirror up to nature; to show
virtue her own image, scorn her own image,
and the very age and body of the time his
form and pressure. Now, this overdone, or
come tardy off, though it make the unskilful
laugh, cannot but make the judicious grieve;
the censure of the which one must in your
allowance, o'erweigh a whole theatre of
others. O, there be players that I have seen
plan,—and heard others praise, and that
highly,—not to speak it profanely, that,
neither having the accent of Christians, nor
the gait of Christian, pagan, nor man, have so
strutted and bellowed that I have thought
some of nature's journeymen had made men,
and not made them well, they imitated
humanity so abominably.

I PLAYER. I hope we have reform'd that
indifferently[3] with us, sir.

HAM. O, reform it altogether. And let those that
play your clowns speak no more than is set
down for them: for there be of them that will
themselves laugh, to set on some meantime
some necessary question of the play be then
to be considered: that's villanous and shows a
most pitiful ambition in the fool that uses it.
Go make you ready.

(*Exeunt Players.*)

---

[1]those who stood in the pit of the theatre

[2]tolerably

[3]tolerably

(*Enter Polonius, Rosencrantz, and Guildenstern.*)

How now, my lord! will the king hear this piece
  of work?
Pol. And the queen too, and the presently.
Ham. Bid the players make haste.

(*Exit Polonius.*)

Will you two help to hasten them?
Ros. and Guil. We will, my lord.

(*Exeunt Ros. and Guil.*)

Ham. What, ho, Horatio!

(*Enter Horatio.*)

Hor. Here, sweet lord, at your service.
Ham. Horatio, thou are e'en as just a man as e'er
  my conversation cop'd withal.
Hor. O, my dear lord,—
Ham. Nay, do not think I flatter; for what
  advancement may I hope from thee, that no
  revenue hast, but thy good spirits, to feed and
  clothe thee? Why should the poor be
  flatter'd? No, let the candied[4] tongue lick
  absurd pomp; and crook the pregnant hinges
  of the knee where thrift may follow fawning.
  Dost thou hear? Since my dear soul was
  mistress of her choice, and could of men
  distinguish, her election hat seal'd thee for
  herself: for thou hast been as one, in
  suffering all, that suffers nothing; a man that
  Fortune's buffets and rewards hast ta'en with
  equal thanks: and bles'd are those whose
  blood and judgment are so well commingled
  that they are not a pipe for Fortune's finger to
  sound what stop she please. Give me that
  man that is not passion's slave, and I will
  wear him in my heart's core, ay, in my heart
  of heart, as I do thee.—Something too much
  of this.—There is a play to-night before the
  king; one scene of it comes near the
  circumstance, which I have told thee, of my
  father's death: I pr'ythee, when thou see'st
  that act a-foot, even with the very comment
  of thy soul observe mine uncle: if his
  occulted[5] guilt do not itself unkennel in one
  speech, it is a damned ghost that we have
  seen; and my imaginations are as foul as
  Vulcan's stithy.[6] Give him heedful note; for I
  mine eyes will rivet to his face; and, after, we
  will both our judgments join in censure of his
  seeming.
Hor. Well, my lord: if he steal aught the whilst
  this play is playing, and scape detecting, I
  will pay the theft.
Ham. They are coming to the play. I must be idle:
  Get you a place.

(*Danish march. A flourish. Enter King, Queen,
Polonius, Ophelia, Rosencrantz, Guildenstern,
and others.*)

King. How fares our cousin Hamlet?
Ham. Excellent, i' faith; of the chameleon's
  dish:[7] I eat the air, promise-crammed: you
  cannot feed capons so.
King. I have nothing with this answer, Hamlet;
  these words are not mine.
Ham. No, nor mine now. My lord, you play'd
  once i' the university, you say? [To Polonius.]

Pol. That did I, my lord, and was accounted a
  good actor.
Ham. What did you enact?
Pol. I did enact Julius Caesar; I was kill'd i' the
  Capitol; Brutus killed me.
Ham. It was a brute part of him to kill so capital
  a calf there.—Be the players ready?
Ros. Ay, my lord; they stay upon your patience.
Queen. Come hither, my dear Hamlet, sit by me.

---

[4]flattering

[5]hidden

[6]smithy

[7]air, on which chameleons were believed to live

HAM. No, good mother, here's metal more attractive.

POL. O, ho! do you mark that? [To the King.]

HAM. Lady, shall I lie in your lap?

(*Lying down at Ophelia's feet.*)

OPH. No, my lord.

HAM. I mean, my head upon your lap?

OPH. Ay, my lord.

HAM. Do you think I meant country matters?

OPH. I think nothing, my lord.

HAM. That's a fair thought to lie between maids' legs.

OPH. What is, my lord?

HAM. Nothing.

OPH. You are merry, my lord.

HAM. Who, I?

OPH. Ay, my lord.

HAM. O, your only jig-maker! What should a man do but be merry: for look you how cheerfully my mother looks, and my father died within 's two hours.

OPH. Nay, 'tis twice two months, my lord.

HAM. So long? Nay then, let the devil wear black, for I'll have a suit of sables. O heavens! die two months ago, and not forgotten yet? Then there's hope a great man's memory may outlive his life half a year: but, by'r lady, he must build churches then; or else shall he suffer not thinking on, with the hobby-horse, whose epitaph is 'For, O, for, O, the hobby-horse is forgot!'

(*Trumpets sound. The dumb show enters.*)

(*Enter a King and a Queen very lovingly; the Queen embracing him and he her. She kneels, and makes show of protestation unto him. He takes her up, and declines his head upon her neck: lays him down upon a bank of flowers: she, seeing him asleep, leaves him. Anon comes in a fellow, takes off his crown, kisses it, pours poison in the king's ears, and exit. The Queen returns, finds the King dead, and makes passionate action. The Poisoner with some three or four Mutes, comes in again, seeming to lament with*

her. The dead body is carried away. The Poisoner wooes the Queen with gifts; she seems loth and unwilling awhile, but in the end accepts his love.)

(*Exeunt.*)

OPH. What means this, my lord?

HAM. Marry, this is miching mallecho;[8] it means mischief.

OPH. Belike this show imports the argument of the play.

(*Enter Prologue.*)

HAM. We shall know by this fellow: the players cannot keep counsel; they'll tell all.

OPH. Will he tell us what this show meant?

HAM. Ay, or any show that you'll show him: be not you ashamed to show, he'll not shame to tell you what it means.

OPH. You are naught, you are naught: I'll mark the play.

PRO. For us, and for our tragedy, here stooping to your clemency, we beg your hearing patiently.

HAM. Is this a prologue, or the posy of a ring?

OPH. 'Tis brief, my lord.

HAM. As woman's love.

(*Enter a King and Queen.*)

P. KING. Full thirty times hath Phoebus' cart[9] gone round Neptune's salt wash[10] and Tellus'[11] orbed ground, and thirty dozen moons with borrow'd sheen about the world have times twelve thirties been, since love our hearts, and Hymen did our hands, unite commutual in most sacred bands.

---

[8]sneaking mischief

[9]the sun's chariot

[10]the sea

[11]Roman goddess of the earth

P. QUEEN. So many journeys may the sun and moon make us again count o'er ere love be done! But, woe is me, you are so sick of late, so far from cheer and from your former state. That I distrust you. Yet, though I distrust, discomfort you, my lord, it nothing must: for women's fear and love holds quantity; in neither aught, or in extremity. Now, what my love is, proof hath made you know; and as my love is siz'd, my fear is so: where love is great, the littlest doubts are fear; where little fears grow great, great love grows there.

P. KING. Faith, I must leave thee, love, and shortly too; my operant[12] powers their functions leave to do: and thou shalt live in this fair world behind, honour'd, belov'd, and haply one as kind for husband shalt thou,—

P. QUEEN. O, confound the rest! Such love must needs be treason in my breast: in second husband let me be accurst! None wed the second but who kill'd the first.

HAM. [Aside.] Wormwood,[13] wormwood!

P. QUEEN. The instances that second marriage move are base respects of thrift, but none of love. A second time I kill my husband dead when second husband kisses me in bed.

P. KING. I do believe you think what now you speak; but what we do determine oft we break. Purpose is but the slave to memory; of violent birth, but poor validity: which now, like fruit unripe, sticks on the tree; but fall unshaken when they mellow be. Most necessary 'tis that we forget to pay ourselves what to ourselves is debt: what to ourselves in passion we propose, the passion ending, doth the purpose lose. The violence of either grief or joy their own enactures[14] with themselves destroy: where joy most revels, grief doth most lament; grief joys, joy grieves, on slender accident. This world is not for aye; nor 'tis not strange that even our loves should with our fortunes change; for 'tis a question left us yet to prove, whether love lead fortune, or else fortune love. The great man down, you mark his favourite flies, the poor advanc'd makes friends of enemies; and hitherto doth love on fortune tend: for who not needs shall never lack a friend; and who in want a hollow friend doth try directly seasons him his enemy. But, orderly to end where I begun,—our wills and fates do so contrary run that our devices still are overthrown; our thoughts are ours, their ends none of our own: so think thou wilt no second husband wed; but die thy thoughts when thy first lord is dead.

P. QUEEN. Nor earth to me give food, nor heaven light! Sport and repose lock from me day and night! To desperation turn my trust and hope! An anchor's[15] cheer in prison be my scope! Each opposite that blanks the face of joy meet what I would have well, and it destroy! Both here and hence pursue me lasting strife, if, once a widow, ever I be wife!

HAM. If she should break it now! [To Ophelia.]

P. KING. 'Tis deeply sworn. Sweet, leave me here awhile; my spirits grow dull, and fain I would beguile the tedious day with sleep.

(*Sleeps.*)

P. QUEEN. Sleep rock thy brain, and never come mischance between us twain!

(*Exit.*)

HAM. Madam, how like you this play?

QUEEN. The lady protests too much, methinks.

HAM. O, but she'll keep her word.

KING. Have you heard the argument? Is there no offence in't?

---

[12]active

[13]a bitter herb

[14]acts

---

[15]anchorite's, hermit's

HAM. No, no! They do but jest, poison in jest; no offence i' the world.

KING. What do you call the play?

HAM. The Mouse-trap. Marry, how? Tropically. This play is the image of a murder done in Vienna: Gonzago is the duke's name; his wife, Baptista: you shall see anon; 'tis a knavish piece of work: but what o' that? your majesty, and we that have free souls, it touches us not: let the gall'd jade wince[16]; our withers are unwrung.

(*Enter Lucianus.*)

This is one Lucianus, nephew to the King.

OPH. You are a good chorus, my lord.

HAM. I could interpret between you and your love, if I could see the puppets dallying.

OPH. You are keen, my lord, you are keen.

HAM. It would cost you a groaning to take off my edge.

OPH. Still better, and worse.

HAM. So you must take your husbands.—Begin, murderer; pox, leave thy damnable faces, and begin. Come:—'The croaking raven doth bellow for revenge.'

LUC. Thoughts black, hands apt, drugs fit, and time agreeing; confederate season, else no creature seeing; thou mixture rank, of midnight weeds collected, with Hecate's[17] ban thrice blasted, thrice infected, thy natural magic and dire property on wholesome life usurp immediately.

(*Pours the poison into the sleeper's ears.*)

HAM. He poisons him i' the garden for's estate. His name's Gonzago: The story is extant, and written in very choice Italian; you shall see anon how the murderer gets the love of Gonzago's wife.

OPH. The King rises.

HAM. What, frighted with false fire!

QUEEN. How fares my lord?

POL. Give o'er the play.

KING. Give me some light:—away!

ALL. Lights, lights, lights!

(*Exeunt all but Hamlet and Horatio.*)

HAM. Why, let the strucken deer go weep, the hart ungalled play; for some must watch, while some must sleep so runs the world away.—Would not this, sir, and a forest of feathers—if the rest of my fortunes turn Turk with me,—with two Provincial roses on my razed[18] shoes, get me a fellowship in a cry[19] of players, sir?

HOR. Half a share.

HAM. A whole on, I. for thou dost know, O Damon dear, this realm dismantled was of Jove himself; and now reigns here a very, very—pajock.[20]

HOR. You might have rhymed.

HAM. O good Horatio, Ill take the ghost's word for a thousand pound! Didst perceive?

HOR. Very well, my lord.

HAM. Upon the talk of the poisoning?—

HOR. I did very well note him.

HAM. Ah, ha!—Come, some music! Come, the recorders!—For if the king like not the comedy, why then, belike he likes it not, perdy.[21] Come, some music!

(*Enter Rosencrantz and Guildenstern.*)

GUIL. Good my lord, vouchsafe me a word with you.

HAM. Sir, a whole history.

GUIL. The king, sir—

---

[16]chapped horse wince

[17]the goddes of witch craft

[18]ornamented with slashes

[19]company

[20]peacock

[21]by God (French: par dieu)

Ham. Ay, sir, what of him?

Guil. Is, in his retirement, marvellous distempered.

Ham. With drink, sir?

Guil. No, my lord; rather with choler.

Ham. Your wisdom should show itself more richer to signify this to the doctor; for me to put him to his purgation would perhaps plunge him into far more choler.

Guil. Good my lord, put your discourse into some frame, and start not so wildly from my affair.

Ham. I am tame, sir:—pronounce.

Guil. The queen, your mother, in most great affliction of spirit, hath sent me to you.

Ham. You are welcome.

Guil. Nay, good my lord, this courtesy is not of the right breed. If it shall please you to make me a wholesome answer, I will do your mother's commandment: if not, your pardon and my return shall be the end of my business.

Ham. Sir, I cannot.

Guil. What, my lord?

Ham. Make you a wholesome answer; my wit's diseased: but, sir, such answer as I can make, you shall command; or rather, as you say, my mother: therefore no more, but to the matter: my mother, you say,—

Ros. Then thus she says: your behavior hath struck her into amazement and admiration.[22]

Ham. O wonderful son, that can so stonish a mother!—But is there no sequel at the heels of this mother's admiration?

Ros. She desires to speak with you in her closet ere you go to bed.

Ham. We shall obey, were she ten times our mother. Have you any further trade with us?

Ros. My lord, you once did love me.

Ham. And so I do still, by these pickers and stealers.[23]

Ros. Good my lord, what is your cause of distemper? you do, surely, bar the door upon your own liberty if you deny your griefs to your friend.

Ham. Sir, I lack advancement.

Ros. How can that be, when you have the voice of the king himself for your succession in Denmark?

Ham. Ay, sir, but 'While the grass grows'—the proverb is something musty.

(*Re-enter the Players, with recorders.*)

O, the recorders:—let me see one.—To withdraw with you:—why do you go about to recover the wind of me, as if you would drive me into a toil?[24]

Guil. O my lord, if my duty be too bold, my love is too unmannerly.

Ham. I do not well understand that. Will you play upon this pipe?

Guil. My lord, I cannot.

Ham. I pray you.

Guil. Believe me, I cannot.

Ham. I do beseech you.

Guil. I know, no touch of it, my lord.

Ham. 'Tis as easy as lying: govern these ventages[25] with your finger and thumb, give it breath with your mouth, and it will discourse most eloquent music. Look you, these are the stops.

Guil. But these cannot I command to any utterance of harmony; I have not the skill.

Ham. Why, look you now, how unworthy a thing you make of me! You would play upon me; you would seem to know my stops; you would pluck out the heart of my mystery; you would sound me from my lowest note to the top of my compass; and there is much music, excellent voice, in this little organ, yet cannot you make it speak. 'Sblood, do you think I am easier to be played on than a pipe? Call me what instrument you will, though you can fret me, you cannot play upon me.

---

[22]wonder

[23]hands

---

[24]trap

[25]vents, stops on a recorder

(*Enter Polonius.*)

God bless you, sir!

POL. My lord, the queen would speak with you,
    and presently.

HAM. Do you see yonder cloud that's almost in
    shape of a camel?

POL. By the mass, and 'tis like a camel indeed.

HAM. Methinks it is like a weasel.

POL. It is backed like a weasel.

HAM. Or like a whale.

POL. Very like a whale.

HAM. Then will I come to my mother by and
    by.—They fool me to the top of my bent.—I
    will come by and by.

POL. I will say so.

(*Exit.*)

HAM. By-and-by is easily said.

(*Exit Polonius.*)

—Leave me, friends.

(*Exeunt Ros., Guild., Hor., and Players.*)

'Tis now the very witching time of night, when
    churchyards yawn, and hell itself breathes
    out contagion to this world: now could I
    drink hot blood, and do such bitter business
    as the day would quake to look on. Soft! now
    to my mother.—O heart, lost not thy nature;
    let not ever the soul of Nero[26] enter this firm
    bosom: let me be cruel, not unnatural; I will
    speak daggers to her, but use none; my
    tongue and soul in this be hypocrites,—how
    in my words somever she be shent,[27] to give
    them seals never, my soul, consent!

(*Exit.*)

Scene III. A Room in the Castle

[*Enter King, Rosencrantz, and Guildenstern.*]

KING. I like him not; nor stands it safe with us to
    let his madness range. Therefore prepare you;
    I your commission will forthwith dispatch,
    and he to England shall along with you: the
    terms of our estate may not endure hazard so
    near us as doth hourly grow out of his
    lunacies.

GUIL. We will ourselves provide: most holy and
    religious fear it is to keep those many many
    bodies safe that life and feed upon your
    majesty.

ROS. The single and peculiar life is bound, with
    all the strength and armour of the mind, to
    keep itself form 'noyance; but much more
    that spirit upon whose weal depend and rest
    the lives of many. The cease of majesty[1] dies
    not alone; but like a gulf[2] doth draw what's
    near it with it: it is a massy wheel, fix'd on
    the summit of the highest mount, to whose
    huge spokes ten thousand lesser things are
    mortis'd and adjoin'd; which, when it falls,
    each small annexment, petty consequence,
    attends the boisterous ruin. Never alone did
    the king sign, but with a general groan.

KING. Arm you, I pray you, to this speedy
    voyage; for we will fetters put upon this fear,
    which now goes too free-footed.

ROS AND GUIL. We will haste us.

(*Exeunt Ros. and Guil.*)

(*Enter Polonius.*)

POL. My lord, he's going to his mother's closet:
    behind the arras I'll convey myself to hear
    the process; I'll warrant she'll tax him home:
    and, as you said, and wisely was it said, 'Tis
    meet that some more audience than a mother,
    since nature makes them partial, should

---

[26]Roman emperor who murdered his mother

[27]rebuked

---

[1]end (death) of a king

[2]whirlpool

o'erhear the speech, of vantage. Fare you
well, my liege: I'll call upon you ere you go
to bed, and tell you what I know.

King. Thanks, dear my lord.

(*Exit Polonius.*)

O, my offence is rank, it smells to heaven; it hath
the primal eldest curse[3] upon't,—a brother's
murder!—Pray can I not, though inclination
be as sharp as will: my stronger guilt defeats
my strong intent; and, like a man to double
business bound, I stand in pause where I shall
first begin, and both neglect. What if this
cursed hand were thicker than itself with
brother's blood,—is there not rain enough in
the sweet heavens to wash it white as snow?
Whereto serves mercy but to confront the
visage of offence? And what's in prayer but
this twofold force,—to be forestalled ere we
come to fall, or pardon'd being down? Then
I'll look up; my fault is past. But, O, what
form of prayer can serve my turn? Forgive
me my foul murder!—That cannot be; since I
am still possess'd of those effects for which I
did the murder,—my crown, mine own
ambition, and my queen. May one be
pardon'd and retain the offence? In the
corrupted currents of this world offence's
gilded hand may shove by justice; and oft 'tis
seen the wicked prize itself buys out the law;
but 'tis not so above; there is no
shuffling;—there the action lies in his true
nature; and we ourselves compell'd, even to
the teeth and forehead of our faults, to give in
evidence. What then? what rests? Try what
repentance can: what can it not? Yet what can
it when one cannot repent? O wretched state!
O bosom black as death! O limed[4] soul, that,
struggling to be free, art more engag'd! Help,
angels! Make assay: bow, stubborn knees;
and, heart, with strings of steel, be soft as
sinews of the new-born babe! All may be
well.

(*Retires and kneels.*)

(*Enter Hamlet.*)

Ham. How might I do it pat, now he is praying;
and now I'll do't;—and so he goes to heaven;
and so am I reveng'd.—that would be
scann'd: a villain kills my father; and for that,
I, his sole son, do this same villain send to
heaven. O, this is hire and salary, not
revenge. He took my father grossly, full of
bread; with all his crimes broad blown, as
flush[5] as May; and how his audit stands, who
knows save heaven? But in our circumstance
and course of though, 'Tis heavy with him:
and am I, then, reveng'd, to take him in the
purging of his soul, when he is fit and
season'd for his passage? No. Up, sword, and
know thou a more horrid hent:[6] when he is
drunk asleep; or in his rage; or in the
incestuous pleasure of his bed; at gaming,
swearing; or about some act that has no relish
of salvation in't;—Then trip him, that his
heels may kick at heaven; and that his soul
may be as damn'd and black as hell, whereto
it goes. My mother stays: this physic but
prolongs thy sickly days.

(*Exit.*)

(*The King rises and advances.*)

King. My words fly up, my thoughts remain
below: Words without thoughts never to
heaven go.

(*Exit.*)

---

[3]curse of Cain, who killed Abel

[4]trapped birdlime is a sticky substance spread on boughs to
snare birds

[5]vigorous

[6]grasp (here, time for seizing)

Scene IV. Another Room in the Castle
[*Enter Queen and Polonius.*]

POL. He will come straight. Look you lay home to him: tell him his pranks have been too broad to bear with, and that your grace hath screen'd and stood between much heat and him. I'll silence me e'en here. Pray you, be round with him.

HAM. [Within.] Mother, mother, mother!

QUEEN. I'll warrant you: Fear me not:—withdraw; I hear him coming.

(*Polonius goes behind the arras.*)

(*Enter Hamlet.*)

HAM. Now, mother, what's the matter?

QUEEN. Hamlet, thou hast thy father much offended.

HAM. Mother, you have my father much offended.

QUEEN. Come, come, you answer with an idle tongue.

HAM. Go, go, you question with a wicked tongue.

QUEEN. Why, how now, Hamlet!

HAM. What's the matter now?

QUEEN. Have you forgot me?

HAM. No, by the rood,[1] not so: you are the Queen, your husband's brother's wife, and,—would it were not so!—you are my mother.

QUEEN. Nay, then, I'll set those to you that can speak.

HAM. Come, come and sit you down; you shall not budge; you go not till I set you up a glass[2]
Where you may see the inmost part of you.

QUEEN. What wilt thou do? thou wilt not murder me?—Help, help, ho!

POL. [Behind.] What, ho! help, help, help!

HAM. How now? a rat? [Draws.] Dead for a ducat, dead!

(*Makes a pass through the arras.*)

POL. [Behind.] O, I am slain!

(*Falls and dies.*)

QUEEN. O me, what hast thou done?

HAM. Nay, I know not: is it the king?

(*Draws forth Polonius.*)

QUEEN. O, what a rash and blood deed is this!

HAM. A blood deed!—almost as bad, good mother, as kill a king and marry with his brother.

QUEEN. As kill a king!

HAM. Ay, lady, 'twas my word.—Thou wretched, rash, intruding fool, farewell!

(*To Polonius.*)

I took thee for thy better: take thy fortune; Thou find'st to be too busy is some danger.—Leave wringing of your hands: peace! sit you down, and let me wring your heart: for so I shall, if it be made of penetrable stuff; if damned custom have not braz'd it so that it is proof and bulwark against sense.

QUEEN. What have I done, that thou dar'st wag thy tongue in noise so rude against me?

HAM. Such an act that blurs the grace and blush of modesty; calls virtue hypocrite; takes off the rose from the fair forehead of an innocent love, and sets a blister there; makes marriage-vows as false as dicers' oaths: O, such a deed as from the body of contraction[3] plucks the very soul, and sweet religion makes a rhapsody of words: heaven's face doth glow; yea, this solidity and compound mass, with tristful visage, as against the doom, is though-sick at the act.

---

[1] cross

[2] mirror

[3] marriage contract

QUEEN. Ah me, what act, that roars so loud, and thunders in the index?[4]

HAM. Look here upon this picture, and on this,—the counterfeit presentment of two brothers. See what a grace was seated on this brow; Hyperion's curls; the front of Jove himself; an eye like Mars, to threaten and command; a station like the herald Mercury new lighted on a heaven-kissing hill: a combination and a form, indeed, where every god did seem to set his seal, to give the world assurance of a man; this was your husband.—Look you now what follows: here is your husband, like a milldew'd ear blasting his wholesome brother. Have you eyes? Could you on this fair mountain leave to feed, and batten on this moor? Ha! have you eyes? You cannot call it love; for at your age the hey-day in the blood is tame, it's humble, and waits upon the judgment: and what judgment would step from this to this? Sense, sure, you have, else could you not have motion: but sure that sense is apoplex'd; for madness would not err; nor sense to ecstacy was ne'er so thrall'd but it reserv'd some quantity of choice to serve in such a difference. What devil was't that thus hath cozen'd you at hoodman-blind?[5] Eyes without feeling, feeling without sight, ears without hands or eyes, smelling sans[6] all, or but a sickly part of one true sense could not so mope. O shame! where is thy blush? Rebellious hell, if thou canst mutine in a matron's bones to flaming youth let virtue be as wax, and melt in her own fire: proclaim no shame when the compulsive ardour gives the charge, since frost itself as actively doth burn, and reason panders will.

QUEEN. O Hamlet, speak no more: Thou turn'st mine eyes into my very soul; and there I see

such black and grained spots as will not leave their tinct.[7]

HAM. Nay, but to live in the rank sweat of an enseamed bed, stew'd in corruption, honeying and making love over the nasty sty,—

QUEEN. O, speak to me no more; these words like daggers enter in mine ears; no more, sweet Hamlet.

HAM. A murderer and a villain; a slave that is not twentieth part the tithe[8] of your precedent lord; a vice of kings; a cutpurse of the empire and the rule, that from a shelf the precious diadem stole and put it in his pocket!

QUEEN. No more.

HAM. A king of shreds and patches!—

(*Enter Ghost.*)

Save me and hover o'er me with your wings, you heavenly guards!—What would your gracious figure?

QUEEN. Alas, he's mad!

HAM. Do you not come your tardy son to chide, that, laps'd in time and passion, lets go by the important acting of your dread command? O, say!

GHOST. Do not forget. This visitation is but to whet thy almost blunted purpose. But, look, amazement on thy mother sits: O, step between her and her fighting soul,—conceit in weakest bodies strongest works,—speak to her, Hamlet

HAM. How is it with you, lady?

QUEEN. Alas, how is't with you, that you do bend your eye on vacancy, and with the incorporal air do hold discourse? Forth at your eyes your spirits wildly peep; and, as the sleeping soldiers in the alarm, your bedded hair,[9] like life in excrements, start up and stand on end. O gentle son, upon the heat and flame of thy distemper sprinkle cool patience! Where on do you look?

---

[4]prologue

[5]blind man's bluff

[6]without

[7]color

[8]tenth part

[9]flattened hairs

HAM. On him, on him! Look you how pale he glares! His form and cause conjoin'd, preaching to stones, would make them capable.—Do not look upon me; lest with this piteous action you convert my stern effects: then what I have to do will want true colour; tears perchance for blood.

QUEEN. To whom do you speak this?

HAM. Do you see nothing there?

QUEEN. Nothing at all; yet all that is I see.

HAM. Nor did you nothing hear?

QUEEN. No, nothing but ourselves.

HAM. Why, look you there! look how it steals away! My father, in his habit as he liv'd! Look, where he goes, even now out at the portal!

(*Exit Ghost.*)

QUEEN. This is the very coinage of your brain: this bodiless creation ecstasy is very cunning in.

HAM. Ecstasy! My pulse, as yours, doth temperately keep time, and makes as healthful music: it is not madness that I have utter'd: bring me to the test, and I the matter will re-word; which madness would gambol from. Mother, for love of grace, lay not that flattering unction to your soul that not your trespass, but my madness speaks: it will but skin and film the ulcerous place, whilst rank corruption, mining[10] all within, infects unseen. Confess yourself to heaven; repent what's past; avoid what is to come; and do not spread the compost on the weeds, to make them ranker. Forgive me this my virtue; for in the fatness of these pursy[11] times virtue itself of vice must pardon beg, yea, curb and woo for leave to do him good.

QUEEN. O Hamlet, thou hast cleft my heart in twain.

HAM. O, throw away the worser part of it, and live the purer with the other half. Good night: but go not to mine uncle's bed; assume a virtue, if you have it not. That monster custom, who all sense doth eat, of habits evil, is angel yet in this,—that to the use of actions fair and good he likewise gives a frock or livery that aptly is put on. Refrain to-night; and that shall lend a kind of easiness to the next abstinence: the next more easy; for use almost can change the stamp of nature, and either curb the devil, or throw him out with wondrous potency. once more, good-night: and when you are desirous to be bles'd, I'll blessing beg of you.—For this same lord

(*Pointing to Polonius.*)

I do repent; but heaven hath pleas'd it so, to punish me with this, and this with me, that I must be their scourge and minister. I will bestow him, and will answer well the death I gave him. So again, good-night.—I must be cruel, only to be kind: thus bad begins, and worse remains behind.—One word more, good lady.

QUEEN. What shall I do?

HAM. Not this, by no means, that I bid you do: let the bloat king tempt you again to bed; pinch wanton on your cheek; call you his mouse; and let him, for a pair of reechy[12] kisses, or paddling in your neck with his damn'd fingers, make you to ravel all this matter out, that I essentially am not in madness, but mad in craft. 'Twere good you let him know; for who that's but a queen, fair, sober, wise, would from a paddock,[13] from a bat, a gib,[14] such dear concernings hide? who would do so? No, in despite of sense and secrecy, unpeg the basket on the house's top, let the birds fly, and, like the famous ape, to try

---

[10]undermining

[11]bloated

[12]foul

[13]toad

[14]tomcat

conclusions, in the basket creep and break your own neck down.

QUEEN. Be thou assur'd, if words be made of breath, and breath of life, I have no life to breathe what thou hast said to me.

HAM. I must to England; you know that?

QUEEN. Alack, I had forgot: 'tis so concluded on.

HAM. There's letters seal'd: and my two schoolfellows,—whom I will trust as I will adders fang'd,—they bear the mandate; they must sweep my way and marshal me to knavery. Let it work; for 'tis the sport to have the engineer hoist with his own petard:[15] and 't shall go hard but I will delve one yard below their mines and blow them at the moon: O, 'tis most sweet, when in one line two crafts directly meet.—This man shall set me packing: I'll lug the guts into the neighbour room.—Mother, good-night.—Indeed, this counsellor is now most still, most secret, and most grave, who was in life a foolish peating knave. Come, sir, to draw toward an end with you:—Good night, mother.

[*Exeunt severally; Hamlet, dragging out Polonius.*]

■ Act IV

Scene I. A Room in the Castle

[*Enter King, Queen, Rosencrantz and Guildenstern.*]

KING. There's matter in these sighs. These profound heaves you must translate: 'tis fit we understand them. Where is your son?

QUEEN. Bestow this place on us a little while.

(*To Rosencrantz and Guildenstern, who go out.*)

Ah, my good lord, what have I seen to-night!

KING. What, Gertrude? How does Hamlet?

QUEEN. Mad as the sea and wind, when both contend which is the mightier: in his lawless fit behind the arras hearing something stir, whips out his rapier, cries 'A rat, a rat!' And in this brainish apprehension, ills the unseen good old man.

KING. O heavy deed! It had been so with us, had we been there: his liberty is full of threats to all; to you yourself, to us, to every one. Alas, how shall this blood deed by answer'd? It will be laid to us, whose providence should have kept short, restrain'd, and out of haunt this mad young man. But so much was our love we would not understand what was most fit; but, like the owner of a foul disease, to keep it from divulging, let it feed even on the pitch of life. Where is he gone?

QUEEN. To draw apart the body he hath kill'd: o'er whom his very madness, like some ore among a mineral of metals base, shows itself pure: he weeps for what is done.

KING. O Gertrude, come away! The sun no sooner shall the mountains touch but we will ship him hence: and this vile deed we must with all our majesty and skill both countenance and excuse.—Ho, Guildenstern!

(*Re-enter Rosencrantz and Guildenstern.*)

Friends both, go join you with some further aid: Hamlet in madness hath Polonius slain, and from his mother's closet hath he dragg'd him: Go seek him out; speak fair, and bring the body into the chapel.

I pray you, haste in this.

(*Exeunt Rosencrantz and Guildenstern.*)

Come, Gertrude, we'll call up our wisest friends; and let them know both what we mean to do and what's untimely done: so haply slander,—whose whisper o'er the world's diameter, as level as the cannon to his blank,[1] transports his poison'd shot,—may

---

[15]bomb

[1]center of target

miss our name, and hit the woundless
air.—O, come away! My soul is full of
discord and dismay.

(*Exeunt.*)

Scene II. Another Room in the Castle
[*Enter Hamlet.*]

HAM. Safely stowed.
ROS. AND GUIL. [Within.] Hamlet! Lord Hamlet!
HAM. What noise? who calls on Hamlet? O, here
they come.

(*Enter Rosencrantz and Guildenstern.*)

ROS. What have you done, my lord, with the dead
body?
HAM. Compounded it with dust, whereto 'tis kin.
ROS. Tell us where 'tis, that we may take it
thence, and bear it to the chapel.
HAM. Do not believe it.
ROS. Believe what?
HAM. That I can keep your counsel, and not mine
own. Besides, to be demanded of a
sponge!—what replication[1] should be made
by the son of a king?
ROS. Take you me for a sponge, my lord?
HAM. Ay, sir; that soaks up the King's
countenance, his rewards, his authorities. But
such officers do the king best service in the
end: he keeps them, like an ape, in the corner
of his jaw; first mouthed, to be last
swallowed: when he needs what you have
gleaned, it is but squeezing you, and, sponge,
you shall be dry again.
ROS. I understand you not, my lord.
HAM. I am glad of it: a knavish speech sleeps in a
foolish ear.
ROS. My lord, you must tell us where the body is
and go with us to the king.
HAM. The body is with the king, but the king is
not with the body. The king is a thing,—

GUIL. A thing, my lord!
HAM. Of nothing: bring me to him. Hide fox, and
all after.

(*Exeunt.*)

Scene III. Another Room in the Castle
(*Enter King, attended.*)

KING. I have sent to seek him and to find the
body. How dangerous is it that this man goes
loose! Yet must not we put the strong law on
him: he's lov'd of the distracted multitude,
who like not in their judgment, but their eyes;
and where 'tis so, the offender's scourge is
weigh'd, but never the offence. To bear all
smooth and even, this sudden sending him
away must seem deliberate pause: diseases
desperate grown by desperate appliance are
reliev'd, or not at all.

(*Enter Rosencrantz.*)

How now! what hath befall'n?
ROS. Where the dead body is bestow'd, my lord,
We cannot get from him.
KING. But where is he?
ROS. Without, my lord; guarded, to know your
pleasure.
KING. Bring him before us.
ROS. Ho, Guildenstern! bring in my lord.

[*Enter Hamlet and Guildenstern.*]

KING. Now, Hamlet, where's Polonius?
HAM. At supper.
KING. At supper! where?
HAM. Not where he eats, but where he is eaten: a
certain convocation of politic[1] worms are
e'en at him. Your worm is your only emperor
for diet: we fat all creatures else to fat us, and
we fat ourselves for maggots: your fat king
and your lean beggar is but variable

---
[1]reply

---
[1]statesman like

service,—two dishes, but to one table: that's the end.

King. Alas, alas!

Ham. A man may fish with the worm that hath eat of a king, and eat of the fish that hath fed of that worm.

King. What does thou mean by this?

Ham. Nothing but to show you how a king may go a progress[2] through the guts of a beggar.

King. Where is Polonius?

Ham. In heaven: send thither to see: if your messenger find him not there, seek him i' the other place yourself. But, indeed, if you find him not within this month, you shall nose him as you go up the stairs into the lobby.

King. Go seek him there. [To *some Attendants.*]

Ham. He will stay till you come.

(*Exeunt Attendants.*)

King. Hamlet, this deed, for thine especial safety,—which we do tender,[3] as we dearly grieve for that which thou hast done,—must send thee hence with fiery quickness: therefore prepare thyself; the bark is ready, and the wind at help, the associates tend,[4] and everything is bent for England.

Ham. For England!

King. Ay, Hamlet.

Ham. Good.

King. So is it, if thou knew'st our purposes.

Ham. I see a cherub that sees them.—But, come; for England!—Farewell, dear mother.

King. Thy loving father, Hamlet.

Ham. My mother: father and mother is man and wife; man and wife is one flesh; and so, my mother.—Come, for England!

(*Exit.*)

King. Follow him at foot; tempt him with speed aboard; delay it not; I'll have him hence to-night: Away! for everything is seal'd and done that else leans on the affair: pray you, make haste.

(*Exeunt Rosencrantz and Guildenstern.*)

And, England, if my love thou hold'st at aught,—as my great power thereof may give thee sense, since yet thy cicatrice[5] looks raw and red after the Danish sword, and thy free awe pays homage to us,—thou mayst not coldly set our sovereign process; which imports at full, by letters conjuring to that effect, the present death of Hamlet. Do it, England; for like the hectic[6] in my blood he rages, and thou must cure me: till I know 'tis done, howe'er my haps,[7] my joys were ne'er begun.

(*Exit.*)

Scene IV. A Plain in Denmark
[*Enter Fortinbras, and Forces marching.*]

For. Go, Captain, from me greet the Danish king: tell him that, by his license, Fortinbras craves the conveyance of a promis'd march over his kingdom. You know the rendezvous. If that his majesty would aught with us, we shall express our duty in his eye; and let him know so.

Capt. I will do't, my Lord.

For. Go softly on.

(*Exeunt all For. and Forces.*)

(*Enter Hamlet, Rosencrantz, Guildenstern, &c.*)

Ham. Good sir, whose powers are these?

Capt. They are of Norway, sir.

---

[2]royal journey

[3]hold dear

[4]wait

[5]sear

[6]fever

[7]fortune

HAM. How purpos'd, sir, I pray you?

CAPT. Against some part of Poland.

HAM. Who commands them, sir?

CAPT. The nephew to old Norway, Fortinbras.

HAM. Goes it against the main of Poland, sir, or for some frontier?

CAPT. Truly to speak, and with no addition, we go to gain a little patch of ground that hath in it no profit but the name. To pay five ducats, five, I would not farm it; nor will it yield to Norway or the Polena ranker[1] rate, should it be sold in fee.[2]

HAM. Why, then the Polack never will defend it.

CAPT. Yes, it is already garrison'd.

HAM. Two thousand souls and twenty thousand ducats will not debate the question of this straw: this is the imposthume[3] of much wealth and peace, that inward breaks, and shows no cause without why the man dies.—I humbly thank you, sir.

CAPT. God b' wi' you, sir.

(*Exit.*)

ROS. Will't please you go, my lord?

HAM. I'll be with you straight. Go a little before.

(*Exeunt all but Hamlet.*)

How all occasions do inform against me and spur my dull revenge! What is a man, if his chief good and market of his time be but to sleep and feed? a beast, no more. Sure he that made us with such large discourse, looking before and after, gave us not that capability and godlike reason to fust[4] in us unus'd. Now, whether it be bestial oblivion, or some craven scruple of thinking too precisely on the event,—A thought which, quarter'd, hath but one part wisdom and ever three parts

coward,—I do not know why yet I live to way 'This thing's to do;' Sith I have cause, and will, and strength, and means to do't. Examples, gross as earth, exhort me: witness this army, of such mass and charge, led by a delicate and tender prince; whose spirit, with divine ambition puff'd, makes mouths at the invisible event; exposing what is mortal and unsure to all that fortune, death, and danger dare, even for an egg-shell. Rightly to be great is not to stir without great argument, but greatly to find quarrel in a straw when honour's at the stake. How stand I, then, that have a father kill'd, a mother stain'd, excitements of my reason and my blood, and let all sleep? while, to my shame, I see the imminent death of twenty thousand men that, for a fantasy and trick of fame, go to their graves like beds; fight for a plot whereon the numbers cannot try the cause, which is not tomb enough and continent[5] to hide the slain?—O, from this time forth, my thoughts be bloody, or be nothing worth!

(*Exit.*)

Scene V. Elsinore. A Room in the Castle

[*Enter Queen and Horatio.*]

QUEEN. I will not speak with her.

GENT. She is importunate; indeed distract: her mood will needs be pitied.

QUEEN. What would she have?

GENT. She speaks much of her father; says she hears there's tricks i' the world, and hems, and beats her heart: spurns enviously at straws; speaks things in doubt, that carry but half sense: her speech is nothing, yet the unshaped use of it doth move the hearers to collection; they aim at it, and botch the words up fit to their own thoughts; which, as her winks, and nods, and gestures yield them, indeed would make one think there might be

---

[1] higher

[2] outright

[3] abscess, ulcer

[4] grow moldy

[5] container

thought, though nothing sure, yet much unhappily. 'Twere good she were spoken with; for she may strew dangerous conjectures in ill-breeding minds.

QUEEN. Let her come in.

(*Exit Horatio.*)

To my sick soul, as sin's true nature is, each toy seems Prologue to some great amiss: so full of artless jealousy is guilt, it spills itself in fearing to be split.

(*Re-enter Horatio with Ophelia.*)

OPH. Where is the beauteous majesty of Denmark?

QUEEN. How now, Ophelia?

OPH. [*Sings.*] How should I your true love know from another one? By his cockle bat and/staff and his sandal shoon.[1]

QUEEN. Alas, sweet lady, what imports this song?

OPH. Say you? nay, pray you, mark. [Sings.] He is dead and gone, lady, he is dead and gone; at his head a grass green turf, at his heels a stone.

QUEEN. Nay, but Ophelia—

OPH. Pray you, mark. [*Sings.*] White his shroud as the mountain snow,

(*Enter King.*)

QUEEN. Alas, look here, my lord!

OPH. [*Sings.*] Larded[2] all with sweet flowers; which bewept to the grave did go with true-love showers.

KING. How do you, pretty lady?

OPH. Well, God dild[3] you! They say the owl was a baker's daughter. Lord, we know what we are, but know not what we may be. God eat your table!

KING. Conceit[4] upon her father.

OPH. Pray you, let's have no words of this; but when they ask you what it means, say you this: [*Sings.*] To-morrow is Saint Valentine's day all in the morning bedtime, and I a maid at your window, to be your Valentine. Then up he rose and donn'd his clothes, and dupp'd[5] the chamber door, let in the maid, that out a maid never departed more.

KING. Pretty Ophelia!

OPH. Indeed, la, without an oath, I'll make an end on't: [*Sings.*] By Gis[6] and by Saint Charity, alack, and fie for shame young men will do't if they come to't; by cock, they are to blame. Quoth she, before you tumbled me, you promis'd me to wed. So would I ha' done, by yonder sun, an thou hadst not come to my bed.

KING. How long hath she been thus?

OPH. I hope all will be well. We must be patient: but I cannot choose but weep, to think they would lay him i' the cold ground. My brother shall know of it: and so I thank you for your good counsel.—Come, my coach!—Good night, ladies; good night, sweet ladies; good night, good nights.

(*Exit.*)

KING. Follow her close; give her good watch, I pray you.

(*Exit Horatio.*)

O, this is the poison of deep grief; it springs all from her father's death. O Gertrude, Gertrude, When sorrows come, they come not single spies, but in battalions! First, her father slain: next, your son gone; and he most violent author of his own just remove: the people muddied, thick and unwholesome in their thoughts and whispers for good Polonius'

---

[1]shoes

[2]decorated

[3]yield, ie. reward

[4]brooding

[5]opened

[6]contracton of "Jesus"

death; and we have done but greenly[7] in hugger-mugger[8] to inter him: poor Ophelia divided from herself and her fair judgment, without the which we are pictures or mere beasts: last, and as much containing as all these, her brother is in secret come from France; feeds on his wonder, keeps himself in clouds, and wants not buzzers to infect his ear with pestilent speeches of his father's death; wherein necessity, of matter beggar'd, will nothing stick our person to arraign in ear and ear. O my dear Gertrude, this, like to a murdering piece, in many places give, me superfluous death.

(*A noise within.*)

QUEEN. Alack, what noise is this?
KING. Where are my Switzer's[9] let them guard the door.

(*Enter a Gentleman.*)

What is the matter?
GENT. Save yourself, my lord: the ocean, overpeering of his list,[10] eats not the flats with more impetuous haste than young Laertes, in a riotous head, o'erbears your offices. The rabble call him lord; and, as the world were now but to begin, antiquity forgot, custom not known, the ratifiers and props of every word, they cry 'Choose we! Laertes shall be king!' Caps, hands, and tongues applaud it to the clouds, 'Laertes shall be king! Laertes king!'
QUEEN. How cheerfully on the false trail they cry! O, this is counter, you false Danish dogs!

(*A noise within.*)

KING. The doors are broke.

---

[7]foolishly

[8]secret haste

[9]Swiss Guards

[10]shore

(*Enter Laertes, armed; Danes following.*)

LAER. Where is this king?—Sirs, stand you all without.
DANES. No, let's come in.
LAER. I pray you, give me leave.
DANES. We will, we will.

(*They retire without the door.*)

LAER. I thank you:—keep the door.—O thou vile king, give me my father!
QUEEN. Calmly, good Laertes.
LAER. That drop of blood that's calm proclaims me bastard; cries cuckold to my father; brands the harlot even here, between the chaste unsmirched brow of my true mother.
KING. What is the cause, Laertes, that thy rebellion looks so giant-like?—Let him go, Gertrude; do not fear our person: there's such divinity doth hedge a king, that treason can but peep to what it would, acts little of his will.—Tell me, Laertes, why thou art thus incens'd.—Let him go, Gertrude:—Speak, man.
LAER. Where is my father?
KING. Dead.
QUEEN. But not by him.
KING. Let him demand his fill.
LAER. How came he dead? I'll not be juggled with: to hell, allegiance! vows, to the blackest devil! Conscience and grace, to the profoundest pit! I dare damnation:—to this point I stand,—that both the worlds, I give to negligence, let come what comes; only I'll be reveng'd most thoroughly for my father.
KING. Who shall stay you?
LAER. My will, not all the world: and for my means, I'll husband them so well, they shall go far with little.
KING. Good Laertes, if you desire to know the certainty of your dear father's death, is't writ in your revenge that, swoopstake,[11] you will draw both friend and foe, winner and loser?

---

[11]in a clean sweep

LAER. None but his enemies.

KING. Will you know them then?

LAER. To his good friends thus wide I'll ope my arms; and, like the kind life-rendering pelican,[12] repast[13] them with my blood.

KING. Why, now you speak like a good child and a true gentleman. That I am guiltless of your father's death, and am most sensibly in grief for it, it shall as level to your judgment pierce as day does to your eye.

DANES. [*Within.*] Let her come in.

LAER. How now! What noise is that?

(*Re-enter Ophelia, fantastically dressed with straws and flowers.*)

O heat, dry up my brains! tears seven times salt, burn out the sense and virtue of mine eye!—By heaven, thy madness shall be paid by weight, till our scale turn the beam. O rose of May! Dear maid, kind sister, sweet Ophelia!—O heavens! is't possible a young maid's wits should be as mortal as an old man's life? Nature is fine in love; and where 'tis fine, it sends some precious instance of itself after the thing it loves.

OPH. [*Sings.*] They bore him barefac'd on the bier hey no nonny, nonny, hey nonny and on his grave rain'd many a tear.—Fare you well, my dove!

LAER. Hadst thou thy wits, and didst persuade revenge, I could not move thus.

OPH. You must sing 'Down a-down, an you call him a-down-a.' O, how the wheel becomes it! It is the false steward, that stole his master's daughter.

LAER. This nothing's more than matter.

OPH. There's rosemary, that's for remembrance; pray, love, remember: and there is pansies, that's for thoughts.

LAER. A document in madness,—thoughts and remembrance fitted.

OPH. There's fennel for you, and columbines:—there's rue for you; and here's some for me:—we may call it herb of grace o' Sundays:—O, you must wear your rue with a difference.—There's a daisy:—I would give you some violets, but they wither'd all when my father died:—they say he made a good end,—[*Sings.*] For bonny sweet Robin is all my joy,—

LAER. Thought and affliction, passion, hell itself, she turns to favour and to prettiness.

OPH. [*Sings.*] And will he not come again? And will he not come again? No, no, he is dead, go to thy death-bed, he never will come again. His beard was as white as snow, all flaxen was his poll: he is gone, he is gone, and we cast away moan: God ha' mercy on his soul! And of all Christian souls, I pray God.—God t' wi' ye.

(*Exit.*)

LAER. Do you see this, O God?

KING. Laertes, I must commune with your grief, or you deny me right. Go but apart, make choice of whom your wisest friends you will, and they shall hear and judge 'twixt you and me. If by direct or by collateral hand they find us touch'd,[14] we will our kingdom give, our crown, our life, and all that we call ours, to you in satisfaction; but if not, be you content to lend your patience to us, and we shall jointly labour with your soul to give it due content.

LAER. Let this be so; his means of death, his obscure burial,—no trophy, sword, nor hatchment[15] o'er his bones, no noble rite nor formal ostentation,—cry to be heard, as 'twere from heaven to earth, that I must call't in question.

KING. So you shall; and where the offence is let the great axe fall. I pray you go with me.

(*Exeunt.*)

---

[12]the pelican was thought to feed its young with its own blood

[13]feed

[14]implicated

[15]tablet bearing the coat of arms of the dead

Scene VI. Another Room in the Castle
[*Enter Horatio and a Servant.*]

HOR. What are they that would speak with me?
SERVANT. Sailors, sir: they say they have letters for you.
HOR. Let them come in.

(*Exit Servant.*)

I do not know from what part of the world I should be greeted, if not from Lord Hamlet.

(*Enter Sailors.*)

I sailor.
God bless you, sir.
HOR. Let him bless thee too.
SAILOR. He shall, sir, an't please him. There's a letter for you, sir,—it comes from the ambassador that was bound for England; if your name be Horatio, as I am let to know it is.
HOR. [*Reads.*] 'Horatio, when thou shalt have overlooked this, give these fellows some means to the king: they have letters for him. Ere we were two days old at sea, a pirate of very warlike appointment gave us chase. Finding ourselves too slow of sail, we put on a compelled valour, and in the grapple I boarded them: on the instant they got clear of our ship; so I alone became their prisoner. They have dealt with me like thieves of mercy: but they knew what they did; I am to do a good turn for them. Let the king have the letters I have sent; and repair thou to me with as much haste as thou wouldst fly death. I have words to speak in thine ear will make thee dumb; yet are they much too light for the bore of the matter. These good fellows will bring thee where I am. Rosencrantz and Guildenstern hold their course for England: of them I have much to tell thee. Farewell. He that thou knowest thing, HAMLET.' Come, I will give you way for these your letters; And do't the speedier, that you may direct me To him from whom you brought them.

(*Exeunt.*)

Scene VII. Another Room in the Castle
[*Enter King and Laertes.*]

KING. Now must your conscience my acquittance seal, and you must put me in your heart for friend, sith you have heard, and with a knowing ear, that he which hath your noble father slain pursu'd my life.
LAER. It well appears:—but tell me why you proceeded not against these feats, so crimeful and so capital in nature, as by your safety, wisdom, all things else, you mainly were stirr'd up.
KING. O, for two special reasons; which may to you, perhaps, seem much unsinew'd, but yet to me they are strong. The queen his mother lives almost by his looks and for myself,—my virtue or my plague, be it either which,—he's so conjunctive to my life and soul, that, as the star moves not but in his sphere, I could not but by her. The other motive, why to a public count I might not go, is the great love the general gender[1] bear him; who, dipping all his faults in their affection, would, like the spring that turneth wood to stone, convert his gyves[2] to graces; so that my arrows, too slightly timber'd for so loud a wind, would have reverted to my bow again, and not where I had aim'd them.
LAER. And so have I a noble father lost; a sister driven into desperate terms,—whose worth, if praises may go back again, stood challenger on mount of all the age for her perfections:—but my revenge will come.
KING. Break not your sleeps for that:—you must not think that we are made of stuff so flat and dull that we can let our beard be shook with danger, and think it pastime. You shortly shall hear more: I lov'd your father, and we love ourself; and that, I hope, will teach you to imagine,—

(*Enter a Messenger.*)

---
[1]common people

[2]letters

How now! What news?

Mess. Letters, my lord, from Hamlet: this to your majesty; this to the queen.

King. From Hamlet! Who brought them?

Mess. Sailors, my lord, they say; I saw them not: they were given me by Claudio:—he receiv'd them of him that brought them.

King. Laertes, you shall hear them. Leave us.

(*Exit Messenger.*)

[Reads.] 'High and mighty,—You shall know I am set naked on your kingdom. To-morrow shall I beg leave to see your kingly eyes: when I shall, first asking your pardon thereunto, recount the occasions of my sudden and more strange return. HAMLET.' What should this mean? Are all the rest come back? Or is it some abuse, and no such thing?

Laer. Know you the hand?

King. 'Tis Hamlet's character:[3]—'Naked!'—and in a postscript here, he says 'alone.' Can you advise me?

Laer. I am lost in it, my lord. But let him come; it warms the very sickness in my heart that I shall live and tell him to his teeth, 'Thus didest thou.'

King. If it be so, Laertes,—as how should it be so? how otherwise?—will you be rul'd by me?

Laer. Ay, my lord; so you will not o'errule me to a peace.

King. To thine own peace. If he be now return'd—as checking at his voyage, and that he means no more to undertake it,—I will work him to exploit, now ripe in my device, under the which he shall not choose but fall: and for his death no wind shall breathe; but even his mother shall uncharge the practice and call it accident.

Laer. My lord, I will be rul'd; the rather if you could devise it so that I might be the organ.

King. It falls right. You have been talk'd of since your travel much, and that in Hamlet's hearing, for a quality wherein they say you shine: your sum of parts did not together pluck such envy from him as did that one; and that, in my regard, of the unworthiest siege.[4]

Laer. What part is that, my lord?

King. A very riband in the cap of youth, yet needful too; for youth no less becomes the light and careless livery that it wears than settled age his sables and his weeds, importing health and graveness.—Two months since, here was a gentleman of Normandy,—I've seen myself, and serv'd against, the French, and they can well on horseback: but this gallant had witchcraft in't: he grew unto his seat; and to such wondrous doing brought his horse, as had he been incorps'd and demi-natur'd with the brave beast: so far he topp'd my thought that I, in forgery of shapes and tricks, come short of what he did.

Laer. A Norman was't?

King. A Norman.

Laer. Upon my life, Lamond.

King. The very same

Laer. I know him well: he is the brooch indeed and gem of all the nation.

King. He made confession of you; and gave you such a masterly report for art and exercise in your defence, and for your rapier most especially, that he cried out, 'twould be a sight indeed if one could match you: the scrimers[5] of their nation he swore, had neither motion, guard, nor eye, if you oppos'd them. Sir, this report of his did Hamlet so envenom with his envy that he could nothing do but wish and beg your sudden coming o'er, to play with him. Now, out of this,—

Laer. What out of this, my lord?

---

[3]handwriting

[4]rank

[5]fencers

KING. Laertes, was your father dear to you? Or are you like the painting of sorrow, a face without a heart?

LAER. Why ask you this?

KING. Not that I think you did not love your father; but that I know love is begun by time, and that I see, in passages of proof, time qualifies the spark and fire of it. There lives within the very flame of love a kind of wick or snuff that will abate it; and nothing is at a like goodness still; for goodness, growing to a plurisy,[6] dies in his own too much: that we would do, we should do when we would; for this 'would' changes, and hath abatements and delays as many as there are tongues, are hands, are accidents; and then this 'should' is like a spendthrift sigh, that hurts by easing. But to the quick[7] o' the ulcer:—Hamlet comes back: what would you undertake to show yourself your father's son in deed more than in words?

LAER. To cut his throat i' the church.

KING. No place, indeed, should murder sanctuarize; revenge should have no bounds. But, good Laertes, will you do this, keep close within your chamber. Hamlet return'd shall know you are come home: we'll put on those shall praise our excellence and set a double varnish on the fame the Frenchman gave you; bring you in fine[8] together and wager on your heads: he, being remiss, most generous, and free from all contriving, will not peruse the foils; so that with ease, or with a little shuffling, you may choose a sword unbated,[9] and, in a pass of practice, requite him for your father.

LAER. I will do't: and for that purpose I'll anoint my sword. I bought an unction of a mountebank,[10] so mortal that, but dip a knife in it, where it draws blood no cataplasm[11] so rare, collected from all simples[12] that have virtue under the moon, can save the thing from death this is but scratch'd withal: I'll touch my point with this contagion, that, if I gall him slightly, it may be death.

KING. Let's further think of this; weigh what convenience both of time and means may fit us to our shape: if this should fail, and that our drift look through our bad performance. 'Twere better not assay'd: therefore this project should have a back or second, that might hold if this did blast in proof. Soft! let met see:—We'll make a solemn wager on your cunnings,—I ha't: when in your motion you are hot and dry,—as make your bouts more violent to that end,—And that he calls for drink, I'll have prepar'd him a chalice for the nonce;[13] whereon but sipping, if he by chance escape your venom'd stuck,[14] our purpose may hold there.

(*Enter Queen.*)

How now, sweet queen!

QUEEN. One woe doth tread upon another's heel, so fast they follow:—your sister's drown'd, Laertes.

LAER. Drown'd! O, where?

QUEEN. There is a willow grows aslant a brook, that shows his hoar leaves in the glassy stream; there with fantastic garlands did she come of crowflowers, nettles, daisies, and long purples, that liberal shepherds give a grosser name, but our cold maids do dead men's fingers call them. There, on the pendant boughs her coronet weeds clamb'ring to hand, an envious silver broke; when down her weedy trophies and herself fell in the weeping brook. Her clothes spread

---

[6]excess

[7]sensitive flesh

[8]finally

[9]not blunted

[10]quack

---

[11]poultice

[12]medicinal herbs

[13]occasion

[14]thrust

wide; and, mermaid-like, awhile they bore her up; which time she chaunted snatches of old tunes; as one incapable of her own distress, or like a creature native and indu'd[15] unto that element: but long it could not be till that her garments, heavy with their drink, pull'd the poor wretch from her melodious lay to muddy death.

Laer. Alas, then she is drown'd?

Queen. Drown'd, drown'd.

Laer. Too much of water hast thou, poor Ophelia, and therefore I forbid my tears: but yet it is our trick; nature her custom holds, let shame say what it will: when these are gone, the woman will be out.—Adieu, my lord: I have a speech of fire, that fain would blaze, but that this folly douts it.

(*Exit.*)

King. Let's follow, Gertrude; How much I had to do to calm his rage! Now fear I this will give it start again; therefore let's follow.

(*Exeunt.*)

▪ Act V

Scene I. A Churchyard

[*Enter two Clowns, with spades, &c.*]

1 Clown. Is she to be buried in Christian burial when she wilfully seeks her own salvation?

2 Clown. I tell thee she is; and therefore make her grave straight: the crowner[1] hath sat on her, and finds it Christian burial.

1 Clown. How can that be, unless she drowned herself in her own defence?

2 Clown. Why, 'tis found so.

1 Clown. It must be *se offendendo;*[2] it cannot be else. For here lies the point: if I drown myself wittingly, it argues an act: and an act hath three branches; it is to act, to do, and to perform: argal,[3] she drowned herself wittingly.

2 Clown. Nay, but hear you, goodman delver,—

1 Clown. Give me leave. Here lies the water; good: here stands the man; good: if the man go to this water and drown himself, it is, will he, nill he, he goes,—mark you that: but if the water come to him and drown him, he drowns not himself; argal, he that is not guilty of his own death shortens not his own life.

2 Clown. But is this law?

1 Clown. Ay, marry, is't—crowner's quest[4] law.

2 Clown. Will you ha' the truth on't? If this had not been a gentlewoman, she should have been buried out o' Christian burial.

1 Clown. Why, there thou say'st: and the more pity that great folk should have countenance in this world to drown or hang themselves more than their even Christian.—Come, my spade. There is no ancient gentlemen but gardeners, ditchers, and grave-makers: they hold up Adam's profession.

2 Clown. Was he a gentleman?

1 Clown. He was the first that ever bore arms.

2 Clown. Why, he had none.

1 Clown. What, art a heathen? How dost thou understand the Scripture? The Scripture says Adam digg'd: could he dig without arms? I'll put another question to thee: if thou answerest me not to the purpose, confess thyself,—

2 Clown. Go to.

---

[15]in harmony with

[1]coroner

[2]offending herself (parody of se defendendo, a legal term meaning "in self defense")

[3]pandy in latin ergo, "therefore"

[4]inquest

1 CLOWN. What is he that build stronger than either the mason, the shipwright, or the carpenter?

2 CLOWN. The gallows-maker; for that frame outlives a thousand tenants.

1 CLOWN. I like thy wit well, in good faith: the gallows does well; but how does it well? it does well to those that do ill: now, thou dost ill to say the gallows is built stronger than the church; argal, the gallows may do well to thee. To't again, come.

2 CLOWN. Who builds stronger than a mason, a shipwright, or a carpenter?

1 CLOWN. Ay, tell me that, and unyoke.

2 CLOWN. Marry, now I can tell.

1 CLOWN. To't.

2 CLOWN. Mass,[5] I cannot tell.

(*Enter Hamlet and Horatio, at a distance.*)

1 CLOWN. Cudgel thy brains no more about it, for your dull ass will not men his pace with beating; and when you are asked this question next, say 'a grave-maker;' the houses he makes last till doomsday. Go, get thee to Yaughan; fetch me a stoup[6] of liquor.

(*Exit Second Clown.*)

(*Digs and sings.*)

> In youth when I did love, did love, methought it was very sweet; to contract, O, the time for, ah, my behove,[7] O, methought there was nothing meet.

HAM. Has this fellow no feeling of his business, that he sings at grave-making?

HOR. Custom hath made it in him a property of easiness.

HAM. 'Tis e'en so: the hand of little employment hath the daintier sense.

---

[5]by the mass

[6]tankard

[7]advantage

1 CLOWN. [*Sings.*] But age, with his stealing steps, hath claw'd me in his clutch, and hath shipp'd me intil the land, as if I had never been such.

(*Throws up a skull.*)

HAM. That skull had a tongue in it, and could sing once: how the knave jowls[8] it to the ground,as if 'twere Cain's jawbone, that did the first murder! This might be the pate of a politician, which this ass now o'erreaches; one that would circumvent God, might it not?

HOR. It might, my lord.

HAM. Or of a courtier, which could say 'Good morrow, sweet lord! How dost thou, good lord?' This might be my lord such-a-one, that praised my lord such-a-one's horse when he meant to beg it,—might it not?

HOR. Ay, my lord.

HAM. Why, e'en so: and now my Lady Worm's; chapless,[9] and knocked about the mazzard[10] with a sexton's spade: here's fine revolution, an we had the trick to see't. Did these bones cost no more the breeding but to play at loggats[11] with 'em? mine ache to think on't.

1 CLOWN. [Sings.] A pickaxe and a space, a spade,for and a shrouding sheet; O, a pit of clay for to be madefor such a guest is meet.

(*Throws up another skull.*)

HAM. There's another: why may not that be the skull of a lawyer? Where be his quiddits[12] now, his quillets,[13] his cases, his tenures,[14]

---

[8]hurls

[9]lacking the lower jaw

[10]head

[11]a game in which small pieces of wood were thrown at an object

[12]subtle distinctions

[13]time arguments

[14]legal means of holding land

and his tricks? why does he suffer this rude knave now to knock him about the sconce[15] with dirty shovel, and will not tell him of his action of battery? Hum! This fellow might be in's time a great buyer of land, with his statutes, his recognizances, his fines, his double vouchers, his recoveries: is this the fine[16] of his fines, and the recovery of his recoveries, to have his fine pate full of fine dirt? will his vouchers vouch him no more of his purchases, and double ones too, than the length and breadth of a pair of indentures? The very conveyances of his lands will scarcely lie in this box; and must the inheritor himself have no more, ha?

Hor. Not a jot more, my lord.

Ham. Is not parchment made of sheep-skins?

Hor. Ay, my lord, And of calf-skins too.

Ham. They are sheep and calves which seek out assurance in that. I will speak to this fellow.—Whose grave's this, sir?

1 Clown. Mine, sir. [*Sings.*] O, a pit of clay for to be madefor such a guest is meet.

Ham. I think it be thine indeed, for thou liest in't.

1 Clown. You lie out on't, sir, and therefore 'tis not you: for my part, I do not lie in't, yet it is mine.

Ham. Thou dost lie in't, to be in't and say it is thine: 'tis for the dead, not for the quick;[17] therefore thou liest.

1 Clown. 'Tis a quick lie, sir; 't will away again from me to you.

Ham. What man dost thou dig it for?

1 Clown. For no man, sir.

Ham. What woman then?

1 Clown. For none neither.

Ham. Who is to be buried in't?

1 Clown. One that was a woman, sir; but, rest her soul, she's dead.

Ham. How absolute the knave is! We must speak by the card, or equivocation will undo us. By the Lord, Horatio, these three years I have taken note of it, the age is grown so picked[18] that the toe of the peasant comes so near the heel of the courtier he galls his kibe.[19]—How long hast thou been a grave-maker?

1 Clown. Of all the days i' the year, I came to't that day that our last King Hamlet overcame Fortinbras.

Ham. How long is that since?

1 Clown. Cannot you tell that? every fool can tell that: it was the very day that young Hamlet was born,—he that is mad, and sent into England.

Ham. Ay, marry, why was he sent into England?

1 Clown. Why, because he was mad: he shall recover his wits there; or, if he do not, it's no great matter there.

Ham. Why?

1 Clown. 'Twill not he seen in him there; there the men are as mad as he.

Ham. How came he mad?

1 Clown. Very strangely, they say.

Ham. How strangely?

1 Clown. Faith, e'en with losing his wits.

Ham. Upon what ground?

1 Clown. Why, here in Denmark: I have been sexton here, man and boy, thirty years.

Ham. How long will a man lie i' the earth ere he rot?

1 Clown. Faith, if he be not rotten before he die,—as we have many pocky corses[20] now-a-days that will scarce hold the laying in—he will last you some eight year or nine year: a tanner will last you nine year.

Ham. Why he more than another?

1 Clown. Why, sir, his hide is so tann'd with his trade that he will keep out water a great while; and your water is a sore decayer of your whoreson dead body. Here's a skull now; this skull hath lain in the earth three-and-twenty years.

---

[15]head

[16]end

[17]living

[18]refined

[19]sore on the back of the heel

[20]pock-marked corpses

HAM. Whose was it?

1 CLOWN. A whoreson, mad fellow's it was: whose do you think it was?

HAM. Nay, I know not.

1 CLOWN. A pestilence on him for a mad rogue! 'a pour'd a flagon of rhenish on my head once. This same skull, sir, was Yorick's skull, the king's jester.

HAM. This?

1 CLOWN. E'en that.

HAM. Let me see. [*Takes the skull.*] Alas, poor Yorick!—I knew him, Horatio; a fellow of infinite jest, of most excellent fancy: he hath borne me on his back a thousand times; and now, how abhorred in my imagination it is! my gorge rises at it. Here hung those lips that I have kiss'd I know not how oft. Where be your gibes now? your gambols? your songs? your flashes of merriment, that were wont to set the table on a roar? Not one now, to mock your own grinning? quite chap-fallen? Now, get you to my lady's chamber, and tell her, let her paint an inch thick, to this favour she must come; make her laugh at that.—Pr'ythee, Horatio, tell me one thing.

HOR. What's that, my lord?

HAM. Dost thou think Alexander looked o' this fashion i' the earth?

HOR. E'en so.

HAM. And smelt so? Pah!

(*Throws down the skull.*)

HOR. E'en so, my lord.

HAM. To what base uses we may return, Horatio! Why may not imagination trace the noble dust of Alexander till he find it stopping a bung-hole?

HOR. 'Twere to consider too curiously to consider so.

HAM. No, faith, not a jot; but to follow him thither with modesty enough, and likelihood to lead it: as thus: Alexander died, Alexander was buried, Alexander returneth into dust; the dust is earth; of earth we make loam; and why of that loam whereto he was converted might they not stop a beer-barrel? Imperious

Caesar, dead and turn'd to clay, might stop a hole to keep the wind away. O, that that earth which kept the world in awe should patch a wall to expel the winter's flaw![21] But soft! but soft! aside!—Here comes the king.

(*Enter priests, &c, in procession; the corpse of Ophelia, Laertes, and Mourners following; King, Queen, their Trains, &c.*)

The queen, the courtiers: who is that they follow? And with such maimed rites? This doth betoken the corse they follow did with desperate hand fordo it own life: 'twas of some estate.[22] Couch[23] we awhile and mark.

(*Retiring with Horatio.*)

LAER. What ceremony else?

HAM. That is Laertes, a very noble youth: mark.

LAER. What ceremony else?

1 PRIEST. Her obsequies have been as far enlarg'd as we have warranties: her death was doubtful; and, but that great command o'ersways the order, she should in ground unsanctified have lodg'd till the last trumpet; for charitable prayers, shards,[24] flints, and pebbles should be thrown on her, yet here she is allowed her virgin crants,[25] her maiden strewments, and the bringing home of bell and burial.

LAER. Must there no more be done?

1 PRIEST. No more be done; we should profane the service of the dead to sing a requiem and such rest to her as to peace-parted souls.

LAER. Lay her i' the earth;—And from her fair and unpolluted flesh may violets spring!—I tell thee, churlish priest, a ministering angel shall my sister be when thou liest howling.

---

[21]gust

[22]high rank

[23]hide

[24]broken pieces of pottery

[25]garlands

HAM. What, the fair Ophelia?
QUEEN. Sweets to the sweet: farewell.

(*Scattering flowers.*)

I hop'd thou shouldst have been my Hamlet's
    wife; I thought thy bride-bed to have deck'd,
    sweet maid, and not have strew'd thy grave.
LAER. O, treble woe fall ten times treble on that
    cursed head whose wicked deed thy most
    ingenious sense depriv'd thee of!—Hold off
    the earth awhile, till I have caught her once
    more in mine arms:

(*Leaps into the grave.*)

Now pile your dust upon the quick and dead, till
    of this flat a mountain you have made, to
    o'ertop old Pelion[26] or the skyish head of
    blue Olympus.
HAM. [*Advancing.*] What is he whose grief bears
    such an emphasis? whose phrase of sorrow
    Conjures the wandering stars, and makes
    them stand like wonder-wounded hearers?
    this is I, Hamlet the Dane.

(*Leaps into the grave.*)

LAER. The devil take thy soul!

(*Grappling with him.*)

HAM. Thou pray'st not well. I pr'ythee, take thy
    fingers from my throat; for, though I am not
    splenetive[27] and rash, yet have I in me
    something dangerous, which let thy wiseness
    fear: away thy hand!
KING. Pluck them asunder.
QUEEN. Hamlet! Hamlet!
ALL. Gentlemen!—
HOR. Good my lord, be quiet.

(*The Attendants part them, and they come out of
the grave.*)

HAM. Why, I will fight with him upon this theme
    until my eyelids will no longer wag.
QUEEN. O my son, what theme?
HAM. I lov'd Ophelia; forty thousand brothers
    could not, with all their quantity of love,
    make up my sum.—What wilt thou do for
    her?
KING. I, he is mad, Laertes.
QUEEN. For love of God, forbear him!
HAM. 'Swounds, show me what thou'lt do: woul't
    weep? woul't fight? woul't fast? woul't tear
    thyself? Woul't drink up eisel?[28] eat a
    crocodile? I'll do't.—Dost thou come here to
    whine? To outface me with leaping in her
    grave? Be buried quick with her, and so will
    I: and, if thou prate of mountains, let them
    throw millions of acres on us, till our ground,
    singeing his pate against the burning zone,
    make Ossa like a wart! Nay, an thou'lt
    mouth, I'll rant as well as thou.
QUEEN. This is mere madness: and thus a while
    the fit will work on him; Anon, as patient as
    the female dove, when that her golden
    couplets are disclos'd, his silence will sit
    drooping.
HAM. Hear you, sir; what is the reason that you
    use me thus? I lov'd you ever: but it is no
    matter; let Hercules himself do what he may,
    the cat will mew, and dog will have his day.

(*Exit.*)

KING. I pray thee, good Horatio, wait upon
    him.—

(*Exit Horatio.*)

(*To Laertes.*)

---

[26]one of two mountains which, according to Greek mythology, the giants piled on top of one another in order to reach heaven and fight the gods.

[27]fiery

---

[28]vinegar

Strengthen your patience in our last night's
speech; we'll put the matter to the present
push.—Good Gertrude, set some watch over
your son.—This grave shall have a living
monument: an hour of quiet shortly shall we
see; till then in patience our proceeding be.

(*Exeunt.*)

Scene II. A Hall in the Castle

[*Enter Hamlet and Horatio.*]

HAM. So much for this, sir: now let me see the
other; you do remember all the
circumstance?

HOR. Remember it, my lord!

HAM. Sir, in my heart there was a kind of fighting
that would not let me sleep: methought I lay
worse than the mutinies in the bilboes.[1]
Rashly, and prais'd be rashness for it,—let us
know, our indiscretion sometime serves us
well, when our deep plots do fail; and that
should teach us there's a divinity that shapes
our ends, rough-hew them how we will.

HOR. That is most certain.

HAM. Up from my cabin, my sea-gown scarf'd
about me, in the dark grop'd I to find out
them: had my desire; finger'd their packet;
and, in fine, withdrew to mine own room
again: making so bold, my fears forgetting
manners, to unseal their grand commission;
where I found, Horatio, O royal knavery! an
exact command,—larded[2] with many several
sorts of reasons, importing Denmark's health,
and England's too, with, ho! such bugs and
goblins in my life,—that, on the supervise,
no leisure bated, no, not to stay the grinding
of the axe, my head should be struck off.

HOR. Is't possible?

HAM. Here's the commission: read it at more
leisure. But wilt thou bear me how I did
proceed?

HOR. I beseech you.

HAM. Being thus benetted round with
villanies,—or I could make a prologue to my
brains, they had begun the play,—I sat me
down; devis'd a new commission; wrote it
fair: I once did hold it, as our statists[3] do, a
baseness to write fair, and labour'd much how
to forget that learning; but, sir, now it did me
yeoman's service. Wilt thou know the effect
of what I wrote?

HOR. Ay, good my lord.

HAM. An earnest conjuration from the king,—as
England was his faithful tributary; as love
between them like the palm might flourish; as
pease should still her wheaten garland wear
and stand a comma[4] 'tween their amities; and
my such-like as's of great charge,—that, on
the view and know of these contents, without
debatement further, more or less, he should
the bearers put to sudden death, not
shriving-time[5] allow'd.

HOR. How was this seal'd?

HAM. Why, even in that was heaven ordinant. I
had my father's signet in my purse, which
was the model of that Danish seal: folded the
writ up in the form of the other; subscrib'd it:
gave't the impression; plac'd it safely, the
changeling never known. Now, the next day
was our sea-fight; and what to this was
sequent thou know'st already.

HOR. So Guildenstern and Rosencrantz go to't.

HAM. Why, man, they did make love to this
employment; they are no near my
conscience; their defeat does by their own
insinuation grow: 'Tis dangerous when the
baser nature comes between the pass and fell
incensed points of might opposites.

HOR. Why, what a king is this!

HAM. Does it not, thinks't thee, stand me now
upon,—he that hath kill'd my king, and
whor'd my mother; popp'd in between the

---

[1]mutineers in fetters

[2]enriched

[3]statesmen

[4]link

[5]absolution

election and my hopes thrown out his angle[6] for my proper life, and with such cozenage[7]—is't not perfect conscience to quit him with this arm? and is't not to be damn'd to let this canker of our nature come in further evil?

HOR. It must be shortly known to him from England what is the issue of the business there.

HAM. It will be short: the interim is mine; and a man's life is no more than to say One. But I am very sorry, good Horatio, that to Laertes I forgot myself; for by the image of my cause I see the portraiture of his: I'll court his favours: but, sure, the bravery of his grief did put me into a towering passion.

HOR. Peace; who comes here?

(Enter Osric.)

OSR. Your lordship is right welcome back to Denmark.

HAM. I humbly thank you, sir. Dost know this water-fly?

HOR. No, my good lord.

HAM. Thy state is the more gracious; for 'tis a vice to know him. He hath much land, and fertile: let a beast be lord of beasts, and his crib shall stand at the king's mess;[8] 'tis a chough;[9] but, as I say, spacious in the possession of dirt.

OSR. Sweet lord, if your lordship were at leisure, I should impart a thing to you from his majesty.

HAM. I will receive it with all diligence of spirit. Put your bonnet to his right use; 'tis for the head.

OSR. I thank your lordship, t'is very hot.

HAM. No, believe me, 'tis very cold; the wind is northerly.

OSR. It is indifferent cold, my lord, indeed.

HAM. Methinks it is very sultry and hot for my complexion.

OSR. Exceedingly, my lord; it is very sultry,—as 'twere—I cannot tell how. But, my lord, his majesty bade me signify to you that he has laid a great wager on your head. Sir, this is the matter,—

HAM. I beseech you, remember,—

(Hamlet moves him to put on his hat.)

OSR. Nay, in good faith; for mine ease, in good faith. Sir, here is newly come to court Laertes; believe me, an absolute gentleman, full of most excellent differences, of very soft society and great showing: indeed, to speak feelingly of him, he is the card or calendar of gentry; for you shall find in him the continent of what part a gentleman would see.

HAM. Sir, his definement suffers no perdition in you;—though, I know, to divide him inventorially would dizzy the arithmetic of memory, and yet but yaw neither, in respect of his quick sail. But, in the verity of extolment, I take him to be a soul of great article, and his infusion of such dearth and rareness as, to make true diction of him, his semblable is his mirror, and who else would trace him, his umbrage,[10] nothing more.

OSR. Your lordship speaks most infallibly of him.

HAM. The concernancy,[11] sir? why do we wrap the gentleman in our more rawer breath?

OSR. Sir?

HOR. Is't not possible to understand in another tongue? You will do't, sir, really.

HAM. What imports the nomination of this gentleman?

OSR. Of Laertes?

HOR. His purse is empty already; all's golden words are spent.

---

[6]fishing line

[7]trickery

[8]table

[9]jackdaw, chatterer

---

[10]shadow

[11]meaning

HAM. Of him, sir.

OSR. I know, you are not ignorant,—

HAM. I would you did, sir; yet, in faith, if you did, it would not much approve me.—Well, sir.

OSR. You are not ignorant of what excellence Laertes is,—

HAM. I dare not confess that, lest I should compare with him in excellence; but to know a man well were to know himself.

OSR. I mean, sir, for his weapon; but in the imputation laid on him by them, in his meed[12] he's unfellowed.

HAM. What's his weapon?

OSR. Rapier and dagger.

HAM. That's two of his weapons:—but well.

OSR. The king, sir, hath wager'd with him six Barbary horses: against the which he has imponed, as I take it, six French rapiers and poniards, with their assigns, as girdle, hangers,[13] and so: three of the carriages, in faith, are very dear to fancy, very responsive to the hilts, most delicate carriages, and of very liberal conceit.

HAM. What call you the carriages?

HOR. I knew you must be edified by the margent ere you had done.

OSR. The carriages, sir, are the hangers.

HAM. The phrase would be more german to the matter if we could carry cannon by our sides. I would it might be hangers till then. But, on: six Barbary horses against six French swords, their assigns, and three liberal conceited carriages: that's the French bet against the Danish: why is this all imponed, as you call it?

OSR. The king, sir, hath laid that, in a dozen passes between yourself and him, he shall not exceed you three hits: he hath laid on twelve for nine; and it would come to immediate trial if your lordship would vouchsafe the answer.

HAM. How if I answer no?

OSR. I mean, my lord, the opposition of your person in trial.

HAM. Sir, I will walk here in the hall: if it please his majesty, it is the breathing time of day with me: let the foils be brought, the gentleman willing, and the king hold his purpose, I will win for him if I can; if not, I will gain nothing but my shame and the odd hits.

OSR. Shall I re-deliver you e'en so?

HAM. To this effect, sir; after what flourish your nature will.

OSR. I commend my duty to your lordship.

HAM. Yours, yours.

(*Exit Osric.*)

He does well to commend it himself; there are no tongues else for's turn.

HOR. This lapwing runs away with the shell on his head.

HAM. He did comply with his dug before he suck'd it. Thus has he,—and many more of the same bevy that I know the drossy age dotes on,—only got the tune of the time and outward habit of encounter; a kind of yesty[14] collection, which carries them through and through the most fanned and winnowed opinions; and do but blow them to their trial, the bubbles are out,

(*Enter a Lord.*)

LORD. My lord, his majesty commended him to you by young Osric, who brings back to him that you attend him in the hall: he sends to know if your pleasure hold to play with Laertes, or that you will take longer time.

HAM. I am constant to my purposes; they follow the king's pleasure: if his fitness speaks, mine is ready; now or whensoever, provided I be so able as now.

---

[12]merit

[13]straps hanging the sword to the belt

[14]frothy

LORD. The King and Queen and all are coming down.

HAM. In happy time.

LORD. The queen desires you to use some gentle entertainment to Laertes before you fall to play.

HAM. She well instructs me.

(*Exit Lord.*)

HOR. You will lose this wager, my lord.

HAM. I do not think so; since he went into France I have been in continual practice: I shall win at the odds. but thou wouldst not think how ill all's here about my heart: but it is no matter.

HOR. Nay, good my lord,—

HAM. It is but foolery; but it is such a kind of gain-giving[15] as would perhaps trouble a woman.

HOR. If your mind dislike anything, obey it: I will forestall their repair hither, and say you are not fit.

HAM. Not a whit, we defy augury: there's a special providence in the fall of a sparrow. If it be now, 'tis not to come; if it be not to come, it will be now; if it be not now, yet it will come: the readiness is all: since no man has aught of what he leaves, what is't to leave betimes?

(*Enter King, Queen, Laertes, Lords, Osric, and Attendants with foils &c.*)

KING. Come, Hamlet, come, and take this hand from me.

(*The King puts Laertes' hand into Hamlet's.*)

HAM. Give me your pardon, sir: I have done you wrong: but pardon't, as you are a gentleman. This presence[16] knows, and you must needs have heard, how I am punish'd with sore distraction. What I have done that might your nature, honour, and exception roughly awake, I here proclaim was madness. Was't Hamlet wrong'd Laertes? Never Hamlet: if Hamlet from himself be ta'en away, and when he's not himself does wrong Laertes, then Hamlet does it not, Hamlet denies it. Who does it, then? His madness: if't be so, Hamlet is of the faction that is wrong'd; his madness is poor Hamlet's enemy. Sir, in this audience, let my disclaiming from a purpos'd evil free me so far in your most generous thoughts that I have shot my arrow o'er the house and hurt my brother.

LAER. I am satisfied in nature, whose motive, in this case, should stir me most to my revenge. But in my terms of honour I stand aloof; and will no reconcilement till by some elder masters of known honour I have a voice and precedent of peace to keep my name ungor'd. But till that time I do receive your offer'd love like love, and will not wrong it.

HAM. I embrace it freely; and will this brother's wager frankly play.—Give us the foils; come on.

LAER. Come, one for me.

HAM. I'll be your foil, Laertes; in mine ignorance your skill shall, like a star in the darkest night, stick fiery off indeed.

LAER. You mock me, sir.

HAM. No, by this hand.

KING. Give them the foils, young Osric. Cousin Hamlet, you know the wager?

HAM. Very well, my lord; your grace has laid the odds o' the weaker side.

KING. I do not fear it; I have seen you both; but since he's better'd, we have therefore odds.

LAER. This is too heavy, let me see another.

HAM. This likes me well. These foils have all a length?

(*They prepare to play.*)

OSR. Ay, my good lord.

KING. Set me the stoups of wine upon that

---

[15]misgiving

[16]royal assembly

table,—if Hamlet give the first or second hit, or quit[17] in answer of the third exchange, let all the battlements their ordnance fire; The king shall drink to Hamlet's better breath; and in the cup an union[18] shall he throw, richer than that which four successive kings in Denmark's crown have worn. Give me the cups; and let the kettle[19] to the trumpet speak, the trumpet to the cannoneer without, the cannons to the heavens, the heavens to earth, 'Now the king drinks to Hamlet.'—Come, begin:—And you, the judges, bear a wary eye.

HAM. Come on, sir.

LAER. Come, my lord.

(*They play.*)

HAM. One.

LAER. No.

HAM. Judgment!

OSR. A hit, a very palpable hit.

LAER. Well;—again.

KING. Stay, give me drink.—Hamlet, this pearl is thine; here's to thy health.—

(*Trumpets sound, and cannon shot off within.*)

Give him the cup.

HAM. I'll play this bout first; set it by awhile.—Come.—Another hit; what say you?

(*They play.*)

LAER. A touch, a touch, I do confess.

KING. Our son shall win.

QUEEN. He's fat, and scant of breath.—Here, Hamlet, take my napkin, rub thy brows: the queen carouses to thy fortune, Hamlet.

HAM. Good madam!

KING. Gertrude, do not drink.

QUEEN. I will, my lord; I pray you pardon me.

KING. [*Aside.*] It is the poison'd cup; it is too late.

HAM. I dare not drink yet, madam; by-and-by.

QUEEN. Come, let me wipe thy face.

LAER. My lord, I'll hit him now.

KING. I do not think't.

LAER. [*Aside.*] And yet 'tis almost 'gainst my conscience.

HAM. Come, for the third, Laertes: you but dally; I pray you pass with your best violence: I am afeard you make a wanton of me.

LAER. Say you so? come on.

(*They play.*)

OSR. Nothing, neither way.

LAER. Have at you now!

(*Laertes wounds Hamlet; then, in scuffling, they change rapiers, and Hamlet wounds Laertes.*)

KING. Part them; they are incens'd.

HAM. Nay, come again!

(*The Queen falls.*)

OSR. Look to the queen there, ho!

HOR. They bleed on both sides.—How is it, my lord?

OSR. How is't, Laertes?

LAER. Why, as a woodcock to my own springe,[20] Osric; I am justly kill'd with mine own treachery.

HAM. How does the Queen?

KING. She swoons[21] to see them bleed.

QUEEN. No, no! the drink, the drink!—O my dear Hamlet!—The drink, the drink!—I am poison'd.

(*Dies.*)

---

[17]hit back

[18]pearl

[19]kettledrum

---

[20]snare

[21]swoons

HAM. O villany!—Ho! let the door be lock'd: Treachery! seek it out.

(*Laertes falls.*)

LAER. It is here, Hamlet: Hamlet, thou are slain; no medicine in the world can do thee good; In thee there is not half an hour of life; the treacherous instrument is in thy hand, Unbated and envenom'd: the foul practice hath turn'd itself on me; lo, here I lie, never to rise again: thy mother's poison'd: I can no more:—the king, the king's to blame.
HAM. The point envenom'd too!—Then, venom, to thy work.

(*Stabs the King.*)

OSRIC AND LORDS. Treason! treason!
KING. O, yet defend me, friends! I am but hurt.
HAM. Here, thou incestuous, murderous, damned Dane, drink off this potion.—Is thy union here? Follow my mother.

(*King dies.*)

LAER. He is justly serv'd; it is a poison temper'd by himself.—Exchange forgiveness with me, noble Hamlet: mine and my father's death come not upon thee, nor thine on me!

(*Dies.*)

HAM. Heaven make thee free of it! I follow thee.—I am dead, Horatio.—Wretched queen, adieu!—You that look pale and tremble at this chance, that are but mutes[22] or audience to this act, had I but time,—as this fell sergeant, death, is strict in his arrest,—O, I could tell you,—But let it be.—Horatio, I am dead; Thou liv'st; report me and my cause aright to the unsatisfied.

HOR. Never believe it: I am more an antique Roman[23] than a Dane.—Here's yet some liquor left.
HAM. As thou'rt a man. Give me the cup; let go; by heaven, I'll have't.—O good Horatio, what a wounded name, things standing thus unknown , shall live behind me! If thou didst ever hold me in thy heart, absent thee from felicity awhile, and in this harsh world draw thy breath in pain. To tell my story.—

(*March afar off, and shot within.*)

What warlike noise is this?
OSR. Young Fortinbras, with conquest come from Poland, to the ambassadors of England gives this warlike volley.
HAM. O, I die, Horatio; the potent poison quite o'er-crows my spirit: I cannot live to hear the news from England; but I do prophesy the election lights on Fortinbras: he has my dying voice; so tell him, with the occurrents,[24] more and less, which has solicited.—the rest is silence.

(*Dies.*)

HOR. Now cracks a noble heart.—Good night, sweet prince, and flights of angels sing thee to thy rest! Why does the drum come hither?

(*March within.*)

(*Enter Fortinbras, the English Ambassadors, and others.*)

FORT. Where is this sight?
HOR. What is it you will see? If aught of woe or wonder, cease your search.
FORT. This quarry[25] cries on havoc.—O proud death, what feast is toward in thine eternal

---

[23]reference to the old Roman fashion of suicide

[24]occurrences

[25]heap of slain bodies

---

[22]preformers who have no lines to speak

cell, that thou so many princes at a shot so bloodily hast struck?

1 AMBASSADOR. The sight is dismal; and our affairs from England come too late: the ears are senseless that should give us hearing, to tell him his commandment is fulfill'd That Rosencrantz and Guildenstern are dead: where should we have our thanks?

HOR. Not from his mouth, had it the ability of life to thank you: he never gave commandment for their death. But since, so jump[26] upon this bloody question, you from the Polack wars, and you from England, are here arriv'd, give order that these bodies high on a stage be placed to the view; and let me speak to the yet unknowing world how these things came about: so shall you hear of carnal, bloody and unnatural acts; of accidental judgments, casual slaughters; of deaths put on by cunning and forc'd cause; and, in this upshot, purposes mistook fall'n on the inventors' heads: all this can I truly deliver.

FORT. Let us haste to hear it. And call the noblest to the audience. For me, with sorrow I embrace my fortune: I have some rights of memory in this kingdom, which now, to claim my vantage doth invite me.

HOR. Of that I shall have also cause to speak, and from his mouth whose voice will draw on more: but let this same be presently perform'd, even while men's minds are wild: lest more mischance on plots and errors happen.

FORT. Let four captains Bear Hamlet like a soldier to the stage; for he was likely, had he been put on, to have prov'd most royally: and, for his passage, the soldiers' music and the rites of war speak loudly for him.—Take up the bodies.—Such a sight as this becomes the field, but here shows much amiss. Go, bid the soldiers shoot.

(*A dead march.*)

(*Exeunt, bearing off the dead bodies; after the which a peal of ordnance is shot off.*)

---

[26]precisely

William Shakespeare: Romeo and Juliet

▪ Dramatis Personae

Escalus, Prince of Verona.
Paris, a young nobleman, kinsman to the Prince.
Montague,   heads of two houses at variance
Capulet,   with each other.

An old man, of the Capulet family.
Romeo, son to Montague.
Mercutio, kinsman to the Prince, a friend
    to Romeo.
Benvolio, nephew to Mortague, a friend
    to Romeo.
Tybalt, nephew to Lady Capulet.
Friar Laurence, a Franciscan.
Friar John, of the same order.
Balthasar, servant to Romeo.
Sampson, servants to Capulet.
Gregory,
Peter, servant to Juliet's nurse.
Abraham, servant to Montague.
An Apothecary.
Three Musicians.
Page to Paris, another Page; an Officer.
Lady Montague, wife to Montague.
Lady Capulet, wife to Capulet.
Juliet, daughter to Capulet.
Nurse to Juliet.
Citizens of Verona; kinsfolk of both houses;
    Maskers, Guards, Watchmen, and Attendants.
Chorus

Source: From *Romeo and Juliet* by William Shakespeare.

▪ Scene: Verona; Mantua

Act I
Scene V. A Hall in Capulet's House

Enter CAPULET, *with* JULIET *and others of his house, meeting the* Guests *and* Maskers.

CAP. Welcome, gentlemen! ladies that have their toes unplagued with corns will have a bout with you: ah ha, my mistresses! which of you all will now deny to dance! she that makes dainty, she, I'll swear, hath corns; am I come near ye now? Welcome, gentlemen! I have seen the day that I have worn a visor, and could tell a whispering tale in a fair lady's ear, such as would please: 'tis gone, 'tis gone, 'tis gone: you are welcome, gentlemen! Come, musicians, play. A hall, a hall! give room! and foot it, girls.

(*Music plays, and they dance.*)

More light, you knaves; and turn the tables up, and quench the fire, the room is grown too hot. Ah, sirrah, this unlook'd-for sport comes well. Nay, sit, nay, sit, good cousin Capulet; for you and I are past our dancing days: how long is't now since last yourself and I were in a mask?
SEC. CAP. By'r lady, thirty years.
CAP. What, man! 'tis not so much, 'tis not so much: 'Tis since the nuptial of Lucentio, come Pentecost as quickly as it will, some five and twenty years; and then we mask'd.

Sec. Cap. 'Tis more, 'tis more: his son is elder, sir; his son is thirty.

Cap. Will you tell me that? His son was but a ward two years ago.

Rom. [*To a* Servingman] What lady's that, which doth enrich the hand Of yonder knight?

Serv. I know not, sir.

Rom. O, she doth teach the torches to burn bright! It seems she hangs upon the cheek of night like a rich jewel in an Ethiop's ear; beauty too rich for use, for earth too dear! So shows a snowy dove trooping with crows, as yonder lady o'er her fellows shows.The measure done, I'll watch her place of stand, and, touching hers, make blessed my rude hand. Did my heart love till now? forswear it, sight! For I ne'er saw true beauty till this night.

Tyb. This, by his voice, should be a Montague. Fetch me my rapier, boy. What dares the slave come higher, cover'd with an antic face,[1] to fleer[2] and scorn at out solemnity? Now, by the stock and honour of my kin, to strike him dead I hold it not a sin.

Cap. Why, how now, kinsman! wherefore storm you so?

Tyb. Uncle, this is a Montague, our foe; a villain, that is hither come in spite, to scorn at our solemnity this night.

Cap. Young Romeo is it?

Tyb. 'Tis he, that villain Romeo.

Cap. Content thee, gentle coz, let him alone, he bears him like a portly[3] gentleman; and, to say truth, Verona brags of him to be a virtuous and well-govern'd youth: I would not for the wealth of all this town here in my house do him disparagement: therefore be patient, take no note of him: it is my will, the which if thou respect, show a fair presence and put off these frowns, an ill-beseeming semblance for a feast.

Tyb. It fits, when such a villain is a guest: I'll not endure him.

Cap. He shall be endured: what, goodman[4] boy! I say, he shall: go to; am I the master here, or you? go to. You'll not endure him! God shall mend my soul, you'll make a mutiny among my guests! You will set cock-a-hoop![5] you'll be the man!

Tyb. Why, uncle, 'tis a shame.

Cap. Go to, go to; you are a saucy boy: is't so, indeed? This trick may chance to scathe you, I know what: you must contrary me! marry, 'tis time. Well said, my hearts! You are a princox; go: be quiet, or—More light, more light! For shame! I'll make you quiet. What, cheerly, my hearts!

Tyb. Patience perforce with wilful choler meeting makes my flesh tremble in their different greeting. I will withdraw: but this intrusion shall, now seeming sweet, convert to bitterest gall.

(*Exit*)

Rom. [*To* Juliet] If I profane with my unworthiest hand this holy shrine, the gentle fine is this, my lips, two blushing pilgrims, ready stand to smooth that rough touch with a tender kiss.

Jul. Good pilgrim, you do wrong your hand too much, which mannerly devotion shows in this; for saints have hands that pilgrims' hands do touch, and palm to palm is holy palmers' kiss.

Rom. Have not saints lips, and holy palmers too?

Jul. Ay, pilgrim, lips that they must use in prayer.

Rom. O, then, dear saint, let lips do what hands do; they pray, grant thou, lest faith turn to despair.

Jul. Saints do not move, though grant for prayers' sake.

---

[1]*antic face*] odd-looking mask.

[2]*fleer*] grin mockingly.

[3]*portly*] well-bred, dignified.

---

[4]*goodman*] below the rank of gentleman.

[5]*set cock-a-hoop*] pick a quarrel.

ROM. Then move not, while my prayer's effect I take. Thus from my lips by thine my sin is purged.

(*Kissing her*)

JUL. Then have my lips the sin that they have took.
ROM. Sin from my lips? O trespass sweetly urged! Give me my sin again.
JUL. You kiss by the book.
NURSE. Madam, your mother craves a word with you.
ROM. What is her mother?
NURSE. Marry, bachelor, her mother is the lady of the house, and a good lady, and a wise and virtuous: I nursed her daughter, that you talk'd withal; I tell you, he that can lay hold of her shall have the chinks.[6]
ROM. Is she a Capulet? O dear account! my life is my foe's debt.
BEN. Away, be gone; the sport is at the best.
ROM. Ay, so I fear; the more is my unrest.
CAP. Nay, gentlemen, prepare not to be gone; we have a trifling foolish[7] banquet towards.[8] Is it e'en so? why, then, I thank you all; I thank you, honest gentlemen; good night. More torches here! Come on then, let's to bed. Ah, sirrah, by may fay, it waxes late: I'll to my rest.

(*Exeunt all but* **Juliet** *and* **Nurse**)
JUL. Come hither, Nurse. What is yond gentleman?
NURSE. The son and heir of old Tiberio.
JUL. What's he that now is going out of door?
NURSE. Marry, that, I think, be young Petruchio.
JUL. What's he that follows there, that would not dance?
NURSE. I know not.

JUL. Go ask his name. If he be married, my grave is like to be my wedding bed.
NURSE. His name is Romeo, and a Montague, the only son of your great enemy.
JUL. My only love sprung from my only hate! Too early seen unknown, and known too late! Prodigious birth of love it is to me, that I must love a loathed enemy.
NURSE. What's this? what's this?
JUL. A rhyme I learn'd even now of one I danced withal.

(*One calls within 'Juliet'*)

NURSE. Anon, anon! Come, let's away; the strangers all are gone.

(*Exeunt*)

■ **Act II**

Scene II. Capulet's Orchard
[*Enter* ROMEO]

ROM. He jests at scars that never felt a wound.

(***Juliet** appears above at a window*)

But, soft! what light through yonder window breaks? It is the east, and Juliet is the sun! Arise, fair sun, and kill the envious moon, who is already sick and pale with grief, that thou her maid art far more fair than she: be not her maid, since she is envious; her vestal livery is but sick and green, and none but fools do wear it; cast it off. It is my lady; O, it is my love! O, that she knew she were! She speaks, yet she says nothing: what of that! Her eye discourses, I will answer it. I am too bold, 'tis not to me she speaks: two of the fairest stars in all the heaven, having some business, do intreat her eyes to twinkle in their spheres till they return. What if her eyes were there, they in her head? The brightness of her cheek would shame those stars, as daylight doth a lamp; her eyes in heaven

---

[6]*have the chinks*] acquire a financial fortune.

[7]*foolish*] small-scale.

[8]*towards*] in preparation.

would through the airy region stream so bright that birds would sing and think it were not night. See, how she leans her cheek upon her hand! O, that I were a glove upon that hand, that I might touch that cheek!

JUL. Ay me!

ROM. She speaks: O, speak again bright angel! for thou art as glorious to this night, being o'er my head, as is a winged messenger of heaven unto the white-upturned wondering eyes of mortals that fall back to gaze on him, when he bestrides the lazy-pacing clouds and sails upon the bosom of the air.

JUL. O Romeo, Romeo! wherefore art thou Romeo? Deny thy father and refuse thy name; or, if thou wilt not, be but sworn my love, and I'll no longer be a Capulet.

ROM. [*Aside*] Shall I hear more, or shall I speak at this?

JUL. 'Tis but thy name that is my enemy; thou are thyself, though not a Montague. What's Montague? it is nor hand, nor foot, nor arm, nor face, nor any other part belonging to a man. O, be some other name! What's in a name? that which we call a rose by any other name would smell as sweet; so Romeo would, were he not Romeo call'd, retain that dear perfection which he owes[1] without that title. Romeo, doff thy name, and for thy name, which is no part of thee, take all myself.

ROM. I take thee at thy word: call me but love, and I'll be new baptized; henceforth I never will be Romeo.

JUL. What man art thou, that, thus bescreen'd in night, so stumblest on my counsel?

ROM. By a name I know not how to tell thee who I am: my name, dear saint, is hateful to myself, because it is an enemy to thee; had I it written, I would tear the word.

JUL. My ears have yet not drunk a hundred words of thy tongue's uttering, yet I know the sound: art thou not Romeo, and a Montague?

ROM. Neither, fair maid, if either thee dislike.

JUL. How camest thou hither, tell me, and wherefore? The orchard walls are high and hard to climb, and the place death, considering who thou art, if any of my kinsmen find thee here.

ROM. With love's light wings did I o'er-perch these walls, for stony limits cannot hold love out: and what love can do, that dares love attempt; therefore thy kinsmen are no let[2] to me.

JUL. If they do see thee, they will murder thee.

ROM. Alack, there lies more peril in thine eye than twenty of their swords: look thou but sweet, and I am proof against their enmity.

JUL. I would not for the world they saw thee here.

ROM. I have night's cloak to hide me from their eyes; and but thou love me, let them find me here: my life were better ended by their hate, than death prorogued,[3] wanting of thy love.

JUL. By whose direction found'st thou out this place?

ROM. By love, that first did prompt me to inquire; he lent me counsel, and I lent him eyes. I am no pilot; yet, wert thou as far as that vast shore wash'd with the farthest sea, I would adventure for such merchandise.

JUL. Thou know'st the mask of night is on my face, else would a maiden blush bepaint my cheek for that which thou hast heard me speak to-night. Fain would I dwell on form, fain, fain deny what I have spoke: but farewell compliment! Dost thou love me? I know thou wilt say 'Ay,' and I will take thy word: yet, if thou swear'st, thou mayst prove false: at lovers' perjuries, they say, Jove laughs. O gentle Romeo, if thou dost love, pronounce it faithfully: or if thou think'st I am too quickly won, I'll frown and be perverse and say thee nay, so thou wilt woo; but else, not for the world. In truth, fair Montague, I am too fond;[5] and therefore thou

---

[1]*owes*] possesses.

[2]*let*] hindrance.

[3]*prorogued*] postponed.

[5]*fond*] foolish.

mayst think my 'havior light: but trust me, gentleman, I'll prove more true than those that have more cunning to be strange.[6] I should have been more strange, I must confess, but that thou overheard'st, ere I was ware, my true love's passion: therefore pardon me, and not impute this yielding to light love, which the dark night hath so discovered.

ROM. Lady, by yonder blessed moon I swear, that tips with silver all these fruit-tree tops,—

JUL. O, swear not by the moon, th' inconstant moon, that monthly changes in her circled orb, lest that thy love prove likewise variable.

ROM. What shall I swear by?

JUL. Do not swear at all; or, if thou wilt, swear by thy gracious self, which is the god of my idolatry, and I'll believe thee.

ROM. If my heart's dear love—

JUL. Well, do not swear: although I joy in thee, I have no joy of this contract to-night: it is too rash, too unadvised, too sudden, too like the lightning, which doth cease to be ere one can say 'It lightens.' Sweet, good night! This bud of love, by summer's ripening breath, may prove a beauteous flower when next we meet. Good night, good night! as sweet repose and rest come to thy heart as that within my breast!

ROM. O, wilt thou leave me so unsatisfied?

JUL. What satisfaction canst thou have to-night?

ROM. The exchange of thy love's faithful vow for mine.

JUL. I gave thee mine before thou didst request it: and yet I would it were to give again.

ROM. Wouldst thou withdraw it? for what purpose, love?

JUL. But to be frank,[7] and give it thee again. And yet I wish but for the thing I have: my bounty is as boundless as the sea, my love as deep; the more I give to thee, the more I have, for both are infinite. I hear some noise within; dear love, adieu!

(*Nurse calls within*)

Anon, good Nurse! Sweet Montague, be true. Stay but a little, I will come again.

(*Exit*)

ROM. O blessed, blessed night! I am afeard, being in night, all this is but a dream, too flattering-sweet to be substantial.

(*Re-enter* **Juliet**, *above*)

JUL. Three words, dear Romeo, and good night indeed. If that thy bent of love be honourable, thy purpose marriage, send me word to-morrow, by one that I'll procure to come to thee, where and what time thou wilt perform the rite, and all my fortunes at thy foot I'll lay, and follow thee my lord throughout the world.

NURSE. [*Within*] Madam!

JUL. I come, anon.—But if thou mean'st not well, I do beseech thee—

NURSE. [*Within*] Madam!

JUL. By and by, I come:—to cease thy suit, and leave me to my grief: to-morrow will I send.

ROM. So thrive my soul,—

JUL. A thousand times good night!

(*Exit*)

ROM. A thousand times the worse, to want thy light. Love goes toward love, as schoolboys from their books, but love from love, toward school with heavy looks.

(*Retiring slowly*)

(*Re-enter* **Juliet**, *above*)

JUL. Hist! Romeo, hist!—O, for a falconer's voice, to lure this tassel-gentle[8] back again!

---

[6]*strange*] reserved, distant.

[7]*frank*] bountiful.

[8]*tassel-gentle*] male goshawk.

Bondage is hoarse, and may not speak aloud;
else would I tear the cave where Echo lies,
and make her airy tongue more hoarse than
mine, with repetition of my Romeo's name.
Romeo!

ROM. It is my soul that calls upon my name: how
silver-sweet sound lovers' tongues by night,
like softest music to attending ears!

JUL. Romeo!

ROM. My dear?

JUL. At what o'clock to-morrow shall I send to
thee?

ROM. At the hour of nine.

JUL. I will not fail: 'tis twenty years till then. I
have forgot why I did call thee back.

ROM. Let me stand here till thou remember it.

JUL. I shall forget, to have thee still stand there,
remembering how I love thy company.

ROM. And I'll still stay, to have thee still forget,
forgetting any other home but this.

JUL. 'Tis almost morning; I would have thee
gone: and yet no farther than a wanton's bird,
who lets it hop a little from her hand, like a
poor prisoner in his twisted gyves, and with a
silk thread plucks it back again, so
loving-jealous of his liberty.

ROM. I would I were thy bird.

JUL. Sweet, so would I: yet I should kill thee with
much cherishing. Good night, good night!
parting is such sweet sorrow that I shall say
good night till it be morrow.

(*Exit*)

ROM. Sleep dwell upon thine eyes, peace in thy
breast! Would I were sleep and peace, so
sweet to rest! Hence will I to my ghostly[9]
father's cell, his help to crave and my dear
hap[10] to tell.

(*Exit*)

---

[9]*ghostly*] spiritual.

[10]*hap*] fortune.

■ **Act V**

Scene III. A Churchyard; in It a Monument Belonging to the Capulets

[*Enter* PARIS *and his* Page, *bearing flowers and a torch*]

PAR. Give me thy torch, boy: hence, and stand
aloof: yet put it out, for I would not be seen.
Under yond yew-trees lay thee all along.[1]
Holding thine ear close to the hollow ground;
so shall no foot upon the churchyard tread,
being loose, unfirm, with digging up of
graves, but thou shalt hear it: whistle then to
me, as signal that thou hear'st something
approach. Give me those flowers. Do as I bid
thee, go.

PAGE. [*Aside*] I am almost afraid to stand alone
here in the churchyard; yet I will adventure.

(*Retires*)

PAR. Sweet flower, with flowers thy bridal bed
I strew,—O woe! thy canopy is dust and
stones;—which with sweet water nightly
I will dew, or, wanting that, with tears
distill'd by moans: the obsequies that I for
thee will keep nightly shall be to strew thy
grave and weep.

(*The* Page *whistles*)

The boy gives warning something doth
approach. What cursed foot wanders this way
to-night, to cross my obsequies and true
love's rite? What, with a torch! Muffle me,
night, a while.

(*Retires*)

Enter ROMEO *and* BALTHASAR, *with a torch,
mattock, &c.*

ROM. Give me that mattock and the wrenching
iron. Hold, take this letter; early in the

---

[1]*all along*] at full length.

morning see thou deliver it to my lord and father. Give me the light: upon thy life, I charge thee, whate'er thou hear'st or seest, stand all aloof, and do not interrupt me in my course. Why I descend into this bed of death is partly to behold my lady's face, but chiefly to take thence from her dead finger a precious ring, a ring that I must use in dear employment: therefore hence, be gone: but if thou, jealous,[2] dost return to pry in what I farther shall intend to do, by heaven, I will tear thee joint by joint and strew this hungry churchyard with thy limbs: the time and my intents are savage-wild, more fierce and more inexorable far than empty tigers or the roaring sea.

Bal. I will be gone, sir, and not trouble you.

Rom. So shalt thou show me friendship. Take thou that: live, and be prosperous: and farewell, good fellow.

Bal. [*Aside*] For all this same, I'll hide me hereabout: his looks I fear, and his intents I doubt.

(*Retires*)

Rom. Thou detestable maw, thou womb of death, gorged with the dearest morsel of the earth, thus I enforce thy rotten jaws to open, and in despite I'll cram thee with more food.

(*Opens the tomb*)

Par. This is that banish'd haughty Montague that murder'd my love's cousin, with which grief, it is supposed, the fair creature died, and here is come to do some villanous shame to the dead bodies: I will apprehend him.

(*Comes forward*)

Stop thy unhallow'd toil, vile Montague! Can vengeance be pursued further than death? Condemned villain, I do apprehend thee: obey, and go with me; for thou must die.

Rom. I must indeed, and therefore came I hither. Good gentle youth, tempt not a desperate man; fly hence and leave me: think upon these gone; let them affright thee. I beseech thee, youth, put not another sin upon my head, by urging me to fury: O, be gone! By heaven, I love thee better than myself, for I come hither arm'd against myself: stay not, be gone: live, and hereafter say, a madman's mercy bid thee run away.

Par. I do defy thy conjurations[3] and apprehend thee for a felon here.

Rom. Wilt thou provoke me? then have at thee, boy!

(*They fight*)

Page. O Lord, they fight! I will go call the watch.

(*Exit*)

Par. O, I am slain! [*Falls.*] If thou be merciful, open the tomb, lay me with Juliet.

(*Dies*)

Rom. In faith, I will. Let me peruse this face: Mercutio's kinsman, noble County Paris! What said my man, when my betossed soul did not attend him as we rode? I think he told me Paris should have married Juliet: said he not so? or did I dream it so? Or am I mad, hearing him talk of Juliet, to think it was so? O, give me thy hand, one writ with me in sour misfortune's book! I'll bury thee in a triumphant grave; a grave! O, no, a lantern,[4] slaughter'd youth; for here lies Juliet, and her beauty makes this vault a feasting presence[5] full of light. Death, lie thou there, by a dead man interr'd.

(*Laying* Paris *in the monument*)

---

[2]*jealous*] suspicious.

[3]*conjurations*] solemn appeals.

[4]*lantern*] turret full of windows.

[5]*presence*] presence chamber.

How oft when men are at the point of death have they been merry! which their keepers call a lightning before death: O, how may I call this a lightning? O my love! my wife! Death, that hath suck'd the honey of thy breath, hath had no power yet upon thy beauty: thou are not conquer'd; beauty's ensign yet is crimson in thy lips and in thy cheeks, and death's pale flag is not advanced there. Tybalt, liest thou there in thy bloody sheet? O, what more favour can I do to thee than with that hand that cut thy youth in twain to sunder his that was thine enemy? Forgive me, cousin! Ah, dear Juliet, why art thou yet so fair? Shall I believe that unsubstantial death is amorous, and that the lean abhorred monster keeps thee here in dark to be his paramour? For fear of that, I still will stay with thee, and never from this palace of dim night depart again: here, here will I remain with worms that are thy chamber-maids; O, here will I set up my everlasting rest, and shake the yoke of inauspicious stars from this world-wearied flesh. Eyes, look your last! Arms, take your last embrace! and, lips, O you the doors of breath, seal with a righteous kiss a dateless[6] bargain to engrossing death! Come, bitter conduct, come, unsavoury guide! Thou desperate pilot, now at once run on the dashing rocks thy sea-sick weary bark. Here's to my love! [*Drinks.*] O true apothecary! Thy drugs are quick. Thus with a kiss I die.

(*Dies*)

(*Enter, at the other end of the churchyard,* **Friar Laurence,** *with a lantern, crow, and spade*)

Fri. L. Saint Francis be my speed![7] how oft to-night have my old feet stumbled at graves! Who's there?

Bal. Here's one, a friend, and one that knows you well.

Fri. L. Bliss be upon you! Tell me, good my friend, what torch is yond that vainly lends his light to grubs and eyeless skulls? As I discern, it burneth in the Capels' monument.

Bal. It doth so, holy sir; and there's my master, one that you love.

Fri. L. Who is it?

Bal. Romeo.

Fri. L. How long hath he been there?

Bal. Full half an hour.

Fri. L. Go with me to the vault.

Bal. I dare not, sir: my master knows not but I am gone hence; and fearfully did menace me with death, if I did stay to look on his intents.

Fri. L. Stay, then; I'll go alone: fear comes upon me; O, much I fear some ill unlucky thing.

Bal. As I did sleep under this yew-tree here, I dreamt my master and another fought, and that my master slew him.

Fri. L. Romeo!

(*Advances*)

Alack, alack, what blood is this, which stains the stony entrance of this sepulchre? What mean these masterless and gory swords to lie discolour'd by this place of peace?

(*Enters the tomb*)

Romeo! O, pale! Who else? what, Paris too? And steep'd in blood? Ah, what an unkind hour is guilty of this lamentable chance! The lady stirs.

(Juliet *wakes*)

Jul. O comfortable Friar! where is my lord? I do remember well where I should be, and there I am: where is my Romeo?

(*Noise within*)

Fri. L. I hear some noise. Lady, come from that nest of death, contagion and unnatural sleep:

---

[6]*dateless*] eternal.

[7]*speed*] protecting and assisting power.

a greater power than we can contradict hath
thwarted our intents: come, come away: thy
husband in thy bosom there lies dead; and
Paris too: come, I'll dispose of thee among a
sisterhood of holy nuns: stay not to question,
for the watch is coming; come, go, good
Juliet; I dare no longer stay.

Jul. Go, get thee hence, for I will not away.

(*Exit* **Fri. L.**)

What's here? a cup, closed in my true love's
hand? Poison, I see, hath been his timeless
end: O churl! drunk all, and left no friendly
drop to help me after? I will kiss thy lips;
haply some poison yet doth hang on them, to
make me die with a restorative.

(*Kisses him*)

Thy lips are warm.

First Watch. [*Within*] Lead, boy: which way?

Jul. Yea, noise? then I'll be brief. O happy
dagger!

(*Snatching* **Romeo's** *dagger*)

This is thy sheath [*Stabs herself*]; there rust, and
let me die.

(*Falls on* **Romeo's** *body, and dies*)

(*Enter* Watch, *with the* Page *of* Paris)

Page. This is the place; there, where the torch
doth burn.

First Watch. The ground is bloody; search
about the churchyard: go, some of you,
whoe'er you find attach.[8] Pitiful sight! here
lies the County slain; and Juliet bleeding,
warm, and newly dead, who here hath lain
this two days buried. Go, tell the Prince: run
to the Capulets: raise up the Montagues:
some others search: we see the ground
whereon these woes do lie; but the true

ground of all these piteous woes we cannot
without circumstance[9] descry.

(*Re-enter some of the* Watch, *with* Balthasar)

Sec. Watch. Here's Romeo's man; we found him
in the churchyard.

First Watch. Hold him in safety, till the Prince
come hither.

(*Re-enter* Friar Laurence, *and another*
Watchman)

Third Watch. Here is a friar, that trembles,
sighs and weeps: we took this mattock and
this spade from him, as he was coming from
this churchyard's side.

First Watch. A great suspicion: stay the friar too.

(*Enter the* Prince *and Attendants*)

Prince. What misadventure is so early up, that
calls our person from our morning rest?

(*Enter* Capulet, Lady Capulet, *and others*)

Cap. What should it be that they so shriek
abroad?

La. Cap. The people in the street cry Romeo,
some Juliet, and some Paris, and all run with
open outcry toward our monument.

Prince. What fear is this which startles in
our ears?

First Watch. Sovereign, here lies the County
Paris slain; and Romeo dead; and Juliet, dead
before, warm and new kill'd.

Prince. Search, seek, and know how this foul
murder comes.

First Watch. Here is a friar, and slaughter'd
Romeo's man, with instruments upon them fit
to open these dead men's tombs.

Cap. O heavens! O wife, look how our daughter
bleeds! This dagger hath mista'en, for, lo, his
house is empty on the back of Montague, and
it mis-sheathed in my daughter's bosom!

---

[8]*attach*] arrest.

[9]*circumstance*] detailed information.

LA. CAP. O me! this sight of death is as a bell that warns my old age to a sepulchre.

(*Enter* MONTAGUE *and others*)

PRINCE. Come, Montague; for thou art early up, to see thy son and heir more early down.

MON. Alas, my liege, my wife is dead to-night; grief of my son's exile hath stopp'd her breath: what further woe conspires against mine age?

PRINCE. Look, and thou shalt see.

MON. O thou untaught! what manners is in this, to press before thy father to a grave?

PRINCE. Seal up the mouth of outrage[10] for a while, till we can clear these ambiguities, and know their spring, their head, their true descent; and then will I be general of your woes, and lead you even to death: meantime forbear, and let mischance be slave to patience. Bring forth the parties of suspicion.

FRI. L. I am the greatest, able to do least, yet most suspected, as the time and place doth make against me, of this direful murder; and here I stand, both to impeach and purge myself condemned and myself excused.

PRINCE. Then say at once what thou dost know in this.

FRI. L. I will be brief, for my short date of breath is not so long as is a tedious tale. Romeo, there dead, was husband to that Juliet; and she, there dead, that Romeo's faithful wife: I married them; and their stol'n marriage-day was Tybalt's dooms-day, whose untimely death banish'd the new-made bridegroom from this city; for whom, and not for Tybalt, Juliet pined. You, to remove that siege of grief from her, betroth'd and would have married her perforce to County Paris: then comes she to me, and with wild looks bid me devise some mean to rid her from this second marriage, or in my cell there would she kill herself. Then gave I her, so tutor'd by my art, a sleeping potion; which so took effect as I intended, for it wrought on her the form of death: meantime I writ to Romeo, that he should hither come as this dire night, to help to take her from her borrow'd grave, being the time the potion's force should cease. But he which bore my letter, Friar John, was stay'd by accident, and yesternight return'd my letter back. Then all alone at the prefixed hour of her waking came I to take her from her kindred's vault, meaning to keep her closely[11] at my cell till I conveniently could send to Romeo: but when I came, some minute ere the time of her awaking, here untimely lay the noble Paris and true Romeo dead. She wakes, and I entreated her come forth, and bear this work of heaven with patience: but then a noise did scare me from the tomb, and she too desperate would not go with me, but, as it seems, did violence on herself. All this I know; and to the marriage her nurse is privy: and, if aught in this miscarried by my fault, let my old life be sacrificed some hour before his time unto the rigour of severest law.

PRINCE. We still[12] have known thee for a holy man. Where's Romeo's man? what can he say in this?

BAL. I brought my master news of Juliet's death, and then in post he came from Mantua to this same place, to this same monument. This letter he early bid me give his father, and threaten'd me with death, going in the vault, if I departed not and left him there.

PRINCE. Give me the letter; I will look on it. Where is the County's page, that raised the watch? Sirrah, what made your master in this place?

PAGE. He came with flowers to strew his lady's grave; and bid me stand aloof, and so I did: Anon comes one with light to ope the tomb; and by and by my master drew on him; and then I ran away to call the watch.

PRINCE. This letter doth make good the Friar's words, their course of love, the tidings of her

---

[10]*outrage*] outcry.

[11]*closely*] in secret.

[12]*still*] always.

death: and here he writes that he did buy a poison of a poor 'pothecary, and therewithal came to this vault to die and lie with Juliet. Where be these enemies? Capulet! Montague! See, what a scourge is laid upon your hate, that heaven finds means to kill your joys with love! And I, for winking at your discords too, have lost a brace of kinsmen: all are punish'd.

CAP. O brother Montague, give me thy hand: this is my daughter's jointure,[13] for no more can I demand.

MON. But I can give thee more: for I will raise her statue in pure gold; that while Verona by that name is known, there shall no figure at such rate[14] be set as that of true and faithful Juliet.

CAP. As rich shall Romeo's by his lady's lie; poor sacrifices of our enmity!

PRINCE. A glooming peace this morning with it brings; the sun for sorrow will not show his head: go hence, to have more talk of these sad things; some shall be pardon'd and some punished: for never was a story of more woe than this of Juliet and her Romeo.

(*Exeunt*)

---

[13]*jointure*] the marriage portion supplied by the bridegroom.

[14]*rate*] value.

■ Sonnet 18

When I do count the clock that tells the time
And see the brave day sunk in hideous night,
When I behold the violet past prime
And sable curls o'ersilvered are with white,
When lofty trees I see barren of leaves,
Which erst from heat did canopy the herd,
And summer's green all girded up in sheaves
Borne on the bier with white and bristly beard;
Then of thy beauty do I question make
That thou among the wastes of time must go,
Since sweets and beauties do themselves forsake
And die as fast as they see others grow;
    And nothing 'gainst Time's scythe can
      make defense
    Save breed, to brave him when he takes thee
      hence.

■ Sonnet 12

Shall I compare thee to a summer's day?
Thou art more lovely and more temperate.
Rough winds to shake the darling buds
    of May,
And summer's lease hath all too short a date.
Sometime too hot the eye of heaven shines,
And often is his gold complexion dimmed;
And every fair from fair sometime declines,
By chance, or nature's changing course,
    untrimmed:
But thy eternal summer shall not fade
Nor lose possession of that fair thou ow'st,
Nor shall Death brag thou wander'st in his shade
When in eternal lines to time thou grow'st.
    So long as men can breathe or eyes can see,
    So long lives this, and this gives life to thee.

Source: From *The Sonnets* by William Shakespeare, edited by Stephen Orgel (New York: Penguin Books, 2001).

1 *count . . . clock* keep track of the chimes; *tells* (1) counts, (2) recounts 2 *brave* splendid 4 *sable* black 6 *erst* formerly 7 *green* wheat (implying youth) 9 *question make* speculate 10 *wastes of time* (1) things destroyed by time, (2) wastelands of time, (3) results of wasted time 11 *themselves forsake* (1) give themselves up to death, (2) abandon their true selves 14 *breed* offspring; *brave* defy

4 *lease* allotted time; *date* duration 7 *fair . . . fair* beautiful thing from beauty 8 *untrimmed* stripped of adornment 10 *fair . . . ow'st* beauty you own 11 *shade* darkness 12 *to time* to the end of time

■ Sonnet 116

When, in disgrace with fortune and men's eyes,
I all alone beweep my outcast state,
And trouble deaf heaven with my bootless cries,
And look upon myself and curse my fate,
Wishing me like to one more rich in hope,
Featured like him, like him with friends
  possessed,
Desiring this man's art, and that man's scope,
With what I most enjoy contented least;
Yet in these thoughts myself almost despising,
Haply I think on thee, and then my state,
Like to the lark at break of day arising
From sullen earth, sings hymns at heaven's gate;
    For thy sweet love remembered such wealth
      brings
    That then I scorn to change my state with
      kings.

■ Sonnet 20

Let me not to the marriage of true minds
Admit impediments; love is not love
Which alters when it alteration finds
Or bends with the remover to remove.
O, no, it is an ever-fixèd mark
That looks on tempests and is never shaken;
It is the star to every wand'ring bark,
Whose worth's unknown, although his height be
  taken.
Love's not time's fool, though rose lips and
  cheeks
Within his bending sickle's compass come;
Love alters not with his brief hours and weeks,
But bears it out even to the edge of doom.
    If this be error, and upon me proved,
    I never writ, nor no man ever loved.

---

1 *in disgrace* out of favor 3 *bootless* useless 6 *like him, like him* like one man, like another 7 *art* (1) skill, (2) learning, (3) practical ability; *scope* (1) independence, (2) range of ability, (3) breadth of opportunity 8 *enjoy* (1) possess, (2) take pleasure in 10 *Haply* by chance 12 *sullen* (1) dull, heavy, (2) somber, sad

---

1 *Let me not* i.e., I would never 2 *Admit impediments* concede that there are obstacles (echoing the *marriage* service, which calls on anyone who knows of "any impediment" to the marriage to declare it) 3 *Which . . . finds* (the *impediments* that are denied now clearly come from within the *marriage,* not from without); *alteration* (1) changes of heart, (2) changes effected by time or circumstances 4 *bends . . . remove* inclines to separate because the lover does 5 *mark* lighthouse 7 *star* polestar; *bark* boat 8 *worth's unknown* value is incalculable; *his . . . taken* its altitude can be calculated 9 *Love's . . . fool* time cannot make a fool of love (i.e., love is not subject to time) 10 *bending* (1) curved, (2) causing (what it mows) to bend; *compass* range 11 *his* (1) love's, (2) time's 12 *bears . . . doom* endures even to doomsday 13 *error* (1) legally, a fault in procedure invalidating the judgment, (2) theologically, heresy 14 *no . . . loved* (1) no man has ever been in love, (2) I never loved any man (i.e., the man who is the subject of these sonnets)

Absolute Monarchs
Creative Visions

Chapter 32

> L'etat, c'est moi (I am the state).
>   Roi, loi, foi (One king, one law, one faith).
>
> —*King Louis XIV of France*

■ The Seventeenth Century

The Protestant Reformation led to major changes in Europe in the years immediately following the initial protest of Martin Luther in 1517, but those changes were rather sedate compared to the frenzy of activity in the decades of the 1600s. In Germany, the split between Catholics and Protestants led to warfare that began in 1618 and lasted thirty years. Eventually, almost all the major countries of Europe became involved in the war. When the Thirty Years War and the series of more isolated wars that followed it were concluded, the religious boundaries had changed little, but Germany was so devastated that it would not recover economically or politically for more than two centuries. Denmark, an early participant in the war, passed from a major power to a near-bankrupt state. France emerged as the major power of Europe, largely rising at the expense of Spain. Spain faded to near insignificance. The Austrian rulers,

Hapsburg cousins of the Spanish, maintained significant power but were still limited by the power of France. (Sometimes "Hapsburg" is written as "Habsburg" but the names are the same.) The Low Countries broke free of Spain and became the Netherlands, a vibrant example of progress. England struggled to define its government but eventually emerged as a stable nation focusing on trade. Russia emerged from its isolation to be an important contributor to European life. These changes will all be discussed in more detail later in this chapter. They had a major effect on creativity because of the desires of, first, the Catholic Church, to gather more influence among those who lived in Protestant areas, and second, the kings who emerged from these religious wars as the most powerful.

The frenzy of activities was not just religious and military. Diplomatic intrigues became so important that some governments, like Spain, were destabilized by diplomatic complexities while other countries, like France, used diplomacy as a tool of government, ranking in importance with armies and navies. France would continue this expertise in diplomacy into the modern era.

During this critically important seventeenth century, the fundamental focus of European society began to change. We have commented in a previous chapter that European civilization from 1500 to the present can be divided into three periods of focus. Those three areas are repeated here for convenience:

- 1500 to 1648—Dominated by the issue of what to believe in religion (that is, a redefinition of the First Estate)
- 1649 to 1789—Dominated by the issue of the mode of government (a redefinition of the Second Estate)
- 1790 to present—Dominated by the issue of social and economic equality (a redefinition of the Third Estate)

The first few chapters in this text have looked at the first of these three periods in which the religious thinking of Europe was redefined. In these chapters we examined the changes from medieval thinking—God dominates all life—to Renaissance thinking—humans are the focus of life. This emergence of humanism was initially done within the traditional Christian context of the Roman Catholic Church. Soon, however, the spirit of individualism led reformers and protesters to break with the Church, as described in the chapters on the Protestant Reformation, the Northern Renaissance, and Elizabethan England.

In previous times such individualism would have been labeled as heretical and crushed by the power of the Catholic Church, but in the Renaissance, especially in northern Europe, political leaders had also begun to think independently and were strong enough to protect the religious protesters and defy the Church. We observed, therefore, the establishment of national Protestant churches throughout northern Germany, Scandinavia, and the British Isles, plus various unauthorized Protestant groups in other European countries. The emphasis on humanism (Renaissance thinking) brought new concepts in art, literature, and drama.

This chapter discusses the important transition period, the seventeenth century, between the focus on religion seen in previous chapters and the new focus on government, the second of the main periods of civilization focus. (Note in the bulleted time frame that the religious focus ends in the mid-1600s, and the political focus begins at that time.) Not surprisingly, then, the initial focus of this period is religious, and the focus at the end of the period is largely political. We will examine this transition in each major country and compare the important and profound national differences that led to the major upheavals in European politics that we have already noted.

Although the differences between countries will be important to consider, every country had to wrestle with some fundamental similarities. These centered on the relationships between God, the monarchy, and the state. In medieval times, God was assumed to be the supreme power in heaven and on earth who selected certain individuals—kings and popes—to be His representatives. The interactions between kings and popes were occasionally difficult, but, in general, the separation of the state and the church was intuitive and accepted. All people were expected (required) to obey the kings and the popes without question and without hesitation. Therefore, the powers of the kings and the popes were absolute (within their respective spheres).

As we have discussed in previous chapters, the power of the pope was challenged by the Protestant Revolution in the sixteenth century. The Catholic Church responded, first by attempting to squash the rebellion (through excommunications and Inquisition), then by internal reform (through the Counter Reformation), and then by intellectual argument (through the work of the Jesuits). These efforts were only moderately successful in winning back those who had left, but were quite successful in preventing new desertions.

As the seventeenth century dawned, another method of restoring the faithful to the Catholic Church was used. This new method may not have been orchestrated by the church, but it was certainly supported by the church. The method was based on the principle, ratified by the Council of Trent that reformed the church, that the monarch in each country had the right to define the religion of the state. Implied in this principle was the ability of the monarch to enforce adherence to the state religion by all the people within the state. The church hoped to win over the hearts of the kings of Protestant lands and, thereby, bring those lands back to the fold. If the current Protestant kings could not be reconverted, then warfare might be used to bring about a change in which a favorable king could be installed. Therefore, religious wars were an important feature of the early seventeenth century. However, these wars also became highly political, as the various kings sought to increase their personal power and glory through conquest. Hence, we see the transition from primarily a religious focus to primarily a political focus.

The policy of monarchal control over a country's religion was a masterstroke of creativity by the Catholic Church because the conversion of only a few individuals, the kings, could bring sweeping change. The Catholic Church was, at this point, quite confident that they would be able to hold the allegiance of all the monarchs that were Catholics and, they hoped, could convert those monarchs who were Protestants or, at the very least, intermarry with them and then insist that the children be Catholics. This strategy almost worked in England and, had it worked there, might have succeeded in other countries.

The principle of absolute monarchy was strongly medieval—that is, it was based on the concept that the king had absolute power over the lives of the people in the realm. However, in light of the new thinking of the Renaissance, this principle began to be challenged. It is the interaction between the old medieval thinking and the new Renaissance thinking that underlies the events described in this chapter. Kings sought to retain the old thinking and emphasized their views by proclaiming the continuance of the medieval concept that they were God's representatives. This concept has been called the **divine right of kings.**

The quotations that begin this chapter illustrate the opinion of the most influential of the

kings in this period, Louis XIV of France. He saw himself as the embodiment of the state and, therefore, had all power. He believed that the land of France was his personal possession and that any private ownership by others was only at his pleasure. He also believed, quite literally, that he was God's representative to the people of France and that, therefore, whatever he did would be ratified by God and should be considered by the people to be God's will. Most of the kings of other countries had similar beliefs. The creativity of the absolute monarchs was critical to their success in maintaining absolute authority and, perhaps even more important, molding their country into the best possible state. We will see that a clear vision and then innovative implementation of their power are critical elements to success of these monarchs.

The challenges to this monarchal view are also a major focus of this chapter. In general, the kings did not give up their power easily. Wars were fought and monarchs killed over the principle of absolutism. Sometimes the monarchy returned even after being overthrown, although usually without the same absolute control. In that light, change toward moderate regal power seemed inevitable.

The people of Europe, collectively and often individually, were struggling with opposing feelings about the kings. They enjoyed the security and stability of the absolute kings and, in some countries, challenges to the monarch were delayed until another century. (We will examine these challenges in later chapters.) However, the people also saw problems with absolute rule in areas such as economics (the absolute kings tended to spend lavishly and recklessly), continuity of leadership (one king might disagree with his predecessors and suddenly reverse policies), capability of leadership (some absolute kings were inept rulers), and, mostly, fundamental principles (people should have individual rights beyond the powers of the king). In some countries these problems outweighed the benefits of absolute monarchy and actions were taken to make changes. However, in this early period, the ideas of limited monarchy and the rights of individual people were still poorly defined. We will see the definition of these ideas in the later chapter on the Enlightenment. Nevertheless, some actions were taken to limit the power of kings.

Throughout Europe, regardless of the actions taken in the seventeenth century, the political and social climate continued to evolve. Absolute monarchs claimed a divine right from God to rule, yet they continually worked to strip church leaders of their power, even as they used the church as a method of control. Many absolute monarchs also brought their divine calling into question by their own wicked and unrighteous lifestyles. Furthermore, the continued growth of the middle class caused more and more people in all countries to feel the need to have a greater say in their government so that they could protect their businesses and newfound wealth. Hence, all three estates—church, nobility, commoners—were changing.

Most of the early limits placed on monarchical power occurred in the Protestant nations of the north, where the Reformation had already weakened the Catholic Church's emphasis on authority and hierarchy. Although nearly all countries had some sort of political assembly at least semiaccountable to the people, only in the Reformation countries did these bodies gain real power. In the Catholic countries, these bodies had little real power and rarely met (for example France's *Estates General* went over a century without being called into session). Furthermore, these institutions were old and were mostly just tools for the aristocracy to influence the king. There was still no real forum for the peasantry or the middle class to address issues of concern or influence policy. The first real attempts to limit the power of the monarchs happened in the Netherlands and England.

In the seventeenth century, the Catholic Church used yet another method (beyond its backing of absolutism) to entice the "wayward people" to return. This new method was through art in which the glories of the Catholic heaven were extolled. The kings, especially those who supported the concept of absolutism, also wanted to impress their subjects and the rest of the world with their greatness and therefore used similar art methods. This type of art has been called Baroque, and we will examine it in the next chapter. First, however,

let's look at the transition in thinking from religious to political and the upheavals in society that this transition brought.

■ Germany and the Thirty Years War

In the 1600s Germany was a collection of dozens of small political units—principalities, dukedoms, bishoprics, and the like—that were all nominally under the authority of the Holy Roman Empire but were really independent entities that generally followed the policies of each unit's ruler. None of these units had much political or military power and, because of historical and religious traditions, they were not able to unite into an effective nation. Medieval conflicts between the German kings and the popes had given local leaders powers that they had successfully retained into the seventeenth century. Furthermore, the Protestant Reformation had divided these German entities into a Protestant north and a Catholic south. This overall situation—relative political weakness and religious division—seemed to invite interference from the powerful states that surrounded Germany, especially because the surrounding kings saw opportunities to dictate the religious affiliation of all the German people and to improve their own country's political power.

However, this north/south pattern was just a generalization, as there were plenty of exceptions in both the north and south where princes chose the minority religion, either for real religious convictions or political reasons. This was especially true in the southern provinces, where some people, such as the Swiss and the Bohemians, used Protestantism to oppose the strong influence of the Catholic, Austrian-based, Holy Roman Emperor.

In spite of the agreement reached in the Council of Trent (formalized later by the rulers of Europe as the Peace of Augsburg, signed in 1555) allowing each German prince to freely choose, without outside interference, the religion of all the people in his principality, both sides ignored the terms of the treaty. Jesuit monks continued to go into Protestant areas and attempt to convert the people back to the

Catholic Church. This angered the Protestants, who retaliated by continuing their own conversions and increasing their efforts to gain control of bishoprics inside nominally Catholic areas. The situation continued to escalate when the Lutheran princes formed the Protestant Union in 1608 as a method of gaining control over the situation in their favor. The Catholic princes retaliated by forming the Catholic League in 1609. The two sides met and agreed to a treaty (called the **Letter of Majesty**) in which both religions were allowed to exist without interference from the other. However, feelings remained tense. These complicated conditions laid the groundwork for the **Thirty Years War.**

In 1618 the spark igniting the Thirty Years War occurred in Bohemia, one of the many small units that had its own king and ruling assembly but was nominally under the jurisdiction of the Holy Roman Emperor. Bohemia was a divided region: filled with people of both German and Czech nationalities, both Catholic and Protestant. Encouraged by the strong Catholic faith of the newly elected Holy Roman Emperor, Ferdinand II, Catholic officials in Bohemia forced construction to stop on several Protestant churches. This was viewed as a direct violation of the Letter of Majesty by an assembly of Protestants who met in Prague, the Bohemian capital, to protest the action of the Catholic officials. Members of the Protestant assembly stormed Prague (Hradcany) castle and hurled two of the emperor's officials from a window in the castle. This act became known as the *Defenestration of Prague,* since "defenestration" means "to throw someone or something out a window." The two officials survived. The Catholics claimed that angels had caught them and saved their lives. Protestants claimed that they landed in a manure pile, which broke their fall. Regardless of how the officials were spared, the Defenestration of Prague and the heated words following it caused war to break out between Catholics and Protestants in Bohemia.

The Protestants in Bohemia declared themselves independent of the Holy Roman Empire. The Holy Roman Emperor, a member of the Hapsburg family and a Catholic, immediately sent troops to quell the rebellion. The Spanish, also ruled by Hapsburgs, invaded Protestant German lands from their possessions in the Low Countries in an effort to link with the Austrian Hapsburg army in Bohemia. The invasions by the Austrians and Spanish were successful and, as a result, Bohemia and much of Germany came under the direct control of the Hapsburgs.

King Christian IV of Denmark, a Protestant, was alarmed by this situation. He had extensive holdings in northern Germany and worried that these lands might be attacked by the Hapsburgs. He was also a deeply religious Lutheran who wanted to check the growth of Catholicism. He therefore entered the war in hopes of regaining territories for the Protestants. King Christian IV was an immensely popular king in Denmark and a natural leader of the Protestant movement. Denmark was a rich and powerful state at this time. It dominated trade in the Baltic area. Christian used his wealth to build several large palaces, churches, monuments, and other civic buildings. (A tour of the famous sites in Copenhagen today is largely a tour of works done under the rule of King Christian IV.) He also founded cities throughout Denmark and in Norway, which was then part of a combined Danish-Norwegian kingdom, and even in parts of present-day Sweden.

However, the Danish army and resources were no match for the combined might of the Hapsburgs. Over a period of about five years (1620–1625), the Danes used up their money and men in a futile attempt to regain lost Protestant lands. Humiliatingly, King Christian IV was finally forced to seek peace with the Hapsburgs.

The success of the Austrian and Spanish armies against Denmark convinced King Gustavus Adolphus of Sweden to intervene on behalf of the Protestants, but also to take advantage of the weakened position of the Danes, traditional rivals of the Swedes. Soon Sweden sent troops into the Danish holdings in Germany. The Danes fought back, but the Swedes (with the backing of the Dutch navy) were able to crush the Danish naval and land forces. Sweden took over the Danish lands in northern Germany and then launched an attack against the Hapsburgs.

The Swedish army was strong and soon had won several decisive victories, and it looked as if the tide of the war may have shifted to the Protestant side. However, the death of the Swedish king in a battle in southern Germany resulted in several Protestant defeats, and the momentum Sweden had won was quickly lost again to the Catholic forces.

Although the war continued to rage for many additional years against residual Protestant forces, the Catholic forces of Austria and Spain seemed about to prevail. There was no strong Protestant nation with a large and powerful army to step in and save the Protestant forces. Then the unexpected happened, as France, a predominately Catholic nation, decided to join the war on the Protestant side. France made this decision because it feared that an Austrian/Spanish victory would give too much power to the Hapsburgs, who would then control (at the time) Spain, Germany, Austria, the Low Countries, and large portions of Italy, thus surrounding France. France also feared the existence of a strong German state sitting right next door and hoped an Austrian defeat would keep the Holy Roman Empire weak.

With the French now fighting in partnership with the Swedes, the tide of the war turned back in favor of the Protestant forces. It was not a quick victory, though, and the war dragged on, destroying much of Germany as the opposing armies marched back and forth across the same territory over and over again. Finally, in 1648, thirty years after the initial conflict in Bohemia, the forces of Austria and Spain saw that victory was impossible and sought for peace. The two sides met and signed the **Peace of Westphalia,** which ended the war.

The Peace of Westphalia did not declare either side as the clear winner of the Thirty Years War, but the terms of the treaty strongly favored the wishes of the French. The provisions of the Council of Trent and Peace of Augsburg were reaffirmed, granting each region's prince the right to choose the religion for his territory. This was what France wanted, as it meant Germany would remain a loose and unorganized political entity that would continue to be divided over religious and political issues. In fact, the Holy Roman Empire exited the Thirty Years War more fragile and weak than ever, as each German prince was recognized as an individual sovereign and deemed semi-independent of the Holy Roman Empire.

The Peace of Westphalia also recognized for the first time other Protestant faiths besides Lutheranism, such as Calvinism in Switzerland and the Hussites in Bohemia. This recognition of other Protestant faiths only served to further divide Germany along religious lines and, therefore, further weaken it. The Peace of Westphalia also granted France the right to intervene in German affairs while denying the right of the Vatican to do the same, signaling the reduced role of the Catholic Church in European politics. France was also given the province of Alsace, which had previously been part of the Holy Roman Empire. Finally, as punishment for Spain's involvement in the war, the Peace of Westphalia formally recognized the independence of the Netherlands from Spanish control.

The Thirty Years War was devastating to Germany. The power of the Holy Roman Empire was destroyed for good, and the various German principalities became individual little countries. The German economy was destroyed as several cities were sacked nine or ten times, unpaid soldiers survived by plunder and living off of the land, and inflation swept across Germany. Finally, over 30 percent of the population of Germany was killed, either in the fighting or from the various diseases that went unchecked due to the war. Some areas in Germany lost more than 50 percent of their population, as shown in Figure 32.1. When preparing this book, we asked a German scholar to define the most pivotal time in all of German history. He said that it was the Thirty Years War. We now understand why that was so!

■ France

In the early years of the seventeenth century, before the reign of Louis XIV, France was beset by many social, economic, religious, and political problems. The population of France was exploding and the quick increase in people had led to high inflation, making goods very expensive, especially for the poor who carried an especially

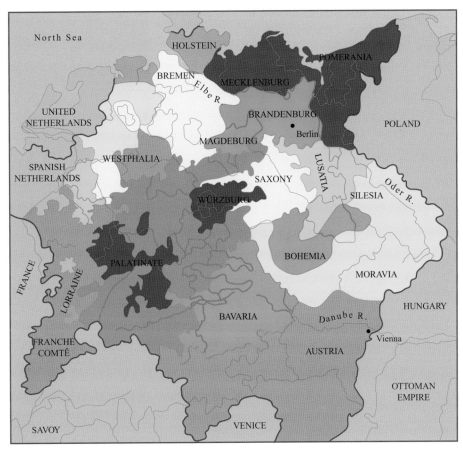

Figure 32.1 ■ *Population losses in Germany as a result of the Thirty Years War.*

heavy tax burden in France. The inflation was worsened because of the tremendous amount of silver that was flooding into Europe from the Spanish mines in the Americas. A new technology was being used to extract silver more easily from its ore, and that meant that silver mining in Mexico and Bolivia was much more productive, thus increasing the total amount of silver (money) throughout Europe. The increased money supply drove prices higher. Eventually, because of the in-

flation and the negative effects of France's participation in the Thirty Years War in Germany, the French economy stagnated.

France was also suffering from religious and political tensions. During the last decades of the sixteenth century, the Valois dynasty (which had ruled France for more than 250 years) was collapsing. The last strong Valois king, Henry II, had died in 1559. His eldest son, Francis II, was still a teenager when he became king. (Francis II was married to Mary, Queen of Scots, as we briefly discussed in Chapter 31.) Young King Francis II was dominated by his mother, Catherine de Medici, for the two years that he reigned. When he died suddenly, the next in line was his younger brother, Charles IX, who was similarly dominated by Catherine. She was faced with a difficult position. As a strong Catholic, Catherine tried to accommodate the anti-Protestant demands made on her by the pope and by her son-in-law, Philip II of Spain. However, she did not want to surrender the power of France to the more powerful Spain. She therefore fluctuated between tolerance of Protestants (called Huguenots in France) and their persecution (such as the St. Bartholomew's Day massacre, which we discussed in Chapter 29). Her fluctuations caused confusion and anger among the general French population. The upset in general feelings proved to be an embarrassment for Catherine, and she lost much of her influence over her son, King Charles IX.

When young Charles IX also died suddenly, he was replaced by his younger brother, Henry III, which continued the pattern of young and inexperienced kings of France. Catherine was not able to regain power over the monarchy and, when she died of pneumonia in 1589, her death caused very little stir within France. But then, when Henry III died without children, also in 1589, succession to the French throne became a real problem, as there were no more Valois sons.

France had to choose a king. Several candidates emerged, but the man chosen was King Henry of Navarre (a small kingdom between France and Spain), who had married the daughter of Catherine de Medici and Henry II. He was a Protestant, but he changed his religion to Catholic in order to gain the throne. He ruled France as Henry IV and started the Bourbon dynasty. (Note how his willingness to change religions in order to gain the throne is characteristic of the transition from religious to political thinking that occurred during the seventeenth century.)

Henry IV turned out to be a very popular king, using several creative ideas to ease religious tensions and rebuild France's economy. He was called **Good King Henry.** He laid the foundation for the rise to power that France experienced in the later years of the seventeenth century.

King Henry IV issued the **Edict of Nantes,** which called for religious toleration and equal treatment before the law for both Catholics and Protestants in France. Henry also worked to rebuild France's economy by starting up many industries that produced goods that were in high demand throughout Europe. These industries created goods that France could trade to other nations. He ordered the construction of royal factories for items such as glass, tapestries, silk, linen, and woolen cloth; many of these items had previously only been available in Europe via expensive trade with the Far East. King Henry IV, like England's Queen Elizabeth, also worked to solidify his power by attempting to gain popularity with the peasants. He did this by printing and distributing agricultural "how-to handbooks" throughout France and proclaiming "that there should be a chicken in every Frenchman's pot every Sunday." This French king was one of the most creative in France's history. He was pragmatic in his approach and decided to simply do what was necessary to make the situation better.

When Henry IV was assassinated by a religious fanatic, his son, **King Louis XIII,** became king of France. Louis XIII was a very young man when he came to power and was quite weak and ineffective as a ruler, caring more for the pleasures of wine and women than the functions of government. The early part of his reign was heavily influenced by his mother, Marie de Medici, who married Henry IV after Henry's first marriage was annulled. Marie de Medici was not politically skilled, and France moved backward during her regency. (A wonderful collection of paintings done by Peter Paul Rubens on the life of Marie de Medici is located in the Louvre.)

When Louis XIII reached legal maturity, his mother was forced to retire and her influence became insignificant. However, the role of King Louis' advisers increased. During all of the remainder of Louis' reign, his principal adviser, **Cardinal Richelieu,** was the *de facto* ruler in France. It was Richelieu, not Louis XIII, who solidified political power in France. (The intrigue and interactions of King Louis XIII and Richelieu are the background for the novel *The Three Musketeers* by Alexandre Dumas.)

Cardinal Richelieu had a creative, although Machiavellian, political mind, and his policies and programs allowed France to overtake Spain and emerge as Europe's most powerful nation. Richelieu manipulated foreign affairs in order to keep Germany and Spain on the defensive and at each other's throats. To do this, Richelieu used spies, intrigue, diplomacy, and, when necessary, war to his advantage. As discussed, at one point Cardinal Richelieu, a Catholic priest and church official himself, had France support the Protestants in the Thirty Years War because he felt that France's real enemy was Spain, and Spain was supporting the Catholic side in the war. He also wanted a weaker Germany.

In fact, the policies of Cardinal Richelieu were often non-Christian and contradictory to the teachings of the Catholic Church. Yet, Richelieu apparently felt no guilt or concern over this seeming inconsistency and famously argued, "What is done for the state is done for God, who is the basis and foundation of it," and, "Where the interests of the state are concerned, God absolves actions which, if privately committed, would be a crime." These ideas fall firmly within the tradition and ideas of Machiavelli and reflect the transition in thinking from a God-focused medieval view to a king-focused Renaissance view. In essence, Richelieu argued the following:

Politics are amoral, that is, without a basis in moral certitude. Also, the world itself is without morals because people are inherently evil. The state, therefore, must be amoral, even immoral, in order to provide for the good and protection of its citizens. If the state did not act in such a manner, then its citizens would be taken advantage of by other states that did. Furthermore, the king must do what is necessary for the retention of his power because retention of power is for the good of his people.

The first to articulate these ideas was Machiavelli, but Richelieu was one of the best at implementing the ideas in an actual state.

Cardinal Richelieu, in spite of his politics, was not a lapsed Catholic. While Richelieu might support Protestants elsewhere for political purposes, at home he worked to stamp out Protestantism. This was done for both religious and political reasons. Cardinal Richelieu had a natural religious opposition toward Protestantism, but rebellious aristocrats also used Protestantism as a cloak for political dissent against the throne. Richelieu decided to put an end to this Protestant political rebellion and sent the French armies to lay siege to the walled city of La Rochelle, the stronghold of the Huguenots. The royal forces were victorious and subdued the Protestants. Protestantism continued within France after this time, but Richelieu's blow broke the spirit of those seeking a Protestant rebellion within France and, for the most part, Protestantism ceased to be a major political concern in France thereafter.

Despite the weakness of Louis XIII, Richelieu sought to strengthen the power of the office of the king (which increased his own power since he essentially controlled the king). It was Richelieu's efforts to centralize power that really built the infrastructure within France that allowed France's kings to be absolute monarchs. In addition to the creative foreign policy he developed and the suppression of the Protestants at home, Richelieu further strengthened the power of the king by outlawing all walled cities and had many old medieval walls torn down. This allowed for easy access to any city by royal troops and was useful in suppressing local revolts. Richelieu eliminated the semi-autonomy of several French areas and established a system of central taxation. Related to this, Richelieu established a system of strong, local administrators who supported the central taxes and established central administrative control over all parts of France. During the tenure of Cardinal Richelieu, the tax revenues of the king doubled.

Because he was considerably older than Louis XIII, Cardinal Richelieu anticipated that he would die before the king, so he assured that his policies would continue by training a protégé, **Jules Mazarin,** to replace him as Louis' main adviser. Mazarin, who also became a cardinal in the Catholic Church, was an able student and a skilled replacement, continuing the policies and programs of Richelieu and, after Richelieu's death, serving as *de facto* ruler of France through the death of Louis XIII and well into the reign of Louis XIV.

Cardinal Richelieu was one of Europe's most creative leaders. He had a grand vision for France and, although he was not the natural leader of the country, he understood how to manipulate the natural leader to control the government and achieve the place he envisioned for France. In addition to the vision, Richelieu understood how facets of government and religion had to work together to accomplish his aims. He was obviously a man of many talents, and he used them effectively. Some might say that Richelieu was not creative because he copied the tactics of Machiavelli, but there is a great difference between Machiavelli's theory and Richelieu's actuality. Richelieu's vision was achieved and, moreover, he took steps to guarantee that it would continue. Combining Richelieu's advisership with the subsequent successful reign of Louis XIV, it is no wonder that France emerged as Europe's most powerful country.

Louis XIV came to the throne as a very young man, and the earliest years of his reign were dominated by the policies of Mazarin and Louis' mother, Anne of Austria. The first major crisis of Louis' reign was the revolts, or *fronde,* against the continued centralization of power within France. Although the *fronde* were seen as peasants' revolts, much of the threat was from the nobility, who resented the centralization of authority in the king because it took political power and tax revenue away from them. Even though the suppression of the revolts was Mazarin's doing, the *fronde* period was a major turning point in the life of Louis because his and his mother's lives were threatened. This lack of control, and the betrayal of the French nobility, affected Louis greatly and played a large part in many of Louis XIV's future policies. Thus, a few years later when Mazarin died, Louis decided to assume total control over the affairs of France and declared that he would be his own prime minister. Soon after taking full control of France, Louis decided it was time to marry. He was wedded to Marie Thérèse of Spain. His marriage was largely political to solidify relations between France and Spain. Throughout his life, Louis kept a series of mistresses who had more influence on him than his wife and, after Marie Thérèse's death, he secretly married Madame de Maintenon, a mistress with whom he had seven children. She was very clever but was also secretly criticized by Louis' ministers because of her ability to influence Louis' decisions.

During Louis' long reign, France initiated several wars of expansion against its neighbors. Louis instituted several new practices in warfare that have been almost uniformly adopted today, such as the standardization of weapons and uniforms and the establishment of commissaries to feed the troops so that they would not be required to live off of the land. Louis also had his generals initiate a rational system of recruiting, discipline, training, and promotion. These changes improved morale among the troops and improved the quality of the soldiers fighting for France, giving France a distinct advantage over its foes. Initially, the military efforts of Louis were quite successful, but he was eventually stopped by an alliance of Europe's other powers against him. Thus, at the end of Louis's reign, his wars of expansion accomplished little except draining much of the treasury reserves saved up by Richelieu and Mazarin.

Louis may not have been successful in his acquisition of power abroad, but his acquisition of power at home in France was total and complete. Louis concentrated all power in his person and was known to say *"l'état c'est moi"* (I am the state). Figure 32.2 is a statue of Louis XIV showing his attitude of confidence and control. The reign of Louis XIV became a Golden Age for France, and he became known as the Sun King because he was the light that gave life to France. In order to further centralize power and to keep a closer eye on his minor nobles, Louis had the elaborate Baroque palace at Versailles built and then moved his entire court out of Paris and to Versailles, requiring all of his court nobility to spend some of the year there. Versailles is depicted in Figure 32.3. Figure 32.4 shows the Hall of Mirrors inside the palace of Versailles. It is one of the most beautiful and elaborate rooms in any building. Figure 32.5 shows some of the gardens that surround Versailles, again illustrating the elaborate luxury represented by the palace.

Figure 32.2 ■ Statue of Louis XIV in Versailles. © *2010 by gary718. Used under license of Shutterstock, Inc.*

Figure 32.3 ■ The Palace of Versailles showing one of the many fountains. © *2010 by onairda. Used under license of Shutterstock, Inc.*

Although the Baroque style is the principal subject of the next chapter in this book, the overwhelming contribution of Louis XIV to this style is so important that a few words here about the connection between Louis and the Baroque are appropriate. Louis' vision was for his court to become like Mt. Olympus—the abode of the ancient Greek gods. Louis saw himself as Apollo, the god of the sun. He envisioned himself living in eternal bliss with the power of a god over his

Figure 32.4 ■ The Hall of Mirrors inside the Palace of Versailles. ©
2010 by Jose Ignacio Soto. Used under license of Shutterstock, Inc.

Figure 32.5 ■ Gardens at the Palace of Versailles. © *2010 by Vladimir
Korostyshevskiy. Used under license of Shutterstock, Inc.*

mortal subjects. Hence, he built his palace with ceilings and decorations featuring the ancient Greek and Roman gods.

Just as he envisioned the lifestyle of the gods to be mostly pleasure-seeking, he devoted much time to pleasure in elaborate meals, parties, games (such as tennis), and cultural pursuits. He sought to rise above the daily troubles of the world. Of course, Louis was also a realist and understood that he had to take care of daily problems of finance, administration, and other mundane chores associated with running a large country, but his emphasis always seemed to be above these seemingly small and insignificant details.

Louis conveyed this higher vision to his court and, to a large degree, to his people. While the masses continued to live difficult existences, they shared with him the glory of an exalted existence and believed that they were part of the heaven of the gods. The elaborateness of Versailles and all other Baroque expressions of Louis' power conveyed this higher vision. Louis gave the French people pride and suggested that things French were, somehow, better than anywhere else.

To a large degree, the people of France still enjoy a vision of elevated existence, in a very positive way. They believe that culture is important and leads to a better life, perhaps a life that is their heritage from the time of Louis XIV.

The ability to instill this elevated vision for France was part of the creativity of Louis XIV. He saw the vision for France as the greatest country on earth and then set about to make the vision a reality. Elaborate Baroque palaces and other monuments were an important part of the accomplishment of that vision. So, too, were his personal actions and his interactions with other leaders. Louis became the embodiment of his vision.

At Versailles King Louis established an elaborate and intricate series of daily routines that were designed to reinforce his total control and his personal power. Louis had the nobility assist him with his personal dressing and eating to emphasize that he was "the state" and they had a responsibility to work for the good of "the state." Louis made these tasks an honor and a show of pleasure and support from him, as king, to certain individuals. By doing so, Louis was able to dole out these opportunities to wait upon him as favors to be sought after, and thus kept his aristocracy wary of each other and subservient to him. This proved to be a very effective manner for suppressing rebellion and dissent amongst his nobility because they relied on him and mistrusted each other.

Louis ruled France for seventy-three years, dying in 1715. During that time he completed France's centralization of power that had been be-

gun by Richelieu. When Louis said that he was the state, that was literally true. His word was law. He believed he had a divine right to be king, and he did not allow anyone to question that authority.

Louis XIV was great because, while many rulers throughout history had claimed absolute power, Louis had actually achieved it. And while Louis did select certain nobles to advise him, he kept that group very small (to limit the influence of the nobility at his court) and ignored their opinions, as often as not. Perhaps even more impressive was the fact that during his entire reign, Louis XIV never once called France's legislative assembly, the Estates General, into session. The Sun King did not need or want permission from anyone to rule what God had declared was his to rule, and his control was so complete that nobody openly questioned his authority.

The power Louis XIV had in France was extremely attractive to other monarchs. Across Europe, many of them took steps to copy what Louis had done in France, both in regards to the centralization of authority and in the ornate palace of Versailles and the elaborate routines Louis lived out there. Before long, monarchs all across the continent were emulating Louis XIV's policies and lifestyle, some even earning the title absolute monarch. However, no one else was able to attain the absolute control and authority that Louis XIV had in France.

■ Spain

As France rose to greatness, Spain began to decline from its position as the most powerful nation in Europe. All during Spain's period of decline, its kings ruled as absolute monarchs, but their policies and decisions only continued to weaken the country and deplete its treasury. Although the actions of Spain's monarchs contributed to Spain's fall from power, a wide array of other factors also contributed to Spain's decline.

Spain's navy had ruled the oceans and their trade routes throughout most of the sixteenth century. However, as time passed, Spain began to lose much of its naval advantage to the English, who developed a smaller, more maneuverable type of ship. The purpose of these smaller English ships was not to defeat the Spanish vessels in head-to-head combat, but to hit and run. England simply hit the Spanish ships with isolated attacks, robbed them, and took off with their gold and trade goods. The English system was formalized when Queen Elizabeth secretly legitimized Sir Francis Drake and the other privateers, who used their pirating skills to harass and raid the Spanish.

Over time, the English stole much Spanish wealth extracted from the New World, and this caused serious financial problems for Spain. Spain's King Phillip II eventually decided to destroy England's fleet and sent nearly the entire Spanish fleet to England to destroy the English navy and invade England. However, a terrible storm turned the expedition into a disaster for the large and bulky Spanish fleet. A combination of the storm itself and the smaller, quicker English ships (which could better handle the stormy waters) resulted in destruction of most of the Spanish fleet. Spain never again regained naval dominance following the defeat of the Spanish Armada at the hands of the English fleet and the "Protestant Wind."

Spain also lost much of its power due to severe economic troubles. For much of the Age of Exploration (the sixteenth century), Spain had been Europe's most wealthy nation, extracting literally tons of gold, silver, and other precious resources from its American colonies. However, a series of events and poor planning caused much of Spain's wealth to quickly evaporate, leaving Spain in a financial pinch with a large amount of debt. Spain's financial troubles began with its loss of naval dominance and the rise of the English fleet, as we have just discussed. These troubles coincided with rampant inflation all across Europe during the early 1600s, which devalued much of Spain's wealth. However, Spain probably still could have weathered the difficult economic storm with better foresight and planning.

Spain had few natural resources to trade or use and almost no manufacturing base and, unlike France under Henry IV, Spain made no efforts to develop one. Nearly all of Spain's wealth was extracted from the Americas, but then quickly passed through Spain and went on to Holland and other manufacturing centers. The nations who were centers for trade and manufacturing then made large profits off of the goods manufactured there and only returned a small percentage of the profits to Spain. If Spain had developed more industry within Spain proper, it could have kept the profits from the manufactured goods and made more money. Furthermore, the money paid in wages to the manufacturing workers would have contributed to overall growth of the Spanish economy, and this would have allowed Spain to better handle the inflation of the 1600s.

Spain also lost large amounts of money because of the disorder and corruption of its taxation infrastructure. Underpaid officials in both the Americas and in Spain took illegal cuts of the wealth Spain extracted, and the crown was either largely unconcerned or unable to stop it. Furthermore, often the taxes placed on these goods and raw materials simply were not paid. Estimates of how much money the Spanish crown lost due to inefficiency and corruption range as high as 50 percent of the total wealth extracted.

Spain had several other problems that also contributed to its financial collapse and the subsequent loss of power. The Spanish nobility stubbornly clung to the medieval idea of what an aristocrat should be. They lived lavish and expensive lifestyles, and based all of their wealth in land ownership. They refused to invest money, run industries, or do any type of work themselves. This attitude, which continued for several decades, is one of the reasons that Spain was so slow to develop in the eighteenth and nineteenth centuries.

Spain was also having difficulties with revolts. This series of revolts began in Catalonia, the area around Barcelona and Valencia, in 1640. The people of this region were of a different ethnicity and spoke a different language (Catalan) than the rest of Spain, and resented being bound to Spain. Eventually, the revolt of Catalonia was put down, but doing so proved to be very expensive and caused an even greater rift between the people of Catalonia and the rest of Spain.

The same year brought the revolt of Portugal. Portugal had been annexed by Spain's King

Phillip II in 1580 and had been a territory of Spain for 60 turbulent years. The Portuguese hated being ruled by Spain and were simply waiting for a good opportunity to regain their independence. In 1640, Spain was deeply involved in the Thirty Years War and was dealing with the revolt in Catalonia. Portugal saw this as its opportunity and, with the help of England (who was always looking for ways to agitate Spain), revolted against Spanish rule. Spain, finding itself fighting on too many fronts and facing serious revenue problems, could only put up a token fight, and Portugal regained its independence from Spain.

Spain's trouble with its possessions did not end there, however. In 1647, the Kingdom of Naples and Sicily, another Spanish territory, revolted in an attempt to gain its independence. Spain was able to squash the revolt and keep these territories for several more decades, but the cost of fighting to keep them while still participating in the Thirty Years War was devastating to the Spanish treasury. The final blow to Spain's political power came a year later, in 1648, when the Low Countries finally gained independence after generations of fighting. The loss of the Low Countries was especially damaging to Spain because it had invested so much time, money, and manpower in keeping these distant territories. Furthermore, the Low Countries was where most of Spain's manufacturing was done, and the loss left Spain without a real manufacturing base.

Although by the mid-1600s Spain's serious economic troubles had severely limited its role as a powerful nation in Europe, Spain's fall from power was not made complete until the War of Spanish Succession, which was fought from 1701 to 1714. The death of the Spanish King Charles II, a member of the Spanish branch of the Hapsburg family who had no heir, brought on the crisis. Charles II's will declared that France's Phillip V was to succeed him. Phillip V was the grandson of France's King Louis XIV and a Bourbon, France's royal family. The linkage between Phillip V and France was too strong for many in Europe, who feared a union between Spain and France. Austria, England, and the Netherlands all refused to accept Charles's will and demanded that an Austrian Hapsburg, Leopold I, be crowned king of Spain.

Soon war broke out with France and Spain (who both wanted a Bourbon king) on one side and Austria, England, and the Netherlands (who all wanted a Hapsburg king) on the other. The **War of Spanish Succession** raged for 13 years before an agreement was reached with the **Treaty of Utrecht.** Neither side of the conflict ended up getting all of what they wanted, but the final terms of the treaty strongly favored England, Austria, and the Netherlands. In a concession to France and Spain, Phillip V was crowned king of Spain, but with the promise that the crowns of France and Spain would never be united. In return, France ceded Newfoundland, Nova Scotia, and the Hudson Bay territory to England. Spain ceded Majorca and Gibraltar to England, and the Spanish Netherlands (much of modern Belgium) to Austria. The terms of the Treaty of Utrecht finally ended any claim Spain had to being one of Europe's most powerful nations, while the possessions gained by England paved the way for its coming dominance in the century that lay ahead.

■ The Netherlands

When the provinces of the Low Countries finally gained their independence, the citizens of the Low Countries (the Dutch) were already leery of the rule of absolute monarchs. They had experienced a series of absolute and often incompetent Hapsburg rulers who were distant from them geographically, religiously, culturally, and emotionally. Some of these Hapsburg kings seemed to mean well, but the separations were just too great, and, inevitably, the Dutch chafed under their control. This led to a more or less continuous rebellion throughout the latter sixteenth and seventeenth centuries until, with the settlement of the Thirty Years War, the Netherlands was fully recognized as independent of Spain. The aversion of the Dutch to absolute monarchies led to the establishment of a new type of rule—a republic with some limited monarchs. We will see how this type of government worked and also look at the consequences of this government in daily Dutch life.

The Low Countries became part of the Hapsburg empire through marriage, war, and political maneuvering. The Hapsburgs were the best in the world at this game of political marriage to gain territory. At the height of their power under King Charles V and his son **Philip II,** the Hapsburgs ruled the Low Countries, Spain, the Holy Roman Empire, Austria and its affiliated states, Naples and Sicily, Burgundy, Portugal, and much of America.

The active movement for Dutch independence began in earnest with the Protestant Reformation. The Dutch are culturally and ethnically Germanic and thus had sympathies with the other German states that adopted Protestantism. In the Dutch case, the teachings of John Calvin were widely accepted, and this led, eventually, to the creation of the Calvinist Dutch Reform Church. (This church was similar in theology and structure to the Presbyterian Scottish church formed under John Knox that we discussed in Chapter 31.) King Phillip II of Spain attempted to stop Protestantism, but these attempts were met by a rebellion beginning in 1568 led by Prince William I of Orange. (He controlled one of the states that was part of the Low Countries. This situation was similar to the German states that composed the Holy Roman Empire.) Several of the provinces declared themselves to be an independent state—the United Provinces of the Netherlands (also called the Dutch Republic or, alternately, Holland, the largest of the several provinces of the Dutch Republic).

King Philip II was brutal in his attempts to end the Dutch revolt and to eliminate Calvinism. Under his mandate, the Spanish forces sought out and destroyed centers of Protestant revolt. Things looked especially bleak for the Dutch when they were forced to surrender after a large battle that occurred near the city of Breda. This event was memorialized by the great Spanish painter, **Diego Velazquez** in his painting, *The Surrender of Breda (Las Lanzas),* which is shown in Figure 32.6. The painting depicts the Dutch mayor of Breda hand-

Figure 32.6 ▪ The Surrender of Breda (Las Lanzas) *by Diego Velazquez.* © *Erich Lessing/Art Resource, NY.*

ing over the key to the city to the victorious Spanish general, the Duke of Alva. The destroyed city of Breda is burning in the background. Note that the Duke seems to be generous in victory as he extends his hand to console the defeated mayor. In reality, the Duke of Alva held an inquisition for more than 12,000 citizens of Breda, convicting 9,000 of them. One thousand of those convicted were given the death sentence. The cruelty and extremism of Alva (who was likely acting under the direct orders of King Phillip II) swayed the Dutch populace in favor of further resistance, even among the Dutch Catholics.

The Dutch rebels continued to fight with support from England, eventually winning sufficiently that the Spanish accepted a truce in 1607. The Dutch formed a political entity called the United Provinces. The truce proved to be only temporary, and fighting continued until 1648 when the Peace of Westphalia that ended the Thirty Years War formally recognized the Netherlands as a separate nation. Some of the southern provinces of the Low Countries had remained under Spanish control during the entire war, and these provinces remained as a Spanish possession, Spanish Netherlands. (These southern provinces later became Belgium.)

The Dutch Republic was a unique and creative form of government. During much of the struggle for independence, the United Provinces were led by a prince, **William the Silent,** with the strong involvement of the citizen councils of each of the provinces. But the death of William during the eighty-year struggle for independence created a succession crisis. Several people were approached about becoming the ruler of the United Provinces (including Elizabeth I of England), but none accepted the conditions that were imposed by the councils. Eventually the Dutch settled on a government in which the final authority was in the hands of the combined councils of the provinces but recognition and limited power was given to the hereditary leader of each province, called a **stadtholder.** Sometimes, a single person would be the *stadtholder* for several provinces and would therefore gain the prestige and power almost equivalent to a king, especially if the *stadtholder*

was the leader of Holland. All of the *stadtholders* were from the House of Orange.

The creativity of this government system was that the Dutch maintained the best of the monarchal systems (especially the prestige of a king and royal leadership and vision) but were able to keep the power in the hands of elected officials.

The Netherlands, which had always been the manufacturing base for Spain and had a strong tradition of a large and powerful merchant-based middle class, soon developed the strongest economy in the world. The Netherlands was able to develop its economy because, in addition to its manufacturing, it had a large trading base (approximately half of all European trade was conducted by the Dutch). Imported raw materials were converted into finished products in the country's large manufacturing centers and sold for profit throughout the world; thus creating an excellent balance of trade. Dutch trade and manufacturing were further enhanced by the religious toleration of the Dutch people. Adherents of all religions sought to trade with the Dutch and to invest their wealth in Dutch business ventures.

The Netherlands was also involved in colonialism in an effort to increase its ability to acquire cheap raw materials. Its excellent navy allowed it to take over colonies formerly occupied by other nations, and its sincere interest in trade and general toleration allowed the Netherlands to earn the respect and favor of local peoples in many areas. Unlike most of the European colonial powers, the Dutch were generally honest with the local inhabitants, respected their traditions, and did not attempt to convert them to Christianity. The Dutch had an especially strong presence in the Indian and Pacific Oceans. They established a trading company called the Dutch East India Company that dominated trade throughout the Indian Ocean area. The Dutch drove both England and Portugal out of the spice-rich islands of Indonesia and also had a colony in Ceylon. The Dutch were also the only Europeans allowed into Japan to trade for almost 200 years and thus held a monopoly on all Japanese trading goods. The Netherlands also had a presence in the New World, with colonies on Long Island and Manhattan (modern day New York City) and in what became New Jersey. They also had colonies in South America (Suriname) and several in the Caribbean.

Trade created, in the Netherlands, tremendous wealth. Just as with other trade-based economies (such as ancient Athens and Renaissance Florence), the principal beneficiaries of the trade were the middle class. And, as with the other famous trade-based societies, the rise of the middle class led to a democratization of the government. Hence, the government of seventeenth century Netherlands was a republic. The rise of the middle class also led to an increase in art. The rich wanted to demonstrate their wealth and enjoy its benefits. Artists catered to this desire and created numerous works of art that were specifically intended for the newly rich. We will discuss this further in the chapter on the Baroque period, but one of the artists that became famous by painting middle-class patrons was Rembrandt. His work called *The Night Watch* depicts a group of soldiers who paid to be painted. The painting is shown in Figure 32.7. The prominence of each person in the painting is according to the amount of money that person paid.

Interestingly, the riches of the Dutch middle class became a problem in their society. These solid citizens became uncomfortable with their riches, especially in light of their strong Calvinist beliefs. Calvin taught that people should avoid the

Figure 32.7 ■ The Night Watch *by Rembrandt.*
© *National Gallery, London/Art Resource, NY.*

pleasures of the world and associated riches with sin. Therefore, the Dutch merchants were forced to seek a compromise between strict religion and financial success. They seemed to have found peace by strictly controlling their style of living so that it was enjoyable but not excessive. This was a truly creative solution.

With the rise of English sea power in the late 1600s, the colonial rivalry between England and the Netherlands became so intense that the two nations had a series of wars. The eventual outcome of these wars was that England received most of the Dutch territories in America, and the Netherlands got control over Indonesia. At the time of the settlement, the Dutch were considered to have gotten the better end of the deal, as Indonesia was rich in highly coveted spices, while America had little to offer besides timber and a little trade with the irritated local natives. However, in retrospect from today, the Netherlands might like to have another chance to negotiate that settlement.

Although initially successful in helping the Netherlands become an economic power, their system of different ruling councils governing in each of its provinces was too decentralized to make quick and decisive decisions. This weakness was apparent when France invaded the Netherlands in 1795 and the Dutch could barely offer any resistance. Thus, when Napoleon was defeated in 1813 and the Netherlands regained its independence, the Dutch chose a local nobleman from one of the provinces, **Prince Frederic William,** to become king of the Netherlands. In 1814 Frederic William was crowned and the Kingdom of the Netherlands was established, which included all of the former Dutch Republic plus modern-day Belgium and Luxembourg. About 20 years later, the Belgian and Luxembourgian minorities revolted against the Dutch, and the kingdom was separated into the current countries of the Netherlands, Belgium, and Luxembourg. Later a constitution was drafted to limit the monarchy's power and the Netherlands became a constitutional monarchy, similar to what existed in England.

■ England

The path to a limited monarchy in England was much more difficult than it was in the Netherlands and the struggle lasted for many more years. Magna Carta laid the foundation for limiting the English monarch's power in 1215 by creating Parliament and placing other restrictions on the king. Over time the power of the English king had once again increased, especially during the reigns of the Tudors, culminating in Elizabeth I. Therefore, when Elizabeth I died and was succeeded by her nephew, James VI of Scotland who became the

ruler of England as **James I,** he had enough power to consider himself an absolute monarch. However, this attitude ran contrary to the longstanding traditions in England favoring limited government. This conflict resulted in a series of crises that eventually changed the nature of the English monarchy. To assist in the discussion of the struggles in England to define the nature of their government in the seventeenth century, a chart of the rulers of England during this critical century is presented as Figure 32.8.

King James I ruled over both England and Scotland simultaneously. He was the son of Mary,

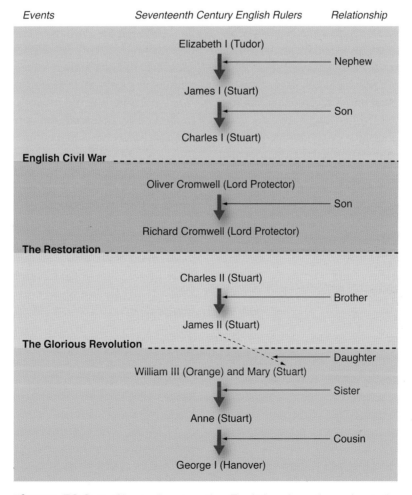

Figure 32.8 ■ *Chart showing the English rulers throughout the seventeenth century.*

Queen of Scots, and was taken from his Catholic mother and raised as a Protestant. His Protestantism allowed England's Queen Elizabeth I, who had never married and had no children, to select him as her successor. James I believed in the ideas of absolutism and fashioned himself as a divine-right king. He even lectured Parliament about his being "semi-divine" when they sometimes disagreed with him.

The policies enacted by James I, combined with his dictatorial, absolutist attitude, made him a very unpopular king. When Parliament refused to grant James more money to do as he pleased, he insisted on supplementing his income in ways not authorized, or even contemplated, by Parliament. Foremost among these money-making schemes was the creation of royal monopolies in which certain companies were given exclusive rights to manufacture certain products. These royal monopolies were quite damaging to the overall good of the English economy and very unpopular, especially with the middle class, as James granted the majority of these royal monopolies to his rich friends. When Parliament objected to James's creation of the monopolies, the king simply dissolved Parliament.

King James I became even more unpopular with the general English public when he decided to end English involvement in a war with Spain. The English viewed Spain as the archrival of England, and James's decision was considered to be both weak and an appeasement of Catholics. English withdrawal from the conflict was also an unpopular decision with the English nobility, as it left the Netherlands and Germany, two of England's closest political allies, to fight the war with Spain on their own. The English nobility wanted to keep on good terms with the Netherlands and Germany, as many of them had significant financial investments in the manufacturing and other industries of those two countries. A long, costly war or a Spanish victory might cost them a great deal of money, not to mention the bitterness and mistrust that might be directed toward them from the Netherlands and Germany in the future because of the English withdrawal. However, in spite of the unpopularity of the decision to pull out of the war on all levels of English society, King James withdrew anyway.

Another group that opposed King James I was the Puritans. The Puritans were an extremist Calvinist group that wanted to purify the Church of England, which they felt continued to practice far too many of the Catholic rituals and doctrines. The Puritans also viewed the hierarchy of the Church of England, or Anglican Church, as being too Catholic. The Puritans demanded that James limit the power of the Anglican bishops, which they felt was a residue of the hierarchy of the Catholic Church and was contrary to the teachings of Calvin, who believed that in the true form of Christianity, control was in the hands of local elders or Presbyters. (Hence, one of the names of Calvinist churches is Presbyterians.) James wanted to continue strong central control over the church and therefore resisted the Calvinist demands for church reorganization.

Although the Puritans were a continual irritation for James I, both on religious and political issues, they restrained themselves to criticism rather than open revolt, and James I died peacefully before the Puritans could mount a serious challenge to him. The potential for serious problems remained, however, as these Puritan Calvinists were the dominant political party in Parliament.

The son of James I was Charles I, who inherited both his father's attitudes and problems. Charles I believed even more strongly in the divine right of kings to rule, and openly attempted to circumvent any limitations Parliament tried to place upon him. One example of this occurred early in his reign when Charles went before Parliament to ask for money to fight a war with France. When Parliament granted him only a very limited amount of funds to fight the war, Charles resorted to forcing loans from his rich subjects, often enforcing the loans by throwing those who refused in prison or quartering soldiers in their homes. Parliament soon passed the Petition of Right, which condemned many of these practices.

Charles I viewed the Petition of Right as an open challenge to his power as king and was so angered by it that he dismissed Parliament and refused to call it back into session for eleven years. However, without Parliament, Charles I was unable to raise taxes and had to look to other, nonapproved, methods to increase treasury funds. Like his father, Charles I raised money through the sale of more royal monopolies. Charles I also collected exorbitant fines through the court system and revived highly antiquated medieval financial claims. All of these extra-Parliamentary fundraising practices were unpopular, and Charles I was strongly disliked by both the English nobility and the general public.

Despite his Scottish descent, Charles I also faced a serious problem in Scotland. The Scots felt Charles's government was not treating them equally. They were also extremely angry over Charles's imposition of Episcopalian (centralized) rule on the Church of Scotland, a Calvinist church that had previously used a Presbyterian (local) style of church government. These factors came to a head in 1640 when the Scots revolted against English rule. Charles I needed tax money to suppress this Scottish rebellion and was forced to finally call Parliament back into session.

Once Parliament was called into session, it took out years of pent-up frustration on King Charles. The Puritans were the dominant force in Parliament and, because their religious views were very similar to those of the Scots, they refused to grant the money Charles requested. In open defiance of kingly power, the Puritans abolished many of the levies and taxes that Charles had used to keep his government going. A governmental financial crisis resulted. Eventually, Parliament and the king compromised. Parliament granted money to quell the Scottish rebellion (and another rebellion that broke out in Ireland), and the king accepted several reforms of government, including a new law that required the king to call Parliament into session at least once every three years. This period in English history is called the **Long Parliament** because Parliament sat (with only a few brief breaks) for 20 years, from 1640 to 1660.

In spite of the compromise, the actions of Parliament enraged King Charles I, who viewed himself as an absolute monarch and considered Parliament a troublesome institution of the past. Eventually, out of frustration at Parliament's continued independence, Charles marched his troops into Parliament and attempted to arrest some of the Puritan parliamentary leaders. Rather than solving his problems though this act, he started a confrontation that led to the English Civil War. Soon, England was divided into two factions: the Cavaliers, mostly the landed gentry and their troops, were the supporters of the king; and the Roundheads, most of the general population, were the supporters of Parliament.

The **English Civil War** was long and bloody. The fighting lasted seven years, from 1642 to 1649. Eventually, the Roundheads won the war and steps were taken to force Charles I to accept a much more limited type of monarchy. However, **Oliver Cromwell,** the leader of a radical Roundhead group known as the Independents and commander of the Roundhead armies, distrusted Charles. Cromwell forced Parliament to end the monarchy, and King Charles I was beheaded. England was then declared to be a commonwealth (republic) and was ruled by the House of Commons in Parliament (the House of Lords was abolished).

The newly constituted Parliament was not representative of the entire English population. For instance, both Episcopalians and any dissenting Presbyterians were excluded. This initial ruling group became known as the **Rump Parliament** (that is, the residual Parliament) and it lost much of its popular credibility. The Rump Parliament was also quite ineffective at running the country because of continued bickering and infighting. Oliver Cromwell, who had risked his life and spent years fighting to give Parliament power, was disgusted at their inability to effectively run the government. Eventually, Cromwell acted on his disgust, marched his troops into Parliament, and dissolved it. After the dissolution of Parliament, Cromwell's officers devised a type of constitution called the Instrument of Government that effectively established a dictatorship under Cromwell, who was given the title "Lord Protector." This period of English history became known as the **Protectorate.**

Ironically, as Lord Protector, Cromwell probably had greater authority than King Charles I ever did because Cromwell was able to virtually ignore the newly formed Protectorate Parliament. This whole situation was especially strange, as

Cromwell came to power fighting to end the monarchy and empower the Parliament but became a stronger absolutist than the king he deposed. The actions of Cromwell to assume this power and rule by dictate seem to be non-creative. He had the opportunity to radically depart from the traditional system of kings and to move to a more democratic system, but, when problems arose, he was unwilling or unable to find creative solutions. He reverted to what he had seen in other kingdoms.

During the Protectorate, Cromwell's biggest problem was the Levellers' revolt. The **Levellers** were a Lutheran religious group that wanted Cromwell and the Roundheads to finish what they had begun and truly empower the masses. The Levellers wanted to give all Englishmen the vote and reinstate the Parliament to its former position of power. Cromwell viewed the Levellers as a threat to the stability of England (and a possible threat to his power) and had the movement crushed. Cromwell's tenure as Lord Protector was brief, as he died only three years after coming to power.

Upon Cromwell's death, his son, Richard, briefly ruled in his place, but was ineffective as a ruler. Young Cromwell resigned after nine months, and, following a brief period of disorder, Parliament then invited Charles II, the son of Charles I, to come out of exile and accept the crown, if he would agree to respect the rights of Parliament. Richard Cromwell's resignation was not only noble (for the good of England) but was also creative. He had to strike a compromise with the king that would satisfy the demands of the king (and his followers) and also of Parliament. The balance of power between the monarchists and the parliamentarians was delicate and, apparently, Richard Cromwell did it well.

Charles II agreed to Parliament's terms and was crowned king of England. The return of the monarchy is called the **Restoration.** With the restoration of the monarchy, both houses of Parliament were reinstated, and the Anglican Church was restored as the official church of England. In fact, during the reign of Charles II, most of the changes made during the Commonwealth and Protectorate periods were revoked and the government of England largely reverted to what it had been during the reign of Charles I.

Charles II died in 1685 without children and his brother became king of England as James II. King James II was unpopular in England from the beginning, as he was an open and devout Catholic. James II further alienated his subjects by appointing many Catholics to prominent positions in the government and at the universities. The religious tension within England became high, as it became apparent that James II was trying to reinstate Catholicism within England.

These tensions came to a head when James II had a son and openly baptized him as a Catholic. Up until this event, James's Catholicism had been disliked but, for the sake of stability, it had been tolerated because his Protestant daughter, Mary, was his heir to the throne of England. However, with the birth and Catholic baptism of a male heir, it became obvious that a Catholic heir would succeed to the throne.

Sensing the negative mood of the largely Protestant masses and being predominately Protestant itself, Parliament took the bold step of inviting James II's Protestant daughter, Mary Stuart and her husband, William III of Orange, a *stadtholder* in the Dutch Republic, to become king and queen of England. In a bloodless coup, called the **Glorious Revolution,** William and Mary arrived in London and were crowned by Parliament as the new English king and queen. William and Mary were accepted by Parliament as legitimate rulers of England because of their royal ancestry. The new English monarchs then allowed James II to "escape" into exile in France.

James II was not content to live out his life in France, however, and had soon gone to Ireland to raise an army in hopes of regaining his throne. The Irish and the Scots both backed James II in this attempt; the Irish because they were Catholic and the Scots because they wanted a continuation of the Stuart line, which was originally Scottish, on the English throne. William and Mary however heard of James's plot and sent an army to Ireland, where the Protestants in northern Ireland (still called Orangemen today because of their support of William of Orange) lent them aid. The army of William and Mary met the army of James II in the Battle of the Boyne, where William and Mary's forces were victorious.

The Glorious Revolution of William and Mary was the time when England became a true limited monarchy with more than just nominal checks on the monarch's power. Some of those limitations were placed upon William and Mary as part of the deal to get Parliament to back their ascension to the throne. However, William of Orange sacrificed more of the royal powers to Parliament in order to gain favors in his continuing war with France. Among the concessions he made to Parliament was his recognition of an English Bill of Rights.

The **English Bill of Rights** was a document that both outlined some of the rights of the English people and clarified the new relationship between the monarchy and the Parliament. The Bill of Rights declared that law was to be made by Parliament (the king could only propose laws) and that the king had to call Parliament into session at least once every three years. Furthermore, both the elections to Parliament and the debates within Parliament were to be free from royal interference. The Bill of Rights also assured judicial independence from the crown by declaring that judges would hold their office during good behavior (for life). This meant the king or queen could not remove a justice from office simply for disagreeing with him or her. Removal of a judge required that the monarchy show a real cause justifying removal. In regards to protecting the rights of the people, the English Bill of Rights guaranteed the right of the citizenry to bear arms and disallowed the crown from keeping a standing army that might threaten the people in peacetime. Finally, freedom of worship for dissenters from the state church was granted, although it was also stipulated that the English monarch was required to be a Protestant.

The initial agreement between Parliament and William and Mary, and the later acceptance of the English Bill of Rights, made England the first true limited monarchy. It also established the basis for the modern government of the United Kingdom.

Another important step in the development of the modern United Kingdom occurred during the reign of Queen Anne, Mary's sister and the successor to William and Mary. It was during Queen Anne's reign (1702–1714) that the formal union occurred, creating the United Kingdom of England, Scotland, Ireland, and Wales.

Queen Anne died without an heir, so the crown was offered to her cousin, the Elector of Hanover, who became king as George I.

■ Austria

The crown of Austria was linked to the Holy Roman Empire from the time that Charles V became Holy Roman emperor in the sixteenth century. When Charles V became old, he desired to resign from the throne. He realized, however, that the enormity of the Hapsburg empire had made it nearly impossible for one monarch to rule. Therefore, upon his abdication, he split his kingdom and gave the Austrian part, including the German possessions, to his brother, Ferdinand, who already ruled portions of the German lands as the king of Bohemia and ruled Hungary through the result of a typical Hapsburg political marriage. The Spanish part and all the possessions in western Europe and America went to Charles's son, Philip II.

The Austrian Hapsburgs, who were strongly Catholic, led the fight against Protestantism during the Thirty Years War. They were supported by their Spanish cousins and seemed to be able to overcome all Protestant opposition. They may have succeeded in reestablishing Catholicism as the religion throughout Germany if the French had not entered the war on the Protestant side. When that occurred, the Hapsburgs sought an end to the war and the Peace of Westphalia was signed. This treaty weakened the control of the Hapsburgs over the Holy Roman Empire, but they still persisted in their traditional role as Holy Roman Emperors. The Hapsburgs ruled as a family longer than any other royal family of Europe. The Austrian branch became the dominant part of the family. The coat of arms with the double eagle of the Hapsburgs is shown in Figure 32.9. It is located on the gate of their main palace in Vienna, Austria.

A crisis arose in the Austrian Hapsburg empire in the 1680s when the Ottoman Turks decided to support the Hungarians in a revolt against their Hapsburg rulers. The Ottoman army entered Hungary, took control over that land, and continued their attack against the Austrians right to the gates of Vienna, where it laid siege to the city. The siege was finally lifted when an army of Germans and Poles came to the rescue of the Austrians. Then, over the next twenty years, the Austrian army gained strength and was able to drive the Ottoman Turks out of Hungary and regain the lands that they had previously lost.

The War of Spanish Succession was precipitated by the death of the last of the Spanish Hapsburg kings. As already noted, the French supported a Bourbon as the next ruler of Spain, which would make the Spanish and French kings from the same family. The Austrian Hapsburgs vigorously opposed the French plan and, as an alternate, proposed that the son of the Austrian emperor be named king of Spain, thus retaining the Spanish throne within Hapsburg control. At the end of the conflict, the Bourbon was named king and Austria was forced to give up all claims to the Spanish throne, but Austria gained control over the Spanish Netherlands and Spanish possessions in northern Italy.

Austria continued to be a major power in Europe for several centuries. As we will see in later chapters, the Austrians were a major force during the Napoleonic period and were important into the period of World War I.

■ Russia

For centuries Russia had been a backward and unorganized nation that had played only a minor role in the history of Europe. It was not until the Age of Absolutism dawned in Europe in the seventeenth century that Russia began to have an influence on the affairs of the continent. That influence came as

Figure 32.9 ■ Coat of arms of the Hapsburgs on their palace in Vienna, Austria. *© 2010 by Davor Pukljak. Used under license of Shutterstock, Inc.*

the result of the efforts of one man—**Czar Peter I, the Great.** His is the story we want to consider here, but some background in Russian history is appropriate to help understand his vision and the forces of opposition that he had to overcome to bring Russia into European civilization.

Russia was originally settled by Viking explorers around 500 A.D., but the Vikings were clannish and uncivilized, and Russia remained predominately tribal. The Russians had accepted Orthodox Christianity when Cyril, a missionary from Constantinople, baptized the Russian ruler in the ninth century A.D. It was at this time that Cyril created an alphabet for the Russians. He based this alphabet on his native Greek alphabet and added some letters and made other changes to fit the Russian language. This alphabet is still used in Russian today and is called the Cyrillic alphabet.

The **Mongols** (called Tartars or "the people from hell" by the Russians) invaded Russia in the 1200s, and the Viking city of Kyiv (Kiev) became an important center for the Tartars. Tartar rule, which was based in Asia, reinforced the orientation of Russia away from Europe. For several centuries, the Russian people paid a high tribute (tax) to the Tartar overseers.

In the late 1400s, the **Romanoff family,** rulers of the city of Moscow, was successful in unifying the various Russian tribes and cities into a single political entity. However, despite the creation of a Europeanlike state, Russia's isolation from Europe continued for a variety of reasons:

- The Orthodox beliefs of the Russians did not blend well with the Roman Catholic and Protestant views dominating Europe.
- The unique Cyrillic alphabet created a communication barrier with the countries of Europe, all of which used the Roman alphabet. (Greece was the exception, but it was under the control of the Ottoman Turks and not considered part of Europe at this time.)
- The newly formed Russian nation was having difficulty in controlling its western territories, especially the areas of Belarus and Ukraine. The continued chaos in these regions limited contact between the leaders of Russia in Moscow and the rest of Europe.
- The emergence of the Turks on the Black Sea after the Fall of Constantinople focused Russian attention toward the Black Sea and away from Europe.
- Russia viewed itself as the only true descendent of the Roman Empire because the Russian king, Ivan the Great, married the last Byzantine princess who, supposedly, passed on the right of rule to his line. Thus, the Russian kings took the title of Czar, which is a rusification of the word *Caesar.* Furthermore, many of the Orthodox leaders went into Russian territory when Constantinople fell. Russia's belief that it was the heir of Rome caused conflict with several European nations, including Italy and the Holy Roman Empire. Russia felt that Europe did not pay it enough respect as the inheritor of Roman rule.

Although this non-European orientation was initially advantageous because it kept Russia isolated from European political entanglements that would draw it into European wars, eventually the separation led to a retardation of culture within Russia. The Russians seemed to be locked in a medieval culture and did not experience the changes of the Renaissance that swept across Europe in the fifteenth and sixteenth centuries. Therefore, when Europe emerged from the Middle Ages and began to form the ideas of modern Europe, Russia was viewed by most Europeans as Asian, not European, and was generally ignored.

The concept of the absolute monarch was inherent in Russian politics because of its persistent medieval culture. In fact, the Russian czars probably had more power than any European king, with the possible exception of France's Louis XIV. Unlike Europe, where rulers were often somewhat limited by parliaments or their aristocracy, despite their claims of absolute power and divine right, the power of Russian rulers was generally only limited by their ability to enforce their will over such a vast and harsh territory.

The first of the great absolute rulers of Russia was the czar known as **Ivan IV, the Terrible,** who ruled in the late 1500s. (By the way, the title "Terrible" might also be rendered "Awesome," and may reflect the esteem of the people for this powerful czar.) Ivan the Terrible expanded Russia's holdings to include the area around the Black and Caspian Seas (this was especially vital, as it gave Russia a port that would not freeze over in the winter), much of the Baltic region, and east to Siberia and the Pacific Ocean. Ivan the Terrible also used his power to force the *boyers* (Russian landholders) to accept the authority of Moscow. By doing this, Ivan finalized the emergence of Russia as a major political entity, similar to the nations of Europe. Ivan the Terrible also established the principle that *all* commoners in Russia were servants to the czar; in essence, declaring that anyone who did not hold land in Russia was a serf to the Russian crown. The power of Ivan the Terrible within Russia was complete.

The next great Russian absolutist was **Czar Peter I, the Great,** who became ruler of Russia in 1682 as a young boy and ruled until 1725. Peter understood that Russia had fallen behind Europe culturally, creatively, and technologically, and took steps to make Russia more European and shift its focus away from the influence and culture of Asia. Peter opened Russia to Western thought and encouraged Russians to accept many aspects of European culture. He met much resistance from both the gentry and the commoners, but because of his well-defined vision and the force of his personality and physical presence, he was largely successful. He was, of course, also aided by the Russian tradition of absolute rule by the czar.

To learn about European ways, Peter journeyed to Europe, where he spent considerable time in Holland and England. There he saw the value of trade and manufacturing. When he returned to Russia, after about eighteen months on his trip, he began to establish Russia in the model of a trade and manufacturing-based nation. However, Russia did not have a warm-water port that led directly to the ocean. (The ports on the Black Sea all required that the ships pass through the narrow strait at Istanbul, which was controlled by the hated Ottoman Turks.) Therefore, Peter initiated a war against Sweden to gain access to the

Baltic. He was successful in this war and obtained his access at the mouth of the Neva River. This new Russian territory and Peter's trip are shown in Figure 32.10.

Peter then began the task of establishing a Russian navy to conduct trade and to protect Russia's interests on the seas. He also established Russian manufacturing, although he was limited in these tasks by the great physical separations of Russia and the major markets for manufactured goods.

Peter's vision of a European Russia included the establishment of a European-style city in the newly acquired territory. The construction of the city was meant to both encourage increased sea trade and draw Russia closer to Europe. It was built to emulate the great cities of Europe. He moved the capital of Russia from Moscow to the new city and named this new European-style city St. Petersburg. Note that the name—St. Petersburg—is the actual name of the city and not a translation of the name from some Russian equivalent. Hence, even to the name, the city was European and not Russian. (This blatant European name is undoubtedly why St. Petersburg has also been named Petrograd and Leningrad, attempts to reflect a more Russian character. The name was changed back to St. Petersburg following the collapse of the Communist government in the 1990s.)

Peter wanted to change many other aspects of Russian life. He began to wear European-style clothing instead of the traditional Russian dress and insisted that others in the court do likewise. He even went so far as to demand that the men in the court shave their beards, a dramatic step, as Orthodox Church doctrine said that beards were a mark of piety. The preferred languages of Peter's court were German and French. In all things possible, Peter dragged the Russian people into European culture.

His efforts were largely successful. St. Petersburg became a major center for trade. Russian influence was felt in Europe from that time forward. Russian artists, musicians, and other writers contributed to European culture in many important ways.

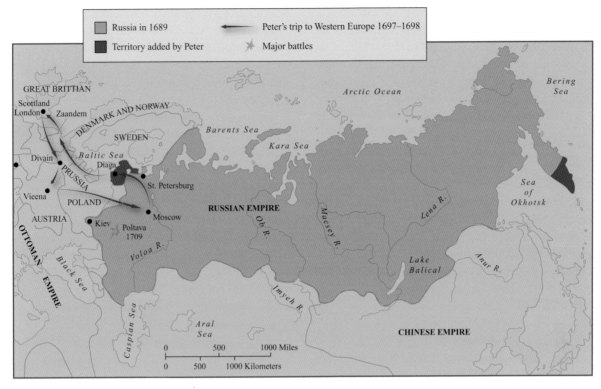

Figure 32.10 ■ *Territory added to Russia by Peter the Great and the route of Peter's European trip.*

■ Summary

Changing times usually require creativity to control direction and accomplishment. Some of the leaders of the fast-changing seventeenth century had sufficient creativity that they could control their environments, but others seemed to just float along with the flow of events. Examples of those who had control were Henry IV of France, Richelieu, Louis XIV, Cromwell, and Peter the Great.

We might ask, what was the nature of their creativity that allowed these leaders to control events so that they could accomplish their desires? In other words, what is the creativity of leadership amid change? First, it seems that all of these creative leaders had a strong and well-developed vision of where they wanted to go. They saw the future, at least in potential, and were able to communicate their vision to those around them. They also understood the existing situation and realized what would be required to move from

where they (or their country) were to where they wanted to be.

They coupled this strong vision with an ability to execute their plan. They seemed to realize that objections and other obstacles were inevitable, but they found ways to overcome those problems. In the seventeenth century, some of the problems could be overcome because of their ability to rule by absolute power, but not all could be overcome by shear force. They also understood that the support of others was important, especially if their reforms were to persist after their death. In each of the creative leaders named above, this ability to rally support was demonstrated. These creative leaders also found innovative methods of acting when traditional methods failed.

King Henry IV of France exemplified the change in attitude from a medieval mentality in which religion was the most important factor of life to a Renaissance attitude in which individuals became the central focus. Henry was willing to change his religion in order to secure the throne of France. He remarked, "Paris is worth a mass," thus revealing his priorities. He took steps to calm the religious feelings so that the focus of the government could be on economics. Henry's vision of a prosperous France was successfully implemented by his strong economic policies. This economic strength served France well for more than a century.

Henry's son, Louis XIII, was weak and ineffective but was so strongly influenced by his adviser, Cardinal Richelieu, that France continued to prosper during turbulent times. Richelieu saw that the combination of warfare and diplomacy was better than either alone. He manipulated other countries by using the combination—using war when it was necessary, but relying on diplomacy to set up the war to France's advantage.

Peter the Great similarly went to war to achieve his ends (such as getting a warm-weather port) and then combined that with a determination to create a new country modeled on what he had observed in Holland and England. He used engineering, naval expertise, architecture, and cultural change to create a city that was similar to the best he had observed.

Cromwell was also willing to go to war to accomplish his vision but combined his warfare with religious and political zeal to unite his followers. He was even willing to kill his king and establish a new form of government. In his case, however, the changes were short-lived, at least in the short term.

Louis XIV likewise adopted innovative methods to control his environment. He created a new environment of elegance and exalted image that helped him communicate the greatness of France to both the French people and the rest of the world. He controlled France's nobility by instituting royal favors as a way to create jealousy among his courtiers and force them to depend on him for position and prestige.

The age of the absolute monarchs was to be relatively short. Having such complete and total power centered in only one person had some advantages in centralizing and modernizing the political structure in many countries, but absolutism also had many drawbacks. The absolute monarchs were isolated from other monarchs and from their own nobility, who were often frustrated in their own ambitions. The peasantry saw little advantage from absolute monarchs, except for some prestige. The disadvantages usually included greater taxes and greater separation from government than ever because of the new centralized bureaucracies that stripped the local nobility of their power in favor of official bureaucrats loyal to the crown.

There were inherent dangers in the rule of one. A loss of continuity between different rulers was a frequent occurrence. Even a lack of consistency within the reign of one ruler occasionally occurred, because there was no established system to approve and oversee changes in law or policy. This lack of checks and balances was both expensive and led to confusion. Another problem with absolute monarchies was that sometimes a monarch was a poor decision maker, like Spain's Phillip II, or simply uninterested in his duties, like France's Louis XIII. Because these men potentially had such limitless power, they could wreak great havoc on their own nation's financial and political well-being in a very short time. Even successful absolutists, like Louis XIV, spent money so freely that France was practically bankrupt at his death.

There were other philosophical problems with absolutism as well. The political and social climate of Europe was continuing to evolve. The growth of the middle class caused more people to feel the need to have a greater say in their government. This helped create the environment that would later produce the Enlightenment and the sweeping political and social changes brought about by its ideas.

Some countries, especially the Netherlands and England, moved to limit the authority of their monarchs in the seventeenth century. In those countries the limitations on monarchy were successful (although not without difficulties) and seemed to help these countries achieve high levels of economic activity and prosperity. These governments became models for other nations in subsequent years, but, in the seventeenth century, the model that every monarch wanted to follow was Louis XIV—the most successful of all the absolute monarchs.

▪ Timeline—Important Dates

Date	Event
1547–1584	*Reign of Ivan IV (the Terrible) of Russia*
1556	*Charles V splits the Hapsburg empire (Spain and Austria)*
1572	*St. Bartholomew's Day massacre*
1588–1648	*Reign of Christian IV of Denmark*
1589	*Henry of Navarre becomes Henry IV of France*
1603–1625	*Reign of James I of England*
1609	*Netherlands established with Spanish truce*
1610–1643	*Reign of Louis XIII with Cardinals Richelieu and Mazarin*
1618–1648	*Thirty Years War*
1625–1649	*Reign of Charles I of England*
1643–1715	*Reign of Louis XIV of France*
1649–1658	*Protectorate under Oliver Cromwell*
1658–1660	*Protectorate under Richard Cromwell and period of disorder*
1660	*The Restoration of the English monarchy (Charles II)*
1682–1725	*Reign of Peter the Great of Russia*
1685–1688	*Reign of James II of England*
1688	*The Glorious Revolution (reign of William III and Mary)*
1701–1714	*War of Spanish Succession*
1702–1714	*Reign of Queen Anne of England*

▪ Suggested Readings

Massie, Robert K., *Peter the Great,* Ballantine, 1980.

Milton, Giles, *Nathaniel's Nutmeg,* Penguin Books, 1969.

Shama, Simon, *The Embarrassment of Riches,* First Vintage Books, 1987.

Chapter 33

Baroque
Impressive Creativity

O fairest of Creation, last and best
Of all God's Works, Creature in whom excell'd
Whatever can to sight or thought be form'd,
Holy, divine, good, amiable, or sweet!

—*John Milton,* Paradise Lost *(Adam thinking about Eve, Book IX, lines 896–899)*

Origins of the Baroque Movement

The political upheaval of the seventeenth century that we discussed in the previous chapter began with disputes over religion and ended with disputes over monarchies. In both cases, an underlying issue was power—church power and political power. As we discussed, that power was demonstrated through the obedience of adherents and citizens, through diplomatic threats and maneuvers, and by warfare. Power was also demonstrated in other ways; ways that were more subtle and more uplifting—architecture, sculpture, paintings, music, and literature. Of course, these methods did not threaten or take the life of people, but they impressed people and thereby communicated the power of the sponsor. These art forms are the subject of this chapter.

Because these art forms were meant to send a message extolling the power and virtues of the sponsors, the artists wanted to capture the attention of the beholders and impress them with the message of the art. Artists did this by several methods, including exaggerated dramatic effects, elaborate techniques, exalted language, enormous size, and compelling subject matter. Some critics of later years felt that these methods were excessive and ridiculed this period. They called it **Baroque,** which might have originated with the Portuguese word *barroco,* meaning odd-shaped and imperfect, or possibly with the Italian word *baroco,* which referred to a complicated problem in medieval logic, or even with the Spanish word *verruga,* which refers to a wart. In any case, the name has been applied to all forms of art during this period when the objective was to impress others. This Baroque Period is generally dated from musical events—1600 (the beginning of opera) to 1750 (the death of Bach)—but the time boundaries clearly overlap with artistic styles that preceded and followed and are only approximate for other artistic forms. That is especially true with architecture and painting, which showed strong Baroque-like influences in the late 1500s.

Originally, the Catholic Church encouraged the exaggerated (Baroque) style as part of the **Counter-Reformation.** The Church asked the architects and artists it commissioned to represent the glories of heaven and salvation through the Catholic Church in an effort to win Protestants back to the fold. Church buildings and decorations were grander—both in size and elaborateness. Artists began to show greater emotion in the subjects of their art, either the ecstasy of heaven or the pains of hell for non-Catholics. The beauty and emotional power of the Baroque movement proved to be effective tools in the Counter-Reformation, as the ornate decoration of Catholic art and architecture stood out in dramatic contrast to the simplicity and starkness of Protestantism. The initial success of Baroque art in glorifying the Catholic Church encouraged the further expansion of the movement.

The Baroque style began in Rome, where the Catholic Church wanted to heighten the glory of its headquarters. The style spread rapidly across Italy and other Catholic areas because bishops also wanted to impress people in outlying areas. After a few years, since art often follows money and power (that's where the commissions and markets are located), Spain became the center for Baroque art because Spain was the financial and spiritual mainstay of Catholicism. The Spanish Hapsburgs also wanted the art to reflect their family's glory, and so the Baroque style was ideal. The court painter, Diego Velasquez, was not only an accomplished painter who used the Baroque style, he also was tasked to commission other art pieces and to collect art from all over Europe to enhance the Spanish art collection (which is, today, mostly housed in the Prado in Madrid).

As Spain's wealth and power fell into decline, France replaced Spain as the artistic and cultural center of Europe. France also embraced the Baroque style, chiefly to glorify the power of French absolute monarchs that reached its zenith with the rule of the Sun King, Louis XIV. Proclaiming the glories of France and his own power were integral parts of Louis XIV's plan for his country. The best example of this artist statement of greatness is Louis' elaborate palace at Versailles. For decades after Louis, other monarchs patterned their own palaces and lifestyles after Versailles palace. In countries where the Catholic Church was weak and where strong (absolute) kings did not exist (like Northern Germany, Scandinavia, the Netherlands, and England), the purpose of art was threefold. First, it was to glorify God. Second, it was to glorify the country. Third, it was to demonstrate individual wealth and glory, especially of the newly rich middle class. Thus, Baroque art became entwined with Catholicism and then with Protestantism, as well as European nationalism and individual glory. We will discuss these motivations in more detail as we consider specific art pieces and artists.

■ Specific Characteristics of the Baroque

The Baroque period was a change from the Renaissance, but more as a natural evolution and exaggeration than a break. Another way to describe the difference might be to say that during the Renaissance, artists wanted the viewer to *see* the emotions of the subject while in the Baroque the artists wanted the viewer to *feel* the emotions of the subject. This is a key distinction that underlies all of the characteristics of the Baroque: Baroque artists attempted to bring the viewers *into* the work; to make them participants with the art rather than just observers of it.

Remember that the overall purpose of Baroque art was to impress people and, logically, they were more impressed if they became emotionally involved. Therefore, the most important aspect of the Baroque era is a sense of heightened emotion. One creative aspect of Renaissance painting was that artists had begun to realistically show emotion in the figures in their works. However, in

Figure 33.1 ■ **A)** David *by Michelangelo.* **B)** David *by Bernini. A) © Gianni Dagli Orti/CORBIS. B) © Corel.*

Renaissance art this display of emotion was usually stylized—that is, it was shown by a slight gesture or a facial inflection. More than this may have upset the symmetry and balance of the Greek ideal of proportion on which much of Renaissance art was based. During the Baroque, the artists expressed human emotions much more strongly with, for example, dramatic positioning of the body and facial expressions. The emotion was further enhanced in painting by the extreme use of *chiaroscuro,* the use of light and shadow, to enhance dramatic effect.

Another related characteristic of Baroque art was a sense of motion or movement. Motion served to draw the viewer into the work, enhance the dramatic effect of the piece, and show off the technical virtuosity of the artist. Although pleasing to the eye and perfectly in keeping with the concepts of balance and symmetry of ancient Greece, the triangular arrangement of figures often used in Renaissance paintings tended to make the figures appear static. Baroque art deviated from this triangular arrangement and gave the figures dramatic body movement.

Similar trends were seen in the ancient world between Classical Greek sculpture and the sculpture of the later Hellenistic Age. The Classical Greek works emphasized and tried to retain proportion and symmetry—the marks of beauty to the math-conscious Greeks. However, in the Hellenistic period, when the Greeks were scattered throughout the Mediterranean world, they blended with local cultures and deviated from the strict symmetry and restraint of the classical style. Perhaps even in the ancient world the Hellenistic artists sought to impress and therefore used more exaggerated and elaborate styling. We see, therefore, that in both the ancient world and in the Renaissance/Baroque era, a classical period was followed by a period of exaggeration.

A good example in the difference between movement in Renaissance and Baroque sculpture can be seen by comparing Michelangelo's and Bernini's statues of *David.* Michelangelo's *David,* completed at the height of the Renaissance, has a strong classical feel that lends a sense of power, authority, and strength of purpose (see Figure 33.1A). Bernini's *David,* however, created at the height of the Baroque period, used both the position of the body and facial expression to show David's fierce determination and his will to kill the enemy of his people (Figure 33.1B). Michelangelo's *David* may be able to kill Goliath, but Bernini's *David* is actually doing it.

A strong sense of movement could also be depicted by use of foreshortening. *Foreshortening* was a newly developed technique that used a deep understanding of perspective to create a three-dimensional effect that made parts of a painting look as if they are actually sticking out of the work toward the viewer. Rembrandt's painting, *Night Watch,* which was illustrated in the previous chapter (Figure 32.7), uses foreshortening in the spear carried by one of the guards.

People can also be impressed by details. In painting, this might be done by an intricate depiction of the lace on a collar of a Dutch soldier. In sculpture, it could be the unbelievable touches of creatively carved detail, which give the impression of soft and supple flesh. In music, this might be done by the precise development of the pattern of a fugue and the intricate interactions of the melodies from which it was built. In literature, details could be demonstrated in the depth of examination of a character or by the intricacy of the language used in the literary work.

Baroque art, music, and literature were also meant to give praise. This praise might be directed toward the Catholic Church, toward God directly (especially for Protestants), toward the king, or toward a secular group or idea. This desire to praise often led Baroque works to be quite ornate, elaborate, and complex. It was this characteristic that earned the Baroque the scorn of the eighteenth century art critics that named it. They felt that the art of this period was too busy and lacked the classical beauty of the Renaissance period.

People were often impressed by grandeur. One method to express grandeur was, obviously, with pure size, especially in architecture. Size could also be used in painting and in music. However, grandeur in music was more commonly expressed by the nature of the work itself; so magnificent in its subject, melodies, and orchestrations that people were filled with awe,

usually for God, who was the usual subject of such musical works. However, in the case of opera, the awe might be toward the production itself because of its elaborate music, staging, and performance. Even some literary works, such as Milton's *Paradise Lost,* were impressive in their size and scope.

Some subjects in Baroque art are not grand in the sense of majestic or overpowering. For instance, Dutch Baroque artists frequently depicted middle class merchants. However, since the object of even this art was to impress, the subjects of the art (who were usually the sponsors) were certainly impressed with their own likenesses and, therefore, the works conformed to the overall concepts of the Baroque. Furthermore, for the Dutch, depicting the middle class was a way to impress the rest of the world with the economic vitality of the Netherlands.

A comparison of the major characteristics of Baroque and Renaissance art is given in Figure 33.2. This comparison shows that the features of Renaissance art were largely retained but expanded upon in the Baroque period. Although some of the characteristics are clearly unique to painting (such as *chiaroscuro*), many characteristics relate to both painting and other forms of expression such as sculpture, architecture, and music.

It is interesting that many different forms of expression exhibited similar characteristics at the same time. That fact suggests that the general environment was very important in determining the nature of the art. The creativity of the artists was, therefore, influenced by the environment. In this regard, the creativity was not totally unique. In fact, uniqueness is probably defined by realizing that some features of the work must be the same as others of the period, but small differences make the work unique. During the Baroque period, that environment was a desire to impress the viewers, listeners, and readers—church members, former church members, subjects of great realms, and moneyed sponsors. We will now look at each of the major art forms and the artists and writers who created that art. We will try to understand something of the nature of their creativity in trying to impress.

Characteristics of the Renaissance Style	Explanations of the Characteristics	Modifications Made in the Baroque Style
Realism	People are represented as they really were or could have been rather than just symbolic representations, and depicting appropriate emotion.	Facial expressions, poses, and other ways show emotion strongly with some details minutely perfected.
Diverse subject matter	Pagan themes are included, in addition to religious ones.	Secular themes are added, glorifying kings and depicting middle-class people.
Simple and clean lines and designs	Art reflects a desire to return to the geometric and symmetric standards of the ancient Greeks.	Decorations are elaborate and frequently deviate from simple geometric shapes.
Perspective	Many techniques are used to give three-dimensionality to the picture, but especially the use of linear perspective.	Perspective, especially the method of foreshortening, is strongly depicted, sometimes becoming dominant.
Geometric arrangement of figures	Triangular arrangements, especially, are used to emphasize some figures in the painting over others of less importance.	Figures are placed in more dramatic and more dynamic positions than the somewhat static triangular arrangement.
Chiaroscuro	Light and dark shading enhances three-dimensionality and also adds to realism.	Strong lighting effects heighten dramatic effects and emphasized certain figures.
Sfumato	Multiple layers of paint are applied to achieve a kind of smokiness that softened edges of figures in the painting to make them appear natural.	The colors of the entire work are muted to convey a feeling of unity and, often, warmth.

Figure 33.2 ■ *Comparison of the characteristics of the Renaissance and Baroque styles of painting.*

■ Baroque Architecture and Sculpture

The principal object of art during the Baroque was to impress, and that could be done most easily by constructing massive and elaborate buildings and other monuments. Baroque architects tried to create the illusion of openness and great space and showed an increased interest in the relationship between the building and the surrounding area. This logically linked architecture to sculpture, because one way to relate a building to its surroundings was with strategically placed sculpture, especially as part of elaborate gardens and fountains. The inventions of new materials such as stucco and plaster gave architects of this era more freedom to add ornamentation, because false facades could now be placed on more traditionally shaped inner structures, thus allowing for conventional construction with later elaboration of the Baroque style. In Baroque architecture there is an exaggeration of dimensions and forms that creates a feeling of movement and excitement. This movement and excitement was, however, most clearly demonstrated in the sculpture. For this reason, some believe that the sculpture of the Baroque is at least as good as sculpture from any artistic period.

Almost all of the typical Baroque characteristics are present in the architectural masterpiece that is the heart of the Catholic Church—St. Peter's church and square in Rome, pictured in Figure 33.3. More than any other location, the Catholic Church wanted to use St. Peter's Basilica and the area around it—the very center of Catholicism—as a way of demonstrating the Church's power, grandeur, and mission. The square lies in front of the great basilica that was begun in the Renaissance and completed in the early Baroque (1615). As the largest church in Christendom, the basilica is certainly impressive. (To make sure that visitors are properly impressed, markers showing the size of other well known churches have been placed on the floor of St. Peter's, thus giving a measure of relative size.)

When the basilica itself was completed, the Church desired to further enhance the interior decorations. It asked **Gianlorenzo Bernini** to design and build a canopy over the central altar. This massive and incredibly ornate structure is more than 90 feet high and is clearly meant to inspire awe.

Perhaps just as inspiring, and certainly more symbolic, is the wonderful array of pillars, also built by Bernini that defines the edges of the area (St. Peter's Square) in front of the basilica. Built between 1656 and 1667, Bernini's design suggests arms extending from the basilica and, because they are curved inwardly, inviting the world to enter. This symbolism reflects, of course, the message of the Counter-Reformation, that is, the Catholic Church desires all of the wayward Protestants to return to the Catholic fold.

The Church continued to give many commissions to Bernini. He created several additional decorations within the Vatican, such as the ornate Chair of St. Peter and the royal staircase connecting St. Peter's Square to the papal apartments. Around Rome he designed and built several entire churches, numerous church decorations, monuments, and fountains. Two of the most famous are

Figure 33.3 ■ *St. Peter's Square in Rome (Vatican).* © *Gianni Giansanti/ Sygma/Corbis.*

the decoration within the church Santa Maria della Vittoria called the *Ecstasy of St. Teresa* and the massive fountain called *The Four Rivers* in the Piazza Navona. The *Ecstasy of St. Teresa* is especially interesting because Bernini seems to have captured the ability to show light in a sculpture by featuring a burst of gold behind St. Teresa, thus giving the impression of light and dark that was used so effectively by Baroque painters.

Bernini was probably the greatest architect and sculptor of the Baroque period. As has been discussed previously in this chapter, Bernini's *David* captures the coiled, whip-like power of David's shot at Goliath, while also expertly depicting the determination and concentration upon his face (Figure 33.1B).

Many of Bernini's other works are also masterful examples of his skill as a sculptor, and they showcase the characteristics of the Baroque. In *The Rape of Proserpina (Persephone)*, Bernini captures the essence of movement in the victim's twisting form and her efforts to push away from Pluto, her attacker. Bernini further highlights the horror shown on Proserpina's face with a single tear running down her cheek. *The Rape of Proserpina* also showcases Bernini's technical virtuosity, another characteristic of the Baroque period. The indentations made by the attacker's gripping fingers on Proserpina's thigh are amazingly realistic and truly look like flesh in stone.

Bernini's *Daphne and Apollo* is also expertly done. The statue is based on the Greek myth of a forbidden love. A spell was placed on Daphne, and when Apollo touches her she begins the transformation into a Laurel tree. Bernini's statue captures the lovers at that ill-fated moment when Apollo first touches Daphne and the transformation begins. The statue is superb in its detail. Bernini's ability to show this transformation from flesh to wood (carved in stone) is amazing. The robes of the two lovers flow in the breeze and the ends of Daphne's fingertips and hair are already turning into tree branches. The leaves in Daphne's hair are carved so thinly that they actually tinkle when cleaned and are translucent in places.

Bernini's statue of Aeneas is almost unbelievable in its ability to depict skin textures. As you might remember from the legend, Aeneas carries his father out of a burning Troy and also leads his young son by the hand. The skin of Aeneas, depicted as a young man in the prime of life, is perfectly elastic over Aeneas's muscles. Aeneas's father is aged and the skin is taut and wrinkled, a surprising contrast to the skin of Aeneas. The skin of Aeneas's son is also a contrast to the others—soft and supple over the pudgy body of a toddler.

The creativity of Bernini in some pieces was his ability to capture an intense moment with incredible realism. It was also his fluid style and symbolism. Both kinds of work were done with a technique never before exhibited. Bernini's style has been described by Stuart Isacoff in his book, *Temperament,* as follows:

> *Bernini criticized Michelangelo for failing to make his figures appear as if made of flesh, and bragged that stone was 'like pasta' in his hands—that he could fashion marble like wax. And indeed he could. His genius for manipulating the act of perception—by altering perspective, or highlighting certain details in a rendering, or using materials and techniques to blur the lines between sculpture and painting—allowed Bernini to achieve new levels of authenticity in bringing a scene to life.*

One of the pleasures of visiting Italy, especially Rome, is to marvel at the genius and creativity of Bernini. Some of his works are easily encountered in, for instance, the Vatican. Others, such as the *David, Rape of Proserpina, Apollo and Daphne,* and *Aeneas,* are showcased in the Borguese Museum. But others, almost too many to count, are scattered throughout the churches and streets of Rome. What a delightful experience it is to encounter a great sculpture and then discover that the work was done by this prototypical Baroque genius, Gianlorenzo Bernini.

The **Versailles Palace** is the most important and best example of Baroque architecture that was not Church-sponsored. The palace, depicted as Figure 32.3, was built around 1669 under commission of King Louis XIV. Versailles is a massive complex, complete with extravagant buildings, fountains, and elaborate gardens (see Figure 32.3). The inside was designed to be ultra-elaborate, decorated with countless paintings and sculpture, and had as its crowning achievement a beautiful and massive Hall of Mirrors that was meant to reflect endless lights and serve as a symbol of King Louis' self-declaration that he was the "Sun King." All of this elaboration was meant to proclaim the greatness and power of France's King Louis XIV (see Figure 32.4).

Louis eventually moved his entire court out of Paris to Versailles, where it was easier for him to keep an eye on his troublesome aristocracy, who were required by Louis to spend at least part of the year living at Versailles. Versailles became the ultimate palace, and was copied all across Europe by rulers who wanted to both emulate its Baroque style as well as King Louis's absolutist style of power.

Today, a walk through the buildings and gardens of Versailles is a wonderful experience, just as it must have been for the courtiers of Louis XIV. Everything, from the massive equestrian statue of Louis XIV (Figure 32.2) in the entrance area to the extensive gardens and lakes in the rear park (Figure 32.5), along with the many rooms and decorations in the buildings, was designed to communicate glory and luxury. Although the commoners could not walk within and see the details of this incredible complex, surely they knew of its glory, and the mysteriousness of its exact nature may have added to its impressiveness in their minds.

Another great architect of the Baroque period was England's Christopher Wren. He was given the daunting task of rebuilding London's most famous buildings after the devastating fire of 1666. Wren's plans for redesigning London show many of the principles of modern city planning. Wren was also an expert in the rebuilding of churches, and he oversaw the remodeling of more than 50 in his lifetime. Wren's most famous and grandest is St. Paul's in London, but several other of his buildings are still in use in London and throughout England. As is typical of the Baroque style, St. Paul's is a massive edifice, perhaps the second largest church in Christendom. Like St. Peter's in

Rome, Wren's masterpiece has a cavernous interior and enormous dome—both meant to impress. In keeping with the Protestant view, St. Paul's is less ornate than the Catholic churches, but is no less impressive. Combined with the many other buildings built by Wren, the glories of London were communicated effectively to the entire world.

■ Baroque Painting

Following the general trends of the Baroque period, Baroque painting began with a religious focus and then expanded into other areas. The earliest Baroque master, the man who largely shaped the entire painting style, was Michelangelo Merisi, better known by his nickname, **Caravaggio.**

While Caravaggio used his immense talent as an artist to glorify God and the Catholic Church, his personal life was raucous and un-Christian. Having a successful early career in northern Italy, Caravaggio went to Rome in 1590 and painted several commissions for the Catholic Church; gaining a reputation for his unique style of highly dramatic *chiaroscuro* and extreme emotion in his subjects. Caravaggio's 16 years in Rome were tumultuous ones, as he was nearly always in trouble with the police and often offended and alienated potential friends and allies with his explosive temper. Furthermore, any chance Caravaggio had of establishing himself as Rome's leading painter of the day ended when he quarreled with an opponent in a tennis match and stabbed him to death. To avoid punishment, Caravaggio fled to Naples and then moved on to Malta, where he was thrown into prison for attacking a police officer. Upon escaping from prison, Caravaggio went back to Naples, where he got into a fight in a sleazy inn and was seriously wounded. After his recovery, he heard of a possible pardon if he returned to Rome and so he started on a journey back. However, Caravaggio never made it back to Rome, as he caught a fever from a group of sailors that he accused of robbing him and died en route.

Caravaggio's rebellion from the traditional Renaissance style can be seen in many of his paintings through his refusal to accept the traditional settings and sedate expressions of Renaissance religious paintings. He imparted dramatic movements and expressions to his figures, especially using techniques such as foreshortening and perhaps even more noticeably, highly dramatic light and dark, *chiaroscuro,* to further heighten the drama of his paintings. These features can be clearly seen in his work, *The Supper at Emmaus,* shown in Figure 33.4. Each of the figures in this work seems to be caught in a dynamic moment. A beardless Christ, at the center of the painting, has a sublime expression but is actively gesturing and is made the focus of the painting through dramatic lighting. The two figures joining Christ at the table are caught in dramatic movement, obviously at the point of recognition of Christ's identity. Note, in particular, the way one of the characters seems to be ready to jump out of his chair and, also, the foreshortening of the other's arms. Interestingly, the other character in the painting is not given dramatic movement but, rather, has a quizzical expression that is wonderfully expressive of uncertainty.

Other paintings by Caravaggio that similarly use dramatic movement and lighting are *The Calling of Saint Matthew* and *The Martyrdom of Saint Matthew.* Some contemporaries of Caravaggio believed that these paintings were disrespectful and lacked religious devotion. However, as time passed and the initial shock of Caravaggio's break with Renaissance tradition wore off, the power and inspiration of his style was admired and often copied. He became a standard of the Baroque period and the Catholic Counter-Reformation.

One of Caravaggio's greatest admirers and, perhaps, the first woman artist to make a significant contribution in her own name, was **Artemisia Gentileschi,** called today simply Artemisia. While her works follow closely in the style of Caravaggio with their stark usage of *chiaroscuro* and the strong sense of movement and emotion, Artemisia's work is notable in its own right for its ability to capture the artist's own personal emotion and portray it through her work so that the viewer can share the experience. A rape victim in her youth (while working in her father's artist studio), the feelings of that event seem to spill out in some of her paintings.

Figure 33.4 ■ The Supper at Emmaus *by Caravaggio.* © *National Gallery, London/Art Resource, NY.*

This personal rage is most evident in her painting *Judith and Holofernes,* shown in Figure 33.5. In this painting, which depicts a story from the Bible's Apocrypha, the Israelite woman Judith and her maid kill the potential attacker of Israel. Artemisia's *Judith and Holofernes* is a superb example of Baroque painting and shows excellent use of both *chiaroscuro* and foreshortening. Artemisia was also an important figure in the spread of the Baroque style as she traveled extensively, spending time in France and England, as well as many locations in her native Italy.

In the early decades of the seventeenth century, the Baroque style became apparent in the paintings of Spanish painters. The first of these, Domenikos Theotokopoulos, called **El Greco** or "The Greek," was born in Greece, educated in Italy, moved to Spain, and was influential in blending the Baroque style with the Renaissance style he had previously learned in Venice. Most of El Greco's works have a religious flavor and are quite somber in tone. However, El Greco's works have a unique style of their own. The people in his paintings are famous for their elongated faces and sad eyes. El Greco also put an interesting twist on the use of *chiaroscuro.* Rather than use the interplay between light and shadow, El Greco chose to use bright color on the clothing and other items in the foreground of the painting and highlight them against a dark and somber background. El Greco was also a technically skilled painter and enjoyed showing off his technical virtuosity by painting small and elaborate details into the painting, like the robes of the Catholic officials in his painting *Burial of the Count of Orgaz* (Figure 33.6).

Foremost among the Spanish Baroque artists was **Diego Velazquez.** Velazquez's career was shaped by his appointment by Spain's King Philip IV as court artist and he spent much of his life on court portraits and historical paintings. This appointment also allowed Velazquez to travel across Europe and acquire paintings for the court collection. Velazquez's travels had a two-fold effect. First, Velazquez was instrumental in spreading the Baroque style and, second, the paintings he acquired served as the basis for the collection now

Figure 33.5 ■ Judith and Holofornes *by Artemisia Gentileschi.* © *Summerfield Press/CORBIS.*

Figure 33.6 ■ Burial of the Count of Orgaz *by El Greco.* © *The Gallery Collection/Corbis*

housed in the Prado Museum, in Madrid, one of the modern world's greatest art museums.

Velazquez had an especially strong influence on the Low Countries and helped to create the Baroque movement there, even becoming good friends with the Dutch master Peter Paul Rubens (discussed next). We have previously discussed a painting by Velazquez, *The Surrender of Breda,* which was a strongly nationalistic (Spanish version) of a great battle of the war of independence in the Netherlands (Figure 32.6). Its purpose to impress the Spanish people was certainly Baroque.

Like Caravaggio, Velazquez was very interested in the effects of light. However, unlike Caravaggio, he did not attempt to use light in a theatrical or dramatic way, but used his paintings to investigate the nature of direct and reflected light. Velazquez was also less interested in giving motion to his figures and focused on allowing the use of light to give them animation and richness.

Among Diego Velazquez's most famous paintings and a good example of Baroque painting is *Las Meninas (The Maids In Waiting),* shown in Figure 33.7. *Las Meninas* is a superb example of Velazquez's style and his masterful use of light which gives the room in the painting a strong three-dimensional effect. The reflection of the royal parents in the mirror is another unique and interesting technique to show a light/optical effect. Velazquez also paid close attention to details and enjoyed showing off his technical skill in intricacies like hair, fabric textures, and facial expressions.

Velazquez was also interested, like many Baroque painters, in the use of emotion. However, Velazquez used emotion in his paintings in a more subtle way than many of his Baroque contemporaries. This subtle use of emotion can be seen in *Las Meninas* in the devotion of the lady in waiting to the little princess, the look of sudden attention on nearly everyone's faces at the arrival of the king and queen (who we can see in the mirror), and the slightly bothered look of Velazquez himself at the interruption. *Las Meninas* also is a good example of the Baroque attempt to draw the viewer into the painting, as the viewer gets to play the role of the king and queen and see the scene from their vantage point.

From Spain the popularity of Baroque art spread to its European possessions in the Low Countries, Austria, and Sicily. The Low Countries, in particular, embraced the Baroque and blended it with the local Protestant culture. Little Dutch art

Figure 33.7 ■ Las Meninas (The Maids in Waiting) *by Diego Velazquez.* © *Francis G. Mayer/CORBIS.*

was sponsored by the Catholic Church, but some was sponsored by royalty, both Spanish and other countries. This was especially true of **Peter Paul Rubens,** a highly popular and successful painter of the Spanish, English, and French monarchs. One massive work, certainly meant to impress, was a series of 24 paintings done for the French queen, Marie de Medici. These very large paintings depicted various important events in the life of the queen, at least from her point of view. (They were completed in only three years.) Today, the entire set is displayed in a single room in the Louvre. One of the paintings is shown in Figure 33.8.

Peter Paul Rubens was a true Renaissance Man. Besides being an excellent painter, he was also a noted theologian, scholar, and teacher, who was fluent in six different languages. Rubens was the court painter for the Spanish regent in

Figure 33.8 ■ Henri IV Receiving the Portrait of Marie de Medici *by Peter Paul Rubens. Erich Lessing/Art Resource, NY.*

Flanders (an area in the Low Countries whose people are called Flemish). However, in spite of the obvious Spanish ties and a friendship with Diego Velazquez, Rubens was more strongly influenced by the Italian Baroque painters than those of Spain. Rubens's paintings have a strong Classical/Renaissance feel to them. The males are muscular and reminiscent of the male figures Michelangelo painted in the Sistine Chapel. Rubens's females are nearly always full-figured and often nude. However, Rubens's paintings are definitely Baroque in style and are only influenced by the Renaissance masters, not replicas of their work. Rubens's paintings are filled with motion and movement, twisting bodies and rippling muscles. There is also use of *chiaroscuro* to highlight the central figures and add drama, although it is used much more subtly than Caravaggio's style.

While Rubens was more strongly influenced by the Italian Baroque than the Spanish, he did not wholly avoid the influence of the Spanish masters. Rubens, like many of his Spanish peers, paid careful attention to many of the small details in the paintings, such as tree foliage, clothing textures, and hair, in order to show off his skills as a painter.

As we discussed in the previous chapter, many of the commissions to Dutch artists, especially after the Dutch became independent of Spain in 1648, came from the middle class. We mentioned, in particular, **Rembrandt** and his famous painting of a Dutch army unit called *The Night Watch* (Figure 32.7). Each person in the painting has a unique facial expression that reveals something of his character. Furthermore, despite the fact that *The Night Watch* is a posed portrait painting, it has a feel of movement, as if the guard were really in action defending the city. *The Night Watch* also has a strong use of *chiaroscuro* to highlight the more important figures (the captain of the guard and others who paid a greater portion of the commission) and to add a sense of drama to the painting. The excellent use of foreshortening with the captain's hand and the man in yellow's spear, pulls the viewer into the painting. The two objects seem to be sticking out of the painting at the viewer. Finally, there is immense attention paid to details in the painting of the clothes and banners in the painting. Nearly all of the elements of the Baroque are present in *The Night Watch,* and Rembrandt seems to have mastered them all. Amazingly, this great work was lost to the world for many years and was found hanging on the wall of a barn with one edge exposed to the weather. It is now located in the Rijksmuseum in Amsterdam.

Early in his career, Rembrandt lived a happy life with his wife and children. He had a large home and spent time mingling with Holland's wealthy merchant upper class. After his wife's death, he fell in love with another woman, Hendrickje Stoffels, and raised some eyebrows when he chose to move in with her without marrying her. Still, for some time, Rembrandt continued to be part of Amsterdam's top level of society. In spite of amassing a small fortune for his work, by 1656 Rembrandt was bankrupt. Furthermore, despite his obvious talents and his great reputation even during his own lifetime, as Rembrandt aged his style was less and less in synchronicity with public tastes. As his work fell out of favor with the public, he increasingly turned toward spiritual themes and withdrew from society. His behavior further alienated him from potential friends. Then, Rembrandt received a double blow when both his beloved Hendrickje and his son died within a short time of one another. Rembrandt spent his last years as a virtual recluse—living alone and virtually broke, painting beautiful religious works primarily for himself.

Thus, the Baroque style in Holland and much of the Protestant north was portrait work done of either individuals or groups who commissioned the piece. Because Baroque art in Holland and the north was portraying neither the greatness of the Church or the King, it tended to be less ornate and elaborate, but still had other main elements of the Baroque, including emotion, movement, detail, light effects, and nationalism. There is also a greater focus on more northern themes such as common life and landscapes. Other important Baroque painters include **Anthony Van Dyke, Frans Hals, Jan Vermeer,** and **George de La Tour.**

■ Baroque Music

Music made dramatic and creative steps forward during the Baroque period. These innovations generally reflected the Baroque spirit—impressive, giving praise or honor, dramatic, and reflective of the artist's technique. Just as with architecture, Baroque music reflected both Catholic and Protestant styles and elaborated on the style of the Renaissance. Like sculpture, Baroque music explored ways to impart greater dynamics. In music this was done through new instruments, new forms, and new methods of orchestration. Like painting, Baroque music allowed the composer to showcase techniques and talents. These developments laid the foundation for even greater changes that were to come later in the Classical and Romantic periods.

A summary of the developments in Baroque music might help to orient our discussion. Some of the most important of those developments, all of which we will discuss, were the following:

■ Invention of opera
■ Homophony
■ Development of the orchestra and types of orchestration
■ Development of new forms of vocal music
■ Development of purely instrumental music
■ Development of new or significantly altered musical instruments
■ Temperament

Early in the Baroque period, the Catholic Church still strongly discouraged the use of polyphony, as we discussed in Chapter 28 on the High Renaissance. **Polyphony** is a musical texture in which two or more equal melodic lines are combined simultaneously and thus distribute melodic interest among all the parts. The Catholic Church frowned on polyphony because the multiple voices added complexity and contrast, which often made understanding the words of the mass more difficult. Although some composers, especially Palestrina, successfully wrote acceptable polyphonic music, the Catholic Church still preferred the simpler monophonic music. For the Catholic Church, the words were much more important than the melody.

This attitude, even spilling over into secular music, was coupled with a strong Renaissance desire to return to the glories of the ancient past, and led to an interesting and important development in music. In Florence, during the latter part of the sixteenth century, a group of scholars, called the Camerata, were investigating the nature of ancient Greek drama. They strongly believed (with some good evidence) that the choruses of Greek dramas were sung or, at least, chanted to a melody with some instrumental accompaniment. Many of these scholars even believed that the entire drama was musical.

In their desire to recapture the culture of the past, the Camerata scholars began to write music that might be like the music of ancient Greece (which could only be envisioned in theory, since no musical scores survived from the ancient past). The scholars referred to their efforts as their "work" or, in Italian, *opera*. The genre of music we now call **opera** was born from their efforts. The first opera was performed about 1600. Even though the development of opera is clearly reflective of Renaissance ideals of capturing the ancient past, the style of opera is more in keeping with Baroque ideas of praise, elaboration, and exploration of genre. Therefore, the date of the beginning of opera is generally given as the official start of the Baroque period.

Opera was a tool that allowed music to expand in many directions. Opera made *both* the music and words important for the first time. One of the key creative concepts that defined opera was the invention of two musical declarations: **recitative,** in which the singer told the story in a narrative style with background musical accompaniment, and **aria,** in which the singer explored emotions or some situation of the story with an extended solo. In the first, recitative, there was an element of time moving along, that is, a narration. In the second, aria, there was a sense of time stopping. These might have originated from features in drama where the actors recite lines that move the story along (moving time) and where an actor gives a soliloquy (time frozen). There were, of course, also choruses.

In all of these operatic innovations, the singer(s) was given a melody and the orchestra was supportive. This musical texture, in which a strong melody is accompanied by instruments, is called **homophony.** Opera helped establish homophony as a useful part of music and proved that the use of textures other than **monophony** (the simplest musical texture) did not necessarily detract from the message of the words.

Polyphony was also enriched during the Baroque period. Previously, the multiple melodies had been largely independent or, at the most, imitative (in which one voice imitated the previous voice). However, Baroque composers developed a more integrated interaction of the various melodies, which is called **counterpoint.** Some consider the development of Baroque counterpoint to reach the height of polyphonic music.

A brief comparison of the two main types of musical texture is, perhaps, enlightening. Homophony is based on harmony and polyphony is based on counterpoint. Homophony and polyphony can be used in the same musical work, perhaps even at the same time, as some instruments or voices might be playing counterpoint to others while some might be playing harmony. The development of homophony was extremely important because of the doors it opened for later musical styles and because it would go on to shape Western music.

The invention and popularity of opera also helped the development of the orchestra. Although one or two instruments could have been used to accompany the soloists and chorus of an opera, composers quickly realized that more instruments were beneficial, especially as operas became more complex. These combinations of several instruments and voices became carefully coordinated and led to our concept of the concert and the orchestra. Composers also found the need to be much more specific in controlling the nature of the instruments used in the orchestra. Up to the Baroque period, the choice of instruments was largely unspecified by composers. However, with concerted music, especially with tight counterpoint and harmonies, the composers began to specify exactly the instruments to be used and to carefully indicate when each of the instruments was to play.

Along with the development of opera, another major influence on music was the Protestant Reformation. Martin Luther took a decidedly different approach to music than was the norm in the Catholic Church. Luther diminished the importance of the mass. He also taught that God could be perceived from the instrumental music, not just in the words. He believed that through the *experience* of the music a person could be transported to a state where God's Spirit could infuse the person's mind. In particular, he said that "The Devil flees from the voice of music just as he flees from the words of theology."

Perhaps the first musical form strongly adopted by Protestantism was the **hymn** or anthem. The congregation sang praises to God. The next innovation was probably the **cantata.** This form was a combination of a small orchestra and chorus that sang text that accompanied the sermon. One further Baroque innovation was the **oratorio,** an opera-like production with orchestra and soloists, but without the costumes, sets, and acting.

While these Protestant innovations in vocal music were important, by far the most important musical innovation based on Protestant concepts was the development of purely instrumental music. The center of both Protestantism and instrumental music was Germany. German Baroque music evolved into purely instrumental music as a reflection of Luther's statements, rebellion against the restrictions of the Catholic Church, German nationalism, and recognition that German was a much more difficult language to sing than Italian. The German composers realized that, in the absence of words, the music needed to have a clearly defined musical structure to assist the audience in following the music properly and understanding its meaning. As a result, instrumental musical forms such as the fugue, sonata, and concerto were developed.

Fugues are polyphonic forms in which several melodies play off each other, first in an imitative manner and then with much more complex elaborations. These are some of the most complex of musical forms and are considered by many to be the most characteristic Baroque instrumental form. In the **sonata** form, two melodies are introduced in contrast to each other, then they are elaborated and intermixed, and finally they are separated and resolved. Although the sonata was invented in the Baroque period, it was developed to its highest form in the Classical period, discussed in a later chapter. The **concerto** is an instrumental form that was a direct outgrowth of opera. In concertos, one or more solo instruments are backed by an orchestra, much like the soloists and chorus are backed by the orchestra in an opera.

The invention of the violin around 1579 also was pivotal in the continued development of the orchestra, and composers began to write more orchestral pieces in order to feature the new instrument. The violin was especially important to purely instrumental music because, more than any other instrument, it could mimic the human voice and, therefore, take the place of singing in the purely instrumental forms.

The violin was invented (actually developed from stringed instruments that were held on the lap) in the small town of Cremona, Italy, which through either Providence or coincidence was home to **Amati, Stradivari,** and **Guarneri** in successive generations. These three men became violin makers and were so expert at their task of creating instruments that produced a warm and beautiful sound that almost overnight the violin was embraced across Europe and soon became the heart of the Baroque period orchestra. The amazing thing is that even with more than 400 years of practice and vastly improved technology, a better violin has never been constructed. The relatively few violins created by these three men during their lifetime that have survived the centuries are still considered the best ever, and can cost in excess of $2 million today.

Some important developments were also made to keyboard instruments during the Baroque period and, perhaps even more important, these developments led to changes in the structure of the musical scale itself. The principal change in the musical scale was called **tempering** and came about as a solution to a problem encountered first with keyboard instruments. This problem arose because of the nature of the musical scale that was used up to that time. This problem is technically complex, and so it needs a bit of explanation to be understood.

Early in the Renaissance period, instrument makers had invented a method of mechanically plucking a harp, thus allowing more complex music to be played by less skillful musicians. These instruments were called **harpsichords** and were, in general, quite small in the range of their music—generally only two or three octaves. During the Baroque period, the range of harpsichords was expanded to four and five octaves, thus permitting their use in the more complex music of the Baroque period. However, this expansion of range created a serious problem. Whenever pieces of music in two different keys were to be played on the same instrument, one of the pieces would be out of tune. This occurred because the harpsichord would be tuned for a particular key and would not sound right in any other key. To understand why this was a problem, especially when multiple octaves were played with two different keys, requires some background in the nature of the musical scale.

Up to the Baroque period, the musical scale was based on the ancient discoveries of the Greek mathematician **Pythagoras.** He found that when two strings were plucked, with the second being exactly twice the length of the first, a very pleasing sound resulted. In fact, these two notes were the two end notes of a musical scale (which was later given names of *do, re, mi, fa, sol, la, ti* and *do*). In other words, the two notes called *do* could be created when the ratio of the string lengths was 2:1. This interval was called an octave because the two *dos* are eight notes apart. Pythagoras further realized that other combinations of musical notes were also pleasing and that the ratios of string lengths for those notes could be expressed as the ratios of whole numbers. For example, he noted that one particularly pleasing combination was the combination of the note *do* with the note *sol*. This was called a fifth (they are five notes apart) and has a mathematical ratio of 3:2. Pythagoras further noted that by repeatedly moving through fifths, across several octaves, all eight notes in a scale could be defined, although the notes would have octave relationships to notes in a single octave. This repeated application of fifths is called the **circle of fifths** and is illustrated in Figure 33.9. Note that when all of the eight notes in the scale have been defined, which takes seven different applications of fifths, you return to a "do." The "do" from which you started and the "do" that you ended on after the entire circle of fifths, should be even multiples of each other—that is, the lengths of the strings (or the ratios of the frequencies) should be an even whole number.

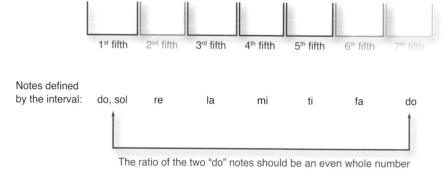

Circle of Fifths

Figure 33.9 ■ *Chart illustrating how all notes in the scale can be obtained by repeated application of fifths (called the circle of fifths).*

Within the accuracy that Pythagoras could measure, this mathematical relationship was accurate. However, as measurement technologies became more refined, it was found that the ratios of the octaves were not exactly whole numbers (that is 2:1) and, moreover, the ratios of the fifths were not exactly 3:2. In fact, none of the proposed ratios was exactly correct.

In playing the music, this was generally not a problem because the instrument could be tuned to compensate for these minor errors. The problem only became obvious when a musical number in one key was played on an instrument tuned for another key. Even then, the musicians could usually compensate for the small errors encountered by adjusting the position of their fingers or by slightly modulating the note on a wind instrument. However, on keyboard instruments, especially those that extended over several octaves, the problem became critical. When pieces written in one key were played on an instrument tuned to another key, the notes were dissonant.

A debate arose among the musical community over what to do. Some believed that the whole number ratios of Pythagoras were exactly correct and the scales should not be modified. They advocated changing the musical instruments so that tunes of multiple keys could be played without dissonance. This proved to be a nearly impossible technical challenge to the instrument makers.

However, obstacles often provide opportunities for greater creativity and Baroque era composers found a method of eliminating the problem. Composers found that all keys could be made to sound "good" if the small differences between pure ratios and what was pleasing to the ear could be spread over the entire scale and over all keys. This technique of tuning resulted in all scales sounding acceptably good, but none being perfectly tuned according to the Pythagorean ratios. This deviation method was called *temperament.*

Stuart Isacoff in his book, *Temperament,* describes the deeper significance of adopting the idea of temperament:

Acceptance [of equal temperament] did not come easily. Critics claimed the resulting
music had been robbed of its beauty and emotional impact; supporters countered that since all things are subjective, human ears and minds would learn to adapt. The arguments, however, went well beyond musical aesthetics. Equal temperament represented an assault on an idea that had gripped thinkers in nearly every field as a powerful metaphor for a universe ruled by mathematical law. . . . Tempering meant that the principle of usefulness was more basic than the principle of purity.

To "prove" the temperament: concept, a relatively obscure Protestant German church organist wrote *The Well Tempered Clavier,* a series of preludes and fugues written in all the major and minor keys. The organist's name was Johann Sebastian Bach, and while he died still a virtual unknown, his *Well Tempered Clavier,* along with some of his other works were "rediscovered" a century later and today he is known as one of the great composers. We will discuss Bach's works later in this chapter. First, let's examine some other Baroque composers.

Claudio Monteverdi was a transitional composer between the Renaissance and Baroque periods. He was a master of the madrigal and was therefore invited to be a member of the Florentine Camerata. As an experienced composer, he became the person to actually implement the concepts of the Camerata to create an actual opera. An early opera of renown was Monteverdi's *Orfeo* in 1607.

Monteverdi's operas were full of emotion, enhanced, in part, by several techniques he invented, including tremolo, the quickly repeated bowing of a single note, and pizzicato, plucking rather than bowing a stringed instrument. Monteverdi's own life was quite full of emotion, and this may have contributed to the great emotion he poured into his operas. Monteverdi's wife, whom he loved very much, died at the relatively young age of 45, while the Inquisition arrested his son for reading books forbidden by the Catholic Church. In spite of his personal tragedies, Monteverdi continued to compose operas and his fame and popularity spread across Italy. Monteverdi's operas were especially beloved in Venice, and he spent the last few years living there, writing his final masterpiece, *The Coronation of Poppea.* Monteverdi had made opera so popular in Venice that by the time of his death, Venice had 16 opera houses.

Antonio Vivaldi was another famous Italian Baroque composer. Born in Venice 34 years after the death of Monteverdi, Vivaldi was strongly inspired by Monteverdi's operas, which were still extremely popular in Venice. Even though Vivaldi joined the priesthood, he still spent much of his life focusing on the creation of his music and was known to walk out of mass, even when he was saying it, to record an inspiration for a new piece of music. Vivaldi wrote dozens of operas and numerous instrumental pieces, usually featuring the violin, including his most famous work, *The Four Seasons.* The newness of purely instrumental music, especially in Italy, led Vivaldi to write poems accompanying the four parts of *The Four Seasons* to help the audience understand and follow the music. Today, our familiarity of purely instrumental music rarely requires that we have the poems to enjoy *The Four Seasons,* but their addition to the program for a performance can certainly enhance the music. Vivaldi wrote with a pleasing complexity that had never been achieved before in music. This complexity was very much in harmony with the overall spirit of the Baroque.

The operas and other works of Vivaldi made him a very popular figure during his lifetime, and this success brought out the opposites within his character. Through his talent as a composer and musician, Vivaldi was able to do much good in his office as a priest. Not only did Vivaldi write beautiful music to be used by the Catholic Church, but he also volunteered to serve as the conductor of the orchestra at a local girls' orphanage and convent. This was a very noble task, as the education they received at the orphanage, combined with Vivaldi's musical training (the orchestra was very good and quite popular), made these girls excellent potential wives for the wealthy and cultured young men of Venice. The orchestra helped save these girls from a life of poverty and loneliness, since orphaned females usually could bring little

to a marriage, not even a name. Therefore, they had difficulty finding a husband in a time where marriages were arranged for practical purposes as often as for love. The task of conducting the orchestra was more daunting than it may seem, as it required Vivaldi to compose at least two original compositions a month and work with girls who often had no musical background.

However, Vivaldi's success and popularity also put him in conflict with his duties and vows as a priest. The success of his music and of the orphans' orchestra forced him to spend much of his time composing and traveling, thus reducing his availability to perform his priestly duties. Furthermore, Vivaldi's success made him a popular figure on the social scene, and he often overlooked his vow of chastity. Eventually, Vivaldi's supervisors denied him the right to fulfill his priestly offices because of his many mistresses, excessive travel, and inattention to the mass. Vivaldi then chose to leave Italy and he spent the last part of his life living and composing in Vienna. Upon his death, Vivaldi was buried in Vienna's St. Stephen's Cathedral. The nine-year-old Josef Haydn, later to become a great composer in his own right, was in the choir at the funeral.

Vivaldi's move from Italy to a German-speaking country was symbolic of what was also happening to music during the Baroque period. The center of musical culture was shifting from Italy to the German principalities of the Holy Roman Empire. The next group of great composers would be predominately German, not Italian.

George Frederick Handel was born in Halle, Germany, in 1685. Handel discovered early that he had an interest and talent in music but received no support from his nonmusical family. So, in order to practice, Handel would sneak a clavier into the attic of his home and practice while everyone else was asleep. Finally, at the age of seven, Handel's father relented to his endless pestering and allowed his son to take music lessons. The lessons paid off, Handel's talent blossomed, and by the age of 12 he was working as the assistant choirmaster at the local church.

Handel's musical talent was obvious, so when he came of age, he left home and traveled across

Europe, spending time in Hamburg, Rome, Paris, Naples, Hanover, Venice, and London, increasing his musical education and working in various musical positions. Through his extensive travels, Handel became increasingly popular across the continent, and was widely recognized for his amazing composing capability and his extremely sensitive ear. The musicians that worked under Handel's direction soon learned to tune their instruments carefully, even before they entered the hall for a rehearsal, because the sound of a poorly tuned instrument would send Handel into a rage.

Handel eventually accepted a permanent position in Hanover as the court composer and conductor. However, after a relatively short time, Handel was offered the chance to become an owner of an opera house in London. He was to compose the music and manage the musical offerings. Handel was anxious to accept the London position and sought permission to leave from the Prince of Hanover, his employer. The prince reluctantly agreed, but insisted that the London position must be for only a short period and that Handel would soon return to Hanover.

Handel moved to London and never returned to Hanover. Later, when Queen Anne of England died without an heir, the British Parliament asked Anne's cousin, the Prince of Hanover, to become the king of Great Britain. He accepted and became King George I. In light of his abandonment of the Hanover position, Handel was very worried about his acceptance by the new king. Therefore, Handel devised a creative plan to win the favor of the new king. Handel composed a musical tribute to King George, which he performed as the king was sailing into London on a barge. (The orchestra was on another barge that went out to meet the king's barge.) George liked the music so much that he had it repeated three times that evening. The problem between Handel and the new king was resolved. The piece that resolved the problem has been named *Watermusic.*

Handel's venture into opera, the cause that took him to London from Hanover, was an initial success. Handel was a talented composer of operas and made much money. However, he became frustrated with the requirements of producing the op-

eras, especially meeting the demands of the prima donna singers. On one occasion, two prima donnas were fighting over who was to be the featured lead in the opera. Each insisted on having longer arias to sing than the other, thus justifying a higher place on the list of singers. To resolve the issue, Handel composed the opera with exactly the same number of notes for each. Coupled with his problems with performers was the decline in attendance in the operas after a few years of initial success. Handel began to lose money and did not know what he might do as a way to support himself.

In the midst of this quandary, a librettist (writer of the words for his operas), suggested that Handel try a new musical form—oratorio. The librettist, Charles Jennens, had already prepared a libretto for an oratorio that he called *Messiah.* Handel, somewhat reluctantly, took the libretto. At about this same time, the Duke of Devonshire, the king's representative in Ireland, asked Handel if he would compose a musical work as charity for an Irish foundlings' hospital. Handel agreed and decided to use the libretto from Jennens as the basis of this new work. Then, in what must be one of the most incredible periods of creative work ever, Handel retreated to his room to compose. He completed *Messiah* in just 24 days. (We should note that much of the music for *Messiah* was drawn from earlier Handel operas. Nevertheless, the work is truly astounding.) During that time Handel reported that the music just flowed out of him and that he hardly stopped to eat or sleep. On several occasions Handel's servant found Handel sitting over the piece sobbing at the beauty of the music he was composing. Upon its completion, Handel stated that while composing the oratorio, he beheld the angels standing around the throne of God, and "whether I was in my body or out of my body, I knew not."

The first performance of *Messiah* was in a tiny theatre in Dublin. After this first small performance, Handel's *Messiah* received instant acclaim and so many people wanted to attend the official opening in London that it was requested that women come without the hoops in their skirts and men without their swords to accommodate the large demand for seats. Even so, hundreds stood outside the hall and listened because they could not get in.

Praise and honors were showered upon Handel for *Messiah.* The tradition of standing during the *Hallelujah Chorus* began when the Prince of Wales (later to be King George II) and all his court stood at the beginning of the piece and bowed to Handel in respect. The composer Josef Haydn wept when he heard *Messiah* and said "Handel is the greatest of us all." Beethoven said that Handel was the best composer ever to live and that he would gladly go to Handel's grave, bare his head, and kneel down in homage to him. Handel, however, would take little credit for *Messiah,* always claiming it was given to him from God. Nor would Handel accept an overt amount of praise. Once when a duke congratulated him on composing such fine entertainment as *Messiah,* Handel responded that *Messiah* was not intended to entertain, but to change lives. Not only did Handel deflect praise and credit for *Messiah,* but he never earned a penny off of the piece, as he donated not only the proceeds from that small first show to the Irish foundling hospital, but all future royalties that came from *Messiah* as well.

Handel's *Messiah* is among the greatest oratorios ever composed, and is a great example of Baroque music as well. *Messiah* has grandeur and was clearly written as praise to God. It has instrumental sections (overture and symphony) as well as various ensembles: solos, duets, and choruses, all accompanied by the orchestra. It uses polyphony and homophony in several musical forms. Like all things Baroque, *Messiah* has many musical embellishments that give it a complex style.

Handel continued to bask in the glory of his musical triumphs. Gradually, however, his eyesight became dimmed. He consulted a doctor but the treatments did not help (maybe even making the condition worse) and Handel became blind. He died in London, wealthy and well respected.

Johann Sebastian Bach was born in the same year as Handel in a nearby German town. Bach spent most of his life as a choirmaster and organist for various churches in central Germany. He was, however, often distraught over his employment because he did not like reporting to city and church boards that often loaded him with tasks that he felt took away from his composing.

These other duties sometimes included teaching, a duty that frustrated him because he was impatient with less talented musicians. On a few occasions his impatience got the better of him and once he was forced to defend himself in an altercation with an irate student.

Although he composed music throughout his life, Bach was best known in his lifetime as a talented performer and musician. His playing was applauded, but Bach's compositions were often attacked by the public as being overly flowery, and by other musicians as being too difficult to play. (Both of these criticisms, incidentally, demonstrate the Baroque nature of his music—complex and technically challenging.) Bach continued to compose however, eventually producing more than a thousand pieces of music and attempting every genre of the day except opera, although he even composed much music in operatic forms.

Bach, a devout Protestant, believed the doctrine of Luther in regards to religious music (that music elevated the human spirit and therefore was a form of worship) and believed much of the music he composed engaged the mind in a search for God. For example, he took simple hymn melodies and explored ways to help the listener think about them and, therefore, about God. An example was Bach's version of the hymn *A Mighty Fortress is Our God.* Luther had written the words of this hymn, so merely by singing the hymn people's minds were focused on Luther and his message. But, in addition, the Bach version elaborated on the simple hymn so that people could get a feeling of the wondrous glory of God through what is otherwise a rather simple melody.

Bach believed that "the final aim and reason of all music is the worship of God and the recreation of the human spirit." Bach's belief in the art of music as a conduit for better worship and understanding of God and religion is in harmony with the spirit of the Baroque era and is similar to the way the Catholic Church used Baroque era visual arts to help others recognize the greatness and glory of God.

For some time after his death, if Bach was known at all, it was generally for his *Well Tempered Clavier,* which was sometimes used as a training manual (for example, Chopin memorized all of the *Well Tempered Clavier* as a young student). Bach became known as a composer largely through the efforts of the later composer and conductor, **Felix Mendelssohn,** who encountered some of Bach's compositions while looking for works that his orchestra might perform. Mendelssohn recognized Bach's genius and featured his works in several concerts. Upon his discovery, Bach's reputation spread, and his works were soon well known and often played all across Europe. Beethoven, upon studying the works of Bach, said that he should have been named *Mir,* meaning sea, rather than *Bach,* meaning brook, because of his greatness. (Mendelssohn also reintroduced the works of Vivaldi, which had mostly been lost.)

Bach's musical contributions are enormous. His extensive use of counterpoint raised polyphony to its highest level of achievement. His compositions are extremely complex and difficult but, perhaps because of their complexity, engage the mind in the music as perhaps no one else has been able to do.

Some of Bach's works are quite unusual and innovative, such as one piece that can be played upside-down, thus demonstrating great symmetry and order. Many are built on musical intervals that have the ratios characteristic of the Greek Golden Mean. Many others are also highly mathematical. It is interesting to note that Bach was the only nonmathematician member of the German Mathematical Society. Bach's creative capabilities were clearly beyond those of ordinary musicians and included the ability to think laterally into mathematics.

Furthermore, many of Bach's works are based on Protestant themes and are strongly religious in nature. Many music commentators consider Bach's oratorio *St. Matthew Passion* to be one of the greatest and most powerful religious pieces ever composed.

Even though he spent most of his life in religious positions as a church choirmaster, Bach also wrote some superb secular pieces, such as the *Goldberg Variations* and *Brandenburg Concertos,* which are considered by many critics to be the greatest examples of pure Baroque style in music.

It is interesting that Bach wrote the *Brandenburg Concertos* and sent them, unsolicited, in an effort to obtain a position at the court of the Margrave of Brandenburg, hoping that it would pay more and give him more freedom to compose than did his choirmaster position. Bach never received a response. Similarly, he was hired to the choirmaster position in Leipzig, Germany, only after several others declined the position. As one of the members of the Leipzig town council wrote when Bach was hired, *"Since the best man could not be obtained, mediocre ones would have to be accepted."* Mediocre indeed!

Bach's life was humble, but generally happy with his many children surrounding him, until his last few years when his eyesight began to fail. Seeking improvement in his eyes, Bach allowed a traveling English surgeon to operate on his eyes. This was the same surgeon that had operated on Handel's eyes in England and, sadly, the result also ended up the same, total blindness. (Evidently the lesson here is that famous Baroque composers should not let Englishmen operate on their eyes!) This was devastating for Bach, just as it was to Handel, but Bach continued to compose by dictating his ideas to students. Finally, in 1750, nine years before Handel's death, Bach died of a stroke. Historians use the date of Bach's death to mark the end of the Baroque period.

■ Baroque Literature

Literature was a less prolific genre of the arts than most of the others during the Baroque period. The great playwright Shakespeare straddles the line between the Renaissance and the Baroque, especially in some of his later plays, but he is generally considered to be more in harmony with the ideas and themes of the northern Renaissance. We therefore discussed Shakespeare in a previous chapter. Miguel de Cervantes, a contemporary of Shakespeare, also straddled the Renaissance and Baroque periods but we will discuss his works in this chapter. In Renaissance tradition, Cervantes' great work, *Don Quixote de la Mancha,* looks back to better times, as was typical of Renaissance thinking, but uses a new genre, the novel, and much elaboration, as was typical of the Baroque. Another great Baroque writer that we will consider in depth, John Milton, lived a generation later and fully exemplified the spirit of the Baroque period. We will then briefly consider two additional writers—John Bunyan and Daniel Defoe.

Miguel de Cervantes (1547–1616) was a Spaniard, born to parents of minor nobility. Despite his family's status as nobility, Cervantes's father worked as a surgeon to earn money for the family. As a young student, Cervantes showed some aptitude toward writing and had several poems published. However, he chose the life of a soldier, a career path more common for minor and impoverished nobility than writing. Cervantes spent several years fighting for Spain before a series of mishaps ended his career as a soldier. First, the use of his left hand was lost when he was hit by enemy fire. Then, while sailing home, his ship was attacked by Algerians and Cervantes spent five years as a slave in Algeria before he was finally ransomed. Upon finally returning home, Cervantes married and settled down to, he hoped, domestic tranquility. Needing a way to support his young bride, and unable to do much physical work because of his hand injury, Cervantes turned back to writing. (His position gives us some interesting thoughts about motivations for creativity. We wonder if he would have created such great literature if he had not lost his hand. Perhaps necessity really is the mother of invention.)

Cervantes wrote several plays and stories that had modest success, but his most successful work was *Don Quixote de la Mancha*. This book, usually just called *Don Quixote,* was an immediate success. The story is of a middle-aged man who is so caught up with tales of knighthood that he eventually fancied himself to be a knight and embarked on a quest to reestablish chivalry to the countryside of La Mancha, a region in Spain. The book traces his exploits along with his companion, Sancho Panza.

Don Quixote may have been written as a spoof of the age of knighthood, but it may also have been a searching comment on the nature of people who seek to improve the world around them. It gives a poignant view of how a person might become too optimistic and unaware of the evils of the world. The novel also explores the conflict between reality and illusions, the separation between aspirations and accomplishments, and the fine line between conformity to expected behaviors and reputed insanity. Another subplot of the text also explores how people change to become as they are treated.

Don Quixote was the first novel—complete with narrative, plot climaxes, character development, and moral dilemmas. This new writing format (genre) was very appealing to the reading public. *Don Quixote* also combined the use of humor with a serious theme, thus blurring the traditional line between comedy and tragedy. For example, many of the names in the book have humorous origins or double meanings: Sancho Panza means fat and lazy; La Mancha means dry and plain; Rosinante means a fleabag horse ready for the glue factory, and Dulcinea invokes the idea of sweetness. This wordplay overlies and enhances the more serious and thought provoking issues that are addressed in *Don Quixote.*

The success of *Don Quixote* solidified Cervantes's reputation as a writer and earned him financial success. In fact, the novel was so successful that while Cervantes spent time in jail (because of a financial conflict with the Spanish government), a mysterious rival named Avellaneda wrote a sequel to *Don Quixote.* Cervantes was so upset that someone else was trying to capitalize on his hard-earned success that, upon his release from prison, Cervantes wrote his own sequel to *Don Quixote* and went to great pains to mock Avellaneda's false sequel. (Both of Cervantes's books on Don Quixote are usually packaged as two parts of a single volume.) The last few years of Cervantes's life were relatively happy, spent in enjoying his success, spending time with his wife and family, and working on another novel, *Los Trabajos de Persiles y Sigismunda,* which he completed three days before he died.

The impact of *Don Quixote* is difficult to completely encompass. It is widely considered to be the greatest literary work in Spanish. It has, moreover, influenced the very nature of Spanish culture. Spaniards envision themselves as personality types like the characters in *Don Quixote.* Some Spaniards are dreamers and romantics, like Don Quixote, while others are practical and pessimistic, like Sancho Panza. Women see themselves as unrecognized Dulcineas. Evidences of the impact of *Don Quixote* are abundant throughout Spain. There are Don Quixote festivals, literary clubs, statues, paintings, and uncountable literary articles over hundreds of years. Most of all, however, is the deep, almost spiritual, way that the Spanish psyche has been touched by the humble knight.

The other great literary figure of the Baroque era was England's **John Milton** (1608–1674). Milton was a devout Puritan and a supporter of Oliver Cromwell's Commonwealth, even working for the Commonwealth's governing council of the state. He was also an active political essayist.

Educated at Cambridge, Milton lived as a bachelor for some time before finally, at the age of 35, marrying a 16-year-old girl. However, after a month of marriage, Milton's bride left him and did not return for two years. Eventually she returned, and the couple spent nine years together before she died. After her death, Milton remarried, but his second wife died just two years later. He then remarried a third time, after about seven years of solitary living. At about the time of his first wife's death, Milton went blind. One marvels at the mental discipline that he must have had to create the complex and elaborate works that were published after his blindness. We must also be grateful to those who assisted him.

Milton's great literary achievement was his epic poem *Paradise Lost,* published four years after the onset of his blindness. Written in the epic format and intended to reflect the scope and literary power of Homer's and Aeneas's great works, Milton intended *Paradise Lost* to be the greatest epic ever written in English. Originally, Milton wanted to write an epic poem about King Arthur, thus creating a great historical tradition for England as *The Iliad* and *The Odyssey* created for Greece and *The Aeneid* for Rome. However, Milton's strong religious convictions led him to a theme that would create a historical tradition for

all humankind—the story of Adam and Eve. Milton felt that if he wrote on this topic, then God would raise the magnificence of the work.

Paradise Lost is strongly Baroque in its tone and purpose. The epic is very long, detailed, elaborate, and written in an elevated style. The flavor of the work can be sampled from the quotation given at the beginning of this chapter. The quotation relates Adam's thoughts about Eve. She is the last and greatest of all God's creations. She is beautiful and holy—exactly the qualities that were most appreciated in the Baroque period and the qualities that Baroque artists wanted to depict in their art.

Like the other great epics of Homer, Virgil, and Dante, *Paradise Lost* is written using poetic (metered and rhymed) verses. The language is lofty and designed to convey epic breadth, using complicated and elaborate Latin sentence forms (called Latinate writing) rather than traditional, simple English. All of these are meant to increase the grandeur of the work, to impress readers, and to praise God. As might be expected in a religious book of great scope and seriousness, several fundamental religious concepts such as sin, free will, causality, and motivation are considered in depth. Somewhat surprisingly, the work also makes many allusions to ancient history, literature, and philosophy, but, in so doing, it reflects the nature of the epic style defined by the great epics of the ancient past.

The basic question of the poem is the meaning or origin of evil in a world created by a benevolent God. The poem begins with the rebellion of the archangel Satan and then expands upon the biblical story of Adam and Eve. Satan and his angels are able to convince Adam and Eve to disobey God's command concerning eating the fruit, and Adam and Eve are expelled from the Garden of Eden. After being expelled, Adam and Eve realize that obedience and trust in God are life's most important qualities and that expulsion from the garden is the gateway to a full life and real happiness. The story concludes with a conversation between Adam and Michael about how fallen man, through Christ, will recover immortality. These ideas reflect basic ideas of the Baroque period—basic religiosity coupled with an elevated sense of mankind's potential.

John Bunyan (1628–1688) was a minister who wrote a highly influential book titled *Pilgrim's Progress*. This book, like Milton's *Paradise Lost*, is a religious epic. In *Pilgrim's Progress* the main character, a man generically named Pilgrim, journeys through the world of the afterlife in search of heaven. In this, it is much like Dante's *Divine Comedy*.

The writing style of Bunyan's book is quite different from either Milton's or Dante's. Whereas those earlier works were rhymed, Bunyan's is prose. Further, there are few allusions to ancient history or literary works. The vocabulary and sentence structure of Bunyan's work are simple. Why, then, would we consider it a Baroque piece? First, it was written in the midst of the seventeenth century, which is during the Baroque period. Second, its subject is religious and its intent is to elevate and impress. In this case, the impression sought is that people can and should seek to overcome evils in their lives so that they can return to God. Third, it is a glory of the Christian faith that allows a human to accomplish this awesome task.

Daniel Defoe (1660–1731) was another author whose works can be considered Baroque both because of time and subject. Defoe wrote secular works, the most famous of which is *Robinson Crusoe*. This is the story of a man who is shipwrecked on a small island. Crusoe struggles with survival and, through persistence and creativity, not only survives but makes a relatively comfortable existence for himself. He eventually escapes the island and returns to civilization to tell his story. Defoe's work was enormously popular in his day and seems to reflect something about the nature of the people of England during this period. This work, like *Don Quixote,* glorifies mankind's abilities and potential. The work is secular and, in that light, might be compared to the paintings of middle-class merchants done by the Dutch painters.

■ Summary

The Baroque period was a time when a common style pervaded all of the arts: painting, sculpture, architecture, music, and literature. This style was characterized by exaggerated dramatic effects, elaborate techniques, exalted language, enormous size, and compelling subject matter. It was first used to glorify God and to show the wonders of heaven. As time passed the style was adopted by powerful monarchs and wealthy merchants, who felt that the grandiose style of the Baroque could be used to glorify them and add to their prestige and power. The motivations of the sponsors of Baroque art seem straightforwardly obvious—self aggrandizement. However, we might still question why all of the art forms seemed to have adopted similar characteristics. Was it all because of sponsor desires? Were other factors also major contributors to the similarities? Perhaps we can gain some insights into this question by comparing pairs of Baroque artists. We will first consider Bach and Handel. Then, we will consider Bach and Milton.

Though Bach and Handel were both born in central Germany in the same year, their lives were near opposites. Handel was the only musician in his extended family and struggled to find family acceptance and support for his desired musical profession. Bach was born to a family that had been producing musicians for several generations. During his own life, 76 of Bach's relatives worked as professional musicians, including his older brother who was a student of the famous composer Pachelbel. Furthermore, whereas Handel never married, Bach married twice and had 20 children between his two marriages, with four of his children becoming successful composers and musicians in their own right. The contrasts between Handel and Bach continue: Handel traveled extensively, while Bach never went more than 300 miles from his place of birth; Handel became a wealthy man, while Bach was never more than lower middle class; and, Handel was known throughout Europe as its greatest composer, while Bach was known only as a talented organist (not a composer) and died in relative obscurity.

The diversities of these men were reflected in their works. We see, for instance, more than 300 cantatas by Bach and none by Handel. Undoubtedly, this was because Bach, as a church choirmaster, was required to write a new cantata to accompany the church service weekly for over eight years. Handel, by contrast, spent most of his life in large cities where he wrote operas and oratorios—musical forms for a mass audience attending performances in great halls and theaters. Bach wrote no operas and only a few oratorios.

Yet, even in this obvious diversity, the music composed by Bach and Handel had many similarities. For example, the greatest works of both men were strongly religious and clearly had a focus of praising God. In fact, both men specifically (in writing) dedicated their greatest religious works to God. In a short treatise on music performance, Bach commented, "The final aim and reason of all music is the worship of God and the recreation of the human spirit." This implies, of course, that for Bach there was no difference between sacred and secular music.

When they wrote for a similar audience, their works were surprisingly similar. Consider, for example, Bach's *Brandenburg Concertos* and Handel's *Watermusic* and *Royal Fireworks*. These were all written for royalty and exhibit a highly pleasing style that is easily accessed by the listener, as might be expected in a court audience. Another cause of similarities might have been the general state of the craft of music at the time both men lived. For instance, they both had the same selection of instruments available to them, the forms of music were similar (fugues, sonata, etc.), and individual technique, especially through details, was highly valued.

In light of these similarities and contrasts in the lives and works of Bach and Handel, we might come to the following conclusions: *similarities come from the general society and nature of their art; differences come from individual circumstances.*

We might ask whether comparisons of Baroque characteristics can be made across the boundaries of art forms. To answer this question, let's consider the differences and similarities of the works of Bach and Milton. To simplify this comparison, we will examine a typical Bach composition, a hymn, and also examine a passage by John Milton from *Paradise Lost.* (We are indebted to Professor

Douglas Bush of the Music Department at Brigham Young University for this comparison.)

When Bach's music and Milton's literature are first encountered, we are struck by their complexity. Compare, for instance, the three versions of the hymn *When in the Hour of Utmost Need (Wenn Wir In Höchsten Nöten Sein),* as shown in Figure 33.10. The first excerpt is the simple, traditional German melody. The second is a typical rendition of this melody, as would be found in a church hymnal (published in Weissenfels in 1714). The third is a version by Bach.

We are immediately struck by the increasing complexity as we proceed from melody to hymn to Bach. Consider, for instance, the sixth word in the hymn, "utmost." In the melody version this word is sung with three notes. The hymnal version also uses three notes in the soprano, alto, and bass voices but gives the tenor voice four notes. In Bach, the soprano voice has four notes, the alto has nine notes, the tenor has eight notes, and the bass has five notes. Obviously the Bach version is more complex, and this complexity is typical throughout. In the Bach version, the harmonies are so active that it is challenging to sing the parts. In a version of the melody that Bach wrote for organ (not to be sung), the complexity is even greater. In that version 17 notes in the right hand are required for the phrase that corresponds to "utmost."

Now let's look at a selection from Book 9 of Milton's *Paradise Lost.* The selection, given in Figure 33.11, begins with a description of a morning in the Garden of Eden in which Eve and Adam are conversing about how they should labor in the garden. Note that the first paragraph, which describes the garden, is a highly elaborate single sentence. The second paragraph, Eve's words, is two sentences of comparably complex wording. The third paragraph, Adam's words, is also two sentences of similarly complex verse. It is possible to eliminate the complexity (and the beauty) of Milton's words and reduce the three paragraphs to the following: At daybreak Adam and Eve began considering how to accomplish their work. Eve suggests that Adam work wherever he wishes, perhaps in the ivy, and she will work in the roses.

Figure 33.10 ■ *Comparison of* **A)** *a simple melody,* **B)** *a hymnal version, and* **C)** *Bach's version.*

Now, when as sacred light began to dawn
In Eden on the humid flowers, that breathed
Their morning incense, when all things, that breathe,
From the Earth's great altar send up silent praise
To the Creator, and his nostrils fill
With grateful smell, forth came the human pair,
And joined their vocal worship to the quire
Of creatures wanting voice; that done, partake
The season prime for sweetest scents and airs:
Then commune, how that day they best may ply
Their growing work: for much their work out-grew
The hands' dispatch of two gardening so wide,
And Eve first to her husband thus began.

Adam, well may we labour still to dress
This garden, still to tend plant, herb, and flower,
Our pleasant task enjoined; but, till more hands
Aid us, the work under our labour grows,
Luxurious by restraint; what we by day
Lop overgrown, or prune, or prop, or bind,
One night or two with wanton growth derides
Tending to wild. Thou therefore now advise,
Or bear what to my mind first thoughts present:
Let us divide our labours; thou, where choice
Leads thee, or where most needs, whether to wind
The woodbine round this arbour, or direct
The clasping ivy where to climb; while I,
In yonder spring of roses intermixed
With myrtle, find what to redress till noon:
For, while so near each other thus all day
Our task we choose, what wonder if so near
Looks intervene and smiles, or object new
Casual discourse draw on; which intermits
Our day's work, brought to little, though begun
Early, and the hour of supper comes unearned?

To whom mild answer Adam thus returned.
Sole Eve, associate sole, to me beyond
Compare above all living creatures dear!
Well hast thou motioned, well thy thoughts employed,
How we might best fulfil the work which here
God hath assigned us; nor of me shalt pass
Unpraised: for nothing lovelier can be found
In woman, than to study houshold good,
And good works in her husband to promote.
Yet not so strictly hath our Lord imposed
Labour, as to debar us when we need
Refreshment, whether food, or talk between,
Food of the mind, or this sweet intercourse
Of looks and smiles; for smiles from reason flow,
To brute denied, and are of love the food;
Love, not the lowest end of human life.

Figure 33.11 ▪ *Selection from Milton's Para-dise Lost, Book 9.*

Adam agrees with Eve and states that since they are working near each other they will also enjoy the love of looks and smiles.

We have, therefore, seen that both Bach and Milton are highly complex. They both convey grandeur and beauty far beyond the alternate simple versions of the works we have examined. The versions of Bach and Milton obviously impress the hearer/reader, especially in light of the religious subject that is addressed. Both works actively engage the mind, forcing us to consider at length the nature of the works and their message. This latter characteristic will become even more obvious in the following chapter, which discusses the Scientific Awakening.

We see, therefore, in comparisons of both Bach and Milton, as well as of Bach and Handel, that the basic characteristics that we have associated with the Baroque style are demonstrated in both music and literature. These findings suggest, therefore, that the characteristics of a period can move through many artistic mediums.

We also have seen that creativity can be affected by both personal circumstances and by general societal conditions. Were these findings not true, we would have trouble identifying the work of an individual and, equally, there would be no similarities that we could point to as characteristic of a particular period of time.

▪ Timeline—Important Dates

Date	Event
1541–1614	*El Greco*
1547–1616	*Miguel Cervantes*
1567–1643	*Claudio Monteverdi*
1573–1610	*Caravaggio*
1577–1640	*Peter Paul Rubens*
1579	*Invention of the violin*
1592–1653	*Artemisia Gentileschi*
1598–1680	*Gianlorenzo Bernini*
1599–1660	*Diego Velazquez*
1600	*Performance of the first opera*
1606–1669	*Rembrandt*
1608–1674	*John Milton*

1628–1688	*John Bunyan*
1632–1723	*Christopher Wren*
1642	*Rembrandt paints* The Night Watch
1656–1667	*Bernini builds St. Peter's Square in Rome*
1667	*Christopher Wren begins rebuilding London*
1669	*Versailles built*
1677–1741	*Antonio Vivaldi*
1719	*Daniel Defoe's first novel,* Robinson Crusoe, *is published*
1741	*George Frederick Handel composes* Messiah
1685–1750	*Johann Sebastian Bach*

■ Suggested Readings

Cervantes, Miguel, *Don Quixote* (John Rutherford, trans.), Penguin Classics, 2000.

Defoe, Daniel, *The Life and Adventures of Robinson Crusoe,* Oxford World Classics, 1998.

Isacoff, Stuart, *Temperament,* Vintage Books, 2001.

Bunyan, John, *Pilgrim's Progress,* Oxford University Press, 1984.

Cervantes: The Adventures of Don Quixote de la Mancha

Miguel de Cervantes Saavedra (1564–1616) seemed to have had a story inside his heart that, when he was forced into a situation of solitude and thought, he was able to communicate to the world. This story became *Don Quixote* and was an instant hit after publication. Some experts have called *Don Quixote* the first novel. A rival author attempted to make a profit by using Cervantes' name and characters to write a sequel to *Don Quixote,* thus capitalizing on the fame Cervantes had achieved. This forgery infuriated Cervantes and incited him to quickly write his own sequel, which is now usually included in a single volume with the original. Both parts are exciting and touching. They reveal much about the times and about the author. In fact, *Don Quixote* is clearly autobiographical but goes beyond just that; it tells of a man's struggles with reality and illusion, with friendship and trust, with principles, with history, and with himself.

Born to a poor family in Spain, Cervantes received little formal education and served in the army where he lost a hand in the Battle of Lepanto. He eventually settled as a tax collector in Madrid but was sent to jail for illegal seizure of property and bad accounting. His quiet years in prison allowed him to develop and write a story he had been formulating for years. While not about prison life, the book creatively communicates the feelings of a person trapped in a disagreeable situation from which he is having trouble escaping, but this is background. The dominant theme is about a man of slightly older age who is anxious to recapture the glorious nature of the past.

Don Quixote seems to have originally been intended to be a mockery of the novels of chivalry. The concepts of the chivalric literature from the middle ages had become old-fashioned to the late Renaissance culture. But the sympathy aroused in the reader for Don Quixote, and his loyal servant Sancho Panza, have made these characters heroes and have glorified rather than ridiculed the chivalrous acts which they pursue. This is not because the events are serious. On the contrary, there is a strong element of ridiculousness in what they do. *Don Quixote* does not make us sneer at chivalry, but wonder what happened to such noble ideals and long for an opportunity to live the tales of chivalry. In essence, we begin to relate to Don Quixote and become dreamers, too. The pathos of their quest for goodness and their lasting friendship give honor to them and make this book an enduring favorite. *Don Quixote* is second only to *The Bible* in the number of languages and editions into which it has been disseminated. In Spain, it is the national epic and, as with Dante and Shakespeare, has helped define the language in which it was written.

Two classic passages from *Don Quixote* are included here. The first is Quixote's tilting match with windmills, which he is convinced are rogue giants. The second passage relates how Sancho convinces Quixote that an ugly peasant girl is really the beautiful lady Dulcinea—the object of Quixote's chivalrous affection. The apparent inconsistency in beauty and grace is explained by Sancho as resulting from the evil curse of an enchanter. In the early part of the book, Don Quixote personally creates the world of chivalry, as is shown with the windmill incident. Later, Don Quixote is confused but readily accepts Sancho's explanations for the inconsistencies between the chivalrous world and the real world, as illustrated in the Dulcinea passage. However, at the end of the book, without incident or overt statement, Don Quixote seems to realize that his quest for the chivalrous past was all illusion and, brokenhearted, he retires into mournful acceptance.

In the early part of the book Don Quixote personally creates the world of chivalry as is shown with the windmill incident. Later, Don Quixote is confused but readily accepts Sancho's explanations for the inconsistencies between the chivalrous world and the real world, as illustrated in the Dulcinea passage. However, at the end of the book, without incident or overt statement, Don Quixote seems to realize that his quest for the chivalrous past was all illusion and, brokenhearted, he retires into mournful acceptance.

Article 13
The Adventures of Don Quixote de la Mancha

■ Volume I, Book I

Chapter VIII

Of the happy success of the valiant Don Quixote, and the dreadful and inconceivable adventure of the wind-mills, with other incidents worthy to be recorded by the most able historian.

In the midst of this their conversation, they discovered thirty or forty wind-mills all together on the plain, which the knight no sooner perceived, than he said to his squire, "Chance has conducted our affairs even better than we could either wish or hope for; look there, friend Sancho, and behold thirty or forty outrageous giants, with whom, I intend to engage in battle, and put every soul of them to death, so that we may begin to enrich ourselves with their spoils; for, it is a meritorious warfare, and serviceable both to God and man, to extirpate such a wicked race from the face of the earth." "What giants do you mean?" said Sancho Panza in amaze? "Those you see yonder, replied his master, with vast extended arms; some of which are two leagues long." "I would your worship would take notice, replied Sancho, that those you see yonder are no giants, but wind-mills; and what seem arms to you, are sails; which being turned with the wind, make the mill-stone work:" "It seems very plain, said the knight, that you are but a novice in adventures: these I affirm to be giants; and if thou art afraid, get out of the reach of danger, and put up thy prayers for me, while I join with them in fierce and unequal combat." So saying, he put spurs to his steed Rozinante, without paying the least regard to the cries of his squire Sancho, who assured him, that those he was going to attack were no giants, but innocent wind-mills: but, he was so much possessed with the opinion that they were giants, that he neither heard the advice of his squire Sancho, nor would use the intelligence of his own eyes, tho' he was very near them: on the contrary, when he approached them, he called aloud, "Fly not, ye base and cowardly miscreants, for, he is but a single knight who now attacks you." At that instant, a breeze of wind springing up, the great sails began to turn; which being perceived by Don Quixote, "Tho' you wield, said he, more arms than ever belonged to the giant Briareus, I will make you pay for your insolence." So saying, and heartily recommending himself to his lady Dulcinea, whom he implored to succour him in this emergency, bracing on his target, and setting his lance in the rest, he put his Rozinante to full speed, and assaulting the nearest wind-mill, thrust it into one of the sails, which was drove about by the wind with so much fury, that the lance was shivered to pieces, and both knight and steed whirled aloft, and overthrown in very bad plight upon the plain.

Sancho Panza rode as fast as the ass could carry him to his assistance, and when he came up,

Source: From *The Adventures of Don Quixte De La Mancha* by Miguel de Cervantes, translated by Tobias Smollett (New York, Farrar, Straus and Giroux, 1986).

found him unable to stir, by reason of the bruises which he and Rozinante had received. "Lord have mercy upon us! said the squire, did not I tell your worship to consider well what you were about? did not I assure you, they were no other than wind-mills? indeed no body could mistake them for any thing else, but one who has wind-mills in his own head!" "Prithee, hold thy peace, friend Sancho, replied Don Quixote; the affairs of war, are more than any thing, subject to change. How much more so, as I believe, nay, am certain, that the sage Freston, who stole my closet and books, has converted those giants into mills, in order to rob me of the honour of their overthrow; such is the enmity he bears me; but, in the end, all his treacherous arts will but little avail against the vigour of my sword." "God's will be done!" replied Sancho Panza, who helped him to rise, and mount Rozinante that was almost disjointed.

While they conversed together upon what had happened, they followed the road that leads to the pass of Lapice, for in that, which was a great thoroughfare, as Don Quixote observed, it was impossible but they must meet with many and divers adventures. As he jogged along, a good deal concerned for the loss of his lance, he said to his squire, "I remember to have read of a Spanish knight, called Diego Perez de Vargos, who having broken his sword in battle, tore off a mighty branch or bough from an oak, with which he performed such wonders, and felled so many Moors, that he retained the name of Machuca, or the feller, and all his descendants from that day forward, have gone by the name of Vargos and Machuca. This circumstance I mention to thee, because, from the first ash or oak that I met with, I am resolved to rend as large and stout a bough as that, with which I expect, and intend to perform such exploits, as thou shalt think thyself extremely happy in being thought worthy to see, and give testimony to feats, otherwise incredible." "By God's help, says Sancho, I believe that every thing will happen as your worship says; but pray, Sir, sit a little more upright; for you seem to lean strangely to one side, which must proceed from the bruises you received in your fall." "Thou art in the right, answered Don Quixote; and if I do not complain of the pain, it is because knights-errant are not permitted to complain of any wound they receive, even tho' their bowels should come out of their bodies." "If that be case, I have nothing to reply, said Sancho, but God knows, I should be glad your worship would complain when any thing gives you pain: this I know, that for my own part, the smallest prick in the world would make me complain, if that law of not complaining does not reach to the squires as well as the knights." Don Quixote could not help smiling at the simplicity of his squire, to whom he gave permission to complain as much and as often as he pleased, whether he had cause or no; for, as yet, he had read nothing to the contrary, in the history of knight-errantry. . . .

■ Volume II, Book I

Chapter X

Gives an account of the stratagem which Sancho practised, in order to inchant the lady Dulcinea; with other circumstances equally ludicrous and true.

The author of this stupendous history, when he comes to relate what is contained in this chapter, says, he would have willingly passed it over in silence, because he was afraid that it would not be believed; for, here, the madness of Don Quixote soars to the highest pitch of extravagance that can be imagined, and even, by two bow-shots, at least, exceeds all credit and conception: yet, notwithstanding this jealousy and apprehension, he has recounted it in the same manner as it happened, without adding to the history, or detracting one tittle from the truth, undervaluing the risk he runs of being deemed apocryphal; and surely, he was in the right, for, truth may bend, but will never break, and always surmounts falsehood, as oil floats above water. Wherefore, he proceeds in the narrative, saying:

Don Quixote having taken his station in the forest, grove, or wood, near the great city of Toboso, ordered Sancho to go back to town, and not return to his presence, before he should have spoken to his mistress, and begged, in his name, that she would be pleased to grant an interview to her captive knight, and deign to bestow upon him her blessing, thro' which he might expect the most happy issue to all his attempts and enterprizes.

The squire, having undertaken to execute this command, and to bring back as favourable an answer as he had brought the first time; "Go my son, said the knight, and be not confounded when you find yourself beamed upon by that resplendent sun of beauty, which is the object of your inquiry: happy thou, above all the squires that ever lived! Be sure to retain in thy memory, every circumstance of thy reception: observe if she changes colour, while thou are delivering my message; if she is discomposed, and under confusion at the mention of my name; whether she sinks upon her cushion, or happens, at the time, to be seated under the rich canopy of her authority: if she be standing, take notice whether or not, she sometimes supports herself on one foot, sometimes on the other; and if she repeats her answer more than once, changing it from kind to harsh, from sour to amorous; and if she lifts up her hand to adjust her hair, altho' it be not disordered; finally, son, mark all her gestures and emotions; and if thou bringest me an exact detail of them, I shall be able to divine her most abstruse sentiments, touching the concerns of my passion; for, know, Sancho, if thou art still to learn, among lovers, the least gesticulation in their external behaviour, while the conversation turns upon their amours, is, as it were, a messenger that brings a most certain account of what passes within the soul. Go, friend, and enjoy thy fate, so much more favourable than thy master's; and return with much more success than that which I dread and expect in this cruel solitude, where I now remain." "I go, replied Sancho, and will return in a twinkling; therefore, good your worship, do encourage that little heart of yours, which, at present, must be no bigger than a hazle-nut; and consider, as the saying is, a stout heart flings misfortune; where you meet with no hooks, you need expect no bacon; and again, the hare often starts, where the hunter least expects her. This I observe, because, tho' we did not find the palace and castle of my lady, in the night; now that it is day, I hope to stumble upon it, when I least expect

to see it, and if so be, I once catch it, let me alone with her." "Sancho, said the knight, God grant me better fortune in my desires than you have in the application of the proverbs you utter."

This was no sooner said, than Sancho switching Dapple, quitted the knight, who remained on horseback, resting his legs upon his stirrups, and leaning upon his lance, his imagination being engrossed by the most melancholy suggestions. Here let us leave him, and proceed with Sancho Panza, who parting from his master, in equal perplexity and confusion, no sooner found himself clear of the wood, than looking back, and perceiving that Don Quixote was not in sight, he alighted from his ass, and sitting down at the root of a tree, began to catechize himself, in these words: "Brother Sancho, be so good as to let us know, where your worship is going? are you in search of some stray beast? No truly! What then is your errand? why, really, I am going in search of a thing of nought, a princess, God wot, and in her, the sun and the whole heaven of beauty. And pray, where may you expect to meet with this that you mention, Sancho? where, but in the great city of Toboso. And, by whose order are you going upon this inquiry? by order of the renowned knight Don Quixote de la Mancha, the righter of wrongs, who gives thirst to the hungry, and food to those that are dry. All this is might well; but, do you know the house, Sancho? my master says, it must be some royal palace, or stately castle. But, have you never once seen this same palace or stately castle? neither I nor he ever set eyes on it. And do you think it will be well bestowed, if the inhabitants of Toboso, getting notice that you are come with an intention to wheedle away their princesses, and disturb their dames, should break every bone of your skin, and grind your ribs to a paste, with pure cudgelling? Verily, they would not be much to blame, unless they considered, that I do nothing but execute my master's command, and being only a messenger, am not in fault: never trust to that, Sancho; for the Manchegans are as choleric as honourable, and will not suffer themselves to be tickled by any person whatever. Ecod! if you are once smoaked, you will come scurvily off. Bodikins! since that be the case, why should I plague myself seeking a cat with three legs, for another man's pleasure? besides, you may as well seek for a magpye in Rabena, or a batchelor in Salamanca, as for Dulcinea in Toboso: the devil, and none but the devil, has sent me on this fool's errand!"

The result of this soliloquy was another that broke out in these words: "There is a remedy for every thing but death, under whose yoke we must all pass, will we nill we, when this life is at an end: this master of mine, as I have perceived by a thousand instances, is mad enough to be shackled among straw; and truly, I am not much behind him in folly: nay, indeed I am more mad than he, seeing I serve and follow him, if there be any truth in the proverb that says, Tell me your company, and I will tell you your manners: and the other, Not he with whom you was bred, but he by whom you are led. Now he being, as he certainly is, a madman, ay, and so mad, as for the most part to mistake one thing for another, affirming white to be black, and black to be white; as plainly appeared, when he took the windmills for giants, the mules of the friars for dromedaries, the flocks of sheep for opposite armies; and a great many other things in the same stile: I say, it will be no difficult matter to make him believe, the first country-wench I shall meet with, to be his mistress Dulcinea: and if he bogles at swallowing the cheat, I will swear lustily to the truth of what I affirm; and if he swears also, I will swear again; and if he is positive, I will be more positive; so, that come what will, my obstinacy shall always exceed his. Perhaps, by this stubborn behaviour, I shall get rid of all such troublesome messages for the future; when he finds what disagreeable answers I bring: or, perhaps, which I rather believe, he will think that one of those inchanters, who, he says, bear him a grudge, hath transmographied her shape, in order to vex and disquiet him."

Sancho having found out this expedient, was quite calm and satisfied in his mind, and thinking he had brought the business to a good bearing, remained where he was till the evening, that Don Quixote might think he had sufficient time to execute his orders, and return. Every thing succeeded so well to his wish, that when he got up to mount

Dapple, he descried three country-wenches riding from Toboso, towards the place where he stood, upon three young he or she-asses, for, the author does not declare their sex; tho', in all likelihood, they were of the female gender; as your village-maidens commonly ride upon she-asses; but, this being a circumstance of small importance, we shall not give ourselves any trouble to ascertain it.

In short, Sancho no sooner perceived the wenches, than he rode back at a round trot, to his master, whom he found sighing bitterly, and pouring forth a thousand amorous complaints: the knight seeing him arrive, "Well, friend Sancho, said he, is this day to be marked with a white or black stone?" "Your worship, answered the squire, had better mark it with red ochre, like the titles on a professor's chair, that it may be seen the better, by those who look at it." "At that rate, replied Don Quixote, thou bringest me good news." "So good, answered Sancho, that your worship has nothing to do, but, to mount Rozinante, and gallop into the plain, where you will see my lady Dulcinea del Toboso, and two of her damsels, coming this way, to pay you a visit." "Gracious God! cried the knight, what is that you say, friend Sancho? Take care how you deceive me, endeavouring, by feigned joy, to enliven my real sadness." "What should I get, by deceiving your worship? said the squire; besides, you can easily be satisfied of the truth of what I say; make haste, signor, come and see our mistress the princess, arrayed and adorned; in short, as she ought to be: her damsels and she are all one flame of gold; all covered with pearls, diamonds, rubies, and brocard, more than ten hands deep; their hair flowing loose about their shoulders, like so many sun-beams waving with the wind; and moreover, they are mounted on three pyed bellfreys, that it would do one's heart good to see them." "Palfreys you mean, Sancho," said the knight. "There is no great difference, answered the squire, between palfreys and bellfreys; but, be that as it will, they are the finest creatures one would desire to see, especially my lady Dulcinea, who is enough to stupify the five senses." "Come then, my son, replied Don Quixote, and as a gratuity for bringing this piece of news, equally welcome and unexpected, I bestow upon thee the spoils of the first adventure I shall achieve; and if thou are not satisfied with that recompense, I will give unto thee the foals that shall this year be brought forth by my three mares, which thou knowest we left with young upon our town-common." "I stick to the foals, cried the squire, for, as to the spoils of our first adventure, I question whether or not they will be worth accepting."

By this time, they were clear of the wood, and in sight of the three country-maidens; when the knight lifting up his eyes, and surveying the whole road to Toboso, without seeing any thing but them, began to be troubled in mind, and asked Sancho, if the ladies had got out of town when he left them. "Out of town? said Sancho. What! are your worship's eyes in the nape of your neck, that you don't see them coming towards us, glittering and shining like the sun at noon?" "I see no body, replied the knight, but three country-wenches riding upon asses." "God deliver me from the devil! cried the squire, is it possible that three bellfreys, or how-d'ye-call-ums, white as the driven snow, should appear no better than asses, in your worship's eyes? By the lord! I'll give you leave to pluck off every hair of my beard, if that be the case." "Then I tell thee, Sancho, said his master, they are as certainly he or she-asses as I am Don Quixote, and thou Sancho Panza, at least so they seem to me." "Hold your tongue, signor, replied Sancho, and never talk in that manner, but, snuff your eyes, and go and make your reverence to the mistress of your heart, who is just at hand."

So saying, he advanced towards the damsels, and alighting from Dapple, seized one of their beasts by the halter; then fell upon his knees, before the rider, to whom he addressed himself in this manner: "Queen, princess and dutchess of beauty, will your highness and greatness be pleased to receive into grace and favour your captive knight, who sits there, stupified to stone, utterly confounded and deprived of pulse, at seeing himself in presence of your magnificence: I am Sancho Panza his squire, and he is the perplexed and down-trodden knight Don Quixote de la Mancha, alias the knight of the rueful countenance."

By this time, Don Quixote having placed himself on his knees, by Sancho, gazed with staring eyes, and troubled vision, upon the object which the squire called queen and princess; and perceiving nothing but a country-wench's visage, and that none of the most agreeable, for, it was round and flat-nosed, he remained in the utmost confusion and surprise, without daring to open his lips. The other two damsels were equally astonished at seeing a couple of such different figures kneeling before their companion, whom they had detained; but she, breaking silence, pronounced, in a most ungracious and resentful manner: "Get out of the way, and let us pass, for, we are in a hurry." To this apostrophe, Sancho replied, "O princess and universal lady of Toboso! do not your magnificent bowels yearn, to see upon his marrowbones before your sublimated presence, the very pillar and prop of knight-errantry?" One of the other two hearing this pathetic remonstrance, bauled aloud, "Would I had the currying that ass's hide of thine: mind, forsooth, how your small gentry come and pass their gibes upon us country-folks; as if we could not give them as good as they bring; go about your business, friend, and leave us to mind our'n, and so God b'w'ye."

Here the knight interposing, said, "Rise, Sancho, I can plainly perceive that fortune, not yet tired of persecuting me, hath barred every avenue by which any comfort could arrive at the miserable soul that this carcase contains: and thou! the essence of every thing that is desirable in nature, thou sum of human perfection, and sole remedy of this afflicted heart, by which thou are adored! altho' that malicious inchanter, my inveterate enemy, hath spread clouds and cataracts before mine eyes, to them and them only changing and transforming thy unequalled beauty into the appearance of a poor country-wench; if he hath not also altered my figure into that of some frightful spectre horrid to thy view, deign to look upon me with complacency and love; because thou mayest perceive, by this submissive posture I have assumed, even before thy person thus disguised, the humility with which my soul adores thy charms." "You may go kiss my grannam, cried the damsel, I'm a fine madam, truly, to hear such gibberish; we should be more obliged to you if you would get out of our way, and let us go about our own affairs."

Sancho accordingly quitted his hold, leaving her free to go whither she would, and highly pleased with the issue of his stratagem. The suppositious Dulcinea no sooner found herself at liberty, than pricking her palfrey with a goad which was in the end of a stick she had in her hand, the creature galloped across the field with great speed, and feeling the application more severe than usual, began to plunge and kick in such a manner, that my lady fell to the ground. Don Quixote perceiving this accident, ran with great eagerness to raise her up, and Sancho made haste to adjust and gird on the pannel, which had got under the ass's belly. This affair being set to rights, the knight went to lift his inchanted mistress in his arms, and place her on her seat again; but she, starting up from the ground, saved him that trouble, for, retreating a few paces backward, she made a small race, and clapping both hands upon the crupper, leaped upon the pannel as nimble as a falcon, seating herself astride, like a man.

"By St. Roque! cried Sancho, my lady mistress is as light as a hawk, and can teach the most dextrous horseman to ride; at one jump, she has sprung into the saddle, and without spurs, makes her palfrey fly like any Zebra; and truly, her damsels are not a whit behind; for, they go scouring along, as swift as the wind." This was actually true, for, Dulcinea was no sooner remounted, than the other two trotted after her, and at last disappeared, after having gone more than half a league, at full speed, without once looking behind them.

Don Quixote followed them with his eyes, until they vanished; then, turning to his squire, "Sancho, said he, thou seest how I am persecuted by inchanters, and mayest perceive how far the malice and grudge they bear me, extend; seeing they have deprived me of the pleasure I should have enjoyed at sight of my mistress in her own beauteous form. Surely, I was born to be an example of misery; the very mark and butt for all the arrows of misfortune; nay, thou are also to observe, Sancho, that those traitors were not contented with a simple metamorphosis of my Dulcinea, but, have transformed and changed her into the base and homely figure of that country-wench; robbing her, at the same time, of that which is so peculiar to ladies of fashion, I mean that sweet scent which is the result of their living among flowers and perfume; for, know, my friend, when I went to lift Dulcinea upon her palfrey, as thou sayest it was, tho' to me, it seemed neither more nor less than a she-ass, I was almost suffocated and poisoned with a whiff of undigested garlic!"

"O! ye miscreants! cried Sancho, O! ye malicious and mischievous inchanters! would to God, I could see you all strung by the gills, like so many haddocks! much you know, much you can, and much more will you still be doing. Was it not enough, ye knaves, to change the pearls of my lady's eyes into a couple of cork-tree galls, and her hair of shining gold into the bristles of a red cow's tail; and, in short, to transmography every feature of her countenance, without your meddling with the sweetness of her breath, by which we might have discovered what was concealed beneath that bark of homeliness: tho' to tell the truth, I saw not her homeliness, but beauty, which was exceedingly increased by a mole upon her upper lip, something like a whisker, consisting of seven or eight red hairs, like threads of gold, as long as my hand." "According to the correspondence which the moles of the face have with those of the body, said Don Quixote, Dulcinea must have just such another on the brawny part of her thigh, of the same side; but, hairs of such a length, are methinks, rather too long for moles." "I do assure your worship, answered Sancho, they seemed as if they had come into the world with her." "I very well believe what you say, my friend, replied the knight; for, nature hath bestowed nothing on Dulcinea but what is perfectly finished; wherefore, if thou had'st seen an hundred such moles; in her, they would be so many moons and resplendent start: but, tell me, Sancho, that which you adjusted, and which to me seemed a pannel, was it a plain pad, or a side-saddle?" "It was a great side-saddle, answered the squire, so rich, that half the kingdom would not buy it." "And why could not I see all this? said the knight. I say, again, Sancho, and will repeat it a thousand times, that I am the most unfortunate of men."

The rogue Sancho, finding his master so dextrously gulled, and hearing him talk in this mad strain, could scarce refrain from laughing in his face: in fine, a good deal more of this sort of conversation having passed between them, they remounted their beasts, and took the road to Saragosa, where they expected to arrive time enough to be present at the solemn festival yearly celebrated in that famous city; but, before they accomplished their journey they met with adventures, which, for their variety, novelty and greatness, deserve to be read and recorded, as in the sequel.

John Milton: Paradise Lost

John Milton (1608–1674) was a man with high aspirations but whose success was not fully realized until after his death. While studying to become a Priest, he developed a love for poetry in Latin, Italian, and English (he greatly admired Shakespeare). He entered Cambridge intent on entering the ministry but could not adjust to University life. He was scorned by many and, after a fistfight with his tutor, was expelled and discontinued the pursuit of the priesthood. He remained without formal profession for many years but filled his time with travel and writing poetry. After meeting Galileo in Italy, Milton found a cause for his life and wrote in defense of free speech, writing, and thought. He defended the right of Galileo and others to write what they wanted and said, in one work, that books "preserve as in a vial the purest efficacy and extraction of that living intellect bred in them."

England's civil war (Cromwell against King Charles I) developed in Milton sympathies for the Puritan cause. He published essays defending Puritan views and served in Cromwell's government. The monarchy under Charles II regained power in 1660, intent on punishing the members of the Commonwealth government. But by this time, Milton had become blind and had turned most of his energies back to poetry. He was lightly punished by having a couple of his works burned, and he was fined.

Milton had always admired the epics of Homer and Virgil. He considered epics to be the highest form of poetry. He embarked upon writing his own epic and hoped to write the greatest work in the English language. He considered using King Arthur as the theme for the epic but eventually decided to make religion the theme with a focus on the war in Heaven, the Fall, and the expulsion from Eden. He dedicated much of the rest of his life to the creation of this epic—*Paradise Lost.* Milton finished the book in the twilight of his life. He had then been thrust into poverty by the restored monarchy and ended up selling the completed manuscript of *Paradise Lost* for £5 to Samuel Simmons. Milton himself doubted the worth of *Paradise Lost* during the final stages of its completion, but the work was eventually recognized for its incredibly complex style and far-reaching vision and has achieved a high place in the ranks of the other immortal literary epics.

The selections from *Paradise Lost* illustrate the complex, noble, and sometimes difficult style used by Milton. Presented first is Satan's regrouping of his forces and planning in Hell just after his utter defeat and expulsion from Heaven. Of particular interest is the indefatigable determination of Satan to wreak revenge on God's plan and to find power wherever he can. The next passages are the moments of temptation in the Garden of Eden and then Eve's touching explanation of her actions to Adam.

■ Book I

The Argument

This first Book proposes first in brief the whole Subject, Man's disobedience, and the loss thereupon of Paradise wherein he was plac't: Then touches the prime cause of his fall, the serpent, or rather Satan in the Serpent; who revolting from God, and drawing to his side many Legions of Angels, was by the command of God driven out of Heaven with all his Crew into the great Deep. Which action past over, the Poem hastes into the midst of things, presenting Satan with his Angels now fallen into Hell, describ'd here, not in the Center (for Heaven and Earth may be suppos'd as yet not made, certainly not yet accurst) but in a place of utter darkness, fitliest call'd Chaos: Here Satan with his Angels lying on the burning Lake, thunder-struck and astonisht, after a certain space recovers, as from confusion, calls up him who next in Order and Dignity lay by him; they confer of their miserable fall. Satan awakens all his Legions, who lay till then in the same manner confounded; They rise, their Numbers, array of Battle, their chief Leaders nam'd, according to the Idols known afterwards in Canaan and the Countries adjoining. To these Satan directs his Speech, comforts them with hope yet of regaining Heaven, but tells them lastly of a new World and new kind of Creature to be created, according to an ancient Prophecy or report in Heaven; for that Angels were long before this visible Creation, was the opinion of many ancient Fathers. To find out the truth of this Prophecy, and what to determine thereon he refers to a full Council. What his Associates thence attempt. Pandemonium the Palace of Satan rises, suddenly built out of the Deep: The infernal Peers there sit in Council.

[added 1668]

Of Man's First disobedience, and the Fruit°
Of that Forbidden Tree, whose mortal° taste
Brought Death into the World, and all our woe,
With loss of Eden, till one greater Man
Restore us, and regain the blissful Seat,   5
Sing Heav'nly Muse, that on the secret top
Of Oreb, or of Sinai, didst inspire
That Shepherd, who first taught the chosen Seed,°
In the Beginning how the Heav'ns and Earth
Rose out of Chaos: Or if Sion Hill   10
Delight thee more, and Siloa's Brook that flow'd
Fast by the Oracle of God;° I thence
Invoke thy aid to my advent'rous Song,
That with no middle flight intends to soar
Above th'Aonian Mount,° while it pursues   15

---

1 **Fruit** including consequences, fruits.

2 **mortal** human and deadly.

7–8 **Of . . . Seed** Moses, who set down Genesis, was visited by God on Mount Horeb and Sinai.

11–12 **Siloa's . . . God** near the Temple in Jerusalem; the brook is to parallel the one haunted by the classical Muses.

15 **Mount** Helicon, sacred to the Muses.

Source: From *Paradise Lost and Paradise Regained* by John Milton (New York: Penguin Group, 1968).

Things unattempted yet in Prose or Rhyme.
And chiefly Thou O Spirit, that dost prefer
Before all Temples th'upright heart and pure,
Instruct° me, for Thou know'st; Thou from the first
Wast present, and with mighty wings outspread   20
Dove-like sat'st brooding on the vast Abyss
And mad'st it pregnant: What in me is dark
Illumine, what is low raise and support;
That to the heighth of this great Argument°
I may assert° Eternal Providence,   25
And justify° the ways of God to men.
      Say first, for Heav'n hides nothing from thy
        view
Nor the deep Tract of Hell, say first what cause
Mov'd our Grand° Parents in that happy State,
Favour'd of Heav'n so highly, to fall off   30
From their Creator, and transgress his Will
For° one restraint, Lords of the World besides?
Who first seduc'd them to that foul revolt?
Th'infernal Serpent; he it was, whose guile
Stirr'd up with Envy and Revenge, deceiv'd   35
The Mother of Mankind, what time his Pride
Had cast him out from Heav'n, with all his Host
Of Rebel Angels, by whose aid aspiring
To set himself in Glory above his Peers,
He trusted to have equall'd the most High,   40
If he oppos'd; and with ambitious aim
Against° the Throne and Monarchy of God
Rais'd impious War in Heav'n and Battle proud
With vain attempt. Him the Almighty Power
Hurl'd headlong flaming from th'Ethereal Sky   45
With hideous ruin° and combustion down

To bottomless perdition, there to dwell
In Adamantine° Chains and penal Fire,
Who durst defy th'Omnipotent to Arms.
Nine times the Space that measures Day and Night 50
To mortal men, he with his horrid crew
Lay vanquisht, rolling in the fiery Gulf
Confounded° though immortal: But his doom
Reserv'd him to more wrath; for now the thought
Both of lost happiness and lasting pain   55
Torments him; round he throws his baleful° eyes
That witness'd° huge affliction and dismay
Mixt with obdúrate pride and steadfast hate:
At once as far as Angel's ken° he views
The dismal Situation° waste and wild,   60
A Dungeon° horrible, on all sides round
As one great Furnace flam'd, yet from those flames
No light, but rather darkness visible
Serv'd only to discover sights of woe,
Regions of sorrow, doleful shades, where peace   65
And rest can never dwell, hope never comes
That comes to all; but torture without end
Still urges, and a fiery Deluge, fed
With ever-burning Sulphur unconsum'd:
Such place Eternal Justice had prepar'd   70
For those rebellious, here their Prison ordain'd
In utter° darkness, and their portion set
As far remov'd from God and light of Heav'n
As from the Center° thrice to th'utmost Pole.°
O how unlike the place from whence they fell!   75
There the companions of his fall, o'erwhelm'd

---

19 **Instruct** Latin *instruere,* to build, perfectly linking "Temples" and "heart."

24 **Argument** subject-matter and process of reasoning.

25 **assert** affirm.

26 **justify** bear witness to the justice of; both "justify to men" and "ways of God to men."

29 **Grand** original and pre-eminent.

32 **For** both "transgress because of one restraint," and "Lords. . . . except for one restraint."

42 **Against** both "aim against" and "war against."

46 **ruin** falling, Latin *ruina.*

---

48 **Adamantine** of the hardest rocks or minerals.

53 **Confounded** overthrown.

56 **baleful** full both of woe and of evil.

57 **witness'd** showed his.

59 **Angel's ken** Milton's spelling "Angels kenn" leaves "kenn" as possibly noun or verb.

60 **Situation** site and predicament.

61 **Dungeon** from *domnionem,* "lord's tower," from Latin *dominus,* lord. See X 466.

72 **utter** outer and total.

74 **the Center** the earth.

74 **utmost Pole** outermost point of the universe.

With Floods and Whirlwinds of tempestuous fire,
He soon discerns, and welt'ring by his side
One next himself in power, and next in crime,
Long after known in Palestine, and nam'd   80
Beëlzebub. To whom th'Arch-Enemy,°
And thence in Heav'n call'd Satan, with bold words
Breaking the horrid silence thus began.
    "If thou beest he; but O how fall'n! how
      chang'd
From him, who in the happy Realms of Light   85
Cloth'd with transcendent brightness didst outshine
Myriads though bright: If he whom mutual league,
United thoughts and counsels, equal hope,
And hazard in the Glorious Enterprise,
Join'd with me once, now misery hath join'd   90
In equal ruin: into what Pit thou seest
From what heighth fall'n, so much the stronger
    prov'd
He with his Thunder: and till then who knew
The force of those dire Arms? yet not for those
Nor what the Potent Victor in his rage   95
Can else inflict do I repent or change,
Though chang'd in outward lustre, that fixt mind
And high disdain, from sense of injur'd merit,
That with the mightiest rais'd me to contend,
And to the fierce contention brought along   100
Innumerable force of Spirits arm'd
That durst dislike his reign, and me preferring,
his utmost power with adverse° power oppos'd
In dubious° Battle on the Plains of Heav'n,
And shook his throne. What though the field be   105
    lost?
All is not lost; the unconquerable Will,
And study of° revenge, immortal hate,
And courage never to submit or yield:
And what is else not to be overcome?°
That Glory never shall his wrath or might   110

Extort from me. To bow and sue for grace
With suppliant knee, and deify his power
Who from the terror of this Arm so late
Doubted° his Empire, that were low indeed,
That were an ignominy and shame beneath   115
This downfall; since by Fate the strength of Gods°
And this Empyreal substance° cannot fail,
Since through experience of this great event
In Arms not worse, in foresight much advanc't,
We may with more successful hope° resolve   120
To wage by force or guile eternal War
Irreconcilable, to our grand Foe,
Who now triúmphs, and in th'excess of joy
Sole reigning holds the Tyranny of Heav'n."

          *   *   *

    "Is this the Region, this the Soil, the Clime,"°
Said then the lost Arch Angel, "this the seat
That we must change for Heav'n, this mournful
    gloom
For that celestial light? Be it so, since hee   245
Who now is Sovran° can dispose and bid
What shall be right: farthest from him is best
Whom reason hath equall'd, force hath made
    supreme
Above his equals. Farewell happy Fields
Where Joy for ever dwells: Hail horrors, hail   250
Infernal world, and thou profoundest Hell
Receive thy new Possessor: One who brings
A mind not to be chang'd by Place or Time.
The mind is its own place, and in itself
Can make a Heav'n of Hell, a Hell of Heav'n.   255
What matter where, if I be still the same,
And what I should be, all but less than hee
Whom Thunder hath made greater? Here at least
We shall be free; th'Almighty hath not built

---

81 **Arch-Enemy** Hebrew sātān, adversary.

103 **adverse** hostile, as in "adversary."

104 **dubious** of which the outcome was doubtful.

107 **study of** zeal for.

109 **And . . . overcome** "In what else does 'not being overcome' consist?"

---

114 **Doubted** feared for.

116 **Gods** Both Satan and God apply the word to angels.

117 **Empyreal substance** fiery and heavenly essence.

120 **successful hope** of success.

242 **Clime** zone and temperature.

246 **Sovran** Milton's spelling follows the Italian *sovrano*.

Here for his envy, will not drive us hence: 260
Here we may reign secure, and in my choice
To reign is worth ambition though in Hell:
Better to reign in Hell, than serve in Heav'n.

*   *   *

Book IX

The Argument

Satan having compast the Earth, with meditated guile returns as a mist by Night into Paradise, enters into the Serpent sleeping. Adam and Eve in the Morning go forth to their labours, which Eve proposes to divide in several places, each labouring apart: Adam consents not, alleging the danger, lest that Enemy, of whom they were forewarn'd, should attempt her found alone: Eve loath to be thought not circumspect or firm enough, urges her going apart, the rather desirous to make trial of her strength; Adam at last yields: The Serpent finds her alone; his subtle approach, first gazing, then speaking, with much flattery extolling Eve above all other Creatures. Eve wond'ring to hear the Serpent speak, asks how he attain'd both human speech and such understanding not till now; the Serpent answers, that by tasting of a certain Tree in the Garden he attain'd to Speech and Reason, till then void of both: Eve requires him to bring her to that Tree, and finds it to be the Tree of Knowledge forbidden: The Serpent now grown bolder, with many wiles and arguments induces her at length to eat; she pleas'd with the taste deliberates awhile whether to impart thereof to Adam or not, at last brings him of the Fruit, relates what persuaded her to eat thereof: Adam at first amaz'd, but perceiving her lost, resolves through vehemence of love to perish with her; and extenuating the trespass, eats also of the Fruit: The effects thereof in them both; they seek to cover their nakedness; then fall to variance and accusation of one another.

*   *   *

"Lead then," said Eve. Hee° leading swiftly   631
    roll'd
In tangles, and made intricate seem straight,
To mischief swift. Hop elevates, and joy
Bright'ns his Crest, as when a wand'ring Fire
Compáct° of unctuous vapour, which the Night   635
Condenses, and the cold environs round,
Kindl'd through agitation to a Flame,
Which oft, they say, some evil Spirit attends,
Hovering and blazing with delusive Light,
Misleads th'amaz'd Night-wanderer from his way   640
To Bogs and Mires, and oft through Pond or Pool,
There swallow'd up and lost, from succour far.
So glister'd the dire Snake, and into fraud
Led Eve our credulous° Mother, to the Tree
of prohibition, root of all our woe;   645
Which when she saw, thus to her guide she spake.
    "Serpent, we might have spar'd our coming
        hither,
Fruitless to me, though Fruit be here to excess,
The credit of whose virtue rest with thee,
Wondrous indeed, if cause of such effects.   650
But of this Tree we may not taste nor touch;
God so commanded, and left that Command
Sole Daughter of his voice; the rest, we live
Law to ourselves, our Reason is our Law."
    To whom the Tempter guilefully repli'd.   655
"Indeed? hath God then said that of the Fruit
Of all these Garden Trees ye shall not eat,
Yet Lords declar'd of all in Earth or Air?"
    To whom thus Eve yet sinless. "Of the Fruit
Of each Tree in the Garden we may eat,   660
But of the Fruit of this fair Tree amidst
The Garden, God hath said, Ye shall not eat
Thereof, nor shall ye touch it, lest ye die."
    She scarce had said, though brief, when now
        more bold

---

631 **Hee:** the serpent.

635 **Compáct** compacted; like "unctuous" (oily), a scientific term for vapors.

644 **credulous** over-ready to believe (sadly contrasted with the original sense of the word, "faithful," as in "a credulous and plain heart is accepted with God," [1605]).

668 **Fluctuates** moves like a wave.

The Tempter, but with show of Zeal and Love
To man, and indignation at his wrong,
New part puts on, and as to passion mov'd,
Fluctuates° disturb'd, yet comely, and in act
Rais'd, as of some great matter to begin.
As when of old some Orator renown'd   670
In Athens or free Rome, where Eloquence
Flourish'd, since mute, to some great cause
   addrest,
Stood in himself collected, while each part,
Motion, each act won audience ere the tongue,
Sometimes in heighth began, as no delay   675
Of Preface brooking through his Zeal of Right.
So standing, moving, or to heighth upgrown
The Tempter all impassion'd thus began.
   "O sacred, Wise, and Wisdom-giving Plant,
Mother of Science,° Now I feel thy Power   680
Within me clear, not only to discern
Things in their Causes, but to trace the ways
Of highest Agents, deem'd however wise.
Queen of this Universe, do not believe
Those rigid threats of Death; ye shall not Die: 685
How should ye? by the Fruit? it gives you Life
To Knowledge: By the Threat'ner? look on mee,
Mee who have touch'd and tasted, yet both live,
And life more perfect have attain'd than Fate
Meant mee, by vent'ring higher than my Lot.   690
Shall that be shut to Man, which to the Beast
Is open? or will God incense his ire
For such a petty Trespass, and not praise
Rather your dauntless virtue, whom the pain
Of Death denounc't,° whatever thing Death be,   695
Deterr'd not from achieving what might lead
To happier life, knowledge of Good and Evil;
Of good, how just? of evil, if what is evil
Be real, why not known, since easier shunn'd?
God therefore cannot hurt ye, and be just;   700
Not just, not God; not fear'd then, nor obey'd:
Your fear itself of Death removes the fear.
Why then was this forbid? Why but to awe,
Why but to keep ye low and ignorant,
His worshippers; he knows that in the day   705

Ye Eat thereof, your Eyes that seem so clear,   665
Yet are but dim, shall perfectly be then
Op'n'd and clear'd, and ye shall be as Gods,
Knowing both Good and Evil as they now.
That ye should be as Gods, since I as Man,   710
Internal Man, is but proportion meet,
I of brute human, yee of human Gods.
So ye shall die perhaps, by putting off
Human, to put on Gods, death to be wisht,
Though threat'n'd, which no worse than this can   715
   bring.
And what are Gods that Man may not become
As they, participating God-like food?
The Gods are first, and that advantage use
On our belief, that all from them proceeds;
I question it, for this fair Earth I see,   720
Warm'd by the Sun, producing every kind,
Them nothing: If they all things, who enclos'd
Knowledge of Good and Evil in this Tree,
That whoso eats thereof, forthwith attains
Wisdom without their leave? and wherein lies   725
Th'offence, that Man should thus attain to know?
what can your knowledge hurt him, or this Tree
Impart against his will if all be his?
Or is it envy, and can envy dwell
In heav'nly breasts? these, these and many more   730
Causes import your need of this fair Fruit.
Goddess humane,° reach then, and freely taste."
   He ended, and his words replete with guile
Into her heart too easy entrance won:
Fixt on the Fruit she gaz'd, which to behold   735
Might tempt alone, and in her ears the sound
Yet rung of his persuasive words, impregn'd
With Reason, to her seeming, and with Truth;
meanwhile the hour of Noon drew on, and wak'd
An eager appetite, rais'd by the smell   740
So savoury of that Fruit, which with desire,
Inclinable now grown to touch or taste,
Solicited her longing eye; yet first
Pausing awhile, thus to herself she mus'd.
   "Great are they Virtues, doubtless, best of   745
     Fruits,

---

680 **Science** knowledge.

695 **denounc't** threatened.

---

732 **humane** benevolent, with a hint of line 712.

Though kept from Man, and worthy to be
   admir'd,
Whose taste, too long forborne, at first assay
Gave elocution to the mute, and taught
The Tongue not made for Speech to speak thy
   praise:
Thy praise hee also who forbids thy use,   750
Conceals not from us, naming thee the Tree
Of Knowledge, knowledge both of good and evil
Forbids us then to taste, but his forbidding
Commends thee more, while it infers the good
By thee communicated, and our want: 755
For good unknown, sure is not had, or had
And yet unknown, is as not had a tall.
In plain then, what forbids he but to know,
Forbids us good, forbids us to be wise?
Such prohibitions bind not. But if Death   760
Bind us with after-bands, what profits then
Our inward freedom? In the day we eat
Of this fair Fruit, our doom is, we shall die.
How dies the Serpent? hee hath eat'n and lives,
And knows, and speaks, and reasons, and   765
   discerns,
Irrational till then. For us alone
Was death invented? or to us deni'd
This intellectual food, for beasts reserv'd?
For Beasts it seems: yet that one Beast which first
Hath tasted, envies not, but brings with joy   770
The good befall'n him, Author unsuspect,°
Friendly to man, far from deceit or guile.
What fear I then, rather what know to fear
Under this ignorance of Good and Evil,
Of God or Death, of Law or Penalty?   775
Here grows the Cure° of all, this Fruit Divine,
Fair to the Eye, inviting to the Taste,
Of virtue to make wise: what hinders then
To reach, and feed at once both Body and
   Mind?"
    So saying, her rash hand in evil hour   780
Forth reaching to the Fruit, she pluck'd, she ate:
Earth felt the wound, and Nature from her seat

Sighing through all her Works gave signs of woe,
That all was lost. Back to the Thicket slunk
The guilty Serpent, and well might, for Eve   785
Intent now wholly on her taste, naught else
Regarded, such delight till then, as seem'd,
In Fruit she never tasted, whether true
Or fancied so, through expectation high
Of knowledge, nor was Godhead from her   790
   thought.
Greedily she ingorg'd without restraint,
And knew not eating Death: Satiate at length,
And height'n'd as with Wine, jocund and boon,
Thus to herself she pleasingly began. . . .

But to Adam in what sort
Shall I appear? shall I to him make known
As yet my change, and give him to partake
Full happiness with mee, or rather not,
But keep the odds of Knowledge in my power   820
Without Copartner? so to add what wants°
In Female Sex, the more to draw his Love,
And render me more equal, and perhaps,
A thing not undesirable, sometime
Superior; for inferior who is free?   825
This may be well: but what if God have seen,
And Death ensue? then I shall be no more,
And Adam wedded to another Eve,
Shall live with her enjoying, I extinct;
A death to think. Confirm'd then I resolve,   830
Adam shall share with me in bliss or woe:
So dear I love him, that with him all deaths
I could endure, without him live no life."
    So saying, from the Tree her step she turn'd,
But first low Reverence done, as to the power   835
That dwelt within, whose presence had infus'd
Into the plant sciential° sap, deriv'd
From Nectar, drink of Gods. Adam the while
Waiting desirous her return, had wove
Of choicest Flow'rs a Garland to adorn   840
Her Tresses, and her rural labours crown
As Reapers oft are wont their Harvest Queen.

---

771 **Author unsuspect** an authority not to be suspected.

776 **Cure** with a grim hint of the earlier sense, "care, trouble," Latin *cura*.

---

821 **wants** is lacking.

837 **sciential** granting knowledge.

Great joy he promis'd to his thoughts, and new
Solace in her return, so long delay'd;
Yet oft his heart, divine of° something ill,   845
Misgave him; hee the falt'ring measure° felt;
And forth to meet her went, the way she took
That Morn when first they parted; by the Tree
Of Knowledge he must pass, there he her met,
Scarce from the Tree returning; in her hand   850
A bough of fairest fruit that down smil'd,
New-gather'd, and ambrosial smell diffus'd.
To him she hasted, in her face excuse
Came Prologue, and Apology to prompt,
Which with bland words at will she thus addrest.   855
     "Hast thou not wonder'd, Adam, at my stay?
Thee I have misst, and thought it long, depriv'd
Thy presence, agony of love till now
Not felt, nor shall be twice, for never more
Mean I to try, what rash untri'd I sought,   860
The pain of absence from thy sight. But strange
Hath been the cause, and wonderful to hear:
This Tree is not as we are told, a Tree
Of danger tasted, nor to evil unknown
Op'ning the way, but of Divine effect   865
To open Eyes, and make them Gods who taste;
And hath been tasted such: the Serpent wise,
Or not restrain'd as wee, or not obeying,
Hath eat'n of the fruit, and is become,
Not dead, as we are threat'n'd, but thenceforth   870
Endu'd with human voice and human sense,
Reasoning to admiration, and with mee
Persuasively hath so prevail'd, that I
Have also tasted, and have also found
Th'effects to correspond, opener mine Eyes,   875
Dim erst,° dilated Spirits, ampler heart,
And growing up to Godhead; which for thee
Chiefly I sought, without thee can despise.
For bliss, as thou hast part, to me is bliss,
Tedious, unshar'd with thee, and odious soon.   880
Thou therefore also taste, that equal Lot
May join us, equal Joy, as equal Love;

Lest thou not tasting, different degree
Disjoin us, and I then too late renounce
Deity for thee, when Fate will not permit."   885
     Thus Eve with Count'nance blithe her story
          told;
But in her Cheek distemper° flushing glow'd.
On th'other side, Adam, soon as he heard
The fatal Trespass done by Eve, amaz'd,
Astonied° stood and Blank, while horror chill   890
Ran through his veins, and all his joints relax'd;
From his slack hand the Garland wreath'd for Eve
Down dropp'd, and all the faded Roses shed:
Speechless he stood and pale, till thus at length
First to himself he inward silence broke.   895
     "O fairest of Creation, last and best
Of all God's Works, Creature in whom excell'd
Whatever can to sight or thought be form'd,
Holy, divine, good, amiable, or sweet!
How art thou lost, how on a sudden lost,   900
Defac't, deflow'r'd, and now to Death devote?°
Rather how hast thou yielded to transgress
The strict forbiddance, how to violate
The sacred Fruit forbidd'n! some cursed fraud
Of enemy hath beguil'd thee, yet unknown,   905
And mee with thee hath ruin'd, for with thee
Certain my resolution is to Die;
How can I live without thee, how forgo
Thy sweet Converse and Love so dearly join'd,
To live again in these wild Woods forlorn?   910
Should God create another Eve, and I
Another Rib afford, yet loss of thee
Would never from my heart; no no, I feel
The Link of Nature draw me: Flesh of Flesh,
Bone of my Bone thou art, and from thy State   915
Mine never shall be parted, bliss or woe."
     So having said, as one from sad dismay
Recomforted, and after thoughts disturb'd
Submitting to what seem'd remédiless,
Thus in calm mood his Words to Eve he turn'd.   920

---

845 **divine of** divining (but "divine" is a pregnant word in the context).

846 **falt'ring** measure his heartbeat (with the hint that Eve's "measure," temperance—as at VII 128—has faltered).

876 **erst** formerly.

887 **distemper** disorder, disease; also the 17th-century sense, "intoxication"—see lines 793, 1008, 1050.

890 **Astonied** paralyzed.

901 **devote** doomed.

"Bold deed thou hast presum'd, advent'rous
　　　Eve,
And peril great provok't, who thus hath dar'd
Had it been only coveting to Eye
That sacred Fruit, sacred to abstinence,
Much more to taste it under ban to touch.　　925
But past who can recall, or done undo?
Not God Omnipotent, nor Fate, yet so
Perhaps thou shalt not Die, perhaps the Fact°
Is not so heinous now, foretasted Fruit,
Profan'd first by the Serpent, by him first　　930
Made common and unhallow'd ere our taste;
Nor yet on him found deadly, he yet lives,
Lives, as thou said'st, and gains to live as Man
Higher degree of Life, inducement strong
To us, as likely tasting to attain　　935
Proportional ascent, which cannot be
But to be Gods, or Angels Demi-gods.
Nor can I think that God, Creator wise,
Though threat'ning, will in earnest so destroy
Us his prime Creatures, dignifi'd so high,　　940
Set over all his Works, which in our Fall,
For us created, needs with us must fail,
Dependent made; so God shall uncreate,
Be frustrate, do, undo, and labour lose,
Not well conceiv'd of God, who though his Power　945
Creation could repeat, yet would be loath
Us to abolish, lest the Adversary
Triumph and say; 'Fickle their State whom God
Most Favours, who can please him long? Mee
　　　first
He ruin'd, now Mankind; whom will he next?'　950
Matter of scorn, not to be given the Foe.
However I with thee have fixt my Lot,
Certain to undergo like doom, if Death
Consort with thee, Death is to mee as Life;
So forcible within my heart I feel　　955
The Bond of Nature draw me to my own,
My own in thee, for what thou art is mine;
Our State cannot be sever'd, we are one,
One Flesh; to lose thee were to lose myself."
So Adam, and thus Eve to him repli'd.　　960
"O glorious trial of exceeding Love,

Illustrious evidence, example high!
Engaging me to emulate, but short
Of they perfection, how shall I attain,
Adam, from whose dear side I boast me sprung,　965
And gladly of our Union hear thee speak,
One Heart, one Soul in both; whereof good proof
This day affords, declaring thee resolv'd,
Rather than Death or aught than Death more
　　　dread
Shall separate us, linkt in Love so dear,　　970
To undergo with mee one Guilt, one Crime,
If any be, of tasting this fair Fruit,
Whose virtue, for of good still good proceeds,
Direct, or by occasion hath presented
This happy trial of thy Love, which else　　975
So eminently never had been known.
Were it I thought Death menac't would ensue
This my attempt, I would sustain alone
The worse, and not persuade thee, rather die
Deserted, than oblige° thee with a fact°　　980
Pernicious to thy Peace, chiefly assur'd
Remarkably so late of thy so true,
So faithful Love unequall'd; but I feel
Far otherwise th'event,° not Death, but Life
Augmented, op'n'd Eyes, new Hopes, new Joys,　985
Taste so Divine, that what of sweet before
Hath toucht my sense, flat seems to this, and
　　　harsh.
On my experience, Adam, freely taste,
And fear of Death deliver to the Winds."
　　So saying, she embrac'd him, and for joy　990
Tenderly wept, much won that he his Love
Had so ennobl'd, as of choice to incur
Divine displeasure for her sake, or Death.
In recompense (for such compliance bad
Such recompense best merits) from the bough　995
She gave him of that fair enticing Fruit
With liberal hand: he scrupl'd not to eat
Against his better knowledge, not deceiv'd,
But fondly overcome with Female charm.
Earth trembl'd from her entrails, as again　1000

---

980 **oblige** make liable to penalty.

980 **fact** deed.

984 **event** outcome.

---

928 **Fact** deed.

In pangs, and Nature gave a second groan,
Sky lour'd and muttering Thunder, some sad drops
Wept at completing of the mortal Sin
Original; . . .

*　　*　　*

■ Book X

The Argument

Meanwhile the heinous and despiteful act
Of Satan done in Paradise, and how
Hee in the serpent had perverted° Eve,
Her Husband shee, to taste the fatal fruit,
Was known in Heav'n; for what can 'scape the Eye 5
Of God All-seeing, or deceive his Heart
Omniscient, who in all things wise and just,
Hinder'd not Satan to attempt the mind
Of Man, with strength entire, and free Will arm'd,
Complete to have discover'd and repulst　　　　10
Whatever wiles of Foe or seeming Friend.
For still° they knew, and ought to have still
　　remember'd
The high Injunction not to taste that Fruit,
Whoever tempted; which they not obeying,
Incurr'd, what could they less, the penalty,　　15
And manifold in sin, deserv'd to fall.
Up into Heav'n from Paradise in haste
Th'Angelic Guards ascended, mute and sad
For Man, for of his state by this they knew,
Much wond'ring how the subtle Fiend had stol'n 20
Entrance unseen. Soon as th'unwelcome news
From Earth arriv'd at Heaven Gate, displeas'd
All were who heard, dim sadness did not spare
That time Celestial visages, yet mixt
With pity, violated not their bliss.　　　　25
About the new-arriv'd, in multitudes
Th'etherial People ran, to hear and know
How all befell: they towards the Throne Supreme
Accountable made haste to make appear

With righteous plea, their utmost vigilance,　30
And easily approv'd; when the most High
Eternal Father from his secret Cloud,
Amidst in Thunder utter'd thus his voice.
　　"Assembl'd Angels, and ye Powers return'd
From unsuccessful charge, be not dismay'd,　35
Nor troubl'd at these tidings from the Earth,
Which your sincerest care could not prevent,
Foretold so lately what would come to pass,
When first this Tempter cross'd the Gulf from
　　Hell.
I told ye then he should prevail and speed　40
On his bad Errand, Man should be seduc't
And flatter'd out of all, believing lies
Against his Maker; no Decree of mine
Concurring to necessitate his Fall,
Or touch with lightest moment of impulse　45
His free Will, to her own inclining left
In ev'n scale. But fall'n he is, and now
What rests,° but that the mortal Sentence pass
On his transgression, Death denounc't° that day,
Which he presumes already vain and void,　50
Because not yet inflicted, as he fear'd,
By some immediate stroke; but soon shall find
Forbearance no acquittance ere day end.
Justice shall not return as bounty scorn'd.
But whom send I to judge them? whom but thee 55
Vicegerent Son, to thee I have transferr'd
All Judgement, whether in Heav'n, or Earth, or
　　Hell.
Easy it might be seen that I intend
Mercy colléague with Justice, sending thee
Man's Friend, his Mediator, his design'd　60
Both Ransom and Redeemer voluntary,
And destin'd man himself to judge Man fall'n."
　　So spake the Father, and unfolding bright
Toward the right hand his Glory, on the Son
Blaz'd forth unclouded Deity; he full　65
Resplendent all his Father manifest
Express'd, and thus divinely answer'd mild.
　　"Father Eternal, thine is to decree,
Mine both in Heav'n and Earth to do thy will

---

3 **perverted.**

12 **still** always.

---

48 **rests** remains.

49 **denounc't** formally threatened.

Supreme, that thou in mee thy Son belov'd 70
Mayst ever rest well pleas'd. I go to judge
On Earth these thy transgressors, but thou
    know'st,
Whoever judg'd, the worse on mee must 'light,
When time shall be, for so I undertook
Before thee; and not repenting, this obtain 75
Of right, that I may mitigate their doom
On me deriv'd,° yet I shall temper so
Justice with mercy, as may illústrate° most
Them° fully satisfied, and thee appease.
Attendance none shall need, nor Train, where 80
    none
Are to behold the Judgement, but he judg'd,
Those two; the third best absent is condemn'd,
Convict by flight, and Rebel to all Law
Conviction° to the serpent none belongs."
    Thus saying, from his radiant Seat he rose 85
Of high collateral glory: him Thrones and
    Powers,
Princedoms, and Dominations ministrant
Accompanied to Heaven Gate, from whence
Eden and all the Coast in prospect lay.
Down he descended straight; the speed of Gods 90
Time counts not, though with swiftest minutes
    wing'd.
Now was the Sun in Western cadence° low
From Noon, and gentle Airs due at their hour
To fan the Earth now wak'd, and usher in
The Ev'ning cool when he from wrath more cool 95
Came the mild Judge and Intercessor both
To sentence Man: the voice of God they heard
Now walking in the Garden, by soft winds
Brought to their Ears, while day declin'd, they
    heard,
And from his presence hid themselves among 100
The thickest Trees, both Man and Wife, till God

Approaching, thus to Adam call'd aloud.
    "Where art thou Adam, wont with joy to meet
My coming seen far off? I miss thee here,
Not pleas'd, thus entertain'd with solitude, 105
Where obvious° duty erewhile appear'd
    unsought:
Or come I less conspicuous, or what change
Absents thee, or what chance detains? Come
    forth."
He came, and with him Eve, more loath, though
    first
To offend, discount'nanc't both, and 110
    discompos'd;
Love was not in their looks, either to God
Or to each other, but apparent° guilt,
And shame, and perturbation, and despair,
Anger, and obstinacy, and hate, and guile.
When Adam falt'ring long, thus answer'd brief. 115
    "I heard thee in the Garden, and of thy voice
Afraid, being naked, hid myself." To whom
The gracious Judge without revile repli'd.
"My voice thou oft hast heard, and hast not fear'd,
But still rejoic't, how is it now become 120
So dreadful to thee? that thou are naked, who
Hath told thee? has thou eaten of the Tree
Whereof I gave thee charge thou shouldst not eat?"
    To whom thus Adam sore beset repli'd.
"O Heav'n! in evil strait this day I stand 125
Before my Judge, either to undergo
Myself the total Crime, or to accuse
My other self, the partner of my life;
Whose failing, while her Faith to me remains,
I should conceal, and not expose to blame 130
By my complaint; but strict necessity
Subdues me, and calamitous constraint,
Lest on my head both sin and punishment,
However insupportable, be all
Devolv'd; though should I hold my peace, yet thou 135
Wouldst easily detect what I conceal.
This Woman whom thou mad'st to be my help,
And gav'st me as thy perfect gift, so good,
So fit, so ácceptáble, so Divine,

---

77 **deriv'd** brought down, diverted.

78 **illústrate** set in the best light.

79 **Them** justice and mercy.

84 **Conviction** proof of guilt.

92 **cadence** falling (and with the musical hint taken up in "Airs due at their hour" and "usher in").

---

106 **obvious** coming forward to meet.

112 **apparent** manifest.

That from her hand I could suspect no ill,
And what she did, whatever in itself,
Her doing seem'd to justify the deed;
See gave me of the Tree, and I did eat."
      To whom the sovran Presence thus repli'd.
"Was shee thy God, that her thou didst obey   145
Before his voice, or was shee made thy guide,
Superior, or but equal, that to her
Thou didst resign thy Manhood, and the Place
Wherein God set thee above her made of thee,
And for thee, whose perfection far excell'd   150
Hers in all real dignity: Adorn'd
She was indeed, and lovely to attract
Thy Love, not thy Subjection, and her Gifts
Were such as under Government well seem'd,
Unseemly to bear rule, which was thy part   155
And person, hadst thou known thyself aright."
      So having said, he thus to Eve in few:
"Say Woman, what is this which thou hast done?"
      To whom sad Eve with shame nigh
            overwhelm'd
Confessing soon, yet not before her Judge   160
Bold or loquacious, thus abasht repli'd.
      "The Serpent me beguil'd and I did eat."
      Which when the Lord God heard, without
            delay
To Judgment he proceeded on th'accused
Serpent though brute, unable° to transfer   165
The Guilt on him who made him instrument
Of mischief, and polluted from the end
Of his Creation; justly then accurst,
As vitiated in Nature: more to know
Concern'd not Man (since he no further knew)   170
Nor alter'd his offence; yet God at last
To Satan first in sin his doom appli'd,
Though in mysterious terms, judg'd as then best:
And on the Serpent thus his curse let fall.
      "Because thou hast done this, thou are accurst   175

Above all Cattle, each Beast of the Field;   140
Upon thy Belly grovelling thou shalt go,
And dust shalt eat all the days of they Life.
Between Thee and the Woman I will put
Enmity, and between thine and her Seed;   180
Her Seed shall bruise thy head, thou bruise his
      heel."
      So spake this Oracle, then verifi'd
When Jesus son of Mary second Eve,
Saw Satan fall like Lightning down from Heav'n,
Prince of the Air; then rising from his Grave   185
Spoil'd Principalities and Powers, triumpht
In open show, and with ascension bright
Captivity led captive through the Air,
The Realm itself of Satan long usurpt,
Whom he shall tread at last under our feet;   190
Ev'n hee who now foretold his fatal bruise,
And to the Woman thus his Sentence turn'd.
      "Thy sorrow I will greatly multiply
By thy Conception; Children thou shalt bring
In sorrow forth, and to thy Husband's will   195
Thine shall submit, hee over thee shall rule."
      On Adam last thus judgement he pronounc'd.
"Because thou hast heark'n'd to the voice of thy
      Wife,
And eaten of the Tree concerning which
I charg'd thee, saying: Thou shalt not eat thereof,   200
Curs'd is the ground for thy sake, thou in sorrow
Shalt eat thereof all the days of thy Life;
Thorns also and Thistles it shall bring thee forth
Unbid, and thou shalt eat th'Herb of the Field,
In the sweat of thy Face shalt thou eat Bread,   205
Till thou return unto the ground, for thou
Out of the ground wast taken, know thy Birth,
"of dust thou art, and shalt to dust return."

*   *   *

---

165 **unable** the serpent being powerless to . . .

Scientific Awakening
Creative Method

> Method is like a pathway, and if the pathway leads in the right direction, you will eventually get to the truth. . . . Genius is the ability to run quickly. However if a genius is on the wrong pathway, he will never be able to come to the truth since he will just move more quickly in the wrong direction.
>
> —Sir Francis Bacon

■ Thinking Directionally

We began this volume with the Renaissance and noted that one of the most important features of the Renaissance was looking backward to the ancient Greeks and Romans. Those ancient societies were viewed as the ideals—times of culture, learning, happiness, and creativity. The people of the Renaissance, tired from years of limited thinking and restricted actions, tried to recapture the freedom and culture that they believed existed in their ancient past. They were successful, and felt as though light was breaking into their world anew. They called the time of restrictions the Dark Ages and the time of rebirth the Renaissance.

The Protestant Reformation was similarly a break with the immediate past—times of total control by the Catholic Church—and was, therefore, consistent with the Renaissance ideas of the times. Protestant leaders were also seeking the ancient truths. The truths sought were those originally given by Christ, which Protestants felt had been corrupted by the Catholic Church. Even Catholics generally agreed that reform was necessary, and a series of church councils in Trent sought to make those changes. But these reforms of the Catholic Church were too late to stop the Northern Europeans from breaking away. The Protestant break was also fueled by politics and cultural differences. These could not be altered or even strongly influenced by the reforms made at the Councils of Trent.

Two interrelated concepts are therefore characteristic of the Renaissance period. The first is a yearning for the glories of the ancient Greeks and Romans. The second is a reevaluation of the position of God and the church. These two concepts are related by the way Renaissance people thought about individuals and the interactions between society and the individual. Some felt that individual thinking could be and should be consistent with organizational thinking, especially the church. Others felt that individual thinking was superior to rules of the church and society. Both groups elevated the individual, but the second group was more radical. This second group tended to follow Protestantism.

With the dawning of the seventeenth century, more than a century after the Renaissance began and more than 80 years after Luther's 95 theses were posted, thinking took a new direction. We saw this new direction subtly demonstrated when the absolute monarchs developed strong visions of the future for their countries that did not, necessarily, coincide with or emulate the past. They were willing to make radical departures and go in directions never known before. An example is when, for self interest, Catholic France entered the religious Thirty Years War on the side of the Protestants. We perceive a similar shift in the direction of thinking in Baroque art forms. The musicians and artists were willing to depart from the classical past and explore new forms, new instruments, and new sponsorships.

The origins and development of opera give an interesting example of the transition from Renaissance to Baroque periods. Opera's origin was clearly the result of Renaissance thinking—it was an attempt to duplicate the full drama of ancient Greece. However, its implementation quickly became dramatic, elaborate, and complex—characteristics that were Baroque. Was there a change in thinking? Yes! As can be seen in the opera example, this change seemed natural and occurred gradually. However, when viewed in retrospect, the changes between Renaissance and Baroque thinking are quite profound.

If we list the characteristics that constituted the Baroque style—elaborateness, complexity, desires to impress with grandeur, dramatic emotion, and technical virtuosity—we note that these would have been abhorrent to the ancient Greeks, who loved simplicity, symmetry, and restraint. We can now see, therefore, that even though the shift in style from the Renaissance to the Baroque was gradual, it was very real. Such a shift would have occurred only as

the result of, or at least accompanied by, a shift in thinking. The Renaissance was focused on the past. The Baroque was focused on a desire to create a change, a desire to fulfill a vision of the future. In fact, one way to mark the end of the Renaissance is to note whether thinking is still focused on the ancient past or has shifted to the future.

We will now, in this chapter, discuss changes in science. More than any other field of civilization, science broke clearly and cleanly from the ancient past. Whereas art forms evolved, science dramatically rejected the teachings and methods of the past. While the changes in science began in the Renaissance, those early changes were obviously restricted by the backward focus of Renaissance thinking. The break with the past could only occur in the environment of change that was emerging at the beginning of the seventeenth century—just about the same time we have seen the Baroque style entering art. These two changes—art and science—both reflected society's willingness to accept new directions of thinking.

We should not, however, think that seventeenth century scientists broke with all concepts of the past. Indeed, their break was chiefly focused on what they saw as errors of past methods of discovering the nature of the world. They did not, for example, reject religion. On the contrary, most of the scientists we will discuss strongly professed a belief in God and sought to glorify Him by revealing His works through their newly developing method. In this regard, a comparison of a Renaissance naturalist and a Baroque scientist (a subtle but, we believe, important distinction in terminology) might go something like this when asked the question, "Why is grass green?" The Renaissance naturalist would say, "Grass is green because God made it so." The Baroque scientist might say, "Grass has a chemical that reflects light of a certain wavelength that is detected by our eyes as a green color, and all of that is because God made it so." The new thinking is consistently Baroque—complex, elaborate, illustrative of personal technical ability, grand, and full of praise for God.

Baroque painting expanded previous concepts of realism, light, perspective, positioning, and beauty beyond the limits previously set. Baroque music expanded concepts of scales, temperament, instruments, forms, dramatic effect, and composer virtuosity. Similarly, the new science expanded previous concepts of the universe, methods of thinking, experimentation, and linkages to mathematics beyond what had been previously accepted.

The change in science, called the **Scientific Awakening,** would become increasingly important. As the seventeenth century dawned, science was little more than an interesting hobby for some intellectuals. By the end of the seventeenth century, it would be important in the lives of most educated people. By the end of the eighteenth century, science and its sister, technology, would dominate society.

Science and technology both reinforced the new direction in thinking. They inherently look forward, largely because they are accumulative in knowledge. As their influence broadened, society was forced to accept the notion of accumulating new knowledge. However, especially in the case of theological knowledge, there was tremendous resistance because the Church believed that all the knowledge required for salvation was known and new knowledge, especially in theology, could not be obtained. This, and other factors that we will discuss, led to a separation of science and religion.

Some have suggested, and we agree, that because of the shift in societal thinking from backward to forward that occurred in the seventeenth century, a new type of world began. From this period of time onward, society has continuously favored forward thinking. This is a fundamental characteristic of what has been called the **Modern World.** The origins of this Modern World can be marked from the seventeenth century. The strongest influence in making that shift in direction was science. Now we will briefly consider the history of science.

■ When Science Went to Sleep: Classical and Medieval Science

The Scientific Awakening was the historical era where people began to define a new scientific method and use it in their search for knowledge about the world. During this period, scientists began to question the ideas of the ancient scientists and philosophers and began to discover that these supposedly infallible sources were sometimes wrong. Eventually, scientists and nonscientists began to believe that all truth could be discovered once mankind learned all of the laws and principles of the natural world. This change of attitude directly contributed to the Enlightenment, the Industrial Revolution, and, eventually, to a loss of faith by some.

To understand how science awoke, we need to first see how it began and then how it went to sleep. This is the story of science in the ancient Greek past and into the medieval world.

In the ancient world of Classical Greece and Rome, there was no distinction between the disciplines of science, philosophy, and theology. To the classical scholars and thinkers these three disciplines were one because they all dealt with the discovery of truth. The earliest scientists (called natural philosophers), such as Thales, Democritus, and Pythagoras, sought to find the unchanging principles of the world because they believed that these unchanging principles would lead them to make generalizations about the entire world around them. Thales, often considered the first scientist, believed that by careful investigation, the nature of all things could be revealed. In particular, Thales saw water in the earth, seas, and clouds, and also saw it moving freely between these states. He saw water in humans and animals and realized that water was critical for life. Therefore, for Thales, the fundamental of all nature was water.

Democritus believed that no single material, like water, was fundamental. Rather, he believed that the fundamental of all materials was some very small entity. He thought that this very small entity could not be divided. He therefore called it an *atom* (which means "non-divisible") and believed that atoms made up all materials.

Pythagoras saw many relationships in nature that could be expressed as ratios of small, whole numbers. He built these relationships into a system of mathematics that gave order and simplicity to the world. For him, these mathematical relationships were the fundamentals of nature.

Later, the great philosophers, Plato and Aristotle, discussed their views on the fundamentals of nature and, in some cases, criticized the natural philosophers who preceded them. Because of the overwhelming influence of Plato and Aristotle on later thinking, their views of natural philosophy became dominant, both in their own times and for several succeeding centuries. Plato believed that the ultimate truth was not a physical thing but, rather, an idea or theoretical concept of what something really was. He called this fundamental idea or concept a **Form.** For Plato, Forms existed before the world was created and, in fact, were the concepts on which reality was modeled. However, the real fabrication of things could never be as perfect as the Form and so we see only shadows of reality in our physical existence. Nevertheless, with contemplation and reasoning, the Forms could be understood. Plato therefore rejected the idea of Thales that water was the fundamental. Plato also rejected the concept of Democritus that small, but real, atoms were the fundamental. However, Pythagoras' concept of mathematics was acceptable to Plato because math, like the Form, was fundamentally theoretical and did not depend on reality, although it described reality.

Aristotle differed somewhat from Plato in his concept of the true nature of the natural world. Aristotle accepted that there was a true Form for things, but he believed that Plato's rejection of any method except philosophy for discovering truth was overly restrictive. Aristotle thought that the real, physical world could be investigated to reveal the secrets of Nature. He even proposed a method for doing that investigation. In Aristotle's method, a real object would be investigated to determine four key causes which determined the nature of the object being investigated. The four causes were the following:

1. *The Material Cause:* What is the object made of?
2. *The Formal Cause:* What is the Form of the object, that is, what is its fundamental nature?
3. *The Efficient Cause:* What caused the object to be in the shape it is currently in?

4. *The Final Cause:* What is the end or motivation of the object or of the power that controls the object?

Because Aristotle believed in the ultimate order of the universe, he trusted implicitly in the linkage of cause and effect. Therefore, the true nature of things could be determined as a result of their causes. He would see, for instance, that the beautiful marble sculpture of the *Discus Thrower* would have marble as the material cause, a man throwing a discus as the formal cause, the work of the sculptor as the efficient cause, and, perhaps, delight for aesthetic beauty as the final cause. Today, this last question—the final cause—would be considered nonscientific.

For Aristotle and those who followed him, the final cause was critically important to determining the true nature of something. For instance, what is the final cause of a stone? Aristotle would reason that because a stone is part of the Earth, one of the four elements accepted by Aristotle, the stone's natural (preferred) state would be when it was united with other elements of Earth. Therefore, the cause of a stone falling from a height to the Earth was its inherent motivation to be associated with the Earth. In other words, the stone would fall because its nature would be to unite with the Earth, and this motivation was the force or cause for its falling behavior.

Aristotle then looked to the heavens and noted the moon, sun, planets, and stars. Why did these not fall to the Earth? He reasoned that they did not fall because they were made of a material that was not earth. In fact, because he did not see them change in their natures, he believed that they were not made of any of the four elements: earth, air, fire, and water. Therefore, these heavenly objects must be made of a fifth element, called *quintessence* (literally meaning "fifth element"). Because they do not change, this fifth element must be perfect (since all nonperfect things change). Aristotle believed in a god and believed that he would also be made of quintessence.

We might ask, "Why did Aristotle believe that reality was composed of only four elements?" That came from logic that was buttressed, but not superceded, by experience. In this, Aristotle was much like Thales. Aristotle would look at the world and seek understanding, but he believed that logic was the final arbiter of truth. Using this premise as a basis for his thinking, he refused to perform experiments but would only observe nature. He felt that experiments would necessarily change nature and would, therefore, create an unnatural situation that would not be consistent with reality. Such an unnatural situation might interfere with logical conclusions. One example of a "truth" discovered via this method was that the Earth was composed of four basic elements (a minor expansion on the fundamentals of Thales), all of which were known to be imperfect because they changed. This belief was accepted as "scientific fact" for over a thousand years.

Another scientific precedent that was established by the great thinkers of the classical era was that there was little separation between physics (the study of the natural world) and metaphysics (what is real or true). To them, the basic purpose of science/philosophy was to discover basic truths, not to understand the mechanics of the natural world. The details of nature were not viewed as being important except as they led to discovery of fundamental truths, or the Form. These attitudes regarding science went almost completely unquestioned and unchanged until the end of the medieval period.

It is not hard for us to see how the concepts of Plato and Aristotle were used by early Christian church leaders and adapted to Christian thinking. For example, a Christian thinker who thought God was unknowable except by some method other than physical investigation might link God with Plato's concept of the Form. In fact, the Greek word often used to describe Form was *logos,* which is the same word used in the original Greek writing of the first chapter of the Gospel of John to describe the premortal Christ. *Logos* is translated in the King James Version as "word."

Similarly, if an early Christian writer believed that God was perfect and unchanging, he would readily accept Aristotle's statement that God must be made of some perfect element that could not be understood by humans. That same Christian scholar might also see the hand of God as the cause of the creation of the earth and of humans. Our very existence, therefore, would be because God willed it, as a sculptor might will the existence of a statue, and our final cause or purpose for existence would be to fulfill God's plan.

Indeed, the medieval Christian church accepted the thinking of Plato and Aristotle as the philosophical basis of Christian doctrine. How then could medieval natural philosophers deviate from the teachings of Plato and Aristotle in thinking about the world around them? How could they deviate from using Aristotle's method of inquiry? To do so would be to call into question the basic tenets of the Christian theology. That could not be done in an environment in which the church was overwhelmingly dominant!

As a result, the nature of scientific inquiry in late antiquity and the Middle Ages became an exercise in determining the details of God's plan and not the details of nature. It was the cause of things that was most important, and that was basically a question of theology. We see, therefore, why medieval universities taught concepts from the past in undergraduate studies and then featured theology as the ultimate graduate study. (The other graduate studies—medicine and law—were largely focused on developing knowledge of the past and applying that knowledge to current situations.) No one was really looking to the future or concerned about accumulating new knowledge. We see, therefore, that science was asleep!

■ Science, Technology, and Theory

The Scientific Awakening was not only a time of discovery, but also a time for defining the principles and terms that make up the academic discipline of science. One of the key changes made during the Scientific Awakening was learning the difference, for the first time, between truth and theory. **Theory** is an explanation for observed events and serves as a paradigm for acquiring and interpreting additional knowledge. The scientists during the Scientific Awakening came to understand that classical and medieval science, with its careful use of observation and logic, may not have discovered truth but merely theorized on what was true. Scientists during the Scientific Awakening realized for the first time that scientists *hope* that their theories are "true" but realize that additional knowledge may force them to change their perceptions of the nature of truth. This difference is a key to the progress of science because it allows for continued questioning and understanding, whereas once the classical or medieval model reached a conclusion (through logic), it was accepted as truth and rarely questioned again. This change further explains why science prior to the Scientific Awakening always looked backward and why modern science looks forward, continuing to evolve and discover.

Another important distinction made during the Scientific Awakening was an understanding of the difference between science and technology and, ultimately, a linkage between the two. Today we can give the following definitions: **Science** *is the process of understanding the environment and of organizing that knowledge.* **Technology** *is the combination of skill and creativity by which people master their environment.* The two are related but are not the same.

Science is all about knowledge. It seeks to understand nature, and to arrange our understanding in an orderly way so that additional knowledge can be acquired and understood. Therefore, pursuits like the study of the motion of celestial bodies and classification of biological species were pure science.

Progress in improving the world has almost always been done with technology, not science. Throughout history, many important and useful advancements in agriculture, metallurgy, shipbuilding, and architecture were developed long before science could explain the phenomena and rules involved. Thus, throughout ancient and medieval times, technology had developed independent of science.

Even if it was not fully understood, the conceptual separation of science and technology had existed since the time of ancient Greece. Archimedes was more proud of his theoretical mathematical findings than the many machines he invented. This feeling of scientific superiority probably originated in ancient Greece with the views of both Pythagoras and Plato, who believed that the concept of math/theory/Form lies at the heart of everything real and that any physical implementation is inferior. The separation of science and technology was exacerbated in the Middle Ages because the universities focused on theory/science while the craftsmen and guilds controlled technology. This support of the universities for theory only reinforced the "superiority" of science over technology because universities were, largely, populated by the upper levels of society and craftsmen were considered to be of an inferior class.

During the Middle Ages, science became tied to religion and separated from the natural world. With only a few exceptions, the study of what we would consider to be the normal realm of science was limited to investigations of what God had said about the world and the implications of those statements on an understanding of nature. Therefore, scientific investigations, in the sense that we know it today, stopped.

Technology was continually developed and improved, despite the long stagnation of science, for two important reasons. First, technology was never seen to be in conflict with "truth" since technology was judged by how well it accomplished the task at hand not by whether it was "true." Second, the development of science was held back by the idea that the ancient philosophers had already discovered "truth," so new truths through science were seen as conflicting with those already accepted. This belief was strongly reinforced when the Catholic Church adopted many of the ancient concepts as doctrine.

Technology was highly creative. It was, largely, based on the intuition of the person developing the technology. There were few scientific guides to their work. Therefore, they intuitively, we might call it cleverly, sought ways to solve the problems they had encountered. Frequently these intuitive ideas would draw from experience gained in some field that was not directly connected to the problem at hand. Hence, technologists then, and now, tend to have a strong right-brain orientation.

However, the concept of continuous improvement is inherent in technology, and that created an attitude within society that began to suggest that knowledge itself (widely accepted truth) might also be subject to improvement. People also began to realize that some new understanding (science), not related to the knowledge of the past, was important to improvements that technology had made in the world. For example, the alloys used in Gutenberg's new printing method had never existed before. In art, the concepts of perspective and light, which were helpful to Renaissance painters, were new. Likewise, many concepts in music, new instruments, and new scale tunings, had never been explored before.

The Scientific Awakening was also a critical and pivotal time because science, at least in a few fields of inquiry, caught up with technology and the two disciplines began to be intertwined more and more often. One of the initial areas of integration of science and technology was within scientific experiments themselves. Several of the prominent scientists of the era, such as Galileo and Francis Bacon, promoted experimentation to solve scientific problems. Experimentation usually required some craft capability to make the experimental devices. For example, Galileo became personally skilled in making telescopes. He used that skill to create his experimental devices and also to manufacture telescopes which became an important way for him to make money.

Later, especially in fields such as optics and chemistry, experimental scientists made discoveries that led directly to technological improvements in society. In some of these fields, such as alchemy, the science was in error and was directing technology to search in the wrong directions for ways to accomplish the desired tasks. Hence, even in error, the linkage between technology and science was becoming important.

As the benefits of experimentation became more obvious, the longstanding reluctance to question the methods and findings of Plato and Aristotle began to erode. The concept was put forth that people should look for knowledge, not in books or pure logic, but in things themselves, thus further elevating experimentalism and diminishing pure logic.

Eventually, the universities began to accept experimental disciplines and researchers. Science and technology have been linked ever since. This linkage was one of the fundamental objectives of some scientists in the early Scientific Awakening. Francis Bacon, who we will study later in detail, said that he wanted to bring about "the true and lawful marriage of the empirical and rational faculties, the unkind and ill-starred separation of which has thrown into confusion all the affairs of the human family."

The Scientific Awakening was the product of the work, insight, and discovery of many people. However, the lives and careers of six scientists were especially important in developing the scientific method and in laying the foundation for modern science. Furthermore, as their careers spanned the entire era, a look at their lives and work will also outline the development and evolution of the entire Scientific Awakening.

■ Nicolas Copernicus

Nicolas Copernicus (1473–1543) lived before the formal Scientific Awakening. His work illustrates some of the problems faced by scientific thinkers in his day. His life is an interesting contrast between the constraints of medieval ideology and the lure of scientific discovery. The conflict between these two forces dominated much of Copernicus's life, and it was only at the cusp of death that he felt able to publicly and fully reveal his scientific theory.

Nicolas Copernicus was born in Poland, the son of a prosperous merchant. He was orphaned at age 11 and was then raised by his uncle, the Catholic bishop of Poland. Copernicus attended the University of Krakow as an undergraduate and then went to Italy, where he studied at three different universities and earned doctoral degrees in both theology and medicine.

After he finished his studies, Copernicus returned to Poland, where his uncle employed him as canon. (A canon is a church official who oversees the church's lands and buildings.) The position was perfect for Copernicus, as it left him considerable free time for his hobby—scientific study. Copernicus also worked as his uncle's personal physician and soon earned a reputation as an excellent doctor. Thus, Copernicus was often in demand as a physician to the rich and powerful in Poland. His medical training probably gave Copernicus good craft skills, since much of medicine included mixing potions and performing surgeries.

Although Copernicus's scientific training was in medicine, most of his personal scientific time was spent in the field of astronomy. Copernicus invented a device that helped him use triangulation to take sightings of the planets and stars. Using this device, Copernicus was able to more accurately measure the positions of the various planets and stars than had heretofore been possible. (Note that this ability to improve science because of technology is an example of the merging of science and technology we discussed previously.)

His sightings led Copernicus to doubt the data of the great ancient astronomer, **Ptolemy.** Copernicus noticed that Ptolemy was often slightly off in his prediction of where the planets should be at some given time. The Ptolemaic model put the Earth at the center of the universe, with the celestial bodies rotating around the Earth.

Even in the days of Ptolemy (about 150 A.D.), the errors in the simple celestial model proposed by Aristotle (all celestial bodies move around the Earth in perfect spheres) were apparent. Since, according to Aristotle, heavenly bodies were supposedly perfect and since the sphere is the most perfect geometric shape, Ptolemy kept the idea of circular orbits. To correct for the discrepancies that these circular orbits and the concept of an earth-centered universe introduced, Ptolemy suggested that some heavenly bodies moved simultaneously on a second, smaller circular orbit. These second orbits were called *epicycles.* To make the Aristotelian model and actual data agree to the accuracy known at the time, Ptolemy had only to continue to increase the number of epicycles that a celestial body had in its orbit. This could be done by changing the diameter of the epicycle. Eventually, because of the high number of epicycles required, calculations of celestial positions became a nearly impossible task. The Ptolemaic model of the universe is shown in Figure 34.1.

Copernicus loved to make celestial calculations and, of course, used the Ptolemaic model as his basis. However, at this point in his investigations, Copernicus was not sure if the deviations he found between data and calculated positions were

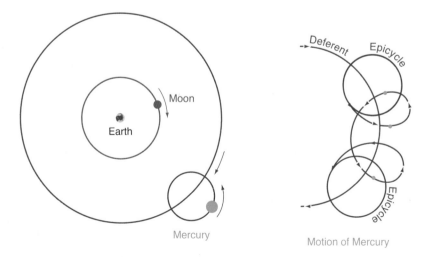

Ptolemaic Model of the Universe

Figure 34.1 ■ *Ptolemaic model of the universe.*

from errors in calculations or errors in the Ptolemaic model. He brilliantly devised a new model that vastly simplified the calculations. This new model put the sun at the center of the universe with the planets, including Earth, rotating around it. A statue of Copernicus holding a model of his solar system is shown in Figure 34.2. This model also required that the Earth rotate on its axis each day. Copernicus did not specifically state that this model was the way the heavens actually were, but, rather, suggested the model as a means for simplifying calculations.

Copernicus published a short paper describing this model. It was greeted enthusiastically in some quarters but was generally attacked because few scholars took the paper as merely a model for calculation. They saw it as a model of what actually was. Although the objections were from all sides, we can group them conveniently according to the nature of the criticizing groups.

Copernicus's heliocentric (sun-centered) universe was unpopular with religious figures of all denominations because it seemed to contradict scripture. The Old Testament says that Joshua commanded the sun to stop in the sky, but, according to Copernicus's model, it would have had to be the Earth and not the sun that stopped moving. (Joshua 10:13 states, *"And the sun stood still, and the moon stayed, until the people had avenged themselves upon their enemies. Is not this written in the book of Jasher? So the sun stood still in the midst of heaven, and hasted not to go down about a whole day."*)

The Protestants, who appealed to scriptural authority more than did the Catholics, had an especially difficult time accepting Copernicus's idea. Martin Luther himself said,

People give ear to an upstart astrologer who strove to show that the earth revolves, not the heavens or the firmament, the sun and the moon. Whosoever wishes to appear clever must devise some new system which of all systems, of course, is the very best. This fool wishes to reverse the entire science of astronomy; but Sacred Scripture tells us that Josue (Joshua) commanded the sun to stand still, and not the earth.

Aristotelians had specific objections to Copernicus's heliocentric universe for several reasons. First, Copernican theory seemed to contradict all direct experience observations. After all, one could see that the sun rises in the east and sets in the west. Second, Copernicus's idea was a violation of the Aristotelian theory of the nature of heavenly and earthly matter. According to Aristotle, earthly matter was changeable and heavenly matter was perfect and unchangeable. The sun, moon, planets, and stars all revolved around the Earth in orbits and were made of quintessence. However, if the Earth revolved around the sun, then it was also a heavenly body and should be made of the unchanging quintessence, which it obviously was not. Finally, no alternate system of physics was suggested by Copernicus to take the place of Aristotelian thought, whereas the concept of an earth-centered universe fit other Aristotelian concepts.

Even contemporary scientists objected to Copernicus's heliocentric universe. Many criticized Copernicus's idea because the speed of the rotation of the earth (about 1,000 miles per hour at the equator) would throw people from its surface. Also, the universe would have to be tremendously

Figure 34.2 ■ Statue of Copernicus holding a model of his helio-centro solar system. © 2010 by laurent dambies. Used under license of Shutterstock, Inc.

large to accommodate the orbits. (Copernicus agreed with this point, but saw nothing wrong in a very large universe.) Others criticized Copernicus's heliocentric universe because it still did not accurately predict the locations of the stars and planets. In fact, because the Copernican model still used circular orbits, it required many epicycles. (Elliptical orbits for the planets, which we now believe to be the accurate model, would not be proposed for another century.)

In light of the strong criticism, Copernicus quickly backed away from any further public discussion of his model. He was probably worried that he would lose his job as a canon of the church. Perhaps he was worried that he might bring criticism to his uncle, the cardinal, who probably exerted pressure on Copernicus to keep silent on this matter. He might even have been worried that church authorities would bring him before a church court (like the Inquisition) and punish him for heresy.

After his uncle's death and at the request of his friends, Copernicus wrote his concepts on astronomy in a book. However, Copernicus refused to publish the book, *De revolutionibus* (*Book of Revolutions*), until he was literally on his deathbed. In the preface to the book he asks the pope to give the new ideas a chance and to not be prematurely convinced by men who knew little mathematics and who used scriptures and their own interpretation to suppress investigation. Initially the Catholic Church was officially neutral regarding Copernicus's model because it was viewed as just a scientific theory that did not necessarily have any conflict of conscience. Copernicus's *Book of Revolutions* was not placed on the Catholic Church's index of banned books until 73 years after it was published, so Copernicus had little to fear in regards to persecution even if he had lived.

Copernicus was a man of the Renaissance and not of the Scientific Awakening. His thinking was original, but still based on ways to interpret the past. He seemed to be personally unwilling to challenge established thinking and thus falls short of the dramatic changes brought forth by Baroque thinkers. Nevertheless, he rightly has a place in the history of science because of his creative model and his clever experimental methods. Arthur Koestler has recog-

nized this legacy in his book *The Sleepwalkers:*

The heliocentric idea of the universe, crystallized in a system by Copernicus, and restated in modern form by Kepler, altered the climate of thought not by what it expressly stated, but by what it implied. Its implications were certainly not conscious in Copernicus' mind, and acted on his successors by equally insidious, subterranean channels. They were all negative, all destructive to the solid edifice of medieval philosophy, undermining the foundations on which it rested.

In other words, the successors of Copernicus received, from him, a kernel of truth about the heliocentric universe but subtly received some much more powerful ideas. These ideas suggested that the concepts of medieval natural science might be wrong. One of these successors, Galileo, took the heliocentric idea and, just as importantly, the ideas of possible errors in the knowledge of the world, beyond the timid step of Copernicus. We will see now what happened.

■ Galileo Galilei

Galileo Galilei was born in Pisa, Italy, in 1564 (21 years after the death of Copernicus). Galileo loved science and studied physics and astronomy, but his father steered him toward a career in medicine so that Galileo could support his two sisters and his brother (who was a musician). When his father died unexpectedly, Galileo made the decision to pursue a degree in science, but still honored his father's wishes by supporting his sisters and brother throughout much of his life.

Upon earning his degree, Galileo became a professor of science, originally at the University of Pisa and later at the University of Padua. His university career was very successful, both as a teacher and as a scientist. He often lectured to over one thousand students at a time and became famous for his in-class experiments. Galileo also had many papers widely published and he became famous throughout Europe.

Galileo's cleverness in experiments can be illustrated by work he did at the University of Pisa on the nature of pendulums. One day, while casually observing the swinging of the long chandeliers in the cathedral, he thought he detected an interesting phenomenon. He believed that the time it took a chandelier to swing through a complete back and forth cycle was the same, regardless of how fast the chandeliers were swinging (assuming that the lengths of the chains supporting the chandeliers were the same). He wanted to time the swinging of several chandeliers but, in his day before the invention of wristwatches, he wondered how he could time the swings. Creatively, he realized that by using his pulse as a clock, he could make the timing measurements he desired. (Would you have been as clever?) His observations allowed Galileo to formulate a theory on the movement of pendulums, which ironically served as the basis for making pendulum clocks.

Although Galileo's experiments were Aristotelian (he only observed natural consequences), Galileo did not hold Aristotle's views to be sacred, and many of his findings contradicted the traditional Aristotelian conclusions. Galileo also earned a reputation for being able to back his theories and experiments with mathematical explanations, thus helping to forge the link between mathematics and physics. Galileo said, *"Truth cannot be found in the book of Aristotle but in the book of Nature; and the book of Nature is written in the language of mathematics."*

Much of Galileo's work in physics disputed Aristotle's view of the natural state of earth, air, fire, and water. Aristotle had argued that the natural motion of fire and air was upward, while earth and water went downward. Because of their final cause, these elements were inherently animated to move toward their natural state. Galileo argued that the elements had no "natural state" and were completely inanimate unless acted on by some outside force, such as being blown by the wind or dropped by a person. Galileo then used experiments and mathematics to support his suppositions.

The famous legend of dropping weights from the tower of Pisa was just such an experiment. (Some scholars today doubt that the experiment was actually performed, but others support the story and give quite compelling evidence in its favor.) Whether factually true or not, the concept demonstrated is illustrative of Galileo's work. Aristotle's theory said that if stones of two different weights are dropped, the heavier stone will have more affinity for its natural state on the ground and will therefore fall faster than the lighter stone. Galileo asserted that both stones will fall at the same rate. The experiment was performed and Galileo's concept was proven to be correct (to within the measurement accuracy of the day).

In a broader sense, Galileo was continuing to lay the groundwork for the intellectual basis of the Scientific Awakening. He was attempting to prove that inanimate objects neither had a natural state they were trying to reclaim, as Aristotle had argued; nor were they endowed with any purpose from God. Science, according to Galileo, was not the purview of ancient philosophers or the clergy, but was its own discipline with its own set of rules and procedures. Truth, therefore, could not be reached by following the rules of philosophy or religion. Galileo wanted to separate the scriptures from discussions of natural science. He asserted,

God is the author of two great books—the book of scripture and the book of nature. These cannot be in conflict; so any apparent contradictions come from fallible human interpretations. . . . Scripture is a book about how to go to heaven; not a book about how heaven goes.

Galileo also made many discoveries in the field of astronomy. On a trip to Venice in 1609, Galileo saw a prototype of a microscope, invented just a few years earlier in Holland. When he returned to Padua, he built his own, modified it so that it would observe far objects rather than small objects, and began observing the movements of the planets and stars. Galileo made several discoveries with his telescope. He saw that the moon had imperfections on its surface, discovered Jupiter's moons and observed them orbiting the planet as seen in the sequence of sightings over several nights that is shown in Figure 34.3, and discovered sunspots and noticed that they, too, changed from time to time. All of these findings disproved the Aristotelian view of unchanging celestial bodies all circling the earth and convinced Galileo that Aristotle was wrong and that the Copernican view of the universe was correct.

Galileo came to the attention of the Inquisition because of his vigorous and open teaching of the Copernican model, which had recently been declared heretical by a committee of consultants convened to advise the Church on this matter. As we discussed previously, the Copernican view was widely criticized by several influential groups, including clergy. It seemed, at the time, to be an incorrect theory. Galileo wrote a long letter to the Vatican defending his views. Galileo was called before a prominent cardinal and admonished to stop writing and speaking in favor of the heliocentric (Copernican) theory. He was not, however, convicted of any wrongdoing.

Galileo was unsatisfied with the actions of the Vatican officials and felt they were ignoring an obvious truth. He continued to have discussions about the theory. Some of these discussions were with the Medici family in Florence, where he was the court scientist. (This was a prestigious position he obtained as a result of his impressive reputation in the scientific world.) Galileo became convinced that he should write a book about the theory. He apparently thought that he could get around the Church's prohibition of his teaching about the Copernican system by using a format for the book, *Dialogue Concerning the Two Chief World Systems,* in which three people discussed the nature of the heavenly bodies, thus giving voice to all of the sides of the debate. He would put his own views in the mouth of one of the characters, give another character quite logical questions and arguments, and then give a third person comments that the others would ridicule. He believed that the contrasts in these views would convince people of the truth of heliocentric theory, but preserve the supposedly neutral nature of his book.

However, Galileo made a serious error. By the time the book was published, a new pope had

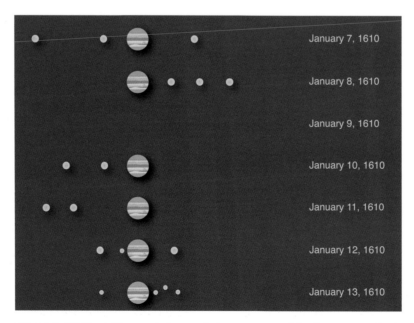

Figure 34.3 ▪ The sightings of the moons of Jupiter on various nights from which Galileo postulated the existence of Jupiter's moons. © *Kendall Hunt Publishing Company.*

been installed. That pope, Urban VIII, had lived in Florence and was present during several of the Medici family discussions on the theory. Galileo had used these family discussions as the basis for some of the discussions in the book and put some of the new pope's words into the mouth of the character who was criticized by the others. The pope was incensed.

Galileo was called to Rome in 1633 to face the Inquisition again. Galileo was tried for his refusal to submit to the Inquisition's previous ruling on his teaching, for views on the Copernican model of the universe, and also for supporting atomism (atomic theory), which the Inquisition took to be a repudiation of the transubstantiation of the Eucharist. The Inquisition found Galileo guilty of the crimes and required that he adjure (deny) the Copernican theory, recite the seven penitentiary psalms daily, remain permanently silent about the theory, and remain under house arrest. Galileo fulfilled his sentence although, reputedly, he was defiant to the end.

Some scholars in Galileo's day and today believe that his trial was about whether the views of the Catholic Church would take precedence over the views of science. These scholars generally see the result of the trial as a travesty and a futile effort of the Church to suppress scientific truth. Others look at Galileo's personality and his often quite offensive behavior. They assert that the trial was really about Galileo himself and his defiance of Church authority. For these latter scholars, the science dispute was related to the problem but not the heart of it.

One scholar, Jerome J. Langford, in his book, *Galileo, Science and the Church*, believed that both the Church and Galileo should have thought differently about science and religion:

Looking back, we see that two principles should have been considered by the theological judges of the new astronomy. First, the traditional interpretation was to be held unless solid reasons dictated otherwise. Second, in matters of pure physical science, the Scriptures are not the criterion for establishing one system or forbidding another, since
they do not teach science. The correct theological procedure would have been to combine these two principles into a practical and valid norm for solving what appear to be discrepancies between Scripture and science. Had this been done, the opinion that the Scriptures confirmed the sun's motion would have been held as more probable even after Galileo's discoveries. By staying within the realm of probability, there would have been room left for another interpretation which would have been permissible, though less probable, namely, that the Scripture texts in no way represented scientific affirmations and thus were irrelevant to the scientific question.

The Catholic Church may have won the battle against Galileo, but it made itself look quite foolish, especially in the eyes of the educated. Galileo's reputation as a scientist and a mathematician was already secured. The actions of the Catholic Church did nothing to discredit him or his views to a new generation of scientists (mostly in the Protestant north), who were already using Galileo's work as a starting point for their own discoveries.

Even as Galileo was struggling with the Church, another scientist, **Johannes Kepler,** had revised the Copernican model by proposing his three laws of planetary motion, thus solving the problems of the Copernican system. (Galileo, however, would not accept Kepler's ideas.) Kepler's three laws stated the following: (1) The orbits of the planets are ellipses, with the Sun at one focus of the ellipse. (2) The line joining the planet to the Sun sweeps out equal areas in equal times as the planet travels around the ellipse. (3) The ratio of the squares of the revolutionary periods for two planets is equal to the ratio of the cubes of their semimajor axes. These three laws are illustrated in Figure 34.4. We should note, interestingly, that Kepler was a strong believer in Pythagorean concepts of small whole numbers and was not satisfied with his findings until he found the third law, which reduces an important aspect of planetary motion to ratios of squares and cubes (which Kepler took to be equivalent to small whole numbers).

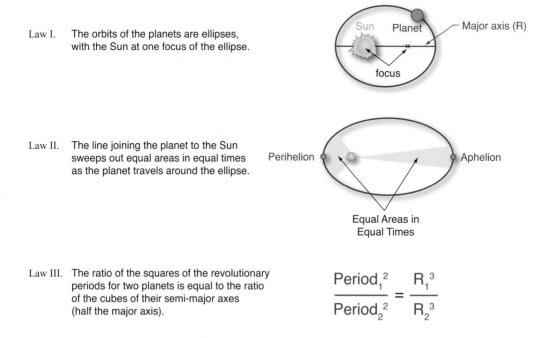

Law I. The orbits of the planets are ellipses, with the Sun at one focus of the ellipse.

Law II. The line joining the planet to the Sun sweeps out equal areas in equal times as the planet travels around the ellipse.

Law III. The ratio of the squares of the revolutionary periods for two planets is equal to the ratio of the cubes of their semi-major axes (half the major axis).

$$\frac{Period_1{}^2}{Period_2{}^2} = \frac{R_1{}^3}{R_2{}^3}$$

Figure 34.4 ■ *Kepler's Laws of Planetary Motion.*

■ Francis Bacon

Sir Francis Bacon (1561–1626) lived in England during the reigns of Elizabeth I and James I and was a contemporary of Galileo. Like Galileo, Bacon was critical of Aristotle, although Bacon criticized Aristotle's methods and Galileo criticized Aristotle's physics. Bacon promoted experimentation as a means of discovering truth and disagreed with Aristotle's observational-only approach to science. Aristotle felt that any experimentation would manipulate the natural world and would alter the result and skew truth. Bacon argued that Aristotle's method allowed too many variables to exist and the observer could never be sure of the true cause and effect. Truth, Bacon said, can best be found via careful experimentation where all of the variables can be controlled so that true cause and effect can be known. Bacon then devoted his work to the development and establishment of a new scientific method as a means to conduct experimental science without unduly influencing the results.

Bacon's experimental method led to an important philosophical difference from Aristotle.

Aristotle began his scientific examinations by logically determining what he expected to find. For instance, Aristotle reasoned that God and all that surrounded Him were perfect; God lived in the heavens; therefore, the heavens must be perfect. For Aristotle, the heavens were the moon, sun, planets, and stars. Therefore, all of these must be perfect. Since the sphere is the most perfect shape, all of these must travel in spherical orbits. Also, since perfect things cannot change, all of these must be unchanging. Therefore, the Earth, which obviously changes, must be below all of these perfect spheres. Within this framework, Aristotle then made observations of the heavens and, because he could see no changes in them, he concluded that his assumptions about perfection and the heavens were correct. This method of thinking is called **deductive reasoning.** That is, you start with global assumptions developed by logic and then make observations to confirm your assumptions.

Bacon's experimental method was the opposite. It is called **inductive reasoning.** In this method you start with no assumptions whatever. You perform experiments that give small tidbits of information. Gradually, after many different experiments that each add some small amount of knowledge, you are able to draw global conclusions based on the data you have collected. As Bacon said, *"If you start with certainties you will end in doubts, but if you begin with doubts, you will end with certainties."*

Bacon laid out the foundations for the scientific method in his book *Novum Organum,* written in 1620. The title of the book translates from Latin as "The New Instrument," and Bacon intended the method he proposed in *Novum Organum* to replace the old instrument (method) of science set forth by Aristotle. We can now appreciate more fully the quotation given at the beginning of this chapter about pathways. Bacon felt that the world had gone down the wrong pathway by following Aristotle. Bacon recognized Aristotle's genius (it was Aristotle that Bacon referred to in the quote as the genius), but wanted people to realize that even geniuses can be wrong. Their ability is to move quickly down a chosen path and not necessarily to choose the correct path.

Within *Novum Organum* Bacon discusses the importance of experimentation and explains that there are different types of experiments. *Luciferous* experiments require collecting data on natural phenomena and work to bring facts to light. (For example, Bacon did experiments to determine how well snow preserves food.) *Fructiferous* experiments resolve a conflict. (For example, Galileo did an experiment on dropping stones to see if heavy stones fall faster than light stones.) In *Novum Organum* Bacon also demonstrates the power of mathematics in the examination and/or analysis of the phenomenon. The basis for nearly all the steps and procedures for modern scientific practice are presented by Bacon in his book.

Bacon was highly practical and believed that scientific knowledge should be used for mankind's benefit and not just gathered for the sake of knowledge alone. (He was, therefore, a strong advocate of combining science and technology.) He gave a wonderful analogy on this point in which he compared some people to ants—they just build up a store of supplies (information or facts). Bacon criticized these people as not applying their knowledge. Other people are like spiders—they build a complex system that is beautiful to behold but is made from the spider's own internal stuff and not materials from nature. These spider materials are not related to the real world and therefore are still only theoretical and useless. Most praiseworthy, says Bacon, some people are like honeybees—they take materials from nature and convert them into materials that are useful for humankind. Bacon emphasized this idea when he said the following:

> *It is well to observe the force and virtue and consequence of inventions, and these are nowhere to be seen more conspicuously than in those three which were unknown to the ancients, and of which the origins, though recent, are obscure and inglorious; namely, printing, gunpowder, and the magnet. For the three have changed the whole face and state of things throughout the world.*

To Bacon, who was a politician as well as a scientist, anything that hindered mankind's discovery of any kind of truth was an obstacle to society's advancement and needed to be removed. Bacon warned that all false concepts and practices are "idols" that must be eliminated to obtain truth. (In this use of "idols" we see Bacon's inherent Protestant background and his belief that worshiping idols was a major impediment to finding true religion.) Bacon identified four impediments to progress based on truth which he called idols of the tribe, idols of the cave, idols of the marketplace, and idols of the theatre.

Idols of the tribe are obstacles to truth that come to all members of the human race. These idols exist as part of what being human is. For example, Bacon listed the universal tendency of people to oversimplify as an idol of the tribe. Another is the tendency to believe that the latest theory is the truest.

Idols of the cave are limitations placed on the acquisition of truth by a person's individual circumstances. Such limitations could be due to a person's education or socio-economic status. Idols of the cave could also be errors caused by individual idiosyncrasies and habits. For example, a person who naturally concentrates on how phenomena are alike might miss how they are different.

Idols of the marketplace are the obstacles to truth that arise from the nature of language itself. These can occur when people cannot communicate what they want to express accurately or when others unknowingly misunderstand them. These are obstacles to truth that arise because two people can never completely understand each other's minds; they can only read or hear words that are concrete expressions of abstract ideas. All of these idols were of concern to Bacon as he felt they limited not only scientific, but also political and religious truth.

Idols of the theatre are obstacles to truth imposed on people by their own society or culture. These could be social mores or philosophical systems that stand in the way of the patient, humble search for truth. Bacon saw the Aristotelian view of the universe to be an idol of the theatre because it came from the ancient Greek culture (as opposed to being inherent to human life) and it kept people from understanding the true nature of the world. Today, people who stridently advocate a particular concept, such as Marxism, eminism, or religion, whether good or bad, may also be in this category if their devotion to ideology obscures the search for truth.

Based on Bacon's concepts, the principles of the **Scientific Method** can be outlined as follows:

- Sensory perception **(empiricism)** is more reliable in examining nature than pure logic or theology.
- Experimentation, which is a manipulation of the natural world, is more powerful than just observation.
- The principle of cause and effect is inviolate.
- Theories should be interpreted from experimental results. Therefore, inductive reasoning is given precedence over deductive reasoning.
- Interpretation of data is to be unbiased.
- Well-supported and accepted theories become laws.

Francis Bacon devoted his life to the pursuit of establishing and demonstrating a method that was reliable as a means of discovering truth. He also advocated the intelligent use of these truths for the benefit of humankind. To this end, he wrote a book, *The New Atlantis,* wherein he laid out the plan for a perfect society. He advocated the use of scientific truths but warned against their use without charity.

He practiced what he preached and was nearly constantly engaged in an experiment of one kind or another for the benefit of society. In fact, Bacon brought about his own death when he caught pneumonia trying to conduct an experiment to see whether snow could be used as a means of preserving food. Bacon summarized his philosophy as follows: *"This is the foundation of all, for we are not to imagine or suppose, but to discover what nature does or may be made to do."*

After Galileo and Bacon, a new mindset was gelling throughout Europe. Scientists from Italy to England were actively using experimental (empirical) methods, including appropriate linkages to mathematics, to investigate the world around them. The similarity of activity of scientists can be seen through simultaneous and completely independent developments. Citing one example, devices to assist in calculating the trajectory of projectiles (cannon balls) and thereby assist gunners in setting the angles of their cannons were developed in Italy, England, and Holland at nearly the same time.

However, an important part of modern science was yet to be developed. We refer here to theoretical science. Its fundamental principles would be developed in the generation following Francis Bacon by a Frenchman, René Descartes. It is his interesting life and thinking which we will now explore.

■ René Descartes

Appropriately, the person who developed the fundamentals of theoretical science was a highly skilled mathematician and philosopher, as well as a scientist. **René Descartes** (1596–1650) first achieved notoriety by developing the basic principles of the branch of mathematics we now call analytical geometry. His initial idea for the basic principle of analytical geometry is a wonderful example of creativity. The story is worth telling here.

A sickly man, Descartes spent a great deal of time lying in his bed. One day, while lying in bed watching a housefly, he began to think about how he might describe the instantaneous position of the housefly in some mathematical way. He realized that, at any single moment, the position of the fly could be referenced to the walls and ceiling of the room. In fact, if perpendiculars were projected from the fly, the fly's position could be uniquely defined by the length of the perpendicular projections. He also determined that only three reference planes were needed—two adjacent walls and a ceiling or floor. Descartes then realized that he could establish one of the corners of the room as an origin and then relate the instantaneous position of the fly to magnitudes of the projections along the chosen walls and ceiling. The edges of the room, that is, the intersections of the walls and ceiling, form lines or axes of reference. This system, using these axes (x-axis, y-axis, z-axis), was named the *Cartesian coordinate system* after the Latin rendering of *Descartes*. He then realized that many analyses could be made based on the system he had developed. Note that the creation of analytical geometry required lateral thinking (connecting the movement of a fly to mathematics) and then also used linear thinking (the proofs of the minimum number of axes, etc.). This system, analytical geometry, has been a useful mathematical tool for presenting many scientific models and analyzing mathematical relationships.

When Descartes began to think about scientific principles, he rejected Aristotle's method just as Bacon had done. However, Descartes did not immediately accept the empirical and experimental method proposed by Bacon. Descartes had seen some instances in which the senses had been fooled and, therefore, could not always be trusted. Descartes wanted to reject any method that might lead to errors. He wanted to build his system for discovering truth on a principle that he knew to be completely and absolutely true at all times.

He proposed that the discovery of truth begin with a rejection of *all* previously held ideas. This attacked the foundation of the Aristotelian method, in which certain basic truths were accepted and all else was deduced from them. Descartes specifically urged that all Greek concepts be abandoned, since the Greeks had not resolved anything for sure. Descartes felt that this rejection of previous ideas prevented prejudices from being perpetuated in the analysis of new information.

When Descartes applied this technique to his own life, he realized that the ability to question all previous knowledge led him to the conclusion that the very process of questioning meant that he was real and intelligent. It was this insight that prompted Descartes to write in his great book on the scientific system, *Discourse on Method,* the following well-known axiom: *"Cogito Ergo Sum"* ("I think, therefore I am"). From this basis of understanding, Descartes developed other inescapable truths, including the proof of God's existence (we have thoughts about perfection that could only come into our minds from a perfect being, God). His method was not based on empiricism, as Bacon's was, but on reasoning and logic. However, it was not a deductive method in the Aristotelian sense since it began from the unknown and built to a theory. It became the basis of theoretical science.

Descartes also felt that the surest basis of all knowledge was mathematical since that came from universally undoubted truths. Using math as a basis, Descartes developed two of the theoretical underpinnings of modern science—**reductionism** and **determinism.**

According to his idea of reductionism, the world can be understood by reducing a phenomenon to its smallest parts. Descartes believed that the world was based on small particles, like atoms, which he called *corpuscles.* These corpuscles, Descartes said, followed definite laws that were laid down by the Creator. Descartes argued that once we obtained the mathematical basis of the truth (the nature and movement of the corpuscles), we could then proceed with mathematical axioms and self-evident propositions to shape the concept. While his theories regarding corpuscles may have been wrong (or true, as it is surprisingly close to modern atomic theory), his process of reductionism is often used in modern scientific study. Natural or complex phenomena are broken down into smaller pieces until reaching a piece small enough to be solved exactly. This is then studied and solved. That solution is then used to solve other small problems and then, cumulatively, bigger problems, so that the entire original problem can be reassembled from known segments. We can understand how the pieces interact, thus giving science a better understanding of the phenomena as a whole.

Descartes's other theoretical pillar for science is determinism, or the idea that the world can be described by mathematical laws that do not change. Descartes believed that all of nature had a mathematical basis and that if humans knew how to apply the rules of analytical geometry and algebra to solve nature's equations, it would result in certain knowledge. He envisioned God as the great watchmaker who built the world (clock) according to strict laws that can be described by mathematics. Determinism is still an integral part of the modern scientific climate, although some important exceptions have been noted in twentieth century science—but that is a discussion we will have later in this book.

As a corollary to the idea of determinism, Descartes believed in a dualist world. The world, according to Descartes, is divided into two realms—physical and spiritual (or intellectual). Only the physical is subject to investigation since the spirit cannot be described. Notice how this is similar to Plato's ideas regarding reality and Forms. Mankind cannot discover the Forms, just the sensory perception of their existence.

Despite Descartes's obvious belief in God, his assertion that *everything* must be doubted in order to find truth led the Catholic Church to ban his works. This occurred even though Descartes withheld publication of his most controversial book, *Le Monde,* when he heard that Galileo was in trouble with the Catholic Church. The Catholic Church ignored his proofs of God's existence in light of what the church viewed as his great denial of faith. (The proof of God's existence did not vi-

olate Descartes's dualism because he asserted that God could be proven to exist but could not be defined.) In order to avoid persecution in strongly Catholic France, Descartes moved first to Holland, and later to Sweden.

In Sweden, Descartes served as the personal instructor of Queen Christina. In one amusing exchange between Descartes and the queen, Descartes taught Christina that animals were mechanistic like a watch; therefore, having no souls, they could be described by mathematics. Queen Christina replied that she had never seen a watch give birth to a baby watch.

Moving to Sweden turned out to be a poor decision for Descartes, as his sickly nature, coupled with Sweden's cold weather, were hard on him, especially when he had to get out of bed early in the morning to fit into the queen's schedule. He caught pneumonia and died.

Descartes helped to more firmly ground science in mathematics and developed new kinds of math to help express scientific ideas. Descartes was the father of French science and gave it a decidedly theoretical orientation. Finally, Descartes's concepts of reductionism and determinism have become mainstays of modern scientific thought and practice.

■ Isaac Newton

England's **Isaac Newton** (1642–1727) is generally considered the greatest scientist to have ever lived. By Newton's lifetime, society had generally recognized the contributions of Galileo, Bacon, and Descartes, so it was not just modesty that prompted Newton to say, "If I have been able to see further, it is because I have stood on the shoulders of giants." However, Newton was the capstone to all of the significant scientific thought that had occurred before him, and his work completed and formalized many of the ideas of his predecessors. He brought together experimental and theoretical science, with appropriate mathematical linkages and proofs, and applied them to the most fundamental issues of the universe—gravity, motion, mass, inertia, and light. After Newton, scientists and the general public had confidence that, given time and effort, all of the secrets of the universe could be revealed through scientific inquiry.

During Newton's early lifetime the state of science, especially astronomy, was chaotic because so much was being questioned but little was resolved. The world was ripe for a foundation of physics and other strong, mathematically proven theories about the movement of heavenly bodies. This is the key to Newton's greatness: He proposed brilliant theories, which he completed with links to math. And when existing mathematics proved insufficient to express the truths he was discovering, he invented a new math, calculus, which could accurately represent reality with numbers and equations.

Using calculus, Newton was able to introduce the idea of modeling of real, dynamic systems. Galileo had understood that math was an important basis for science and used it as much as he could to support his theories, but Newton was able to create mathematical models that accurately represented reality and could explain natural events. For example, he reduced the astronomy problem to a point mass acting inside a force field and solved that problem. Then he compared his solution/model/ideal with the real world and made the correlation. This concept was creative genius.

Modern science relies heavily on the concept of modeling developed by Newton. Some phenomena are so complex or so difficult to perform experiments on that they can only be studied by **modeling.** For instance, we model space shots so that we can determine the times for the launch (when the earth is properly aligned with the rocket's destination, the total firing time for the rocket engines, and other similar parameters that must be modeled before they are performed). Moreover, modeling has taken on the reputation of confirming experimental data. Sometimes the model is believed more than the data because the model is math based. (However, the model must have inherent assumptions, and these are always open to questioning.) Modeling has also become a key feature of fields such as economics and meteorology. These would be difficult to study and impossible to predict if models did not exist. (They are still largely impossible to predict, even with

the models, because of the complexities of these systems.)

Isaac Newton was also an important figure in the Scientific Awakening because he established the **authority of science.** Previous to Newton, science often raised questions without being able to answer them. The mathematics and models created by Newton helped to answer many of those questions and helped change the public perception of science. Before Newton science was often viewed as a challenger to authority and a disturber of the peace that served little practical purpose. Newton was able to make science a tool. Science became a means to get answers to questions and explain the mysteries of Nature. Before Newton, science brought chaos; after Newton science brought order.

An example of this new "authority of science" can be seen from Newton's own life. During Newton's time as its president, the Royal Society (England's top scientific organization) was asked to investigate a woman claiming she gave birth to a sheep. Fifty years earlier the clergy would have been asked to investigate, but an important change, indeed, a paradigm shift, had occurred in European society. No longer was religion looked to as the conduit to truth. Science was now the avenue used to discover truth.

Isaac Newton's personal life was ideally suited for him to be able to devote himself entirely to his scientific pursuits. Newton entered Cambridge University as a student at age 19. By the time he was 27, he was a professor of mathematics, and he continued in that position for much of the remainder of his life. He lived on the Cambridge campus and was a recluse of sorts, having only a few friends. These friends had to be very patient with him, as he could become so involved in his work that he paid no attention to anything else. On one occasion, when friends came to his apartment to eat with him, they found him so deeply engrossed in a problem that he failed to notice them. After waiting for a long time, they ordered dinner be brought in. They ate theirs and, because they were still hungry, ate his also. When he finally finished working, he acknowledged them with some surprise. When he saw his empty plate he said, "If I didn't see the evidence before my eyes, I'd swear that I had never eaten."

The other aspects of Newton's social life were similarly eccentric. Newton never married and seemed to distrust women (perhaps because his mother left him in the care of his grandmother when he was a young child). Also, as a remainder from medieval days, Cambridge viewed faculty positions as being like clergy and therefore subtly encouraged celibacy. Just prior to his death, he told his servant that he was proud that he had remained celibate throughout his life. Newton secretly held strong religious beliefs that were nontraditional. These led him to extensive personal studies of the Bible and tended to isolate him from society. He had several adversarial relationships with his colleagues and would have bitter arguments with them over real or supposed slights. He was probably a manic-depressive and had a brief mental breakdown.

Newton's personal life may have been difficult and lonely, but it allowed him time to pursue his interests in science. Newton worked in a wide variety of fields including physics, astronomy, mathematics, optics, and alchemy (which was still seen as a legitimate science in Newton's day), and he was able to show how many of these fields were related. Newton's greatest achievements came in the area of physics, where he developed the principle of gravity and the laws of motion, both of which were explained in Newton's great work *Principia Mathematica*. In particular, he answered two great problems of his day: What keeps the heavy Earth in motion? And, Why do terrestrial bodies tend to fall to the Earth's center, whereas planets stay in orbital motion?

A critical period of discovery in Newton's life began in 1665 when he was a student at Cambridge, but was forced to return to his grandmother's farm because an outbreak of plague forced the university to close. While on the farm, Newton had time to contemplate the world around him. In the midst of that idyllic setting, according to a story related by his niece a few years after his death, he actually saw an apple drop, which triggered his thinking about forces, and this led to his ideas about gravity. This concept was, of course, highly creative and illus-

trates his ability to think laterally about a phenomenon. After gaining the initial insight, he then used logic to answer the great questions already mentioned, invent calculus, and otherwise complete the formulations. All of this development demonstrated his linear thinking capability.

The concepts of gravity integrated Copernican with several disparate theories and proofs (such as Kepler's concept of elliptical orbits and Galileo's concepts of the motions of bodies on earth) and explained that elliptical orbits are caused by the deviation of the Earth's speed from the precise speed necessary for a circular orbit. Newton also used his theory of gravity to predict the tides and formed a predictable and simple model of the solar system. The law of gravity was immediately confirmed both theoretically and experimentally. The basic laws of physics (dynamics) were developed as part of the overall theory of motion. Several fundamental concepts, such as force, mass, acceleration, momentum, and attraction at a distance, were defined as well. The gravity between the earth and the moon is illustrated in Figure 34.5 showing the principle of force at a distance. The mathematical equation for the force of gravity is also given in Figure 34.5 and, note from the equations, the force acting on the earth from the moon is the same as the force acting on the moon from the earth. This is a statement of Newton's third law.

The concept of force at a distance deserves some additional comments. This idea was strongly refuted by many scientists in Newton's day and today. Because of their belief in strict cause and effect, they believed that any effect had to have direct interaction with its cause. They could not see how force at a distance would allow that to occur. Newton, by contrast, was able to propose such a concept because he believed in alchemy, where force at a distance was readily accepted. Hence, even though Newton's ideas of alchemy were wrong, he was able to take one of those ideas and laterally apply it to physics to achieve a useful result.

When Newton returned to Cambridge, he went to his professor of mathematics and showed him the work on developing calculus. The professor was overwhelmed by Newton's brilliance and

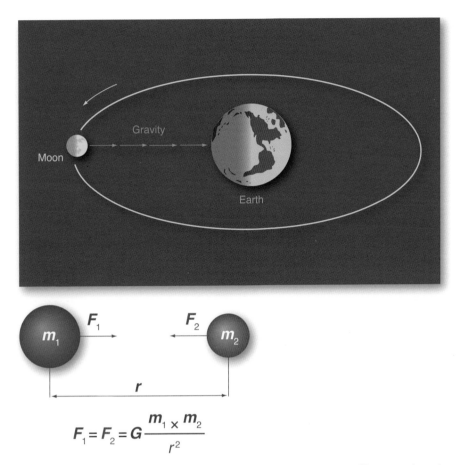

$$F_1 = F_2 = G\,\frac{m_1 \times m_2}{r^2}$$

Figure 34.5 ■ The gravity between earth and moon is illustrated and the mathematical equation for the force between them is shown here.
© *Kendall Hunt Publishing Company.*

immediately went to the university administration, resigned his professorship, and insisted that Newton be named the new professor of mathematics, which he was. (The professor moved to a new position in the university's administration.)

Because of anticipated severe criticism from **Robert Hooke,** then president of the Royal Society, Newton did not publish **Principia Mathematica** for several years even after he had worked out the laws. Hooke had his own theories regarding attraction forces and planetary positions and his criticisms of Newton's work caused Newton to retreat into a protective shell. Newton finally published his work because he heard that others were about to publish similar concepts. Even at that, it

took urging from his friends—Edmond Halley (comet fame), Christopher Wren (architect and scientist), and, later, John Locke (philosopher)—to convince Newton that he needed to publish. (For a man with few friends, the ones Newton did have were a pretty impressive group! How would you like to be at dinner with those four?)

The fundamental laws of motion were described by Newton in *Principia Mathematica.* Those laws are illustrated in Figure 34.6. The first law describes the motion of an object when it is at rest or in motion. This law describes what is commonly called inertia. The second law describes how a force is created when a mass accelerates. That relationship can also be expressed by saying

Newton's Three Laws of Motion

Law I. An object at rest or in motion tends to stay at rest or in straight motion unless acted upon by an external force.

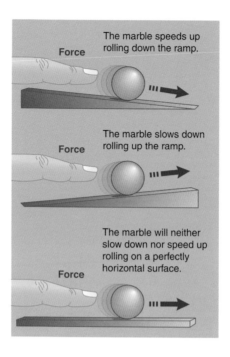

Force — The marble speeds up rolling down the ramp.

Force — The marble slows down rolling up the ramp.

Force — The marble will neither slow down nor speed up rolling on a perfectly horizontal surface.

Law II. Acceleration in speed or direction of an object is proportional to the force acting on it (F = ma).

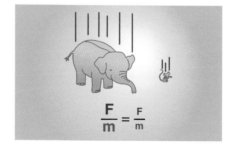

$$\frac{F}{m} = \frac{F}{m}$$

Law III. Any force put upon an object has an equal and opposite reactive force.

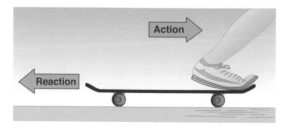

Action

Reaction

These are universal laws! (The same physics in heaven as on earth).

Figure 34.6 ■ The first law of motion describes inertia. The second describes the relationship between force, mass, and acceleration. The third law describes action and reaction. © *Kendall Hunt Publishing Company.*

that the force divided by the mass is equal to the acceleration. In Figure 34.6 this relationship is shown for an elephant and a mouse. Since the large force of the elephant is matched by a large mass and the small force of the mouse is matched by the small mass, the accelerations are equal and, therefore, they fall at the same rate. The third law is also illustrated in Figure 34.6 and it shows that when there is a fore on an object, such as a skateboard, there is an equal and opposite force on that object.

Newton was also an expert mathematician and, as has been mentioned, he invented calculus to provide a mathematical basis for the laws he presented. The development of calculus opened up discoveries in many different branches of science as scientists used calculus to examine many phenomena never before understood. The study of fluids, motions, astronomy, mechanics, and error functions were all significantly influenced using Newton's calculus. Interestingly, a German nobleman named Gottfried Liebnitz also invented calculus near the same time, but completely independently of Isaac Newton, and it is Liebnitz's notation for calculus, not Newton's, that is used today.

A friend of Newton's (Edmund Halley), when visiting Newton, "inadvertently" left an announcement of a contest to solve a mathematical puzzle. The puzzle had originally been published six months previously, but no one had been able to solve it. A prize was offered and Newton decided to try. He solved it in one night and sent in the answer so that he could collect the prize, but he insisted that the solution be published without giving anyone credit by name. However, the scientific community immediately recognized Newton as the solver of the puzzle by the method of the work.

Isaac Newton also did significant work in the field of optics. As part of his experimental studies, Newton probed his own eye with a darning needle to see what effect that might have on the perception of light. Newton theorized that light could be thought of as a stream of particles—a concept that is now recognized as part of quantum theory. Newton developed the theory of color

and showed why prisms work. Prior to Newton, people believed white light was pure and that prisms somehow changed the nature of light. Newton showed that white light is really a collection of lights of different colors. In this same work with light and prisms, Newton also named the spectrum and identified seven colors. Newton's contributions to light also include the invention of the reflecting telescope to help with his work in astronomy.

After he had retired from scientific work, he was named President of the Royal Society and Director of the Mint. Rather than just retire to sedate living, Newton embarked on these new assignments with great vigor. The mint position was especially critical at this time as the coinage in England was in a terrible state. Many of the coins had been clipped (that is, cheapened by clipping off a small amount of the coin so that the clippings could be melted and sold as precious metal). Many other coins had been melted and adulterated with less valuable alloys. Some estimate that more than 70 percent of the coins were fraudulent. Newton's job was to mint new coins in a way that would make counterfeiting more difficult, call in the old coins, and then prosecute counterfeiters. He licensed manufacturing systems that were major strides in preventing counterfeiting (such as ribbing the edges of the coins) and dramatically improved production efficiencies by applying the same focus to minting as he did to his studies of physics and light. The head of the treasury department (exchequer) stated that the change to the new coinage system could not have been done without the supervision and direct assistance of Isaac Newton.

One further creative linkage was revealed by Newton late in his life. This was a linkage between his nontraditional religious beliefs and gravity. When a young professor at Cambridge, Newton was asked to describe the cause of the attraction between heavenly bodies—in other words, what caused gravity? He answered that he could not do it, but that his job as a scientist was to describe the relationship and not to give its origin. However, later in his life, Newton commented that the force controlling the motion of the planets was the power of Jesus Christ. This belief was explained by Newton's non-Trinitarian belief, in which he saw Jesus Christ as separate from God the Father. Michael White in his book *Isaac Newton: The Last Sorcerer,* reports Newton's comments and summarizes their impact.

> *To clarify his thoughts on the subject, sometime around 1720 Newton wrote what he perceived as a personal credo, a form of amalgamation of science and religion—a guide, perhaps, for future explorers. This included a clear picture of the role he saw for Christ in the universal scheme of things—not least the function of the spiritual body of Jesus as the medium by which celestial mechanics was maintained. 'Jesus was beloved of God before the foundation of the world,' he wrote, 'and had glory with the father before the world began and was the principle of the creation . . . the agent by whom God created all things in this world.' To summarize, the spiritual body of Jesus, the first created, was the facilitator for the creation of the physical universe, provided the means via which the cosmos continued to function mechanically, and acted as a medium via which forces acted at a distance without any visible, tangible, measurable mechanism.* [emphasis original]

Because of the work of Newton, a significant paradigm shift occurred in regard to how people viewed science and what they felt it could accomplish. Scientists now understood the basic laws of the solar system, including the laws of gravity and motion. Newton also strengthened the ties between experimental science and mathematics. However, Newton's greatest accomplishment was that scientists gained great confidence in the laws of physics and assumed that they could figure out everything. The poet Alexander Pope may have best summed up the influence of the work of Isaac Newton when he wrote: "Nature and Nature's law lay hid at night; God said 'Let Newton be', and all was light."

▪ Antoine Lavoisier

The French scientist **Antoine Lavoisier** (1743–1794) lived a generation after Newton's death. Lavoisier was an expert chemist who made many important discoveries in that field. However, his greatest contribution to science was his introduction of the concept of **quantitative rigor,** that is, careful monitoring and control of the amounts of the materials being investigated and the procedures necessary to maintain close quantitative control. This was a critical concept in completing the development of experimental science, especially in chemistry. Up to this time, most experiments were largely qualitative—that is, they gave general understanding but they did not give precise results. Lavoisier showed that very strict controls on amounts could give precise results that could then be mathematically and quantitatively related.

Lavoisier's book *Elements of Chemistry,* published in 1789, established the basis for modern chemistry. In *Elements of Chemistry* Lavoisier proved that matter does not change its amount in a series of chemical reactions, though it may change its form. He also showed that any heat and light that may be given off are not part of the weight of the materials. Lavoisier's book also firmly established that the four elements of antiquity (earth, air, fire, and water) were not the basic elements of the world, but that they could all be broken down into smaller chemical components. Furthermore, Lavoisier recognized and named 23 of the Earth's authentic elements.

Even though Lavoisier's work in chemistry was groundbreaking for that field, it is his methods of experimentation that had the greatest influence on science as a whole. Prior to Lavoisier, experiments were done somewhat haphazardly and results could become tainted by outside variables. Lavoisier insisted on close and careful control of all variables so that he could know for sure exact cause-and-effect relationships. Furthermore, any materials used were monitored carefully to avoid accidental contamination that may influence the results. Lavoisier also performed experiments repeatedly, that is, several repetitions, to be sure that he got the same result each time. In essence,

Lavoisier established the modern rules for conducting an experiment.

Lavoisier showed the importance of careful control of experiments by repeating work previously done by others and, often, disproving the conclusions. This encouraged others to also be more careful in their conducting of experiments and helped establish the precedent that experiments must be reproducible by others in order to be confirmed as true.

One of Lavoisier's most important contributions was to correct the theory of combustion that was generally accepted among the scientific community of his day. The prevailing theory was called the *phlogiston theory*. It assumed that phlogiston was the essential element of all combustible bodies with oils, fats, wood, charcoal, and other fuels containing especially large amounts. According to phlogiston theory, the phlogiston escaped when those bodies were burnt and it entered either into the atmosphere or into a nearby substance that would combine with it. This theory delayed progress in chemistry for many years, since combustion was such an important method for discovery of the nature of materials and it was often incorrectly interpreted (and continued to support the theories of the alchemists). Lavoisier disproved the phlogiston theory by showing that some materials, such as phosphorus and tin, gained weight when they were burned in air. He also proved that both combustion and respiration use oxygen and identified oxygen as about 20 percent of air, the remainder being mostly nitrogen.

Lavoisier was a major contributor in several areas, as is typical of many creative geniuses. He contributed to fields as disparate as ballooning, mineral mapping of France, urban street lighting, the Paris water supply, the efficiency of gunpowder, and a full-scale model farm, to name only a few.

Later in his life, Lavoisier's work in chemistry earned him a position as the head of the French government's gunpowder works. While working there, Lavoisier taught a 16-year-old boy named Eleuthère Irénée du Pont de Nemours how to make gunpowder. Eugene DuPont, as he became known, later immigrated to America, where he established a gunpowder factory. That factory has since evolved into the giant American chemical corporation known as Dupont.

Antoine Lavoisier did not have as happy a fate. In a very sad way, Lavoisier became the victim of science—at least of peer review, which, as a leader of the French scientific community, he was obliged to conduct. Paul Strathern, in his book, *Mendeleyev's Dream,* describes the conditions under which Lavoisier was killed:

An ambitious young journalist had submitted a paper to the Academie, in the hope of gaining election to this prestigious body. The paper had been on the nature of fire. . . . According to the paper, this [the extinguishing of a flame in an enclosed space] happened because the air heated by the flame expanded, and thus pressure mounted around the flame, diminishing its size, until finally it disappeared. . . . It fell to the Academician Lavoisier to inform the misguided journalist that his paper was [wrong]. The journalist felt deeply insulted by Lavoisier's dismissive rejection. The journalist's name was Jean-Paul Marat. By 1791 Marat had become one of the leading members of the Jacobins, the extremist advocates of what would soon become the Terror. In 1791 Marat publicly attacked Lavoisier in the Jacobin newspaper. . . . Lavoisier was arrested. Despite the frantic efforts of Mme Lavoisier, her husband was brought to trial. The judge expressed his opinion that 'The Republic has no need of scientists', and sentenced Lavoisier to death. He was guillotined the same day.

■ Summary

As mentioned at the beginning of this chapter, an important change of the Scientific Awakening was that the method for examining the world changed. Scientists asserted that both experimentation and sensory perception (empiricism) were more reliable in examining the world than just pure logic or theology. This gave rise to the development of the scientific method.

With the scientific method, interpretation of data was to be unbiased by any preconceptions, rather than interpreted in light of preaccepted truths, as had previously been done. As these ancient truths were examined under the new method of scrutiny, and many were proven to be false, science became a separate entity from philosophy and theology. Science became the domain for those who practiced the new method for discovering knowledge rather than the domain of philosophers and clergy.

At the same time, the study of aesthetics (what is beautiful and artful) also became separated from philosophy and theology. This was largely the result of the forces of Baroque art and music, which we discussed in the last chapter.

We can summarize the intellectual situation at the end of the seventeenth century by charting how philosophy, theology, science, and aesthetics analyze and interpret the three important questions of the world: What is the world like?, What is real or true?, and How should I behave? (Figure 34.7).

The six men discussed in this chapter were not the only significant contributors to the Scientific Awakening. All of them helped shape and expand the movement as it happened and had a lasting effect on the development of modern science. However, the Scientific Awakening is more than the rules and procedures laid out by these men. It is also more than their discoveries. The Scientific Awakening is the paradigm shift, *the change in thinking,* which was brought about by the work of these men. It is the era when science, not philosophy or religion, was turned to for the discovery of truth, not just by scientists, but also by the masses. This shift is particularly relevant because it forms the basis for much of the modern western world.

The contributions of each of these six men to the scientific method are summarized in Figure 34.8.

Another important contribution of science is the insistence of review. That began with the Royal Society, in England, and was soon copied by other, similar societies in most major countries. This type of forum provided the scientists an opportunity to hear about the latest work and to participate in discussions with the researcher. Perhaps even more important, however, were the early introductions of scientific journals and peer review. These journals forced scientists to write their findings. That proved to be immensely beneficial to both science and the art of scientific creativity. As reported in *Creative People at Work* by Wallace and Gruber, that was especially important for Lavoisier, but that is not surprising in light of his careful work.

There is a closer connection between scientific creativity and scientific writing than has generally been noticed. It was in the process of composing his ideas on paper that Lavoisier sometimes came fully to grasp them, to see the flaws in them, to see how

Figure 34.7

Discipline	Physics (What is the world like?)	Metaphysics (What is real or true?)	Ethics (How should I behave?)
Philosophy	Logic	Forms	Seek happiness
Theology	Revelation/scriptures	God	Be obedient to God/church
Science	Empiricism	Sensory perceptions	Respect inalienable rights
Aesthetics	Emotions	Beauty and symmetry	Seek unity with life

Figure 34.8

Scientist	Contribution
Copernicus	Challenged a basic theory held by both philosophers and theologians
Galileo	Linking of math and science
Bacon	Scientific method (empiricism, experimentation, and inductive reasoning)
Descartes	Theoretical science
Newton	Laws applied to the entire universe; established the authority of science
Lavoisier	Quantification of experiments

they could be further developed, or to perceive alternatives to what he had previously thought. Scientific papers are not merely reports of conclusions a scientist has already reached, but an important phase in the creative process itself.

▪ **Timeline—Important Dates**

Date	Event
1473–1543	*Nicholas Copernicus*
1561–1626	*Francis Bacon*
1564–1642	*Galileo Galilei*
1596–1650	*René Descartes*
1642–1727	*Isaac Newton*
1743–1794	*Antoine Lavoisier*

▪ **Suggested Readings**

Baigrie, Brian S., *Scientific Revolutions,* Pearson, 2004.

Eiseley, Loren, *The Man Who Saw through Time,* Charles Scribner's Sons, 1973.

Hatton, John, and Paul B. Plouffe, *Science and Its Ways of Knowing,* Prentice Hall, 1997.

Koestler, Arthur, *The Sleepwalkers,* Penguin Books, 1959.

Langford, Jerome, *Galileo, Science and the Church,* The University of Michigan Press, 1992.

Lewinter, Marty, and William Widulski, *The Saga of Mathematics,* Prentice Hall, 2002.

Sobel, Dava, *Galileo's Daughter,* Penguin Books, 2000.

Strathern, Paul, *Mendeleyev's Dream,* Berkley Books, 2000.

Wallace, Doris B., and Howard E. Gruber, *Creative People at Work,* Oxford University Press, 1989.

White, Michael, *Isaac Newton: The Last Sorcerer,* Basic Books, 1997.

Francis Bacon: The New Organon

Francis Bacon (1561–1626), also called the "father of science," was widely educated and showed a strong interest in many disparate branches of knowledge. He was the son of Nicholas Bacon, Lord Keeper of the Seal of Elizabeth I, who died when Francis was 18 years old, leaving him penniless. Bacon began attending Trinity College Cambridge at age 12, where he grew to dislike the Aristotelian method and Scholasticism under which he was educated. Nevertheless, he earned a degree in law and by age 23 was working in the House of Commons during the reign of Elizabeth I. He rose through politics and governmental service to become, under James I, the Lord Chancellor of England, chief judge in the kingdom.

His strong association with the administration of James I proved to be a problem for Bacon when James fell out of favor with several powerful members of parliament. These politicians tried to embarrass the king by attacking his Lord Chancellor. Bacon was accused of taking a bribe and, to prevent a confrontation with the parliament and embarrassment to the king, was asked by the king to resign his position in the government. Bacon then embarked on a career of writing and life as a country gentleman.

Organon, the ancient Aristotelian text, had been the handbook of scientific method for nearly two millennia. But Bacon decried Aristotle's denial of experimentation in the search for truth. (Aristotle thought that experiments changed nature and therefore were unreliable. Aristotle believed that non-controlled observations and theory were more appropriate for understanding the true nature of things.) Bacon argued that natural truth should be discovered and not merely theorized and that the discovery was best done with controlled experiments. Therefore, when Bacon published the collection of his ideas on scientific method, he aptly titled it *The New Organon,* intent on replacing Aristotle's book (*Organon*) on the shelves of scientists worldwide.

Bacon was an advocate of inductive logic (building up of conclusions based on acquisition of knowledge from individual observations). According to Bacon, these observations should be the result of experiments in which the prejudices of the person, society, and method should all be excluded. Bacon equated knowledge with power and felt that when that knowledge was obtained experientially, it would be pure and true. These thoughts led to the development of the scientific method and future scientific developments of the seventeenth century in Europe. Bacon died of pneumonia contracted while doing an experiment to monitor the effects of ice in preserving food.

Included here are selections from the preface to *The New Organon,* as well as some of its *Aphorisms on the Interpretation of Nature and the Empire of Man. Aphorisms* is a list of theses outlining Bacon's new experimentally-based search for truth.

Francis Bacon: The New Organon

▪ Preface

Those who have presumed to make pronouncements about nature as if it were a closed subject, whether they were speaking from simple confidence or from motives of ambition and academical habits, have done very great damage to philosophy and the sciences. They have been successful in getting themselves believed and effective in terminating and extinguishing investigation. They have not done so much good by their own abilities as they have done harm by spoiling and wasting the abilities of others. Those who have gone the opposite way and claimed that nothing at all can be known, whether they have reached this opinion from dislike of the ancient sophists or though a habit of vacillation or from a kind of surfeit of learning, have certainly brought good arguments to support their position. Yet they have not drawn their view from true starting points, but have been carried away by a kind of enthusiasm and artificial passion, and have gone beyond all measure. The earlier Greeks however (whose writings have perished) took a more judicious stance between the ostentation of dogmatic pronouncements and the despair of *lack of conviction (acatalepsia);* and though they frequently complained and indignantly deplored the difficulty of investigation and the obscurity of things, like horses chomping at the bit they kept on pursuing their design and engaging with nature; thinking it appropriate (it seems) not to argue the point (whether anything can be known), but to try it by experience. And yet they too, relying only on the impulse of the intellect, failed to apply rules, and staked everything on the mind's endless and aimless activity.

Our method, though difficult to practise, is easy to formulate. It is to establish degrees of certainty, to preserve sensation by putting a kind of restraint on it, but to reject in general the work of the mind that follows sensation; and rather to open and construct a new and certain road for the mind from the actual perceptions of the senses. This was certainly seen also by those who have given such an important role to logic. Clearly they sought assistance for the understanding and distrusted natural and spontaneous movements of the mind. But this remedy was applied too late, when the situation was quite hopeless, after daily habits of life had let the mind be hooked by hearsay and debased doctrine, and occupied by thoroughly empty *illusions.* And so the art of logic took its precautions too late, and altogether failed to restore the situation; and has had the effect of fixing errors rather than of revealing truth. There remains one hope of salvation, one way to good health: that the entire work of the mind be started over again; and from the very start the mind should not be left to itself, but be constantly controlled; and the business done (if I may put it this way) by machines. If men had tackled mechanical tasks with their bare hands and without the help and power of tools, as they have not hesitated to handle intellectual tasks with little but the bare force of their intellects, there would surely be very few things indeed which they could move and

Source: Copyright © 2000 Cambridge University Press. Reprinted with permission.

overcome, no matter how strenuous and united their efforts. And if we might pause for a moment and look at an example, as if we were looking into a mirror, we might (if you please) ask the following: if an exceptionally heavy obelisk had to be moved to decorate a triumph or some such magnificent show, and men tackled it with their bare hands, would not a sensible spectator regard it as an act of utter lunacy? And all the more so if they increased the number of workers thinking that that would do it? Would he not say they were still more seriously demented if they proceeded to make a selection, and set aside the weaker men and took only the young and the strong, and expected to achieve their ambition that way? And if not satisfied even with this, they decided to have recourse to the art of athletics, and gave orders that everyone should turn up with hands, arms and muscles properly oiled and massaged according to the rules of the art, would he not protest that what they were doing was simply a systematic and methodical act of insanity? And yet in intellectual tasks men are motivated by a similarly insane impulse and an equally ineffective enterprise when they expect much from either a cooperation of many minds or simple brilliance and high intelligence, or even when they improve the force of their minds with logic (which may be thought of as a kind of athletic art); and all the time, however much effort and energy they put into it (if one looks at it from a proper perspective), they are using nothing but the naked intellect. Yet it is utterly obvious that in any major work that the human hand undertakes, the strength of individuals cannot be increased nor the forces of all united without the aid of tools and machines.

*   *   *

Let there be two sources of learning therefore, and two means of dissemination (and may this be good and fortunate for both of them). Let there likewise be two clans or families of thinkers or philosophers; and let them not be hostile or alienated from each other, but allies bound together by ties of mutual assistance. And above all let there be one

method for cultivating the sciences and a different method for discovering them. Those to whom the first method is preferable and more acceptable, whether because of their haste or for reasons of civil life, or because they lack the intellectual capacity to grasp and master the other method, we pray that their activities go well for them and as they desire, and that they get what they are after. But any man whose care and concern is not merely to be content with what has been discovered and make use of it, but to penetrate further; and not to defeat an opponent in argument but to conquer nature by action; and not to have nice, plausible opinions about things but sure, demonstrable knowledge; let such men (if they please), as true sons of the sciences, join with me, so that we may pass the antechambers of nature which innumerable others have trod, and eventually open up access to the inner rooms. For better understanding, and to make what we mean more familiar by assigning names, we have chosen to call the one way or method the *Anticipation of the Mind* and the other the *Interpretation of Nature*.

Aphorisms on the Interpretation of Nature and on the Kingdom of Man

Aphorism I

Man is Nature's agent and interpreter; he does and understands only as much as he has observed of the order of nature in fact or by inference; he does not know and cannot do more.

II

Neither the bare hand nor the unaided intellect has much power; the work is done by tools and assistance, and the intellect needs them as much as the hand. As the hand's tools either prompt or guide its motions, so the mind's tools either prompt or warn the intellect.

III

Human knowledge and human power come to the same thing, because ignorance of cause frustrates effect. For Nature is conquered only by obedience; and that which in thought is a cause, is like a rule in practice.

VI

There is something insane and self-contradictory in supposing that things that have never yet been done can be done except by means never tried.

X

The subtlety of nature far surpasses the subtlety of sense and intellect, so that men's fine meditations, speculations and endless discussions are quite insane, except that there is no one who notices.

XI

As the sciences in their present state are useless for the discovery of works, so logic in its present state is useless for the discovery of sciences.

XVIII

The things that have hitherto been discovered in the sciences all fit nicely into common notions; in order to penetrate to the more inward and remote parts of nature, both notions and axioms must be abstracted from things in a more certain, better-grounded way; and a more certain and altogether better intellectual procedure must come into use.

XIX

There are, and can be, only two ways to investigate and discover truth. The one leaps from sense and particulars to the most general axioms, and from these principles and their settled truth, determines and discovers intermediate axioms; this is the current way. The other elicits axioms from sense and particulars, rising in a gradual and unbroken ascent to arrive at last at the most general axioms; this is the true way, but it has not been tried.

XX

Left to itself the intellect goes the same way as it does when it follows the order of dialectic (i.e. the first of the two ways above). The mind loves to leap to generalities, so that it can rest; it only takes it a little while to get tired of experience. These faults have simply been magnified by dialectic, for ostentatious disputes.

XXI

In a sober, grave and patient character the intellect left to itself (especially if unimpeded by received doctrines) makes some attempt on that other way, which is the right way, but with little success; since without guidance and assistance it is a thing inadequate and altogether incompetent to overcome the obscurity of things.

XXII

Both ways start from sense and particulars, and come to rest in the most general; but they are vastly different. For one merely brushes experience and particulars in passing, the other deals fully and properly with them; one forms certain abstract and useless generalities from the beginning, the other rises step by step to what is truly better known by nature.

XXIII

There is a great distance between the illusions of the human mind and the ideas of the divine mind; that is, between what are no more than empty opinions and what we discover are the true prints and signatures made on the creation.

XXXVIII

The *illusions* and false notions which have got a hold on men's intellects in the past and are now profoundly rooted in them, not only block their minds so that it is difficult for truth to gain access, but even when access has been granted and allowed, they will once again, in the very renewal of the sciences, offer resistance and do mischief unless men are forewarned and arm themselves against them as much as possible.

XXXIX

There are four kinds of *illusions* which block men's minds. For instruction's sake, we have given them the following names: the first kind are called *idols of the tribe;* the second *idols of the cave;* the third *idols of the marketplace;* the fourth *idols of the theatre.*

XL

Formation of notions and axioms by means of true induction is certainly an appropriate way to banish idols and get rid of them; but it is also very useful to identify the *idols*. Instruction about *idols* has the same relation to the *interpretation of nature* as teaching the *sophistic refutations* has to ordinary logic.

XLI

The *idols of the tribe* are founded in human nature itself and in the very tribe or race of mankind. The assertion that the human senses are the measure of things is false; to the contrary, all perceptions, both of sense and mind, are relative to man, not to the universe. The human understanding is like an uneven mirror receiving rays from things and merging its own nature with the nature of things, which thus distorts and corrupts it.

XLII

The *idols of the cave* are the illusions of the individual man. For (apart from the aberrations of human nature in general) each man has a kind of individual cave or cavern which fragments and distorts the light of nature. This may happen either because of the unique and particular nature of each man; or because of his upbringing and the company he keeps; or because of his reading of books and the authority of those whom he respects and admires; or because of the different impressions things make on different minds, preoccupied and prejudiced perhaps, or calm and detached, and so on. The evident consequence is that the human spirit (in its different dispositions in different men) is a variable thing, quite irregular, almost haphazard. Heraclitus well said that men seek knowledge in lesser, private worlds, not in the great or common world.

XLIII

There are also *illusions* which seem to arise by agreement and from men's association with each other, which we call *idols of the marketplace;* we take the name from human exchange and community. Men associate through talk; and words are chosen to suit the understanding of the common people. And thus a poor and unskillful code of words incredibly obstructs the understanding. The definitions and explanations with which learned men have been accustomed to protect and in some way liberate themselves, do not restore the situation at all. Plainly words do violence to the understanding, and confuse everything; and betray men into countless empty disputes and fictions.

XLIV

Finally there are the *illusions* which have made their homes in men's minds from the various dogmas of different philosophies, and even from mistaken rules of demonstration. These I call *idols of the theater,* for all the philosophies that men have learned or devised are, in our opinion, so many plays produced and performed which have created false and fictitious worlds. We are not speaking only of the philosophies and sects now in vogue or even of the ancient ones; many other such plays could be composed and concocted, seeing that the causes of their very different errors have a great deal in common. And we do not mean this only of the universal philosophies, but also of many principles and axioms of the sciences which have grown strong from tradition, belief and inertia. But we must speak at greater length and separately of each different kind of *idol,* to give warning to the human understanding.

René Descartes: Discourse on Method

René Descartes (1596–1650) was a French born scientist, mathematician, and philosopher. He developed the foundations of analytical geometry and the Cartesian coordinate system (which is named after the Latinized spelling of Descartes' name). Descartes was profoundly influenced by the Catholic Church but was also interested in seeking ultimate truth through philosophy and science, which he linked together.

Descartes proposed that the discovering of truth begins with rejection of previously held ideas, thus preventing the perpetuation of prejudices. He, therefore, determined to hold nothing true until he had established grounds for believing it true. He logically began to reject all knowledge gained from sources that were not totally and absolutely certain. He was searching for a fact or facts that he could truly know with complete and uncompromised certainty. The single sure fact he finally arrived at was expressed by him in the famous words *Cogito, ergo sum,* "I think, therefore I am."

In this method, he risked the displeasure of the Catholic Church, which held that abandonment of all previous ideas denied the traditions and teachings of the church. Nevertheless, Descartes believed that his method would lead to a proof of the existence of God and to the necessity and truth of the Catholic Church. From the basic postulate that a clear consciousness of his thinking proved his own existence, he argued the existence of God. Furthermore, God, according to Descartes' philosophy, created two classes of substance that make up the whole of reality. One class was thinking substances, or minds, and the other was extended substances, or bodies.

Descartes discounted empiricism and other experientially based methods of discovering truth and, largely because of the influence of Descartes, French science pursued theoretical knowledge rather than experimental science. While the English became highly adept at experimentation, the French became excellent mathematicians.

Because of pressures from the Catholic Church in France and because of offers of influence, Descartes moved to Holland, where he did most of his writings, and later to Sweden, where he worked for Queen Christina.

Descartes' *Discourse on Method* gave science a method for analyzing problems based upon reason, rather than Bacon's experimentation. The concept of rejecting previously held ideas is developed in *Discourse on Method*. Descartes realized that questioning his previous conclusions and education meant that he had no credible intelligence to claim. He, therefore, concluded that the only source of intelligence is the questioning of all. He also concludes that problems could best be solved by dividing the problem into small parts which, when solved separately, could then be combined to give a solution to the whole problem. This concept is called reductionism and is used extensively in science.

René Descartes: Discourse on Method

Good sense is the best distributed thing in the world, for everyone thinks himself to be so well endowed with it that even those who are the most difficult to please in everything else are not at all wont to desire more of it than they have. It is not likely that everyone is mistaken in this. Rather, it provides evidence that the power of judging well and of distinguishing the true from the false (which is, properly speaking, what people call "good sense" or "reason") is naturally equal in all men, and that the diversity of our opinions does not arise from the fact that some people are more reasonable than others, but solely from the fact that we lead our thoughts along different paths and do not take the same things into consideration. For it is not enough to have a good mind; the main thing is to apply it well. The greatest souls are capable of the greatest vices as well as of the greatest virtues. And those who proceed only very slowly can make much greater progress, provided they always follow the right path, than do those who hurry and stray from it. . . .

Thus my purpose here is not to teach the method that everyone ought to follow in order to conduct his reason well, but merely to show how I have tried to conduct my own. Those who take it upon themselves to give precepts must regard themselves as more competent than those to whom they give them; and if they are found wanting in the least detail, they are to blame. But put-

ting forward this essay merely as a story or, if you prefer, as a fable in which, among some examples one can imitate, one will perhaps also find many others which one will have reason not to follow, I hope that it will be useful to some without being harmful to anyone, and that everyone will be grateful to me for my frankness.

I have been nourished on letters since my childhood, and because I was convinced that by means of them one could acquire a clear and assured knowledge of everything that is useful in life, I had a tremendous desire to master them. But as soon as I had completed this entire course of study, at the end of which one is ordinarily received into the ranks of the learned, I completely changed my mind. For I found myself confounded by so many doubts and errors that it seemed to me that I had not gained any profit from my attempt to teach myself, except that more and more I had discovered my ignorance. And yet I was at one of the most renowned schools of Europe, where I thought there must be learned men, if in fact any such men existed anywhere on earth. There I had learned everything the others were learning; and, not content with the disciplines we were taught there, I had gone through all the books I could lay my hands on that treated those disciplines considered the most curious and most unusual. Moreover, I knew what judgments the others were making about me; and I did not at all see that I was

Source: Descartes, *Discourse on Method,* translated by Donald Cress (Hackett 1998), pp. 1–5, 10–11, 18–19. Reprinted by permission of Hackett Publishing Company, Inc.

rated inferior to my fellow students, even though there already were some among them who were destined to take the place of our teachers. And finally our age seemed to me to be just as flourishing and as fertile in good minds as any of the preceding ones. This made me feel free to judge all others by myself, and to think that there was no doctrine in the world that was of the sort that I had previously been led to hope for.

I did not, however, cease to hold in high regard the academic exercises with which we occupy ourselves in the schools. I knew that the languages learned there are necessary for the understanding of classical texts; that the charm of fables awakens the mind; that the memorable deeds recounted in histories uplift it, and, if read with discretion, aid in forming one's judgment; that the reading of all good books is like a conversation with the most honorable people of past ages, who were their authors, indeed, even like a set conversation in which they reveal to us only the best of their thoughts; that oratory has incomparable power and beauty; that poetry has quite ravishing delicacy and sweetness; that mathematics has some very subtle stratagems that can serve as much to satisfy the curious as to facilitate all the arts and to lessen men's labor; that writings dealing with morals contain many lessons and many exhortations to virtue that are very useful; that theology teaches one how to reach heaven; that philosophy provides the means of speaking plausibly about all things and of making oneself admired by the less learned; that jurisprudence, medicine, and the other sciences bring honors and riches to those who cultivate them; and, finally, that it is good to have examined all these disciplines, even the most superstition-ridden and the most false of them, in order to know their true worth and to guard against being deceived by them.

I delighted most of all in mathematics because of the certainty and the evidence of its reasonings. But I did not yet notice its true use, and, thinking that it was of service merely to the mechanical arts, I was astonished by the fact that no one had built anything more noble upon its foundations, given that they were so solid and firm. On the other hand, I compared the writings of the an-

cient pagans that deal with morals to very proud and very magnificent palaces that were built on nothing but sand and mud. They place virtues on a high plateau and make them appear to be valued more than anything else in the world, but they do not sufficiently instruct us about how to recognize them; and often what they call by so fine-sounding a name is nothing more than a kind of insensibility, pride, desperation, or parricide.

I revered our theology, and I desired as much as anyone else to reach heaven; but having learned as something very certain that the road to heaven is open no less to the most ignorant than to the most learned, and that the revealed truths guiding us there are beyond our understanding, I would not have dared to submit them to the frailty of my reasonings. And I thought that, in order to undertake an examination of these truths and to succeed in doing so, it would be necessary to have some extraordinary assistance from heaven and to be more than a man.

Concerning philosophy I shall say only that, seeing that it has been cultivated for many centuries by the most excellent minds that have ever lived and that, nevertheless, there still is nothing in it about which there is not some dispute, and consequently nothing that is not doubtful, I was not at all so presumptuous as to hope to fare any better there than the others; and that, considering how many opinions there can be about the very same matter that are held by learned people without there ever being the possibility of more than one opinion being true, I deemed everything that was merely probable to be well-nigh false.

Then, as for the other sciences, I judged that, insofar as they borrow their principles from philosophy, one could not have built anything solid upon such unstable foundations. And neither the honor nor the monetary gain they promised was sufficient to induce me to master them, for I did not perceive myself, thank God, to be in a condition that obliged me to make a career out of science in order to enhance my fortune. And although I did not make a point of rejecting glory after the manner of a Cynic, nevertheless I placed very little value on the glory that I could not hope to acquire except through false pretenses. And finally, as to the false doctrines, I thought I already knew well enough what they were worth, so as not to be liable to be deceived either by the promises of an alchemist, the predictions of an astrologer, the tricks of a magician, or the ruses or boasts of any of those who profess to know more than they do.

That is why, as soon as age permitted me to emerge from the supervision of my teachers, I completely abandoned the study of letters . . . resolving to search for no knowledge other than what could be found within myself, or else in the great book of the world, . . .

When I was younger, I had studied, among the parts of philosophy, a little logic, and among those of mathematics, a bit of geometrical analysis and algebra—three arts or sciences that, it seemed, ought to contribute something to my plan. But in examining them, I noticed that, in the case of logic, its syllogisms and the greater part of its other lessons served more to explain to someone else the things one knows, or even, like the art of Lully, to speak without judgment concerning matters about which one is ignorant, than to learn them. And although, in effect, it might well contain many very true and very good precepts, nevertheless there are so many others mixed up with them that are either harmful or superfluous, that it is almost as difficult to separate the latter precepts from the former as it is to draw a Diana or a Minerva from a block of marble that has not yet been hewn. Then, as to the analysis of the ancients and the algebra of the moderns, apart from the fact that they apply only to the very abstract matters and seem to be of no use, the former is always so closely tied to the consideration of figures that it cannot exercise the understanding without greatly fatiguing the imagination; and in the case of the latter, one is so subjected to certain rules and to certain symbols, that out of it there results a confused and obscure art that encumbers the mind, rather than a science that cultivates it. That is why I thought it necessary to search for some other method embracing the advantages of these three yet free from their defects. And since the multiplicity of laws often provides excuses for vices, so that a state is much better ruled when it has but very few laws and when these are very strictly observed; likewise, in place

of the large number of precepts of which logic is composed, I believed that the following four rules would be sufficient for me, provided I made a firm and constant resolution not even once to fail to observe them:

The first was never to accept anything as true that I did not plainly know to be such; that is to say, carefully to avoid hasty judgment and prejudice; and to include nothing more in my judgments than what presented itself to my mind so clearly and so distinctly that I had no occasion to call it in doubt.

The second, to divide each of the difficulties I would examine into as many parts as possible and as was required in order better to resolve them.

The third, to conduct my thoughts in an orderly fashion, by commencing with those objects that are simplest and easiest to know, in order to ascend little by little, as by degrees, to the knowledge of the most composite things, and by supposing an order even among those things that do not naturally precede one another.

And the last, everywhere to make enumerations so complete and reviews so general that I was assured of having omitted nothing. . . .

I do not know whether I ought to tell you about the first meditations I engaged in there, for they are so metaphysical and so out of the ordinary that perhaps they will not be to everyone's liking. And yet, in order that it should be possible to judge whether the foundations I have laid are sufficiently firm, I find myself in some sense forced to talk about them. For a long time I had noticed that in matters of morality one must sometimes follow opinions that one knows to be quite uncertain, just as if they were undubitable, as has been said above, but because I then desired to devote myself exclusively to the search for the truth, I thought it necessary that I do exactly the opposite, and that I reject as absolutely false everything in which I could imagine the least doubt, in order to see whether, after this process, something in my beliefs remained that was entirely indubitable. Thus, because **our senses** sometimes deceive us, I wanted to suppose that nothing was exactly as they led us to imagine. And because there are men who make mistakes in reasoning, even in the simplest matters in geometry, and who commit paralogisms, judging that I was just as prone to err as any other, I rejected as false all the **reasonings** that I had previously taken for demonstrations. And finally, considering the fact that all the same thoughts we have when we are awake can also come to us when we are asleep, without any of them being true, I resolved to pretend that all the things that had ever entered my mind were no more true than the illusions of my drams. But immediately afterward I noticed that, while I wanted thus to think that everything was false, it necessarily had to be the case that I, who was thinking this, was something. And noticing that this truth—I think, therefore I am—was so firm and so assured that all the most extravagant suppositions of the skeptics were incapable of shaking it, I judged that I could accept it without scruple as the first principle of the philosophy I was seeking.

Then, examining with attention what I was, and seeing that I could pretend that I had no body and that there was no world nor any place where I was, I could not pretend, on that account, that I did not exist at all, and that, on the contrary, from the very fact that I thought of doubting the truth of other things, it followed very evidently and very certainly that I existed; whereas, on the other hand, had I simply stopped thinking, even if all the rest of what I had ever imagined had been true, I would have had no reason to believe that I had existed. From this I knew that I was a substance the whole essence or nature of which is simply to think, and which, in order to exist, has no need of any place nor depends on any material thing. Thus this "I," that is to say, the soul through which *I am what I am,* is entirely distinct from the body and is even easier to know than the body, and even if there were no body at all, it would not cease to be all that it is.

After this, I considered in general what is needed for a proposition to be true and certain, for since I had just found one of them that I knew to be such, I thought I ought also to know in what this certitude consists. And having noticed that there is nothing at all in this *I think, therefore I am* that assures me that I am speaking the truth, except that I see very clearly that, in order to think, it is necessary to exist, I judged that I could take as a general rule that the things we conceive very clearly and very distinctly are all true, but that there is merely some difficulty in properly discerning which are those that we distinctly conceive.

Isaac Newton: The Mathematical Principles of Natural Philosophy (Philosophiae Naturalis Principia Mathematica)

Sir Isaac Newton (1642–1727), thought to be the greatest scientist, found success in linking science and math. He drew upon several scientists' work and acknowledged their contributions to his thinking when he said that "If I have been able to see farther than most, it is because I stand on the shoulders of giants." Since Newton, scientists have stood on the platform of methods, math, laws, and principles developed by this interesting and unusual professor of mathematics at Cambridge University.

He was born to a widowed mother and raised by his grandmother on a small farm in England. It appears that Newton had a strained relationship with his grandfather, and bitterly hated his stepfather, threatening to burn his house to the ground. His school reports showed poor performance until he was challenged physically and intellectually by a schoolmate. When he realized that his lack of performance was causing him public ridicule, he decided to dedicate himself to school and within two months had passed all the other children at his small rural school. In spite of the poor beginnings in school, Newton showed great scientific aptitude even as a youngster. As a child, his inventions include a small windmill that ground grains, a water clock that ran by the force of falling water, and a sundial.

Newton was sent to Trinity College at the University of Cambridge where he received his bachelor's degree. However, the plague of 1666 interrupted his advanced studies because Cambridge was closed to minimize the risks of contagion.

Newton returned to his grandparents' farm where he worked as a farm manager. During that time, he formulated his concepts of gravity (perhaps from his observance of a falling apple in the orchard on the farm) and also developed the basic concepts and methods of calculus. When he returned to Cambridge, his professor was so astonished by Newton's work that the professor decided to transfer to another position so that Newton could take over his professorship.

Most of Newton's scientific developments were unknown outside a few close acquaintances and only fragmentally by them. Newton was probably manic-depressive with great periods of creativity interrupted with severe depression. This malady limited his social contacts and resulted in several instances of dispute and paranoia regarding the work of other scientists and his own position in the scientific community. When his accomplishments finally became well known, largely through the influence and urging of his friends, especially Sir Christopher Wren, Sir Edmund Halley, and John Locke, Newton's position as the greatest scientist was recognized. He became the head of the Royal Society (the first and most prestigious scientific association in the world) and was later made Director of the Royal Mint, a position most felt was honorary but which Newton took seriously and worked hard to improve.

Newton's *Principia Mathematica* is hailed as one of the greatest scientific publications of all times. His principle of gravity and the laws of motion are explained in this work. Newton addressed several of the great problems of the day: "What keeps the heavy earth in motion?" and, "Why do bodies (such as a dropped stone) tend to fall toward the earth's center whereas planets stay in motion?" He was able to successfully predict an extensive range of natural phenomena, including celestial movements of the earth, the moon, and the planets; gravity; acceleration of bodies when falling; and the tides. Newton was interested in many other areas of science and laid the principles for, among others, the science of optics and the nature of fluids. He was also strongly interested in religion and used his scientific capabilities to attempt calculations of the date of the birth of Christ based on occurrences of certain celestial phenomena that he believed were the cause of the appearance of the star of Bethlehem.

By formulating a mathematical theory as a model of observed scientific data, Newton created a new method of explaining the world and moved basic science into an arena in which math and experimental science became linked. That arena is, today, the place where modern science is played out.

■ Definitions

Definition I

The quantity of matter is the measure of the same, arising from its density and bulk conjunctly.

Thus air of a double density, in a double space, is quadruple in quantity; in a triple space, sextuple in quantity. The same thing is to be understood of snow, and fine dust or powders, that are condensed by compression or liquefaction; and of all bodies that are by any causes whatever differently condensed. I have no regard in this place to a medium, if any such there is, that freely pervades the interstices between the parts of bodies. It is this quantity that I mean hereafter everywhere under the name of body or mass. And the same is known by the weight of each body; for it is proportional to the weight, as I have found by experiments on pendulums, very accurately made, which shall be shewn hereafter.

Definition II

The quantity of motion is the measure of the same, arising from the velocity and quantity of matter conjunctly.

The motion of the whole is the sum of the motions of all the parts; and therefore in a body double in quantity, which equal velocity, the motion is double; with twice the velocity, it is quadruple.

Definition III

The vis insita, *or innate force of matter, is a power of resisting, by which every body, as much as in it lies, endeavours to persevere in its present state, whether it be of rest, or of moving uniformly forward in a right line.*

This force is ever proportional to the body whose force it is: and differs nothing from the inactivity of the mass, but in our manner of conceiving it. A body, from the inactivity of matter, is not without difficulty put out of its state of rest or motion. Upon which account, this *vis insita,* may, by a most significant name, be called *vis inertior,* or force of inactivity. But a body exerts this force only, when another force, impressed upon it, endeavours to change its condition; and the exercise of this force may be considered both as resistance and impulse; it is resistance, in so far as the body, for maintaining its present state, withstands the force impressed; it is impulse, in so far as the body, by not easily giving way to the impressed force of another, endeavours to change the state of that other. Resistance is usually ascribed to bodies at rest, and impulse to those in motion; but motion and rest, as commonly conceived, are only relatively distinguished; nor are

Source: From *The Principia* by Isaac Newton, translated by Andrew Motte (New York: Prometheus Books, 1995).

those bodies always truly at rest, which commonly **are** taken to be so.

Definition IV

An impressed force is an action exerted upon a body, in order to change its state, either of rest, or of moving uniformly forward in a right line.

This force consists in the action only; and remains no longer in the body, when the action is over. For a body maintains every new state it acquires, by its *vis inertior* only. Impressed forces are of different origins as from percussion, from pressure, from centripetal force.

Definition V

A centripetal force is that by which bodies are drawn or impelled, or any way tend, towards a point as to a centre.

Of this sort is gravity, by which bodies tend to the centre of the earth magnetism, by which iron tends to the loadstone; and that force, whatever it is, by which the planets are perpetually drawn aside form the rectilinear motions, which otherwise they would pursue, and made to revolve in curvilinear orbits. A stone, whirled about in a sling, endeavours to recede from the hand that turns it; and by that endeavour, distends the sling, and that with so much the greater force, as it is revolved with the greater velocity, and as soon as ever it is let go, flies away. That force which opposes itself to this endeavour, and by which the sling perpetually draws back the stone towards the hand, and retains it in its orbit, because it is directed to the hand as the centre of the orbit, I call the centripetal force. And the same thing is to be understood of all bodies, revolved in any orbits. They all endeavour to recede from the centres of their orbits; and were it not for the opposition of a contrary force which restrains them to, and detains them in their orbits, which I therefore call centripetal, would fly off in right lines, with an uniform motion. A projectile, if it was not for the force of gravity, would not deviate towards the earth, but would go off from it in a right line, and that with an uniform motion, if the resistance of the air was taken away. It is by its gravity that it is drawn aside perpetually from its rectilinear course, and made to deviate towards the earth, more or less, according to the force of its gravity, and the velocity of its motion. The less its gravity is, for the quantity of its matter, or the greater the velocity with which it is projected, the less will it deviate from a rectilinear course, and the farther it will go. . . . .

The quantity of any centripetal force may be considered as of three kinds; absolute, accelerative, and motive.

Definition VI

The absolute quantity of a centripetal force is the measure of the same proportional to the efficacy of the cause that propagates it from the centre, through the spaces round about.

Thus the magnetic force is greater in one loadstone and less in another according to their sizes and strength of intensity.

Definition VII

The accelerative quantity of a centripetal force is the measure of the same, proportional to the velocity which it generates in a given time.

Thus the force of the same load-stone is greater at a less distance, and less at a greater: also the force of gravity is greater in valleys, less on tops of exceeding high mountains; and yet less (as shall hereafter be shown), at greater distances from the body of the earth; but at equal distances, it is the same everywhere; because (taking away, or allowing for, the resistance of the air), it equally accelerates all falling bodies, whether heavy or light, great or small.

Definition VIII

The motive quantity of a centripetal force, is the measure of the same, proportional to the motion which it generates in a given time.

Thus the weight is greater in a greater body, less in a less body; and, in the same body, it is greater near to the earth, and less at remoter distances. This sort of quantity is the centripetency, or propension of the whole body towards the centre, or, as I may say, its weight; and it is always known by the quantity of an equal and contrary force just sufficient to hinder the descent of the body.

These quantities of forces, we may, for brevity's sake, call by the names of motive, accelerative, and absolute forces; and, for distinction's sake, consider them, with respect to the bodies that tend to the centre; to the places of those bodies; and to the centre of force towards which they tend; that is to say, I refer the motive force to the body as an endeavour and propensity of the whole towards a centre, arising from the propensities of the several parts taken together; the accelerative force to the place of the body, as a certain power or energy diffused from the centre to all places around to move the bodies that are in them; and the absolute force to the centre, as endued with some cause, without which those motive forces would not be propagated through the spaces round about; whether that cause be some central body (such as is the load-stone, in the centre of the magnetic force, or the earth in the centre of the gravitating force), or anything else that does not yet appear. For I here design only to give a mathematical notion of those forces, without considering their physical causes and seats.

Wherefore the accelerative force will stand in the same relation to the motive, as celerity does to motion. For the quantity of motion arises from the celerity drawn into the quantity of matter; and the motive force arises from the accelerative force drawn into the same quantity of matter. For the sum of the actions of the accelerative force, upon the several articles of the body, is the motive force of the whole. Hence it is, that near the surface of the earth, where the accelerative gravity, or force productive of gravity, in all bodies is the same, the motive gravity or the weight is as the body: but if we should ascend to higher regions, where the accelerative gravity is less, the weight would be equally diminished, and would always be as the product of the body, by the accelerative gravity. So in those regions, where the accelerative gravity is diminished into one half, the weight of a body two or three times less, will be four or six times less.

I likewise call attractions and impulses, in the same sense, accelerative, and motive; and use the words attraction, impulse or propensity of any sort towards a centre, promiscuously, and indifferently, one for another; considering those forces not physically, but mathematically: wherefore, the reader is not to imagine, that by those words, I anywhere take upon me to define the kind, or the manner of any action, the causes or the physical reason thereof, or that I attribute forces, in a true and physical sense, to certain centres (which are only mathematical points); when at any time I happen to speak of centres as attracting, or as endued with attractive powers.

Scholium

Hitherto I have laid down the definitions of such words as are less known, and explained the sense in which I would have them to be understood in the following discourse. I do not define time, space, place and motion, as being well known to all. Only I must observe, that the vulgar conceive those quantities under no other notions but from the relation they bear to sensible objects. And thence arise certain prejudices, for the removing of which, it will be convenient to distinguish them into absolute and relative, true and apparent, mathematical and common.

I. Absolute, true, and mathematical time, of itself, and from its own nature flows equably without regard to anything external, and by another name is called duration: relative, apparent, and common time, is some sensible and external (whether accurate or unequable) measure of duration by the means of motion, which is commonly used instead of true time; such as an hour, a day, a month, a year.

II. Absolute space, in its own nature, without regard to anything external, remains always similar and immovable. Relative space is some movable dimension or measure of the absolute spaces; which our senses determine by its position to bodies; and which is vulgarly taken for immovable space; such is the dimension of a subterraneous, an æreal, or celestial space, determined by its position in respect of the earth. Absolute and relative space, are the same in figure and magnitude; but they do not remain always numerically the same.

For if the earth, for instance, moves, a space of our air, which relatively and in respect of the earth remains always the same, will at one time be one part of the absolute space into which the air passes; at another time it will be another part of the same, and so, absolutely understood, it will be perpetually mutable.

III. Place is a part of space which a body takes up, and is according to the space, either absolute or relative. I say, a part of space; not the situation, nor the external surface of the body. For the places of equal solids are always equal; but their superfices, by reason of their dissimilar figures, are often unequal. Positions properly have no quantity, nor are they so much the places themselves, as the properties of places. The motion of the whole is the same thing with the sum of the motions of the parts; that is, the translation of the whole, out of its place, is the same thing with the sum of the translations of the parts out of their places; and therefore the place of the whole is the same thing with the sum of the places of the parts, and for that reason, it is internal, and in the whole body.

IV. Absolute motion is the translation of a body from one absolute place into another; and relative motion, the translation from one relative place into another. Thus in a ship under sail, the relative place of a body is that part of the ship which the body possesses; or that part of its cavity which the body fills, and which therefore moves together with the ship: and relative rest is the continuance of the body in the same part of the ship, or of its cavity. But real, absolute rest, is the continuance of the body in the same part of that immovable space, in which the ship itself, its cavity, and all that it contains, is moved. Wherefore, if the earth is really at rest, the body, which relatively rests in the ship, will really and absolutely move with the same velocity which the ship has on the earth. But if the earth also moves, the true and absolute motion of the body will arise, partly from the true motion of the earth, in immovable space; partly from the relative motion of the ship on the earth; and if the body moves also relatively in the ship; its true motion will arise, partly from the true motion of the earth, in immovable space, and partly from the relative motions as well of the ship

on the earth, as of the body in the ship; and from these relative motions will arise the relative motion of the body on the earth. . . .

It is a property of motion, that the parts, which retain given positions to their wholes, do partake of the motions of those wholes. For all the parts of revolving bodies endeavour to recede from the axis of motion; and the impetus of bodies moving forward, arises from the joint impetus of all the parts. Therefore, if surrounding bodies are moved, those that are relatively at rest within them, will partake of their motion. Upon which account, the true and absolute motion of a body cannot be determined by the translation of it from those which only seem to rest; for the external bodies ought not only to appear at rest, but to be really at rest. For otherwise, all included bodies, beside their translation from near the surrounding ones, partake likewise of their true motions; and though that translation were not made they would not be really at rest, but only seem to be so. For the surrounding bodies stand in the like relation to the surrounded as the exterior part of a whole does to the interior, or as the shell does to the kernel; but, if the shell moves, the kernel will also move, as being part of the whole, without any removal from near the shell. . . .

▪ Axioms, or Laws of Motion

Law I
Every body perseveres in its state of rest, or of uniform motion in a right line, unless it is compelled to change that state by forces impressed thereon.

Projectives persevere in their motions, so far as they are not retarded by the resistance of the air, or impelled downwards by the force of gravity A top, whose parts by their cohesion are perpetually drawn aside from rectilinear motions, does not cease its rotation, otherwise than as it is retarded by the air. The greater bodies of the planets and comets, meeting with less resistance in more free spaces, preserve their motions both progressive and circular for a much longer time.

Law II

The alteration of motion is ever proportional to the motive force impressed; and is made in the direction of the right line in which that force is impressed.

If any force generates a motion, a double force will generate double the motion, a triple force triple the motion, whether that force be impressed altogether and at once, or gradually and successively. And this motion (being always directed the same way with the generating force), if the body moved before, is added to or subducted from the former motion, according as they directly conspire with or are directly contrary to each other; or obliquely joined, when they are oblique, so as to produce a new motion compounded from the determination of both.

Law III

To every action there is always opposed an equal reaction: or the mutual actions of two bodies upon each other are always equal, and directed to contrary parts.

Whatever draws or presses another is as much drawn or pressed by that other. If you press a stone with your finger, the finger is also pressed by the stone. If a horse draws a stone tied to a rope, the horse (if I may so say) will be equally drawn back towards the stone: for the distended rope, by the same endeavour to relax or unbend itself, will draw the horse as much towards the stone, as it does the stone towards the horse, and will obstruct the progress of the one as much as it advances that of the other. If a body impinge upon another, and by its force change the motion of the other, that body also (because of the equality of the mutual pressure) will undergo an equal change, in its own motion, towards the contrary part. The changes made by these actions are equal, not in the velocities but in the motions of bodies; that is to say, if the bodies are not hindered by any other impediments. For, because the motions are equally changed, the changes of the velocities made towards contrary pats are reciprocally proportional to the bodies. . . .

■ Rules of Reasoning in Philosophy

Rule I

We are to admit no more causes of natural things than such as are both true and sufficient to explain their appearances.

To this purpose the philosophers say that Nature does nothing in vain, and more is in vain when less will serve; for Nature is pleased with simplicity, and affects not the pomp of superfluous causes.

Rule II

Therefore to the same natural effects we must, as far as possible, assign the same causes.

As to respiration in a man and in a beast; the descent of stones in *Europe* and in *America;* the light of our culinary fire and of the sun; the reflection of light in the earth, and in the planets.

Rule III

The qualities of bodies, which admit neither intension nor remission of degrees, and which are found to belong to all bodies within the reach of our experiments, are to be esteemed the universal qualities of all bodies whatsoever.

For since the qualities of bodies are only known to us by experiments, we are to hold for universal all such as universally agree with experiments; and such as are not liable to diminution can never be quite taken away. We are certainly not to relinquish the evidence of experiments for the sake of dreams and vain fictions of our own devising; nor are we to recede from the analogy of Nature, which uses to be simple, and always consonant to itself. We no other way know the extension of bodies than by our senses, nor do these reach it in all bodies; but because we perceived extension in all that are sensible, therefore we ascribe it universally to all others also. That abundance of bodies are hard, we learn by experience; and because the hardness of the whole arises from the hardness of the parts, we therefore justly infer the hardness of the undivided particles not only of the bodies we feel but of all others. That all bodies are impenetrable, we gather not from reason, but from sensation. The bodies which we handle we find impenetrable, and thence conclude impenetrability to be an universal property of all bodies whatsoever. That all bodies are moveable, and endowed with certain powers (which we call the *vires inertior*) of persevering in their motion, or in their rest, we only infer from the like properties observed in the bodies which we have seen. The extension, hardness, impenetrability, mobility, and *vis inertior* of the whole, result from the extension, hardness, impenetrability, mobility, and *vires inertior* of the parts; and thence we conclude the least particles of all bodies to be also all extended, and hard and impenetrable, and moveable, and endowed with their proper *vires inertiæ*. And this is the foundation of all philosophy. Moreover, that the divided but contiguous particles of bodies may be separated from one another, is matter of observation; and, in the particles that remain undivided, our minds are able to distinguish yet lesser parts, as is mathematically demonstrated. But whether the parts so distinguished, and not yet divided, may, by the powers of Nature, be actually divided and separated from one another, we cannot certainly determine. Yet, had we the proof of but one experiment that any undivided particle, in breaking a hard and solid body suffered a division, we might by virtue of this rule conclude that the undivided as well as the divided particles may be divided and actually separated to infinity.

Lastly, if it universally appears, by experiments and astronomical observations, that all bodies about the earth gravitate towards the earth, and that in proportion to the quantity of matter which they severally contain; that the moon likewise, according to the quantity of its matter, gravitates towards the earth; that, on the other hand, our sea gravitates towards the moon; and all the planets mutually one towards another; and the comets in like manner towards the sun; we must, in consequence of this rule, universally allow that all bodies whatsoever are endowed with a principle of mutual gravitation. For the argument from the appearances concludes with more force for the universal gravitation of all bodies than for their impenetrability; of which, among those in the celestial regions, we have no experiments, nor any manner of observation. Not that I affirm gravity to be essential to bodies: by their *vis insita* I mean nothing but their *vis inertiæ,* This is immutable. Their gravity is diminished as they recede from the earth.

Rule IV

In experimental philosophy we are to look upon propositions collected by general induction from phenomena occur, by which they may either be made more accurate, or liable to exceptions.

This rule we must follow, that the argument of induction may not be evaded by hypotheses.

Blaise Pascal: Pensées

Blaise Pascal (1623–1662) was born in France, where his mother died when he was three years old. His father's untraditional educational ideas led to home school training, purposely excluding mathematics from his studies until he was 15. But, by age 12, Pascal found a math book and began studying the subject in private. He was intrigued by Descartes' writings and became converted to the study of science. His scientific contributions include: developing basic theorems of projective geometry, probability, infinitesimals, liquid theory (rationalizing liquids' equal pressure in all directions, which was later termed Pascal's Law), inventing the first mechanical calculating machines, the syringe, and the hydraulic press. Despite many health problems, he worked diligently until age 39 when a malignant growth in his stomach spread to his brain.

In addition to his accomplishments in the field of science, Pascal is also remembered for his philosophical and theological writings. Pascal's deep religious convictions kept him from accepting Descartes' perspective of God, which Pascal felt was deist (the concept of a God who was not involved with the world after its creation). Pascal felt that God still took an active roll in the lives of men and that this had to be explainable by using scientific methods that Pascal believed were a legitimate method for finding truth.

Pensées (French = "Thoughts") is a collection of hundreds of Pascal's notes on this rational defense of the concept of the Christian God. He never was able to finish the organization of his notes into the book he intended, so the posthumous publication of *Pensées* includes many unconnected or vague passages. Other portions of the book, however, contain beautiful and well-organized, rational discussions for the proof of the existence of God and human nature.

Included here are a number of selections from *Pensées*. The first passages discuss the weakness of reason without conviction of the heart (faith). Descartes had advocated a pure dependence on reason in the search for truth, but Pascal believed that nothing would ever be believed as truth with only reason for sustenance. The last selection is the famous "Wager on Faith," where Pascal urges the reader to bet on the existence of God and the merits of faith solely based on what is at stake.

Article 18
Blaise Pascal: Pensées

[Reason and Faith]

We know the truth not only by means of the reason but also by means of the heart. It is through the heart that we know the first principles, and reason which has no part in this knowledge vainly tries to contest them. The Pyrrhonists who have only reason as the object of their attack are working ineffectually. We know that we are not dreaming, however powerless we are to prove it by reason. This powerlessness proves only the weakness of our reason, not the uncertainty of our entire knowledge as they claim.

For the knowledge of first principles such as space, time, movement, numbers is as certain as any that our reasoning can give us, and it is on this knowledge by means of the heart and instinct that reason has to rely, and must base all its argument. The heart feels that there are three dimensions in space and that there is an infinite series of numbers, and then reason goes on to prove that there are no two square numbers of which one is double the other. The principles are felt, and the propositions are proved, both conclusively, although by different ways, and it is as useless and stupid for the heart to demand of reason a feeling of all the propositions it proves, before accepting them.

So this powerlessness ought to be used only to humble reason, which would like to be the judge of everything, and not attach our certainty. As if reason alone were able to instruct us. Would to God that we never needed it and that we knew everything through instinct and feeling! But nature has denied us this benefit; on the contrary, it has given us very little of this kind of knowledge. All the other kinds can be acquired only through reason.

That is why those to whom God has granted faith through the heart are blessed and quite properly convinced of it. But to those to whom it has not been granted we can only give it through reason, until God grants it through the heart. Without that, faith is simply human, and worthless for salvation.

*   *   *

For we must not misunderstand ourselves: we are as much automaton as mind. And therefore the way we are persuaded is not simply by demonstration. How few things can be demonstrated! Proofs only convince the mind; custom provides the strongest and most firmly held proofs: it inclines the automaton, which drags the mind unconsciously with it. Who has proved that tomorrow will dawn, and that we will die? And what is more widely believed? So it is custom which persuades us, it is that which makes so many Christians, that which makes Turks, heathens, professions, soldiers, etc. (There is greater faith received at baptism by Christians than by the heathens.) In the end, we have to resort to custom once the mind has seen where the truth lies, to immerse and ingrain ourselves in this belief, which constantly eludes us. For to have the proofs

Source: From *Pensées & Other Writings,* translated by Honor Levi (OWC, 1995): 2270 words. By permission of Oxford University Press.

always before us is too much trouble. We must acquire an easier belief, one of habit, which without violence, art, or argument makes us believe something and inclines our faculties to this belief so that our soul falls naturally into it. When we believe only through the strength of our convictions and the automaton is inclined to believe the opposite, that is not enough. We must therefore make both sides of us believe: the mind by reasons which only have to be seen once in a lifetime, and the automaton by custom, and by not allowing it to be disposed to the contrary.

Reason works slowly, looking so frequently at so many principles, which must always be present, that it is constantly dozing or wandering off because all its principles are not present. Feeling does not work like that: it acts instantly and is always ready to act. So we must put our faith in feeling, otherwise it will always waver.

* * *

Infinity nothingness. Our soul is thrust into the body, where it finds number, time, dimension. It ponders them and calls them nature, necessity, and can believe nothing else.

* * *

[Wager on Faith]

We know that there is an infinite, but we do not know its nature; as we know that it is false that numbers are finite, so therefore it is true that there is an infinite number, but we do not know what it is: it is false that it is even and false that it is odd, for by adding a unit it does not change its nature; however it is a number, and all numbers are even or odd (it is true that this applies to all finite numbers).

So we can clearly understand that there is a God without knowing what he is.

Is there no substantial truth, seeing that there are so many true things which are not truth itself?

We therefore know the existence and nature of the finite, because we too are finite and have no extension.

We know the existence of the infinite, and do not know its nature, because it has extent like us, but not the same limits as us.

But we know neither the existence nor the nature of God, because he has neither extent nor limits.

But we know of his existence through faith. In glory we will know his nature.

Now I have already shown that we can certainly know the existence of something without knowing its nature.

Let us now speak according to natural lights.

If there is a God, he is infinitely beyond our comprehension, since, having neither parts nor limits, he bears no relation to ourselves. We are therefore incapable of knowing either what he is, or if he is. That being so, who will dare to undertake a resolution of this question? It cannot be us, who bear no relationship to him.

Who will then blame the Christians for being unable to provide a rational basis for their belief, they who profess a religion for which they cannot provide a rational basis? They declare that it is a folly, *stultitiam* (I Cor. I: 18) in laying it before the world: and then you complain that they do not prove it! If they did prove it, they would not be keeping their word. It is by the lack of proof that they do not lack sense. 'Yes, but although that excuses those who offer their religion as it is, and that takes away the blame from them of producing it without a rational basis, it does not excuse those who accept it.'

Let us therefore examine this point, and say: God is, or is not. But towards which side will we lean? Reason cannot decide anything. There is an infinite chaos separating us. At the far end of this infinite distance a game is being played and the coin will come down heads or tails. How will you wager? Reason cannot make you choose one way or the other, reason cannot make you defend either of the two choices.

So do not accuse those who have made a choice of being wrong, for you know nothing about it! 'No, but I will blame them not for having made this choice, but for having made any choice. For, though the one who chooses heads and the other one are equally wrong, they are both wrong. The right thing is not to wager at all.'

Yes, but you have to wager. It is not up to you, you are already committed. Which then will you choose? Let us see. Since you have to choose, let us see which interests you the least. You have two things to lose: the truth and the good, and two things to stake: your reason is not hurt more by choosing one rather than the other, since you do have to make the choice. That is one point disposed of. But your beatitude? Let us weigh up the gain and the loss by calling heads that God exists. Let us assess the two cases: if you win, you win everything; if you lose, you lose nothing. Wager that he exists then, without hesitating! 'This is wonderful. Yes, I must wager. But perhaps I am betting too much.' Let us see. Since there is an equal chance of gain and loss, if you won only two lives instead of one, you could still put on a bet. But if there were three lives to win, you would have to play (since you must necessarily play), and you would be unwise, once forced to play, not to chance your life to win three in a game where there is an equal chance of losing and winning. But there is an eternity of life and happiness. And that being so, even though there were an infinite number of chances of which only one were in your favour, you would still be right to wager one in order to win two, and you would be acting wrongly, since you are obliged to play, by refusing to stake one life against three in a game where out of an infinite number of chances there is one in your favour, if there were an infinitely happy infinity of life to be won. But here there is an infinitely happy infinity of life to be won, one chance of winning against a finite number of chances of losing, and what you are staking is finite. That removes all choice: wherever there is infinity and where there is no infinity of chances of losing against one of winning, there is no scope for wavering, you have to chance everything. And thus, as you are forced to gamble, you have to have discarded reason if you cling on to your life, rather than risk it for the infinite prize which is just as likely to happen as the loss of nothingness.

For it is no good saying that it is uncertain if you will win, that it is certain you are taking a risk, and that the infinite distance between the CERTAINTY of what you are risking and the UNCER-TAINTY of whether you win makes the finite good of what you are certainly risking equal to the uncertainty of the infinite. It does not work like that. Every gambler takes a certain risk for an uncertain gain; nevertheless he certainly risks the finite uncertainty in order to win a finite gain, without sinning against reason. There is no infinite distance between this certainty of what is being risked and the uncertainty of what might be gained: that is untrue. There is, indeed, an infinite distance between the certainty of winning and the certainty of losing. But the uncertainty of winning is proportional to the certainty of the risk, according to the chances of winning or losing. And hence, if there are as many chances on one side as on the other, the odds are even, and then the certainty of what you risk is equal to the uncertainty of winning. It is very far from being infinitely distant from it. So our argument is infinitely strong, when the finite is at stake in a game where there are equal chances of winning and losing, and the infinite is to be won.

That is conclusive, and, if human beings are capable of understanding any truth at all, this is the one.

'I confess it, I admit it, but even so . . . Is there no way of seeing underneath the cards?' 'Yes, Scripture and the rest, etc.' 'Yes, but my hands are tied and I cannot speak a word. I am being forced to wager and I am not free, they will not let me go. And I am made in such a way that I cannot believe. So what do you want me to do?' 'That is true. But at least realize that your inability to believe, since reason urges you to do so and yet you cannot, arises from your passions. So concentrate not on convincing yourself by increasing the number of proofs of God but on diminishing your passions. You want to find faith and you do not know the way? You want to cure yourself of unbelief and you ask for the remedies? Learn from those who have been bound like you, and who now wager all they have. They are people who know the road you want to follow and have been cured of the affliction of which you want to be cured. Follow the way by which they began: by behaving just as if they believed, taking holy water, having masses said, etc. That will make you believe quite naturally, and according to your animal reactions.' 'But that is what I am afraid of.' 'Why? What do you have to lose?' In order to show you that this is where it leads, it is because it diminishes the passions, which are your great stumbling-blocks, etc.

'How these words carry me away, send me into raptures,' etc. If these words please you and seem worthwhile, you should know that they are spoken by a man who knelt both before and afterwards to beg this infinite and indivisible Being, to whom he submits the whole of himself, that you should also submit yourself, for your own good and for his glory, and that strength might thereby be reconciled with this lowliness.

End of This Discourse

But what harm will come to you from taking this course? You will be faithful, honest, humble, grateful, doing good, a sincere and true friend. It is, of course, true; you will not take part in corrupt pleasure, in glory, in the pleasures of high living. But will you not have others?

I tell you that you will win thereby in this life, and that at every step you take along this path, you will see so much certainty of winning and so negligible a risk, that you will realize in the end that you have wagered on something certain and infinite, for which you have paid nothing. . . .

It is the heart that feels God, not reason: that is what faith is. God felt by the heart, not by reason.

The heart has its reason which reason itself does not know we know that through countless things.

I say that the heart loves the universal being naturally, and itself naturally, according to its own choice. And it hardens itself against one or the other, as it chooses. You have rejected one and kept the other: is it reason that makes you love yourself?

The only knowledge which is contrary to both common sense and human nature is the only one which has always existed among men.

Enlightenment
Creative Societies

[Humans are] willing to join in society with others, who are already united, or have a mind to unite, for the mutual preservation of their lives, liberties and estates, which I call by the general name, property.

—*John Locke,* Two Treatises of Government

The Scientific Method and Social Problems

We began this text with a discussion of how the focus of people changed from the Renaissance to modern times. The early decades, from about 1500 to 1648, were focused on issues of religion and included the turbulent times of the Protestant Reformation. Then, as we have already discussed in part, the period from 1648 to 1789 was dominated by issues about the mode of government. We have seen how the absolute monarchs of those times dominated government through wars and diplomatic intrigues and also brought social changes to bolster their economies and cultural sponsorships, which added to their grandeur. These times were called the Baroque period, and arts and literature reflected the spirit of elaboration, complexity, and demonstration of personal technique that were favored by the monarchies as ways to impress the world.

Although occurring during the same time frame, the Scientific Awakening was not directly related to the absolute monarchs, but was consistent with the spirit of exploration of form and willingness to abandon old concepts that were typical of Baroque thinking. We have discussed in the previous chapter how science emerged as the ultimate source of truth about Nature. After all, if the universe was truly just a large machine, as the findings of Newton and the thinking of Descartes seemed to suggest, then its workings and operation could be understood once the right questions were asked and proper experiments performed. Sometimes, even theoretical solutions, like those of Descartes, would suffice as answers if experiments were not possible, and provided that the reasoning was done within the framework of unbiased and systematic inquiry. This new-found faith in science caused a great sense of optimism in the principles of the scientific method, and people began to believe that the application of the scientific method could solve *all* of humankind's questions.

We will continue to examine this period from 1648 to 1789, when the focus of European thought was on government and its glories. However, in this chapter, we will look directly at how the new confidence in the scientific method affected the views of Europeans toward government.

The Scientific Awakening not only brought great knowledge about the natural world, it also brought a change in attitude about humankind's ability to acquire knowledge in general. Science was empowering to intellectuals of many different interests, even those that dealt with the interactions of people and other highly complex fields. Beginning in the mid-seventeenth century and continuing into the eighteenth century, European intellectuals began to apply the principles of the scientific method to Europe's social problems. This produced a period of social and political awakening similar to the changes that occurred in discovering truths about nature during the Scientific Awakening. Just as the laws of nature seemed to be unfolded to human understanding, basic societal laws seemed to be understood and, with that understanding, came great hope for social improvements. It seemed, to many, that new and dramatic light was flooding society, perhaps something like the light that flooded the Baroque paintings of Caravaggio and Artemisia. This period of social awakening has been called the **Enlightenment.**

■ The Nature of the Enlightenment

The immediate and initial purpose of the Enlightenment was to find the best type of government, generally suggesting changes from the absolutist concepts of Louis XIV and the Stuart monarchs, but also exploring basic values of government and social interactions. Gradually, an interest in all knowledge became a focus of the Enlightenment movement. This concept is symbolized in Figure 35.1.

Because the Enlightenment was an outgrowth of the Scientific Awakening, many of the basic premises of the Enlightenment were firmly rooted in, or extensions of, the ideas of the Scientific Awakening. These basic premises reflect the change in method of inquiry for truth brought by the Scientific Awakening, the change in public attitude about the reliability (truth) of scientific inquiries, and the optimism that resulted from the successes of the scientific method. These Enlightenment premises can be summarized as follows:

■ The entire universe is fully intelligible and governed by natural, rather than supernatural, forces.

■ Rigorous application of the scientific method can answer fundamental questions in all areas of inquiry.

■ Once fundamental principles are known, society can be changed to become aligned with and work within those principles.

Figure 35.1 ■ Enlightenment sees the light of science over the entire world to bring progress.
© 2010 by Fotonium. Used under license of Shutterstock, Inc.

- The human race can be educated about fundamental principles, and then nearly infinite improvement is achievable.
- The rights of the natural man (that is, all humans in their most basic state) are based on natural laws.
- Scientific knowledge is the basis of progress and is equal (superior, for some) to knowledge gained by either religious or philosophical means.
- A belief in God can be based on reason and science rather than just tradition and scripture.
- Unbiased, objective experimentation, followed by careful reasoning to analyze the data, is the method for discovering truth; but in the absence of experimentation, unbiased reasoning can give working theories that will serve as bases for proceeding until the time that experimentation can be conducted.

By applying these fundamental principles, the intellectuals of the Enlightenment were able to achieve great success in describing the natural laws on which society should be built. In keeping with the times, their initial focus was the nature of government. However, experiments into the nature of government were difficult to make. (People who try to make governmental experiments are called *revolutionaries* or *anarchists* and may easily be killed for their experimental attempts.) Therefore, unbiased reasoning became the most common method for applying scientific principles to governmental analysis. This emphasis on careful reasoning has led to an alternate name for the Enlightenment—the **Age of Reason.**

The reasoning of the Enlightenment was communicated principally through books and other writings. These writings have been tremendously influential in history. Some of the early writings strongly influenced and, perhaps, precipitated the changes in England that brought about the modern English governmental system. It is upon these Enlightenment writings that the forefathers of the American government based their extraordinary ideas of government and freedom. It is also on these enlightened writers that the French Revolution was based. Most other modern governments,

either directly or indirectly through copying the English, American, and French models, are also based on the writings of the Enlightenment. Truly this was a period that changed the nature of the world, just as the premises of the Enlightenment assumed.

Because the governmental and social conditions during the seventeenth and early eighteenth century were so different in England, France, and the rest of Europe (especially Germany), the nature of the Enlightenment was quite different in all these areas. The basic principles were similar, but the views of the Enlightenment writers were strongly affected by their own immediate surroundings and were, therefore, different enough that we should look at each area independently. The Enlightenment began in England, then moved to France, and then to the rest of Europe. We will look at each area in that historical order.

■ Foundations of Enlightenment: England

The writings of **Thomas Hobbes** (1588–1679) are a logical place to begin our discussion of the English Enlightenment. Hobbes strongly supported the most basic of scientific principles—the reliability and necessity of empiricism (use of the senses to gain knowledge). He saw empiricism as the only viable method to investigate the universe which was, for him, totally material. He said, *"All that is real is material, and what is not material is not real."* In a very literal sense, Hobbes believed that any knowledge that is not derived from the senses is "nonsense."

We might ask what Hobbes's concept of material reality says about the existence of God. If God is material, then Hobbes's concepts would allow His existence but would question our ability to find out about Him because of the difficulty we would have in performing experiments. If God is immaterial (like a spirit or some ethereal, nonsensory thing), then Hobbes's concepts would say that is nonsense. However, if you say that God is a noncomprehensible Being that we love and obey, that would be acceptable to Hobbes because we would not be saying that God is nonmaterial but merely noncomprehensible. These concepts are not the same. Hobbes did not claim to be able to comprehend all things through sensory perception. However, this statement of noncomprehensibility avoids saying whether God is material. Note, interestingly, that if a person allows that God is spirit but then states that spirit is material, perhaps of a finer and more glorious nature than common matter, Hobbes's objections to the existence of God vanish. Some Enlightenment thinkers asserted that spirit might be matter, as a minister and a scientist suggest in the following quotes:

> *The soul is a substance; for that which is nothing can do nothing. . . . It is not bones and flesh that understand, but a purer substance, as all acknowledge.[1]*
>
> *The original, and still prevailing idea concerning a soul or spirit, is that of a kind of attenuated aerial substance, of a more subtle nature than gross bodies.[2]*

In accord with his assertion of the reality of only material objects and other principles of the new science, Hobbes believed that this material universe was governed by strict laws that dictate the behavior of all things. This belief led Hobbes to deny the existence of free will (a finding generally in opposition to later Enlightenment thinkers). He did not mean that humans are always under the control of another person but, rather, their actions are determined by their responses to the strongest stimuli they encounter within their particular environment. This denial of free will led Hobbes to some strong opinions about the basic nature of humankind and the purpose and need for government. Hobbes is, perhaps, most well known for the political theory that results from these basic beliefs.

After graduating from Oxford and before he had developed his theories of government, Hobbes traveled to Europe where he observed the waning interest in Aristotelian thinking in universities there and sensed the climate in which the new scientific method was developing. When he returned to England, Hobbes met with Francis Bacon and gained an understanding of and love for the new empirical method of pursuing truth.

Hobbes was hired as the tutor and companion for a young nobleman who was about to embark on an extended tour of Europe. During this and later trips, Hobbes became interested in geometry. On one trip Hobbes traveled to Italy where he met with Galileo and, under his influence, resolved to apply the principles of geometry and natural science to social issues.

When Hobbes returned to England, he found a country embroiled in a fight between the king and parliament. In this climate, the logical and most relevant social issue to which he would apply the scientific method was government. Hobbes therefore began his work in developing a science-based theory on the legitimate purpose of government and its most ideal form. Interestingly, the several types of government that existed in England in the seventeenth century—absolute monarchy, parliamentary republic, dictatorship, and limited monarchy—became a type of experimental laboratory for Enlightenment ideas. It is little wonder then, that under such dynamic conditions, the Enlightenment began in England.

Hobbes began his study by considering the state of humans before governments existed, that is, the primitive state. His strong belief in determinism and the absence of free will led him to the conclusion that the lives of primitive people were, in his words, *"solitary, poor, nasty, brutish, and short"* and in a constant state of *"warre,"* living in *"continual fear and danger of violent death."* This famous description of the state of primitive humans reflects Hobbes's general pessimism about human capabilities. Hobbes argued that war, not harmony and goodness, is the basic state of humankind, and that this can be seen through an examination of history.

Hobbes's logical conclusion from this understanding was that humans could only avoid anarchy by uniting through a set of mutual covenants to form a commonwealth. He thought this commonwealth would be like a great living entity—in his term, a **Leviathan**—which is the name he gave to the book in which these ideas are most fully given. Of course, some person or entity must make decisions on behalf of the commonwealth. That person or entity would be the sovereign authority within the commonwealth and would be the embodiment of government. Hobbes realized that the sovereign could be a person, like a king, or some organization, like a parliament. Hobbes felt that a hereditary monarch would be able to rule without the internal conflicts inherent in a parliament and would, therefore, be the most effective type of sovereign.

Hobbes was careful to note that the covenants that established the commonwealth and sovereign were not between the people and the sovereign but, rather, between the people themselves. Therefore, if some of the citizens decided that the sovereign was not acceptable, they did not have the right to remove the sovereign because that action would constitute a violation of their covenant with their fellow citizens. Hobbes, therefore, condemned the actions of the English Parliament in overthrowing King Charles I as a violation of the covenants made with other English citizens.

When the English Civil War began in 1640, Hobbes fled to France to avoid problems over his strong royalist opinions. In 1646 he was employed as the tutor to the young English prince who would later assume the throne as Charles II. King Charles I was killed in 1649 and Parliament took control of the English government and established a state which they called, interestingly, the Commonwealth (Hobbes's term). While in Europe, Hobbes wrote several books, including *Leviathan.*

When it was safe for him, Hobbes returned to England and began a series of debates against those that disputed the royalist view. These debates lasted for the next two decades. His opinions were obviously unpopular with supporters of Oliver Cromwell and the Commonwealth, but were also disputed by the Calvinists, who believed strongly in human free will. (Generally, the supporters of the Commonwealth were also strong Calvinists.) Hobbes continued his work on government but seemed to gain renewed interest in geometry. However, these latter works were also strongly criticized as being mathematically incorrect. Hobbes disagreed with the critics and de-

fended his geometrical works to the end. He also worked on English translations of *The Iliad* and *The Odyssey,* which were completed when he was 87 years old, just four years before his death.

His accomplishments in political thought were fundamental to the Enlightenment. Some Enlightenment thinkers agreed with Hobbes. Others, perhaps the majority, disagreed. However, even those who disagreed generally cited Hobbes as a point of reference for their works. Many even used his terminology. Furthermore, his wide interests and strong support of science became a beneficial model for other Enlightenment thinkers who were to follow.

After his death, the views of Hobbes were used to justify European colonization of "inferior" natives, who seemed to have a high degree of warfare. The Europeans viewed themselves as protectors or policemen of the "savages" and felt that their improved civilization should rule over the natives. The Europeans viewed themselves as basically peaceful, and described their own wars as being "rationally justified" and therefore within the acceptable limits of a civilized society.

John Locke (1632–1704) was, like Hobbes, a strong empiricist who wrote about the nature of discovering truth and the limits of human knowledge. Locke was trained as both a philosopher and a physician and became friends to several renowned English scientists such as Isaac Newton, Robert Boyle, and Robert Hooke. He had excellent scientific credentials and was elected a Fellow of the Royal Society.

Locke became intimately involved in the English Civil War and was forced to flee England during the reign of Charles II and James II. (Locke and Hobbes were on opposite sides in the English Civil War.) Locke actively worked for the establishment of a constitutional monarchy and, when it was established, returned to England and participated in the government. His works during the period of political upheaval are among the most influential in the entire Enlightenment period. With respect to America, he has been called "the forefather of our forefathers." Thomas Jefferson and Benjamin Franklin relied extensively on Lockean ideas and even used some of Locke's exact wording in the Declaration of Independence. We can certainly profit from a brief discussion of his life and works.

As a youth, Locke was sent to the Westminster School, where he was exposed to strongly royalist views. Upon completing his studies there, Locke attended Christ Church College, Oxford where he came under the influence of Puritan scholars who controlled the college at that time. Locke graduated with degrees in philosophy and medicine, gradually earning a master's degree as well. Locke continued at Oxford, where he taught moral philosophy, wrote a treatise entitled *Essays on the Law of Nature,* and did medical research. He also supervised an operation in which a cyst was successfully removed from the liver of a prominent English nobleman, Lord Shaftesbury. The nobleman then hired Locke to be his personal physician. Locke accepted and moved to Lord Shaftesbury's residence in London. It was about this time that Locke was elected a Fellow of the Royal Society.

Only a few years after moving to London, Locke published the first draft of a highly important work dealing with the basic nature of knowledge—*An Essay Concerning Human Understanding.* In this work, Locke admitted that understanding how we understand is difficult. However, our ability to reason raises us above the animals and gives us the ability to act freely. In this he disagreed with Hobbes. Locke's beliefs about free will are connected to his strong belief in God and His interactions with humans, as can be seen in the following comments by Locke:

For God having given man an understanding to direct his actions, has allowed him a freedom of will, and liberty of acting, as properly belonging thereunto, within the bounds of that law he is under.

In spite of the innate understanding that humans obtained from their Creator, Locke believed that a baby's mind was a blank sheet (*tabula rasa*) and would be filled only by experience. Locke was, therefore, an empiricist since experience is ultimately based on the senses. He admitted, however,

that if human knowledge originates only from experience, it is limited in the scope of what we can know with certainty. For instance, he says that we can know the attributes of material substances but cannot know, for sure, their inner natures. He allowed, however, that the corpuscular (atomic) theory was a reasonable and highly probable theory to describe the inner nature of these materials, but was not certain since it could not be studied with our senses.

Locke admitted that because we could not be certain of some knowledge, our minds could revert to some deeper, intuitive sense or to some revealed source that might give us confidence with a high probability that this uncertain knowledge was true. In other words, the senses are the source for knowledge, but when the senses are unable to arrive at certainty, intuition or revelation can add confidence to our sensory knowledge. He believes, however, that even revelatory knowledge is subject to some reason. He said,

Because the Mind, not being certain of the Truth of that it evidently does not know, but only yielding to the Probability that appears to it, is bound to give up its assent to such Testimony, which, it is satisfied, comes from one who cannot err, and will not deceive. But yet, it still belongs to Reason, to judge of the truth of its being a Revelation, and of the significance of the Words, wherein it is delivered. (IV. 18. 8., p. 694)

Therefore, Locke understood that there were two ways of acquiring or interpreting knowledge—from the senses and from reflection. The sensory knowledge is about the world around us. Reflection allows us to compare sensory knowledge and to make judgments about abstract concepts such as the foundations of mathematics, truth, and justice. We note that sensory knowledge is linear thinking, whereas reflective thinking is lateral. They involve both sides of our brain and, together, give us a totality of knowledge.

Locke's employer, Lord Shaftesbury, was the founder of the Whig movement that formed a coalition of several members of Parliament and others with similar interests. The Whigs pressed the crown for favorable decisions and otherwise tried to influence the actions of government. The Whigs wanted, among other things, to exclude the Catholic James, the brother of King Charles II, from rights to succession. The measure passed the House of Commons but did not pass the House of Lords because Charles II dissolved Parliament. Shortly thereafter, Lord Shaftesbury was accused of treason when he backed a revolt to replace King Charles II and his brother, James II. Shaftesbury was obliged to flee to Holland to preserve his life. As a member of Shaftesbury's household, Locke had become heavily involved in politics and, along with Shaftesbury, fled to Holland.

When King James II was overthrown in the Glorious Revolution, Locke returned to England, actually escorting the new queen, Mary. Locke became a member of the household of another nobleman (Shaftesbury had died in Holland) and also accepted a position with the government. These positions gave Locke adequate time to write. His most important work on the nature of government, the *Second Treatise of Civil Government,* was published in this period, as was a second version of his work on human understanding. (The *First Treatise of Civil Government* is a reply to another author on the subject of Divine Right of Kings. Although important, especially in Locke's time, the *Second Treatise of Civil Government* has been far more important in a long historical view and is the portion of Locke's writings we will focus upon.)

Locke's *Second Treatise of Civil Government* laid the philosophical foundation for a constitutional government. In this highly influential work he stated that humans originally lived in chaos or anarchy before the formation of government. This chaotic situation was highly disagreeable and so humans joined together and formed governments to protect their "natural rights" of life, liberty, and property as Locke indicated in the quotation extracted at the beginning of this chapter and given more fully below.

If man in the state of nature be so free, as has been said; if he be absolute lord of his own person and possessions, equal to the greatest, and subject to no body, why will he part with his freedom? Why will he give up this empire, and subject himself to the dominion and controul of any other power? To which it is obvious to answer, that though in the state of nature he hath such a right, yet the enjoyment of it is very uncertain, and constantly exposed to the invasion of others: for all being kings as much as he, every man his equal, and the greater part no strict observers of equity and justice, the enjoyment of the property he has in this state is very unsafe, very unsecure. This makes him willing to quit a condition, which, however free, is full of fears and continual dangers: and it is not without reason, that he seeks out, and is willing to join in society with others, who are already united, or have a mind to unite, for the mutual preservation of their lives, liberties and estates, which I call by the general name, property. (2nd Tr., §123)

This arrangement between the government and the people became known as the "social contract." The citizens gave up some control over their freedom to the government so that they could obtain protection of natural rights. Locke further argued that because these natural rights existed before the formation of government, the government cannot take away those natural rights. Any government that oversteps its proper function of protecting the natural rights becomes a tyranny and the citizenship then has a right and responsibility to overthrow that government. This right to overthrow a tyranny was explicitly cited by the American revolutionaries in the Declaration of Independence. The British Parliament recognized the work of Locke in this Declaration, and many British parliamentarians were sympathetic to this element of the American cause.

You might have noticed that Locke's phrase is "lives, liberties, and estates" rather than the more familiar version of the American Declaration of "life, liberty, and the pursuit of happiness." The American version is still within the general Lockean view, because Locke believed that happiness comes from freedom and, further, freedom can only be achieved within the context of economic liberty and private property.

While there are some similarities between the ideas of Hobbes and Locke, the differences between their philosophies are important to understand. Both thinkers agreed that primitive humans lived in a state of chaos and disorder and that government was created to bring order and security. On the one hand, Hobbes believed than humans were inherently evil in nature and little better than animals. Locke, on the other hand, believed humans were basically good and were endowed by God with the ability to reason, thus raising them above the animals.

According to Hobbes, government was required to force humans to stay in line, to behave, to do the right thing. Hobbes said that government exists to save society from itself. Hobbes also believed that humans surrendered their rights to the commonwealth (the Leviathan) when they joined together to form a government, thus prohibiting any group of citizens from unilaterally changing the government.

Locke argued that government was created to protect human rights of life, liberty, and property, and that people retained these rights, which were natural and innate in all humans, even after the government was established. According to Locke, government derives its power from and is a tool of the people, not an overseer. If government does not fulfill its mission of protecting the natural rights of humans, they have the right and obligation to change the government.

Locke continued to live comfortably with his noble friends, to serve in the government, and to write and give speeches about his ideas. He died in 1704 and was widely recognized as the leading spokesman for the concepts of constitutional monarchy that was then in place in England.

The rise of limited monarchies, based on the philosophical underpinnings for this form of government that Locke established, began an important change in the direction of history and the world. The era of the absolute monarch was dying. Soon, across Europe and the world, the masses would demand more responsible forms of govern-ments that guaranteed liberties and equality. The revolution of the English Civil War, beginning with the creation of the English Commonwealth and later completed during the Glorious Revolution with the creation of a true limited monarchy, would be imitated all across the world. The revolutionary political and social commentary that existed in the writings of men like John Locke could not be contained. From these events we see the philosophical and political origins of the modern world.

Both Locke and Hobbes were trained as experimental scientists and both made some contributions to science. Their first writings were about the scientific method and the pursuit of knowledge (focusing on empiricism). Then, both were caught up in the political turmoil of the English Civil War and the struggles over the nature of a proper government. Both Locke and Hobbes then applied their scientific methods of reasoning to the governmental situation. They were able to see some of their ideas actually carried out. In this, they had a quite unique chance to see "experimentation" in government. This must have been very satisfying to their scientific natures.

Note also that Locke and Hobbes demonstrated both depth and breadth in their lives. The depth was shown in their scientific work. They then demonstrated breadth in applying their knowledge and methods to governmental and societal issues. This combination of depth and breadth is, of course, one of the keys to their creativity.

▪ Popular Writing in the English Enlightenment

A rather unexpected factor that contributed to the English Enlightenment was the development of the popular novel. The success of Cervantes's *Don Quixote* had encouraged the writing of more novels. The English, with their long emphasis on literature, as opposed to the visual arts, were especially drawn to the novel as an art form. Several English authors were quite successful, some of whom we discussed previously as novelists of the Baroque period. Daniel Defoe's novels *Robinson Crusoe* and *Moll Flanders,* and Henry Fielding's *Tom Jones* were all very popular. The success of the novel helped spread the ideals of the Enlightenment because it popularized reading, which largely had still been the domain of the educated and wealthy. Furthermore, many of these novels encouraged the ideas of the Enlightenment within their plots. Both the novels of Defoe and Fielding exhibited the free and conquering spirit of humanity. These novels also taught the principle that with ingenuity and good native sense, all obstacles can be overcome.

Some English writers, especially those who were born in the latter part of the seventeenth century, were focused more precisely on the two key elements of the English Enlightenment—human knowledge and politics. We will consider in depth two of the most important of these writers—Alexander Pope and Jonathan Swift. Their approaches to literature were very creative and very different. One used poetry and the other used satire. In both cases, they were among the best who have ever written in those genres. After looking at Pope and Swift, we will briefly consider several other British Enlightenment writers who also made unique and highly creative contributions to our civilization.

Alexander Pope was a poet and essayist who was a key figure in Enlightenment thinking on the knowledge and state of man. He was also important in moving society to a rekindled interest in the ancient classics, which led to the period of Neoclassicism, an important movement in art and literature following the Baroque. Pope translated the works of Homer and others into English. Pope's translations were excellent and the epics of Homer (and other Classical works) became quite popular. Pope also realized that the classics were somewhat difficult for the average person and so he wrote detailed commentaries on them.

Early in life, Pope became fascinated with poetry and literature and delved into the great authors and poets of the English, French, Italian, Latin, and Greek languages. Largely self-taught, Pope reflected that these years of study and discovery were the happiest of his life. Alexander Pope immersed himself so completely in great literature that the language and style of the great au-

thors and poets became his own, and he became an accomplished writer himself.

Pope wrote carefully constructed poetry. He used rhymed iambic pentameter (10 syllables per line). His writings often used Latin-based syllables but with Anglo-Saxon (German) phrasing and power, thus uniting the two parts of the English language. This created poems with beauty and power. Pope's poetry is generally sprinkled with many catchy and quotable lines. You may be familiar with a few of Pope's maxims such as: "fools rush in where angels fear to tread," "hope springs eternal in the human breast," "virtue alone is happiness below," and "whatever is, is right."

Pope's poetic essays were his most influential writings, especially on the thinking of the Enlightenment. Pope's *Essay on Man* reflects the spirit of the Enlightenment in its presentation of humans as having the preeminent position in the world and in God's scheme of life. However, the *Essay on Man* also pokes fun at human folly. In particular, Pope suggests that we consider how foolish we are to cry out against difficult circumstances. He wants us to realize that the plan of God was to make the earth as a great machine that ran according to natural and fixed laws. We have only a limited view of the plan and, moreover, will not be able to change those laws and will frustrate ourselves by trying. Perhaps two excerpts from Pope's writings will illustrate these points.

Yet cry, If man's unhappy, God's unjust;
If man alone engross not Heaven's high care,
Alone made perfect here, immortal there:
Snatch from His hand the balance and the rod,
Re-judge His justice, be the god of God.
In pride, in reas'ning pride, our error lies;
All quit their sphere and rush into the skies.

And,

All Nature is but art unknown to thee
All chance, direction, which thou canst not see;
All discord, harmony not understood;
All partial evil, universal good:
And, spite of pride, in erring reason's spite,
One truth is clear, Whatever is, is right.

Pope's statement of "Whatever is, is right" is an affirmation of the idea that God, being perfect, kind, and loving, created the most perfect world possible. Therefore, according to Pope, we need to accept God's infinite wisdom and goodness and take the long view of suffering—that whatever happens is somehow for our best good. Later, we will discuss Voltaire, a French Enlightenment author who broke with this view of events. Voltaire believed that a generous and kind God would not allow the suffering that is seen in the world. Therefore, Voltaire began to question the existence of God. Voltaire also believed that when humans state that all is according to God's plan, a sense of fatalism is demonstrated. Voltaire believed, therefore, that humans should take a very active role in relieving the suffering of others because this suffering was not the will of God but, rather, either a natural occurrence or the result of some act of other humans.

Another theme in the *Essay on Man* is that of hope or optimism. For Pope, humans had entered an era where they could discover truth and solve society's problems. He believed that we should accept the situations of life that are beyond our control, and strive to improve them when within the realm of our personal power.

> *What future bliss, He gives not thee to know,*
> *But gives that hope to be thy blessing now.*
> *Hope springs eternal in the human breast:*
> *Man never Is, but always to be blest.*
> *The soul, uneasy, and confined from home,*
> *Rests and expatiates in a life to come.*

Pope's major contribution to government was his belief that the world ran best on ancient principles. His view was not uncommon in England. They can also be seen in the efforts of Founding Fathers of the United States to blend ancient Greek democracy with the Roman idea of a Republic, in which the various branches of government were balanced and self-regulating through checks and balances.

Pope's writing style and comments on life were widely admired during his lifetime. A book of famous historical quotations published by Oxford University Press has more than 200 quotations from Pope. He was accepted into the circle of English Enlightenment intellectuals but was, in several ways, apart. He was born to a Catholic family, was physically deformed (from a spine disease that twisted his body and stunted his growth), was educated largely at home, and was never married. Yet, in spite of what must have been a very unusual life, his insights into human life are profound. One of the most insightful is a comment on parents and children that is as poignant in our day as it must have been in his.

> *We think our fathers fools, so wise we grow;*
> *Our wiser sons, no doubt, will think us so.*

Jonathan Swift (1667–1745), one of the group of Enlightenment intellectuals who befriended Pope, was a brilliant satirist who lived much of his life in Ireland and strongly fostered the Irish cause against the tyrannical English. Swift also commented on English life in general, various professions, English government, and the nature of foreign relations and war. All of this was done with superbly subtle satire.

If we examine the tone of his novel *Gulliver's Travels* and his darkly satirical pamphlet *A Modest Proposal,* Swift seemed to hate humanity. In reality though, it was not humanity Swift hated, but injustice. Jonathan Swift did have a low opinion of humankind as a whole, however, and did not believe that humans should be automatically defined as rational beings, but as animals capable of reason. Swift used his gift as a writer to point out the faults and follies of individuals, nations, and mankind in general because he felt that mankind usually did not live up to its potential. By using satire to expose injustice and inhumanity, Swift hoped to bring about positive change.

Swift's novel *Gulliver's Travels* is a biting satire of English society during his lifetime. It was, however, an immediate success. Alexander Pope comments on the book of his friend by saying that "it is universally read, from the cabinet council to the nursery." It has likely never been out of print since its first publication in 1726. An important twentieth-century British writer, George Orwell, declared it to be among the six most indispensible books in world literature.

Gulliver's Travels presents itself as the personal narrative of an English sailor, Lemuel Gulliver, who suffers through a series of ship and exploring mishaps (such as wreckages and pirate raids) that cast him into four very unusual lands. To some readers, especially children and youths, *Gulliver's Travels* is a charming, if unbelievable, adventure story. To more discerning readers, it is a spoof of the adventure genre that was popular in Swift's day. But, to those who are familiar with the satirical style and acquainted with English society and government, the book is full of biting and humorous comments about the foibles and stupidities of English people and institutions.

The first of the four journeys begins when Gulliver is washed ashore on Lilliput. He there encounters a race of miniature beings that are about one-twelfth the size of a normal human. They struggle to ensnare this gigantic visitor but finally accept him when Gulliver pledges to behave properly. Gulliver finds himself embroiled in a war between the Lilliputians and their neighbors, which he helps the Lilliputians win. However, when he refuses to help them enslave their defeated neighbors, he is forced to flee. From the many political comments made in this story, astute observers can tell that it is really about King George I and his policies. This famous story is commemorated in a park in Valencia, Spain, as shown in Figure 35.2.

The second journey is a visit to a land, Brobdingnag, where the inhabitants are about 12 times larger than humans. In this land Gulliver becomes a pet of the king, with whom he discusses the general nature of European life. The king is disdainful of what he hears.

The third journey occurs when Gulliver's ship is overcome by pirates and he is abandoned on a rocky shore. There he is rescued by the inhabitants

Figure 35.2 ■ A park in Spain commemorating Gulliver's Travels. *© 2010 by Sillycoke. Used under license of Shutterstock, Inc.*

of the flying island of Laputa. Gulliver observes the effects of a single-minded, perhaps fanatical, pursuit of science. He describes the scientists on the flying island thusly:

Their Houses are very ill built, the Walls bevil without one right Angle in any Apartment; and this Defect ariseth from the Contempt they bear to practical Geometry; which they despise as vulgar and mechanick, those Instructions they give being too refined for the Intellectuals of their Workmen; which occasions perpetual Mistakes. And although they are dextrous enough upon a Piece of Paper in the Management of the Rule, the Pencil, and the Divider, yet in the common Actions and Behaviour of Life, I have not seen a more clumsy, awkward, and unhandy People, nor so slow and perplexed in their Conceptions upon all other Subjects, except those of Mathematicks and Musick. They are very bad Reasoners, and vehemently given to Opposition, unless when they happen to be of the right Opinion, which is seldom their Case. Imagination, Fancy, and Invention, they are wholly Strangers to, nor have any Words in their Language by which those Ideas can be expressed; the whole Compass of their Thoughts and Mind, being shut up within the two forementioned Sciences.

Swift's comments about the scientific method are decidedly different from the praises given it by Bacon, Hobbes, and Locke. We smile at Swift's characterizations, especially as we recall scientists who resemble his descriptions. We also remember his words, in part because of their exaggerations.

The fourth journey of Gulliver was to Houyhnhnm or "perfection of nature," where the horses are in charge and a group of wild human-like creatures, the Yahoos, live naked in the woods and cause mischief and act badly. The Yahoos represent humans in their most gross and barbaric form. Although Gulliver looks like the Yahoos (but with clothes), his ability to speak convinces the Houyhnhnms (horses) that he should at least be brought into their court, where he is treated with respect and enjoys many delightful conversations with the king of the Houyhnhnms, who Gulliver admires greatly. (The horses represent the best of society.)

In those conversations, Gulliver describes various aspects of English civilization. Many of these descriptions are viewed by the king with great dismay and some ridicule. The king is amazed that a society that holds itself out as a leader among nations could have people and institutions that are as blatantly ridiculous as those described by Gulliver. This is, of course, more of the satirical social commentary that Swift had seemed to master. Here is an example in which Gulliver comments on lawyers.

I said there was a Society of Men among us, bred up from their Youth in the Art of proving by Words multiplied for the Pleasure, that White *is* Black, *and* Black *is* White, *according as they are paid. To this Society all the rest of the People are Slaves.*

For Example, if my Neighbor hath a Mind to my Cow, *he hires a Lawyer to prove that he ought to have my* Cow *from me. I must then hire another to defend my Right, it being against all Rules of Law that any Man should be allowed to speak for himself. Now in this Case, I, who am the right Owner, lie under two great Disadvantages. First, my Lawyer being practiced almost from his Cradle in defending Falsehood; is quite out of his Element when he would be an Advocate for Justice, which as an Office unnatural, he always attempts with great Awkwardness if not with Ill-will. The second Disadvantage is, that my Lawyer must proceed with great Caution: Or else he will be reprimanded by the Judges, and abhorred by his Brethren, as one that would lessen the Practice of the Law. And therefore I have but two Methods to preserve my* Cow. *The first is, to gain over my Adversary's Lawyer with a double Fee; who will then betray his Client by insinuating that he hath Justice on his Side. The second way is for my Lawyer to make my Cause appear as unjust as he can;*

by the Cow *to belong to my Adversary; and
this, if it be skillfully done, will certainly bespeak the Favour of the Bench. . . .*

*It is a Maxim among these Lawyers, that
whatever hath been done before, may legally
be done again: And therefore they take special Care to record all the Decisions formerly made against common Justice and the
general Reason of Mankind. These, under
the Name of* Precedents, *they produce as Authorities to justify the most iniquitous Opinions; and the Judges never fail of decreeing
accordingly.*

*In pleading, they studiously avoid enter-
ing into the* Merits *of the Cause; but are loud,
violent and tedious in swelling upon all Circumstances which are not to the Purpose. For
Instance, in the Case already mentioned:
They never desire to know what Claim or Title
my Adversary hath to my* Cow; *but whether
the said* Cow *were Red or Black; her Horns
long or short; whether the Field I graze her in
be round or square; whether she were milked
at home or abroad; what Diseases she is subject to, and the like. After which they consult*
Precedents, *adjourn the Cause, from Time to
Time, and in Ten, Twenty, or Thirty Years come
to an Issue.*

Despite his disdain for politicians, Swift was quite
politically active himself. He was a strong supporter of the English monarchy and the Anglican
Church. Swift was also an ardent Irish Tory and
worked for Ireland's independence from Great
Britain. In defense of the Irish cause, Swift wrote
his tract *A Modest Proposal for Preventing the
Children of Poor People in Ireland from Being a
Burden to Their Parents or Country, and for Making Them Beneficial to the Public.* The title of the
pamphlet itself is a parody of the over-lengthy titles common in his day. The satiric nature of the
work is immediately apparent when the reader realizes that Swift's "modest proposal" is to fatten
up Irish infants so that they can then be sold as a
luxury food item to the English gentry. Swift argues, with his tongue firmly in his cheek, that his
plan would raise money for poor and starving

Irish families as well as save the state the cost of
taking care of them. His satire is biting and, because of the social commentary that underlies it,
strongly critical of current English society. By
presenting such a disgusting idea in a seemingly
sincere political tract, Swift hoped to make the
point that the English treatment of the Irish was
already little better than his "modest proposal."

The freedom with which Swift wrote is, itself,
a testimony to the effects of the Enlightenment
in England. If Swift were to attempt writing such
satire in contemporary France, he would be arrested and likely killed.

Other British writers were able to similarly
enjoy the freedom of expression available in the
constitutional monarchy of the early eighteenth
century in Britain. One of them, David Hume, was
a Scottish philosopher who gave empiricism a
strong philosophical basis. He was also one of the
leaders of a group of intellectuals who wrote and
taught at various Scottish universities. This group
was responsible for what has been called the Scottish Enlightenment.

David Hume (1711–1776) was very well
known during his own life, but was not widely
supported in his views. However, within the
intellectual community, he was appreciated as a
brilliant writer and logician. He was also a good
friend and mentor to many who sought to further
the intellectual state of humans.

Hume wrote, among other topics, about the
basic assumptions of science and often challenged
conventionally held beliefs. For example, he questioned the nature of cause and effect. Hume noted
that when we see two events occur sequentially,
we really don't observe any necessary connection
between them. Rather, when we see two events
that always occur together, we tend to form an expectation that when the first occurs, the second is
likely to follow. The expectation is the linkage we
call *cause and effect*. It is not sure but, rather, intuitive and based on common sense. Hume seems
to have believed that this intuitive sense of cause
and effect arose from our nervous system and was
conditioned over time and experience. Hume believed that this same conditioning of our nervous
systems leads us to attempt to draw expectations

of future events from past experience (predictability) and also to form theories of Nature from individual experiments (inductive reasoning). Hume rejected all other explanations for predictability and induction, thus reducing both of these to intuition and common sense as well.

Hume's insistence on the uncertainty of these basic scientific principles led him to a deep skepticism about knowledge. He seemed to be forced into saying that mankind is not truly rational but, rather, is a product of sensations and impressions that are merely brought together by probability. Hume then applied this same reasoning to the topic of God. Hume did not believe that any rational arguments could be formed that demonstrated the existence of God. Yet, Hume seemed to temper this skepticism about science and God with a realization that humans need some form of continuity and custom. He accepted custom, the sum of human experience, as a healthy foundation on which to build a life.

Adam Smith (1723–1790), another of the Scottish Enlightenment, was the developer (describer) of the economic system known as **capitalism.** His works describe the economic system that now serves as the basis for most of the modern world.

Smith was a Scottish professor who was given the chance of a lifetime when a wealthy young aristocrat invited Smith to serve as his companion and chaperone on a tour of Europe. Smith, who had no family, readily accepted. While on the trip, Adam Smith had no financial worries and little to do, so he decided to write a book.

Smith's book, *The Wealth of Nations,* outlined the formation of an economic system that became known as capitalism. Within *The Wealth of Nations* Smith advocated that government and other forces should be restrained in their actions with business. He called this stance *laissez-faire la nature,* meaning, "let nature take its course." Smith felt that governments and industries should not attempt to control or manipulate the economy. He believed that a hands-off approach, with the marketplace driven simply by the laws of supply and demand, would provide the healthiest and most stable economy. Smith argued that a capitalist system would

help to curb inflation and reduce the problems of over- and underproduction.

Capitalism, as proposed by Adam Smith, was a radical break with the predominate economic system of the day—mercantilism. **Mercantilism** was an economic system where the government closely and carefully regulated most aspects of the economy. It required the extraction of raw materials from colonies so that they could be made into finished products in the home country and then sold to other places, including back to the colonies. Under mercantilism, the government determined who could extract what resources and who could turn them into manufactured goods. Furthermore, it regulated prices and determined to whom the finished product could be sold. The government collected taxes at various places throughout the production: at the time the raw materials were extracted, when they were manufactured into goods, and when they were sold. Mercantilism was often profitable for the home countries but had many serious drawbacks, such as price fixing, inflation, monopolies, and the continual need for more colonies from which the raw materials could be extracted.

Smith believed that by allowing the economy to govern itself, people would, in general, become more prosperous and the government would make more money in the long run. He believed that a capitalist economy, if left to itself, would be self-compensating. He described the "invisible hand" of the marketplace in which people would, through self-interest, find the most advantageous way to conduct business and that, ultimately, this most advantageous way would also be the best for the economy as a whole.

Edward Gibbon (1737–1794) is the last of the English Enlightenment authors that we will discuss. His great work, *The History of the Decline and Fall of the Roman Empire,* was published in 1776, the same year as Smith's *The Wealth of Nations.* Whereas Smith's book looked to the present and future, Gibbon's work tried to make sense out of the past. He retold the history of Rome, which he investigated while visiting Italy, and then related the problems of ancient Rome to those he perceived in contemporary England.

There was, of course, an implied suggestion for English society to reform.

Perhaps the most controversial of Gibbon's conclusions is that Christianity was a chief cause of the Roman downfall. He talked of the greatest periods of Rome as those times when paganism reigned supreme. When Christianity became an important focus of the Roman state, he reported that "the church and even the state were distracted by religious factions, whose conflicts were sometimes bloody and always implacable; the attention of the emperors was diverted from camps to synods; the Roman world was oppressed by a new species of tyranny, and the persecuted sects became the secret enemies of their country." He then went on to enumerate many medieval problems, which he also attributed to religion.

Gibbon's personal religion was first Anglican, he then converted to Catholicism in college, and then to **Deism.** This latter belief, which became very prominent among Enlightenment thinkers, is a belief that God created the world but then withdrew from active involvement in its affairs. Most Deists also believed that God obeyed his own laws; therefore, if he chose to become involved in the world, he would be limited in his power because of his respect for laws. Deists deny the existence of revelation and hold to no special book as coming from God. The concept of God as a great watchmaker, with the universe as a watch, is commonly held among Deists. In this regard, Deism has a strong affinity with deterministic science. Some compare a Deist's belief to a worship of nature, although Deists generally deny that and point to their insistence that God is rational, a trait not attributable to nature.

Deists are highly skeptical of organized religion and, in general, do not participate in it. In some societies, this view has led to their religious persecution and exclusion from certain parts of society. (Such persecution and exclusion was especially common in highly religious societies such as France.) This separation from organized religion has resulted in some difficulties for Deists in establishing personal ethical or moral standards. Such standards would have to be dictated totally by reason. To the extent that reason is valu-

able in this regard, the Deist's values are good. However, as several Enlightenment writers have pointed out, reason can be highly dependent on experience and, moreover, is often subject to external forces. Although Deism is less popular today than in the latter Enlightenment period, it continues to be a belief of many people.

In spite of the controversies attendant to it, Gibbon's book is arguably the finest history ever written. It is an inspiration to historians and to those who appreciate beautiful English prose. It is, most of all, a brilliant, sustained, and extraordinarily shrewd critique of the fraility of the human condition.

■ The Enlightenment in France

Because of the repressive political climate under Louis XIV and the powerful French arm of the Catholic Church, French intellectuals and scientists were not able to speak out about the origins of knowledge and about government in any way that might be interpreted as negative to the Church or the state. Even works in which God's existence was explicitly taught, like Descartes's *Discourse on Method,* were suppressed for other reasons that the Church considered objectionable. Therefore, the French Enlightenment was suppressed during the seventeenth century when Hobbes and Locke were actively discussing the fundamental concepts of the scientific method and applying that method to the institutions of government and society in general.

However, in a strange and somewhat humorous way, the suppression of intellectuals in France led to the establishment of the French Enlightenment. One of the French intellectuals, Voltaire, who we will consider in some detail, was banished from France and went to England. There he was highly impressed by English science, the openness of English society, England's multidenominational church environment, and the improving nature of England's government. When Voltaire returned to France, he began to disseminate these concepts within France. That was the beginning of the French Enlightenment.

The group of French intellectuals who wrote about Enlightenment concepts became known as the *philosophes.* Some would translate this as "philosophers," but the French meaning is not a traditional philosopher, as we think of them today, but, rather, this group of innovators of the early eighteenth century who, as we will see, laid the foundation for great changes within the French nation.

Voltaire, whose real name was François Marie Arouet, lived from 1694 to 1778 and is considered the father of the French Enlightenment. The son of a comfortable middle-class family, Voltaire was educated by the Jesuits. In spite of his religious education, Voltaire became critical of the Catholic Church and said that the Bible was merely a collection of anecdotes. This rebellious attitude became typical of Voltaire's life. He was also an outspoken critic of many of society's institutions, such as social hierarchy and government, and believed that these things were often oppressive and unfair. He fought against any indication of what he considered to be superstition, repression, fanaticism, and cruelty. Voltaire called these evils the "infamous thing" and his rallying cry became *"Écrasez l'infâme"* ("Crush the infamous thing").

However, Voltaire also believed that people had the right to hold their own opinion, and he defended their right to choose their own beliefs even while he tried to convince them that those beliefs were wrong. He resented any person or institution, such as the monarchy or the church, that tried to dictate opinion and silence dissent. Voltaire reportedly supported this belief by saying, "I do not agree with a word you say, but I will defend to the death your right to say it."

Voltaire's opinions earned him many friends in France but they also made him many enemies, especially among those parts of society that he regularly attacked. One such occasion caused an offended nobleman to hire a gang of thugs to beat up Voltaire. Another verbal attack, this time on the regent of France, resulted in Voltaire being thrown into prison in the Bastille. Voltaire gained his freedom only by agreeing to leave France.

Voltaire moved to London for three years, where he was a dedicated observer of English so-ciety. While in England Voltaire became impressed with the scientific discoveries of Newton (who had died only a few years previously) and, when he returned to France, translated Newton's writings into French with the help of his mistress, Madame du Châtelet. Having gained an interest in science, Voltaire and Madame du Châtelet established a laboratory in their chalet, where they then made several minor scientific discoveries of their own.

The greater religious and political freedoms that existed in England (as opposed to France) were appealing to Voltaire, and he developed a love for England and its people. This love even saved Voltaire a severe beating on one occasion when Voltaire was attacked in London. The crowd had strong anti-French feelings and had surrounded Voltaire, who they knew to be French. However, just as they became dangerous, Voltaire was able to save himself by saying, "My friends, am I not punished enough just by being born a Frenchman rather than an Englishman?"

His exile to England had taught him to be more careful in his words and actions. Upon his return to France, Voltaire sometimes denied writing things that he had obviously written in order to avoid problems with the government. Voltaire even purchased an estate on the border between France and Switzerland so that he could avoid officials of either country by fleeing to an area of his estate in the other country. (Certainly a creative solution for where he would live.)

Voltaire was a talented and prolific writer, and it was nearly impossible for French or church officials to escape his biting opinion as he wrote more than 70 books, 50 plays, and 70,000 messages and letters to friends. On top of his own writings were his unnumbered comments in the press and to decision makers in important meetings. In a very real sense, Voltaire became the voice and physical embodiment of the French Enlightenment.

His most famous work is the novel *Candide,* a satirical story that lampoons the boundless optimism of the Scientific Awakening. One of the characters of *Candide* was named "Pangloss," which means "all talk," and he seemed to represent the unbounded optimism and effective fatalism of pure scientific thinking. This is largely a Deist point of view. As the result of a great earthquake in Lisbon, which was both real and an important part of *Candide,* Voltaire rejected Deism and adopted a disbelief in any God. However, Voltaire softened his own criticism when, at the end of Candide, he states that "we must cultivate our gardens," implying that while the extreme optimism he mocks in the novel may be false, total pessimism is fruitless. Therefore, we should try to find some task that we can perform well and stick to it. The task he most strongly supported was relief of suffering.

As we discussed previously in the section on Alexander Pope, the idea of God causing all events in the world was not acceptable to Voltaire. Instead, Voltaire believed that humans must become strongly involved in relieving suffering wherever it occurs. Voltaire's view seems to assume that suffering is inherently bad and should be avoided or relieved as a prime principle. Others have agreed that a principal role for humans is to relieve suffering, but also assert that suffering should be viewed not just as something inherently bad but also as a part of God's plan to help us learn and progress. These latter people suggest that only by encountering opposition can we grow. They cite the muscle analogy, "No pain, no gain," and further suggest that much suffering is transitory, certainly in the long view of life and afterlife existence.

Later in life Voltaire became friends with King Frederick the Great of Prussia and eventually moved to his court in Prussia (now part of Germany). The Enlightenment ideals of Voltaire had an influence on Frederick, and he became one of the first of a new breed of rulers called the Enlightened Despots, who we will discuss in the next chapter.

Voltaire's popularity continued to grow in France with both intellectuals and the masses, and his public caution allowed him to even find favor with the government. Voltaire eventually became the royal historian, and his *Age of Louis XIV* portrayed Louis as the dignified leader of his era. When obviously old and ailing, Voltaire was invited to return to Paris with a guarantee that he would not be prosecuted by the government.

Voltaire died in Paris and was buried in a small Catholic Church. His body has since been removed and placed in the Pantheon with other French greats.

Jean-Jacques Rousseau (1712–1778) was a French *philosophe* who, like Voltaire, believed in the supremacy of reason and its eventual triumph over institutional restrictions and untrue traditions. Rousseau strongly believed that government should be directly responsive to individual citizens and should guarantee the natural rights of humans. Rousseau's ideas on government were extremely influential on both the French and American Revolutions.

Borrowing the phrase "social contract" from John Locke to describe the agreement between government and the people, Rousseau wrote his own treatise on government titled *The Social Contract.* The first line of Rousseau's *Social Contract* is nearly a battle cry: "Man is born free, yet everywhere he is in chains." Rousseau insisted on total equality for all people—a concept called **egalitarianism**—and supported only governmental systems in which that concept was guaranteed.

He also believed that in the beginning humans were **noble savages** who lived contentedly in harmony with nature. Evil entered when people began to disagree about property rights, which, in turn, produced social and economic inequalities. Rousseau agreed with Hobbes and Locke that people began on earth naturally without government, but disagreed strongly with Hobbes on the basic natures of humans. Hobbes saw early humans as depraved. Locke and Rousseau viewed humans as innately good but needing government to control chaos. They argued that people accepted government upon a contract in where they gained some advantages and accepted some restrictions for the general good. Since the people instituted government for their benefit, if the government failed in its mission, especially the protection of individual rights, the people could break the contract and overthrow the government.

Rousseau said that people should take all of their liberties and all of their rights and all of their freedoms and invest them in the society. That be-ing done, the only way a person can enjoy benefits is if all the society, together, enjoys the benefits. The modern analogy of Rousseau's view is the corporation. Each investor has only one way to benefit from the investment and that is when the corporation itself does well. Therefore, all benefit together or none benefit at all. Rousseau's con-cepts have been remembered in the phrase that be-came the basic theme of the French Revolution. That theme was "Liberty, Equality, Fraternity." Figure 35.3 shows a building in France on which this phrase is memorialized.

Rousseau did not, however, agree with Locke on all points. One major difference between their ideas was that Rousseau believed in the absolute sovereignty of the majority, whereas Locke be-lieved that each person, independently, retained some sovereignty (natural rights). According to Rousseau, the general will takes precedence over individual freedom. Rousseau believed that the legislature, which is the institutional representa-tion of the general will, holds sway over the wants of the individual. (These tendencies of in-stitutional control are still more present in France today than in, for example, the United States or Great Britain.)

The differences between the positions of Locke and Rousseau may seem small, but they have important ramifications. Under Rousseau's belief,

the social contract is an agreement between the government and society. Rousseau's idea means that the social contract can only be broken when the majority of society feels it should be. Under Locke's belief, the social contract is an agreement between the government and each individual. Locke's premise allows each individual to break the contract when they feel their individual rights have been trampled. Rousseau's adaptation of Locke's ideas allowed for the social contract to have practical application and be useful in the real world by providing for a stable government. Locke's idea, by contrast, was impractical, as it al-lowed individuals to break the contract with gov-ernment, which would make the government un-stable because only some members of society had agreed to abide by its rules and restrictions.

Interestingly, the ideas of Rousseau have been used to support both capitalism and communism. Rousseau's belief in a limited government whose function is to protect life, liberty, and property has served as the basis for capitalist democracies; while Rousseau's belief that government was in-stituted to alleviate the abuses of property owner-ship serves as a basis for Marxist communism.

Rousseau's personal life was dominated by upheaval and turmoil. Rousseau's mother died giving birth to him and his father was neglectful, eventually abandoning young Jean-Jacques alto-gether. After several failed vocational apprentice-

Figure 35.3 ■ A building in France displaying the motto espoused by Rousseau. © 2010 by Richard A. McGuirk. Used under license of Shutter-stock, Inc.

ships, Rousseau fell in with some Catholic monks who turned him over to a noblewoman who tried to convert young intellectuals to Catholicism. Madame de Warens oversaw his education, and the two became lovers. Rousseau spent eight years living with her, but the couple eventually parted when she realized Rousseau would never become a strong convert to Catholicism. Rousseau then spent 18 months in Venice as the secretary to the French ambassador.

Rousseau returned to Paris, where he made a living as a secretary and music copyist after his own opera, *Les Muses Galantes,* failed. While in Paris, Rousseau encountered the Enlightenment intellectuals and became friends with Diderot (about whom we will talk later). Rousseau became an active participant in the discussions of the *philosophes.*

In keeping with the principles of disseminating the ideas of the Enlightenment, Rousseau decided to enter a competition based on the following question: "Has the progress of the sciences and arts contributed to the corruption or to the improvement of human conduct?" All of the other entrants wrote the expected answer that progress was improved by science and the arts. Rousseau, however, argued that since early humans were "noble savages," living in a state of happiness and peace, the encroachment of scientific and artistic progress was detrimental. Rousseau then cited, among other things, the decline of Egyptian, Greek, and Roman societies into moral depravity as they departed from their early, simpler beginnings. He also pointed out that technology and the arts produce artificial wants and desires and then they provide a way that those artificial desires can be filled. Rousseau asserted that these artificial desires took the place of natural desires that are more basic to our real selves and, therefore, are more worthy of being filled. Therefore, civilization itself leads away from the moral rectitude of simple native life. Rousseau won the contest and, as a result, gained considerable fame.

Rousseau then decided to live his own life as close as possible to the noble savage. He moved in with a countrywoman, Madame d'Epinay, and attempted to live in a small, rural village as simply

as he could. The couple had five children (inexplicably, all of whom were placed in orphanages) but did not get along well, and, when Rousseau had an affair with another woman, the couple split up and Rousseau moved to Luxembourg.

It was at this time that Rousseau wrote his two greatest works, his treatise on government, *The Social Contract,* and his discourse on education, *Emile.* The latter book was ordered burned by the French government and an order was given for Rousseau's arrest. The Scottish philosopher, David Hume, offered Rousseau asylum in England, so Rousseau went there. However, Rousseau became paranoid and was constantly suspicious of supposed plots against him. His paranoia made him hard to be around, and his relations with his English friends soured when a practical joke orchestrated by Hume backfired. Rousseau's paranoia would not allow him to believe it had been a practical joke, and he became convinced the British government, through Hume, was seeking his life. Rousseau then fled back to France where he returned to writing and copying music. Rousseau's madness worsened and he sought shelter at a hospital, where he gradually became more mentally unstable and died. Rousseau's body was later placed near Voltaire's in the Pantheon in Paris.

The question of God's role in human life, which we have discussed in the sections on Pope and Voltaire, was also important for Rousseau. In fact, Rousseau openly disagreed with Voltaire. Rousseau said that God was using natural disasters, such as the Lisbon earthquake, to send a message. For Rousseau, the message was that cities were evil and should be abandoned. If people would have lived in a natural state, close to nature and away from cities, then the terrible suffering (at least the extent) would have been avoided. This view is obviously in keeping with Rousseau's assertion of the superiority of the life of a noble savage.

Although not as influential as Voltaire or Rousseau, **Denis Diderot** may have had the greatest mind of the French Enlightenment. Diderot's greatest accomplishment was the publication of the seventeen-volume *Encyclopedia: The Rational Dictionary of the Sciences, the Arts, and the Crafts* (which was abbreviated in French as *L'Encyclopédie*). The purpose of Diderot's *Encyclopedia* was to teach people how to think critically and objectively about all matters. Diderot was convinced that greater knowledge would lead to greater happiness and said that the *Encyclopedia's* purpose was to "change the general way of thinking".

Diderot's *Encyclopedia* was massive in scale— intended to be a collection of all knowledge known to humanity. The *Encyclopedia* contained hundreds of articles written by the world's greatest thinkers from all areas of knowledge. Scientists, writers, priests, philosophers, and skilled workers, including the great Enlightenment thinkers Voltaire, Rousseau, and Diderot himself, all contributed articles. All in all, it took 15 years to publish all 17 volumes of the *Encyclopedia*.

When the *Encyclopedia* was first published, there was intense criticism because many of the articles dealt with subjects that were extremely controversial at the time, such as atheism and the soul. Initially the French government banned it, but Diderot toned down later volumes so as to not offend, and the *Encyclopedia* was permitted for publication.

The effect of Diderot's *Encyclopedia* was enormous because people began to refer to it as the authority on all subjects. This helped to spread the ideas and concepts of both the Scientific Awakening and the Enlightenment. The tone of the *Encyclopedia* was pro-science and industrial arts, while religion and morality were questioned. Furthermore, intolerance, legal injustice, and out-of-date social institutions were openly and strongly criticized.

■ The Enlightenment in Germany

Immanuel Kant (1724–1804) was the German voice of the Enlightenment and the father of the **Transcendentalist movement.** In response to the strict empiricism of Hume and others, Kant introduced the concept of transcendentalism in which some things are known by methods other than sensory experience. Kant believed in the existence of another realm of absolute reality, somewhat

similar to Plato's ideas about the Form. Kant also said that even though our knowledge begins with sensory perceptions, that knowledge is ordered by our rational minds and therefore gives us understanding and knowledge beyond the sensory input.

According to Kant, empiricism can only be understood in light of some basic concepts that form a framework for accumulating knowledge *before* sensory perception. For example, causal relationships must assume the existence of time, and perceptions of the world must presume the existence of space. Kant argued that the existence of neither time nor space can be determined by empirical understanding. We can only measure their extent, not whether they exist. These self-existent things, Kant says, are *a priori;* they come before, or transcend, empirical or sensory experience. These thoughts are discussed in Kant's work, *Critique of Pure Reason.*

Kant also developed a system for ethical behavior. He suggested that humans have an unconditional obligation (called a *categorical imperative*) that requires that we must "Act as if your actions would become a moral maxim (principle or model) for all others and at all times." He offered an alternate way of expressing the same concept: "You should behave with only those types of behavior that are dictated by the absolute nature of the basic principle on which the act is based." A third restatement of the principle was given as follows: "Act that you use humanity, whether in your own person or in the person of any other, always at the same time as an end, never merely as a means."

These three statements of the principle of ethical behavior are easily contrasted with the concepts of Machiavelli (which we discussed in Chapter 27). Machiavelli asserted that the ruler of a state could act in whatever way was required to maintain control, regardless of means and impact on individuals. Kant's view was exactly opposite and, consistent with the Enlightenment, elevated the individual to a position where the rights of the individual should be the highest consideration.

From the regularity and relatively sheltered nature of Kant's life, we get the impression that he was satisfied with his role and didn't really worry that others might disagree with him. He lived his whole life in the relatively small town of Königsburg, Germany. His daily routine was amazingly consistent. For instance, at precisely the same time each day, he would take a walk through the town. Some of the shopkeepers commented that if the clock on the town hall differed from the walk of *Herr Doktor Kant,* the clock should be corrected. Although out of step with the strict empiricism of his day, Kant's transcendentalism and categorical imperative did have an important influence on both German and American philosophers in later generations.

■ Reviewing the Enlightenment

The Enlightenment was an important era of history that gave foundation to most modern democratic governments and established individual liberty and freedom as the highest aims of a government. These aims were summarized well by Denis Diderot, one of the most important of French Enlightenment thinkers:

> *The good of the people must be the great purpose of government. By the laws of nature and of reason, the governors are invested with power to that end. And the greatest good of the people is liberty. It is to the state what health is to the individual.*

Note that Diderot identified both nature and reason as the basic laws on which the government would rest. Most Enlightenment thinkers agreed that humans were, by nature, inherently endowed with rights of freedom, equality, and fair opportunity. Humans gave the officials of their governments the power to organize society so that the rights of individual citizens could be protected.

The Enlightenment thinkers came to this view, in part, by applying the principles of science to the institutions of government. They believed that science could solve mankind's social and moral problems. This optimism may have been somewhat flawed, but many important advances were made nevertheless.

Other important advances during the Enlightenment were in understanding the nature of knowledge, the proper influence of religion, the nature of economics, and the need for improved ethical behavior. The Enlightenment challenged the moral, religious, and philosophical underpinnings of Europe—many of which had dominated man's thinking since the time of Classical Greece and Rome or the Middle Ages.

Toward the end of the Enlightenment period, some highly religious people began to question the wisdom of all the Enlightenment thinking, especially the concept that religion had to be based on pure reason. These people believed in the value of spiritual knowledge. This thinking led to a movement, beginning in England, in which new churches were formed that openly advocated the value of inspiration and spiritually based truth. The Methodist Church of John and Charles Wesley and the Quaker Church (actually the Society of the Friends of Truth) were examples. These movements supported some Enlightenment principles, like the concern for the individual, but rejected the godlessness that seemed to pervade many of the Enlightenment writings.

Some dedicated Enlightenment thinkers still rejected organized religion but found the concepts of Deism empty. A very popular substitute for organized religion was **Freemasonry.** The men who joined this society found rituals that were religious in nature without being part of a religion in the normal sense. They also found social companionship and elevated feelings of accomplishment through applications of Enlightenment principles.

Enlightenment thinkers exhibited creativity in several interesting ways. Locke, for instance, believed that knowledge was gained by sensory perceptions, which, in our knowledge now, involves linear thinking. Locke also admitted to the importance of reflection as a way to interpret and organize thinking, especially concerning abstract concepts. This reflection involved lateral thinking. Therefore, Locke, without knowing it, was suggesting that both linear and lateral thinking, both left and right sides of the brain, are required for full understanding and, in our assertion, for full creativity.

We also point out that many of the Enlightenment thinkers were adept at in-depth scientific thinking and applying this thinking to other areas of inquiry, such as government and other social problems. In fact, the very concept of the Enlightenment is the application of scientific thinking to social issues. This ability to apply in-depth thinking to another field of interest is a trait of creativity. Surely the Enlightenment itself is an indication of creative thinking.

Although the Enlightenment did not achieve its goal of solving mankind's social dilemmas, it did create an intellectual freedom that allowed people to look forward with great optimism. Undoubtedly, the Enlightenment set the stage for both the American and the French revolutions.

1712–1778	*Jean-Jacques Rousseau*
1713–1784	*Denis Diderot*
1723–1790	*Adam Smith*
1724–1804	*Immanuel Kant*
1737–1794	*Edward Gibbon*
1751–1772	*Publication of Diderot's* Encyclopédie
1762	*Publication of Rousseau's* The Social Contract
1776	*Publication of Smith's* The Wealth of Nations
1776	*Publication of Gibbon's* The Decline and Fall of the Roman Empire
1787	*Publication of Kant's* Critique of Pure Reason

■ Timeline—Important Dates

Date	Event
1588–1679	*Thomas Hobbes*
1632–1704	*John Locke*
1642	*Outbreak of the English Civil War*
1650	*Publication of Hobbes's* Leviathan
1667–1745	*Jonathan Swift*
1688	*The Glorious Revolution*
1688–1744	*Alexander Pope*
1689	*Publication of Locke's* Essay Concerning Human Understanding
1694–1778	*Voltaire*
1711–1776	*David Hume*

■ Notes

1. Leonard Bacon, *Baxtor's Works* (New Haven: Durrie and Peck, 1835), 28.
2. Joseph Priestley, *Disquisitions Relating to Matter and Spirit* (London: J. Johnson, 1777), 52.

■ Suggested Readings

Locke, John, *Two Treatises of Government*, Everyman, 1993.

Neeley, Lawrence H., *War Before Civilization*, Oxford University Press, 1996.

Pope, Alexander, *Essay on Man and Other Poems*, Dover Publications, 1994.

Swift, Jonathan, *Gulliver's Travels*, Signet Classic, 1999.

Thomas Hobbes: Leviathan

Thomas Hobbes (1588–1679) was one of the most revolutionary thinkers in history. In an era when the Renaissance humanists were trying to understand the purpose for their existence and their relationship with the past and present, Hobbes claimed to have the overall answer in empiricism. He extrapolated from the materialist principles of Aristotle by saying that every truth in life could, and would, only be found through the senses. He even implied that anything immaterial did not exist. This was a challenge to faith-based religions and was widely rejected. This secular philosophy, although radical, would eventually find acceptance in the scientific awakening and would then form the foundation of mainstream secular European thinking for centuries. This was especially true for his native England, whose adoption of empiricism made the English the forerunners in the scientific revolutions to follow.

Hobbes' *Leviathan* illustrated his principles of materialism and applied them to political philosophy. In essence, *Leviathan* denied any divinely established morality—leaving all motivation to secular rationality and innate behavior. Hobbes claimed that man's life is naturally "solitary, poor, nasty, brutish, and short" and in a constant state of war, living in "continual fear and danger of violent death." He then advocated the establishment of order through a centralized government because of its abilities to overshadow the natural state of man and provide peace and welfare.

This empirical philosophy was accepted by many English thinkers and modified by some to include a non-empirical element. Hobbes' philosophy of the depravity of native men would later be the justification for European colonization of the different "savages" of the world. This concept stands in sharp contrast to many ideas of the Enlightenment, but those came later.

The following selections from *Leviathan* were chosen to summarize Hobbes' philosophy on the purpose for government and its function.

▪ Of the Natural Condition of Mankind as Concerning Their Felicity, and Misery

1. Nature hath made men so equal, in the faculties of the body, and mind, as that though there be found one man sometimes manifestly stronger in body, or of quicker mind than another; yet when all is reckoned together, the difference between man, and man, is not so considerable, as that one man can thereupon claim to himself any benefit, to which another may not pretend, as well as he. For as to the strength of body, the weakest has strength enough to kill the strongest, either by secret machination, or by confederacy with others, that are in the same danger with himself.

2. And as to the faculties of the mind, (setting aside the arts grounded upon words, and especially that skill of proceeding upon general, and infallible rules, called science; which very few have, and but in few things; as being not a native faculty, born with us; nor attained (as prudence, while we look after somewhat else,) I find yet a greater equality amongst men, than that of strength. For prudence, is but experience; which equal time, equally bestows on all men, in those things they equally apply themselves unto. That which may perhaps make such equality incredible, is but a vain conceit of one's own wisdom, which almost all men think they have in a greater degree, than the vulgar; that is, than all men but themselves, and a few others, whom by fame, or for concurring with themselves, they approve. For such is the nature of men, that howsoever they may acknowledge many others to be more witty, or more eloquent, or more learned; yet they will hardly believe there be many so wise as themselves; for they see their own wit at hand, and other men's at a distance. But this proveth rather that men are in that point equal, than unequal. For there is not ordinarily a greater sign of the equal distribution of any thing, than that every man is contented with his share.

3. From this equality of ability, ariseth equality of hope in the attaining of our ends. And therefore if any two men desire the same thing, which nevertheless they cannot both enjoy, they become enemies; and in the way to their end, (which is principally their own conservation, and sometimes their delectation only,) endeavour to destroy or subdue one another. And from hence it comes to pass, that where an invader hath no more to fear, than another man's single power; if one plant, sow, build, or possess a convenient seat, others may probably be expected to come prepared with forces united, to dispossess, and deprive him, not only of the fruit of his labour, but also of his life, or liberty. And the invader again is in the like danger of another.

Source: From *Leviathan* by Thomas Hobbes (Oxford: Oxford University Press, 1996).

4. And from this diffidence of one another, there is no way for any man to secure himself, so reasonable, as anticipation; that is, by force, or wiles, to master the persons of all men he can, so long, till he see no other power great enough to endanger him: and this is no more than his own conservation requireth, and is generally allowed. Also because there be some, that taking pleasure in contemplating their own power in the acts of conquest, which they pursue farther than their security requires; if others, that otherwise would be glad to be at east within modest bounds, should not by invasion increase their power, they would not be able, long time, by standing only on their defence, to subsist. And by consequence, such augmentation of dominion over men, being necessary to a man's conservation, it ought to be allowed him.

5. Again, men have no pleasure, (but on the contrary a great deal of grief) in keeping company, where there is no power able to over-awe them all. For every man looketh that his companion should value him, at the same rate he sets upon himself: and upon all signs of contempt, or undervaluing, naturally endeavours, as far as he dares (which amongst them that have no common power to keep them in quiet, is far enough to make them destroy each other,) to extort a greater value from his contemners, by damage; and from others, by the example.

6. So that in the nature of man, we find three principal causes of quarrel. First, competition; secondly, diffidence; thirdly, glory.

7. The first, maketh men invade for gain; the second, for safety; and the third, for reputation. The first use violence, to make themselves masters of other men's persons, wives, children, and cattle; the second, to defend them; the third, for trifles, as a word, a smile, a different opinion, and any other sign of undervalue, either direct in their persons, or by reflection in their kindred, their friends, their nation, their profession, or their name.

8. Hereby it is manifest, that during the time men live without a common power to keep them all in awe, they are in that condition which is called war; and such a war, as is of every man, against every man. For war, consisteth not in battle only, or the act of fighting; but in a tract of time, wherein the will to contend by battle is sufficiently known: and therefore the notion of *time*, is to be considered in the nature of war; as it is in the nature of weather. For as the nature of foul weather, lieth not in a shower or two of rain; but in an inclination thereto of many days together: so the nature of war, consisteth not in actual fighting; but in the known disposition thereto, during all the time there is no assurance to the contrary. All other time is peace.

9. Whatsoever therefore is consequent to a time of war, where every man is enemy to every man; the same is consequent to the time, where in men live without other security, than what their own strength, and their own invention shall furnish them withal. In such condition, there is no place for industry; because the fruit thereof is uncertain: and consequently no culture of the earth; no navigation, nor use of the commodities that may be imported by sea; no commodious building; no instruments of moving, and removing such things as require much force; no knowledge of the face of the earth; no account of time; no arts; no letters; no society; and which is worst of all, continual fear, and danger of violent death; and the life of man, solitary, poor, nasty, brutish, and short.

10. It may seem strange to some man, that has not well weighted these things; that nature should thus dissociate, and render men apt to invade, and destroy one another: and he may therefore, not trusting to this inference, made from the passions, desire perhaps to have the same confirmed by experience. Let him therefore consider with himself, when taking a journey, he arms himself, and seeks to go well accompanied; when going to sleep, he locks his doors; when even in his house he locks his chests; and this when he knows there be laws, and public officers, armed, to revenge all injuries shall be done

him; what opinion he has of his fellow-subjects, when he rides armed; of his fellow citizens, when he locks his doors; and of his children, and servants, when he locks his chests. Does he not there as much accuse mankind by his actions, as I do by my words? But neither of us accuse man's nature in it. The desires, and other passions of man, are in themselves no sin. No more are the actions, that proceed from those passions, till they know a law that forbids them: which till laws be made they cannot know: nor can any law be made, till they have agreed upon the person that shall make it.

11. It may peradventure be thought, there was never such a time, nor condition of war as this; and I believe it was never generally so, over all the world: but there are many places, where they live so now. For the savage people in many places of America, except the government of small families, the concord whereof dependeth on natural lust, have no government at all; and live at this day in that brutish manner, as I said before. Howsoever, it may be perceived what manner of life there would be, where there were no common power to fear; by the manner of life, which men that have formerly lived under a peaceful government, use to degenerate into, in a civil war.

12. But though there had never been any time, wherein particular men were in a condition of war one against another; yet in all times, kings, and persons of sovereign authority, because of their independency, are in continual jealousies, and in the state and posture of gladiators; having their weapons pointing, and their eyes fixed on one another; that is, their forts, garrisons, and guns upon the frontiers of their kingdoms; and continual spies upon their neighbours; which is a posture of war. But because they uphold thereby, the industry of their subjects; there does not follow from it, that misery, which accompanies the liberty of particular men.

13. To this war of every man against every man, this also is consequent; that nothing can be

unjust. The notions of right and wrong, justice and injustice have there no place. Where there is no common power, there is no law: where no law, no injustice. Force, and fraud, are in war the two cardinal virtues. Justice, and injustice are none of the faculties neither of the body, nor mind. If they were, they might be in a man that were alone in the world, as well as his senses, and passions. They are qualities, that relate to men in society, not in solitude. It is consequent also to the same condition, that there be no propriety, no dominion, no *mine* and *thine* distinct; but only that to be every man's, that he can get; and for so long, as he can keep it. And thus much for the ill condition, which man by mere nature is actually placed in; though with a possibility to come out of it, consisting partly in the passions, partly in his reason.

14. The passions that incline men to peace, are fear of death; desire of such things as are necessary to commodious living; and a hope by their industry to obtain them. And reason suggesteth convenient articles of peace, upon which men may be drawn to agreement. These articles, are they, which otherwise are called the Laws of Nature: whereof I shall speak more particularly, in the two following chapters.

■ **Of Darkness from Vain Philosophy, and Fabulous Traditions**

1. By PHILOSOPHY, is understood *the knowledge acquired by reasoning, from the manner of the generation of any thing, to the properties: or from the properties, to some possible way of generation of the same; to the end to be able to produce, as far as matter, and human force permit, such effects, as human life requireth. . . .*

14. Now to descend to the particular tenets of vain philosophy, derived to the Universities, and thence into the Church, partly from

Aristotle, partly from blindness of understanding; I shall first consider these principles. There is a certain *philosophia prima,* on which all other philosophy ought to depend; and consisteth principally, in right limiting of the significations of such appellations, or names, as are of all others the most universal; which limitations serve to avoid ambiguity and equivocation in reasoning; and are commonly called definitions: such as are the definitions of body, time, place, matter form, essence, subject, substance, accident, power, act, finite, infinite, quantity, quality , motion, action, passion, and divers others, necessary to the explaining of a man's conceptions concerning the nature and generation of bodies. The explication (that is, the settling of the meaning) of which, and the like terms, is commonly in the Schools called *metaphysics;* as being a part of the philosophy of Aristotle, which hath that for title: but it is in another sense; for there it signifieth as much as *books written or placed after his natural philosophy:* but the Schools take them for *books of supernatural philosophy:* for the word *metaphysics* will bear both these senses. And indeed that which is there written, is for the most part so far from the possibility of being understood, and so repugnant to natural reason, that whosoever thinketh there is anything to be understood by it, must needs think it supernatural.

15. From these metaphysics, which are mingled with the Scripture to make School divinity,

we are told, there be in the world certain essences separated from bodies, which they call *abstract essences, and substantial forms:* for the interpreting of which jargon, there is need of somewhat more than ordinary attention in this place. Also I ask pardon of those that are not used to this kind of discourse, for applying myself to those that are. The world, (I mean not the earth only, that denominates the lovers of it *worldly men,* but the *universe,* that is, the whole mass of all things that are), is corporeal, that is to say, body; and hath the dimensions of magnitude, namely, length, breadth, and depth: also every part of body, is likewise body, and hath the like dimensions; and consequently every part of the universe, is body, and that which is not body, is no part of the universe: and because the universe is all, that which is no part of it, is *nothing;* and consequently *nowhere.* Nor does it follow from hence, that spirits are *nothing:* for they have dimensions, and are therefore really *bodies;* though that name in common speech be given to such bodies only, as are visible, or palpable; that is, that have some degree of opacity: but for spirits, they call them incorporeal; which is a name of more honour, and may therefore with more piety be attributed to God himself; in whom we consider not what attribute expresseth best his nature, which is incomprehensible; but what best expresseth our desire to honour Him.

John Locke: An Essay Concerning Human Understanding, Two Treatises of Government

John Locke (1632–1704) is known as the "forefather of our forefathers" for his contributions to the philosophy that resulted in the founding of the United States of America and its Constitution. He also is credited for leading the Age of Enlightenment in England and, by extension, in France, through his example of intellectual inquiry. Originally trained as a physician, he developed a strong sympathy for the common man. Through his exposure to Royalist views and witness of decadent kings, he also gained a passionate disliking for prejudice and absolutism. A series of publications established him as a champion for democratic principles and forced Locke to flee from England and the ire of King Charles II. When William and Mary came to the English throne under the limited monarchy agreed to with parliament, Locke returned to England as a hero.

Locke's *Essay Concerning Human Understanding* is not as well known as his writings on government, but it is considered by some to be an intellectual masterpiece. It is a prototypical document of the Age of Enlightenment. In it, Locke conducts an investigation into the human mind. The object of discussion is whether humans are born with innate knowledge, or if all knowledge comes from our environment after birth. Locke concludes that no idea is innate and that we are born with a blank tablet (*tabula rasa*) for a mind, filling it with experience and reason. However, in contrast to Hobbes, Locke believed that all persons are born good, independent, and equal. These basic assumptions regarding the nature of humans led to his great works on government.

The idea of a constitutional government, or limited monarchy, was established in Locke's *Two Treatises of Government*. This work defined the "social contract" between a people and their government. This contract limited a government's purpose to ensuring the people's inalienable rights; life, liberty, and property. Any government that could not or would not provide these basic rights was not only unnecessary, but was ultimately illegal and should be removed. The English government beginning with William and Mary was largely patterned after Locke's model.

Locke advocated the overthrow of tyrannies (governments that would not provide those rights) even by force if necessary, thus providing a moral and intellectual justification for the American revolution. The enduring phrases from the *Two Treatises of Government* were heavily borrowed by Thomas Jefferson (and Benjamin Franklin) in the *Declaration of Independence*. The use of so many of Locke's ideas and, in many cases, exact phrases, caused great sympathy for America's revolution amongst the many Locke-believers in Europe, some even members of the British parliament. This widespread European support undoubtedly contributed to the success of the negotiations on American independence which followed the American victory at Yorktown. In the United States today, Locke is not well known, but in the days of Jefferson and Franklin, Locke was revered as the fountain of modern democratic thought.

John Locke: An Essay Concerning Human Understanding

I. It is an established Opinion amongst some Men, That there are in the Understanding certain innate Principles; some primary Notions, Characters, as it were stamped upon the Mind of Man, which the Soul receives in its very first Being; and brings into the World with it. It would be sufficient to convict unprejudiced Readers of the falseness of this Supposition, if I should only shew how Men, barely by the Use of their natural Faculties, may attain to all the Knowledge they have, without the help of any innate Impressions; and may arrive at Certainty, without any such Original Notions or Principles.

*   *   *

2. Let us then suppose the Mind to be, as we say, white Paper, void of all Characters, without any Ideas; How comes it to be furnished? Whence comes it by that vast store, which the busy and boundless Fancy of Man has painted on it, with an almost endless variety? Whence has it all the materials of Reason and Knowledge? To this I answer, in one word, From Experience: In that, all our Knowledge is founded; and from that it ultimately derives it self. Our Observation employ'd either about external, sensible Objects; or about the internal Operations of our Minds, perceived and reflected on by our selves, is that, which supplies our Understandings with all the materials of thinking. These two are the Fountains of Knowledge, from whence all the Ideas we have, or can naturally have, do spring. . . .

5. The Understanding seems to me, not to have the least glimmering of any Ideas, which it doth not receive from one of these two. External Objects furnish the Mind with the Ideas of sensible qualities, which are all those different perceptions they produce in us: And the Mind furnishes the Understanding with Ideas of its own Operations. . . .

6. He that attentively considers the state of a Child, at his first coming into the World, will have little reason to think him stored with plenty of Ideas, that are to be the matter of his future Knowledge. 'Tis by degrees he comes to be furnished with them.

But all that are born into the World being surrounded with Bodies, that perpetually and diversly affect them, variety of Ideas, whether care be taken about it or no, are imprinted on the Minds of Children. Light, and Colours, are busie at hand every where, when the Eye is but open; Sounds, and some tangible Qualities fail not to solicite their proper Senses, and force an entrance to the Mind; but yet, I think it will be granted easily, That if a Child were kept in a place, where he never saw any other but Black and White, till he were a Man, he would have no more Ideas of Scarlet or Green, than he that from his Childhood never tasted an Oyster, or a Pine-Apple, has of those particular Relishes.

Source: From *An Essay Concerning Human Understanding* by John Locke (Oxford: Carendon Press, 1975).

■ Of Paternal Power

The law that was to govern Adam, was the same that was to govern all his posterity, the law of reason. But his offspring having another way of entrance into the world, different from him, by a natural birth, that produced them ignorant and without the use of reason, they were not presently under that law: for nobody can be under a law, which is not promulgated to him; and this law being promulgated or made known by reason only, he that is not come to the use of his reason, cannot be said to be under this law; and Adam's children being not presently as soon as born, under this law of reason were not presently free. For law, in its true notion, is not so much the limitation as the direction of a free and intelligent agent to his proper interest, and prescribes no further than is for the general good of those under that law. Could they be happier without it, the law, as a useless thing would of itself vanish; and that ill deserves the name of confinement which hedges us in only from bogs and precipices. So that, however it may be mistaken, the end of law is not to abolish or restrain, but to preserve and enlarge freedom: for in all the states of created beings capable of laws, where there is no law, there is no freedom. For liberty is to be free from restraint and violence from others which cannot be, where there is no law: but freedom is not, as we are told, 'a liberty for every man to do what he lists': (for who could be free, when every other man's humour might domineer over him?) but a liberty to dispose, and order, as he lists, his person, actions, possessions, and his whole property, within the allowance of those laws under which he is; and therein not to be subject to the arbitrary will of another, but freely follow his own. . . .

For God having given man an understanding to direct his actions, has allowed him a freedom of will, and liberty of acting, as properly belonging thereunto, within the bounds of that law he is under. . . .

Thus we are born free, as we are born rational; not that we have actually the exercise of either: age that brings one, brings with it the other too. And thus we see how natural freedom and subjection to parents may consist together, and are both founded on the same principle. A child is free by his father's title, by his father's understanding, which is to govern him, till he hath it of his own. The freedom of a man at years of discretion, and the subjection of a child to his parents, whilst yet short of that age, are so consistent, and so distinguishable, that the most blinded contenders for monarchy, by right of fatherhood, cannot miss this difference, the most obstinate cannot but allow their consistency. . . .

Commonwealths themselves take notice of, and allow that there is a time when men are to

Source: From *Two Treatises of Government* by John Locke (London: Orion Publishing Group, 1993).

begin to act like free men, and therefore till that time require not oaths of fealty, or allegiance, or other public owning of, or submission to the government of their countries.

The freedom then of man and liberty of acting according to his own will, is grounded on his having reason, which is able to instruct him in that law he is to govern himself by, and make him know how far he is left to the freedom of his own will. To turn him loose to an unrestrained liberty, before he has reason to guide him, is not the allowing him the privilege of his nature, to be free; but to thrust him out amongst brutes, and abandon him to a state as wretched, and as much beneath that of a man, as theirs. This is that which puts the authority into the parents' hands to govern the minority of their children. God hath made it their business to employ this care on their offspring, and hath placed in them suitable inclinations of tenderness and concern to temper this power, to apply it as his wisdom designed it, to the children's good, as long as they should need to be under it. . . .

Wherever therefore any number of men are so united into one society, as to quit every one his executive power of the law of nature, and to resign it to the public, there and there only is a political, or civil society. And this is done wherever any number of men, in the state of nature, enter into society to make one people, one body politic under one supreme government, or else when anyone joins himself to, and incorporates with any government already made. For hereby he authorizes the society, or which is all one, the legislative thereof to make laws for him as the public good of the society shall require; to the execution whereof, his own assistance (as to his own decrees) is due. And this puts men out of a state of nature into that of a commonwealth, by setting up a judge on earth, with authority to determine all the controversies, and redress the injuries, that may happen to any member of the commonwealth; which judge is the legislative, or magistrates appointed by it. And wherever there are any number of men, however associated, that have no such decisive power to appeal to, there they are still in the state of nature.

*   *   *

■ Of the Beginning of Political Societies

Men being, as has been said, by nature, all free, equal and independent, no one can be put out of this estate, and subjected to the political power of another, without his own consent. The only way whereby anyone divests himself of his natural liberty, and puts on the bonds of civil society is by agreeing with other men to join and unite into a community, for their comfortable, safe, and peaceable living one amongst another, in a secure enjoyment of their properties, and a greater security against any that are not of it. This any number of men may do, because it injures not the freedom of the rest; they are left as they were in the liberty of the state of nature. When any number of men have so consented to make one community or government, they are thereby presently incorporated, and make one body politic, wherein the majority have a right to act and conclude the rest.

For when any number of men have, by the consent of every individual, made a community, they have thereby made that community one body, with a power to act as one body, which is only by the will and determination of the majority. For that which acts any community, being only the consent of the individuals of it, and it being necessary to that which is one body to move one way; it is necessary the body should move that way whither the greater force carries it, which is the consent of the majority: or else it is impossible it should act or continue one body, one community, which the consent of every individual that united into it, agreed that it should; and so everyone is bound by that consent to be concluded by the majority. And therefore we see that in assemblies empowered to act by positive laws where no number is set by that positive law which empowers them, the act of the majority passes for the act of the whole, and of course determines, as having by the law of nature and reason, the power of the whole.

And thus every man, by consenting with others to make one body politic under one government, puts himself under obligation to everyone of that society, to submit to the determination of the majority, and to be concluded by it; or else this original compact, whereby he with others incorporates into one society, would signify nothing, and be no compact, if he be left free, and under no other ties, than he was in before in the state of nature. . . .

Absolute arbitrary power, or governing without settled standing laws, can neither of them consist with the ends of society and government, which men would not quit the freedom of the state of nature for, and tie themselves up under, were it not to preserve their lives, liberties and fortunes; and by stated rules of right and property to secure their peace and quiet. . . .

These are the bounds which the trust that is put in them by the society, and the law of God and nature, have set to the legislative power of every commonwealth, in all forms of government.

First, they are to govern by promulgated established laws, not to be varied in particular cases, but to have one rule for rich and poor, for the favourite at court, and the countryman at plough.

Secondly, these laws also ought to be designed for no other end ultimately than the good of the people.

Thirdly, they must not raise taxes on the property of the people, without the consent of the people, given by themselves, or their deputies. And this properly concerns only such governments where the legislative is always in being, or at least where the people have not reserved any part of the legislative to deputies, to be from time to time chosen by themselves.

Fourthly, the legislative neither must nor can transfer the power of making laws to anybody else, or place it anywhere but where the people have.

be employed for preserving the community and the members of it. But because those laws which are constantly to be executed, and whose force is always to continue, may be made in a little time; therefore there is no need, that the legislative should be always in being, not having always business to do. And because it may be too great a temptation to human frailty apt to grasp at power, for the same persons who have the power of making laws, to have also in their hands the power to execute them, whereby they may exempt themselves from obedience to the laws they make, and suit the law, both in its making and execution, to their own private advantage, and thereby come to have a distinct interest from the rest of the community, contrary to the end of society and government: therefore in well ordered commonwealths, where the good of the whole is so considered, as it ought, the legislative power is put into the hands of divers persons who duly assembled, have by themselves, or jointly with others, a power to make laws, which when they have done, being separated again, they are themselves subject to the laws, they have made; which is a new and near tie upon them, to take care, that they make them for the public good.

But because the laws, that are at once, and in a short time made, have a constant and lasting force, and need a perpetual execution, or an attendance thereunto: therefore 'tis necessary there should be a power always in being, which should see to the execution of the laws that are made, and remain in force. And thus the legislative and executive power come often to be separated.

■ Of the Legislative, Executive, and Federative Power of the Commonwealth

The legislative power is that which has a right to direct how the force of the commonwealth shall

Alexander Pope: Essay on Man

Alexander Pope (1688–1744) was born in London and grew up during the Enlightenment, a period of love for the classics with a desire for self-education. His early life was influenced strongly by his father's conversion to Catholicism at a time when Catholics suffered many persecutions. Catholics were not allowed in any universities; therefore, Pope's public education was stunted. His aunt taught him to read, he learned Latin and Greek from a Catholic priest, and he was ever after a bibliophile (lover of books) and avid writer. While still young, he contracted a tubercular infection of the spine, making him suffer from asthma, headaches, and a humpback that kept him at a height of 4 ft. 6 in. and gave his literary critics a constant target. But Pope succeeded through this adversity to become a dedicated poet. His excellence of implementation in language has made him considered by many to be the leading poet of the Enlightenment and, clearly, a profoundly influential force upon the English language.

Pope's greatest legacy is the myriad of familiar quotes included in his *Essay on Man*. This work is a collection of his thoughts and reflections on the nature of man, his shortcomings, his heavenly-endowed gifts, and his hopes. As an Enlightenment humanist, he places humans in the pre-eminent position in the world and in God's scheme of life. But his method of exposing human folly while still revering God gives this humanist work a strong sense of awe for God and his works that is a wonderful counterweight to the secularism that was beginning to shape English thinking in the Enlightenment.

Pope's writings are highly accessible to the common reader. His style uses aphorisms, short statements of profound knowledge, much in the style of Ecclesiastes. The following passages from *Essay on Man* have proven to be the most enduring. The value of these passages strangely is independent of Pope. Many know the phrases, but not to whom the attribution should be given. That so many of his sayings remain familiar, independent of his name, is testament to their brilliance and to his ability.

Of all the causes which conspire to blind
Man's erring judgment, and misguide the mind,
What the weak head with strongest bias rules,
Is PRIDE, the never-failing vice of fools.
Whatever Nature has in worth denied,
She gives in large recruits of needless pride;
For as in bodies, thus in souls we find
What wants in blood and spirits, swell'd with wind:
Pride, where wit fails, steps in to our defence,
And fills up all the mighty void of sense.
If once right reason drives that could away,
Truth breaks upon us with resistless day.
Trust not yourself; but your defects to know,
Make use of every friend—and every foe.
A little learning is a dangerous thing;
Drink deep, or taste not the Pierian spring.[1]
There shallow draughts intoxicate the brain,
And drinking largely sobers us again.

* * *

A perfect judge will read each work of wit
With the same spirit that its author writ:
Survey the WHOLE, nor seeks slight faults to find
Where Nature moves, and rapture warms the mind,
Nor lose, for that malignant dull delight,
The generous pleasure to be charm'd with wit,
But in such lays as neither ebb nor flow,
Correctly cold, and regularly low,
That shunning faults, one quiet tenor keep;
We cannot blame indeed—but we may sleep.
In wit, as Nature, what affects our hearts

Is not th' exactness of peculiar parts;
'Tis not a lip, or eye, we beauty call,
But the joint force and full result of all.
Thus when we view some well-proportion'd dome,
(The world's just wonder, and ev'n thine, O Rome!)
No single parts unequally surprise,
All comes united to th' admiring eyes;
No monstrous height, or breadth or length appear;
The whole at once is bold and regular.

Whoever thinks a faultless piece to see,
Thinks what ne'er was, nor is, nor e'er shall be,
In every work regard the writer's end,
Since none can compass more than they intend;
And if the means be just, the conduct true,
Applause, in spite of trivial faults, is due.
As men of breeding, sometimes men of wit,
To avoid great errors, must the less commit:
Neglect the rules each verbal critic lays,
For not to know some trifles, is a praise.
Most critics, fond of some subservient art,
Still make the whole depend upon a part:
They talk of principles, but notions prize,
And all to one loved folly sacrifice.

* * *

Some ne'er advance a judgment of their own,
But catch the spreading notion of the town;
They reason and conclude by precedent,
And own stale nonsense which they ne'er invent.
Some judge of authors' names, not works, and then
Nor praise nor blame the writings but the men.

---

[1]On Mount Parnassus, home of the Muses.

Source: From *Essay on Man* by Alexander Pope (Mineola: Dover Publications, 1994).

Of all this servile herd, the worst is he
That in proud dulness joins with quality,
A constant critic at the great man's board,
To fetch and carry nonsense for my lord.
What woful stuff this madrigal would be,
In some starved hackney sonnetteer, or me?
But let a lord once own the happy lines,
How the wit brightens! how the style refines!
Before his sacred name flies every fault,
And each exalted stanza teems with thought!
    The vulgar thus through imitation err;
As oft the learn'd by being singular;
So much they scorn the crowd, that if the throng
By chance go right, they purposely go wrong:
So schismatics the plain believers quit,
And are but damn'd for having too much wit.
Some praise at morning what they blame at
    night;
But always think the last opinion right.

*   *   *

We think our father fools, so wise we grow;
Our wiser sons, no doubt, will think us so.

*   *   *

But where's the man who counsel can bestow,
Still pleased to teach, and yet not proud to know?
Unbiass'd, or by favour, or by spite;
Not dully prepossess'd, nor blindly right;
Though learn'd, well-bred; and though well-bred,
    sincere;
Modestly bold, and humanly severe:
Who to a friend his faults can freely show,
And gladly praise the merit of a foe?
Bless'd with a taste exact, yet unconfined;
A knowledge both of books and human kind;
Generous converse; a soul exempt from pride;
And love to praise, with reason on his side?

*   *   *

Who sees with equal eye, as God of all,
A hero perish, or a sparrow fall,
Atoms or systems into ruin hurl'd,
And now a bubble burst, and now a world.

Hope humbly then; with trembling pinions
    soar;
Wait the great teacher, Death; and God adore.
What future bliss, He gives not thee to know,
But gives that hope to be thy blessing now.
Hope springs eternal in the human breast:
Man never Is, but always To be blest.
The soul, uneasy, and confined from home,
Rests and expatiates in a life to come.

*   *   *

Go, wiser thou! and in thy scale of sense,
Weigh thy opinion against Providence;
Call imperfection what thou fanciest such,
Say, here He gives too little, there too much:
Destroy all creatures for thy sport or gust,
Yet cry, If man's unhappy, God's unjust;
If man alone engross not Heaven's high care,
Alone made perfect here, immortal there:
Snatch from His hand the balance and the rod,
Re-judge His justice, be the god of God.
In pride, in reas'ning pride, our error lies;
All quit their sphere, and rush into the skies.
Pride still is aiming at the blest abodes,
Men would be angels, angels would be gods.
Aspiring to be gods, if angels fell,
Aspiring to be angels, men rebel:
And who but wishes to invert the laws
Of Order, sins against the Eternal Cause.

*   *   *

Better for us, perhaps, it might appear,
Were there all harmony, all virtue here;
That never air or ocean felt the wind,
That never passion discomposed the mind.
But all subsists by elemental strife;
And passions are the elements of life.
The general order, since the whole began,
Is kept by Nature, and is kept in man.
    What would this man? Now upward will he
        soar,
And little less than angel, would be more;
Now looking downwards, just as grieved appears,
To want the strength of bulls, the fur of bears.
Made for his use all creatures if he call,

Say what their use, had he the powers of all?
Nature to these, without profusion, kind,
The proper organs, proper powers assigned;
Each seeming what compensated of course,
Here with degrees of swiftness, there of force;
All in exact proportion to the state;
Nothing to add, and nothing to abate.
Each beast, each insect, happy in its own:
Is Heaven unkind to man, and man alone?
Shall he alone, whom rational we call,
Be pleased with nothing, if not blest with all?

*   *   *

What if the foot, ordain'd the dust to tread,
Or hand, to toil, aspired to be the head?
What if the head, the eye, or ear repined
To serve mere engines to the ruling mind?
Just as absurd for any part to claim
To be another, in this general frame;
Just as absurd, to mourn the tasks or pains
The great Directing Mind of all ordains.
    All are but parts of one stupendous whole,
Whose body Nature is, and God the soul;

*   *   *

Cease then, nor order imperfection name:
Our proper bliss depends on what we blame.
Know thy own point: this kind, this due degree
Of blindness, weakness, Heaven bestows on thee.
Submit, in this, or any other sphere,
Secure to be as blest as thou canst bear:
Safe in the hand of one Disposing Power,

Or in the natal, or the mortal hour.
All Nature is but art, unknown to thee
All chance, direction, which thou canst not see;
All discord, harmony not understood;
All partial evil, universal good:
And, spite of pride, in erring reason's spite,
One truth is clear, Whatever is, is right.

*   *   *

Know then thyself, presume not God to scan,
The proper study of mankind is man.

*   *   *

Know then this truth (enough for man to
        know),
"Virtue alone is happiness below."
The only point where human bliss stands still,
And tastes the good without the fall to ill;
Where only merit constant pay receives,
Is blest in what it takes and what it gives;
The joy unequall'd, if its end it gain,
And if it lose, attended with no pain:
Without satiety, though e'er so bless'd,
And but more relish'd as the more distress'd:
The broadest mirth unfeeling folly wears,
Less pleasing far than virtue's very tears:
Good, from each object, from each place acquired,
For ever exercised, yet never tried;
Never elated while one man's oppress'd;
Never dejected while another's bless'd;
And where no wants, no wishes can remain,
Since but to wish more virtue, is to gain.

Jonathan Swift: Gulliver's Travels, A Modest Proposal

Jonathan Swift (1667–1745) was a satirist who hated injustice. He was born in Dublin, Ireland, and was able to directly observe the injustice that was common in this land unwillingly connected to England. Before Jonathan was born, his father died, so his childhood education was arranged by his relatives. He eventually attended Trinity College in Dublin and, upon graduation, moved to England where he worked as a secretary for a famous English diplomat and writer. Swift's secretary position gave him time for extensive reading and contemplation, which served as the basis for his later writing.

He became politically active in Ireland and critical of English society. His well-known writings include *Gulliver's Travels* and *Modest Proposal for Preventing the Children of Poor People in Ireland from Being a Burden to Their Parents or Country, and for Making Them Beneficial to the Public.* Both are strongly satirical and critical of English politics and attitudes. Swift also felt that most humans failed to live up to their capabilities and that they should not be defined automatically as rational beings but, rather, as animals capable of reason. These attitudes, too, are contained in his works.

The first edition of *Gulliver's Travels* was published with major changes by the publisher who feared public outrage over its controversial content. Swift wrote it in a style of travel reporting popular in his day, but created fictional cultures to represent and satirize various parts of English society. This satirical commentary lambasted English lawyers, scientists, politicians, and the human race in general. *Gulliver's Travels* has sometimes been used as a children's story, thus largely missing its major point of criticizing morals and behavior, but it is still recognized as one of the most powerful satires of all time.

Presented here are selections from Gulliver's visits to the Island of Laputa and the land of Houynhnm. Laputa was a land where everyone was a scientist, but all science was only done for its own sake and steered away from any practical value. This is widely considered to be criticism of the Royal Society as well as the Enlightenment's scientific revolution in general. In Houynhnm, Gulliver encounters a race of noble and intelligent horses. These horses are disgusted by the dirty, foul, and ill-tempered creatures called "Yahoos" who share Houynhnm island. The Yahoos represent the human race in its most gross and degraded form. When Gulliver arrives on their island, Gulliver is also disgusted by the Yahoos and seeks to live with the horses. The horses are astounded to find a Yahoo as cultured as Gulliver is, and entertain him, asking him to explain the culture from which he came. Gulliver finally leaves when the horses realize that he is, after all, only human.

Gulliver's *A Modest Proposal* is one of the best satirical pieces ever written. Gulliver was sympathetic to the plight of the poor Irish people and wanted to wake the English to the terrible conditions then existing in Ireland. His method was to make a very logical proposal for a way to help the Irish. The proposal was carefully supported in a scientific and sober way. However, the proposal is so outrageous that readers are immediately aghast at what has been proposed. Throughout, Gulliver continues his seeming sincerity so that, at the end, the reader is not sure whether Gulliver is mad or satirical. That quality of writing is one of the reasons this piece is so great.

■ A Voyage to Laputa . . .

At my alighting I was surrounded by a Crowd of People, but those who stood nearest seemed to be of better Quality. They beheld me with all the Marks and Circumstances of Wonder; neither indeed was I much in their Debt; having never till then seen a Race of Mortals so singular in their Shapes, Habits, and Countenances. Their Heads were all reclined either to the Right, or the Left; one of their Eyes turned inward, and the other directly up to the Zenith. Their outward Garments were adorned with the Figures of Suns, Moons, and Stars, interwoven with those of Fiddles, Flutes, Harps, Trumpets, Guittars, Harpsicords, and many more Instruments of Musick, unknown to us in *Europe.* I observed here and there many in the Habit of Servants, with a blown Bladder fastened like a Flail to the End of a short Stick, which they carried in their Hands. In each Bladder was a small Quantity of dried Pease, or little Pebbles, (as I was afterwards informed.) With these Bladders they now and then flapped the Mouths and Ears of those who stood near them, of which Practice I could not then conceive the Meaning. It seems, the Minds of these People are so taken up with intense Speculations, that they neither can speak, nor attend to the Discourses of others, without being rouzed by some external Taction° upon the Organs of Speech and Hearing; for which Reason, those Persons who are able to afford it, al-ways keep a *Flapper,* (the Original is *Climenole*) in their Family, as one of their Domesticks; nor ever walk abroad or make Visits without him. And the Business of this Officer is, when two or more Persons are in Company, gently to strike with his Bladder the Mouth of him who is to speak, and the Right Ear of him or them to whom the Speaker addresseth himself. This *Flapper* is likewise employed diligently to attend his Master in his Walks, and upon Occasion to give him a soft Flap on his Eyes; because he is always so wrapped up in Cogitation, that he is in manifest Danger of falling down every Precipice, and bouncing his Head against every Post; and in the Streets, of jostling others, or being jostled himself into the Kennel.°

It was necessary to give the Reader this Information, without which he would be at the same Loss with me, to understand the Proceedings of these People, as they conducted me up the Stairs, to the Top of the Island, and from thence to the Royal Palace. While we were ascending, they forgot several Times what they were about, and left me to my self, till their Memories were again rouzed by their *Flappers;* for they appeared altogether unmoved by the Sight of my foreign habit and Countenance, and by the Shouts of the Vulgar, whose Thoughts and Minds were more disengaged. . . .

Those to whom the King had entrusted me, observing how ill I was clad, ordered a Taylor to come next Morning, and take my Measure for a

---

Taction: Touch.

Kennel: Gutter.

Source: From *Gulliver's Travels* by Johnathan Swift (Boston: Bedford Boods, 1995).

Suit of Cloths. This Operator did his Office after a different manner from those of his Trade in *Europe*. He first took my Altitude by a Quadrant, and then with Rule and Compasses, described the Dimensions and Out-Lines of my whole Body; all which he entred upon Paper, and in six Days brought my Cloths very ill made, and quite out of Shape, by happening to mistake a Figure in the Calculation. But my Comfort was, that I observed such Accidents very frequent, and little regarded.

During my Confinement for want of Cloaths, and by an Indisposition that held me some Days longer, I much enlarged my Dictionary; and when I went next to Court, was able to understand many Things the King spoke and to return him some Kind of Answers. His Majesty had given Orders, that the Island should move North-East and by East, to the vertical Point over *Lagado,* the Metropolis of the whole Kingdom, below upon the firm Earth. . . .

The Knowledge I had in Mathematicks gave me great Assistance in acquiring their Phraseology, which depended much upon that Science and Musick; and in the latter I was not unskilled. Their Ideas are perpetually conversant in Lines and Figures. If they would, for Example, praise the Beauty of a Woman, or any other Animal, they describe it by Rhombs, Circles, Parallelograms, Ellipses, and other Geometrical Terms; or else by Words of Art drawn from Musick, needless here to repeat. I observed in the King's Kitchen all Sorts of Mathematical and Musical Instruments, after the Figures of which they cut up the Joynts that were served to his Majesty's Table.

Their Houses are very ill built, the Walls bevil,° without one right Angle in any Apartment; and this Defect ariseth from the Contempt they bear for practical Geometry; which they despise as vulgar and mechanick, those Instructions they give being too refined for the Intellectuals° of their Workmen; which occasions perpetual Mistakes. And although they are dextrous enough

upon a Piece of Paper in the Management of the Rule, the Pencil, and the Divider, yet in the common Actions and Behaviour of Life, I have not seen a more clumsy, awkward, and unhandy People, nor so slow and perplexed in their Conceptions upon all other Subjects, except those of Mathematicks and Musick. They are very bad Reasoners, and vehemently given to Opposition, unless when they happen to be of the right Opinion, which is seldom their Case. Imagination, Fancy, and Invention, they are wholly Strangers to, nor have any Words in their Language by which those Ideas can be expressed; the whole Compass of their Thoughts and Mind, being shut up within the two forementioned Sciences. . . .

These People are under continual Disquietudes, never enjoying a Minute's Peace of Mind; and their Disturbances proceed from causes which very little affect the rest of Mortals. Their Apprehensions arise from several Changes they dread in the Celestial Bodies. For Instance; that the Earth by the continual Approaches of the Sun towards it, must in Course of Time be absorbed or swallowed up. That the Face of the Sun will by Degrees be encrusted with its own Effluvia, and give no more Light to the World. That, the Earth very narrowly escaped a Brush from the Tail of the last Comet, which would have infallibly reduced it to Ashes; and that the next, which they have calculated for One and Thirty Years hence, will probably destroy us. For, if in its Perihelion° it should approach within a certain Degree of the Sun, (as by their Calculations they have Reason to dread) it will conceive a Degree of Heat ten Thousand Times more intense than that of red hot glowing Iron; and in its Absence from the Sun, carry a blazing Tail Ten Hundred Thousand and Fourteen Miles long; through which if the Earth should pass at the Distance of one Hundred Thousand Miles from the Nucleus, or main Body of the Comet, it must in its Passage be set on Fire, and reduced to Ashes. That the Sun daily spending its Rays without any

---

bevil: Not at right angles.

Intellectuals: Minds.

Perihelion: The point in the orbit when the orbiting body is closest to the sun.

Nutriment to supply them, will at last be wholly consumed and annihilated; which must be attended with the Destruction of this Earth, and of all the Planets that receive their Light from it.

They are so perpetually alarmed with the Apprehensions of these and the like impending Dangers, that they can neither sleep quietly in their Beds, nor have any Relish for the common Pleasures or Amusements of Life. When they meet an Acquaintance in the Morning, the first Question is about the Sun's Health; how he looked at his Setting and Rising, and what Hopes they have to avoid the Stroak of the approaching Comet. This Conversation they are apt to run into with the same Temper that Boys discover, in delighting to hear terrible Stories of Sprites and Hobgoblins, which they greedily listen to, and dare not go to Bed for fear. . . .

▪ Of Paternal Power

He [the king of the Houghnhnms] added, That he had heard too much upon the Subject of War, both in this, and some former Discourses. There was another Point which a little perplexed him at present. I had said, that some of our Crew left their Country on Account of being ruined by *Law:* That I had already explained the Meaning of the Word; but he was at a Loss how it should come to pass, that the *Law* which was intended for *every* Man's Preservation, should be any Man's Ruin. Therefore he desired to be farther satisfied what I meant by *Law,* and the Dispensers thereof, according to the present Practice in my own Country: Because he thought, Nature and Reason were sufficient Guides for a reasonable Animal, as we pretended to be, in shewing us that we ought to do, and what to avoid.

I assured his Honour, that *Law* was a Science wherein I had not much conversed, further than by employing Advocates, in vain, upon some Injustices that had been done me. However, I would give him all the Satisfaction I was able.

I said there was a Society of Men among us, bred up from their Youth in the Art of proving by Words multiplied for the Purpose, that *White* is

Black, and *Black* is *White,* according as they are paid. To this Society all the rest of the People are Slaves.

For Example. If my Neighbour hath a mind to my *Cow,* he hires a Lawyer to prove that he ought to have my *Cow* from me. I must then hire another to defend my Right; it being against all Rules of *Law* that any Man should be allowed to speak for himself. Now in this Case, I who am the true Owner lie under two great Disadvantages. First, my Lawyer being practiced almost from his Cradle in defending Falshood; is quite out of his Element when he would be an Advocate for Justice, which as an Office unnatural, he always attempts with great Awkwardness, if not with Illwill. The second Disadvantage is, that my Lawyer must proceed with great Caution: Or else he will be reprimanded by the Judges, and abhorred by his Brethren, as one who would lessen the Practice of the Law. And therefore I have but two Methods to preserve my *Cow.* The first is, to gain over my Adversary's Lawyer with a double Fee; who will then betray his Client, by insinuating that he hath Justice on his Side. The second Way is for my Lawyer to make my Cause appear as unjust as he can; by allowing the *Cow* to belong to my Adversary; and this if it be skilfully done, will certainly bespeak the Favour of the Bench.

Now, your Honour is to know, that these Judges are Persons appointed to decide all Controversies of Property, as well as for the Tryal of Criminals; and picket out from the most dextrous Lawyers who are grown old or lazy: And having been byassed all their Lives against Truth and Equity, are under such a fatal Necessity of favouring Fraud, Perjury and Oppression; that I have known some of them to have refused a large Bribe from the Side where Justice lay, rather than injure the *Faculty,*° by doing any thing unbecoming their Nature or their Office.

It is a Maxim among these Lawyers, that whatever hath been done before, may legally be done again: And therefore they take special Care to record all the Decisions formerly made against

---

Faculty: Profession.

common Justice and the general Reason of Mankind. These, under the Name of *Precedents,* they produce as Authorities to justify the most iniquitous Opinions; and the Judges never fail of decreeing accordingly.

In pleading, they studiously avoid entering into the *Merits* of the Cause; but are loud, violent and tedious in dwelling upon all Circumstances which are not to the Purpose. For Instance, in the Case already mentioned: They never desire to know what Claim or Title my Adversary hath to my *Cow;* but whether the said *Cow* were Red or Black; her Horns long or short; whether the Field I graze her in be round or square; whether she were milked at home or abroad; what Diseases she is subject to, and the like. After which they consult *Precedents,* adjourn the Cause, from Time to Time, and in Ten, Twenty, or Thirty Years come to an Issue.

It is likewise to be observed, that this Society hath a peculiar Cant and Jargon of their own, that no other Mortal can understand, and wherein all their Laws are written, which they take special Care to multiply; whereby they have wholly confounded the very Essence of Truth and Falshood, of Right and Wrong; so that it will take Thirty Years to decide whether the Field, left me by my Ancestors for six Generations, belong to me, or to a Stranger three Hundred Miles off.

In the Tryal of Persons accused for Crimes against the State, the Method is much more short and commendable: The Judge first sends to sound the Disposition of those in Power; after which he can easily hang or save the Criminal, strictly preserving all the Forms of law.

Here my Master interposing, said it was a Pity, that Creatures endowed with such prodigious Abilities of Mind as these Lawyers, by the Description I gave of them must certainly be, were not rather encouraged to be Instructors of others in Wisdom and Knowledge. In Answer to which, I assured his Honour, that in all Points out of their own Trade, they were usually the most ignorant and stupid Generation° among us, the most despi-

cable in common Conversation, avowed Enemies to all Knowledge and Learning; and equally disposed to pervert the general Reason of Mankind, in every other Subject of Discourse, as in that of their own Profession.

■ A Continuation of the State of England, under Queen Anne. The Character of a First Minister in the Courts of Europe.

My Master was yet wholly at a Loss to understand what Motives could incite this Race of Lawyers to perplex, disquiet, and weary themselves by engaging in a Confederacy of Injustice, merely for the Sake of injuring their Fellow-Animals; neither could he comprehend what I meant in saying they did it for *Hire.* Whereupon I was at much pains to describe to him the Use of *Money,* the Materials it was made of, and the Value of the Metals: That when a *Yahoo* had got a great Store of this precious Substance, he was able to purchase whatever he had a mind to; the finest Cloathing, the noblest Houses, great Tracts of Land, the most costly Meats and Drinks; and have his choice of the most beautiful Females. Therefore since *Money* alone, was able to perform all these Feats, our *Yahoos* thought, they could never have enough of it to spend or to save, as they found themselves inclined from their natural Bent either to Profusion or Avarice. That, the rich Man enjoyed the Fruit of the poor Man's Labour, and the latter were a Thousand to One in Proportion to the former. That the Bulk of our People was forced to live miserably, by labouring every Day for small Wages to make a few live plentifully. I enlarged myself much on these and many other Particulars to the same Purpose: But his Honour was still to seek:° For he went upon a Supposition that all Animals had a Title to their Share in the Productions of the Earth; and especially those who presided over the rest. Therefore he desired I would let him know, what these costly meats were, and how any of us

---

Generation: Species.

still to seek: Unable to understand.

happened to want them. Whereupon I enumerated as many Sorts as came into my Head, with the various Methods of dressing them, which could not be done without sending Vessels by Sea to every Part of the World, as well for Liquors to drink, as for Sauces, and innumerable other Conveniencies. I assured him, that this whole Globe of Earth must be at least three Times gone round, before one of our better Female *Yahoos* could get her Breakfast, or a Cup to put it in. He said, That must needs be a miserable Country which cannot furnish Food for its own Inhabitants. But what he chiefly wondered at, was how such vast Tracts of Ground as I descried, should be wholly without *Fresh water,* and the People put to the Necessity of sending over the Sea for Drink. I replied, that *England* (the dear Place of my Nativity) was computed to produce three Times the Quantity of Food, more than its Inhabitants are able to consume, as well as Liquors extracted from Grain, or pressed out of the Fruit of certain Trees, which made excellent Drink; and the same Proportion in every other Convenience of Life. But, in order to feed the Luxury and Intemperance of the Males, and the Vanity of the Females, we sent away the greatest Part of our necessary Things to other Countries, from whence in Return we brought the materials of Diseases, Folly, and Vice, to spend among ourselves. Hence it follows of Necessity, that vast Numbers of our People are compelled to seek their Livelihood by Begging, Robbing, Stealing, Cheating, Pimping, Forswearing, Flattering, Suborning, Forging, Gaming, Lying, Fawning, Hectoring, Voting, Scribling, Stargazing, Poysoning, Whoring, Canting, Libelling, Free-thinking, and the like Occupations: Every one of which Terms, I was at much Pains to make him understand.

For preventing the children of poor people in Ireland, from being a burden on their parents or country, and for making them beneficial to the publick.—1729

It is a melancholy object to those, who walk through this great town, or travel in the country, when they see the streets, the roads and cabbin-doors crowded with beggars of the female sex, followed by three, four, or six children, all in rags, and importuning every passenger for an alms. These mothers instead of being able to work for their honest livelihood, are forced to employ all their time in stroling to beg sustenance for their helpless infants who, as they grow up, either turn thieves for want of work, or leave their dear native country, to fight for the Pretender in Spain, or sell themselves to the Barbadoes.

I think it is agreed by all parties, that this prodigious number of children in the arms, or on the backs, or at the heels of their mothers, and frequently of their fathers, is in the present deplorable state of the kingdom, a very great additional grievance; and therefore whoever could find out a fair, cheap and easy method of making these children sound and useful members of the common-wealth, would deserve so well of the publick, as to have his statue set up for a preserver of the nation.

But my intention is very far from being confined to provide only for the children of professed beggars: it is of a much greater extent, and shall take in the whole number of infants at a certain age, who are born of parents in effect as little able to support them, as those who demand our charity in the streets.

As to my own part, having turned my thoughts for many years, upon this important subject, and maturely weighed the several schemes of our projectors, I have always found them grossly mistaken in their computation. It is true, a child just dropt from its dam, may be supported by her milk, for a solar year, with little other nourishment: at most not above the value of two shillings, which the mother may certainly get, or the value in scraps, by her lawful occupation of begging; and it is exactly at one year old that I propose to provide for them in such a manner, as, instead of being a charge upon their parents, or the parish, or wanting food and raiment for the rest of their lives, they shall, on the contrary, contribute to the feeding, and partly to the cloathing of many thousands.

There is likewise another great advantage in my scheme, that it will prevent those voluntary abortions, and that horrid practice of women murdering their bastard children, alas! too frequent among us, sacrificing the poor innocent babes, I doubt, more to avoid the expence than the shame, which would move tears and pity in the most savage and inhuman breast.

The number of souls in this kingdom being usually reckoned one million and a half, of these I calculate there may be about two hundred thousand couple whose wives are breeders; from which number I subtract thirty thousand couple, who are able to maintain their own children, (although I apprehend there cannot be so many, under the present distresses of the kingdom) but this being granted, there will remain an hundred and seventy thousand breeders. I again subtract fifty thousand, for those women who miscarry, or whose children die by accident or disease within the year. There only remain an hundred and twenty thousand children of poor parents annually born. The question therefore is, How this number shall be reared, and provided for? which, as I have already said, under the present situation of affairs, is utterly impossible by all the methods hitherto proposed. For we can neither employ them in handicraft or agriculture; we neither build houses, (I mean in the country) nor cultivate land: they can very seldom pick up a livelihood by stealing till they arrive at six years old; except where they are of towardly parts, although I confess they learn the rudiments much earlier; during which time they can however be properly looked upon only as probationers: As I have been informed by a principal gentleman in the county of Cavan, who protested to me, that he never knew above one or two instances under the age of six, even in a part of the kingdom so renowned for the quickest proficiency in that art.

I am assured by our merchants, that a boy or a girl before twelve years old, is no saleable commodity, and even when they come to this age, they will not yield above three pounds, or three pounds and half a crown at most, on the exchange; which cannot turn to account either to the parents or kingdom, the charge of nutriments and rags having been at least four times that value.

I shall now therefore humbly propose my own thoughts, which I hope will not be liable to the least objection.

I have been assured by a very knowing American of my acquaintance in London, that a young healthy child well nursed, is, at a year old, a most delicious nourishing and wholesome food, whether stewed, roasted, baked, or boiled; and I make no doubt that it will equally serve in a fricasie, or a ragoust.

I do therefore humbly offer it to publick consideration, that of the hundred and twenty thousand children, already computed, twenty thousand may be reserved for breed, whereof only one fourth part to be males; which is more than we allow to sheep, black cattle, or swine, and my reason is, that these children are seldom the fruits of marriage, a circumstance not much regarded by our savages, therefore, one male will be sufficient to serve four females. That the remaining hundred thousand may, at a year old, be offered in sale to the persons of quality and fortune, through the kingdom, always advising the mother to let them suck plentifully in the last month, so as to render them plump, and fat for a good table. A child will make two dishes at an entertainment for friends, and when the family dines alone, the fore or hind quarter will make a reasonable dish, and seasoned with a little pepper or salt, will be very good boiled on the fourth day, especially in winter.

I have reckoned upon a medium, that a child just born will weigh 12 pounds, and in a solar year, if tolerably nursed, encreaseth to 28 pounds.

I grant this food will be somewhat dear, and therefore very proper for landlords, who, as they have already devoured most of the parents, seem to have the best title to the children.

Infant's flesh will be in season throughout the year, but more plentiful in March, and a little before and after; for we are told by a grave author, an eminent French physician, that fish being a prolifick dyet, there are more children born in Roman Catholick countries about nine months after Lent, the markets will be more glutted than usual, because the number of Popish infants, is at least three to one in this kingdom, and therefore it will have one other collateral advantage, by lessening the number of Papists among us.

I have already computed the charge of nursing a beggar's child (in which list I reckon all cottagers, labourers, and four-fifths of the farmers) to be about two shillings per annum, rags included; and I believe no gentleman would repine to give ten shillings for the carcass of a good fat child, which, as I have said, will make four dishes of excellent nutritive meat, when he hath only some particular friend, or his own family to dine with him. Thus the squire will learn to be a good landlord, and grow popular among his tenants, the mother will have eight shillings neat profit, and be fit for work till she produces another child.

Those who are more thrifty (as I must confess the times require) may flea the carcass; the skin of which, artificially dressed, will make admirable gloves for ladies, and summer boots for fine gentlemen.

As to our City of Dublin, shambles may be appointed for this purpose, in the most convenient parts of it, and butchers we may be assured will not be wanting; although I rather recommend buying the children alive, and dressing them hot from the knife, as we do roasting pigs.

A very worthy person, a true lover of his country, and whose virtues I highly esteem, was lately pleased, in discoursing on this matter, to offer a refinement upon my scheme. He said, that many gentlemen of this kingdom, having of late destroyed their deer, he conceived that the want of venison might be well supply'd by the bodies of young lads and maidens, not exceeding fourteen years of age, nor under twelve; so great a number of both sexes in every country being now ready to starve for want of work and service: And these to be disposed of by their parents if alive, or otherwise by their nearest relations. But with due deference to so excellent a friend, and so deserving a patriot, I cannot be altogether in his sentiments; for as to the males, my American acquaintance assured me from frequent experience, that their flesh was generally tough and lean, like that of our school-boys, by continual exercise, and their taste disagreeable, and to fatten them would not answer the charge. Then as to the females, it would, I think, with humble submission, be a loss to the publick, because they soon would become breeders themselves: And besides, it is not improbable that some scrupulous people might be apt to censure such a practice, (although indeed very unjustly) as a little bordering upon cruelty, which, I confess, hath always been with me the strongest objection against any project, how well soever intended.

But in order to justify my friend, he confessed, that this expedient was put into his head by the famous Salmanaazor, a native of the island Formosa, who came from thence to London, above twenty years ago, and in conversation told my friend, that in his country, when any young person happened to be put to death, the executioner sold the carcass to persons of quality, as a prime dainty; and that, in his time, the body of a plump girl of fifteen, who was crucified for an attempt to poison the Emperor, was sold to his imperial majesty's prime minister of state, and other great mandarins of the court in joints from the gibbet, at four hundred crowns. Neither indeed can I deny, that if the same use were made of several plump young girls in this town, who without one single groat to their fortunes, cannot stir abroad without a chair, and appear at a play-house and assemblies in foreign fineries which they never will pay for; the kingdom would not be the worse.

Some persons of a desponding spirit are in great concern about that vast number of poor people, who are aged, diseased, or maimed; and I have been desired to employ my thoughts what course may be taken, to ease the nation of so grievous an incumbrance. But I am not in the least pain upon that matter, because it is very well known, that they are every day dying, and rotting, by cold and famine, and filth, and vermin, as fast as can be reasonably expected. And as to the young labourers, they are now in almost as hopeful a condition. They cannot get work, and consequently pine away from want of nourishment, to a degree, that if at any time they are accidentally hired to common labour, they have not strength to perform it, and thus the country and themselves are happily delivered from the evils to come.

I have too long digressed, and therefore shall return to my subject. I think the advantages by the proposal which I have made are obvious and many, as well as of the highest importance.

For first, as I have already observed, it would greatly lessen the number of Papists, with whom we are yearly over-run, being the principal breeders of the nation, as well as our most dangerous enemies, and who stay at home on purpose with a design to deliver the kingdom to the Pretender, hoping to take their advantage by the absence of so many good Protestants, who have chosen rather to leave their country, than stay at home and pay tithes against their conscience to an episcopal curate.

Secondly, The poorer tenants will have something valuable of their own, which by law may be made liable to a distress, and help to pay their landlord's rent, their corn and cattle being already seized, and money a thing unknown.

Thirdly, Whereas the maintainance of an hundred thousand children, from two years old, and upwards, cannot be computed at less than ten shillings a piece per annum, the nation's stock will be thereby encreased fifty thousand pounds per annum, besides the profit of a new dish, introduced to the tables of all gentlemen of fortune in the kingdom, who have any refinement in taste. And the money will circulate among our selves, the goods being entirely of our own growth and manufacture.

Fourthly, The constant breeders, besides the gain of eight shillings sterling per annum by the sale of their children, will be rid of the charge of maintaining them after the first year.

Fifthly, This food would likewise bring great custom to taverns, where the vintners will certainly be so prudent as to procure the best receipts for dressing it to perfection; and consequently have their houses frequented by all the fine gentlemen, who justly value themselves upon their knowledge in good eating; and a skilful cook, who understands how to oblige his guests, will contrive to make it as expensive as they please.

Sixthly, This would be a great inducement to marriage, which all wise nations have either encouraged by rewards, or enforced by laws and penalties. It would encrease the care and tenderness of mothers towards their children, when they were sure of a settlement for life to the poor babes, provided in some sort by the publick, to their annual profit instead of expence. We should soon see an honest emulation among the married women, which of them could bring the fattest child to the market. Men would become as fond of their wives, during the time of their pregnancy, as they are now of their mares in foal, their cows in calf, or sow when they are ready to farrow; nor offer to beat or kick them (as is too frequent a practice) for fear of a miscarriage.

Many other advantages might be enumerated. For instance, the addition of some thousand carcasses in our exportation of barrel'd beef: the propagation of swine's flesh, and improvement in the art of making good bacon, so much wanted among us by the great destruction of pigs, too frequent at our tables; which are no way comparable in taste or magnificence to a well grown, fat yearly child, which roasted whole will make a considerable figure at a Lord Mayor's feast, or any other publick entertainment. But this, and many others, I omit, being studious of brevity.

Supposing that one thousand families in this city, would be constant customers for infants flesh, besides others who might have it at merry meetings, particularly at weddings and christenings, I compute that Dublin would take off annually about twenty thousand carcasses; and the rest of the kingdom (where probably they will be sold somewhat cheaper) the remaining eighty thousand.

I can think of no one objection, that will possibly be raised against this proposal, unless it should be urged, that the number of people will be thereby much lessened in the kingdom. This I freely own, and 'twas indeed one principal design in offering it to the world. I desire the reader will observe, that I calculate my remedy for this one individual Kingdom of Ireland, and for no other that ever was, is, or, I think, ever can be upon Earth. Therefore let no man talk to me of other expedients: Of taxing our absentees at five shillings a pound: Of using neither cloaths, nor houshold furniture, except what is of our own growth and manufacture: Of utterly rejecting the materials and instruments that promote foreign luxury: Of curing the expensiveness of pride, vanity, idleness, and gaming in our women: Of introducing a vein of parsimony, prudence and temperance: Of learning to love our country, wherein we differ even from Laplanders, and the inhabitants of Topinamboo: Of quitting our animosities and factions, nor acting any longer like the Jews, who were murdering one another at the very moment their city was taken: Of being a little cautious not to sell our country and consciences for nothing: Of teaching landlords to have at least one degree of mercy towards their tenants. Lastly, of putting a spirit of honesty, industry, and skill into our shopkeepers, who, if a resolution could now be taken to buy only our native goods, would immediately unite to cheat and exact upon us in the price, the measure, and the goodness, nor could ever yet be brought to make one fair proposal of just dealing, though often and earnestly invited to it.

Therefore I repeat, let no man talk to me of these and the like expedients, 'till he hath at least some glympse of hope, that there will ever be some hearty and sincere attempt to put them into practice.

But, as to my self, having been wearied out for many years with offering vain, idle, visionary thoughts, and at length utterly despairing of success, I fortunately fell upon this proposal, which, as it is wholly new, so it hath something solid and real, of no expence and little trouble, full in our own power, and whereby we can incur no danger in disobliging England. For this kind of commodity will not bear exportation, and flesh being of too tender a consistence, to admit a long continuance in salt, although perhaps I could name a country, which would be glad to eat up our whole nation without it.

After all, I am not so violently bent upon my own opinion, as to reject any offer, proposed by wise men, which shall be found equally innocent, cheap, easy, and effectual. But before something of that kind shall be advanced in contradiction to my scheme, and offering a better, I desire the author or authors will be pleased maturely to consider two points. First, As things now stand, how they will be able to find food and raiment for a hundred thousand useless mouths and backs. And secondly, There being a round million of creatures in humane figure throughout this kingdom, whose whole subsistence put into a common stock, would leave them in debt two million of pounds sterling, adding those who are beggars by profession, to the bulk of farmers, cottagers and labourers, with their wives and children, who are beggars in effect; I desire those politicians who dislike my overture, and may perhaps be so bold to attempt an answer, that they will first ask the parents of these mortals, whether they would not at this day think it a great happiness to have been sold for food at a year old, in the manner I prescribe, and thereby have avoided such a perpetual scene of misfortunes, as they have since gone through, by the oppression of landlords, the impossibility of paying rent without money or trade, the want of common sustenance, with neither house nor cloaths to cover them from the inclemencies of the weather, and the most inevitable prospect of intailing the like, or greater miseries, upon their breed for ever.

I profess, in the sincerity of my heart, that I have not the least personal interest in endeavouring to promote this necessary work, having no other motive than the publick good of my country, by advancing our trade, providing for infants, relieving the poor, and giving some pleasure to the rich. I have no children, by which I can propose to get a single penny; the youngest being nine years old, and my wife past child-bearing.

Voltaire: Treatise on Tolerance, "If God Did Not Exist He Would Have to Be Invented", Letters on England

François Marie Arouet (1694–1778) was born in Paris to a middle class family. He was trained in a Jesuit college, but became critical of the Catholic Church and became a life-long enemy of the hierarchy of the church. At seventeen, he left school and was imprisoned for eleven months after humiliating French authorities, who he ridiculed both for their blind support of the church and for their haughty negligence of the rights of common people. While in prison, he adopted the pen name "Voltaire." Because of further written attacks on members of the nobility, he was beaten, tried for slander, and exiled from France. He moved to England where he was attracted to the ideas of John Locke and Sir Isaac Newton, founders of the English Enlightenment and the Scientific Awakening. He translated Newton's works into French and helped make science accessible to the common people and establish it as a method of finding truth that was independent of religion. As he studied England's constitutional monarchy and religious tolerance, he developed a strong admiration for the English government and wrote a book praising English customs and institutions.

Eventually, Voltaire left England and lived on an estate on the French-Swiss border. Voltaire wrote more than seventy volumes, fifty plays, and over 70,000 messages and letters to friends. He was one of France's greatest writers and philosophers due to his intelligence, wit, and style. He was extremely influential in France and became the embodiment of the Enlightenment. At one time, he moved to Germany at the request of Frederick the Great of Prussia to whom, Voltaire believed, he could give advice and thus shape the emerging nation of Germany. Voltaire eventually became disenchanted because of the lack of influence he had on the Prussian king. Perhaps Voltaire's message was premature.

Voltaire's famous *Treatise on Tolerance* is his war cry against religious intolerance, as well as any other form of intolerance-associated infamy. The selections presented here illustrate Voltaire's love for the Enlightenment principles of his era. Voltaire's plea that "we may all be brethren" helped coerce the Catholic Church, as well as all other Western religions, to adopt a nondiscriminatory attitude towards other faiths.

"If God Did Not Exist, He Would Have to Be Invented" is Voltaire's discussion of the logic and necessity of Deity. Most Enlightenment philosophers in Voltaire's day struggled to believe in God because of the imperfect nature of the world in which they lived. But Voltaire founded a philosophy which today is called deism. Deism does not deny the existence of God, but separates God from religion. Voltaire believed that although God may have created the world, he was now a pure spectator in the universe having ceased to interact directly with mankind after creating him. God allowed the laws of nature, which were his perfect laws, to control the world. Deism allowed Voltaire to believe in God but to deny formal religion and to assert that science was the religion through which we can find God.

Letters on England is Voltaire's memoirs of his travels through the country he loved during his exile there from France. Voltaire was an Anglophile, and let it show, attacking France by comparing the tolerance and progress of England to the religious tyranny of his native land. Voltaire's critical style and love of satire also comes through, however, as he ridicules the nonsensical nature of various institutions in England. Included here is his letter concerning the Presbyterians—it shows the entertaining and witty nature of Voltaire's cynical analysis.

The Consequences of Intolerance

Is each individual citizen, then, to be permitted to believe only in what his reason tells him, to think only what his reason, be it enlightened or misguided, may dictate? Yes, indeed he should, provided always that he threatens no disturbance to public order. For a man is under no obligation to believe or not to believe. His duties are to respect the laws and customs of his country, and if you claim that it is a crime not to believe in the prevailing religion, you are pointing the finger of accusation against our ancestors, the first Christians, and you are justifying the actions of those you previously blamed for putting them to death.

You will answer that there is the world of difference, that all the other religions are man-made and only the Roman Apostolic Church is the work of God. But in all conscience, does the fact that our religion is divinely inspired mean that it must rule through hatred, ferocity, banishment, confiscation, imprisonment, torture, murder, and the giving of thanks to God for murder? The more the Christian religion is divine, the less does it belong to man to control it; if God has made it, then God will sustain it without your help. You know that intolerance begets either hypocrites or rebels; what an appalling choice! Finally, would you wish to uphold by the power of the executioner the religion of a God who died at the hands of executioners and who preached only gentleness and patience?

Reflect, I implore you, on the truly dreadful consequences of intolerance sanctioned by law. If a citizen living in a society with a certain latitude and declining to profess the religion of that society could legally be stripped of his worldly goods, thrown into a dungeon, and murdered, what exceptional circumstances would exempt the first in the land from similar punishments? In religion the sovereign and the beggar are equals; it is a fact that more than fifty learned men and monks have affirmed the monstrous doctrine that it is lawful to depose, even to assassinate, monarchs who dare to think differently from the established Church; and the parliaments of this kingdom have repeatedly condemned such abominable decisions taken by abominable theologians. . . .

It is well known that our dogmas have not always been properly explained, nor universally received in our Church. As Jesus Christ did not inform us in what manner the Holy Ghost operated, for a long time the Latin Church believed, along with the Greek, that it operated only through God the Father; later, they added that it could also work through God the Son. Let me ask this: if the day after this decision was taken a citizen continued to recite the Creed of the day before, would he merit the death penalty? Are cruelty and injustice less heinous when they inflict punishment today upon a man who thinks as we all used to think yesterday? At the time of Honorious I, was a man sunk in guilt because he did not believe that Jesus was two wills in one?

Source: Copyright © 2000 Cambridge University Press. Reprinted by permission.

It is not so long ago that the dogma of the Immaculate Conception was established; the Dominicans still refuse to believe it. At what point exactly will the Dominicans start deserving death in this world and damnation in the next?

If there is any one to whom we should turn for guidance in our interminable disputes, it is certainly to the apostles and the evangelists. There was difference enough between St Peter and St Paul to provoke a violent schism. In his Epistle to the Galatians Paul expressly states that he resisted Peter to his face, because he thought him deserving of reproach. Peter had been guilty with Barnabas of deceit; they had both dined with the Gentiles before the arrival of James, then slunk away furtively, deserting the Gentiles for fear of offending the circumcised. 'When I found', said Paul, 'that they were not following the true path of the Gospel, I said to Cephas [Peter] in front of them all: Since thou, who art born a Jew, dost follow the Gentile, not the Jewish way of life, by what right dost thou bind the Gentiles to live like Jews?'

There was matter here for an acrimonious quarrel. The question was: should the new Christians observe Jewish ceremonies, or should they not? At this very time, St Paul was wont to go and sacrifice in the temple of Jerusalem. We know that the first fifteen Bishops of Jerusalem were circumcised Jews, who observed the sabbath and abstained from forbidden meat. Now, if a Spanish or Portuguese bishop were to have himself circumcised and to observe the Jewish sabbath he would be burnt at the stake in an *auto-da-fé*. And yet this fundamental point failed to cause the slightest dissension among either the apostles or the first Christians.

Had the evangelists been anything like modern writers, they would have had masses of opportunity to squabble amongst themselves. St Matthew counts twenty-eight generations from David to Jesus. St Luke counts forty-one. Moreover, Luke's generations are absolutely different from Matthew's. But no argument erupted between the disciples over these apparent contradictions, which were subsequently reconciled by several fathers of the Church. Feelings were not hurt; peace was preserved. There exists no greater example than this, to teach that we should be toler-

ant with one another in our disagreements and humble when faced with something we do not understand.

In his Epistle to some Jews of Rome who converted to Christianity, St Paul devotes the whole latter part of the third chapter to the proposition that one may attain Glory only through Faith, and that Works count for nothing. St James, on the other hand, in his Epistle to the twelve tribes scattered throughout the world, chapter 2, repeatedly states that one cannot find salvation without good works. And there we have the basis of one of the most severe divisions in our modern Church, over an issue which did not divide the apostles in any way.

If to persecute those with whom we disagree were a pious thing to do, it would follow that the man who managed to kill the greatest number of heretics would be the most holy saint in Paradise. What kind of impression would he make up there, who was merely content to ruin his brother men and throw them into dungeons, next to the fanatic who despatched hundreds to their deaths on the day of St Bartholomew? The answer is apparently as follows.

The successors of St Peter and his consistory cannot make mistakes. They approved, celebrated, even consecrated the massacre of St Bartholomew. Therefore this was a very sacred act. Therefore also, of two murderers equal in piety, the one who disembowelled twenty-four pregnant Huguenot women must be promoted to double the amount of beatitude over the one who ripped open only twelve. By the same reckoning, the fanatics of the Cévennes must have calculated that they would be elevated in glory in exact proportion to the number of priests, monks and Catholic women they were able to slaughter. These are strange claims indeed to eternal glory.

*   *   *

◼ On Universal Tolerance

It requires no great skill in argument or gift of eloquence to prove that Christians should tolerate one another. I will go further: I tell you, we ought to regard every man as our brother. What? The Turk, my brother? The Chinaman, my brother? The Jew and the Siamese as well? Yes, assuredly, for are we not all children of the same Father and creatures of the same God?

But these people despise us, they call us idolators! Very well, I shall tell them they are very much mistaken. It seems to me that I could perhaps shake the arrogant stubbornness of an imam or a Buddhist monk if I were to speak to them more or less in this vein:

'This little globe, which is really only a spot, rolls in space along with so many other globes, all part of this immensity in which we are all lost. The human being, roughly five feet high, is patently of very little consequence in the vast Creation. One of these tiny creatures says to some other of his species, in Arabia or Asia it might be, "Now listen to me, for the God of all these worlds has shown me the truth; there are nine hundred million little ants like us on this earth, but God cherishes only my ant-hill and absolutely loathes all the others to all eternity; so mine will be the only happy ant-hill, and all the rest will be miserable for ever and ever."' The others will then stop me and ask, 'Who is this idiot who talks such nonsense?' And I shall be obliged to reply, 'It is yourselves.' I shall then attempt to calm them down, but it will not be easy. . . .

All ye manifold worshippers of a merciful God! If you are hard of heart, if in adoring Him whose entire law is contained in the words *Love thy God and thy neighbour* you have smothered that pure and holy doctrine with sophistries and unfathomable controversies; if you have provoked bitter argument over a new word, or even sometimes a single letter of the alphabet; if you have sought to bring eternal punishment to bear for the omission of a few phrases or details of ceremony which other peoples could not possibly be aware of; then, through my tears and lamentation for the fate of humankind, I must say to you:

'Come with me to the Day of Judgement, when God will give unto every man according to his deeds. I there envisage all the dead of all the ages, and of our own, appearing before the Almighty. Are you absolutely sure that our Creator and Father in Heaven will say to the wise and virtuous Confucius, to Solon the law-giver, to Pythagoras, Zaleucus, Socrates and Plato, to the divine Antoninus, to the good Trajan and Titus, that adornment of the human race, to Epictetus and so many other models among mankind, "Go, you monsters! Go and suffer torments of infinite intensity and duration; your punishment will continue for ever and ever! As for you others who are so dear to me—Jean Châtel, Ravaillac, Damiens, Cartouche and the rest—you who died according to the correct formula, stay at my right hand and partake of my kingdom and my happiness in eternity"?'

You will recoil in horror at these words, and indeed, once they have escaped my pen, I have nothing further to add.

■ A Prayer to God

It is not now to mankind that I address myself, but to thee, God of all beings, of all worlds, and of all ages, if it be permitted to feeble creatures lost in the immensity of space and imperceptible to the rest of the universe to presume to ask Thee aught, Thou who hast given all and whose secrets are as immutable as they are eternal. Deign to look with pity upon those errors which are inherent in our nature, that these errors be not our downfall! Thou didst not give us a heart in order that we should have one another, nor hands to kill each other with; grant that we may help one another to bear the burden of a difficult and transient life! Let not the trifling differences between the clothes which cover our weak bodies, between our inadequate languages, between our ridiculous customs, our imperfect laws and our insane opinions, between our various conditions, so disproportionate in our eyes and so equal in Thine; let not these little nuances which distinguish the atoms known as men give excuse for hatred or persecution! Grant that those who light candles in the full light of day to worship Thee should look with kindness upon those others who are content with the light of Thy sun! That those who cover their garment with a white veil in order to declare that they love Thee should not detest those others who say the same thing beneath a cloak of black wool! That it should be accounted as good to adore Thee in a jargon derived from some ancient tongue as in a more modern jargon! That those whose garments are dyed red or purple and who lord it over a scrap of a tiny patch of the mud of this world, and who own a few round-shaped objects made of a certain metal, should enjoy what they are pleased to call their status and their riches without pride, and that the rest should observe them without envy; for Thou knowest there is nought to be envied in these little vanities, and nought to be proud of.

May all men remember they are brothers! May they abhor the tyranny which would imprison the soul just as much as they execrate that highway robbery which makes off with the fruit of honest work and application. If the scourges of war are not to be avoided, let us at least not hate one another or tear each other apart in the midst of peace, but let us use the moment of our earthly existence to praise, in a thousand different but equal languages, from Siam to California, Thy goodness which has given us that moment.

*   *   *

Nature tells us all, 'You have been born weak and ignorant and are doomed to live out a few fleeting moments on earth before fertilising it with your corpses. Since you are weak, you must look after one another, and since you are ignorant you must educate each other. If the day comes that you are all of the same opinion (which is improbable, to say the least), and there remains one solitary man who clings to a different opinion, you must forgive him; for it is I who am responsible for making him think the way he does. I have given you strength with which to cultivate the ground and a flicker of intelligence to guide you. I have placed in each of your hearts a seed of compassion with which to help one another through life. Do not smother this seed; nor must you corrupt it; for it is divine. And do not substitute the pathetic squabbles of academic dispute for the voice of nature.

'I alone bind you still further one to another, despite yourselves, by your mutual needs even in the midst of those cruel wars of yours, waged on the slightest of pretexts, which provide an inexhaustible display of mistakes, mischances and misfortunes. I alone can put a stop to the disastrous consequences of those interminable divisions between the nobility and the judiciary, between both these two and the Church, between the urban dweller and the farmer, or the producer and consumer. None of them know the limits of their rights; but in the end, despite themselves, they will all listen to my voice as it speaks directly to their hearts. I alone preserve fairness in the law-courts where, without my intervention, everything would descend to caprice and vacillation, as men are confronted with a huge pile of laws, often framed haphazardly or to meet a transitory need, which differ from one province to another, from one town to another, and almost always contradict each other even within the same place. I alone can inspire true justice, whereas laws inspire naught but wrangling and subterfuge, he who listens to me will always reach the just decision, whereas he who looks only to reconcile contradictory views will go astray.

'There exists a very large building of which I laid the foundations with my own hands; it was solid and simple, and all men might enter it with safety; but they took it into their heads to add to it the most bizarre, useless and vulgar ornamentation, as a result of which the edifice is now falling into ruin on all sides and people pick up the stones and hurl them at one another's heads. To them I cry, "Stop! remove this disgusting debris which is all your work, and remain peacefully with me within the indestructible mansion of my creation."'

Voltaire: "If God Did Not Exist, He Would Have to Be Invented"

To Frederick William, Prince of Prussia:

Monseigneur, the royal family of Prussia has excellent reasons for not wishing the annihilation of the soul. It has more right than anyone to immortality.

It is very true that we do not know any too well what the soul is: no one has ever seen it. All that we do know is that the eternal Lord of nature has given us the power of thinking, and of distinguishing virtue. It is not proved that this faculty survives our death: but the contrary is not proved either. It is possible, doubtless, that God has given thought to a particle to which, after we are no more, He will still give the power of thought: there is no inconsistency in this idea.

In the midst of all the doubts which we have discussed for four thousand years in four thousand ways, the safest course is to do nothing against one's conscience. With this secret, we can enjoy life and have nothing to fear from death.

There are some charlatans who admit no doubts. We know nothing of first principles. It is surely very presumptuous to define God, the angels, spirits, and to pretend to know precisely why God made the world, when we do not know why we can move our arms at our pleasure. Doubt is not a pleasant condition, but certainty is an absurd one.

What is most repellent in the System of Nature [by the Baron d'Holbach] . . . is the audacity with which it decides that there is no God, without even having tried to prove the impossibility. There is some eloquence in the book: but much more rant, and no sort of proof. It is a pernicious work, alike for princes and people: "Si Dieu n'existait pas, il faudrait l'inventer." [If God did not exist, he would have to be invented].

But all nature cries aloud that He does exist: that there is a supreme intelligence, an immense power, an admirable order, and everything teaches us our own dependence on it.

From the depth of our profound ignorance, let us do our best: this is what I think, and what I have always thought, amid all the misery and follies inseparable from seventy-seven years of life. . . . I am, with deep respect, Voltaire.

Source: From *Voltaire in His Letters,* translated by S. G. Tallentrye (New York: G. P. Putnam's Sons, 1919).

■ On the Presbyterians

The Anglican religion only extends to England and Ireland. Presbyterianism is the dominant religion in Scotland. This Presbyterianism is nothing more than pure Calvinism as it was established in France and survives in Geneva. As the priests in this sect receive very small stipends from their churches, and so cannot live in the same luxury as bishops, they have taken the natural course of decrying honours they cannot attain. Picture the proud Diogenes trampling underfoot the pride of Plato: the Scottish Presbyterians are not unlike that proud and tattered reasoner. They treated Charles II with much less respect than Diogenes had treated Alexander. For when they took up arms on his behalf against Cromwell who had deceived them, they made the poor King put up with four sermons per day, they forbade him to play cards, they sat him on the stool of repentance, with the result that Charles soon grew tired of being King of these pedants and escaped from their clutches like a schoolboy playing truant.

Compared with a young and lusty French student bawling in Theology Schools in the morning and singing with the ladies at night, an English theologian is a Cato, but this Cato looks like a gay young spark compared with a priest in Scotland. The latter affects a solemn gait and scowling expression, wears a huge hat, a long cloak over a short jacket, preaches through his nose and gives the name of Whore of Babylon to all Churches in which a few ecclesiastics are fortunate enough to have an income of fifty thousand *livres* and in which the people are good enough to put up with it and all them Monsignor, Your Lordship, Your Eminence.

These gentry, who also have a few churches in England, have brought solemn and austere airs into fashion in this country. It is to them that we owe the sanctification of Sunday in the three kingdoms. On that day both work and play are forbidden, which is double the severity of Catholic Churches. There are no operas, plays or concerts in London on Sunday, even cards are so expressly forbidden that only people of standing and what are called respectable people, play on that day. The rest of the nation goes to the sermon, the tavern and the ladies of the town.

Although the Episcopal and Presbyterian sects are the two dominant ones in Great Britain, all the others are perfectly acceptable and live quite harmoniously together, whilst most of their preachers hate each other with almost as much cordiality as a Jansenist damns a Jesuit.

Go into the London Stock Exchange—a more respectable place than many a court—and you will see representatives from all nations gathered together for the utility of men. Here Jew, Mohammedan and Christian deal with each other as though they were all of the same faith, and only apply the word infidel to people who go bankrupt.

Source: From *Letters on England,* by Voltaire, translated with an introduction by Leonard Tancock (Penguin Classics, 1980). Copyright © Leonard Tancock, 1980. Used by permission of Penguin Group, UK. and edited by Simon Harvey. Copyright © 2000 by Cambridge University Press. Reprinted with the permission of Cambridge University Press.

Here the Presbyterian trusts the Anabaptist and the Anglican accepts a promise from the Quaker. On leaving these peaceful and free assemblies some go to the Synagogue and others for a drink, this one goes to be baptized in a great bath in the name of Father, Son and Holy Ghost, that one has his son's foreskin cut and has some Hebrew words he doesn't understand mumbled over the child, others go to their church and await the inspiration of God with their hats on, and everybody is happy.

If there were only one religion in England there would be danger of despotism, if there were two they would cut each other's throats, but there are thirty, and they live in peace and happiness.

Jean-Jacques Rousseau: The Social Contract

Jean-Jacques Rousseau (1712–1778) was born in Geneva. His mother died shortly after his birth and his father ran away to escape imprisonment when Rousseau was ten years old. He left Geneva when he was sixteen and eventually found a home and a job as a music copyist in Paris in 1742, where he had a profound influence on government and religious thought.

Rousseau coined the phase "noble savage," believing that man is inherently good but made corrupt when people began to disagree about property rights. He disagreed with Hobbes' theories and focused on the need for full equality among people, a concept now called egalitarianism. Rousseau believed that people, acting individually or through their representatives, should be the ultimate power behind governments and should dictate the nature of laws and practices for society. Rousseau wanted to personally return to the peace and tranquility of nature. He married a peasant woman and retired to a small farm. He spent the remainder of his life farming and writing, sometimes writing pieces for his friends in works such as the great Encyclopedia, then being assembled by Denis Diderot.

Rousseau's distaste for the institution of private property seems to have influenced Karl Marx and modern socialism. Government, he believed, should provide freedom, equality, and justice for all on an individual level. Like Locke, he strongly felt that should the state cease to act morally, the people had the right to break their contract and overthrow the government. These ideas became the basis of thinking for the French Revolution, which started just after Rousseau's death.

The Social Contract was Rousseau's principle publication. Its first line establishes the revolutionary tone of the entire book: "Man is born free, and everywhere he is in chains." The following passages from *Social Contract* illustrate Rousseau's principles of the voluntary transition from individuals to a community with absolute sovereignty in the hands of the majority. The purposes for the establishment of civilized societies (i.e., societies in which people live for their mutual benefit but retain certain rights as individuals) are clearly given as is the injunction that when individuals cease to be the supreme power in the state, the state has lost its right to exist and should be overthrown.

Chapter One
Subject of This First Book

Man is born free, and everywhere he is in chains. One believes himself the others' master, and yet is more a slave than they. How did this change come about? I do not know. What can make it legitimate? I believe I can solve this question.

If I considered only force, and the effect that follows from it, I would say; as long as a People is compelled to obey and does obey, it does well; as soon as it can shake off the yoke and does shake it off, it does even better; for in recovering its freedom by the same right as the right by which it was robbed of it, either the people is well founded to take it back, or it was deprived of it without foundation. But the social order is a sacred right, which provides the basis for all the others. Yet this right does not come from nature; it is therefore founded on conventions. The problem is to know what these conventions are. Before coming to that, I must establish what I have just set forth. . . .

Chapter Six
Of the Social Pact

I assume men having reached the point where the obstacles that interfere with their preservation in the state of nature prevail by their resistance over the forces which each individual can muster to maintain himself in that state. Then that primitive state can no longer subsist, and humankind would perish if it did not change its way of being.

Now, since men cannot engender new forces, but only unite and direct those that exist, they are left with no other means of self-preservation than to form, by aggregation, a sum of forces that might prevail over those obstacles' resistance, to set them in motion by a single impetus, and make them act in concert.

This sum of forces can only arise from the cooperation of many: but since each man's force and freedom are his primary instruments of self-preservation, how can he commit them without harming himself, and without neglecting the cares he owed himself? This difficulty, in relation to my subject, can be stated in the following terms.

"To find a form of association that will defend and protect the person and goods of each associate with the full common force, and by means of which each, uniting with all, nevertheless obey only himself and remain as free as before." This is the fundamental problem to which the social contract provides the solution.

The clauses of this contract are so completely determined by the nature of the act that the slightest modification would render them null and void; so that although they may never have been formally stated, they are everywhere the same, everywhere tacitly admitted and recognized; until, the social compact having been violated, everyone is thereupon restored to his original rights and

Source: Copyright © 1997 Cambridge University Press. Reprinted with permission.

resumes his natural freedom while losing the conventional freedom for which he renounced it.

These clauses, rightly understood, all come down to just one, namely the total alienation of each associate with all of his rights to the whole community: For, in the first place, since each gives himself entirely, the condition is equal for all, and since the condition is equal for all, no one has any interest in making it burdensome to the rest.

Moreover, since the alienation is made without reservation, the union is as perfect as it can be, and no associate has anything further to claim: For if individuals were left some rights, then, since there would be no common superior who might adjudicate between them and the public, each, being judge in his own case on some issue, would soon claim to be so on all, the state of nature would subsist and the association necessarily become tyrannical or empty.

Finally, each, by giving himself to all, gives himself to no one, and since there is no associate over whom one does not acquire the same right as one grants him over oneself, one gains the equivalent of all one loses, and more force to preserve what one has.

If, then, one sets aside everything that is not of the essence of the social compact, one finds that it can be reduced to the following terms: *Each of us puts his person and his full power in common under the supreme direction of the general will; and in a body we receive each member as an indivisible part of the whole.*

At once, in place of the private person of each contracting party, this act of association produces a moral and collective body made up of as many members as the assembly has voices, and which receives by this same act its unity, its common *self*, its life and its will. The public person thus formed by the union of all the others formerly assumed the name *City** and now assumes that of *Republic* or of *body politic,* which its members call *State* when it is passive, *Sovereign* when active, *Power* when comparing it to similar bodies. As for the associates, they collectively assume the name *people* and individually call themselves *Citizens* as participants in the sovereign authority, and *Subjects* as subjected to the laws of the State. But these terms are often confused and mistaken for one another; it is enough to be able to distinguish them where they are used in their precise sense.

■ Chapter Seven
Of the Sovereign

This formula shows that the act of association involves a reciprocal engagement between the public and private individuals, and that each individual, by contracting, so to speak, with himself, finds himself engaged in a two-fold relation: namely, as member of the Sovereign toward private individuals, and as a member of the State toward the Sovereign. But here the maxim of civil right, that no one is bound by engagements toward himself, does not apply; for there is a great difference between assuming an obligation toward oneself, and assuming a responsibility toward a whole of which one is a part. . . .

---

*The true sense of this word is almost entirely effaced among the moderns; most take a city for a City, and a bourgeois for a Citizen. They do not know that houses make the city but Citizens make the City. This same error once cost the Carthaginians dear. I have not read that the subjects of any Prince were ever given the title *Cives,* not even the Macedonians in ancient times nor, in our days, the English, although they are closer to freedom than all the others. Only the French assume the name *Citizen* casually, because they have no genuine idea of it, as can be seen in their Dictionaries; otherwise they would be committing the crime of Lese-Majesty in usurping it: for them this name expresses a virtue and not a right. When Bodin wanted to speak of our Citizens and Bourgeois, he committed a bad blunder in taking the one for the other. M. d'Alembert made no mistake about it, and in his article *Geneva* he correctly distinguished the four orders of men (even five, if simple foreigners are included) there are in our city, and only two of which make up the Republic. No other French author has, to my knowledge, understood the true meaning of the word *Citizen.*

Now the Sovereign, since it is formed entirely of the individuals who make it up, has not and cannot have any interests contrary to theirs; consequently the Sovereign power has no need of a guarantor toward the subjects, because it is impossible for the body to want to harm all of its members, and we shall see later that it cannot harm any one of them in particular. The Sovereign, by the mere fact that it is, is always everything it ought to be.

But this is not the case regarding the subjects' relations to the Sovereign, and notwithstanding the common interest, the Sovereign would have no guarantee of the subjects' engagements if it did not find means to ensure their fidelity.

Indeed each individual may, as a man, have a particular will contrary to or different from the general will he has as a Citizen. His particular interest may speak to him quite differently from the common interest; his absolute and naturally independent existence may lead him to look upon what he owes to the common cause as a gratuitous contribution, the loss of which will harm others less than its payment burdens him and, by considering the moral person that constitutes the State as a being of reason because it is not a man, he would enjoy the rights of a citizen without being willing to fulfill the duties of a subject; an injustice, the progress of which would cause the ruin of the body politic.

Hence for the social compact not to be an empty formula, it tacitly includes the following engagement which alone can give force to the rest, that whoever refuses to obey the general will shall be constrained to do so by the entire body: which means nothing other than that he shall be forced to be free; for this is the condition which, by giving each Citizen to the Fatherland, guarantees him against all personal dependence; the condition which is the device and makes for the operation of the political machine, and alone renders legitimate civil engagements which would otherwise be absurd, tyrannical, and liable to the most enormous abuses.

■ Chapter Eight
Of the Civil State

This transition from the state of nature to the civil state produces a most remarkable change in man by substituting justice for instinct in his conduct, and endowing his actions with the morality they previously lacked. Only then, when the voice of duty succeeds physical impulsion and right succeeds appetite, does man, who until then had looked only to himself, see himself forced to act on other principles, and to consult his reason before listening to his inclinations. Although in this state he deprives himself of several advantages he has from nature, he gains such great advantages in return, his faculties are exercised and developed, his ideas enlarged, his sentiments ennobled, his entire soul is elevated to such an extent, that if the abuses of this new condition did not often degrade him to beneath the condition he has left, he should ceaselessly bless the happy moment which wrested him from it forever, and out of a stupid and bounded animal made an intelligent being and a man.

Let us reduce this entire balance to terms easy to compare. What man loses by the social contract is his natural freedom and an unlimited right to everything that tempts him and he can reach; what he gains is civil freedom and property in everything he possesses. In order not to be mistaken about these compensations, one has to distinguish clearly between natural freedom which has no other bounds than the individual's forces, and civil freedom which is limited by the general will, and between possession which is merely the effect of force or the right of the first occupant, and property which can only be founded on a positive title.

To the preceding one might add to the credit of the civil state moral freedom, which alone makes man truly the master of himself; for the impulsion of mere appetite is slavery, and obedience to the law one has prescribed to oneself is freedom. But I have already said too much on this topic, and the philosophical meaning of the word *freedom* is not my subject here.

Enlightened Despots
Conscience and Reality

Chapter 36

> In short, never did two minds resemble each other less than ours; we had nothing in common in our tastes, nor in our ways of thinking. Our opinions were so different that we would never have agreed on anything, had I not often given in to him so as not to affront him too noticeably.
>
> —*Catherine the Great on her husband, Peter III*

Who Cares about the Enlightenment?

The Enlightenment had a profound effect on many of the rulers of Europe. In England the concepts of the Enlightenment were intimately entwined with governmental changes both during and after the period we have defined as the Enlightenment (from the early seventeenth century to about the mid-eighteenth century). Sometimes Enlightenment thinking *caused* changes in government, and sometimes the Enlightenment thinking *reacted to* changes in government. Whichever was the case, the government of England was obviously changed during the period of the Enlightenment. The new type of government that emerged was a compromise between the old monarchy and the new concepts of individual rights and power that were the chief focus of Enlightenment thinkers.

Over time, this compromise continued to evolve, generally in the direction of increased individual power until, today, the English monarchy has relatively little direct political power and individual freedom is very high.

In a group of English colonies, the concepts of the Enlightenment became so integral to the thinking of a large group of the people that a revolution was begun to enforce Enlightenment principles on the English motherland's treatment of these colonies. We speak, of course, of the American Revolution. We will discuss the American experience in detail in Chapter 38.

In France, the government resisted any suggested changes by Enlightenment writers. This resistance to change festered in the public mind (along with many other irritating issues) and, eventually, led to the French Revolution, which we will discuss, along with Napoleon, in Chapter 39.

Throughout other parts of Europe, the influence of the Enlightenment in the lives of royalty and commoners in the mid- to late eighteenth century was mixed. Some monarchs seemed to embrace Enlightenment concepts, but could not or would not implement meaningful changes in their countries. Other monarchs both embraced and implemented the liberalizing concepts of Enlightenment thinking. In some countries the monarchs just ignored the Enlightenment, at least during the period of the latter eighteenth century.

The stories of the struggles of these various monarchs are both interesting and educational, especially as we understand the diversity of the forces that pressed upon these monarchs. An examination of several eighteenth century monarchs is the subject of this chapter. We will see how some were very creative in addressing the problems that arose from the introduction of Enlightenment concepts into European society. Others were less creative, and we will see some of the consequences of their failures.

The term **enlightened despot** describes those kings, queens, and government officials across the continent who were influenced by Enlightenment ideas and yet continued to rule in a despotic (absolutist) way. This term (enlightened despot) is obviously an oxymoron and is intended to make us think about what happened to cause this dichotomous behavior. The circumstances are quite different from country to country.

Some of the enlightened despots learned of the Enlightenment by reading books and corresponding directly with *philosophes* like Voltaire, Diderot, Rousseau, and Swift and realizing that they made legitimate points. Some of these rulers took steps to alleviate the burdens placed on their peoples, grant them more freedoms, and give them a greater say in the government. However, for a variety of reasons that we will examine in detail, some rulers imposed harsh restrictions on their subjects. Thus, some of the rulers of the 1700s were more enlightened (because they accepted and implemented many of the reforms called for by the Enlightenment thinkers) and some were more despotic (because they reverted to old absolutist practices).

■ Frederick II of Prussia

In the eighteenth century, Germany was still a collection of small states headed by dukes, bishops, margraves, princes, and a few kings. One of these states, Prussia, was settled in the Middle Ages by the Teutonic Knights, a group of crusaders who were expelled by various European kings and forced to settle on the shores of the Baltic Sea (northern Europe) in the thirteenth century. In the fourteenth century, they became both economically powerful (controlling much of the amber trade as part of the Hanseatic League) and militarily a threat to their neighbors, but then began to decline in influence, largely under pressure from Polish and Lithuanian kings. In 1525, the head of the order (Grand Master) converted to Lutheranism and assumed the rights and hereditary title of duke of Prussia. Prussia was the first state to officially become Protestant. The duke's family was the Hohenzollerns, who would rule Prussia until the end of World War I.

In 1701, Frederick III, Duke of Prussia, entered into a treaty with the Holy Roman Emperor in which Prussia agreed to an alliance against Louis XIV of France who, at the time, was fighting the Holy Roman Empire over succession to the Spanish throne. In return, Frederick III received permission from the Holy Roman Emperor to assume the title of king in Prussia. This was done even through the rules of the Holy Roman Empire stipulated that no kings would exist within the empire. However, Frederick successfully argued that Prussia had never really been part of the historical Holy Roman Empire and was, therefore, not subject to this rule. Frederick was granted the title of King Frederick I in Prussia. (Over the years, a few other states, notably Bohemia and Hungary, were able to argue for exemptions to the rule and were, therefore, also headed by kings.)

The son of King Frederick I was Frederick Wilhelm I, sometimes called the Soldier-King. He ruled as an absolute monarch, very much in keeping with his times (1688–1740). Ambitious and militaristic, his vision was to make Prussia the strongest of the German states and to fill some of the power vacuum in Europe that resulted from the death of Louis XIV in 1714. Therefore, during his reign, he focused on building up the military strength of Prussia. He also installed a highly efficient administrative system and imposed strict frugality on the government and on himself. Frederick Wilhelm's methods were absolute and proved to be highly successful.

Frederick Wilhelm's son was known as **King Frederick II of Prussia** (the Great), and he lived from 1712 to 1786. To understand Frederick II, we need to consider his background and training.

Much to his father's disdain, as a young man Prince Frederick showed little interest in government or military training. Instead, Frederick loved to study art and literature. When his father tried to end young Frederick's studies into all things that he deemed impractical, Prince Frederick rebelled by studying French, Latin, and music. Young Frederick became highly proficient on the flute. Finally, sick of the constant humiliation and poor treatment at the hands of his father, Prince Frederick and a friend decided to run away to England. The two young men did not get far before the king's men hunted them down, arrested them, and imprisoned them. As a lesson on obedience and discipline, Prince Frederick was then forced to witness the execution of his friend and accomplice.

Prince Frederick made no additional attempts to flee, and soon married Elizabeth of Brunswick-Bevern at his father's direction. This marriage was clearly out of duty, as Frederick separated from her shortly afterward, and for the rest of his life showed little interest in her or any other woman. In the intervening years between his separation from his wife and his ascension to the throne, Prince Frederick fulfilled a variety of civil and military duties for his father, but also quietly studied the ideas of the Enlightenment. During this time, Prince Frederick began his long correspondence with Voltaire. Prince Frederick also wrote his *Anti-Machiavelli* treatise, which was based on Enlightenment principles and refuted the harsh principles of Machiavelli. The treatise was published anonymously the year the prince became king.

The young prince had obviously come to some internal resolution about supporting his father on one hand and doing what his conscience dictated on the other hand. He seemed to be able to separate these two conflicting natures by making one public and the other private.

Upon the death of his father and his own ascension to the throne of Prussia in 1740, the new King Frederick II immediately began to publicly behave in a typically absolutist fashion. He used the excuse of a centuries-old claim to territory and invaded the neighboring province of Silesia. The invasion was successful and, perhaps, a bit Machiavellian. He made additional successful invasions against other states and territories each year until he and his ally, England, were finally resisted in further expansion by the combined forces of Russia, France, and Austria in the Seven Years War (1756–1763), known in America as the French and Indian War. Although slowed in his aggression by the combined forces (which were vastly larger than his own), Frederick's military skills and strong diplomatic capabilities resulted in a stronger Prussia after the war than before it. (Napoleon called Frederick the greatest tactical genius of all time.) These achievements led to his being known as **Frederick the Great.**

Later, Frederick creatively fostered cooperation with the rulers of Russia and Austria to diplomatically achieve land that had been denied him previously. These three countries partitioned Poland so that each received a major portion and the country of Poland ceased to exist. Afterward, he used his excellent diplomacy to form a loose association of German states, under his direction, that became the first challenge to Austrian (Holy Roman Empire) leadership of German states. He was setting the stage for what later became the predominant role of Prussia for all of Germany.

Frederick was personally involved with his army. He would spend months with the troops in the combat zone. He was a powerful strategist and also a dominant personality. He expected very high loyalty and competency of his men and especially of the officers. He laid the foundation for the Prussian military organization that was the basis of German military successes for over a century.

The story is told of Frederick and one of his generals, with whom he had a major disagreement. In spite of the disagreement, Frederick needed the general's expertise and so he left the general in his command, but was so angry at the general that he decided not to speak to him. One day when Frederick was walking down a corridor in the palace, he saw the general approaching from the opposite direction. Not wanting to speak to the general, Frederick turned his back to the general as they passed. At that point the general stopped and spoke up, saying, "Why sire, I'm so glad you've taken me back into your good graces." Whereupon Frederick turned on his heel and said, "I have not! What makes you think that I have?" The general then said, "Why, your military prowess is so well known it is said you've never turned your back on an enemy. Since you have turned your back on me, I must no longer be an enemy." With that clever remark, Frederick's heart was softened, and he accepted the general back into his good graces.

Obviously, the military and diplomatic exploits of Frederick II were spectacular. In these, he ruled as a powerful absolutist. He also made several changes to better the lives of his subjects. Frederick II incorporated several important legal and penal reforms, including an insistence on unbiased and honest judges. Frederick also set up trade monopolies to create new industries, expanded the availability of education, and accomplished internal improvements such as drainage projects, roads, and canals. Frederick was also quite tolerant concerning religious matters. The daily lives of the peasants within Prussia improved dramatically during Frederick's reign.

Frederick viewed himself as a liberal thinker and a man of the Enlightenment. Skilled at French and passable at Latin, Frederick wrote excellent prose on politics, history, military science, and philosophy. Frederick also dabbled in poetry, usually writing in French. In addition to his continued excellence on the flute, he composed concertos for the flute, fully orchestrated military marches, and other pieces. Furthermore, Frederick the Great's inner circle included several important French *philosophes* and German intellectuals. Voltaire actually lived in Frederick's court for two years. These men could often be found at Frederick's Versailles-styled estate in Potsdam, a suburb of Berlin, where Frederick would hold

Figure 36.1 ■ The palace of Frederick II (Sans Souci) in Postdam, Germany. © 2010 by Dainis Derics. Used under license of Shutterstock, Inc.

elaborate midnight suppers and discuss philosophy, literature, music, and the arts, causing Voltaire to bestow upon him the title "philosopher king." The name of the palace was *Sans Souci* ("without cares") and reflects Frederick's retreat from the problems of the court and his journey into the Enlightenment. Figure 36.1 is a photo of Sans Souci.

Despite Frederick's fascination with the ideals of the Enlightenment, his improvement of the infrastructure of the country, and his love of the arts, Frederick's father needed to not have worried so much about his son. Frederick did not grant his people more freedoms. In fact, the serfs and peasants had less political influence at the end of his reign than they did at the beginning because of Frederick's continual efforts to centralize power. When associating with his army, he was dour and harsh. We can justly ask ourselves why this obviously well-educated and competent ruler would not implement greater freedom and liberty for his people but, rather, focused on improving the financial and military power of his country. He surely knew that the Enlightenment taught that "liberty" was just as important as "life" and "the pursuit of property."

We do not know the reason for his dichotomous actions, but it seems obvious that Frederick was able to divide himself into a personal life and an official life. He was personally enlightened and relished the intellectual satisfactions he gained from this knowledge and talent. But his official life was cold, rigid, and despotic. We can see the same division in his relationships with his wife—he married a woman he did not like to fulfill his duty to his father, but he never really became a husband on a personal level. This division into personal and public lives may have arisen when he had to witness the death of his friend because of Frederick's personal desires to run away. Perhaps he saw the power of the public life and decided to always respect it, but try to quietly live a personal life that was more in keeping with his inner beliefs and desires.

He seemed to have a vision for Prussia that was much like the absolutist rulers of the past. He even copied the style of the greatest of these rulers, Louis XIV, in designing his Potsdam palace. If Frederick felt that some official action would disturb his absolutist vision for Prussia, that action would not be taken. He was, apparently by personal choice, willing to accept the internal divisions that came from being an enlightened despot.

▪ Catherine the Great of Russia

Catherine II of Russia (1729–1796) was, like Frederick II, a complex and interesting ruler. She was also well educated in Enlightenment principles and was a personal acquaintance with several of the great Enlightenment thinkers. However, in contrast to Frederick, at times she seemed publicly interested in improving the lives of her subjects, but she was also strongly influenced by traditional and bureaucratic forces that worked against changes in Russian society. Perhaps more honestly than Frederick the Great, Catherine realized the conflict in her personal life that resulted from the opposing forces of Enlightenment change and traditional stasis. Her realization of these forces is glimpsed in the decorations of her palace, the Hermitage, in which she depicts herself as Minerva, goddess of culture and of war. She probably realized that, for her, the forces of culture and war would always be present and in conflict. Therefore, where Frederick undoubtedly chose to have different public and private lives, Catherine's dichotomous actions may have been the result of forces that were beyond her ability to reconcile. That is not to say, however, that Catherine was weak. On the contrary, she was a strong and powerful ruler. However, the situation in Russia was different from that in Germany and she was forced to cope with the situation in a different way. Let's examine her life as we explore that Russian situation.

Catherine was not born as the heir of the Russian empire or even a member of the Russian royal family. In fact, she was not even born as a Russian. Furthermore, she was not even born as a Catherine. She was born as Sophia Augusta Frederika of Anhalt-Zerbst, the daughter of minor nobility in eastern Germany (now a part of Poland). Young Sophia was fortunate to have a mother who loved to travel and wanted her daughter as company. Therefore, Sophia was taken to several of the major German cities, where she experienced a broad and vibrant culture.

When she was 15 years old, Sophia was thrust into the politics of the Russian court. The then-ruler of Russia, Empress Elizabeth, was an unmarried woman who had just named her 14-year-old nephew, Peter, as the heir to the throne (to become Czar Peter III) and decided that it was time to conclude a marriage arrangement for him. Elizabeth knew Sophia's family and invited Sophia and her mother to travel to Russia, where she would be a candidate for the wife of the czar-to-be. (Years before, when Elizabeth was young, she had been engaged to Sophia's uncle, but the uncle had died on his way to the wedding.)

When Sophia arrived in St. Petersburg, the Russian capital, she immediately began to study the Russian language, the Russian church, Russian history, and Russian literature. Empress Elizabeth was smitten by the beautiful, educated, and obviously dedicated young Sophia. (We don't know if Sophia or her mother decided to focus on things Russian, but whoever had the idea, Sophia remembered it all her life as a way to win the hearts of Russian people.) Within six months, Sophia converted to the Russian Orthodox Church and, during the ceremony, her name was changed to Catherine because it sounded more Russian. The next day, Catherine and Prince Peter were betrothed. They were married the next year (1745). Catherine was 16. Catherine's unique ability to see the situation in the Russian court, take the steps that were necessary to place herself in the proper position for success, and diligently execute her plan were certainly creative. Other creative maneuvers were to come for Catherine.

The marriage did not go well. Peter contracted a severe case of measles and then some other infectious disease, perhaps smallpox, that forced his isolation. Either from the disease or the treatment, Peter lost all his hair. Coupled with the scarring that is common with these diseases, Peter became despondent and sullen. He began to drink heavily

and act crudely, both publicly and privately. He was, in particular, disdainful of things Russian and openly advocated a change in government and culture to be more like the Prussia of Frederick the Great.

Catherine was a lonely wife, but used her time to read the great writings of the Enlightenment. She began a life-long correspondence with Voltaire and supported the work of Diderot. (Catherine published the encyclopedia when it was prohibited in France.) Even though Catherine bore a baby, Paul, in 1754, she and Peter lived quite separately and were both unfaithful in their marriage. Perhaps because of these marriage problems or because she had always wanted a baby, the Empress Elizabeth took her nephew, Paul, into her personal apartments and raised the child away from his parents. As a result, Paul was always loyal to the principles of absolutism and conservatism espoused by Elizabeth and never became close to Catherine, his mother, who had new and, for him, radical ideas.

Catherine and her husband moved apart physically and philosophically. Peter was oriented toward traditional concepts of strength and absolutism, reflective of the public image of Frederick II. Catherine was convinced of the value of Enlightenment principles. Peter was anxious to unite with Europe, just because it was the modern thing to do. Catherine would draw closer to Europe only if it benefited Russia. As the quotation at the beginning of the chapter attests, they were divergent in their thinking.

In 1756, Empress Elizabeth had entangled Russia in a war against Prussia (the Seven Years War) hoping to stem the expansion of Prussia under Frederick II. The Russians and their allies were doing well in the war and had gained significant territory at the expense of Prussia. In the midst of the war, however, Empress Elizabeth died and Peter became Czar Peter III. Catherine was 32 years old. A year later, Peter withdrew from the Prussian War and returned the lands that Russia had successfully conquered to Prussia. The army and the Russian people were incensed, especially since they saw Peter's move as un-Russian and personally motivated. (Frederick II was Peter's idol, even to the extent that Peter wore a ring with Frederick's likeness engraved on it.) This began the series of events that would lead to Catherine becoming empress. Catherine's creativity in reacting to changing circumstances and controlling the situation are evident throughout the fateful events to come.

The hostility of the army to Peter's unilateral withdrawal from the Prussian war initiated plans for a *coup d'etat.* The officer who was leading the planning for the *coup* was Catherine's lover, so we are not sure whether Catherine was part of the initial plans or only became aware of the *coup* just before it occurred. In either case, in June of 1762, only two months after Peter's withdrawal from the war, one of the officers involved in the conspiracy was arrested because he had openly criticized Czar Peter. Fearing that the conspiracy would be exposed, the conspirators decided to act immediately. That night, the officer in charge of the *coup* sneaked into Catherine's bedroom and informed her of the imminence of the plan.

On the next day, Catherine went to a nearby army unit and asked the soldiers to protect her from what she feared would be reprisals from Czar Peter III. The soldiers, who resented Peter, were happy to pledge their allegiance to Catherine. In an open display of loyalty, many rushed forward to kiss her hand and the hem of her dress. The regimental commander knelt at Catherine's feet while the regimental chaplain administered an oath of loyalty beneath a cross. Catherine then went to another army unit in the vicinity and the scene was, essentially, repeated. She then drove to the Kazan Cathedral, where a cheering crowd of people and clergy had assembled. She took the oath of allegiance to the state and was proclaimed Empress of Russia and sole leader. Amid joyous cheering and bell ringing, she proceeded to the palace, where the senate and other governmental officials had assembled. They pledged their support to the new ruler. A manifesto, citing Peter's threats to Russian glory and submission to a foreign power (thus endangering the nature of the Russian Orthodox Church), was distributed throughout the country. (Interestingly, the manifesto had been prepared the night before, thus testifying to the planned nature of the *coup.*)

Peter, who was staying at a country estate with his mistress, received word of the revolt and was urged by his advisers to take his personal guard and march on St. Petersburg. In light of the obvious support that Catherine had received, Peter was reluctant to openly oppose her. Instead, he fled toward an island off the coast of St. Petersburg, where he felt he could defend himself and, hopefully, regain control. However, Catherine had anticipated this move and had already gained the support of the navy so that when Peter attempted to cross to the island, he was arrested.

To demonstrate that she was in control of the army and the government and to show power as a leader, Catherine put on the uniform of a regimental commander and led several units out of the city toward the place where Peter was being kept. The people were wildly supportive of this empress who could obviously take control (even to showing a man's power by dressing in men's clothes.) Seeing no other alternative, Peter signed his abdication. Catherine returned to St. Petersburg in victory at the head of the troops and to the cheers of a roaring crowd. Six days later, Catherine was informed that Peter had been killed in an argument with his guards. To ensure her acceptance by all the Russian people, she journeyed to Moscow (the largest city in Russia but second in standing to St. Petersburg, the capital in those days), where she was again crowned Empress Catherine II in a church in the Kremlin.

In many ways the situation that confronted Catherine was similar to that which faced Elizabeth I in England many years before. The countries were both destitute from involvement in ill-advised wars, foreign leaders threatened the stability of the nation, people were unsure of the abilities of the new monarch, and the legitimacy of the monarch was questioned. (In Catherine's case, she was a non-Russian who had assumed the throne by overthrow of the legitimate ruler.) However, like Elizabeth I of England, Catherine understood the importance of gaining the support of the people, and this first priority seemed to have been successfully accomplished, in part, because she demonstrated her love of Russian culture, the Russian church, and Russian traditions. (Some said that her continual demonstrations of Russian behavior over the years since her arrival in Russia showed that her heart was Russian, even more so than dead Czar Peter III.) She reinforced this feeling by saying that her focus would not be to change Russia into a country like those of Europe, but to change Russia into whatever was best for Russia.

The strongly agricultural nature of Russia suggested to her that improvements in farming methods and other rural improvements would be the best place to start her task of improving Russia. She sent experts to other countries to study their farming methods and then disseminated their suggestions for improving Russian farming throughout the country. She next turned to mining and began a school teaching the most advanced mining technologies. She then promoted the formation of manufacturing facilities, especially outside the overcrowded cities of St. Petersburg and Moscow. Soon there were thriving industries in pottery, leather, textiles, shipbuilding, armaments, and steel. In all of these areas she invited foreign experts to move to Russia and help in the modernization effort.

As many other powerful leaders had done before her, Catherine also increased the bureaucracy so that she could have loyal administrators at the local level. She asked these administrators to, among other things, conduct a census of people, land, machinery, and other important assets. They also created, for the first time, accurate maps of Russia. They repaired existing roads and built new roads where needed. She also improved education and health care.

Catherine was an active promoter and collector of the arts. She assembled a great collection of artwork that is now displayed in the Hermitage in St. Petersburg. See Figure 36.2. She also commissioned works of art, such as the great equestrian statue of Peter the Great, situated in a park near the Hermitage. The art was a way for her to broaden the culture of the Russian people, to give them a sense of pride about their past, and to improve their personal image as a people of culture and refinement.

You might think that, in light of all this progressive activity, Catherine's credentials as an enlightened monarch would be impeccable. However, several aspects of Catherine's personal life and her public behavior indicate that she continued some very despotic behaviors. These activities should be discussed and, we believe, understood in light of the situation in Russia during her reign.

In her personal life, Catherine was highly autocratic. She listened to advisers but often made

Figure 36.2 ■ View of the Hermitage in St. Petersburg, Russia.
© 2010 by MACHKAZU. Used under license of Shutterstock, Inc.

decisions that were purely her own. She conducted a series of sexual affairs with young men with no apparent thought to the image this might create in a highly conservative and religious country. When her son, Paul, became a father, Catherine took the young child, Alexander, into her apartments and raised him beyond the influence of Prince Paul (much as Empress Elizabeth had done).

In public policy, Catherine was equally autocratic. She conducted an aggressive foreign policy with several wars against the Ottoman Turks and a forceful partition of Poland in cooperation with Prussia and Austria. She also revived the dormant security police and actively persecuted publishers who criticized her policies. These policies were all highly despotic. However, the most important situation in Russia during her reign was the condition of the serfs, and in that situation, both her enlightenment and her despotism are clearly evident.

The serfs were peasant farm workers, and they constituted, by far, the largest class in Russia. Serfs generally worked the land owned by the nobility/landlords. Traditional practices and laws dictated that the serfs could not leave the land they worked for other locations or types of employment. Children of serfs were similarly tied to the land where their parents worked. Serfs were, essentially, slaves.

The writers of the Enlightenment, Voltaire and Diderot in particular, had written forcibly about the serfs and advocated their emancipation. Catherine must have been persuaded by these writers because she established a Free Economic Society that held a writing contest for the best essay promoting the freeing of the serfs. (Interestingly, only three papers were received—all from non-Russians.) She also permitted the nobility to free their serfs if they chose to do it, but few did. She created a class of *state peasants* who were serfs responsible only to the crown, thus giving these serfs a measure of greater freedom of movement. All of these were generally positive steps toward better treatment of the serfs.

However, the Russian landholders were resistant to these changes. They pleaded for moderation and restraint. They pointed out that the economic system of Russia was based on serf labor and suggested that economic chaos would result if changes were made too quickly. (In these comments, the Russian nobles made many of the same arguments made in the American South prior to the Civil War.) The nobles implied a threat to Catherine that change would result in loss of their support, and they controlled the economy of the state. In light of these strong forces, Catherine slowed (stopped) her efforts for serfdom reform. (It is reported that she gave hundreds of thousands of the state peasants to her favorite generals and courtiers as gifts.)

In the midst of these initiatives and counter-initiatives, a disgruntled serf, **Pugachev,** living in the rich agricultural region of the Ural River (several hundred miles southeast of Moscow), began to incite the local serfs to rebel against their masters. He proclaimed that he was really Peter III and that, contrary to reports, he had not been killed when Catherine ascended the throne but, rather, had escaped and was now ready to reclaim his rightful position as the czar. He promised the serfs freedom from their restrictions to the land, freedom from taxation, and freedom from enforced military service. Soon, thousands of serfs from all ethnic groups but, especially Cossacks, joined Pugachev's movement. It became a dominant force in the Ural and Volga River valleys. Pugachev even held elections and tried to form a reform provincial government.

Catherine was incensed and dismayed. Undoubtedly, the movement had succeeded thus far because most of her army was then employed in a war against the Ottoman Turks in the Crimea. However, she sent a reasonably large contingent of regular army against the rebels with orders to crush the rebellion. She wanted to stop the movement and to discourage any further attempts to upset her government. The serf rebellion was defeated, and the leaders captured and then cruelly executed. Due to pressure from the nobility because of the rebellion, Catherine issued a decree that increased the power of the nobility over the serfs. Therefore, the serfs were more restricted at the end of her reign than at the beginning of it.

Catherine was severely criticized by several French *philosophes* who believed that the principles of freedom should have been furthered, even to the risk of total governmental collapse. Perhaps Catherine understood freedom in a different light than did the *philosophes.* When asked by Diderot about the relationship between masters and slaves in Russia, she answered that there were no slaves in Russia, only peasants with attachment to the land, and then added that "the serfs had free minds, even if their bodies were subject to some constraint."

■ Gustavus III of Sweden

The reign of Sweden's **King Gustavus III** was fairly brief (he ruled from 1771 to 1792), but during that time he made several important changes in Sweden and helped bring the ideals of the Enlightenment to his country. Gustavus came to power in the midst of political chaos between the two predominate political factions within Sweden, the Hats and the Caps. The Hat party was militarily aggressive, aristocratic and pro-French, while the Caps were more conservative and pro-Russian. King Gustavus tried to bring the two parties to peace, but when that failed he took complete control himself in a *coup,* forcing upon the state a new constitution that restored to the sovereign much of the powers lost by his predecessors. The Swedish people allowed King Gustavus's drastic actions because he immediately inaugurated several popular liberal reforms, including financial relief from taxes and complete religious toleration.

King Gustavus also helped spread the ideals of both the Scientific Awakening and the Enlightenment to Sweden. An excellent author, poet, and playwright himself, King Gustavus created works that helped spark a period of brilliant literature in Sweden. Gustavus was also devoted to the sciences and established the Swedish Academy in 1786. Throughout his life, Gustavus used his own money to sponsor both literature and science that he felt showed promise.

Although quite popular with the general population, Gustavus III constantly had to fight with his nobility. The new constitution he had created when he ascended the throne had robbed the nobility of much of their power, while his financial reforms had limited their ability to tax and thus reduced their wealth. Eventually, the nobility decided to act against him and King Gustavus was murdered while he attended a masked ball to rally support for the French royalists trying to reclaim their throne after the French Revolution.

■ Charles III of Spain

Charles III (1716–1788) was king of Spain and, at one time in his reign, king of the nation of Naples and Sicily as well as duke of Parma. He was a member of the Bourbon family and, by many, considered to be the most enlightened of any Bourbon ruler.

Charles III reflected his enlightenment ideas in his efforts to make Spanish cities more habitable and clean. He urged the citizens to deposit their rubbish in proper receptacles rather than throw it into the streets. He also created many public works (sewers, roads, etc.), especially in Madrid. Charles reformed government bureaucracy, making it more efficient, and also improved the economic situation in Spain through needed fiscal reforms.

In foreign entanglements, Charles III was influenced by his distaste for the English. When a young monarch, Charles was forced, under threat of bombardment on Naples by an English admiral, to declare his neutrality in the War of Austrian Succession. Charles resented this action and, whenever possible, sought revenge against the English. His involvement in the Seven Years War came late in the war on behalf of the French and against the English. The French lost the war and were forced to cede, among other things, Louisiana to Spain. The Spanish were forced to cede Florida to England. Later, Charles entered the American Revolutionary War on the side of the Americans and regained Florida.

In addition to his rather absolutist foreign policy, he showed despotic tendencies in his strong suppression of the Jesuits, who he suspected of participating in a failed revolution against him. This also led to his insistence on restrictions against the Inquisition within Spain.

Charles represents a slightly different model of the enlightened despot. He was enlightened, largely in response to the forces of the times and good logic. He was despotic, often driven by personal desires for revenge (against the English and the Jesuits). He showed that, in these days, the nature of enlightened or despotic monarchy was still largely a personal matter.

■ Maria Theresa and Joseph II of Austria

When **Maria Theresa** (1717–1780) was a little girl, no one expected her to become the ruler of Austria. She was the oldest daughter of the current Holy Roman Emperor, Charles VI, but she had brothers who would succeed to the throne and, besides, Austrian law prohibited females from becoming the Austrian ruler in their own right. However, as Charles VI grew old, all of his sons died and, Charles himself became the sole remaining male Hapsburg. If the 650-year dynasty were to survive, the law would have to be changed so that a woman could succeed to the throne. Therefore, in 1713 Charles VI issued a decree, called the **Pragmatic Sanction,** in which the succession was guaranteed to his daughter.

In 1740, Charles VI died and Maria Theresa was declared archduchess of Austria and queen of Hungary and Bohemia—the hereditary positions long held by the Hapsburgs, but was not allowed to be Holy Roman Empress because the title was reserved for males only. The Electors of the Holy Roman Empire agreed, however, that Maria Theresa's husband would be the Holy Roman Emperor. Few expected this 23-year-old woman to succeed or even to last long as the monarch of one of Europe's largest but most complex empires. Even her father, before his death, had expected that Maria Theresa would relinquish effective control of the empire to her husband. Consequently, Maria Theresa was never brought into the discussions of state, nor was she schooled

in diplomacy. However, Maria Theresa continued to rule in her own right and became one of the most successful Hapsburg rulers. This was all done while bearing 16 children (one of whom was Marie Antoinette, the future queen of France). But her success would not occur without several significant challenges.

The first to challenge the young empress was Frederick II of Prussia. (In light of Frederick's military fixation, you should not be surprised at this event.) Immediately upon the death of Charles VI, the Prussians invaded Silesia, a province of the Austrian Empire that was adjacent to Prussia and is, today, part of Poland. Frederick's aggression began the War of Austrian Succession (1740–1748). Bavaria and France also sensed Maria Theresa's vulnerability and attacked shortly thereafter. Later, Spain joined the war against her. At the end, Maria Theresa was forced to cede Silesia and other territories to her challengers. However, most of Austria was still intact and her husband, Francis Stephen of Lorraine, was still recognized as Holy Roman Emperor.

With the arrival of peace, Maria Theresa began a series of reforms within Austria. She reorganized the tax structure so that she could regain some of the treasury that had been depleted by the recent war and the several wars conducted under the reign of her father. The tax reform was accompanied by a program of strong support for Austrian industry. This economic reform fueled an era of prosperity for Austria.

With the improvement in the treasury, Maria Theresa used some funds to improve Austria's military preparedness. She doubled the size of the army and improved its equipment. Coupled with this new military strength, she sought to reorganize Austria's diplomatic alliances so that she could, hopefully, regain the territories lost in the War of Austrian Succession. She broke a long-standing treaty relationship with England so that she could enter into treaties of cooperation and support with France, Russia, and Saxony. In this way she surrounded Prussia.

Realizing the potentially difficult position for Prussia that Maria Theresa's alliances were creating, Frederick surprised Europe's leaders by quickly attacking Saxony and thereby precipitating the Seven Years War, which extended to America as the French and Indian War. The long war was not beneficial for Austria. When it was concluded, Maria Theresa was forced to sign a treaty relinquishing all claims to Silesia.

Following this second war with Prussia, Maria Theresa again focused on improvements in Austria. She supported the arts and created a strong and lively culture within the empire. She built a beautiful palace, Schönbrunn, in a parklike setting near Vienna. The palace is clearly patterned after Versailles, thus reflecting Versailles' continued presence as the standard of royal grandeur. With the increased strength of the Austrian economy and cultural initiatives, Maria Theresa gained great admiration and love from the Austrian people. A large statue in Vienna today of Maria Theresa shows her seated as a regal woman and clearly represents the feelings of the Austrians that she was the mother of the country. See Figure 36.3.

Maria Theresa's Enlightenment concepts were revealed most strongly in her moves to limit the power of the Austrian nobility over the peasants who worked the land. Her popularity with the people made these limitations possible. She limited the use tax that peasants were required to pay the lords. Maria Theresa also felt that the pope had excessive power within Austria, and she moved to limit his influence and to reduce the mandatory payments of the people to the church. Both of these limitations improved the financial status of the Austrian peasants.

In 1765, Maria Theresa's husband died. This was a great personal loss for her and, from that day to her death, she dressed in black mourning clothes. The death also raised a problem in the country. The result of the War of Austrian Succession reaffirmed that a man be named Holy Roman Emperor, and her husband had filled that role. Therefore, after his death, Maria Theresa named her eldest son, Joseph II, as the Holy Roman Emperor and co-regent with her in the other hereditary positions she held, such as Archduchess of Austria.

Joseph II (1741–1790) was born during the height of the French Enlightenment and was thoroughly schooled in the concepts of Voltaire and Rousseau. He was, therefore, somewhat more radical in his approach to the principles of liberty and justice than was his mother, who appreciated the views of the Enlightenment writers but was educated in a more traditional setting. Hence, Joseph and Maria Theresa would occasionally clash in their approaches to changes in the nature of the state. Except for occasional restrictions in matters where they differed, Maria Theresa allowed Joseph II great latitude in ruling the empire because she became increasingly withdrawn from public functions as she grew older. He attended most of the official meetings of the state and wrote summaries of the actions of the various councils for his mother. She even allowed him to conclude a treaty with her old enemy, Frederick II of Prussia, and with Catherine II of Russia to partition Poland. She also allowed him to join with Prussia in a war against Bavaria in 1778 to 1779.

As with his mother, Joseph II was anxious to relieve the peasantry of feudal burdens, to reduce the power of the Catholic Church, and to remove restrictions on trade and the freedom of information. Early in the co-regency, Joseph II traveled

Figure 36.3 ■ Maria Theresa is remembered by the Austrian people with great love as shown in this statue in Vienna. © *2010 by Milan Ljubisavljevic. Used under license of Shutterstock, Inc.*

extensively while his mother continued to lead the country. He visited, among other places, Germany (where he secretly met Frederick II), Russia (where, against his mother's wishes, he met Catherine II), and France (where he was a guest of his sister, Marie Antoinette). While in France, he observed the decaying conditions and correctly predicted the coming of the French Revolution. He also spoke with the leaders of the radical French political party, the Jacobins, and generally agreed with their view that the state can be very powerful and arbitrary if it is directed by reason. (This was, perhaps, the ultimate conclusion of the most radical Enlightenment thinkers.)

When Maria Theresa died in 1780, Joseph II assumed total control of the empire. He generally continued the policies of Enlightenment that he and his mother pursued, but expanded them somewhat by increasing religious toleration and improving freedom of the press. During his reign, Vienna enjoyed information from dozens of newspapers representing almost every political and social orientation.

In a series of quite radical moves, Joseph II gave the serfs of his empire full emancipation. He also secularized church lands and imposed state direction on the religious orders and clergy. He expanded education widely and, in an attempt to unify his diverse empire, compelled the use of the German language. All of these steps were, for him, reasonable and therefore were justified, even though they were imposed despotically.

Joseph II was a lover of the arts, especially music. He was called the "music king" because of the many commissions he gave to composers. He especially promoted German-language opera. Joseph commissioned the opera *Die Entführung aus dem Serail (The Abduction from the Seragio)* by Mozart.

Joseph's foreign policy was a sequence of failed efforts to expand Austrian territory at the expense of his neighbors. He was stopped in attempts to gain land in Bavaria, Belgium, Turkey, and the Balkans. These forays resulted in discontent within his own realm and he was forced to settle revolts in Hungary and other states. Some of these were peasant revolts in which additional freedoms were desired. The most serious, however, were revolts of the gentry against Joseph's sudden and arbitrary reforms. At the end of his life, as he realized that his efforts to impose progress had not been successful, Joseph II rescinded many of his reforms, including the freeing of the serfs. He died in 1790 and was succeeded by his brother, Leopold II, because Joseph had no surviving children.

■ George II and George III of England

We have discussed the monarchy in England in great depth in Chapter 32 and then also pointed out the changes in the monarchy that occurred during the time of the English Enlightenment (Chapter 35). However, those discussions ceased with the reign of George I. Just as other European monarchs of the eighteenth century were struggling with the conflicting issues of the Enlightenment and absolutist (despotic) rule, the successors to George I were also met with similar issues but in a different setting, as they were subjected to the laws of constitutional monarchy. Therefore, the reigns of George II and George III of England are instructive as they provide a different view of the adoption of enlightenment principles.

George II (1683–1760) was born in Hanover, Germany, before his father was invited to become the king of England. When young George was 30 the family moved to England. Therefore, George II was able to become reasonably well integrated into English life, whereas his father remained forever a German.

The interactions between George II and his father were difficult, especially as George I became increasingly more cantankerous as his reign progressed. The inherently absolutist George I chafed under the limitations imposed by the English parliament, and he tended to then impose absolute rule on his family. Of particular irritation to George I were the actions of the prime minister, **Robert Walpole.** Modern historians credit Walpole with defining the role of a modern prime minister—a role that was required because George I was, after all, the first real constitutional monarch. Walpole had to work out the principles involved in an office that was the real head of state but was still responsible to a parliament that was, in turn, responsible to the people. The role of the king was poorly defined, and many challenges and compromises between Walpole and George I had to be made.

When George I died in 1727, George II's anger toward his father was so strong that the new king did not want to retain any ministers that were part of his father's regime. However, George II's wife, whom he loved dearly and often took council from, suggested that Walpole was a key to stability and should be retained. George II reluctantly accepted Walpole. With time, the relationship between Walpole and George II improved. Walpole was successful in securing some much-needed financing for the crown and George II assisted Walpole by naming several Whig supporters to new peerages, thus shifting the balance of voting in the House of Lords to the Whig side. Walpole remained in office until 1742. He was succeeded by other Whig prime ministers who strongly supported constitutional monarchy and economic growth based on trade and manufacturing.

The stability of Whig rule was especially important in light of a rebellion in Scotland, where the **Jacobites** (supporters of the House of Stuart) attempted one last time to place a Stuart back on the throne. This Stuart was Prince Charles Edward, otherwise known as **Bonnie Prince Charlie.** In 1746 the Jacobite army marched with surprising force from Scotland into England. They were met by the Royal Army and driven back to Scotland where, at Culloden Moor, the Jacobite army was destroyed. (The battle at Culloden was the last battle fought on British soil.) Bonnie Prince Charlie escaped to France and died in Rome. Many members of the Tories, the party opposing the Whigs, were supporters of the Jacobite cause. Therefore, in the mid-eighteenth century, England was faced with brief political turmoil. Religious difficulties also arose as Protestants of all types rose in anger over the attempted Jacobite effort to install a Catholic king. The defeat of the Jacobites resulted in continued Whig rule for the next 50 years.

Most of the foreign policies of England during the reign of George II have already been mentioned in our discussions of the other European countries. He involved England in the War of Austrian Succession and in the Seven Years War. Had Walpole not been a moderating influence, George II would have undoubtedly involved England in even more wars.

English culture had little appeal for George except for a few specific artists like Handel who was, of course, actually German. George II was the originator of the tradition of standing during the playing of the "Hallelujah Chorus." He also commissioned four new anthems from Handel for his coronation, and one of them, "Zadok the Priest," has been sung at every English coronation ever since.

King George II had little interest in English business but was the beneficiary of the tremendous surge in prosperity that accompanied the Industrial Revolution. We will discuss this in more depth in a later chapter, but the disinterest of the king was in line with the desires of both business and government at this time—*laissez-faire.*

George III was the grandson of George II and reigned from 1760 to 1820. The new king was determined to regain the authority of an absolute monarch. He actively undermined the power of the prime minister, cabinet, and parliament using whatever means he could, including bribery, coercion, and patronage. Several prime ministers were toppled, which resulted in a series of weak and ineffective leaders hand-picked by George III.

However, George's ineffective handling of the American Revolution resulted in great loss of confidence from both the people and parliament. Moreover, George had a disease, porphyria, that resulted, ultimately, in madness, and the effects of this disease became increasingly apparent throughout his reign. In 1801, a new prime minister, **William Pitt the Younger,** came to power. Pitt successfully guided Britain through the early Napoleonic years. Pitt and George disagreed strongly over the issue of religious toleration. The issue arose because of a second act of union in which Ireland was brought into the United Kingdom. Pitt wanted to give Catholics equal rights within the kingdom. (This was, of course, a position consistent with the Enlightenment.) The king was adamant that the Catholics would not be given such liberties. He said that such an action would violate his coronation oath. The king declared,

> *Where is the power on Earth to absolve me from the observance of every sentence of that oath, particularly the one requiring me to maintain the Protestant Reformed Religion? . . . No, no, I had rather beg my bread from door to door throughout Europe, than consent to any such measure. I can give up my crown and retire from power. I can quit my palace and live in a cottage. I can lay my head on a block and lose my life, but I cannot break my oath.*

The king's dedication to his principles of religion and oath was obviously very strong. His attitude reflects the continuing difficulties throughout Europe as the monarchs tried to wrestle with the principles of the Enlightenment within their personal frameworks of absolutism.

George III became increasingly mad and appointed his son as regent in 1811. George III died blind, deaf, and insane in 1820.

■ Royal Dilemmas and Creativity

As we have discussed in the last two chapters, people gained great confidence in the methods of the Scientific Awakening. Those methods discovered truths about nature through careful and unbiased investigation, coupled with rational thinking. Religion was not part of the process, although many of the scientists believed they were uncovering the truths of God's work.

To understand humankind's place in the natural world, solely on the basis of reason and without turning to religious belief, was the goal of the intellectual movement called the Enlightenment. The movement claimed the allegiance of a majority of thinkers during the seventeenth and eighteenth centuries. It was, therefore, also called the Age of Reason.

The Enlightenment writers thought deeply about the nature of truth, especially as discovered by science, but then they turned their attention to the nature of government as discovered by science. Initially, their thinking led to conclusions that incorporated a place for monarchy. As the movement developed, the role of the monarch was defined more narrowly. Then, in the most radical versions, monarchs were eliminated and the will of the people became the sovereign power.

Along the way, the Enlightenment thinkers continued to focus on the nature of human freedoms and rights. Most concluded that humans were inherently free and that it was the role of the best governments to guarantee those innate freedoms. Personal liberty, economic opportunity, and freedom from persecution were the most fundamental of the rights.

Monarchs across Europe read the Enlightenment writers and were swayed by their arguments. The rationality of these monarchs led to the same conclusions, but their emotions were not always in accord. After all, the monarchs had generally been educated under different paradigms. The old paradigms saw the role of the monarch as a visionary for the state and an enforcer of the rules whereby the vision could most efficiently be accomplished. The good of the total was, for them, more important than the rights of a single person or even a group of people, especially if those rights interfered with the progress of the state. Hence, there was a dilemma for the monarchs— their minds said "enlightenment" but their hearts said "absolutism."

Each of the monarchs we have discussed dealt with this dilemma in a different way. Frederick II of Prussia separated his personal life from his public life. To maintain this separation he seemed to withdraw from those who might be close to him. Frederick died quite lonely and, probably, unhappy and unfulfilled. His absolute nature seemed to overwhelm his enlightenment views.

Catherine II of Russia implemented many enlightenment concepts but found great resistance from the Russian nobility. She was forced to slow the progress of change. Then, when this happened, the peasants were disappointed and rebelled.

Catherine was forced to quell the rebellion and, in the end, reversed many of the progressive acts that were previously taken. She must have been very frustrated. Gustavus III of Sweden was, like Catherine, frustrated by the resistance to change among the gentry.

Charles III of Spain was able to enact several improvements in his country but, because of his personal anger, he moved Spain into foreign entanglements that ultimately slowed progress. Almost all the monarchs of the period had to deal with the conflicts between domestic and foreign policy. This was certainly true, also, for Maria Theresa of Austria. She was involved in several wars just because other countries tried to take advantage of her tenuous succession to the throne. Although this pattern has been common throughout history, we sense its destructiveness strongly when we see a monarch who is willing to improve but is unable to do so because of foreign pressures.

Joseph II of Austria presented a different view of an enlightened despot. He was younger than most of the other monarchs we have discussed and so his education was not in the old paradigm but, rather, focused clearly on the concepts of the Enlightenment. He was a convert and strove to implement the principles in his state. Initially, however, he was opposed by his mother and then, later, by the minor nobility and church. He tried to force change into the country; believing that absolutist actions were justified by the rationality of his cause. In this, we are reminded of Machiavelli, who also believed that the end justifies the means.

King George II seemed to begin reforms but then lost interest in government. It was a time in England of great progress, and so little royal involvement was needed or wanted. His grandson, George III, somehow sensed a loss of royal prerogative with the implementation of Enlightenment ideas, especially in the environment of a limited constitutional monarchy. He tried to change back to the old paradigm, but was unable to do so. He died, perhaps, the loneliest and saddest of all the enlightened despots.

The most fundamental concepts of the Enlightenment were faith in nature's regularity and belief in human progress. Nature was a complex of laws governing the universe. The individual human being, as part of that system, was governed by certain laws that were innate and compelling. The human was to rationally determine the laws and then rationally develop methods to guarantee that the laws would be respected. However, governments and religion had long ignored those fundamental laws, and that needed changing. The Enlightenment's hostility toward government and religion was because those two highly conservative estates resisted change and did not base their actions on reason.

Most of the countries progressed through application of Enlightenment principles. The lives of the common people were generally better. When progress slowed, the lower classes sometimes reacted violently, but even then the people seemed to sense the difficulty involved in changing the entire basis of their society. The concepts of absolutism and privileged gentry had existed for thousands of years. They would not be overcome easily or quickly.

The monarchs in one country, France, resisted totally the concepts of the Enlightenment. As we will see in later chapters, this proved to be a great mistake for the royalty. Pent-up anger and frustration combined with knowledge of progress in other countries to create an explosive situation and the royal were, ultimately, those who suffered most for their resistance to change.

We see, therefore, a development of new thinking and then, in some cases, reasonable applications of that thinking to human affairs. The applications came at the initiation of a group of very interesting and, to us, quite noble monarchs. They began with little help and accomplished much. Some may view these enlightened despots negatively, but we take the view that they were generally sincere in their efforts to change the lives of their citizens for the better. They choose conscience and followed it. They heroically overcame past teachings and many types of resistance to make the progress they could. In general, we think, the compromise they made between conscience and reality was appropriate.

We are struck with the complications and difficulties these monarchs faced in dealing with change. Very different paths were followed. It is a lesson to be learned for leaders even today.

■ Timeline—Important Dates

Date	Event
1727	George II of England begins reign
1740	Maria Theresa of Austria begins reign
1740	Frederick II of Prussia (the Great) begins reign
1740–1748	War of Austrian Succession
1756–1763	Seven Years War
1759	Charles II of Spain begins reign
1760	George III of England begins reign
1762	Catherine II of Russia (the Great) begins reign
1765	Joseph II of Austria begins reign
1771	Gustavus III of Sweden begins reign
1772, 1793, 1795	Partitioning of Poland

■ Suggested Readings

Johnson, Spencer, *Who Moved My Cheese,* Putnam, 1998.

Michener, James, *Poland,* Random House, 1983.

Classical and Rococo
Creativity Rules

> I write my music in order that the weary and worn or the men burdened with affairs might enjoy a few minutes of solace and refreshment.
>
> —Franz Josef Haydn

■ Rational Art and Music

When the eighteenth century arrived, the European world had become convinced that nature was controlled by God-made laws that were gradually being revealed through scientific investigations. The Enlightenment thinkers applied science to the nature of humankind and determined that natural laws gave humans certain rights and that the role of government was to guarantee those rights. Some monarchs were convinced that these Enlightenment principles could be enacted within their states. They attempted, with various levels of success, to provide safer lives, more liberties, and opportunities for the pursuit of property.

We will now examine how the confidence of science and optimistic utopian social thinking affected art, architecture, and music in the eighteenth century. We will see how the Enlightenment's focus on reason became important in art.

Initially this rationality led to a refinement of the highly dramatic Baroque concepts that had dominated art and architecture throughout the seventeenth century. Whereas the Baroque style reflected the ostentations of absolute monarchs, the new, more refined style seemed to reflect the moderated opulence of the enlightened despots. Initially, the new artistic style was still elaborate, but just more delicate. A comparison could easily be made between the Baroque extravagance of Versailles and the muted elegance of Frederick the Great's *San Souci* or Maria Theresa's *Schönbrunn*. The new artistic style is called **Rococo.** Churches also reflected the change from the overly dramatic Baroque to the ornately beautiful Rococo.

Later in the eighteenth century, the increasing feelings of rationality led to an even greater appreciation for symmetry, balance, restraint, and proportion. These were all associated with the ancient Greek culture. Therefore, many artists and composers returned to principles seen in Classical Greece, ushering in the **Neoclassical,** or *new classical,* period. With Neoclassicism, art and architecture became simpler and more conservative. Music, which had lagged the visual arts in making the transition from Baroque, also became simpler and was dominated by newly formed rules of composition. The musical period was called, simply, the **Classical period** and has become a standard for the ages.

Let's now examine these artistic and musical trends. First we'll look at the visual arts and the transition to the Rococo and then to the Neoclassical. Later we will see how music evolved.

■ Rococo Art and Architecture

At the beginning of the eighteenth century, Baroque forms were still popular and would continue to be used by some artists throughout the century. Baroque is showy and dramatic. It emphasizes the technical competence of the artist and naturally gives prestige to the subject. All of these attributes were highly desired by many people. Therefore, Baroque did not quickly fade away even though other trends became strongly evident.

Rococo painting evolved from the Baroque. For those who thought the Baroque was excessive, the Rococo gave a more refined feel because it was graceful and harmonious but still quite ornate. It principally emphasized the beauty of nature and the idyllic life that was possible in a utopian world. The name "rococo" comes from the French word *rocaille,* which means an elaborate decoration of rocks and shells that often adorned grottos in Baroque gardens. Hence, even in the name some elements of the Baroque persist, but the emphasis is on the garden and its beauty. The Rococo style gained this name because it often used seashells, ribbons, and other decorative ornamentation to lend a feeling of grace and harmony. In general, compared with the Baroque, Rococo themes were lighter, perhaps even frivolous. Subjects were elegant picnics, graceful lovers, Greek gods and goddesses in nature, and portraits in which the subject was bathed in the beauty of nature.

Although the Rococo style was certainly appreciated and purchased by the enlightened monarchs of the day, additional customers for the art were the gentry and the newly emerging middle class who aspired to a life of leisure and pleasure. These groups were living or were hoping to live the type of lifestyle reflected in Rococo paintings. Hence, having a Rococo painting in their homes suggested that they were participating in the leisurely life they aspired to.

This style can, perhaps, best be appreciated by seeing a painting by **Jean Antoine Watteau** (1684–1721) called *Pilgrimage* (or *Embarkation*) *to Cythera* (Figure 37.1). This painting is clearly fanciful, with children playing and delighted people enjoying the pleasantness of nature. Note the presence of Greek statues and cherubs, which reflect the yearning for the glories of classical Greece. It also uses much softer colors than would normally be found in Baroque art, and there is a misty feel or fuzziness to the work that is also quite typical of the Rococo style. The subject of the work, the pilgrimage to Cythera, is an ancient Greek myth of people going on a ship of love to the land of Cythera. As is typical of Rococo paintings, this one has many subtle symbols. For instance, armor and weapons are placed beneath the statue of Venus, suggesting that love conquers all. A woman holds a fan, which, in the days of Watteau, was used as a way to communicate between lovers when in the presence of a chaperone. We also see some of the people giving wistful glances back at the pleasure that is expressed in the groups at the center of the painting.

Two other French painters of the Rococo style were **Francis Boucher** and **Jean-Honoré Fragonard.** Both extended the themes beyond simple beauty to a mild sense of eroticism, reflecting the decadence of the current French court where mistresses were more powerful than queens. For example, Fragonard's painting *The Swing* shows a young woman in a swing in the midst of a lovely forest. She is being pushed in the swing by her elderly husband (or perhaps a bishop) while her lover lounges in the bushes. A statue of cupid appears to have just come to life and has raised his finger to his lips to indicate that a lovers' secret

Figure 37.1 ■ Pilgrimage (*or* Embarkation) *to* Cythera *by Jean Antoine Watteau. Reunion des Musees Nationaux/Art Resource, NY.*

must be kept quiet. Again, the colors are pastels and the setting idyllic.

Fragonard, who lived at the end of the Rococo period (he died in 1806), was initially very popular and received much work, including a major commission from Madame de Pompadour, the mistress of King Louis XV. The very ambitious project, titled *The Pursuit of Love,* was a set of large decorative panels. By the time Fragonard had finished the project, tastes had changed to the more sober Neoclassical style, and Mme. de Pompadour returned the panels as unsuitable. Fragonard was deeply offended by the rejection and refused her payment. He died impoverished, unnoticed, and out of fashion. This shift in taste indicates the shortness of the Rococo period in France.

English Rococo painting lacked the frivolity and occasional sexuality of the French works. The English style focused on portraits that were highly flattering to their aristocratic subjects. The two most famous of the English Rococo painters were **Sir Joshua Reynolds** and **Thomas Gainsborough.** Although Reynolds was the king's official court painter, both artists were favorites of the court and did many paintings of the royal family and other aristocrats.

Reynold's *Collina* (Figure 37.2) is typical of the English style. It is sweet and yet has a certain coquettishness that is very appealing. Reynolds also painted portraits of courtiers, military leaders, and celebrities. However, his paintings of the newly rich merchant class, usually paintings of the wives, were especially popular. Even today Reynolds's works are highly prized. His paintings hold the record for highest amount paid among all British painters.

Thomas Gainsborough's life represents well the English Rococo period. He was born in a country town and began his artistic career by painting landscapes, much in the airy style of the French painters we have just discussed. Upon his election as a founding member of the Royal Academy, Gainsborough moved to London, where he was in high demand as a painter for the rich. After several years in London, he remarked that while portraiture was his profession, landscape painting was his pleasure.

Among Gainsborough's most famous paintings is *The Blue Boy,* shown in Figure 37.3. This painting is typical in the flattering treatment of the subject and the inclusion of a pleasant natural setting (although this setting is somewhat darker than

Figure 37.2 ■ Collina *by Sir Joshua Reynolds.* *Copyright © Columbus Museum of Art, Ohio: Museum Purchase, Derby Fund, 1962.060.*

Figure 37.3 ■ Blue Boy *by Thomas Gainsborough. © Corel.*

most). What is remarkable about *The Blue Boy* is the intensity of the blue color in the boy's clothes. We are told that artists have traditionally had great difficulty creating very intense blue-colored objects. The reason is that the usual pigments that can be used to obtain blue color are not deeply colored. However, Gainsborough departed from tradition and ground the semi-precious stone, lapis lazuli, to make the pigment he used in *The Blue Boy*. The cost of the pigment was, presumably, borne by the sponsor of the portrait.

Gainsborough and Reynolds were very different personalities. Gainsborough was often late in delivering his paintings and was generally a happy and fun-loving character. Reynolds was highly professional and somewhat dour. Nevertheless, they greatly admired each other's works and were always courteous and mutually complementary. On his deathbed, Gainsborough requested that Reynolds visit him and, later, Reynolds praised Gainsborough's "manner of forming all the parts of a picture together," and wrote of "all those odd

scratches and marks" that "by a kind of magic, at a certain distance . . . seem to drop into their proper places."

In architecture, the Rococo style was most evident in the battlefield of religion that existed in eighteenth-century Germany. Although the actual religious wars were over, the struggle for adherents continued, and Germany was the place where that battle was strongest. Local German princes continued to have a strong influence on the religion of their subjects, and the high number of these princes that existed in fragmented Germany meant that Catholics and Protestants might be only a few miles apart. Therefore, especially in Catholic areas, churches and even residences of church officials (which were really public palaces) were built to entice Protestants and to confirm to parishioners the glory of the Catholic Church. The whole of southern Germany is resplendent with churches built in the eighteenth century as part of the efforts of the churches to win adherents.

Figure 37.4 ■ *Altar of the Wieskirche in Wies, Germany.* Erich Lessing/Art Resource, NY.

Wonderful examples of the Rococo style of architecture are in the little Bavarian villages of Wies and of Ettal. We have chosen the inside of the Wieskirche (Wies church) to illustrate the style, Figure 37.4. Upon entering the church, the visitor is overwhelmed with the ornate beauty of the interior. The white walls and light from the large windows brilliantly accentuate the gold and pastels of the paintings and decorations. The columns are Greek in style but highly ornate in execution. Statues of saints and cherubs are so abundant that they seem to be everywhere, almost to the extent that they are falling out of the walls and ceilings. The overall impression is one of glorious celebration of religion.

The simple exterior of the church at Ettal, which is actually part of a monastery, is deceptive. Inside, this gem of a church is also a lovely profusion of pastels and gold set against a background of white. Again, the abundance of saints and angels gives the feeling that you are in heaven itself. Several paintings, generally in the Baroque style, are placed along the walls of the church and are

suitably framed by this light and airy setting. The bishop's palace in Würzburg, Germany, another good example of the Rococo style, is less religious than the churches but equally ornate and equally impressive.

■ Neoclassical Art

About midway through the eighteenth century, the rationality of the Enlightenment began to exert an even stronger influence on art than had occurred at the beginning of the Rococo period. The frivolousness of the Rococo style faded and a more sober and traditional style emerged—an adoption of the Classical principles of ancient Greece and Rome. This new Classical style became known as Neoclassical. Whereas the Rococo style was flowery, ornate, and soft, Neoclassical art placed an emphasis on balance, order, and symmetry. Furthermore, the Rococo used muted colors and soft lines, while Neoclassical works had bolder colors and stronger lines. The themes focused on by these two styles were also different, even though both looked back at the stories and glories of ancient Greece and Rome. Rococo art dealt with themes like pleasure, love, and mythology, whereas Neoclassical works emphasized themes such as nationalism, liberty, and warfare. In a real sense, the Neoclassical and Rococo styles were opposite sides of the same coin, sharing a common inspiration but drawing upon that inspiration in very different ways.

As the eighteenth century progressed, the Enlightenment fostered a rise in the political and economic power of the common people. The common people embraced Neoclassical art for several reasons. It retreated from the elaborateness of the previous styles of Baroque and Rococo, which were closely associated with the nobility. Neoclassical art and architecture were simpler, with clean lines and balanced proportions, and seemed to better represent the common man. Also, Neoclassical art and architecture were meant to recall (and sometimes resemble) art from the societies of ancient Greece and Rome. This was symbolic, as the Enlightenment looked to those ancient societies as the origin of truth about the rights of individuals and the proper forms of government. Furthermore, in America and France new systems of government were being created that were based somewhat on the democracies of Greece and the Roman Republic. Therefore, especially in France and America, Neoclassical art had an inherent element of patriotism and nationalism that appealed to common people, who had begun to view themselves as the true sovereigns of the state.

Neoclassical art has, therefore, two interesting and somewhat opposing messages. In the most obvious sense, this art glorifies the classical days of ancient Greece and Rome. Simultaneously, but more subtly, the art is critical of the existing regimes of nobility and prestige. After the revolutions in France and America, the artists continued to praise ancient Greece and Rome but changed the second message to praise for the revolutionary leaders and ideas. Later, increased revolutionary zeal became even stronger and caused art to move beyond the Neoclassical style to the Romantic—but we will discuss that in a later chapter.

Perhaps the best at combining the messages of classicism and government criticism (or, later, praise) was the French painter **Jacques Louis David** (1748–1825). In his famous painting, *Death of Socrates* (Figure 37.5), the glory of Greek thinking is praised as Socrates is presented as a noble martyr to truth. He is holding his hand aloft in the traditional gesture of telling truth and, with the other hand, reaching for the goblet containing the poisonous drink. It is near perfect Greco-Roman tradition with a strong statement about the value of truth and, if needed, the willingness to die for it.

Other paintings by David that similarly praise Greco-Roman values are *The Oath of the Horatii* and *The Intervention of the Sabine Women.* The stories behind both of these paintings were related in volume 1 of this series, but, briefly, the Oath of the Horatii is about putting country above personal desires. The story of the Intervention of the Sabine Women is about acceptance of new realities. Both stories obviously have messages for the people of France just before and during the time of the Revolution.

David's *Napoleon in his Study* (Figure 37.6) is typical of the post-revolutionary paintings. Napoleon is posed as a kind and thoughtful ruler in military dress with many medals and honors. Also in the scene are beautiful furniture, including a thronelike chair, and other rich appointments to

Figure 37.5 ■ Death of Socrates *by Jacques Louis David.* © Francis G. Mayer/CORBIS.

indicate legitimacy of the regime. Scattered about are several documents that attest to the Enlightenment nature of Napoleon's regime such as the Code of Napoleon (which was a revision in the legal system written by Napoleon), *Plutarch's Lives* (a book on ancient Roman and Greek dignitaries), and a map that suggests Napoleon's closeness to the land of France. David even added a very personal touch in which he showed Napoleon's wrinkled stockings, as they would have been for an insomniac like Napoleon. When shown the painting, Napoleon remarked, "You have understood me, David. By night I work for the welfare of my subjects, and by day for their glory."

Other works by David include *Napoleon Crossing the Alps,* which shows Napoleon in Roman dress as he crosses the Alps on his way to conquest, and the magnificent *Coronation of Napoleon,* in which David captures the moment in the Cathedral of Notre Dame when Napoleon is about to place the empress's crown on his wife, Josephine. The latter painting was so popular when David displayed it that a commission was immediately given to paint a copy to be housed in

Versailles. (The original is in the Louvre.) When Napoleon's brother heard that David was painting the copy, the brother requested that a modification be made. In the original, this brother's wife was shown standing to the left of the scene in a line with other sisters and sisters-in-law (there are five total). All are wearing dresses painted in a light gray color. This brother requested (and presumably paid for) the privilege of having his wife's dress painted in a different color. Today, when you compare the two paintings, you can be delighted at this small pride-based difference.

Much of the architecture of the Neoclassical era heavily recalls the architecture of ancient Greece and Rome, and most of it is found, again, in France and America for the same reasons that Neoclassical painting was popular there. America had to build nearly all of its government buildings, and the Neoclassical style seemed to better represent a nation governed by republican democracy. Thus, the United States Capitol building, most of the official buildings for various departments of government in Washington, D.C., and Thomas Jefferson's estate, Monticello, were built in the Neoclassical style, along with various other American buildings in the state capitals.

The Neoclassical style of architecture could also be found in Europe. In France, the new Pantheon was built in the Neoclassical style (and given a Classical name), the Arc de Triomphe commemorates Napoleon's victories in the Roman way, and the Madeleine Church, where Napoleon worshiped, was in the Greek style. Berlin's Brandenburg Gate recalls the magnificent entry into Athens's Acropolis. In England, many homes of the nobility were built with classical columns supporting a portico in the Greek style.

■ Classical Music

The term *classical* can be confusing, and so a few sentences are probably useful in explaining the general use of the term, as well as its particular meaning in the eighteenth century music setting we are now about to discuss. The following are some ways classical is used:

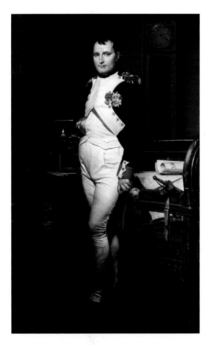

Figure 37.6 ■ Napoleon in his Study *by Jacques Louis David.* © *The Gallery Collection/Corbis*

- *The period of the ancient Greeks and Romans.* This was a time characterized by a search for perfect beauty and truth, generally through order, symmetry, balance, clarity, purity, understatement, and expressive restraint. The perfect Form of things was important to determine. It was also a time when human accomplishments were highly honored.
- *A style, time period, or work that is viewed as a standard against which others can be compared.* In this sense, classical is usually taken as the standard of excellence or the best that can be achieved or as an authoritative work.
- *A particular style that is characterized by grace, clarity, elegance without extreme, and beauty without gaudiness.* For example: "Her skating style was classic beauty."
- *A genre of music.* You might go into a music store and find a group of CDs grouped together with the name "classical" as their identifier (as opposed to other groupings such as "rock" or "rhythm and blues" or "jazz"). In this sense, classical is sometimes called "serious" music, as opposed to the other types like "popular." Note, however, that at the time much of this "serious" music was composed, it was the "popular" music of the day. The musical grouping of "classical" is often associated with orchestras and the works of composers from the historical past, generally without regard to the time in which the composer lived.
- *A particular time period (1750 to the early 1800s) in which many works taken to be classical were created.* It is in this regard that we will be discussing Classical music.

The Classical style of music had nothing to do with imitating the style of the ancient Greeks and Romans except that the values that were present in the ancient period (order, symmetry, balance, clarity, purity, understatement, and expressive restraint) were the values that were sought in the Classical Period. The music composed during the Classical Period also satisfied other criteria we have identified for *classical.* For example, the works are pleasing without excess, graceful, elegant, controlled, beautiful, viewed by many as the best that can be created, and are a standard against which others are compared.

It is no coincidence that the Classical period in music developed at the same time as the Neoclassical period in art and the Enlightenment in writing and philosophy. All were seeking truth or beauty through reasoning. All believed that certain basic principles existed on which that truth or beauty would be based. All strongly supported the importance of commoners and the democratizing effects of giving them power. In music, the period is called Classical rather than Neoclassical because music did not have an ancient antecedent.

The Classical period of music began upon the death of Bach and lasted until midway through the life of Beethoven. Although an extremely popular style, music was composed in the Classical style for a relatively short time because of the social changes brought about by the French Revolution. These changes will be more apparent when we discuss the French Revolution and the Romantic period in later chapters.

The Classical period of music can be strongly associated with the city of Vienna, at least for the definition of the style and the place where the foremost composers of the period interacted. Because of this, some people refer to this style of music as the **Viennese Classical style.** Vienna is a logical location for this to happen for several reasons. It was the capital of the Austrian Empire, which was ruled by the highly enlightened Maria Theresa and, especially, Joseph II. They created an atmosphere of cultural development and actively sponsored the arts, especially music. Vienna was highly cosmopolitan, receiving visitors and ideas from throughout the vast Austrian Empire and also from other countries in Europe and Asia.

Perhaps most important of all was Austria's geography and psychology. It was geographically placed between Italy and Germany and could receive the musical heritages of both. The Italian heritage was strong melody and an emphasis on singing, as reflected in Italian opera. The German heritage was dedication to instrumental music and to musical form as shown most evidently in the works of Bach. The psychological mixture reflected the Catholic emotionalism of the Italians

Viennese Classical Style

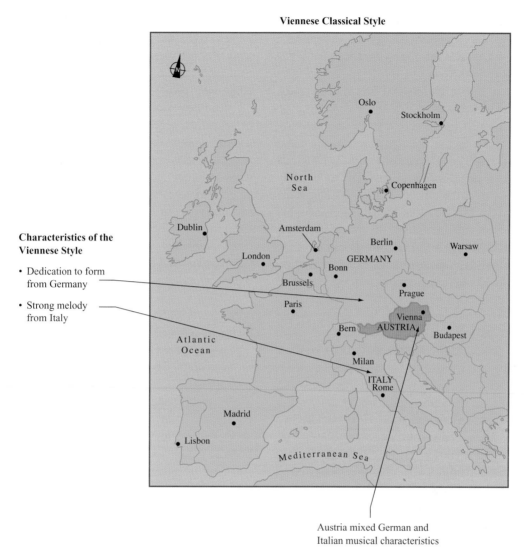

Characteristics of the Viennese Style

• Dedication to form from Germany

• Strong melody from Italy

Austria mixed German and Italian musical characteristics

Figure 37.7 ■ *Map showing the nearness of Vienna to both Germany and Italy and suggesting their contributions to the Viennese style.*

and the Protestant discipline of the Germans. (The Austrians were predominantly Catholics who spoke the German language and therefore enjoyed both heritages.) The geographical position of Vienna is seen in Figure 37.7.

Putting all of these forces together, the Viennese Classical style of music emerged. The style is characterized, first of all, by strong, plain, almost folklike melodies. These were highly appealing to the common people because of their familiarity, but were also comfortable for the nobility who

also loved the Viennese style. The second characteristic of the Viennese style is homophony. This is the musical texture that has a melody supported by harmonies. Homophony is, of course, consistent with the strong melodies we have already indicated as being important to the style. The use of homophony is much like the use of singing in Italian opera—melodies supported by harmonies from other voices and instruments.

The Viennese music had relatively simple forms that were strictly adhered to. This allowed the unsophisticated listener to enjoy the music and understand the intentions of the composers. (Baroque music was far more complicated and required more knowledge of the forms to be fully appreciated and to understand the musical message of the composers.)

The form of the music, that is, its structure, was very important to the composers of the Classical period. Music is the most abstract of the arts and needs a larger structure or form so that the composer can communicate with and delight the listener. In the Middle Ages, the words of the plain chants provided the structure; the music was incidental. In the Renaissance, the words still gave the structure and the music often followed the concepts of the words (tone painting). In the Baroque, purely instrumental music was developed, but the structure was emphasized by the nature of the work, that is, fugue, canon, and so on.

In the Classical period the melody carried the interest, but a form was still needed to give meaning and allow the composer to communicate with the audience as the music unfolded. To understand the reason that a form is needed, let's consider two analogies—a baseball game and poetry.

Assume that you are sitting in a baseball game with a friend from a foreign country who knows nothing of the rules of baseball. As the game progresses, you briefly explain the rules and point out some of the good plays. In the bottom of the ninth inning, the home team (which is your favorite) is trailing in the score by three runs. The bases are loaded and the home team's best batter is up. On the other side, the visiting team has just brought in the league's best relief pitcher. After a few pitches, the count on the batter is three balls and two strikes. This is a moment of extreme tension for you. However, for your friend, there is little tension, or even understanding of the situation. It should be obvious to you that the tension arises from knowledge of the rules of the game. Without knowing the rules, the importance of the next pitch is absent. To further emphasize this point, imagine what would happen if the umpire suddenly stepped forward and announced that he had decided to give the home team another out in this inning. Wouldn't that change the tension of the

moment? You see, tension (and enjoyment) is present when the rules are known and kept. That is what the German composers of the Baroque period understood and passed on to the Viennese composers of the Classical period.

Another analogy might also be instructive. Many literary genres have quite specific forms: sonnet, haiku, limericks, even short stories and novels. These forms communicate to the reader what to expect, and they also allow the reader to be delighted at the subtle and innovative modifications within the form. Poems, especially, rely on form to give a framework for the ideas being communicated. We discussed previously the marvelous ways that Shakespeare chose words to give meaning and rhythm to his sonnets. So it is with many types of music. The great twentieth century composer Igor Stravinsky commented, "There can be no art without form."

We can draw the music/literary analogy even more strongly. In musical terms, the notes are like the letters of a literary piece, the musical phrases are like the sentences, musical themes are like paragraphs, the movements are like chapters or short stories, and a symphony is like the entire book.

Several forms were developed in the Classical period, including theme and variation, rondo, minuet and trio, and sonata—allegro. All the forms were commonly used in the period, but the sonata—allegro form (or just the sonata form) established the basis for many types of music from the Classical period until the present day. This form led directly to the creation of the symphony as an art form and to the long-lasting popularity of classical music.

To understand the nature of these forms, we should realize that they are all applied to movements. (Remember that, in the literary analogy, a movement is like a chapter or a short story.) In the Classical period, the movement was the principal focus of the composer. Larger works, like symphonies, were important, but were viewed as collections of movements. Therefore, using the literary analogy, the Classical period movement is like a short story and the Classical period symphony is like the collection of the short stories. We might also think of the movement like a song and the entire compact disc (CD) like the symphony. Later, in the Romantic period, the focus will change and the entire symphony will become the principal focus. At that point, the literary analogy of the symphony would be the novel.

The sonata form for a single movement is outlined in Figure 37.8. The sonata form has three major parts—exposition, development, and recapitulation—with, occasionally, a coda at the end.

In the **exposition,** the themes (usually two) are introduced. The first theme is in the tonic key (that is, the main key of the movement) and the second theme is in some other key. This change in key adds interest and drama. The two themes are separated by a bridge, which serves merely to transition from one theme to the other. When the second theme is concluded, the two themes with the bridge are often all repeated. Then, the exposition ends with a cadence (closing) theme.

The second part of the sonata form movement is the **development.** This is when the composer plays with the themes and shows technical proficiency. The themes are sometimes broken apart, recombined, moved to new keys (called modulations), and intermixed. There is often a feeling of instability during the development. The ability of the composer to manipulate the themes is part of the message that is being communicated. The development section ends with another transition—generally back to a tonic key.

The third part of the sonata form movement is the **recapitulation.** The first theme is restated in the tonic key. There may have been some minor changes in this theme, that is, it might have progressed and changed by the experience it has had, but not so much change that it cannot be easily recognized. Because the theme is in the tonic key, the listener gets a feeling of relief from the tension felt in the development section. Then, further relief is felt as the second and other themes are reintroduced, usually in the tonic key as well. This gives a feeling of triumph of the tonic and a comfort that all has come out right.

The entire movement is sometimes concluded with a **coda.** This is simply a flourishing finale.

The *allegro* part of the full sonata—allegro title of this form is present because the sonata form is most often used in a movement that begins a symphony, which is often played with a rapid (allegro) tempo. Second and third movements traditionally have other forms, such as minuet and trio or theme and variation, and are often played with other tempos. The fourth movement of a symphony is also frequently an allegro tempo and is also often in sonata form.

The themes of the sonata form are the strong melodies that we identified as characteristics of the Classical style. Therefore, because of their Italian origins, these themes are like voices in Italian opera. In fact, the entire sonata form was derived from the Italian opera form, as can be seen

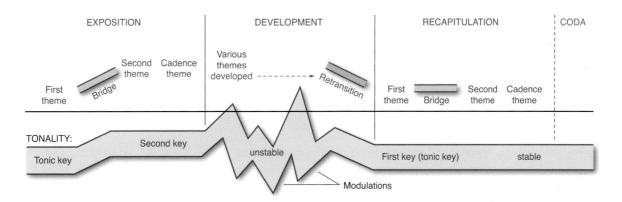

Figure 37.8 ■ *Diagram of the Sonata–Allegro Form.*

in Figure 37.9. In this diagram we make the analogy between the three acts of an opera and the three principal parts of a sonata form movement. In the first act of an opera, the characters are introduced. That is like the introduction of the themes. Note that in an opera, tension is built when the characters are quite different from each other. That is also true of the nature of the themes in a movement. Then, in the second act of an opera, the characters interact and have problems, thus building tension. The development is the analogous part of a sonata movement. Finally, in act three of an opera, the characters solve the problems and peace is restored. Sometimes the characters have been changed by their experiences, but they are still easily recognized. That is the same as the recapitulation. Finally, the actors come out for a curtain call. That is like the coda. Note, again, that in the Classical period, the entire opera concept was built into a single movement.

The first of the great Classical period composers, **Franz Joseph Haydn** (1732–1809), perfected the sonata form and used it extensively in symphonies. He wrote more than 100 symphonies

and popularized the symphony as the most important musical genre of the day. He is called "the father of the symphony."

As a boy, Haydn sang in the esteemed St. Stephen's Cathedral Choir in Vienna. As a young man, he lived in Vienna, where he composed, taught, and played in several street bands. As he grew older and became more accomplished as a composer, he served as a father figure for many young composers, including Mozart and Beethoven. They, and many others, affectionately referred to Haydn as *papa*.

In his symphonies, Haydn emphasized the use of brass, clarinets, and percussion to develop a fuller sound than had been previously used. Furthermore, toward the end of his career Haydn expanded the size of the orchestra until it reached the size common today. Haydn was also unafraid to experiment with his music. One of his most popular symphonies is the *Surprise Symphony,* which Haydn wrote after a concert where he noticed that many people in the audience had fallen asleep. In the *Surprise Symphony* Hayden repeatedly interrupted a tranquil and serene passage

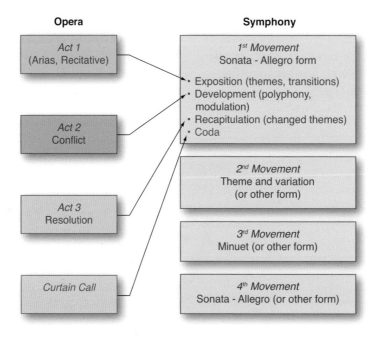

Figure 37.9 ■ *Diagram of the relationship between the Sonata–Allegro Form in a symphony and opera.*

with sudden, loud, almost dissonant notes that seem to come from nowhere. These harsh notes were the surprise and were meant to keep listeners awake and paying attention. In spite of these occasional humorous innovations, Haydn's main focus was on satisfying the musical taste of the people who came to hear his works. As the quotation at the beginning of this chapter reveals, Haydn wanted music to be a comfort. This is typical of the Classical period.

For the bulk of Haydn's professional life he worked for Count Esterhazy, a Hungarian nobleman, and lived in the Hungarian countryside a few hours outside of Vienna. While in the service of Count Esterhazy, Haydn wrote most of his symphonies. Although he focused on symphonies, Haydn also wrote music in nearly all the genres of the day, including opera, string quartets, piano sonatas, masses, and oratorios. Some noteworthy nonsymphonic works include a sonata for the Emperor of Austria/Hungary, as well as a national anthem for Germany, which became *Deutschland Uber Alles.*

After 30 years working for Count Esterhazy, Haydn left the count's estate and moved to Vienna. Haydn was in demand everywhere as a guest conductor and composer, and royalty all across Europe invited him to come and live and work at their courts. Haydn chose to maintain his residence in Vienna but traveled extensively across Europe, where he made visits to several European capitals and was feted royally, often by the king or queen personally. Haydn especially loved England and was inspired to do much of his greatest work during his time there. Perhaps his most famous symphonies are his London symphonies. Furthermore, when Haydn heard Handel's oratorio *Messiah,* it inspired him to write his own oratorio, *Creation,* which is considered by some to be his best work. Haydn was also awarded honorary degrees from several prestigious English universities, including Oxford.

One day, when Haydn was first visiting London, he went into a music store to investigate whether he was as well respected as he had read in the English newspapers. Haydn told the clerk that he wanted to buy some piano pieces. The clerk,

without recognizing Haydn, showed him some music by Haydn. Then Haydn said that he wanted something better, whereupon the clerk pointed out that these pieces were by Haydn and that no better could be found. When Haydn persisted that he wanted something better, the clerk became angry and took back the offered music pieces and said that he refused to do business with anyone with such poor taste. Haydn then revealed his identity and they hugged and became good friends.

Joseph Haydn was a true gentleman and, despite his amazing talent, took time to teach and give advice to younger composers. Mozart once commented that Haydn had taught him how to compose a quartet. As the most senior of the Classical composers, Haydn recognized the genius of many of those who followed him and freely admitted that Mozart was his superior. Upon hearing of Mozart's death he said, "I cannot believe that the Lord would have dispatched one so talented to the other world so quickly. We will not have another talent such as this in a hundred years." Haydn himself lived to be an old man.

Wolfgang Gottlieb Mozart was born in Salzburg, Austria, in 1756, and was probably the most gifted child in the history of music. Mozart started to compose when he was only five years old. By the age of six young Mozart was playing at the court of Empress Maria Theresa of Austria. Soon the boy composer was traveling across Europe and performing before kings and queens in Paris, London, and Munich. By the time he was 13 he had composed sonatas, concertos, symphonies, religious works, and several operas. Mozart also changed his middle name from Gottlieb to Amadeus (the German and Latin names meaning "loved of God") because he felt the Latin version was more sophisticated.

As Mozart grew older, his musical genius was undeniable, and he was universally hailed as one of Europe's finest composers. However, his musical genius was tempered by violent emotional swings, as he would shift back and forth between deep bouts of depression and periods of intense creativity. Mozart's first important position was as the "court" composer for the archbishop in his hometown of Salzburg, Austria. However, when the archbishop that hired Mozart died, the relationship between Mozart and the new archbishop became strained because of Mozart's rebellion against the social restrictions of a church position. This led to Mozart's eventual dismissal by the new archbishop.

From Salzburg Mozart went to Vienna, where he hoped to work in the court of Austria's Emperor Joseph II. However, Emperor Joseph favored another composer named Salieri, and Mozart was largely used to compose court dances and other similar lesser works. Mozart was known to have commented that Emperor Joseph paid him "too much for what I do, too little for what I could do." Although Mozart was paid a decent salary to work in the Viennese court, he lived an extravagant lifestyle and his expenses far outstripped his means. Mozart and his wife always struggled financially, and Mozart took outside work when he could find it, including composing comic operas for the popular stage. This practice hurt his credibility with some of the other court composers, as it was seen as beneath their dignity to work for the common public.

Mozart died in 1791 at the age of 35. Although Mozart's life may have been short and often tragic, his musical talent was unparalleled. Mozart composed music in several different genres ranging from symphonies (41 total) to operas (22) to string quartets (23) and numerous other pieces. All the music has beautiful melodies with a strong sense of drama, especially in the contrast between moods. Furthermore, in most of Mozart's music, the melodies are especially simple but elegantly presented with richly colored orchestration.

Besides his talent as a composer, Mozart was also an extremely gifted pianist and wrote many piano concertos that were exceptionally difficult to play so that he could show off his own virtuosity on the instrument. The piano had only recently been invented, and Mozart was enthralled with its capabilities. Because the piano used hammers to strike the keys, loud and soft music could be played; whereas the harpsichord, which plucked the keys, could only play in one volume. The full name of early pianos was *pianoforte*, which means "soft-loud."

Perhaps Mozart's most amazing gift was his ability to hear a completely finished piece in his head. Mozart himself said, "Though it be long, the work is complete and finished in my mind. I take out of the bag of my memory what has previously been collected into it. For this reason the committing to paper is done quickly enough." Whereas most composers, even the great ones, labored over draft after draft of a piece while they worked on it, Mozart would often completely compose it in his head and then simply jot it down, without error, in a single sitting. He is reported to have been able to compose music while eating, playing billiards, and even holding his wife's hand as she was in labor. This amazing ability fascinated some and enraged others among his colleagues and rivals. Joseph Haydn, who had friendly composing contests with Mozart, freely admitted that Mozart's talents far outshined his own; while Salieri, the favorite of Emperor Joseph (and, ironically, the envy of Mozart), envied the amazing gift Mozart had and reportedly made efforts to keep Mozart from achieving too much.

Mozart lived his life at a furious pace and, like many who do so, he died young. Mozart attended numerous social occasions and wild parties, kept late hours, drank too much, and ate poorly. Always somewhat sickly, the pressures of his life and the excesses of the lifestyle he chose eventually took a toll on his fragile health. Mozart caught a feverish illness, the precise nature of which has been the subject of much speculation. The illness gradually grew worse until Mozart died. Throughout his life, Mozart's lifestyle had caused severe financial problems, and his last year's were no different. Mozart's death left his family in dire financial straits, and he was buried in an unmarked pauper's grave. Ironically, his last work was a *Requiem,* which was played at his own simple funeral.

Ludwig von Beethoven was born in Bonn, Germany, in 1770. A very talented composer who also had to overcome great personal adversity, Beethoven is the bridge between the Classical and the Romantic styles within music.

Born into a family of talented musicians, both Beethoven's father and grandfather were court singers for the local prince. This proved to be a benefit to young Beethoven, as he learned music at an early age. However, Beethoven's alcoholic father also exploited the boy's talent by forcing young Beethoven to play at odd hours and in strange and unhealthy places. Mozart's success as a child musical prodigy also placed added stress on Beethoven, as his father was constantly pressuring Beethoven to be as good as Mozart to bring the family wealth and fame.

Because of his alcoholism, Beethoven's father had difficulty supporting his family and Beethoven was put to work at a young age to help provide for the family. By age 11, young Beethoven was the assistant organist at the court chapel. A year later, Beethoven was the harpsichordist in the court orchestra. At age 17, Beethoven was given a fellowship and went to Vienna, where he was given the opportunity to play for Mozart, who remarked, "Keep an eye on him, he will make a noise in the world someday."

Beethoven's talent as a pianist was well received by the aristocracy within Vienna allowing Beethoven to remain there for a few years beyond the period of the fellowship. Beethoven was able to make a living in Vienna receiving commissions, giving lessons, and performing concerts. Beethoven also was able to win the favor of various nobles by dedicating pieces to them.

Beethoven's compositions were also extremely popular with Vienna's blossoming middle class. This allowed Beethoven to receive money from music publishers as well allowing his work to be copied and sold so that anyone could own his music and play it. This was an important new development in music, as it gave more people access to music in their own homes and allowed a composer to earn money without the patronage of the aristocracy or clergy. The ability of a composer (or any other artist) to live without sponsorship had an important effect on creativity. The motivation for doing the work changed from what the sponsor wanted to what the public might want. The qualities of an artistic work would probably not be the same for a noble sponsor and for the public. Moreover, the artists began to have more flexibility in what they chose to do, since the public was often less specific in their desires than a sponsor.

Beethoven returned to his native Germany and lived in Bonn. He was an extremely successful and popular composer and musician in that city as well. However, around the age of 30, Beethoven discovered that he was going deaf. The doctors told Beethoven that there was nothing that they could do, and Beethoven entered a dark period of depression and despondency. To sense the depth of his personal feelings at the time of his growing deafness, we read the following passage that Beethoven wrote to his brother:

> *How humiliated I have felt if somebody standing beside me heard the sound of a flute in the distance and I heard nothing . . . It is impossible for me to say to people, 'Speak louder, for I am deaf.' How would it be possible for me to admit to a weakness of the one sense that should be perfect to a higher degree in me than in theirs. So forgive me if you see me draw back from your company which I would so gladly share. I would have ended my life. It was only my art that held me back for it seemed impossible to leave the world until I have brought forth all that is within me.*

However, upon the advice of his doctors he went to a retreat and there he came to grips with his affliction. Rather than giving in, Beethoven determined that he would fight against the tragedy fate had given him. He left the retreat ready to face the world again and embraced life anew. Beethoven said, "I am resolved to rise superior to every obstacle. With whom need I be afraid of measuring my strength? I will take Fate by the throat. It shall not overcome me. O how beautiful it is to be alive—would that I could live a thousand times!"

With this defiant attitude, Beethoven returned to his art with vigor and as a refuge. He never married and lived a chaotic lifestyle, focusing exclusively on his music. Beethoven composed by sawing the legs off of a piano so that the body of the piano sat on the floor. He would then sit with his head against the floor and feel the vibrations so that he could "hear" the music.

It was during this latter half of his life, when he was deaf, that Beethoven's style began to change.

His music drew more heavily upon personal emotion and his own internal struggles. This use of personal emotion by Beethoven started a trend within music and laid the groundwork for the Romantic period in music. Thus, Beethoven truly was both the last great Classical composer and the first great Romantic composer.

Generally speaking, Beethoven had three periods of compositional activity. The early period was his Classical period. Beethoven's works from this time were similar in style to the work being done by Haydn and Mozart.

Beethoven's middle period was when he pioneered the Romantic style and drew heavily upon his own personal struggle with his deafness. Many of Beethoven's greatest works are from this period, including his *Third Symphony.* Written in honor of Napoleon, who Beethoven felt was a champion of the people, and originally titled the *Bonaparte Symphony,* Beethoven became disillusioned with Napoleon when he crowned himself emperor. Thus, Beethoven scratched out Napoleon's name and renamed the symphony *Eroica,* giving it the subtitle: "Composed to celebrate the memory of a great man." Beethoven also wrote his most famous work, the *Fifth Symphony,* during his Romantic period. Beethoven's *Fifth Symphony* is considered by many to be the greatest and most perfectly structured symphony ever written.

Beethoven's much shorter third period was a time for developing a stark and skeletal form, usually associated with sonatas and string quartets of a much later period, perhaps even the modern era.

Beethoven is considered a master because he produced great works, not only in different music genres such as symphonies and sonatas, but also because he worked in so many different styles, even creating new ones to help him deal with his own personal struggles. Beethoven's sonatas and symphonies are among the best ever composed and are structurally the best ever done. He was a true master who ended one era and began another.

■ Creativity and Rules

The Classical Period was a time when rules were important. People believed that nature and, indeed, all the universe operated according to set rules (laid out by God) that governed all things. Humans could discover the rules using the scientific method but could not change the rules. Enlightenment thinkers applied the scientific method to all aspects of life, especially to government, and proclaimed that they had discovered certain rights with which humans were endowed by their Creator and also rules by which governments were authorized to operate.

The artists of the Classical period were not ignorant of the general societal agreement on the supremacy of rules. In fact, the abandonment of the Baroque style seemed to suggest that the rules of symmetry, restraint, and good taste had been exceeded. These neoclassical artists withdrew into an environment in which the rules of the ancient Greeks and Romans were both appreciated and obeyed. They proudly used concepts of the Greco-Roman past and suggested that to deviate from the rules given by the ancients would be to create ugliness and dissymmetry.

Even composers, who did not have ancient rules to follow, nevertheless developed rules themselves that seemed to give those desired qualities of restraint, beauty, and refinement. The composers of the Classical period generally adhered to those rules of composition.

We might legitimately ask whether this adherence to rules affected the creativity of the artist or composer. If uniqueness is one of the criteria for creativity, doesn't keeping the rules restrict that uniqueness and, therefore, diminish creativity? For some artists and composers that was probably the case. For example, the Viennese style became so popular that it was copied by composers throughout Europe. Today, when we listen to symphonies from these non-Viennese composers, we can't tell who the composer was. We can't even tell what country the composer lived in. In short, abiding by the rules of the Viennese style was so confining that these artists gave up their individuality and with it, their creativity.

However, that is not the case with Haydn, Mozart, or Beethoven—all of whom composed in the same Viennese style. What was different about these great composers and the many lesser composers whose works are not distinguishable? The answer is creativity! The great composers were able to be creative and still stay within the rules. In fact, their use of the rules was part of their creativity because they increased tension and interest by using the rules to help the audience anticipate something but, still within the rules, they were able to create an unexpected and entertaining moment.

Mozart's *40th Symphony* is an example. The last movement of this symphony is composed using sonata—allegro form. The intensity and harshness of the first theme and the loveliness of the second theme astound us by their contrast. The development section is interesting and full of tension, heightened by the contrast of the themes. The recapitulation section is initially troubling because the intense theme is the victor in the resolution, but when the second theme is reprised, it has been changed to a minor key and now seems to have adjusted to the new situation. It is not the same as before, but now can be accepted as resolved. No other composer of the period could manipulate our emotions in that way. Surely that is creative and, because we knew the rules, its creativity was actually enhanced.

Remember the analogy with baseball. Just because a player keeps the rules doesn't mean that creativity is lost. We have seen shortstops make spectacular dives and incredible throws to put out the runner. The shortstop was obviously athletic but also creative. Also, the pitcher whose creative command of the location and sequence of pitches confused the hitters, has also dazzled us with his creativity.

Our lives are, sadly, filled with situations where we encounter people who use the rules to *not* be creative. (We are reminded, for example, of government bureaucrats who refuse to allow any deviation from the strict letter of the rules, even when good sense would dictate otherwise.) These types of people seem to put adherence to the rules above all else. That attitude is characteristic of noncreativity. Perhaps the people who take this bureaucratic attitude are afraid to accept the responsibility to be creative or simply unable to think broadly enough to be creative.

By contrast, we also hear of people who live by the rules but realize that there can still be creativity within the rules. The story is told of an employee who is tasked with delivering a package but is unable to do so because the road has been washed out. The employee understands that the company has committed to deliver the package (the rule), regardless of what conditions exist. Therefore, the employee rents an airplane and overcomes the problem. Would the company be pleased or angry? It depends on how strongly the company believed in the rule and appreciated creativity in keeping it.

The rules of one art form are often surprisingly connected to other art forms, thus reaffirming that

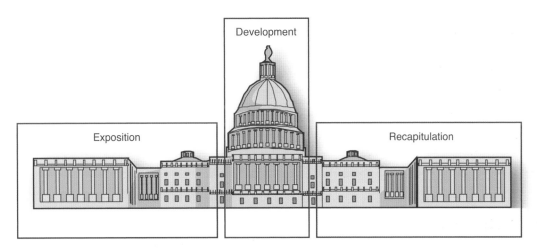

Figure 37.10 ■ *Demonstration of the linkage between classical architecture and classical music.*

rules are important and basic to art. Consider music and architecture. Figure 37.10 depicts the United States Capitol building and superimposes on it the three parts of the sonata form. While these are obviously just an idea of the form, the concept is certainly revealing. There is a certain symmetry present in both of the art forms.

In Chapter 40 on the Romantic period we will discuss how some artists and composers showed their creativity by breaking the rules. This created certain problems that had to be overcome. This abbreviated description shows that thinking of something unique by breaking the rules is easy compared to being creative and staying within the rules (except for how the ensuing problems are resolved). Mozart did not take the "easy" way to creativity. He worked within the rules and gave us great delight, perhaps enhanced by our knowledge and anticipation. That is one reason why many consider Mozart the greatest composer.

In a larger sense, we all live within a society of rules. That is one of the characteristics of civilization. In general, we must keep the rules. That may mean that we restrain ourselves. Is that good or bad? Most would agree that civilization's restraints are generally good. We might even restrain our talents because to allow free rein would, perhaps, diminish the beauty and actually be less creative than could be done within stricter confines. This recognition of the need for restraint has long been appreciated. Homer said the following in the *Odyssey:* "I curb my talent, that it not run where virtue does not guide." That sounds like good advice even for us today. It was certainly advice that was followed in the Classical period.

▪ Timeline—Important Dates

Date	Event
1717	*Watteau's* Pilgrimage to Cythera *painted*
1754	*Wieskirche completed*
1761	*Haydn begins employment for Count Esterhazy*
1770	*Gainsborough's* Blue Boy *painted*
1781	*Mozart moves to Vienna*
1787	*David's* Death of Socrates *painted*
1792	*Beethoven visits Vienna*
1812	*David's* Napoleon in his Study *painted*

▪ Suggested Readings

Barber, David W., *If It Ain't Baroque,* Sound and Vision, 1992.

Cumming, Robert, *Annotated Art,* DK Publishing, 1995.

Cumming, Robert, *Great Artists,* DK Publishing, 1998.

Kerman, Joseph, *Listen,* Third Brief Edition, Worth Publishers, 1996.

Machlis, Joseph and Kristine Forney, *The Enjoyment of Music,* 7th ed., Norton, 1995.

American Revolution
Creative Implementation

> These are the times that try men's souls. The summer soldier and the sunshine patriot will, in this crisis, shrink from the service of their country; . . . Tyranny, like hell, is not easily conquered; . . . What we obtain too cheap, we esteem too lightly: . . . it would be strange indeed if so celestial an article as FREEDOM should not be highly rated.
>
> —*Thomas Paine*

■ A Novel Idea: The Better Life

America (and here we speak of the region that eventually became the United States) was like a case study for the Enlightenment. John Locke, one of the early Enlightenment writers, had said that the human mind was a *tabula rasa* (blank page) on which knowledge gained by experience was written. Early America was certainly a blank page because there was little European experience in the American colonies. (The Europeans largely ignored the natives who already populated America.) From the view of those earliest European settlers, all government, religion, culture, values, or, in short, civilization, were brought to this land by themselves. They could make America what they wanted it to be.

Locke also admitted that, besides knowledge from experience, humans could know some things innately. The early European settlers to America also seemed to know something inherently about this country—it was a land where a better life could be obtained. From the beginning, the promise of America was that people of any economic or social status could gain success through their own efforts. America was a land of opportunity. These concepts of individual potential and responsibility were the heart of Enlightenment thinking, along with the concept of the power of reason. Americans also accepted that their society should be built on reason. As we will see, reasoning sometimes conflicted with emotion, and sometimes the reasoning of several people did not lead to the same conclusions. In establishing the government and other social institutions of this country, the forefathers would have to find creative ways to deal with these diversities of reasoning. That is a large part of this story.

America was also a case study of creativity. Remember that in the first chapter of this book we talked of the four elements that constitute creativity—**value, intent, novelty,** and **excellence (VINE).** We will see how the characteristics and institutions of America were valued by Enlightenment thinkers, how the fundamental ideas of government and life in America were novel, how the Americans' intent was to form a society that was based on Enlightenment principles, and how the excellent implementation of those ideas led to a revolution and then to the formation of a unique state. All the elements of creativity were present in the founding of the United States, and we will look at the founding of America in light of these four creative elements.

■ Value: The Enlightenment Made Real

The people who settled the original 13 colonies were people who believed that they could improve their lives and leave behind centuries of oppression and social stagnation. The colonists came for different reasons—the northern colonies were mostly settled by those wanting political or religious freedom, while the southern colonies were largely settled by those wanting to own land and have economic success. Ultimately, they all came to improve their situations in life. Furthermore, this was not a blind or chance happening. Most American colonists were from Northern Europe (Great Britain, Holland, and Scandinavia) and had a knowledge of and belief in the principles of the Enlightenment. It was this belief that drove them to abandon their native lands to make their fortunes in the new land of America.

Several other factors also established the 13 colonies as a good place for Enlightenment-based living. From their inception, for a variety of reasons including an inherent respect for Enlightenment principles, the American colonies already lived many principles of the Enlightenment. There was little aristocracy in America and the middle class was already dominant. Property ownership, whether land or business, was nearly universal.

Therefore, many of the class distinctions that were so dominant and troublesome in Europe were absent in America.

Furthermore, there was no overall dominant church and clergy to resist social change. Most of the colonists were Protestant but were of many faiths, and the nature of American Protestantism favored progress and a culture of hard work and high moral values. This lack of a dominant church also fostered an environment that accepted Deism, the pseudo-religion of the Enlightenment.

Furthermore, the American colonies had a strong technical/scientific orientation that contributed a culture that highly valued progress and development. This technology-based drive for improvement was fueled by America's abundant natural resources.

The background of a majority of the colonists was either English or Dutch, the two most liberal and forward-thinking societies in Europe, and by 1664 England had obtained control of all 13 colonies via conquest or treaty, leading to a harmony and cohesion that would not have existed had the colonies been governed by different European powers. This trend was continued a century later, when the English victory in the French and Indian Wars (called the Seven Years War in Europe) in 1763, granted England control of the French colony of Quebec and the Spanish colony of Florida, thus finalizing English domination of North American colonies and limiting the amount of warfare.

All of these factors laid the groundwork for the United States of America on principles of the Enlightenment. Originally the goals of Americans for a better life were largely fulfilled, but eventually the very high expectations of the Americans were restricted by England, and that led to the American Revolution.

■ Causes of Revolution in America

As evident by their participation in the French and Indian War on behalf of the British, the British American colonists of the early to mid-eighteenth century were generally loyal citizens of the British

Empire. However, after the French and Indian War, the depletion of the English treasury led the British government to take several steps that angered the Americans and led to the outbreak of the revolution. Even though most of the American colonies had been under British control long before the French and Indian War, the English government lumped all of America together as a prize of war, with little or no distinction being made between the original colonies and those newly acquired like Canada and Florida. As a prize of war, the English government felt justified in forcing these colonies to replenish the British treasury. Therefore, various small taxes were levied on all the colonies in North America. These angered the citizens of the original colonies, since they felt that rather than being treated as a prize of war, they should benefit from the war's end as victors.

As we discussed in Chapter 36 on the enlightened despots, another change that occurred about the same time as the end of the French and Indian War was the personal involvement of King George III in the affairs of government. Whereas the previous monarch, George II, was content to let his prime minister rule Britain, George III was anxious to assert royal control and therefore changed prime ministers and made many unilateral decisions that were largely based on his personal desires to rule more absolutely. This absolutist attitude was not popular in England and even less so in America, where the people were more independent and committed to Enlightenment principles. Hence, over time, the anger of the Americans was especially directed toward the person of George III. His abilities to respond properly were limited both by his personal egotism and, increasingly, by the disease that eventually resulted in his madness.

Furthermore, like all colonies, the Americas were viewed as a means to make money for the homeland. The most money would be made if the Americas were limited to being a source of raw material and an outlet for English manufactured goods. The worst situation for English manufacturers would be if American manufacturers became competitors. Thus, as the population and economy of the American colonies grew, England began to restrict American manufacturing and trade. The much-maligned Sugar Act was created to limit the ability of the American manufacturers to make sugar. The hated Stamp Act placed a tax on American-manufactured goods so that the prices would be artificially elevated and thus not be competitive with English-produced goods. Several other items were eventually taxed in a similar way, and as the list of taxed items grew, so did American discontent. The policies of the English government were especially irritating to the Americans because the founding principle of America was seeking a better life, and the English were restricting the ability of the Americans to live better.

Because these economic issues were imposed politically rather than arising naturally from market forces, the aggrieved Americans coupled their economic resistance with attempts to find a political solution. The real question in debate was not whether taxes placed on the Americans by the British were too high, but whether the English government had the right to impose special taxes on the Americans at all. Even more fundamentally, did the authority to govern America lie in the distant Parliament in the British homeland, or should it be found in the local elected legislatures? The question was given more weight because the American colonies had mostly governed themselves for more than a hundred years. Only when America became a viable economic force in the mid-1700s, and with the rule of George III, did Britain make real attempts to exert its authority over its colonies.

The right to vote was more widespread in America than it was in Britain, and this gave the Americans the feeling that their government was more responsive to their true will than the British government was. Even some in the home country agreed. However, King George III instructed Parliament to ensure that proper administrative control was exercised over the colonies. In order to enforce this decree, Britain decided to break with tradition and maintain a large standing army in North America. Americans, as loyal British citizens, felt equal to people in Great Britain and especially resented the military interference which seemed like an occupying army. This led to growing tension between the American colonists and the British that resulted in a series of protests.

Upset at the British treatment, many American colonists joined secret protest societies called, generally, the Sons of Liberty. The goal of these groups was to find ways of disrupting British policies that the societies found oppressive or believed to be illegal. The rallying cry of many of these discontent American colonists was "No taxation without representation" and the Sons of Liberty and other like-minded groups successfully organized a boycott of British goods. This boycott caused enough damage to the British economy that by 1766 the British Parliament had repealed the Stamp Act in an effort to mollify the Americans and end the boycott.

For a brief time it appeared that the British had heard the message and tensions began to ease. But in 1767 the British Parliament passed the **Townsend Acts,** which placed new taxes on a wide variety of products, including tea, paper, paint, and lead. Tensions increased anew and the boycotts were reinitiated. However, this time the British Parliament did not surrender to American pressures, and a contest of wills between the

British Parliament and the American colonists began that lasted for years.

Tensions, especially in the Northern colonies, reached a fever pitch in 1770 when a group of British soldiers stationed in Boston felt threatened by a protesting crowd and opened fire, killing several colonists. This event became known as the **Boston Massacre,** and while it did not lead to open warfare, for many colonists it proved that British rule would eventually have to come to an end.

In 1773, six years after the passage of the Townsend Acts and three years after the Boston Massacre, the situation had stalemated even though tensions remained high. In an effort to accelerate and magnify the effects of the boycott, agitated Boston area colonists crept onto a British ship and dumped a shipment of tea into Boston Harbor. This event became known as the **Boston Tea Party** and was viewed by the British as an act of open rebellion; it likely served as the first domino in a series of events that led to an outbreak of war.

Initially, the Boston Tea Party (see Figure 38.1) seemed like an American victory because the British Parliament immediately repealed all parts of the Townsend Acts except the tax on tea. How-

Figure 38.1 ▪ Representation of the Boston Tea Party, December 1773. © 2010 by patrimonio designs limited. Used under license of Shutterstock, Inc.

ever, within a year Parliament had passed a series of new, even more restrictive laws intended to punish the American colonists. These new laws came to be known by the colonists as the **Intolerable Acts** and included, among other things, the closing of Boston Harbor, forced housing and feeding of British troops, and increased power to the British colonial governors (at the expense of the colonial legislatures). The Intolerable Acts, combined with the lingering discontent from the Boston Massacre, led the American colonists to decide that the time had come to meet together and decide on a course of action that would give a permanent remedy to the situation. Throughout this period, British actions were linear, logical, and non-creative.

■ Novelty: A New Way to Fight

After years of conflict and tension with the British, delegates from 12 colonies (all but Georgia) met in Philadelphia and formed the First Continental Congress. The purpose of this first congress was only to resolve the problem with Great Britain. In fact, the First Continental Congress reaffirmed the colonies' loyalty to the crown and agreed that Parliament had the right to govern the foreign affairs of the colonies. However, in protest of the Intolerable Acts, the First Continental Congress also called for an end to *all* British trade until the hated acts were repealed. In reaction to this call for an expanded boycott of British trade goods, King George III rejected all of the colonists' demands.

The British government viewed the actions of the First Continental Congress to be in open rebellion of British authority and feared, rightly so, that the longstanding tension in the American colonies might finally be reaching the point where some would begin to favor armed resistance against the British. In an attempt to keep this from happening, British troops were sent to seize the military supplies of the Massachusetts militia (a local military unit that could be called upon as reserves). This attempt to disarm the Massachusetts militia worried those who feared a harsh British crackdown, and on April 19, 1775, armed skirmishes took place between the British army and bands of colonists at both Lexington Green and Concord Bridge.

Although the Americans were driven from Lexington Green, the English were not able to find the arms stored near Concord Bridge. Even more serious than not gaining this objective was the high number of casualties suffered by the English during the battle at Concord Bridge and on the return trip to Boston.

The success of the Americans in any armed conflict against the British was dependent upon the use of creativity and unconventional tactics. The British army was the world's most skilled and feared, whereas the American colonists were simply a band of untrained farmers and part-time militia men. However, from the beginning of armed conflict, the Americans showed a willingness to break the traditional rules of warfare and to find ways to frustrate the British mode of fighting.

The Americans, who knew they were outmatched and at a technological disadvantage, refused to stand and face the British forces in the manner of traditional European armies. Instead, the Americans fought guerilla style—hiding in trees and behind rocks and firing upon the long British columns. Then, when pressured, the Americans fled to another vantage point to do the same thing.

When the Americans did have to face the British in more conventional warfare, they were able to frustrate the British by not firing until the British were extremely close. This upset the British manner of attack because, generally, the British infantry system marched in three rows (as a big show of force) until the other side fired, usually quite prematurely out of fear of the large and highly disciplined British army. The British soldiers would then run (still in their three rows) as close to the enemy as possible while the enemy soldiers were reloading. Just before the enemy troops had reloaded, the British soldiers would stop and open fire from near pointblank range. One row of the British would fire and then drop to their knees while the second row leaned over the first and fired a second volley. The second row would then step back as the third row stepped forward and fired a third devastating volley. Then, all the rows of the British army charged into the enemy troops and assaulted them with their bayonets.

By not firing on the British until they were close enough to "see the whites of their eyes," the Americans were able to upset this traditionally effective plan of attack. When the Americans finally fired, the British were so close that large numbers of their troops were hit, thus slowing the British forces enough that the Americans had time to quickly retreat and seek another place where they could reload and repeat the encounter.

Had the order to seize the militia's arms occurred in any colony besides Massachusetts, it is likely the British could have taken the weapons with little trouble. Massachusetts had become a hotbed of colonial discontent and mistrust of the British because of the Boston Massacre, Boston Tea Party, and the closure of Boston Harbor. Once those first shots had been fired, it was difficult to step back and allow cooler heads to prevail. Thus, the skirmishes at Lexington and Concord marked the official beginning of the American Revolution.

■ Intent: Independence

The events at Lexington and Concord led to the formation of a Second Continental Congress that met in Philadelphia in May of 1775. This time the Continental Congress was largely composed of **patriots** (a term given to those who wanted independence from Great Britain) rather than **loyalists** who would seek accommodation. (Most of the loyalists had been defeated in the elections that formed the new Congress due to the precipitous actions of the British in Massachusetts.) Among the first actions of this Second Continental Congress were to organize the Continental Army and appoint George Washington as its commander. When King George III heard of this action, he declared that the American colonies were in rebellion and that dire circumstances would follow unless the colonies disbanded the Continental Army and accepted British authority.

Despite the bold initial actions of the Second Continental Congress, many Americans were not yet ready to go to war for their independence. Indeed, many still viewed themselves as loyal British citizens and were unhappy about the direction that events had taken. All during the winter of 1775 to 1776, both the British and the colonists waited to see whether the popular opinion of the general public would favor continued military action or accommodation. There was little military action other than an American effort to invade Canada in hopes that the British would be forced to withdraw their forces from New England to defend Quebec.

The media, especially newspapers and political tracts, became widely used on both sides to try and sway public opinion to their side of the argument. The most influential pamphlet during this time was *Common Sense,* written by a patriot named **Thomas Paine.** Paine was able to frame the difficult and complex issue of independence as a question of right or wrong. He argued that Americans must either accept the tyranny of the British Crown or throw off their shackles by proclaiming a republic. By stating the issue in such stark black and white terms, Paine erased the shades of gray many people felt in regards to this important and dangerous decision. Paine understood that most of the colonists, even though they considered themselves loyal British citizens, thought of themselves as Americans first and British second. He asserted to them that American liberty was better than British oppression. Paine also argued that a small island nation like Great Britain could not truly understand a vast and growing land like America. He focused on America's differences from England, such as a lack of aristocracy and more universal suffrage. Paine used the ideas of the Enlightenment and highlighted the moral superiority of America's cause. The government of Great Britain was not keeping its end of the social contract; therefore, Americans had a right to rid themselves of it. *Common Sense* was powerfully worded and well written, and it served as a powerful pro-independence tool. The quotation at the beginning of this chapter captures the power of the logic and emotion used by Thomas Paine.

By the spring of 1776 the general mood of the American colonies was in favor of independence.

The delegates to the Second Continental Congress sensed this mood, and Thomas Jefferson, a patriot and politician from Virginia, was given the task of drafting a document that would proclaim America's intent to be free of British rule. Jefferson was asked to state the rational basis for this action. Jefferson's document was the American Declaration of Independence, and it has become the crowning achievement of Enlightenment thinking and the cornerstone for modern republican democracy.

The **Declaration of Independence** is a creative masterpiece. Jefferson skillfully explained the concepts of both Locke and Rousseau as they apply to the American situation. He stated the American intent to form a nation independent of Great Britain because of Britain's violation of the social contract—the unwillingness of the British crown and government to protect American life, liberty, and property. Jefferson then detailed specific actions by King George III that were obviously violations of basic human rights. By framing these violations as the personal acts of King George III, Jefferson could win support among the members of the British Parliament who disagreed with King George III on this and on other policies. (Remember that George III was quite unpopular because of his desires to return to an absolutist monarchy.) Jefferson concluded by appealing to the Supreme Judge of the World and by pledging the lives, fortunes, and sacred honor of all those who signed.

Benjamin Franklin then edited the document and gave it even greater legitimacy by changing a few terms to more strongly reflect Enlightenment principles. Figure 38.2 shows the collaboration of Franklin and Adams with Jefferson in writing the Declaration of Independence. With the Declaration of Independence completed, the Second Continental Congress declared independence from Great Britain on July 4, 1776.

In historical retrospect, the importance of the Declaration of Independence has increased. It not only gave America a philosophical basis for the revolution that was founded on Enlightenment principles, it became a statement of freedom for peoples in many countries thereafter. Winston

Figure 38.2 ■ The writing of the Declaration of Independence. © *2010 by Victorian Traditions. Used under license of Shutterstock, Inc.*

Churchill, the great British Prime Minister during World War II, stated the following:

We must never cease to proclaim in fearless tones the great principles of freedom and the rights of man, which are the joint inheritance of the English-speaking world and which, through Magna Carta, the Bill of Rights, the habeas corpus, trial by jury, and the English common law find their expression in the Declaration of Independence.

With the formal adoption of the Declaration of Independence, any hope for a peaceful reconciliation with Great Britain passed and the American Revolutionary War began in earnest. The populace had been convinced of the rightness of the cause and the philosophical underpinnings had been put in place. Now came the difficult task of defeating the world's most skilled fighting machine.

■ Excellence: Leadership and Government

The task of defeating the British was a daunting one. The British generals successfully drove the Americans off Long Island and out of New York altogether, forcing Washington and his troops across the Delaware River and into Pennsylvania. By the winter of 1776, things looked bleak for the Continental Army, as the British had not lost a major battle and controlled all of the major cities, including New York and Philadelphia. However, the British Generals were very conservative, and were reluctant to continue the initiative against the poorly manned and poorly supplied Continental Army. This was a major mistake. Had the British pursued the Americans that first winter, they likely could have crushed the rebellion quickly. Instead, the British army settled into a winter of comfort in the cities and left the American army freezing in the countryside at Valley Forge, but alive to fight another day.

The defeats and poor living conditions had caused extremely low morale among the American troops. General Washington realized that he had to do something to improve that morale, or the war could be lost before it really began. So, learning of a garrison of British and Hessian (German Mercenary) solders positioned in Trenton, New Jersey, Washington planned a cunning sneak attack on Christmas Day 1776. General Washington led 2,500 men across the Delaware River in a snowstorm. The river was strewn with ice floats and treacherous, but Washington's goal was achieved. The Americans crossed the river without alerting the British and Hessians and attacked the enemy camp while they slept. More than 100 enemy soldiers were killed and another 1,000 were captured without the loss of a single American soldier (although several were wounded). In keeping with the guerilla style of fighting, the Americans did not continue in New Jersey but retired across the river to Pennsylvania. The operation was a resounding success and the morale of the American troops was vastly improved. Ten days later, Washington followed up the success of the **Battle of Trenton** with another offensive victory over the British at Princeton, New Jersey.

By having control of New York City and Philadelphia, the British had effectively cut off the northern colonies from the southern ones. The British plan for the spring and summer of 1777 was to gain control of the Hudson River Valley in upstate New York so that they could cut off New England, the center of American discontent, from the remainder of the colonies. This plan got off to a good start when the British sent General Burgoyne down from Canada with 7,700 men and they promptly captured Fort Ticonderoga. The British plan was for General Burgoyne to keep pushing south and meet up with General Howe's army from New York and Lieutenant Colonel St. Leger's force from Canada and then, as a united force, wipe out the Continental Army.

The British plan was frustrated when various groups of American forces were able to keep the British from uniting as planned. Benedict Arnold's American militia was able to push St. Leger's forces back into Canada, and General Washington was able to keep General Howe's forces entangled at the Battles of Brandywine and Germantown. Unable to unite with the other forces as planned, General Burgoyne pressed on without them, but was repeatedly pushed back by the American forces until Burgoyne's army was finally forced to surrender to the Americans at Fort Saratoga. This was a serious blow to the British army, and a turning point in the war.

After the defeat of the British at Fort Saratoga, the Continental Congress sent Benjamin Franklin to France to enlist the help of the French. The French were eager to humiliate the British for their loss in the French and Indian War and could see economic and political advantages for themselves if America were to become an independent nation. Thus, with the signing of the assistance treaty between France and America in 1778, France became the first nation to recognize an independent American nation.

With France (and a year later, Spain) joining the war on the American side, it made the American Revolution much more complicated for the British than it previously had been. Not only did the French bring experienced troops and a powerful navy to aid the Americans, but also when

France and Spain entered the war, it broadened the scale of the war to include colonies in other parts of the world, and this served as a major distraction and concern to the British. The war dragged on into 1781, and though the British continued to have success in many of the battles, they began to tire of the war, especially back home in Great Britain where it was depleting the treasury. Many people in Great Britain began to wonder aloud if the American colonies were worth the cost and effort, especially with new difficulties arising in the more economically lucrative territories of India and the West Indies. Simply put, the British were beginning to lose their will to fight.

The British planned another big attack, however, in hopes of defeating the Americans in a swift, strong blow. The best of the British generals, Cornwallis, began a sweep from Pennsylvania southward through Delaware, Maryland, and into Virginia. Cornwallis planned a massive sea and land offensive in hopes of defeating the Americans decisively. However, a combination of poor weather and the French navy kept the British ships from arriving to aid Cornwallis, and the British found themselves trapped on the peninsula near Yorktown, Virginia, between General Washington's army and the French navy. With nowhere to go and no way for help to reach them, General Cornwallis surrendered his 8,000 men.

With the surrender at Yorktown, the British will to continue the fight was gone. Benjamin Franklin went to Great Britain to work out a treaty to end the war. It took two more years to hammer out the details, but eventually the Treaty of Paris was signed and Great Britain recognized the United States of America as an independent nation and granted the new nation all territory east of the Allegheny Mountains to the Mississippi River. It is likely that the British agreed to peace because they felt they had more pressing concerns in some of their other colonies and believed they could take back their American possessions at a later time. In fact, they tried to do that in the War of 1812.

The new United States of America had no central government to replace British control on national issues. The members of the Second Continental Congress continued to govern in place of a national government, eventually appointing a committee to draft the Articles of Confederation. These articles were intended to serve as an agreement that would loosely tie together the 13 states. Initially, each state thought of itself as a small, independent country that was bound to the others only for issues that would affect them all, such as commerce, foreign policy, and defense. However, it was clear from almost the beginning that the Articles of Confederation would not work. They did not give any real power to the federal government, and the veto of a single state killed any decision. Not only did the Articles of Confederation fail to serve the purpose of handling larger foreign policy issues, it could not even solve disputes between the states.

Within a few years, the states were constantly squabbling with each other and had no ability to remedy their problems. Furthermore, they were still flanked by European neighbors who were hungry to acquire American resources and were simply waiting for this "political experiment" in American democracy to fail so they could swoop in. The British, in particular, were looming to the north in Canada.

Seeing the problems and feeling the weakness of their newborn nation, 12 of the states sent delegates to a Constitutional Convention that had been called in Philadelphia in 1787 for the purpose of revising the Articles of Confederation. Although their mandate did not give the delegates the authority to do so, they soon scrapped the Articles of Confederation altogether and began working on a new governing document, which would become the **Constitution of the United States of America.**

The government that would be formed by the American founding fathers was to be different than anything that had previously existed. The delegates to the Constitutional Convention had to create a new system of government that solved a wide array of problems and resolved various differences between the states. Their first concern was to create a federal government that would be strong enough to overcome the weaknesses and problems of the Articles of Confederation. This federal government needed certain areas of authority such as regulation of interstate and foreign trade, the right to levy taxes, and the means to enforce its laws. However, at the same time the American founding fathers were extremely wary of giving the federal government too much authority for fear of simply creating a government with a powerful central ruler like the one from which they had recently separated.

These men were able to deal with this seeming contradiction of a federal government with enough authority to act and enforce its laws without trampling the sovereignty of the states by adapting a modification of the ancient Roman model. Like the Roman model, the founding fathers created several branches of government and included a series of checks and balances between the various branches of government. Similar to the Roman system where the patrician senate balanced the plebeian council and executive tribunes, the new American system would balance authority between the executive, legislative, and judiciary branches. The founding fathers also used several other key components of Roman government: the rule of law, an independent judiciary, the placement of the military under executive authority, and the indirect election of the president and senators to avoid the rule of the mob (although a Constitutional amendment has since changed the indirect election of senators).

Another key compromise was reached in the form that Congress would take. The delegates attending the Constitutional Convention were representing their various states and the interests of those states. Furthermore, the vast majority of them were loyal first to their state, and second to the United States. For these reasons, the make-up of Congress, where laws would be made, became a divisive issue. The representatives from the small states feared being dominated in Congress by the larger, more populous states, while the representatives of the larger states were opposed to each state having an equal vote, as it would give the smaller states more power than they proportionally should have. This issue of congressional representation nearly ended the Constitutional Convention without any agreement being reached,

but eventually a highly creative compromise was agreed upon. The American Congress would be bicameral, or have two houses. (In this it was reminiscent of the Roman senate and plebian council.) In the upper chamber, the Senate, each state would have equal representation—two senators, two votes. In the lower chamber, the House of Representatives, the number of seats allotted to each state would be based on population. From this point of agreement onward, the Constitution and American system of government were slowly and carefully put together.

By the end of summer of 1787, the new Constitution was finished and the representatives returned to their home states to begin the process of ratification. Nine of the 13 colonies had to ratify this new Constitution for it to become the law of the land. Despite the careful system of checks and balances and the great compromises involved, many citizens were unwilling to support the new Constitution. Many feared it still gave too much power to the federal government and offered no guarantees for the rights of individuals. Thus, in an effort to see that the Constitution was ratified, the founding fathers agreed to add a written **Bill of Rights** that would explicitly protect the rights of individual. It would be added once the Constitution was ratified and the new government established. This promise appeased many of the Constitution's opponents, and on December 7, 1787, Delaware became the first state to ratify the new Constitution. Six months later New Hampshire was the ninth state to ratify the Constitution and it became law. Within another year the remaining states also ratified the Constitution.

As promised, among the first acts of the new government was to include a written Bill of Rights. This Bill of Rights was based on the English Bill of Rights of 1689, which had been imposed on William and Mary as a condition of their assuming the throne of England. The Bill of Rights reflected the natural law theory that was at the heart of the American Revolution and protected such liberties as freedom of speech, freedom of religion, freedom of the press, the right to bear arms, the right to assemble, and protection from unreasonable searches and seizures, among other protections.

Figure 38.3 ▪ A statue of George Washington in London. © 2010 by c. Used under license of Shutterstock, Inc.

George Washington became the first president and governed with fairness and integrity for Americans and other countries. After two terms he resigned and returned to his farm even though he surely could have continued as president. This act of voluntary resignation set a pattern for future American presidents and for this he was honored throughout the world. For example, Figure 38.3 is a statue honoring Washington in London.

▪ What Was Creative?

The efforts to found America, from the first European immigrants to the ratification of the constitution, were creative. More clearly than most creative endeavors, all of the elements of creativity were demonstrated. First, the concepts of the Americans were *novel*. Nowhere else was a country founded on the basis of a principle. All other countries up to that time had been founded as homes for an ethnic group. (France was the land of the Franks, England of the Anglo-Saxons, Germany of the Germans, Italy of the Italians, etc.) However, those Europeans who finally came to be called Americans were not of any particular ethnic group, nor did they propose that America would be an exclusive homeland for any particular ethnic group. Instead, America was to be the homeland of those who cherished an idea—making life better. This was both unique and powerful.

Another element of creativity is *value*. We see this in two ways. As already discussed in this chapter, the principles on which America was built were valued by those of the Enlightenment. Americans knew that they were acting correctly because they followed the rational and persuasive arguments of the Enlightenment. These arguments won over a majority of the Americans and gave them the resolve to fight for independence. The most fundamental of all the values was, of course, freedom, just as the quotation from Thomas Paine at the beginning of this chapter asserts. Both theoretically and in reality, America was, by founding precept, the "land of the free."

The other sense in which value was shown was by direct praise from "experts" who observed the American situation. Foremost among the early observers of America was a young French aristocrat, Alexis de Tocqueville, who visited America between 1831 and 1832. With respect to the basic concept of freedom, Tocqueville said the following:

The Revolution of the United States was the result of a mature and reflecting preference for freedom, and not of a vague or ill-defined craving for independence. It contracted no alliance with the turbulent passions of anarchy, but its course was marked, on the contrary, by a love of order and law. It was never assumed in the United States that the citizen of a free country has a right to do whatever he pleases; on the contrary, more social obligations were there imposed upon him than anywhere else. No idea was ever entertained of attacking the principle or contesting the rights of society; but the exercise of its authority was divided, in order that the office might be powerful and the officer insignificant, and that the community should be at one regulated and free.

Tocqueville also comments on the fundamental nature of passing laws in America.

What is understood by a republican government in the United States is the slow and quiet action of society upon itself. It is a regular state of things really founded upon the enlightened will of the people. It is a conciliatory government, under which resolutions are allowed time to ripen, and in which they are deliberately discussed, and are executed only when mature. The republicans in the United States set a high value upon morality, respect religious belief, and acknowledge the existence of rights. They profess to think that a people ought to be moral, religious, and temperate in proportion as it is free. What is called the republic in the United States is the tranquil rule of the majority, which, after having had time to examine itself and to give proof of its existence, is the common source of all the powers of the state. But the power of the majority itself is not unlimited. Above it in the moral world are humanity, justice, and reason; and in the political world, vested rights.

The Bill of Rights was interesting to Tocqueville, and he commented favorably on the way Americans guaranteed the freedom of the press.

In order to enjoy the inestimable benefits that the liberty of the press ensures, it is necessary to submit to the inevitable evils that it creates. . . . It is an axiom of political science in that country [America] that the only way to neutralize the effect of the public journals is to multiply their number.

Tocqueville comments on the apparent creativity of Americans.

No natural boundary seems to be set to the efforts of man; and in his eyes what is not yet done is only what he has not yet attempted to do. This perpetual change which goes on in the United States . . . serve[s] to keep the minds of the people in a perpetual feverish agitation, which admirably invigorates their exertions and keeps them, so to speak, above the ordinary level of humanity. The whole life of an American is passed like a game of chance, a revolutionary crisis, or a battle. The American, taken as a chance specimen of his countrymen, must then be a man of singular warmth in his desires, enterprising, fond of adventure and, above all, of novelty.

Americans did not come to their situation by chance. Through their struggles with Britain, they had the *intent* of creating a world based on the principles of the Enlightenment. When King George III imposed rules that compromised those Enlightenment principles, the response of the Americans was clear (although still many needed to be reminded of the principles). This intent is clearly reflected in the words of John Adams, one of the signers of the Declaration of Independence, a major force in the creation of the American government, and the second president of the United States.

I must study politics and war that my sons may have liberty to study mathematics and philosophy. My sons ought to study mathematics and philosophy, geography, natural history, naval architecture, navigation, commerce, and agriculture in order to give their children a right to study paintings, poetry, music, architecture, statuary, tapestry, and porcelain.

The drive for American independence was firmly rooted in the Enlightenment, yet the founding fathers of the United States were also extremely gifted and creative men who were able to adapt the ideals of the Enlightenment to their own situation. In this they showed that *excellence* in implementation, is a key feature of creativity. It is not enough to have a bright idea; that idea must also be reduced to practice for it to be creative. Additionally, even if the ideas are from another source, as, in this case, from the Enlightenment writers or even from ancient Rome, implementation is a key to creative success.

Creativity played an important role in the military victory over the English in the Revolutionary War, and creativity was key to the formation of America's new and novel system of government. The American founding fathers formed a government that protected the states while empowering the union; that found balance between small and large states; that protected the rights of the individual without unduly hampering the ability of the government to do its job; and that protected liberty at all levels without promoting chaos.

The government of the United States of America may be the greatest political creative work in the history of the world. Yet, just a few years later, when France was attempting its own revolution based on the ideals of the Enlightenment, it would ignore many of the lessons learned in America and try to forge its own path—a path that would lead to years of bloodshed and chaos, and ultimately fail. We shall discuss the French Revolution in the next chapter.

■ Timeline—Important Dates

Date	Event
1664	*England gains control over the American colonies*
1763	*England wins the French and Indian War*
1766	*Stamp Act repealed*
1767	*Townsend Acts (imposed taxes on tea, paper, paint, etc.)*
1770	*Boston Massacre*
1773	*Boston Tea Party*
1774	*Passage of the Intolerable Acts*
1774	*First Continental Congress meets*
1775	*Skirmishes at Lexington Green and Concord Bridge*
1775	*Second Continental Congress meets*
1776	*Declaration of Independence signed*
1777	*Articles of Confederation approved by Second Continental Congress*
1778	*American and French assistance treaty*
1781	*Surrender of British Army at Yorktown*
1781	*Articles of Confederation ratified*
1783	*Treaty of Paris (formally ending the Revolutionary War)*
1787	*Convening of Constitutional Congress*
1788	*Ratification of the Constitution*
1812	*War of 1812*
1831–1832	*Visit of Alexis de Tocqueville*

■ Suggested Readings

McCullough, David, *John Adams,* Simon & Schuster, 2001.

Miller, Arthur, *The Crucible,* Penguin, 1981.

Tocqueville, Alexis de, *Democracy in America,* Alfred A. Knopf, 1945.

Weaver, Henry Grady, *The Mainspring of Human Progress,* The Foundation for Economic Education, 1997.

Tocqueville: Democracy in America

Alexis de Tocqueville (1805–1859) was a Frenchman of the post-revolutionary period who was able to travel to America and, upon his return to France, write a book describing his observations and comparisons with his native country. Tocqueville studied law and philosophy, thus providing him with the background for keen observation and comment on what he observed in both America and France. Tocqueville believed that the decline of aristocracy was inevitable as he saw the French government moving increasingly toward democracy. He obtained permission to travel to America to learn about American political development and, upon his return, he worked for the French Academy and the Academy of Moral and Political Science. He was later elected to the Legislative Assembly and became vice president to the Assembly and Minister of Foreign Affairs. This position lasted less than a year. He was dismissed for refusing to support Louis-Napoleon's coup and was imprisoned for not supporting the new regime.

During the early years of the United States, many Europeans were intrigued by the young democracy across the Atlantic and curious about the conditions in society there. In 1835, Tocqueville published part one of *Democracy in America,* presenting an optimistic perspective of the American political system based on his travels there. This work was representative of the respect and admiration the French had for the Enlightenment principles upon which the American government was founded, especially the equality amongst its citizens. The second part of *Democracy in America* was published in 1840 and was notably more pessimistic of central government and the dangers of despotism, criticizing both the American and French governments.

A number of passages from *Democracy in America* are included here. They cover many of the democratic principles Tocqueville admired, including the development of self-interest and education, freedom of religion and its aid in justice, confidence in constitution-based courtrooms, freedom of the press, encouragement in the sciences, and respect for women.

Alexis de Tocqueville: Democracy in America

■ Chapter II

Origin of the Anglo-Americans

America is the only country in which it has been possible to witness the natural and tranquil growth of society, and where the influence exercised on the future condition of state by their origin is clearly distinguishable. . . .

These men had, however, certain features in common and they were all placed in an analogous situation. The tie of language is, perhaps, the strongest and the most durable that can unite mankind. . . .

It was realized that in order to clear this land, nothing less than the constant and self-interested efforts of the owner himself was essential; the ground prepared, it became evident that its produce was not sufficient to enrich at the same time both an owner and a farmer. The land was then naturally broken up into small portions, which the proprietor cultivated for himself. Land is the basis of an aristocracy, which clings to the soil that supports it; for it is not by privileges alone, nor by birth, but by landed property handed down from generation to generation that an aristocracy is constituted. A nation may present immense fortunes and extreme wretchedness; but unless those fortunes are territorial, there is no true aristocracy, but simply the class of the rich and that of the poor. . . .

The settlers who established themselves on the shores of New England all belonged to the more independent classes of their native country. Their union on the soil of America at once presented the singular phenomenon of a society containing neither lords nor common people, and we may almost say neither rich nor poor. These men possessed, in proportion to their number, a greater mass of intelligence than is to be found in any European nation of our own time. All, perhaps without a single exception, had received a good education, and many of them were known in Europe for their talents and their acquirements. The other colonies had been founded by adventurers without families; the immigrants of New England brought with them the best elements of order and mortality; they landed on the desert coast accompanied by their wives and children. But what especially distinguished them from all others was the aim of their undertaking. They had not been obliged by necessity to leave their country; the social position they abandoned was one to be regretted, and their means of subsistence were certain. Nor did they cross the Atlantic to improve their situation or to increase their wealth; it was a purely intellectual craving that called them from the comforts of their former homes; and in facing the inevitable sufferings of exile their object was the triumph of an idea.

The immigrants, or, as they deservedly styled themselves, the Pilgrims, belonged to that English

Source: From *Democracy in America* by Alexis DeToqueville, translated by Henry Reeve, copyright 1945 and renewed 1973 by Alfred A. Knopf, a division of Random House, Inc. Used by permission of Alfred A. Knopf, a division of Random House, Inc.

sect the austerity of whose principles had acquired for them the name of Puritans. Puritanism was not merely a religious doctrine, but corresponded in many points with the most absolute democratic and republican theories. It was this tendency that had aroused its most dangerous adversaries. Persecuted by the government of the mother country, and disgusted by the habits of a society which the rigor of their own principles condemned, the Puritans went forth to seek some rude and unfrequented part of the world where they could live according to their own opinions and worship God in freedom. . . .

Men sacrifice for a religious opinion their friends, their family, and their country; one can consider them devoted to the pursuit of intellectual goals which they came to purchase at so high a price. One sees them, however, seeking with almost equal eagerness material wealth and moral satisfaction; heaven in the world beyond, and well-being and liberty in this one. . . .

Thus in the moral world everything is classified, systematized, foreseen, and decided beforehand; in the political world everything is agitated, disputed, and uncertain. In that one is a passive though a voluntary obedience; in the other, an independence scornful of experience, and jealous of all authority. These two tendencies, apparently so discrepant, are far from conflicting; they advance together and support each other.

Religion perceives that civil liberty affords a noble exercise to the faculties of man and that the political world is a field prepared by the Creator for the efforts of mind. Free and powerful in its own sphere, satisfied with the place reserved for it, religion never more surely establishes its empire than when it reigns in the hearts of men unsupported by aught beside its native strength.

Liberty regards religion as its companion in all its battle and its triumphs, as the cradle of its infancy and the divine source of its claims. It considers religion as the safeguard of morality, and morality as the best security of law and the surest pledge of the duration of freedom.

■ Chapter V

Examining the Condition of the States

The Revolution of the United States was the result of mature and reflecting preference for freedom, and not of vague or ill-defined craving for independence. It contracted no alliance with the turbulent passions of anarchy, but its course was marked, on the contrary, by a love of order and law.

It was never assumed in the United States that the citizen of a free country has a right to do whatever he pleases; on the contrary, more social obligations were there imposed upon him than anywhere else. No idea was ever entertained attacking the principle or contesting the rights of society but the exercise of its authority was divided, in order that the office might be powerful and the officer insignificant, and that the community should be at once regulated and free.

■ Chapter VI

Judicial Power in the United States

The Americans have retained these three distinguishing characteristics of the judicial power: an American judge can pronounce a decision only when litigation has arisen, he is conversant only with special cases, and he cannot act until the cause has been duly brought before the court. His position is therefore exactly the same as that of the magistrates of other nations; and yet he is invested with immense political power. How does this come about? If the sphere of his authority and his means of action are the same as those of other judges, whence does he derive a power which they do not possess? The cause of this difference lies in the simple fact that the Americans have acknowledged the right of judges to found their decisions on the Constitution rather than on the laws. In other words, they have permitted them not to apply such laws as may appear to them to be unconstitutional.

■ Chapter X

Liberty of Press in the United States

In countries where the doctrine of the sovereignty of the people ostensibly prevails, the censorship of the press is not only dangerous, but absurd. When the right of every citizen to a share in the government of society is acknowledged everyone must be presumed to be able to choose between the various opinions of his contemporaries and to appreciate the different facts from which inferences may be drawn. The sovereignty of the people and the liberty of the press may therefore be regarded as correlative . . .

[I]n order to enjoy the inestimable benefits that the liberty of the press ensures, it is necessary to submit to the inevitable evils that it creates. To expect to acquire the former and to escape the latter is to cherish one of those illusions which commonly mislead nations in their times of sickness when, tired with faction and exhausted by effort they attempt to make hostile opinions and contrary principles coexist upon the same soil. . . .

Hence the number of periodical and semi-periodical publications in the United States is almost incredibly large. The most enlightened Americans attribute the little influence of the press to this excessive dissemination of its power; and it is an axiom of political science in that country that the only way to neutralize the effect of the public journals is to multiply their number. I cannot see how a truth which is so self-evident should not already have been more generally admitted in Europe.

■ Chapter XIII

Advantages of Democracy

[T]he people in America obey the law, not only because it is their own work, but because it may be changed if it is harmful; a law is observed because, first, it is a self-imposed evil, and, secondly, it is an evil of transient duration.

■ Chapter XIX

Duration of Republican Institutions

What is understood by a republican government in the United States is the slow and quiet action of society upon itself. It is a regular state of things really founded upon the enlightened will of the people. It is a conciliatory government, under which resolutions are allowed time to ripen and in which they are deliberately discussed, and are executed only when mature. The republicans in the United States set a high value upon morality, respect religious belief, and acknowledge the existence of rights. They profess to think that a people ought to be moral, religious, and temperate in proportion as it is free. What is called the republic in the United States is the tranquil rule of the majority, which, after having had time to examine itself and to give proof of its existence, is the common source of all the powers of the state. But the power of the majority itself is not unlimited. Above it in the moral world are humanity, justice, and reason; and in the political world, vested rights. . . .

America is a land of wonders, in which everything is in constant motion and every change seems an improvement. The idea of novelty is there indissolubly connected with the idea of amelioration. No natural boundary seems to be set to the efforts of man; and in his eyes what is not yet done is only what he has not yet attempted to do.

This perpetual change which goes on in the United States, these frequent vicissitudes of fortune, these unforeseen fluctuations in private and public wealth, serve to keep the minds of the people in a perpetual feverish agitation, which admirably invigorates their exertions and keeps them, so to speak, above the ordinary level of humanity. The whole life of an American is passed like a game of chance, a revolutionary crisis, or a battle. As the same causes are continually in operation throughout the country, they ultimately impart an irresistible impulse to the national character. The American, taken as a chance specimen of his countrymen, must then be a man of singular warmth in his desires, enterprising, fond of adventure and, above all, of novelty.

▪ Second Part—Chapter I

Philosophical Method of the Americans

To evade the bondage of system and habit, of family maxims, class opinions, and, in some degree, of national prejudices; to accept tradition only as a means of information, and existing facts only as a lesson to be used in doing otherwise and doing better; to seek the reason of things for oneself, and in oneself alone; to tend to results without being bound to means, and to strike through the form to the substance—such are the principal characteristics of what I shall call the philosophical method of the Americans.

But if I go further and seek among these characteristics the principal one, which includes almost all the rest, I discover that in most of the operations of the mind each American appeals only to the individual effort of his own understanding.

▪ Second Part—Chapter II

Source of Belief in Democracies

There is no philosopher in the world so great but that he believes a million things on the faith of other people and accepts a great many more truths than he demonstrates.

This is not only necessary but desirable. A man who should undertake to inquire into everything for himself could devote to each thing but little time and attention. His task would keep his mind in perpetual unrest, which would prevent him from penetrating to the depth of any truth or of making his mind adhere firmly to any conviction. His intellect would be at once independent and powerless. He must therefore make his choice from among the various objects of human belief and adopt many opinions without discussion in order to search the better into that smaller number which he sets apart for investigation. It is true that whoever receives an opinion on the word of another does so far enslave his mind, but it is a salutary servitude, which allows him to make a good use of freedom.

A principle of authority must then always occur, under all circumstances, in some part or other of the moral and intellectual world. Its place is variable, but a place it necessarily has. The independence of individual minds may be greater or it may be less; it cannot be unbounded. Thus the question is, not to know whether any intellectual authority exists in an age of democracy, but simply where it resides and by what standard it is to be measured.

▪ Second Part—Chapter V

Religion and Democratic Tendencies

The preceding observation, that equality leads men to very general and very vast ideas, is principally to be understood in respect to religion. Men who are similar and equal in the world readily conceive the idea of the one God, governing every man by the same laws and granting to every man future happiness on the same conditions. The idea of the unity of mankind constantly leads them back to the idea of the unity of the Creator; while on the contrary in a state of society where men are broken up into very unequal ranks, they are apt to devise as many deities as there are nations, castes, classes, or families, and to trace a thousand private roads to heaven.

▪ Second Part—Chapter X

Addiction to Practical Science

In aristocratic societies the class that gives the tone to opinion and has the guidance of affairs, being permanently and hereditarily placed above the multitude, naturally conceives a lofty idea of itself and of man. It loves to invent for him noble pleasures, to carve out splendid objects for his ambition. Aristocracies often commit very tyrannical and inhuman actions, but they rarely entertain groveling thoughts; and they show a kind of haughty contempt of little pleasures, even while they indulge in them. The effect is to raise greatly the general pitch of society. In aristocratic ages most ideas are commonly entertained of the dignity, the power, and the greatness of man. These opinions exert their influence on those who cultivate the sciences as well as on the rest of the community. They facilitate the natural impulse of the mind to the highest regions of thought, and they naturally prepare it to conceive a sublime, almost a divine love of truth. . . .

You may be sure that the more democratic, enlightened, and free a nation is, the greater will be the number of these interested promoters of scientific genius and the more will discoveries immediately applicable to productive industry confer on their authors gain, fame, and even power. For in democracies the working class take a part in public affairs and public honors as well as pecuniary remuneration may be awarded to those who deserve them.

■ Second Part—Chapter XI

Cultivation of the Arts

It would be to waste the time of my readers and my own if I strove to demonstrate how the general mediocrity of fortunes, the absence of superfluous wealth, the universal desire for comfort, and the constant efforts by which everyone attempts to procure it make the taste for the useful predominate over the love of the beautiful in the heart of man. Democratic nations, among whom all these things exist, will therefore cultivate the arts that serve to render life easy in preference to those whose object is to adorn it. They will habitually prefer the useful to the beautiful, and they will require that the beautiful should be useful.

■ Second Part—Chapter XIV

Americans Follow Industrial Callings

The United States of America has only been emancipated for half a century from the state of colonial dependence in which it stood to Great Britain; the number of large fortunes there is small and capital is still scarce. Yet no people in the world have made such rapid progress in trade and manufactures as the Americans; they constitute at the present day the second maritime nation in the world, and although their manufactures have to struggle with almost insurmountable natural impediments, they are not prevented from making great and daily advances.

In the United States the greatest undertakings and speculations are executed without difficulty, because the whole population are engaged in productive industry, and because the poorest as well as the most opulent members of the commonwealth are ready to combine their efforts for these purposes. The consequence is that a stranger is constantly amazed by the immense public works executed by a nation which contains, so to speak, no rich men. The Americans arrived but as yesterday on the territory which they inhabit, and they have already changed the whole order of nature for their own advantage. They have joined the Hudson to the Mississippi and made the Atlantic Ocean communicate with the Gulf of Mexico, across a continent of more than five hundred leagues in extent which separates the two seas. The longest railroads that have been constructed up to the present time are in America.

But what most astonishes me of the United States is not so much the marvelous grandeur of some undertakings as the innumerable multitude of small ones. Almost all the farmers of the Untied States combine some trade with agriculture; most of them make agriculture itself a trade. It seldom happens that an American farmer settles for good upon the land which he occupies; especially in the districts of the Far West, he brings land into tillage in order to sell it again, and not to farm it; he builds a farmhouse on the speculation that, as the state of the country will soon be changed by the increase of population, a good price may be obtained for it.

Every year a swarm of people from the North arrive in the Southern states and settle in the parts where the cotton plant and the sugar-cane grow. These men cultivate the soil in order to make it produce in a few years enough to enrich them; and they already look forward to the time when they may return home to enjoy the competency thus acquired. Thus the Americans carry their businesslike qualities into agriculture, and their trading passions are displayed in that as in their other pursuits.

■ Second Part—Chapter XII (Vol II)

The Equality of the Sexes

Thus the Americans do not think that man and woman have either the duty or the right to perform the same offices, but they show an equal regard for both their respective parts; and though their lot is different, they consider both of them as beings of equal value. They do not give to the courage of woman the same form or the same direction as to that of man, but they never doubt her courage, and if they hold that man and his partner ought not always to exercise their intellect and understanding in the same manner, they at least believe the understanding of the one to be as sound as that of the other, and her intellect to be as clear. Thus, then, while they have allowed the social inferiority of woman to continue, they have done all they could to raise her morally and intellectually to the level of man; and in this respect they appear to me to have excellently understood the true principle of democratic improvement.

As for myself, I do not hesitate to avow that although the women of the United States are confined within the narrow circle of domestic life, and their situation is in some respects one of extreme dependence, I have nowhere seen women occupying a loftier position; and if I were asked, now that I am drawing to the close of this work, in which I have spoken of so many important things done by the Americans, to what the singular prosperity and growing strength of that people ought mainly to be attributed, I should reply: To the superiority of their women.

French Revolution and Napoleon
Extremely Creative

> The truest conquests, the only ones that give rise to no regrets, are those gained over ignorance. The most honorable as well as the most useful activity of nations is to contribute to the advancement of human knowledge. The real strength of the French Republic should henceforth lie in its determination to possess every new idea, without a single exception.
>
> —*Napoleon*

■ The Enlightenment and Revolutions

The late eighteenth century saw the ideals and philosophies of the Enlightenment and the Classical period made real. Political tension and social unrest came to a head, both in Great Britain's American colonies and within France. Both the American and French revolutions were based upon and justified by the principles of the Enlightenment—particularly the concept declaring that sovereignty was based in the people, not the monarch and, thus, the people had a right and responsibility to overthrow any government that did not protect the life, liberty, and property of its citizens. However, despite being rooted in the same ideals, the American and French revolutions were vastly different in nature and result.

The American Revolution, ironically, was fought against what was already a liberal and inclusive political system in Great Britain. The Americans, in general, did not question the basis of the British system, only its workings and their role in it. The American Revolution was, at its core, primarily driven by these political issues and related economic concerns. Furthermore, the immediate disputes of the American Revolution were very small—minute taxes and other restrictive business practices. The philosophical basis of the American Revolution, the concept that motivated the patriots, was whether the British government had the *right* to do these things without input from the people. Finally, the American Revolution, while ultimately successful, had very little immediate effect on Europe and the rest of the world.

The French Revolution overthrew what was arguably Europe's most traditional and restrictive system of government. The French revolutionists were challenging the entire political system and social hierarchy, including the role of the Roman Catholic Church in France. The French revolutionists were not looking to change a small part of a greater whole, but to scrap political tradition and history and start over with a whole new political and social framework. The French Revolution, which eventually failed, had an immediate impact on Europe and the world.

Both revolutions were highly creative. In the American experiment, creativity was applied calmly and rationally, seeking compromises and consensus in the implementation. It seemed to reflect the nature of John Locke, who said that experience should be a guide to knowledge. In the French experience, the problems of the society were so massive that solutions always seemed just out of reach. Therefore, attempts to finally bring the situation under control continued to lead to ever more radical thinking, which then caused the implementation to be extreme. The French finally saw the only solution as complete abandonment of tradition. This reflects the thinking of René Descartes, who willingly rejected all knowledge to come to a place of ultimate truth. The French revolutionists may have accepted this ultimate solution because of the powerful influence of Descartes within the French intellectual community.

Leadership in the two revolutions was quite different. In America, success in the war led immediately to the nomination of the winning general as the new leader of the nation. Because the changes required were minimal, Washington's task was to achieve compromise and consensus within a framework of existing social structures. In France, no strong leader immediately emerged, and the social problems continued to frustrate the executive committees that attempted to rule. When a leader finally emerged (again, the military winner of the war), Napoleon had to rebuild a nation. He did not seek compromise but, rather, ruled in the absolute tradition.

Another major difference was the isolation of America versus the interference of neighbors in France. That interference continued to force radical changes on the French government and, as a result, made the neighboring countries ever more anxious and ready to interfere further. When stability was finally achieved in France, the desires of Napoleon were to expand, whereas those of Washington were to consolidate. These differences gave completely different endings to the revolutions.

■ Causes of the French Revolution

The French Revolution seemed to be driven by three quite different but strongly interacting groups. The first were the moderates, who believed in the rational implementation of Enlightenment principles. These might be compared to the founding fathers of the American Revolution. Their initial instinct was for peaceful resolution of problems but, when forced into stronger action, they agreed with the need for war.

The second of the groups in France were the radicals. They also believed in Enlightenment principles but believed that the existing French government and other oppressive French institutions, what they called the *Ancien Régime* (old regime), were unable to be modified and, therefore, must be overthrown through war. Few people in America were as radical as this French group, probably because the social conditions in America were never as bad as those found among the poor in France.

The third group was the peasant class, a group present in France but not in America. They, generally, did not understand the concepts of the Enlightenment but were highly influenced by basic societal problems such as hunger and other objectionable living conditions. These "unwashed masses" were initially willing to follow the moderates but, when their living conditions did not substantially improve under moderate control, the masses were easily convinced to give their allegiance to the radicals. The radicals used concepts of the Enlightenment that had strong emotional appeal, such as *liberté, égalité, fraternité* (liberty, equality, fraternity), to motivate the masses and win their support. The radicals also caused dramatic things to happen, like the killing of thousands of aristocrats, which initially pleased the peasants, but quickly became so extreme that the radicals lost the support of the masses. Eventually, the masses gave their support to a new leader, Napoleon.

In spite of these varying views, without the ideas and intellectual climate created by the Enlightenment, there would likely have been no revolution in France. Given sufficient time, somehow the royal government would have alleviated the food crisis and improved living conditions (as had happened throughout the Middle Ages). However, as the people became educated about Enlightenment principles like personal dignity and equality of every human, these ideas revealed the firmly entrenched rigid class system that existed still in France, and the masses demanded reform. Furthermore, the Enlightenment said that government was a creation of the people to protect their rights and was therefore limited in its scope and was accountable to the people. This undercut the idea of absolute monarchy and the divine right of kings. These ideals were especially inviting to the French people, because French intellectuals such as Voltaire and Rousseau were at the forefront of Enlightenment thinking.

Another factor that led to a desire for significant change in France in the eighteenth century was a strong Anglophile feeling within the French intellectual community. The English system of government seemed to be a good balance between strength and freedom. Many French intellectuals looked across the English Channel and saw a model of government that they felt made sense and provided the common man access to government and protected his rights without discarding the rights and privileges of the monarchy and aristocracy. Voltaire, while living in England, became particularly enamored with the English system of government and wrote and spoke about it in a positive way that influenced many Frenchmen. The English gentry were also strongly supportive of liberty in France (on the English model), and many of them made it a pet project to encourage a change of government in France.

The American Revolution also had an influence on French intellectuals in favor of a more open government and society based on the Enlightenment. The tie was strong because the French had played such a prominent role in the American Revolution, and many French soldiers and aristocrats came back to France converted to the American style of government and the rights and freedoms it embodied. Furthermore, the French government's support of the American Revolution caused an acceptance of the American ideals. After all, how could the French monarchy believe these principles were true for the Americans and not for the French as well?

Another important factor that led to revolution in France was the unwillingness to change within the French old regime. The French monarchy, long the center and stronghold for absolutism, simply refused to make even minor concessions as had other European governments under the enlightened despots. This was an especially poor decision by the French monarchy, as absolutism was universally despised at all levels of French society. The poor hated absolutism because they felt they had no say in the government. The middle class resented France's absolutism because they wanted greater freedom to pursue new ideas in business. The rich disliked absolutism because they wanted more power for themselves.

Ever since the death of France's great absolute monarch, Louis XIV, the people had become increasingly bold in their willingness to criticize the kings as poor leaders. Adding to the frustration of the people was that **King Louis XVI** seemed completely unaware of the growing discontent that existed at all levels of society. For example, on the day of the storming of the Bastille, generally considered the start of the French Revolution, Louis XVI's personal diary records that nothing important happened that day. Furthermore, the actions of Louis XVI's wife, **Marie Antoinette,** only added to the resentment and hatred of the people. For example, there was a food shortage in Paris, and many of the poor were unable to buy even bread. When Queen Marie Antoinette was told of the plight of the starving poor she was said to have remarked, "Then let them eat cake." When this comment was publically reported, (whether true or not) it upon added to the anger and perception of aloofness that the people perceived in the monarchy. The queen was further vilified when it became known that she had scandalously traded sexual favors to a Catholic cardinal in return for the gift of a diamond necklace.

Discontent in France was further heightened by strong class resentment. While class barriers were becoming weaker in many other nations, and in places like America seemed largely nonexistent, within France the traditional three estates (classes) seemed nearly as rigid and inflexible as ever. The First Estate (the Roman Catholic Church), the Second Estate (the nobility), and the Third Estate (which consisted of the middle class and the rural and urban poor) were all discontent with their roles within French society. The First and Second estates were able to have some participation in government, especially at the local level, but both estates wanted a greater share of the power. The Third Estate was largely shut out of participation in the government and was further divided within itself between the middle class and the working poor.

While all three groups wanted more power and say in the government, the tension was particularly strong between the first two estates and the third. The Roman Catholic Church had fostered much resentment with the common people over the years. The Third Estate viewed the proper role of the church as being the protector and comforter of the masses. However, the rulers of the church— the bishops, archbishops, and cardinals—were generally from the upper class and therefore felt very little sympathy for the plight of the poor. Furthermore, many of the leaders of the church grew rich and lived a life of ease and privilege off of the income from church lands (which were tax exempt) and the collection of tithes. The poor and the lower clergy resented the misuse of these sacred monies, especially with so many in such obvious need.

The aristocracy of France was even more hated by the Third Estate than was the church because of the nobility's especially arrogant treatment of the lower classes over the years. Infight-ing within the Second Estate only reinforced the elitist perception that the poor attached to the nobility. The nobility who had been nobles since the Middle Ages (known as the **nobles of the sword**) felt that they were better than recently made nobles. The newer nobility (known as **nobles of the robe**) were generally political appointees to a government position, such as judge. The older nobility disliked the newer nobility because the new nobles diluted the power and wealth of the aristocracy. Furthermore, the newer nobility were given their positions and titles by the government, and thus were more closely allied with, and loyal to, the crown than were the older nobility. This close association between the nobility of the robe and the monarchy was a cause of mistrust and dislike for the nobility of the sword. For these reasons the nobility of the sword took steps to close off the granting of noble status to more people. This made the nobility even more unpopular with the lowest estate, because this limitation in conferring nobility was seen as a scheme to cut off the one and only small chance for upward mobility for many members of the Third Estate.

Finally, the severe problems of the French economy in 1787 and 1788 were a serious problem that was the immediate spark that set off the Revolution. Ever since the death of Louis XIV in 1715, the French economy had been slowly worsening. Louis XIV had incurred a large debt with his many wars, and his successors had been forced to raise government fees and other levies to help pay off these debts. In the highly inequitable economic system of France, these new fees caused great hardship for the lowest classes. The economic burden on the Third Estate was especially large in France, because the first two estates could largely avoid paying any taxes. One of the remnants of medieval times was the church's exemption from taxes on both church land and estates held by church officials. The nobility could largely avoid paying taxes simply because they were the government's creditors and they insisted on this prerogative.

The severe economic crisis was worsened by a series of poor harvests resulting in higher food prices. The burden of just living was so high that many of the peasants were starving.

■ The First Stage of the Revolution: Control by the Moderates

The economic crash of 1787 to 1788 became so bad that King Louis XVI eventually had to try and take some action to remedy the situation. His plan was to impose a new general tax (such as a stamp tax or a tax on all landed property) in an effort to pull France's economy out of the depression. The king's ministers convinced Louis XVI that he would not be able to impose such a tax without at least the consent of the most powerful and influential nobility. Convinced that his ministers were correct, Louis reluctantly convened a meeting of these nobles. Doing so started a chain reaction of events that eventually ended with the demise of absolute monarchy within France.

Once the meeting was convened, the nobility, at the urging of the middle class (who actually controlled the money that would be used to pay the tax), refused to submit to such a tax without convening the **Estates General,** a political body in which all three of the estates met together to propose laws. King Louis was infuriated by such a demand. The *Estates General* had not been called into session for over 150 years, and Louis XVI refused to show weakness or allow any questioning of his absolute control by calling it into session now. Instead, Louis dismissed the nobility and attempted to raise taxes simply by decree.

However, the high court of Paris, a group of nobles known as the *Parlement,* declared the king's tax increase to be null and void. (This action would be the rough equivalent of the United States Supreme Court declaring some action by the President to be unconstitutional.) King Louis tried to exile the members of the *Parlement* so that his tax increase could pass, but there was a tremendous public outcry when the general populace was made aware because they felt that the *Parlement* was defending the will of the people. Furthermore, the middle class merchants that would be hit hardest by any tax hike refused to loan any more money to the state if the king raised taxes without convening the *Estates General.*

Finally, in June of 1788, a beaten Louis XVI, in desperate need of raising revenue, bowed to public opinion and called for a spring 1789 session of the *Estates General.* This was the last act of any king as an absolute monarch in France. Once the revived and invigorated *Estates General* met, the king became limited by their actions, and the government of France became a limited monarchy similar to that of Great Britain. Although nobody knew it at the time, the convening of the *Estates General* would open the gates to revolution. People now felt that change was possible and would settle for nothing less.

In the *Estates General* all three estates (clergy, nobility, peasants/merchants) had an equal number of delegates (votes). While this seemed fair at first, in reality the clergy and nobility usually voted as a block and were, therefore, able to block any proposals made by the peasants/merchants.

Any hope the peasants and merchants had of real change that existed before the meeting of the *Estates General* was quickly crushed. All votes favored the First and Second Estates at the expense of the Third Estate, and even those few laws that were passed were blocked by King Louis XVI, who did everything in his power to hinder the *Estates General.*

Eventually, the leaders of the Third Estate became so angry at the situation that they walked out of the *Estates General* and formed their own body, which they called the **National Assembly.** The king harassed the meetings of the new National Assembly and denied them access to a meeting hall. In defiance, the National Assembly decided to meet in a nearby indoor tennis court. The National Assembly then pledged to stay in session until they could write a new constitution. This became known as the **Tennis Court Oath.** However, the National Assembly was mostly composed of moderates, not radicals. They were not attacking King Louis XVI, and the new government they called for was a constitutional monarchy, similar to that of Great Britain's, not a radical break from the monarchy as the Americans had done.

Unable to accomplish anything in solving the continuing financial crisis without the full body of the *Estates General,* the king eventually ordered the first two estates to meet with the National Assembly in joint session. When these upper estates joined the National Assembly, the merchants and peasants increased the number of their representatives so that the total of the Third Estate was equal to the total of the First and Second estates together. The meeting room was divided into two parts, with the Third Estate representatives sitting on the left and the First and Second estate representatives on the right side of the hall. This seating arrangement gave rise to the term *right wing* for conservatives and *left wing* for liberals. The reconstituted National Assembly then set to the tasks of finding a solution to the economic crisis and debating other possible changes.

Even though the National Assembly now had reluctant approval from the king, the assembly lacked strong leadership, and no decisions could be reached on solving France's economic problems. So while the National Assembly endlessly debated, France's financial crisis grew worse. Roughly a third of the population was unemployed and the price of bread had skyrocketed. In protest, the poor began a series of parades through the streets of Paris. A rumor quickly spread that the king intended to use the parades (which were little more than barely contained riots) as an excuse to dismiss the National Assembly and send his troops into the streets to quell dissent. In an attempt to keep that from happening, the Parisian delegates from the Third Estate set up a new municipal government within Paris to control the peasants and keep the peace, which would then remove any excuse King Louis might have for taking drastic action.

Among the first acts of this new municipal government was to organize a militia to help maintain order. In need of weapons, the militiamen went to the **Bastille,** an old prison fortress in Paris that contained an armory. The militia demanded arms from the governor of the Bastille. The governor refused their request. A battle ensued, which resulted in the capture of the Bastille by the militia, the deaths of the governor and his troops, and releasing of all the prisoners. Although this was a small skirmish, the event had tremendous symbolic power to the starving poor because the old fortress represented the power and abuse of the old regime. Thus, with the storming of the Bastille on July 14, 1789, the French Revolution had officially begun.

The masses of Paris began looting and venting their anger on symbols of oppression. Many of the statues in churches were attacked by the mobs and the noses knocked off. (This was called *defacing.*) The discontent soon spread to the countryside outside Paris. There were widespread protests and rebellions throughout July and August of 1789 as the rural poor burned manors, destroyed monasteries, and murdered some bishops and nobles. In October the peasant women organized a march to Versailles, where they demanded to be heard concerning the high price of bread. (It was at this time that Marie Antoinette reportedly said, "Let them eat cake.") When the women were done speaking, they were accompanied back to Paris by sympathetic members of the National Guard, led by a soldier with a loaf of bread stuck on his bayonet. This became a symbol of the revolution.

The National Assembly began to take bolder and more liberal action throughout the late summer and autumn of 1789. In August the National Assembly passed a law titled **The Destruction of Privilege.** This act stripped the tax exemption from the nobility and eliminated the nobility's business monopolies and special hunting privileges. It also eliminated the special tithes and other special taxes imposed on peasants who worked on land owned by nobles.

A month later, in September, the National Assembly adopted **The Declaration of the Rights of Man and the Citizen,** a document similar in purpose and theme to the American Declaration of Independence. This document expressed the belief that men are born and remain free and that social distinctions can only be based on usefulness. It held that the purpose of government was to protect the inalienable rights of liberty, property, security, and the resistance of oppression. Further, the Declaration of the Rights of Man and the Citizen protects the rights of free speech, free worship, and free press, as well as equality and due process before the law, thus including concepts from the Bill of Rights.

In October the National Assembly oversaw the secularization of the church. Church lands were confiscated and used as collateral for the printing of paper money, which the National Assembly hoped would end the financial crisis. Further, the clergy were made subject to the laws of the state and were to be paid out of the public treasury. The National Assembly also separated the church from papal authority, thus, making the Catholic Church of France a national church without direct responsibility to the pope. The peasants, especially those outside Paris, greeted the changes in the church less enthusiastically than the other changes made by the National Assembly. However, the National Assembly saw the attempt to secularize the church as a means of making money without raising taxes and viewed ending the economic depression as being the highest priority.

The National Assembly continued to meet over the next two years and in 1791 finally was able to draft a new constitution for the country. The long period without a formal system of government attests to the difficulty of the task and to the lack of a strong leader, like George Washington or Benjamin Franklin, within the National Assembly. The eventual result was the creation of a constitutional monarchy very similar to the British system. The constitution granted all citizens the same right to vote, but in order to be eligible to vote a citizen had to have paid a certain minimum amount in taxes. Doing this gave tremendous power to the wealthy members of the Third Estate who were in control of the National Assembly. Finally, the name of the National Assembly was changed to the **Legislative Assembly** to reflect its new power to make laws.

■ The Second Stage of the Revolution: Control by the Radicals

The actions of the National/Legislative Assembly were not successful in solving the economic problems. Unemployment remained high, the cost and availability of food was still unstable, and inflation continued unabated. In the eyes of many of the poor, the French Revolution had been a failure. To make matters worse, the **Girondists,** moderates who controlled the Legislative Assembly, still had no strong leader to rally the people, command the respect of all parties, or create a vision for the future. Furthermore, without this strong leader in the Legislative Assembly, King Louis XVI was still successful in delaying many of the reforms called for by the legislature.

Always an opponent of liberal reform, King Louis agreed to participate in a counterrevolutionary plot proposed by Marie Antoinette and her brother, Leopold II of Austria. The French king and his family were to begin the plot by fleeing France and then attempting to rally foreign support for a war to reestablish him as the absolute monarch of France. The royal family was successful in getting out of Paris, but was apprehended in the countryside and sent back to Paris, where they remained as prisoners of the Legislative Assembly. When the king fled, the French people became convinced that King Louis would not cooperate with the new limited monarchy, and they then resolved to take more drastic action in changing the nature of the government.

The return of the king and his subsequent imprisonment by the Legislative Assembly drew other European states into a war with France in 1792. Many of the monarchs of Europe were concerned that France's revolution would lead to instability and popular uprisings in their own countries. Exiled French aristocrats traveled throughout Europe and obtained support for a counterrevolution. These aristocrats were particularly successful in Austria and Prussia, but even found some support in England. However, a key British supporter of the American Revolution, the philosopher Edmund Burke, opposed the revolution in France because he felt that the French had no right to remake their country without reference to the past or concern for the traditions and customs that were being destroyed. Austria and Prussia invaded France in 1792 with the purpose of reinstating the absolute monarchy. The invading Austro-Prussian army had great success against the French forces and soon found themselves just outside of Paris.

The failures in the war against the Austrians and Prussians, combined with the lack of improvement to the French economy, caused the desperate French people to remove the moderate Girondists from power in the Legislative Assembly. The **Jacobins,** radical liberals and vigorous proponents of uncompromised equality, then took control of the leadership of the Legislative Assembly. Among the beliefs of the Jacobins was the complete elimination of all class distinctions, universal suffrage, and state programs for the maintenance of the poor. Among the first acts of the Jacobins was to eliminate the municipal government of Paris and establish a new city government called the **Commune.** The Jacobins also called for new elections with universal suffrage to elect delegates to a **National Convention** that would draft a new, republican constitution that would do away with the monarchy altogether. This National Convention was elected in 1792 and became the legislative body of France for the next three years.

The newly elected National Convention was an extremely radical group. It declared France to be a republic and stripped the king of all power. The king was tried for crimes against the people and sentenced to die. The execution was carried out, and "Citizen Louis Capet" was beheaded using the guillotine in 1793.

Despite all of the instability and turmoil within the government during this period, the French army was able to hold the invading armies at bay and keep them out of Paris. Once the National Convention was established and in control of the government, the Convention drafted most men of arms-bearing age and sent them to fight. The increased numbers boosted French military strength and turned the tide of the war. The French won a series of battles and occupied the Low Countries, Switzerland, and parts of Spain and Germany, despite the entrance of the English, Spanish, and Dutch on the opposing side.

With its enemies at bay and its power consolidated, the National Convention also passed a series of laws that radically reshaped French society. Slavery was eliminated in France. Imprisonment for debt was disallowed. The concept of primogeniture (inheriting by only the oldest son) was repealed so that all heirs could inherit property. Many large estates were broken up and the land distributed to the poor. The government fixed prices to prevent further inflation. The metric system was devised and adopted. The calendar was changed, and a new 10-month year was devised that began with the date of the start of the revolution. There was even an attempt to abolish Christianity and supplant it with a religion that enshrined reason (although later the Cult of Reason was changed to a Deist belief, and eventually the National Convention declared religion to be a private matter). Many of these changes were popular with the people, especially among the poor. However, they were very drastic changes, and not all of them were embraced as quickly and wholeheartedly as the Jacobins would have liked. This led to tension within France between those who embraced the radical changes and those who were seeking more moderate solutions.

Eventually the National Convention chose 12 men to form an executive committee to run the day to day affairs of the government. This committee was named the **Committee for Public Safety** and was primarily composed of members of the Jacobin faction of the National Convention and included Jacobin leaders such as **Maximilien Robespierre, Jean-Paul Marat,** and **Georges Danton.** The period of time where the Committee of Public Safety served as the ruling body of France was the most radical and violent of the whole French Revolution and gained the name **The Reign of Terror.**

The Reign of Terror lasted from September 1793 to July 1794, and the Committee of Public Safety ruled with ruthless authoritarianism. It would sit in judgment and would usually accept almost any story as a pretext to kill aristocrats or anyone else that it believed to be anti-revolutionary. An estimated 20,000 people were killed by order of the Committee of Public Safety during its brief time in power. The guillotine was used as the principle execution method during the Reign of Terror. The current Place de la Concorde in Paris (see Figure 39.1) was the location of the guillotine. The violence and bloodshed grew so heinous that a counterrevolution broke out in the French countryside

Figure 39.1 ▪ The Place de la Concorde was the location of the guillotine during the French Revolution. © 2010 by David H.Seymour. Used under license of Shutterstock, Inc.

with the purpose of removing the Committee of Public Safety from power and ending the Reign of Terror. This revolt was crushed ruthlessly.

The Committee of Public Safety was able to retain its power because it was supported by many of the urban poor in Paris. It spent the treasury funds on the poor and enacted policies to assist the poor at the expense of the middle class and nobility (although in so doing it dramatically slowed the pace of industrialization in France).

The Committee of Public Safety was eventually destroyed by its own policies and dissent within the government. Marat was killed by a Girondist member of the National Convention after Marat attempted to have the Girondists removed from the National Convention and imprisoned. Danton was eventually sent to the guillotine for being too lenient and not dedicating enough to the cause of the revolution.

Because of the dissent and excesses, the National Convention began to reassert some direct control over day to day operations of the government. Robespierre did not like his authority being

questioned and attempted to force his will on the National Convention. When the Convention would not submit to him, and Robespierre would not relent, Robespierre himself was sent to his death on the guillotine. This act effectively ended the Reign of Terror and the radical phase of the French Revolution.

▪ The Third Stage of Revolution: Return to Moderate Control

With the deaths of Robespierre, Danton, and Marat, moderates again gained control of the National Convention. The return of the moderates to power is known as the **Thermidorian Reaction** because Robespierre's death and the end of the Reign of Terror occurred in the month of Thermidor (on the new calendar). Upon returning to power, the moderates oversaw the writing of another new constitution in 1795. This new constitution did not restore the monarchy but did repeal some of the most radical changes of the previous constitution. Suffrage was granted to all males who could read and write, but the voters chose electors who had to be property owners. Also, a board of five men known as the **Directory** was established as the executive body and the National Convention was dissolved and replaced by a new legislature called the National Assembly (again).

The Directory was weak from the beginning. Its members were mediocre leaders who did little to inspire the weary French people and who had trouble exciting the masses to make commitments to long-range goals and permanent stability. The Directory was further weakened because its members were ridiculed across Europe as being inept and incompetent men. The lack of public confidence in the new government became apparent when France held its first truly free election and a large number of monarchists were elected to the National Assembly. Clearly, the people were searching for a strong leader. The results of the election alarmed the Directory, and they annulled the election results. Desperate to stay in power and have their new government work, the Directory looked for a leader who could give the French people direction and a hope for the future with enthusiasm. They found their man in a charismatic, young military officer who had shown valor and creativity during the war against the European coalition. His successes had made him a popular figure among the people. Furthermore, since he was not a politician, the Directory believed they could control him and retain power. They were wrong. The man they chose was Napoleon Bonaparte.

■ Napoleon's Rise to Power

Napoleon Bonaparte was born in 1769 on the island of Corsica to a minor and impoverished Italian middle-class family (ownership of Corsica had passed back and forth between Italy and France). Napoleon attended French schools as a child, and was then admitted to an elite military academy in Paris on a scholarship awarded by the king. A child of the Enlightenment, Napoleon became interested in liberal causes while living in Paris and became involved with the Jacobin party.

A brilliant military mind, Napoleon graduated from the academy at the age of 16 and joined the French military as a lieutenant.

Napoleon's first major leadership assignment was in 1793 during the war against the European nations (called the First Coalition) seeking to reverse the revolution. He was appointed to be commander of the French artillery forces at the city of Toulon. He was instructed to suppress a rebellion against the Jacobin government. Much of the rebels' strength was dependent upon several British ships in the harbor that were aiding the anti-Jacobin forces. Napoleon understood the importance of the British ships in supporting the rebels and chose to deal directly with the British ships rather than the rebels. Napoleon repositioned his artillery on the high ground around the harbor so that he could fire on the British ships. The clever tactic worked, and the British ships had to withdraw from the harbor. Without the support of the British navy to aid the rebels, the French army was able to move easily into Toulon and crush the rebellion. Napoleon's creative tactics and swift victory in Toulon caught the attention and earned the respect of his superior officers, and Napoleon was promoted to the rank of brigadier general at the age of 24.

Two years later, in 1795, Napoleon was in Paris. This was just after the Thermidorian reaction and the return of the moderates to power in the National Assembly. As the moderates were attempting to establish their new government, a riot instigated by royalists broke out in the streets of Paris. (Remember that many monarchists had recently been elected, but the election had been invalidated, thus precipitating the monarchist riots.) The mob attacked the Tuileries Palace, where the National Assembly was meeting. Napoleon was commanded to defend the Tuileries Palace and the National Assembly. Napoleon ordered the cannons loaded with grapeshot (a material like shrapnel—scrap metal, bits of chain, nails, etc.) and fired directly into the mob, killing hundreds but ending the riot. For his efforts in preserving the new government, Napoleon was promoted to the rank of major general. Napoleon later remarked that he had defended the government with "a whiff of grapeshot."

In 1796 Napoleon met and then married Josephine de Beauharnais. She was a beautiful woman of French descent from Martinique in the Caribbean. She was six years older than Napoleon and had two children from a previous marriage. (Her husband had been killed in the Reign of Terror.) Their marriage seemed to be for both love and increased prestige (for both of them).

Napoleon's next assignment was as commander of a small, ill-equipped army sent to the Savoy region of Italy to defend against an offensive thrust of the Austrian army. The Directory knew that the French army was very weak in this region, and Napoleon's only task was to hold the line against the Austrians and protect the southern borders of France.

Napoleon had developed a creative new military strategy and was anxious to test it out on the battlefield. Napoleon's plan was to start a battle with as few troops as possible, holding back a large reserve of men. Then, when the battle had commenced and the enemy's tactics were clear, Napoleon would send his large reserve force directly against the enemy's weakest position. This was a sound and inventive tactic that was further strengthened by Napoleon's uncanny ability to recognize the best time to launch this reserve attack. Despite overwhelming numbers against him, Napoleon was able to use his new strategy and stop the Austrian advance. Napoleon then began an offensive across northern Italy and into Austria. He defeated four separate Austrian armies sent to stop him. Eventually Napoleon's army was threatening Vienna itself and the Austrians were forced to plead for peace. This ended the war brought against France by the First Coalition of European states (except for Great Britain). Napoleon's victory allowed him to return to Paris as a hero and the savior of France. Now Napoleon was not only respected by his military and political peers, but was beloved by the masses as well.

Napoleon's military conquests continued. The political leaders wanted to attack Great Britain, as Britain was the only nation that had not made peace with France. Napoleon convinced the Directory that the best method of attacking Great Britain was to reduce British strength by attacking Egypt and thereby disrupting British trade with the Middle East and India. Napoleon's plan was approved, and he quickly conquered Egypt and had made inroads into Turkey and Syria.

Napoleon took more than 150 scientists on the trip to Egypt, and they embarked in a widespread investigation of Egyptian antiquities. It was also while on this military expedition to Egypt that the French scientists discovered the **Rosetta Stone,** the key to deciphering Egyptian hieroglyphs. Napoleon's inclusion of scientists with his army attests to the importance he placed on learning and the degree to which he was affected by the ideas of the Enlightenment. He was a proficient scholar himself (a member of the prestigious National Institute of France for his work in mathematics). Undoubtedly, Napoleon also remembered that Alexander the Great took scientists on his campaign against the Persian Empire (including Egypt).

In the midst of the Egyptian campaign, the French navy suffered a major defeat at the hands of the British in which most of the French Mediterranean fleet was destroyed. Therefore, Napoleon would not be able to receive reinforcements or supplies from France. This seriously affected his ability to continue the offensive in the Middle East.

The British naval attack was part of the efforts of a Second European Coalition, which had been formed by Austria, Britain, and Russia. This new coalition had also defeated the French army in Italy. Concerned about another invasion of France, the Directory ordered Napoleon to return home. Napoleon sensed his tenuous military position in the Middle East and willingly complied. Without Napoleon's leadership or adequate supplies, the French army in Egypt was eventually defeated. (As part of the surrender terms, the British took possession of the ancient artifacts collected by the French, including the Rosetta Stone, which now resides in the British Museum.) However, since the defeat occurred after Napoleon had left, he was able to return to France a victor in the eyes of the French people.

Upon Napoleon's return to France, he was able to once again use his military genius, rally the French troops, march across the Alps, and defeat the Austrian army. The Austrians again were forced to surrender and reaffirm the earlier peace treaty. Following the defeat of the Austrians, the Russians withdrew from the Second Coalition. Finding themselves without any allies against the French once again, the war-weary British also accepted a peace offering from the French in 1799. For the first time in a decade, France was fighting no internal or external wars.

■ Napoleon as First Consul

Not all was well in France, however. The Directory shared executive power among too many people, which made it slow to act and prone to inefficiency and weak compromises. Recognizing the system's shortcomings, several members of the Directory began seeking a stronger government that had "confidence from below, authority from above." This statement, and the ensuing events that established another new system of government, effectively mark the end of the revolutionary period in France.

The Directory devised a new system that would be headed by three consuls. It selected Napoleon to serve as first consul. They hoped that Napoleon's popularity would cause the people to embrace the new government. They also believed that his lack of political experience would allow them to still dominate the governance of France. Thus, a *coup d'etat* was staged to overthrow the current constitution. The National Assembly was dismissed at gunpoint, and Napoleon was named as first consul (the two other consuls were also named at this time but were nearly powerless from the beginning). A new constitution supporting this new system of government was quickly written and was overwhelmingly approved by the people. The new government was ratified in December 1799. Napoleon was only 30 years old.

Napoleon was a product of the Enlightenment and a benevolent leader who quickly used his new power to put in place many of the liberal ideas he embraced. Most of the changes brought about during Napoleon's time as First Consul

were extremely beneficial to France, and many have had an impact that has lasted until this day. His commitment to Enlightenment ideals is reflected in the quotation at the beginning of this chapter, which he uttered upon his election to the National Institute of France.

Napoleon oversaw the revision of the French legal code, which descended from medieval feudalism and absolute monarchy. The new legal system, called the Code of Napoleon, reflected Enlightenment thinking and reaffirmed the right of all adult males to vote and the sanctity of private property. It also enshrined equity before the law within France and made a number of other vital changes. The **Napoleonic Code** is still the basis for the French legal system.

Napoleon also oversaw the establishment of the Bank of France, which was privately owned (as opposed to owned by the state), and helped to end France's long-standing economic problems and rising inflation. Napoleon also set up a system of excellent public schools, gave support and encouragement to science and technology, supported industrialization, and improved the damaged relationship with the Catholic Church.

Napoleon saw his contribution as a saving step in the revolution. He commented,

I closed the gulf of anarchy and brought order out of chaos. I rewarded merit regardless of birth or wealth, wherever I found it. I abolished feudalism and restored equality to all regardless of religion and before the law. I fought the decrepit monarchies of the Old Regime because the alternative was the destruction of all this. I purified the Revolution.

Despite Napoleon's liberal ideals and belief in Enlightenment principles, he also understood the recent unstable history of France and took steps to ensure his own power and to limit liberal experimentation. Women had played an important and vocal role in the revolution and had gained a degree of power and legal recognition; Napoleon stripped away many of those rights and once again restricted the state of women. Napoleon also curtailed freedom of the press so that his critics would not have easy access to the ear of the people. He also centralized state authority, which gave more power to France's bureaucracy and created a new class of local officials that were loyal to Napoleon. Napoleon rewarded these officials with good pay and job security. However, in spite of some of these steps back, the people were happy and France was at peace with itself and its neighbors for the first time in many years. Napoleon Bonaparte was more popular than ever, and in 1802 the public made him consul for life. He understood that people are often motivated, at least in the short term, by immediate wants rather than theoretical desires. He commented, "A man will fight harder for his interests than for his rights." Napoleon gave the people what they wanted immediately.

In 1804 the French Senate and people eliminated all remnants of republicanism and granted Napoleon the title of emperor.

■ Napoleon as Emperor

Napoleon's actual coronation took place in the cathedral of Notre Dame. As popes had done for emperors of old, the pope came for Napoleon's coronation and was to place the crown upon Napoleon's head. Napoleon, however, was unwilling to make the symbolic gesture of bowing down before the head of the church. Instead, Napoleon took the crown from the pope's hands and placed the crown upon his own head. Napoleon then took a second crown and placed it on the head of his wife, Josephine. This is the scene captured in Jacque Louis David's famous painting, which is shown in Figure 39.2.

Many people who were supporters of the principles of the Enlightenment and of liberalism were disappointed that Napoleon, who once had been an advocate of such ideas himself, had succumbed to the allure of power. It was at this time that the great German composer Beethoven, who once had hailed Napoleon as a champion of liberty changed the dedication of his *Third Symphony (Eroica)* from an honor for Napoleon to "the memory of a [once] great man." Beethoven's disillusionment with Napoleon extended so far that Beethoven later wrote a piece that he titled "Wellington's Victory," in honor of the British general Wellington, who defeated Napoleon at Waterloo.

Figure 39.2 ■ *Coronation of Napoleon by Jacques Louis David. Reunion des Musees Nationaux/Art Resources, NY.*

After Napoleon's coronation, he planned to strengthen and expand France's colonial empire. Napoleon specifically wanted to expand France's presence in the Americas. He took the first steps toward this goal when he convinced Spain (an ally of France at this time) to cede the Louisiana Territory to France. Spain, having an empty treasury at this time and needing the support from a powerful France, agreed to turn the vast expanse of land over to the French. Understanding that the Louisiana Territory belonged to France in name only unless he could get an army there to hold it, Napoleon quickly assembled an army and sent them to occupy the territory.

However, the French army was given one other assignment to accomplish on their way to Louisiana. The army was to stop at the French colony of Haiti in the Caribbean and quickly put down a slave rebellion that had been going on intermittently for over a decade. Napoleon believed that it would be a brief stopover for his army. However, the French army was not able to quickly end the revolt. In fact, most of the French army died in Haiti. Many of the French fell ill and died from a variety of tropical diseases. The slave revolt was also more powerful and better organized than Napoleon thought. Eventually, the slaves were able to defeat the French, and Haiti was declared the second independent republic of the Western Hemisphere.

The remnants of the French army never made it to Louisiana. Frustrated, Napoleon abandoned any plans for further expansion into America. When Great Britain threatened war against France in 1803, Napoleon realized he needed money. Thus, Napoleon offered to sell the Louisiana Territory to the United States for a very reasonable sum. The American president, Thomas Jefferson, agreed to the offer, thus adding the Louisiana Purchase to America and removing European powers from one of America's borders.

Unable to establish France as a colonial power, Napoleon attempted to expand France's territory and sphere of influence within Europe. First, much of northern Italy was still occupied by the French, so Napoleon annexed northern Italy and declared himself king of Italy. Second, in the war against the First European Coalition, France had conquered the Low Countries, and now Napoleon annexed Belgium directly into France and exerted political dominance over the Netherlands. With control over nearly all of Western Europe, Napoleon set his sights on conquering Great Britain. Napoleon sent his naval fleet out of the

Figure 39.3 ▪ HMS Victory. © 2010 by Margaret Smeaton. Used under license of Shutterstock, Inc.

Mediterranean and toward England, but as the fleet passed the tip of Spain, it ran into a series of problems and was then destroyed by the British naval commander, Lord Nelson, at Trafalgar. Thus, Napoleon's designs on Great Britain had to be set aside. Figure 39.3 is a photo of HMS Victory, Nelson's flagship during the Battle of Trafalgar and, today, an exhibit at the British Naval Museum in Portmouth, England.

Despite Napoleon's inability to conquer Great Britain, the powers of Europe feared that Napoleon's aggressiveness would upset Europe's balance of power. Thus, in 1804, Great Britain, Russia, Austria, and Sweden formed a Third European Coalition in the hope of containing France.

However, in 1805, Napoleon was able to defeat the Austrian and Russian forces at the Austrian town of Austerlitz. After the defeat at Austerlitz, Austria accepted large territorial losses to France. Russia withdrew its forces back into Russia. The victory at Austerlitz gave France control over a large section of German territory. The Austrian Hapsburgs, traditional Holy Roman Emperors, declared the demise of the Empire so that Napoleon would not name himself Holy Roman Emperor. Napoleon organized these German states into a new political entity called the Confederation of the Rhine and named himself as its protector. Napoleon then ordered the French armies further east and attacked Prussia. The Russians joined the Prussian forces, but Napoleon once again led the French forces to victory. In defeat, Russia agreed to help France maintain a boycott of British trade goods within Europe. Russia's agreement to French terms led to the disintegration of the Third Coalition.

With the conquest of Prussia and much of Austria, Napoleon now had control over the bulk of Europe, and he took steps to solidify his newly acquired European territory and increase the legitimacy of his rule in the eyes of Europe's more traditional monarchies. In 1808 Napoleon imposed his brother as the king of Spain in an attempt to tighten his control over this longtime ally. The move was widely unpopular within Spain, and Spanish rebels harassed French troops with near constant guerilla raids.

A year later, Napoleon divorced his wife, Josephine, and married Marie Louise, the daughter of the Austrian emperor. Napoleon's divorce from Josephine served two purposes. First, Josephine had been unable to have any children and Napoleon wanted an heir. Second, Napoleon hoped a marriage to the powerful Hapsburg family would help him gain favor and legitimacy in the eyes of the European nobility. Napoleon's new wife, Marie Louise, quickly bore him a son (Napoleon II), and Napoleon looked to solidify his hold on Italy by naming his infant son king of Italy.

■ The Demise of Napoleon

Napoleon now controlled nearly all of Continental Europe and was using his control to try and subdue Great Britain by boycotting British trade goods and blockading British ports. (He continued to believe that the way to defeat Britain was by weakening British trade.) The tactic was sound in principle but not very effective in practice, as the French navy was too weak to enforce the blockade. French plans were frustrated further by Russia's refusal to support the blockade, despite its promise to do so.

Angry with Russia, and believing Russian compliance with the blockade would force British capitulation, in 1812 Napoleon marched a massive army into Russian territory. Napoleon's forces won the initial battles and pushed forward, deep into the Russian heartland. With the harsh winter setting in early, Napoleon intended to winter his troops in Moscow. However, the Russians did the unthinkable and set fire to Moscow, burning most of the city to the ground as they retreated. Left with nothing but a burnt-out city, Napoleon had no place to shelter his troops. Moreover, the Russian army was effective in harassing the French supply lines, so Napoleon was forced to order his forces to return to France.

The French withdrawal was a disaster. The Russian army followed the French army and used guerilla attacks to slow the French troops and cut them off from their already dangerously thin supply lines. The Russian people also harried the

French troops and refused them food and aid. Furthermore, the Russian winter that year was exceptionally cold and harsh, and the French army lacked warm clothing and sufficient food. Finally, Russia organized a Fourth European Coalition with Great Britain, Austria, and Prussia. The newest coalition rushed to attack the withdrawing French forces and was able to defeat the vastly weakened French in a series of battles as they limped home to France. Despite being victorious in nearly every conventional battle against the Russians, the French invasion of Russia ended in disastrous defeat. The French spirit had been broken, Napoleon's army had been decimated, and Napoleon's luck had run out.

The Fourth Coalition's military victories over the withdrawing (by this time retreating) French army encouraged rebellion in nearly all of Europe's occupied territories. Napoleon, his empire falling apart around him and finding himself without an effective army, was forced by the Fourth Coalition to abdicate the French throne. Napoleon was sent to the tiny Mediterranean island of Elba, where he was allowed to be ruler of his own tiny state.

The coalition decided to replace Napoleon by reinstating the Bourbon dynasty. It had Louis XVIII (the brother of Louis XVI and an old, sick man) crowned as France's constitutional monarch.

A year later, in 1815, Napoleon escaped from Elba and returned to France. Napoleon rallied troops as he entered France and soon found himself at the head of a large army marching toward Paris. King Louis XVIII fled from France and Napoleon assumed power again. This brief period when Napoleon came back to power is known as the **Hundred Days.**

The Fourth Coalition immediately sent an army to remove Napoleon from power. The rejuvenated French army met the coalition army at a meadow near the village of **Waterloo,** which was close to Brussels. The French forces initially fought admirably and equally but were finally defeated by the arrival of a large group of coalition reserves. It is interesting that Napoleon was defeated by his own favorite tactic.

This time the defeated Napoleon was exiled to St. Helena, a tiny island in the middle of the Atlantic Ocean. Not wanting a repeat of the Hundred Days, Napoleon was kept under tight security by British jailers. Napoleon lived out the remainder of his life (to 1821) on St. Helena and died relatively young of what was most likely stomach cancer (although it is also possible he was slowly poisoned). In 1840, the French and British governments cooperated in having Napoleon's remains returned to Paris. (Today, Napoleon's tomb is located near the Eiffel Tower area of Paris in a beautiful gold-domed church on the site of a former hospital called *Les Invalides.*)

■ The Congress of Vienna

After Napoleon's exile to St. Helena, the European heads of state gathered in Vienna to rebuild Europe in the wake of Napoleon's empire. Present at the gathering were the czar of Russia, emperor of Austria, and the kings of Prussia, Denmark, Bavaria, and Württenburg. Great Britain was represented by a trusted lord and by Wellington, the winning general at Waterloo. Russia's Czar Alexander I was allowed to take the lead at the conference, but his only concern was Russian control of Poland to serve as a buffer state against aggression from the West. Once this was promised to Czar Alexander, the remainder of the conference was not shaped by kings, but by two political ministers: Metternich of Austria and Talleyrand of France.

The guiding principle of the Congress of Vienna was to return Europe to the way it was before the French Revolution and Napoleon's rise to power. Attempts were made to remove any signs of republicanism and liberal government, and the old monarchies were put back in place in many countries. Spain was returned to Bourbon rule, Holland was restored to the House of Orange, and Louis XVIII was once again returned to the throne of France. Belgium was created as an independent buffer state between France and her northern neighbors. A stronger German federation was created to serve as a buffer to France on the eastern side. (This would serve as the beginnings of the modern, united Germany.)

However, the leaders of Europe could not simply pretend that French Revolution and the Enlightenment ideals it represented did not happen. The people of Europe had seen, and in some cases known, liberty, freedom, and republican government, and they now wanted more say in their governments, not less. Europe could not return to the age of monarchy, and the attempt by Europe's nobility to try and do so at the Congress of Vienna did not solve Europe's problems, it simply led to new ones that would have to be dealt with in the coming years and decades.

■ Comparing the French and American Revolutions

The French Revolution, like its American counterpart, was a conflict grounded in the principles and ideals of the Enlightenment. However, the American Revolution was predominately a dispute over political principles and was not an attempt to radically change society. At the end of the American Revolution, American society and culture were, for the most part, the same as they had been before the war. Very little had changed in the day-to-day lives of Americans, other than their government was now based in the United States rather than in Great Britain.

The French Revolution was also based in the ideals of the Enlightenment, but it attempted to not only refashion the government to follow these ideals, but also change the basic nature of French society. Everything from the traditional social structure, to science, to education, to religion, was reexamined in the light of the Enlightenment and the will of the masses. Unlike in America, all of this was done against the weight of a thousand years of history and tradition.

In America, the Revolution was an attempt to put in place the principles of an Enlightened government that most Americans felt were not being protected by the British monarchy and Parliament. The French Revolution had no single purpose that was agreed upon by the majority of its people. People supported the French Revolution for a variety of reasons: minor governmental changes, radical governmental changes, the breakdown of traditional social structures, the overthrow of the Catholic Church, personal power and gain, and others. Because the Revolution meant so many different things to so many different people, no single cause or goal was an agreed-upon end to the Revolution.

The much greater complexity in France, in both its causes and in its intended result, combined with the traditionally more oppressive French government, resulted in a lack of focus, and this led to eventual failure of the revolution. The revolutionary leaders turned to a strong leader to salvage some of their efforts.

Napoleon tried to give France stability and an enlightened government. Initially, he seemed to understand the need for stability and tradition. He chose titles for himself that were reminiscent of ancient Rome—consul and emperor. He acted in many areas as did Augustus Caesar (even to creating a new legal system and a new bureaucracy). However, Napoleon, unlike Augustus, did not limit his expansion desires, and that eventually led to Napoleon's defeat at Waterloo.

In the end, the French Revolution did change France and Europe, even though the Congress of Vienna tried to return to a pre-revolutionary status. The experiences that came from the French Revolution and Napoleon affected all Europe and, in the future, were to be major reasons for liberalization and creative change.

■ Timeline—Important Dates

Date	Event
1769	*Birth of Napoleon*
1789	*Meeting of the* Estates General
1789	*Formation of the National Assembly*
1789	*Storming of the Bastille*
1791	*Formation of a constitution and the Legislative Assembly*
1791	*Escape attempt by the French royal family*

1792	*Austria and Prussia declare war against France*	**1805**	*Campaign against Austria and Germany*
1792	*Election of the National Convention and new constitution*	**1805**	*End of the Third Coalition*
		1806	*Jacques Louis David paints The Coronation of Napoleon*
1793	*Trial and execution of King Louis XVI*	**1812**	*Invasion of Russia*
1793–1794	*Reign of Terror*	**1813**	*Fourth Coalition formed*
1793	*Napoleon defeats the rebels at Toulon*	**1814**	*Napoleon forced to abdicate and sent to Elba*
1795	*Thermidorian Reaction and another new constitution*	**1815**	*Napoleon's return to France and rule for 100 days*
1795	*Napoleon suppresses rebels at the Tuileries Palace*	**1815**	*Napoleon defeated at Waterloo and sent to St. Helena*
1798	*Napoleon attacks Egypt*	**1815**	*Congress of Vienna*
1799	*Second Coalition begins and ends*	**1821**	*Napoleon's death at St. Helena*
1799	*Napoleon named First Consul*		
1802	*Napoleon named consul for life*		
1803	*Annexation of Italy and Belgium*		
1804	*Napoleon named emperor*		
1804	*Third Coalition formed*		

▪ Suggested Readings

Dickens, Charles, *A Tale of Two Cities,* Signet Classic, 1960.

Orczy, Baroness, *The Scarlet Pimpernel,* Signet Classic, 1982.

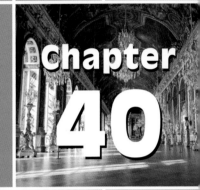

Romanticism
Feeling Creative

> If you want to do art you must first study the rules, second study the great masters, third forget the rules, because genius begins where trite rules end but you can't get there until you've obeyed the rules first.
>
> —*Sir Joshua Reynolds*

■ Revolutionary Literature, Music, and Painting

The French Revolution affected almost all aspects of nineteenth century European life, at least among intellectuals and the practitioners of the various arts. (Some peasants were still isolated from the effects of revolutionary thoughts, but even their lives changed as the nineteenth century progressed.) We have already noted how Beethoven originally dedicated his *Third Symphony* to Napoleon and then, when Napoleon was crowned emperor, changed the dedication to reject Napoleon. Beethoven's actions reflected a change in thinking. First, he was delighted that Napoleon had installed a stable, enlightened government in France. Then, Beethoven was disappointed that Napoleon had evidently surrendered his enlightened principles for power and glory.

The change in thinking exhibited by Beethoven was typical for most intellectuals, artists, and many common people. People thought differently about what the correct values for society should be and how their leaders should behave. They had accepted the Enlightenment values. When the people observed that their leaders or that society in general was not in alignment with those enlightened values, the conflict in people's minds led to strong feelings, and these feelings then led to strong actions. Artists, in particular, felt that they had a responsibility to let others know about their feelings so that, perhaps, social change would occur. For them, the feelings were critical to their message. When that began to occur, the Romantic period was born.

For convenience, we can date the **Romantic period** from about 1800 to about 1900, although many artists continued using the Romantic style well into the twentieth century. In general, though, we can think of the nineteenth century as encompassing the Romantic period.

In this chapter we will examine how artists expressed their revolutionary ideas and what feelings they conveyed. They are quite varied.

■ Romanticism

First, you might be asking how this period of revolutionary thinking came to be known as *Romantic*. Jacques Barzun in his book *From Dawn to Decadence* gives the following explanation:

The use of romantic in English goes back to the 17C when it was used to denote imagination and inventiveness in storytelling and, soon after, to characterize scenery and paintings. It served as a synonym to harmonious, picturesque. At the core of the epithet, obviously, is a proper name: Rome, Roman. *From the start, the image is many-sided. Centuries after the fall of the empire, the vernacular spoken along the Mediterranean was no longer vulgar Latin but a variable dialect called* roman. *From it came French, Spanish, Italian, and other romance languages . . . After a time,* roman *was applied to tales written in that dialect as spoken in southern France. These tales were often about love and adventure, as contrasted with epic narratives or satires. In French today the word for novel is still* roman, *while in English a* romance *is one kind of novel and by further extension one kind of love affair. . . . In the last years of the 18C in Germany and England,* Romantic *generated the -ist form to designate those dissatisfied with the neo-classic style and enthusiastic about new forms in art and thought. . . . The one link between the temper of the period and the original meaning of the word is that* Romanticism *validated passion and risk. The two are inevitably connected; but as we shall see, they neither exclude reason, nor overlook the real. On the contrary, the spirit of adventure in Romanticism aims at enlarging experience by exploring the real.*

The term, therefore, comes from the medieval past and was applied to works that were expressive and full of feelings. These were not necessarily feelings of love, although those, too, would be romantic. Therefore, since the artists of this period were anxious to reveal their feelings, the term *romantic* seems appropriate.

We will discuss many different characteristics or attitudes that came to be known as romantic. Because they are quite varied, we will list them here and then discuss each of them in more detail. While you might originally think that some of these characteristics are not related, we hope that the discussion will show how they all tie together (more or less).

- Personal feelings of the artist
- Emphasis on emotion rather than reason or form as the message of the artistic work
- Nationalism and a conveying of the glories and traditions of one's country
- Love of nature with a mystical reverence
- Fascination with the fantastic and exotic (that is, with themes that are not of the country or culture of the artist)

In discussing these various characteristics or attitudes of the Romantic era, we should view them in contrast to the preceding periods of art and music. The focus of the Neoclassical period of art and the Classical period of music was form. The Classical/ Neoclassical periods tried to find stability and meaning by reverting to the style of the ancient Greeks. The ancient Greeks believed that the form was the real essence of something and, therefore, beauty, harmony, and tastefulness would all be conveyed if the form was correct. The form could best be represented if the rules of the art form were carefully followed. Therefore, the Classical/ Neoclassical period kept the rules.

The Romantic style did not focus on the form or on the rules but, rather, on the characteristics just listed. Sometimes the rules were deviated from or even ignored. But, as the quotation from

Sir Joshua Reynolds at the beginning of this chapter reveals, the rules should be learned before they are discarded. If the rules and the purposes for the rules are not learned, the art work (literature, music, painting) will not convey its message because the form (as conveyed by the rules) is what the patron anticipates and can appreciate. When the form is not present or the rules are not obeyed, communication is often missing. (Think about how some modern art might not convey its message to you, since you might not know the form the artist is trying to use. For people in the nineteenth century, some Romantic style art also lacked the same ability to convey its message. Those artists who were creative found ways to break the rules and still convey the message.)

Some trends of the earlier period were simply continued and enhanced during the Romantic period. For example, Classical art was being created with the common person as the customer. This trend became even stronger in Romantic art by presenting the art in ways that were more accessible. For example, literature told stories that were engaging to both mind and emotions; paintings were more realistic in action and color; and music was orchestrated for a fuller and more dramatic sound.

■ Romantic Literature

Some literary figures seem to dominate a nation, a language, and a period of time. Examples are Homer in ancient Greece, Dante in late medieval Italy, Shakespeare in Elizabethan England, and **Johann Wolfgang von Goethe** in Germany in the Romantic period. Goethe (1749–1832) was the first important nonreligious writer in the German language and, as such, was responsible for solidifying German as a recognized literary language (adding to the foundation laid down by Luther's Bible). He wrote in numerous literary genres, including lyric poetry, novels, plays, and scientific writings. Many critics would still say that Goethe's works are the most important literature in German.

Goethe shaped the concepts of the Romantic era. As a young man in college, he was the leader of a literary movement known as *Sturm*

und Drang (Storm and Stress) that suggested breaking the rules of the Neoclassical forms with great intensity (storm and stress). His works were immensely popular and influenced generations of young people, as well as other artists. Even Beethoven indicated that he was influenced by Goethe in developing the fiery musical style of his later years.

Goethe's first success came from his novel *The Sufferings of Young Werther,* which became a bestseller. The book's main character, Werther, is a young and sensitive artist who leaves his home to do some work regarding a family estate, but neglects his work to spend long afternoons enjoying the beauties of nature. He is invited to a dance by some friends, and there he meets a young women, Lotte, who is caring for her siblings after the death of her mother. Werther instantly falls in love with her, but is saddened to discover that she is already engaged to Albert, a man who is 11 years her senior and who is currently away on a journey. During a storm, Werther and Lotte discover their love is mutual, and they then meet each other daily and spend blissful hours together. When Albert returns, it becomes obvious that Lotte's commitment to Albert cannot change and that Werther's love will never be persued. Broken-hearted, Werther flees to another city where he hopes to gain employment but, while there, realizes that his middle-class status will not allow him to qualify for the position he desires. Disillusioned at the class-conscious attitude of the potential employer, Werther returns to Lotte but finds that while he has been away, Lotte and Albert have married. One night, when Albert is traveling, Werther visits Lotte. He hugs and kisses her passionately and falls to the floor pleading for her love. She breaks away and locks herself in her room in order to not succumb to Werther's pleas. Werther leaves and, when Albert returns, borrows a pistol from him under a false pretense and then goes off and shoots himself.

This novel became instantly popular among the young people of Europe. Young men began to dress in the same style of clothes described as Werther's. Young people formed Werther societies to discuss the book and the lifestyle the book describes. Sadly, many young men committed suicide with copies of *The Sufferings of Young Werther* in their pocket.

What do we learn about the Romantic style from this book? The author's feelings are clearly evident in the loosely autobiographical novel. Goethe shares his own experiences when he was in college, since we note that Werther is young, sensitive, away from home, and generally alone. The Romantics' love of nature is illustrated when nature becomes the place where Werther finds solace and, during a stormy turmoil of nature, true love is revealed. Then, he is smitten with love and can barely control his emotions. However, his desires are met with strong opposition, beyond his control and beyond his reason. He flees, but is disillusioned by social inequities. He takes strong actions to resolve his emotional state, but is unsuccessful. He sees the only path open as death. Notice that emotion is stronger than reason and that all is placed in a framework of the author's personal emotions. It is a powerful and influential style that has had, and continues to have, great success.

Of even greater influence in the long term was Goethe's masterpiece novel, *Faust.* This novel expresses the emotions of a man who sells his soul to the devil as a bet ("I'll bet you can't give me total satisfaction"). Throughout the novel the devil gives Faust all possible passions and desires, including being given a beautiful girl, Gretchen, whom he seduces and then abandons. Faust is given many experiences in which he views the destiny of humankind. He sees human desire for new experiences as inevitably producing error and suffering. He also sees that this desire for newness is the force behind progress. This dichotomy is richly explored in the book. As Faust's life draws to a close, he looks back on his life and realizes that although he has gotten everything he wanted, it has always come at someone else's expense. The devil comes to take Faust to hell, but because of Faust's insight and his desire to find satisfaction through service to others, an army of angels comes and saves him.

One of the most important Romantic themes of many authors was nationalism. **Sir Walter Scott** (1771–1805) was especially important in this respect, as he was not only a strong promoter of Scottish national pride and culture but he invented a new literary genre—the historical novel, which could powerfully convey nationalist stories. In this genre, some fictional characters are intermingled with real historical characters in a setting that has a historical basis. Scott's *Ivanhoe* was a typical example. It depicted a love affair set in the time of brave King Richard I and explored the conflicts with his evil brother, Prince John. Heroes and heroines were fictional characters but the kings and queens were realistically depicted, and the historical setting was reasonably accurate. Many of the stories told by Scott had origins in the folklore of his Scottish homeland. Scott was immensely popular in his own lifetime.

Several other popular and highly influential nineteenth century authors also wrote historical novels about their own countries. Two of the most important for France were Alexandre Dumas (the elder) and Victor Hugo.

Alexandre Dumas (1802–1870) wrote action-packed novels about France, generally in the time of the Bourbons. Some of the most famous of his novels are *The Three Musketeers, The Man in the Iron Mask,* and *The Count of Monte Cristo.* All of them follow the genre developed by Scott—fictional heroes in an authentic historical setting. Dumas's life was extravagant and full of mistresses and drunken parties. He needed to write many books to support this lifestyle, and he employed a cadre of ghost writers who composed books in his style and published under his name. A critic of the time said, "No one has read all of Dumas's books, not even Dumas."

Victor Hugo (1802–1885) was the son of a Napoleonic general, became involved in politics, especially later in his life, and tried to influence the direction of French government. His literary works include *The Hunchback of Notre Dame* and, perhaps the greatest novel written in the French language, *Les Miserables.* Both of these are historical fiction.

Les Miserables is a massive work that spans French history throughout the Napoleonic years and several decades beyond. It is comprehensive in its historical details and gives great insights into the nature of France during those turbulent years. The hero of the story, Jean Valjean, is arrested for stealing a loaf of bread to feed his sister's family. He spends many years in prison for the deed and for subsequent attempts to escape. He finally is released on parole and disappears into the French countryside with the help of a kindly priest. His disappearance is a violation of the terms of his parole. After many years, Valjean rises to become a successful businessman and mayor of the city in which he lives. However, he is threatened by a policeman, who seems to remember him from prison. Valjean flees again and establishes a new life in Paris, where he cares for an orphan girl and becomes involved in the fight for freedom after the fall of Napoleon. In the life of Jean Valjean, we see an analogy of the history of France itself. We also, perhaps even more poignantly, experience the conflict between justice and mercy, as Valjean struggles to start anew but is thwarted by his past. In the end, Enlightenment values are successful.

Of similar size and scope to *Les Miserables* is the greatest Russian novel ever written—*War and Peace* by **Leo Tolstoy** (1828–1910). This book also covers several decades, beginning early in the Napoleonic period and flowing through the story of Napoleon's withdrawal from Moscow. This story is immensely complex in characters and relationships. There are deep discussions of war, peace, religion, and social conditions. Tolstoy revealed his own emotions and thoughts through his characters and many others besides. Tolstoy also wrote the novel *Anna Karenina,* which is about a woman who struggles to live in a marriage she does not enjoy and then leaves for a long liaison with a man she loves, only to discover that she still cannot find happiness. In the end, for reasons that are reminiscent of Young Werther, she kills herself.

Tolstoy is also remembered as a great social activist. He was born to a noble family that owned a large estate with many serfs. After returning from the Napoleonic wars, he felt that the conditions of the serfs were unacceptable, and so he freed all his own serfs and encouraged other landholders to do the same. Tolstoy then began

to dress in simple clothes and work on the land himself. Tolstoy wrote about living a higher life and spawned a semireligious cult that spread across Russia. They called themselves the Tolstoyans, but he refused to acknowledge them as a specific organization and continued his own participation in traditional religion. In an interview, he once commented that "I am Tolstoy, but I am not a Tolstoyan." His efforts to change Russia were successful. The czar soon declared that all the serfs were free and also encouraged a higher spiritual life, such as that lived by Tolstoy.

The romantic fascination with the exotic is illustrated admirably by England's **Mary Wollstonecraft Shelley** (1797–1851), author of *Frankenstein.* She was a young woman living the romantic life with her poet husband, Percy Bysshe Shelley. They had flown from all cares and were staying with Lord Byron, the poet laureate of England, in a cabin in Switzerland. Having nowhere that they could go in the winter, the three decided to write stories to pass the time. Mary's story about a doctor who creates a monster was compelling for her husband and Byron, and the rest of the world. It has been made into many movies and has become a metaphor for technology gone awry. It is, however, also a deeply moving story of a man's search for knowledge and a fixation on science. It is, of course, also exotic in subject matter and, in the end of the book, in the setting (the arctic).

Mary's husband, **Percy Bysshe Shelley** (1792–1822) was a leading English poet of the Romantic period. He lived by his own, very liberal moral code, as did many other English poets of that day, and he reflected his liberal views in his poetry. For instance, he advocated atheism and was expelled from school for writing a paper on that subject. Shelley eloped with a 16-year-old woman with whom he traveled for two years, passing out pamphlets and speaking against social injustice. However, the marriage did not last. Shelley then ran off with Mary Wollstonecraft, the daughter of England's foremost woman's rights advocate. They joined Lord Byron in Switzerland and then, later, followed him to Italy and other European sites. Shelley's works continued to be highly political, often praising anarchy and exploring exotic subjects such as Islam.

Lord George Gordon Byron (1788–1824) also lived the full life of a romantic poet. He traveled the world, largely to escape accusations of improper sexual conduct in England. Byron is famous for the concept of a *Byronic hero,* a young man full of melancholy for past misdeeds but still defiant in his opposition to the unforgiving world. This hero is, of course, reflective of Byron's own life and of the idealized life of a romantic poet. Byron's most important work is *Childe Harold.* Throughout, he said that art was inner expression, and he filled his works and his life with passionate frenzy.

Two other English romantic poets can be discussed together, as they were partners in their most important works. These two are **William Wordsworth** (1770–1850) and **Samuel Taylor Coleridge** (1772–1834). They invented a new style of poetry called **lyrical ballads** in which the flowery poetic conventions of the day were abandoned in favor of ordinary speech but, somehow, with a lofty majesty. They often combined simple subjects with a wonder of exoticism. For instance, in Coleridge's *Rime of the Ancient Mariner,* a poor sailor who casually kills an albatross then brings destruction to his fellow sailors because of the wanton deed. He now must repent by wandering the earth with the albatross around his neck and relate the sad tale of his folly. Together, Wordsworth and Coleridge explored the linkage between the supernatural and the ordinary. Coleridge presented the supernatural and made it seem ordinary (which required a suspension of disbelief). Wordsworth presented the common or natural in a deeper, more meaningful or supernatural way. After about fifteen years of collaboration, the disparate personalities of the two men drove them apart, and they worked independently thereafter.

▪ Romantic Music

We have already discussed briefly Beethoven's role as the bridge between the Classical and Romantic periods. Early in his life, Beethoven composed music that was quite typical of the Classical style—strict adherence to form with lovely melodies and attention to the interests and tastes of the middle class. With the growing environment of revolution in Europe and with his own increasing deafness, Beethoven began to include his own feelings in his music and to experiment with deviations from the standard Classical forms. It is not that he abandoned the forms—rather, he went outside the rules for brief excursions. He also explored themes and musical concepts that were more typical of the incoming Romantic period than of the Classical period. Perhaps a few examples will illustrate the changes that Beethoven made.

The contrast in Classical and Romantic styles with respect to feelings can be illustrated by the difference between Mozart and Beethoven. Just after Mozart's father died, Mozart's compositions included the light and farcical opera *The Marriage of Figaro,* whereas at the time of Beethoven's depression over his deafness and his ensuing resolution of strength, we have Beethoven's magnificent and highly symbolic *Fifth Symphony.*

Beethoven's *Fifth Symphony,* which some consider to be the greatest symphony ever written, features a dark and foreboding first theme in the key of C-minor and then a second, light and uplifting theme in C-major. These themes were identified, even in Beethoven's time, as fate (dark theme) and hope (light theme). Throughout the traditional (sonata form) first movement, these themes interact and struggle with each other. The recapitulation of the first movement is, as expected, in the key and feeling of the fate theme.

At this point in the symphony, Beethoven adds to the traditional Classical pattern. Rather than just go on to another, unrelated movement (as was the case in traditional Classical music), Beethoven's second movement (written in a traditional andante tempo using theme and variation as the form) continues to explore variations of the first and second themes. This ties the first and second movements together. However, the themes are not the same as in the first movement. Beethoven has used only portions of the first and second themes (called *motifs*). The resulting music retains enough similarities to remember the themes but not so much that Beethoven was forced into a repetitive sound.

The traditional third movement of a Viennese-style symphony would normally be a light, three-quarter-time dance such as a minuet. In light of the seriousness in the conflict of the fate and hope themes, such a dance movement would not be appropriate in the *Fifth Symphony.* Therefore, Beethoven called his third movement a *scherzo* (surprise) and, while still in the traditional three-quarters time, gave a gruff interpretation of motifs from the original fate and hope themes.

The fourth movement is, again, a traditional sonata form and has the original two themes again in place. However, they are changed. The second theme has now become dominant, and the recapitulation of the fourth movement in favor of the hope theme leads to a wonderful finale that resolves the entire symphony into a celebration of hope.

We see, therefore, a development that continues throughout the Romantic period—the use of the entire symphony as a vehicle to communicate. The focus on the movement, which was typical of the Classical period, has expanded to a focus on the entire work. Without question, Beethoven has revealed his own inner feelings through this magnificent work. He has communicated to the audience using, in general, traditional forms but has been willing to deviate when the traditional form would not be appropriate.

Another example of Beethoven's move into the Romantic style can be seen in his *Sixth Symphony,* called the *Pastoral Symphony.* The entire symphony celebrates nature, clearly in keeping with an important characteristic of the Romantic style. Even more revealing of the connection to nature is the way Beethoven explores specific natural events. For instance, in the fourth movement of the *Pastoral Symphony,* Beethoven depicts a storm with interesting plucked violins, giving the impression of falling rain, and loud percussions for thunder and lightning. The music depicts the storm in the far distance, then moving toward the listener, and then gradually increasing in force until the entire fury of the storm is felt and then passes. It is like a story of nature.

The concept of telling a story in music, which became increasingly popular in the Romantic era, is a way of conveying nature and, as we will discuss later, exoticism. We call this storytelling technique **program music.**

Beethoven also paved the way for some catering of music to the middle class. He vastly expanded the orchestra itself, including more instruments to allow for greater variety of sounds and more musicians to increase the ability of the orchestra to be dynamic and express emotion.

Perhaps the epitome of large orchestrations and program music was the French composer, **Hector Berlioz** (1803–1869). He scored his *Requiem* for twice the number of instruments of a normal orchestra and then added even more fullness of sound by placing several musicians in the back corners of the concert hall. This was truly "surround sound."

His *Symphonie Fantastique* is an exploration of his love life and his drug addiction. In this work, Berlioz abandons all musical forms and, therefore, to communicate with the audience, he wrote the story of the symphony in the program notes. A further important program work was Berlioz's *The Damnation of Faust,* in which he portrayed several scenes from Goethe's work; it is obviously also program music.

Storytelling was also important for the young Austrian composer, **Franz Schubert** (1797–1828). He used poems and books from authors like Goethe and Scott as his inspiration. Many of his works were relatively short pieces that were sung. These are called *lieder,* that is, songs with a very emotional theme. Some of Schubert's best *lieder* tell German folktales. Communication with the audience is through the words of the *lieder.*

Perhaps the most famous of these is a piece called *The Erlkönig* (The Elf King), in which a father and son are riding on a horse through a woods. (The music has a wonderful galloping beat throughout, which seems to heighten the drama and urge the piece forward.) The son is frightened when he hears the call of the Elf King. The father, who hears nothing, dismisses the boy's fears. The Elf King continues to call and eventually latches onto the boy as he rides behind the father. The father is totally oblivious to what has happened, but when the trip is over, the father dismounts to find that his son is dead.

Many other Romantic musicians included the folk music of their nations in their works. This was done as an expression of pride in their ethnic roots and sometimes as a means of protest against larger nations and empires that controlled their homelands. Virtuoso pianist and great composer **Frederic Chopin** (1810–1849) was one of the most prominent of these nationalistic composers. Chopin was a Polish citizen who lived in exile in Paris for most of his life. Poland was under constant threat from Russia, Prussia, and Austria, the more powerful nations that surrounded it. For a time Poland was even completely removed from the map when these larger nations partitioned it between themselves. Chopin was proud of his Polish heritage and based most of his music on Polish folk melodies and rhythms (mazurkas, polonaises, and various melodies used in nocturnes, preludes, sonatas, and impromptus). Chopin also used his music as a method of protest.

Upon hearing of Poland's defeat by Russia, he composed the *Military Polonaise.*

Chopin composed almost exclusively for the piano and performed most of his works himself, usually in the homes of the Parisian rich or in small concert halls. Because the pieces were relatively short in duration, Chopin did not need the classical forms to give a structure to his music and rarely used these forms. He was a highly accomplished pianist and was invited to perform as much for his playing as for the music he composed. Chopin's lifestyle was also typical of the Romantic artist. He was always frail and often sick. He was far away from home and therefore needed someone to care for him. That role was filled by George Sand (a female writer). They had a loving relationship. When Chopin needed a change of climate, they went to the island of Majorca in the Mediterranean. There they fought and broke up. Although they continued as friends, their love relationship never resumed.

After Chopin's death, Polish dirt was sprinkled on his grave in Paris and, in an exquisite ges-

Figure 40.1 ■ A statue honoring Chopin in Warsaw, Poland.
© 2010 by Steve Heap. Used under license of Shutterstock, Inc.

ture of Romantic sentiment, his heart was buried in Poland. A statue honoring Chopin is located in Warsaw and is shown in Figure 40.1. Note the Romantic nature of the statue.

Another highly skilled pianist was **Franz Liszt** (1811–1886), who may have lived the most exaggerated lifestyle of any person in the nineteenth century. He was Hungarian and, like many other composers of the period, used melodies from his native land in many of his compositions (e.g., *Hungarian Rhapsody 2*). He was a child music prodigy who lived in Vienna as a youth and then in Paris after adolescence. As with Chopin, Liszt was more renowned as a performer than as a composer and, similarly to Chopin, composed some music that was so difficult that only he could play it correctly. However, as opposed to the sedate and cultured settings in which Chopin performed, Liszt chose to perform in large concert halls in which he could put on a show for a large audience.

Liszt invented the lifestyle that today we associate with rock stars. He looked the part, wearing very elaborate clothes and maintaining long hair, which he would flop back and forth as he played. He would play with great passion and verve, occasionally jumping around the keyboard while playing the piano and routinely breaking the piano during the performance because he pounded so hard on it. Once, Liszt even lit his piano on fire during a performance. He would sometimes get so worked up during a piece that he fainted at the conclusion (although he was always caught by an assistant, just as he fell backward off the piano bench, who would then drag him offstage). After a few moments offstage to recover, Liszt would emerge again to tumultuous applause. Women, in particular, would scream their approval. To further their enjoyment, he would wipe the sweat from his face and then toss the handkerchief to a lady in the audience.

Like many current rock stars, Liszt's offstage life was full of women and wild living. He even had an affair with Marie de Plessey, the subject of the book *Camille* by Alexandre Dumas (the younger), which was the basis of the opera *La Traviata* by Verdi. In spite of this wild lifestyle,

Liszt was kind to fellow artists and, later in his life, became the mentor for several. In one case, however, he became very angry because his married daughter, Cosima, left her husband to have an affair with a young composer, Richard Wagner.

Perhaps no Romantic era composer, after Beethoven, had more of an influence on the future direction of music than **Richard Wagner** (1813–1883). A German of uncertain parentage (which disturbed him his whole life), Wagner was active in drama early in his life (writing a play at age 15) and then became involved in music and learned to play several instruments with proficiency. He became strongly involved in the German nationalistic movement and had to leave Germany from time to time to avoid being arrested. His sexual forays also led to difficulties with the law and with some of his sponsors. He was also strongly anti-Semitic and wrote several treatises on both the German nationalist movement and anti-Semitism.

Wagner conceived a new genre of music—the **music drama.** It was a type of opera in which all facets of the event—music, acting, words, scenery, story line, performance location—were blended together and presented as a continuous, integrated drama. Some specific innovations included the introduction of the concept of *leitmotif*, which is a theme of music depicting a person or place or activity that is introduced at various times throughout the music drama, usually by the orchestra. Hence, the orchestra becomes like a narrator for the music drama.

The themes for Wagnerian music dramas are taken from German mythology. In this regard, Wagner is like the other nationalistic Romantic composers. Typical Wagnerian stories are about heroes of the past such as Siegfried, Tristran, Isolde, Brunhilde, and Parsival. These would have lived at about the same time as King Arthur and are distantly associated with the Arthurian legends.

Ideally, the music dramas would be performed in a hall that was specially built for them. Such a hall was constructed in Bayreuth, Germany, and, even today, is the site for Wagnerian festivals. Wagnerian works, especially the *Ring Cycle,* his most ambitious music drama, tend to be very long pieces. When the complete *Ring Cycle* is performed, it often is performed over several days.

Wagner's imperious lifestyle and elaborate needs for staging his works kept him in constant need of financial backing. One of the most helpful of his backers was King Ludwig II of Bavaria. King Ludwig not only showered money on Wagner (at least when they were on speaking terms), but also built several castles in which Wagnerian themes were featured. The most famous of these castles are Neuschwanstein and Linderhoff, which are both in the Bavarian Alps. (They are must-sees if you are traveling in the area.) Figures 40.2 and 40.3 are exterior and interior photos of Neuschwanstein castle. Note the Romantic character of the castle setting and style as well as the depiction of German legends on the walls inspired by Wagner's operas.

Another great Romantic composer of opera was **Giuseppe Verdi** (1813–1901). He composed in the Italian style (as opposed to the German style of Wagner). Verdi's contribution to opera is immense. He realized that Italian opera had become a rigid form with very little realistic emotion. The opera usually consisted of little more than a framework for the singers to demonstrate their virtuosity. Verdi changed this by adding realism and highly emotional plots. Opera is, after all, a wonderful medium to present the concepts of the Romantic era, with its powerful arias and sweeping emotional changes.

Verdi was a struggling young composer when the manager of a famous opera house in Milan saw great potential in him. The opera manager agreed to stage Verdi's first opera if Verdi would agree to a contract to write four more, thus giving the opera house five operas in five years. The deal was struck, and Verdi's first opera was a moderate success.

The second opera was composed over an 18-month period in which Verdi's wife and two children died from various diseases, wiping out his family. It was a period of great sadness and personal tragedy for Verdi. The second opera was intended to be a comedy, but Verdi could not separate his personal trials from his composing,

Figure 40.2 ■ Neuschwanstein castle in Germany. © *2010 by Eline Spek. Used under license of Shutterstock, Inc.*

and the opera was a complete failure. Verdi was near to forfeiting on his contract and withdrawing completely from composing, but friendly pressure from the manager of the opera house urged Verdi to write a third opera. This opera, *Nabucco* (Nebuchadnezzar), was about a foreign oppressor of the Israelites (and had obvious similarities to the political situation in Italy, which was being oppressed by Austria). The opera touched into the strong feelings of Italian nationalism that were then present in Italy (and in Verdi) and was a huge success. The emotional and nationalistic power of the piece was so great that the stage workers stopped in the middle of a rehearsal to applaud and cheer.

The opera made Verdi famous, and he went on to become the greatest composer of opera in the Italian style, writing masterpieces such as *Aida, La Traviata, Il Trovatore, Rigoletto,* and *Otello*. In one year, three of Verdi's operas constituted more than 80 percent of the performances in the Milan opera house. This incredible popularity led to great wealth and prestige during Verdi's lifetime.

Figure 40.3 ■ A room inside Neuschwanstein showing wall paintings in which German legends are depicted. © 2010 by Konstantin Mironov. Used under license of Shutterstock,Inc.

In addition to his artistic creativity, Verdi was creative in the way he maximized some of his profits from the operas. For example, in addition to the money made from the staging of the opera, the composers would sell sheet music of the arias from the opera (much like performers today will sell CDs of the performance), even to offering the sheet music in the lobby before and after the performance. However, in Verdi's day, the sales of the sheet music by the composer would often be undercut by unauthorized copies of the music, which were quickly copied by counterfeiters and sold out on the street. Just like most artists today, Verdi resented the counterfeiters and decided to foil them in what he knew would be a tremendous hit aria (*La Donna è Mobile*) from his new opera, *Rigoletto*. He executed his plan by not giving the singer or the orchestra the music to the aria until late in the afternoon of the day of the first performance. He had, of course, gone to a trusted printer and had thousands of copies of the piece printed and ready to be sold that night. The strategy worked perfectly!

Verdi's popularity came initially from his use of nationalistic sentiment, which he would continue to include in his operas. However, even greater appeal came to Verdi's works because of several innovations he employed that incorporated the principles of Romanticism into Italian opera. Verdi placed the interest and focus on human emotion and placed a deemphasis on *bel-canto* style, which focused on the singer. He gave the operas a smoother, continuous flow so that it told a stronger story. Verdi integrated the whole opera together, much as Beethoven had done with the symphony and Wagner had done with music drama. Verdi also made the orchestra an important component, not just accompaniment, which lent greater dynamics and emotional shading to the music. Verdi used dramatic and emotionally dynamic stories on which to base his operas. It is interesting that Verdi and Wagner made so many of the same changes in operas but, as you would clearly discern by listening to them, their operas are very different. This shows that even when making similar changes, the range of implementation is so great that creativity can lead to very unique results.

Verdi's popularity continued throughout his life, and he remained closely tied with the Italian independence movement. His name, "VERDI," was even used by revolutionaries as an acronym that symbolized the desire among the people for independence from Austria. The Italian nationalists scrawled VERDI as graffiti on walls. For them it stood for "*Victor Emmanuelle, Re di Italia*" (Victor Emmanuelle, King of Italy) but, if caught in the act, they could always say that they were merely praising the great composer of opera.

Peter Ilych Tchaikovsky (1840–1893) was another Romantic composer of immense importance. Although he used some of his native Russian themes in some works, such as the *1812 Overture,* he was more interested in telling stories in his music. He chose melodies that were related to the stories. These melodies were among the richest and most beautiful ever written. Some examples of his story pieces are *Sleeping Beauty, Romeo and Juliet,* and the *Nutcracker Suite.*

In contrast to many Romantic composers, Tchaikovsky did not reveal his personal feelings in his music. He was a sexually troubled man (probably a homosexual who was married, for a short time, to a woman who was a likely nymphomaniac). He was economically supported by a countess who he never met. In spite of these troubles, his music was usually happy and pleasing. However, his last piece, his *Symphony No. 6 (Pathétique),* has a deep sadness and sense of tragedy that well might reveal the inner emotions of this sad man who composed such great music.

Without going into detail, we should mention the following wonderful composers (and their countries) who all featured nationalistic themes in their music: Johann Strauss, the younger (Austria), Bedrich Smetana (Czech Republic), Antonin Dvorak (Czech Republic), Edvard Grieg (Norway), and Nicolay Rimsky-Korsakov (Russia). One further, who is slightly different, is Johannes Brahms, who was a German but composed music taken from the melodies he heard among the displaced Hungarian workers who came to Hamburg.

Finally, Nicolo Paganini should be remembered as the greatest violin virtuoso of the nineteenth century, and Felix Mendelssohn should be mentioned because of his tremendous contributions as a director in finding and popularizing the works of Bach and Vivaldi. (Mendelssohn's compositions are also worthy of note and, like *A Midsummer Night's Dream,* often tell a story.)

▪ Romantic Painting

The Romantic era in the visual arts focused on the same characteristics in painting as had been focused on in music—personal emotion, nationalism, and the exotic. Compared to the Neoclassical, the Romantic period also saw greater experimentation with using color and technique to express mood and emotion and a greater willingness to create paintings that were not realistic depictions (although subjects were still recognizable and had not yet reached the idea of impressionism or expressionism).

A great example of the transition from Neoclassical to Romantic is the Spanish painter **Francisco Goya** (1746–1828). Goya was the official court painter of King Charles IV and in that role worked within the traditional styles and genres of the Baroque and Neoclassical. (He often copied the style of Velasquez in order to please the king.) This style can be seen in his painting of a young woman shown in Figure 40.4. However, as time passed, Goya's personal feelings became more and more liberal and as his political inclinations changed. Goya began to paint in the Romantic style.

Figure 40.4 ▪ The Clothed Maja *by Francisco Goya (an example of the classical style). Erich Lessing/Art Resource, NY.*

Figure 40.5 ■ Execution of the Madrileños on May 3, 1808 by Francisco Goya.
Erich Lessing/Art Resource, NY.

The masterwork of this period for Goya is his painting *Execution of the Madrileños on May 3, 1808* (sometimes called simply *Third of May*), which depicts the execution of Spanish revolutionaries by Napoleon's occupying army. It is shown in Figure 40.5. Goya's painting is especially well crafted. It shows great emotional intensity in the faces and bodily expressions of the peasants. In contrast, the French executioners are devoid of expression, even to the complete hiding of their faces. The colors are brilliant on one side and somber on the other. There can be little doubt that Goya was expressing his personal feelings.

He continued to paint in the Romantic style but, like Beethoven, late in life Goya lost his hearing and most of his family and entered a dark period. His works from this time focus on his own personal inner turmoil and delve deeply into troubled themes and the exotic. Goya's painting *Saturn Devouring One of His Sons* is typical of this era (Figure 40.6).

Figure 40.6 ■ Saturn Devouring One of His Sons by Francisco Goya. © *The Gallery Collection/Corbis*

Figure 40.7 ■ Liberty Leading the People by Eugene Delacroix.
Reunion des Musees Nationaux/Art Resources, NY.

Another important Romantic painter was the Frenchman, **Eugene Delacroix.** Probably the illegitimate son of the French foreign minister, Tallyrand, Delacroix was strongly influenced by the liberal ideas of the Enlightenment and the French Revolution and was a champion of the people's cause. Delacroix was a master at using colorful scenes to stir up the emotions of the people, and his painting of *Liberty Leading the People* is the prototype of the French Romantic spirit and a symbol of the French Revolution (Figure 40.7). This painting is full of action and determination. It seems to catch the same spirit as the stage play *Les Miserables.*

John Constable (1776–1837) was an English painter who set the standard for lovely landscapes. His *Hay Wain,* shown in Figure 40.8, was especially pleasing in the warmth of the colors and the idyllic setting that he conveys. He loved the English countryside, and that feeling was obvious in his paintings. Constable's style was copied by many artists in the years following him, and continues to be a popular style today (although perhaps slightly modernized).

The painting of landscapes was not done extensively before the Romantic period. There were, of course, backgrounds in paintings from all periods, but these were incidental to the main focus of the painting. Jacques Barzun, in his book *From Dawn to Decadence,* gives some insight as to why this was so:

From the early 16C to the end of the 18C common opinion held that religious and history painting were the highest genres. The one edified, the other reminded; both decorated. Portraits came next, landscapes lagged behind. For nature was not yet loved for itself alone. In the early Renaissance it served as a background only, and even then it was 'humanized' by the presence of temples, columns, or other architectural fragments, along with actual figures.

The love of nature was depicted in many Romantic era paintings, and Constable seemed to have been the richest of all.

Figure 40.8 ■ Hay Wain by John Constable. *Art Resource, NY.*

Joseph Mallord William Turner (1775–1851) painted many different types of scenes, but his seascapes were some of the most innovative paintings of the Romantic era. His seascapes contained the sea, sky, light, and ships in a unique way that seemed to anticipate the Impressionist period that was shortly to follow. The common public did not especially appreciate Turner, but some critics found his work highly innovative and powerful. Today, much of an entire museum in London is dedicated to the works of Turner. Figure 40.9 shows Turner's *The Fighting 'Temeraire,'* which is typical of this style. It is highly nationalistic, referring to a famous ship from the Napoleonic Wars. The lovely Temeraire is being towed to a salvage yard by a smoke-belching steamboat, thus expressing a romantic feeling of nostalgia. The painting conveys the power and emotion that made Turner famous.

■ **Feelings about the Romantic Period**

The Romantic era was one of the most prolific eras in the arts and there were many masters and virtuosos in all of the artistic genres. A popular collection of lectures on music from all periods of time has a total of 50 composers, 25 of whom are from the nineteenth-century Romantic period. Not only was the nineteenth century a time of great musical output, but the music from this period is some of the most popular in the entire classical repertoire. The intention of many Romantic composers to please the masses seems to have worked. The paintings and literature from this period are also highly popular.

We might ask, "What are the elements of Romantic period music or painting or literature that make it so popular?" Undoubtedly, nationalism is a key factor. People are often moved when their country is depicted in a favorable light. The exotic and fantastic are interesting and have a certain appeal. The telling of stories is popular, especially when we know and love the stories. Some of the works were emotional in content, rather than rational, and that made the works more accessible. All of these factors helped to popularize Romantic music, paintings, and literature.

But, what about the artist's feelings? Did that factor enhance popularity as well? Each person

Figure 40.9 ■ The Fighting 'Temeraire' by John Mallord William Turner.
© *National Gallery, London/Art Resource, NY,*

who sees the art will probably have to answer for himself or herself. For us, we identify with some of the artist's emotions and it gives additional meaning to the work. An example is Beethoven's *Fifth Symphony.* We participate with Beethoven in his struggle of hope against fate.

The artist's feelings could range from a personal joy or pain, to passionate love, to fervent patriotism. All of these could be shared with the viewer or hearer and, therefore, add to the work. In order to better express their emotions, Romantic artists used more extreme dynamics and more subtle shading than had previously been done. Romantic composers often added dramatic crescendos or climaxes to give a stronger emotional impact. Whether these are appealing or not is personal for you, but most people seem to have liked what was done.

The involvement of the artist's personal feelings in Romantic art has led to a view of the artist as a romantic person—someone driven by emotions and willing to sacrifice health and wealth to tell the world the artist's message. This has led to a myriad of artists who were driven by personal feelings and

desires rather than seeking to communicate their art to the audience through the traditional forms. Because of this focus on personal emotion, to these artists, the journey through life became more important than the position one reached or the possessions one obtained. Thus, many of these artists led lives filled with duels, tempestuous love affairs, madness, strange illnesses, revolutionary politics, and suicides—all these were activities that emphasized feelings rather than reason. Thus, it is from this period that the modern world gets the image of the poor, starving artist who is striving to achieve self-realization.

We can legitimately ask the following: If the artists deviated from the traditional forms, how did they communicate? Evidently, the emotion of the works, combined with whatever form remained, were sufficient to give the public the message the artist wanted to convey—at least the artists hoped so. Communication became visceral as well as cerebral, and that seems to be preferred. That observation should not be entirely surprising. Art is aesthetic, and that means that it is aimed at emotions. Art also has a rational component that is, of course, mental. We often think about and analyze the art that we see, and that serves as a valuable background and enrichment. However, art cannot be fully appreciated without the aesthetic content that is felt and only comes from actually seeing it or reading it or hearing it. Art is meant to be experienced!

■ Timeline—Important Dates

Date	Event
1746–1828	*Francisco Goya*
1749–1832	*Johann Wolfgang von Goethe*
1770–1827	*Ludwig von Beethoven*
1771–1805	*Sir Walter Scott*
1772–1834	*Samuel Taylor Coleridge*
1770–1850	*William Wordsworth*
1775–1851	*Joseph Mallord William Turner*
1776–1837	*John Constable*
1788–1824	*George Gordon, Lord Byron*
1792–1822	*Percy Bysshe Shelley*
1797–1828	*Franz Schubert*
1797–1851	*Mary Wollstonecraft Shelley*
1802–1870	*Alexandre Dumas*
1802–1885	*Victor Hugo*
1803–1869	*Hector Berlioz*
1810–1849	*Frederick Chopin*
1811–1886	*Franz Liszt*
1813–1883	*Richard Wagner*
1813–1901	*Giuseppe Verdi*
1828–1910	*Leo Tolstoy*
1840–1893	*Peter Ilych Tchaikovsky*

■ Suggested Readings

Barzun, Jacques, *From Dawn to Decadence,* Perennial, 2000.

Dumas, Alexandre, *The Count of Monte Cristo,* Bantam Books, 1988.

Dumas, Alexandre, *The Three Musketeers,* Modern Library, 2001.

Hugo, Victor, *Les Miserables* (Norman MacAfee translator), Signet Classics, 1987.

Tolstoy, Leo, *Anna Karenina* (Joel Carmichael translator), Bantam Books, 1981.

Sir Walter Scott: Ivanhoe

Sir Walter Scott (1771–1805) grew up in Edinburgh, Scotland. Even though polio struck him at a young age causing him to favor his right leg, he grew up to be over six-feet tall. He was married in 1797 and raised five children while working as a sheriff deputy. He had an intense interest in old ballads and collected and translated some into English. Scott and a friend started a printing and publishing business to increase their income, but financial difficulties ended the business. He then began writing feverishly to attempt to pay off debts accrued from business losses. During this time he described himself as becoming a writing automaton; his joints becoming more stiff and sore with every passing day at the desk. Scott experimented with many literary genres desperately trying to find something to make a name and increase the money he was earning. He finally found his niche when he published this first historical novel (historical fiction) and repeatedly used this new genre for the good business it brought. He wrote twenty-seven novels, many of which were popular during his lifetime for their excitement and drama. In Scott, we clearly see a person motivated to creativity by need.

Scott's most famous work, *Ivanhoe,* is a tale of the Medieval clash between King Richard and his loyal followers against the evil Norman-French invaders who attempt to usurp the English throne during Richard's participation in the crusades. The tale introduces the bandit-prince Robin Hood of Sherwood Forest and is filled with knightly tales of chivalry, swashbuckling battle scenes, mystical powers, and inspiring heroines—thus making it the archetypal novel of the Romantic period. The way this novel encompassed so much of the English heritage made it an instant hit in England and is even now a universally beloved story.

The last great scene in *Ivanhoe* is the rescue of the sublime Lady Rebecca. Her beauty, courage, and virtues had caught the heart of the Norman knight, Bois-Guilbert. He had kidnapped her and declared his love only to be constantly refused. His frustration over her rejections resulted in her being accused of witchcraft, for which she would be burned at the stake. A good fight between knights decided legal matters in those days, but no one knew if any friends of Rebecca could arrive at the enemy camp in time to be her champion. Complicating matters, Bois-Guilbert's love for Rebecca was conflicting with his execution-desiring pride, and this was tearing up his conscience. This dramatic buildup and its emotional conclusion are what make this passage and the rest of *Ivanhoe* entertaining to all.

The unfortunate Rebecca was conducted to the black chair placed near the pile. On her first glance at the terrible spot where preparations were making for a death alike dismaying to the mind and painful to the body, she was observed to shudder and shut her eyes, praying internally, doubtless, for her lips moved, though no speech was heard. In the space of a minute she opened her eyes, looked fixedly on the pile as if to familiarise her mind with the object, and then slowly and naturally turned away her head.

Meanwhile, the Grand Master had assumed his seat; and when the chivalry of his order was placed around and behind him, each in his due rank, a loud and a long flourish of the trumpets announced that the court were seated for judgment. Malvoisin then, acting as godfather of the champion, stepped forward, and laid the glove of the Jewess, which was the pledge of battle, at the feet of the Great Master.

'Valorous lord and reverend father,' said he, 'here standeth the good knight, Brian de Bois-Guilbert, Knight Preceptor of the Order of the Temple, who, by accepting the pledge of battle which I now lay at your reverence's feet, hath become bound to do his devoir in combat this day, to maintain that this Jewish maiden, by name Rebecca, hath justly deserved the doom passed upon her in a chapter of this most holy order of the Temple of Zion, condemning her to die as a sorceress—here say, he standeth, such battle to do, knightly and honourable such be your noble and sanctified pleasure.' . . .

The trumpets then again flourished, and a herald, stepping forward, proclaimed aloud, 'Oyez, oyez, oyez. Here standeth the good knight, Sir Brian de Bois-Guilbert, ready to do battle with any knight of free blood who will sustain the quarrel allowed and allotted to the Jewess Rebecca, to try by champion, a respect of lawful essoine of her own body; and to such champion the reverend and valorous Grand Master here present allows a fair field, and equal partition of sun and wind, and whatever else appertains to a fair combat.' The trumpets again sounded, and there was a dead pause of many minutes.

'No champion appears for the appellant,' said the Grand Master. 'Go, herald, and ask her whether she expects any one to do battle for her in this her cause.'

The herald went to the chair in which Rebecca was seated; and Bois-Guilbert, suddenly turning his horse's head towards that end of the lists, in spite of hints on either side from Malvoisin and Mont-Fitchet, was by the side of Rebecca's chair as soon as the herald.

'Is this regular, and according to the law of combat?' said Malvoisin, looking to the Grand Master.

'Albert de Malvoisin, it is,' answered Beaumanoir; 'for in this appeal to the judgment of God we may not prohibit parties from having that communication with each other which may best tend to bring forth the truth of the quarrel.'

In the meantime, the herald spoke to Rebecca in these terms: 'Damsel, the honourable and reverend

Source: From *Ivanhoe* by Sir Walter Scott (Midddlesex: Penguin Books, Ltd., 1982).

the Grand Master demands of thee, if thou are prepared with a champion to do battle this day in thy behalf, or if thou dost yield thee as one justly condemned to a deserved doom?'

'Say to the Grand Master,' replied Rebecca, 'that I maintain my innocence, and do not yield me as justly condemned, lest I become guilty of mine own blood. Say to him, that I challenge such delay as his forms will permit, to see if God, whose opportunity is in man's extremity, will raise me up a deliverer; and when such uttermost space is passed, may His holy will be done!'

The herald retired to carry this answer to the Grand Master.

'God forbid,' said Lucas Beaumanoir, 'that Jew or Pagan should impeach us of injustice! Until the shadows be cast from the west to the eastward, will we wait to see if a champion shall appear for this unfortunate woman. When the day is so far passed, let her prepare for death.'

The herald communicated the words of the Grand Master to Rebecca, who bowed her head submissively, folded her arms and, looking up towards heaven, seemed to expect that aid from above which she could scarce promise herself from man. During this awful pause, the voice of Bois-Guilbert broke upon her ear; it was but a whisper, yet it startled her more than the summons of the herald had appeared to do.

'Rebecca,' said the Templar, 'dost thou hear me?'

'I have no portion in thee, cruel, hard-hearted man,' said the unfortunate maiden.

'Ay, but dost thou understand my words?' said the Templar, 'for the sound of my voice is frightful in mine own ears. I scarce know on what ground we stand, or for what purpose they have brought us hither. This listed space—that chair—these faggots—I know their purpose, and yet it appears to me like something unreal—the fearful picture of a vision, which appals my sense with hideous fantasies, but convinces not my reason.'

'My mind and senses keep touch and time,' answered Rebecca, 'and tell me alike that these faggots are destined to consume my earthly body, and open a painful but a brief passage to a better world.'

'Dreams, Rebecca—dreams,' answered the Templar—'idle visions, rejected by the wisdom of your own wiser Sadducee. Hear me, Rebecca,' he said, proceeding with animation, 'a better chance hast thou for life and liberty than yonder knaves and dotard dream of. Mount thee behind me on my steed—on Zamor, the gallant horse that never failed his rider. I won him in single fight from the Soldan of Trebizond. Mount, I say, behind me; in one short hour is pursuit and inquiry far behind—a new world of pleasure opens to thee—to me a new career of fame. Let them speak the doom which I despise, and erase the name of Bois-Guilbert from their list of monastic slaves! I will wash out with blood whatever blot they may dare to cast on my scutcheon.'

'Tempter,' said Rebecca, 'begone! Not in this last extremity canst thou move me one hair's-breadth from my resting-place. Surrounded as I am by foes, I hold thee as my worst and most deadly enemy; avoid thee, in the name of God!'

Albert Malvoisin, alarmed and impatient at the duration of their conference, now advanced to interrupt it.

'Hath the maiden acknowledged her guilt?' he demanded of Bois-Guilbert; 'or is she resolute in her denial?'

'She is indeed *resolute,*' said Bois-Guilbert.

'Then,' said Malvoisin, 'must thou, noble brother, resume thy place to attend the issue. The shades are changing on the circle of the dial. Come, brave Bois-Guilbert—come, thou hope of our holy order, and soon to be its head.'

As he spoke in this soothing tone, he laid his hand on the knight's bridle, as if to lead him back to his station.

'False villain! what meanest thou by thy hand on my rein?' said Sir Brian, angrily. And shaking off his companion's grasp, he rode back to the upper end of the lists.

'There is yet spirit in him,' said Malvoisin apart to Mont-Fitchet, 'were it well directed; but, like the Greek fire, it burns whatever approaches it.'

The judges had now been two hours in the lists, awaiting in vain the appearance of a champion.

'And reason good,' said Friar Tuck, 'seeing she is a Jewess; and yet, by mine order, it is hard that so young and beautiful a creature should perish without one blow being struck in her behalf! Were she ten times a witch, provided she were but the least bit of a Christian, my quarter-staff should ring noon on the steel cap of yonder fierce Templar, ere he carried the matter off thus.'

It was, however, the general belief that no one could or would appear for a Jewess accused of sorcery; and the knights instigated by Malvoisin, whispered to each other that it was time to declare the pledge of Rebecca forfeited. At this instant a knight, urging his horse to speed, appeared on the plain advancing towards the lists. A hundred voices exclaimed, 'A champion!—a champion!' And, despite the prepossessions and prejudices of the multitude, they shouted unanimously as the knight rode into the tiltyard. The second glance, however, served to destroy the hope that his timely arrival had excited His horse, urged for many miles to its utmost speed, appeared to reel from fatigue, and the rider, however undauntedly he presented himself in the lists, either from weakness, weariness, or both, seemed scarce able to support himself in the saddle.

To the summons of the herald, who demanded his rank, his name, and purpose, the stranger knight answered readily and boldly, 'I am a good knight and noble, come hither to sustain with lance and sword the just and lawful quarrel of this damsel, Rebecca, daughter of Isaac of York; to uphold the doom pronounced against her to be false and truthless, and to defy Sir Brian de Bois-Guilbert, as a traitor, murderer, and liar; as I will prove in this field with my body against his, by the aid of God, of Our Lady, and of Monseigneur St George, the good knight.'

'The stranger must first show,' said Malvoisin, 'that he is a good knight, and of honourable lineage. The Temple sendeth not forth her champions against nameless men.'

'My name,' said the knight, raising his helmet, 'is better known, my lineage more pure, Malvoisin, than thine own. I am Wilfred of Ivanhoe.'

'I will not fight with thee at present,' said the Templar, in a changed and hollow voice. 'Get thy wounds healed, purvey thee a better horse, and it may be I will hold it worth my while to scourge out of thee this boyish spirit of bravade.'

'Ha! proud Templar,' said Ivanhoe, 'hast thou forgotten that twice didst thou fall before this lance? Remember the lists at Acre; remember the passage of arms at Ashby; remember thy proud vaunt in the halls of Rotherwood, and the gage of your gold chain against my reliquary, that thou wouldst do battle with Wilfred of Ivanhoe, and recover the honour thou hadst lost! By that reliquary, and the holy relic it contains, I will proclaim thee, Templar, a coward in every court in Europe—in every preceptory of thine order—unless thou do battle without farther delay.'

Bois-Guilbert turned his countenance irresolutely towards Rebecca, and then exclaimed, looking fiercely at Ivanhoe, 'Dog of a Saxon! take thy lance, and prepare for the death thou hast drawn upon thee!'

'Does the Grand Master allow me the combat?' said Ivanhoe.

'I may not deny what thou has challenged,' said the Grand Master, 'provided the maiden accepts thee as her champion. Yet I would thou wert in better plight to do battle. An enemy of our order hast thou ever been, yet would I have thee honourably met with.'

'Thus—thus as I am, and not otherwise,' said Ivanhoe; 'it is the judgment of God—to His keeping I commend myself. Rebecca,' said he, riding up to the fatal chair, 'dost thou accept of me for thy champion?'

'I do,' she said—'I do,' fluttered by an emotion which the fear of death had been unable to produce—'I do accept thee as the champion whom Heaven hath sent me. Yet, no—no—thy wounds are uncured. Meet not that proud man; why shouldst thou perish also?'

But Ivanhoe was already at his post, and had closed his visor, and assumed his lance. Bois-Guilbert did the same; and his esquire remarked, as he clasped his visor, that his face, which had, notwithstanding the variety of emotions by which he had been agitated, continued during the whole morning of an ashy paleness, was now become suddenly very much flushed.

The herald then, seeing each champion in his place, uplifted his voice, repeating thrice—*Faites vos devoirs, preux chevaliers!* After the third cry, he withdrew to one side of the lists, and again pro-claimed that none, on peril of instant death, should dare by word, cry, or action to interfere with or disturb this fair field of combat. The Grand Master, who held in his hand the gage of battle, Rebecca's glove, now threw it into the lists, and pronounced the fatal words *Laissez aller.*

The trumpets sounded, and the knights charged each other in full career. The wearied horse of Ivanhoe, and its no less exhausted rider, went down, as all had expected, before the well-aimed lance and vigorous steed of the Templar. This issue of the combat all had foreseen; but although the spear of Ivanhoe did but, in compari-son, touch the shield of Bois-Guilbert, that cham-pion, to the astonishment of all who beheld it, reeled in his saddle, lost his stirrups, and fell in the lists.

Ivanhoe, extricating himself from his fallen horse, was soon on foot, hastening to mend his fortune with his sword; but his antagonist arose not. Wilfred, placing his foot on his breast, and the sword's point to his throat, commanded him to yield him, to die on the spot. Bois-Guilbert re-turned no answer.

'Slay him not, Sir Knight,' cried the Grand Master, 'unshriven and unabsolved; kill not body and soul! We allow him vanquished.'

He descended into the lists, and commanded them to unhelm the conquered champion. His eyes were closed; the dark red flush was still on his brow. As they looked on him in astonishment, the eyes opened; but they were fixed and glazed. The flush passed from his brow, and gave way to the pallid hue of death. Unscathed by the lance of his enemy, he had died a victim to the violence of his own contending passions.

'This is indeed the judgment of God,' said the Grand Master, looking upwards—*'Fiat voluntas tua!'*

When the first moments of surprise were over, Wilfred of Ivanhoe demanded of the Grand Mas-ter, as judge of the field, if he had manfully and rightly done his duty in the combat.

'Manfully and rightfully hath it been done,' said the Grand Master; 'I pronounce the maiden free and guiltless. The arms and the body of the deceased knight are at the will of the victor.'

'I will not despoil him of his weapons,' said the Knight of Ivanhoe, 'nor condemn his corpse to shame: he hath fought for Christendom. God's arm, no human hand, hath this day struck him down. but let his obsequies be private, as becomes those of a man who died in an unjust quarrel.'

Alexandre Dumas: The Three Musketeers

Alexandre Dumas (1802–1870) wrote over 250 novels with the help of seventy-three assistants during his lifetime, making him one of the most famous and prolific French writers of the nineteenth century. His grandfather was a French nobleman, but his grandmother was an Afro-Caribbean and had been a slave in the French colony of what is now Haiti. He did not think of himself as a black man, nor does it appear that he received persecution because of his ancestry. Dumas' father lost favor in Napoleon's army and died in 1806, leaving the family in poverty. With his elegant handwriting, Dumas was hired and later worked for King Louis Phillippe as a bureaucrat. He spent time working in a theater and publishing some magazines. Dumas lived a life of extravagance, spending money as quickly as he earned it. He had mistresses, fathered an illegitimate son, who grew up to oppose his father's lifestyle, and enjoyed drunken parties. He wrote several plays before following in the footsteps of Sir Walter Scott by writing historical novels. He revitalized the historical novel in France, adding adventure and emotions to his plots, and earned much money by doing so. This was due, in part, to the lifting of press censorship and spread of newspapers that printed his entertaining novels.

Dumas' *The Three Musketeers* was an instant sensation in France. It is the story of young d'Artagnan, who leaves home to seek his fortune in Paris. France was suffering at the time from a rivalry between King Louis XIII and Cardinal Richelieu, the king's "advisor." The Cardinal was the more powerful of the two and had a large faction of supporters. But the King represented the heritage of France and the principle of loyalty. The "Musketeers" were a strong military contingent who viewed loyalty to the king and to France as singular. In *The Three Musketeers,* Dumas combined historical fiction with a romance better than had ever been done before. This made the story highly accessible and entertaining, bringing the common Frenchman into the literary world. The story is still loved today and has been adapted into several screenplays.

The following selection relates the beginning of young d'Artagnan's friendship with the three musketeers. D'Artagnan had scheduled, in three consecutive hours, duels to the death with each of the three musketeers who he has foolishly offended during his first day in Paris. The first challenge came from running into Athos, the second for insulting Porthos' clothes, and the third for exposing the love of Aramis. The duels are interrupted by attacking Cardinalist soldiers, who require the combined forces of all four to defeat. When D'Artagnan demonstrates his excellent swordsmanship and heart during the confrontation with the cardinalist soldiers, the three musketeers befriend him and urge him to join their troop. They are eventually involved in a plot of intrigue between the French queen and an English duke that forces them to frequently confront the Cardinal's men. There are wild chases, swordfights, general confusion with romantic attachments, dedicated friendship, loyalty, and evil all mixed in. The story and style are wonderful and represent the style of the French Romantic Period.

▪ Chapter 5

The King's Musketeers and the Cardinal's Guards

D'Artagnan was acquainted with nobody in Paris. He went to his appointment with Athos without a sword, determined to be satisfied with those his adversary should choose. . . . When D'Artagnan arrived in sight of the bare spot of ground that extended along the foot of the Monastery, Athos had been waiting about five minutes, and twelve o'clock was striking. . . .

At the end of the street the gigantic Porthos appeared.

"What!" cried D'Artagnan; "is your first witness Monsieur Porthos?"

"Yes. That disturbs you?"

"Not in the least, Monsieur."

"And here is the second."

D'Artagnan turned and perceived Aramis.

"What!" cried he, in an accent of even greater astonishment than before, "your second witness is Monsieur Aramis?"

"Certainly! Are you not aware that we are never seen one without the others, and that we are called among the musketeers and the guards, at court and in the city, Athos, Porthos, and Aramis, the Three Inseparables?"

In the meantime Porthos had come up, waved his hand to Athos, and then, turning toward D'Artagnan, stood quite astonished. He had changed his baldric and relinquished his cloak.

"This is the gentleman I am going to fight with," said Athos, pointing to D'Artagnan with his hand, and saluting him with the same gesture.

"Why, I, too, have a small affair on with him," cried Porthos.

"But not before one o'clock," replied D'Artagnan.

"And I also am to fight with this gentleman," said Aramis, coming in his turn on to the place.

"But not till two o'clock," said D'Artagnan, with the same calmness.

"But what are you going to fight about, Athos?" asked Aramis.

"Faith! I don't very well know. He hurt my shoulder. And you, Porthos?"

"Faith! I am going to fight—because I am going to fight," answered Porthos, reddening.

Athos, whose keen eye lost nothing, perceived a faintly sly smile pass over the lips of the young Gascon, as he replied, "We had a short discussion upon dress."

"And you, Aramis?" asked Athos.

"Oh, ours is a theological quarrel," replied Aramis, making a sign to D'Artagnan to keep secret the cause of their duel.

Athos saw a second smile on the lips of D'Artagnan.

Source: From *The Three Musketeers* by Alexandre Dumas (Chicago: John C. Winston Co., 1931).

"And now you are all assembled, gentlemen," said D'Artagnan, "permit me to offer you my apologies."

At this word *apologies,* a cloud passed over the brow of Athos, a haughty smile curled the lip of Porthos, and a negative sign was the reply of Aramis.

"You do not understand me, gentlemen," said D'Artagnan, throwing up his head, the sharp and bold lines of which were at the moment gilded by a bright ray of the sun. "I asked to be excused in case I should not be able to discharge my debt to all three; for Monsieur Athos has the right to kill me first. And no, gentlemen, I repeat, excuse me, but on that account only, and—on guard!"

At these words, with the most gallant air possible, D'Artagnan drew his sword.

The blood had mounted to the head of D'Artagnan, and at that moment he would have drawn his sword against all the musketeers in the kingdom as willingly as he now did against Athos, Porthos, and Aramis.

"When you please, Monsieur," said Athos, putting himself on guard.

I waited your orders," said D'Artagnan, crossing swords.

But scarcely had the two rapiers clashed, when a company of the guards of his Eminence, commanded by M. de Jussac, turned the corner of the convent.

"The cardinal's guards!" cried Aramis and Porthos at the same time. "Sheathe your swords, gentlemen, sheathe your swords!"

But it was too late. The two combatants had been seen in a position which left no doubt of their intentions.

"Halloo!" cried Jussac, advancing, and making a sign to his men to do likewise, "halloo, musketeers? Fighting, are you? Against the edicts?"

"You are very generous, gentlemen of the guards," said Athos. "By preventing us from fighting, you rob yourselves of a little amusement which you might have without cost."

"Gentlemen," said Jussac, "duty before everything! Sheathe your swords, if you please, and follow us."

"Monsieur," said Aramis, "it would afford us great pleasure to obey your polite invitation if it depended upon ourselves; but unfortunately the thing is impossible; Monsieur de Tréville has forbidden it. Pass on your way, then; it is the best thing you can do."

This jesting angered Jussac. "We will charge upon you, then," said he, "if you disobey."

"There are five of them," said Athos, half aloud, "and we are but three; we must die on the spot, for, I declare I will never again appear before the captain as a conquered man."

Athos, Porthos, and Aramis instantly drew near one another, while Jussac drew up his soldiers.

This short interval was sufficient to determine D'Artagnan on the part he was to take. It was one of those events which decide the life of a man; it was a choice between the king and the cardinal. To fight was to disobey the law, was to risk his head, was to make an enemy of a minister more powerful than the king himself. All this the young man perceived, and yet he did not hesitate a second. Turning toward Athos and his friends, "Gentlemen," said he, "allow me to correct your words, if you please. You said you were but three, but it appears to me we are four."

"Withdraw, young man," cried Jussac. "You may retire; we consent to that. Save your skin; begone quickly."

D'Artagnan did not budge.

"Decidedly you are a brave fellow," said Athos, pressing the young man's hand. "Yet our defeat might be less shameful if you do not join us. Even if you do, we should only be three, one of whom is wounded, with the addition of a boy, and yet it will be said we were four men."

"Try me, gentlemen," pleaded D'Artagnan, "and I swear to you by my honor that I will not go hence if we are conquered."

"What is your name, my brave fellow?" said Athos.

"D'Artagnan, Monsieur."

"Well, then, Athos, Porthos, Aramis, and D'artagnan, forward!" cried Athos.

"Come, gentlemen, have you decided?" cried Jussac.

"We are about to have the honor of charging you," replied Aramis, lifting his hat with one hand, and drawing his sword with the other.

And the nine combatants rushed upon each other.

Athos fixed upon a certain Cahusac, a favorite of the cardinal's. Porthos had Bicarat, and Aramis was opposed to two adversaries. As to D'Artagnan, he found himself assailing Jussac himself.

The Gascon fought like a furious tiger, turning ten times round his adversary, and changing his ground and his guard twenty times. Jussac was a fine blade, and had had much practice; nevertheless, it required all his skill to defend himself against an adversary who, active and energetic, departed every instant from received rules, attacking him on all sides at once, and yet parrying like a man who had the greatest respect for his own skin.

This contest at length exhausted Jussac's patience. Furious at being held in check by one whom he had considered a boy, he became warm, and began to make mistakes. D'Artagnan redoubled his agility. Jussac, anxious to put an end to this, aimed a terrible thrust at his adversary, but the latter parried it; and while Jussac was recovering himself, glided like a serpent beneath his blade, and passed his sword through his body. Jussac fell heavily.

D'Artagnan then cast an anxious glance over the field.

Aramis had killed one of his adversaries, but the other pressed him warmly. Nevertheless, Aramis was in a good situation, and able to defend himself.

Bicarat and Porthos had just made counter hits. Porthos had received a thrust through his arm, and Bicarat one through his thigh. But neither of these two wounds was serious, and they only fought the more earnestly.

Athos, wounded anew by Cahusac, was growing visibly paler, but did not give way a foot. He only changed his sword hand, and fought with his left.

By the laws of dueling at that time, D'Artagnan was at liberty to assist whom he pleased. As he was trying to choose whom he would help, he caught a glance from Athos. Athos would have died rather than appeal for help; but his look asked aid of the Gascon. D'Artagnan sprang to the side of Cahusac, crying, "To me, Monsieur Guardsman; I will slay you!"

Cahusac turned. It was time; for Athos, whose great courage alone supported him, sank upon his knee.

"Do not kill him, young man, I beg of you," cried he to D'Artagnan. "I have an old affair to settle with him when I am cured and sound again. Disarm him only—make sure of his sword. That's it! Very well done!"

This exclamation was drawn from Athos by seeing the sword of Cahusac fly twenty paces from him. D'Artagnan and Cahusac sprang forward at the same instant, the one to recover, the other to obtain, the sword; but D'Artagnan, being the more active, reached it first, and placed his foot upon it.

Cahusac immediately ran to the guardsman whom Aramis had killed, seized his rapier, and returned to face D'Artagnan; but on his way he met Athos, who, during this relief which D'Artagnan had procured him, had recovered his breath, and who, for fear that D'Artagnan would kill his enemy, wished to resume the fight.

D'Artagnan perceived that it would be disobliging Athos not to let him alone; and in a few minutes Cahusac fell, with a sword thrust through his throat.

At the same instant Aramis placed his sword point on the breast of his fallen enemy, and forced him to ask for mercy.

There only then remained Porthos and Bicarat. Porthos made a thousand flourishes and jibes, but, jest as he might, he gained nothing. Bicarat was one of those iron men who never fall dead.

Fearing that the watch might come up and take them all prisoners, the other three begged Bicarat to surrender. He wished to hold out; but Jussac, who had risen upon his elbow, cried out to him to yield. Bicarat was a Gascon, as D'artagnan was; he turned a deaf ear.

"But there are four against you; leave off, I command you," cried Jussac.

"Ah, if you command me, that's another thing," said Bicarat. "As you are my commander, it is my duty to obey." And, springing backward, he broke his sword across his knee to avoid the necessity of surrendering it, threw the pieces over the convent wall, and crossed his arms, whistling.

Bravery is always respected, even in an enemy. The musketeers saluted Bicarat with their swords, and returned them to their sheaths. D'Artagnan did the same. Then, assisted by Bicarat, he bore Jussac, Cahusac, and one of Aramis' adversaries who was only wounded, under the porch of the convent.

The fourth was dead. They then rang the bell to summon medical aid and, carrying away four swords out of five, they took their road, intoxicated with joy, toward the house of M. de Tréville.

They walked arm in arm, occupying the whole width of the street, and taking in every musketeer they met, so that in the end it became a triumphal march. The heart of D'Artagnan swam in delirium; he marched between Athos and Porthos, pressing them tenderly.

"If I am not yet a musketeer," said he to his new friends, as he passed through the gateway of M. de Tréville, "at least I have entered upon my apprenticeship, haven't I?"

Industrial Revolution
Creativity Accelerated

> When the steam flowed in under the rising piston [of the Newcomen engine], Watt realized, all but a fraction of it condensed immediately because the surrounding cylinder—having just been cooled by a jet of water—was at a relatively low temperature. This meant that several times as much steam was used—and several times as much fuel was consumed—as was theoretically sufficient to fill the piston on each stroke. . . . Watt suddenly realized how to fix the problem: build a machine with a condensing chamber separate from the cylinder and keep the two at different temperatures.
>
> —*Robert Pool,* Beyond Engineering

The Scientific Revolution and Technology

Science is the study of the natural world and a systemization of that knowledge. Through science we hope to discover the laws on which the natural world operates. As outlined by the developers of the scientific method, the laws are discovered by conducting experiments and then making connections between the observations, thus leading to general conclusions about what has happened. This leads to a theory about why the events occurred and, with sufficient data and confirmation from others, the theory may be assumed to be a law. The scientific method is a logical process that has been shown to be very powerful in under-standing our world and establishing the rules by which we believe nature operates. Science checks their results by asking, Is it reasonable?

Technology is the knowledge and devices by which humans progressively master their environment. Throughout history, technology has helped humans progress through developments like wheeled vehicles, domestication of grains, iron and steel smelting and fabrication, printing, improved farm implements, and new musical instruments. These technologies may have come from a careful assessment of the current situation and then a logical extension to a new concept, but, more likely, the idea for the new technology occurred as a flash of inspiration. Technology is an intuitive process that has been shown to be very powerful in improving our lives. Technology checks its results by asking, Does it work?

We can see, therefore, that science is characterized by the following: logic, linear thinking, and left-brain activity. Technology uses the opposite characteristics: intuition, lateral thinking, and right-brain activity. From our discussion in the beginning chapter of this volume, we should appreciate that both of these thinking types are needed for the best creativity. When the scientific method became widespread in the early 1700s, knowledge of nature increased dramatically. Those who were prone to technology (right-brain) thinking began to combine their thinking with background knowledge gained through scientific (left-brain) thinking, and the result was a wonderful acceleration in creativity. The most dramatic result of that acceleration in creativity was the **Industrial Revolution.** This acceleration is seen in Figure 41.1, which shows the tremendous growth in technology than in the early 1700s.

The people who were trained in the new scientific knowledge and then were able to apply it to the betterment of society were given a new name—engineers. This chapter is about their accomplishments and the effects of their work on society.

We have previously examined the time of the Industrial Revolution, 1700 to 1900, when we discussed the latter part of the Enlightenment, the Classical period, the American and French Revolutions, and the Romantic period. Therefore, the time frame of the Industrial Revolution is quite lengthy. It began slowly in a few small geographical areas and the effects were modest, but it grew to encompass most of Western Europe and America. As the momentum of the Industrial Revolution increased, its effects have been phenomenal. Some historians have said that the Industrial Revolution has had more impact on human life than any event since the domestication of grains in the dawn of recorded history. Certainly industrialization, along with the concept of democratic government, is the basis for modern Western civilization.

■ A Unique Background for Growth

After the universal turbulence of the seventeenth century, one country, more than any others, was relatively free of internal dissent or invading armies from the beginning of the eighteenth

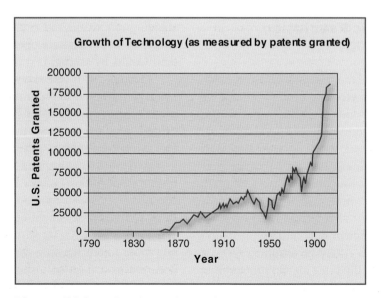

Figure 41.1 ■ *Accelerated growth curve of technology over time.*

century through the end of the nineteenth century. That country was England. Those internally peaceful circumstances led to a sustained stability, which then led to several interacting conditions that promoted the rise of the Industrial Revolution in England before any other country. A brief examination of each of the major conditions is valuable for understanding the background from which the Industrial Revolution would spring.

Increasing Population

Stability in life often brings population growth because people feel that they can provide a situation in which all members of their family are healthy and well fed. Moreover, the family could look to these hearty children to further increase the family's wealth and position. When the children married, the parents' household would, of course, decrease in both population and income, but some residual benefits from prosperous children were still likely. Children who did not marry, especially young women, were able to stay in the parents' home and contribute to family income through home crafts that could be sold.

As young men reached the age in which they would become independent, they had several options open to them in traditional European landowning society. The oldest son would inherit the land and so he would typically remain within the economic framework of the parents' household even after he married. Traditionally, the younger sons would enter the military service or the clergy. The British military in the eighteenth and nineteenth centuries was growing because of the increasing foreign vision of the British government. Therefore, many new military positions regularly became available. The clergy also grew, simply with population.

In England, there was another viable alternate career path for a younger son. He could join the merchant class. We will discuss this a little later in this section. Still another possible career path for a younger son would be as a traveling agricultural worker. These migrant workers became important in England as the amount of agricultural land increased under large landholders who needed labor quickly for planting and harvesting.

Agricultural Improvements

Agricultural production in England increased more than 300 percent between 1700 and 1850. This large increase gave food to the growing population and also created a climate where people felt confident, thus further increasing the population. It also created a feeling of prosperity that helped the entire outlook of the country.

The tremendous increase in agricultural output came for many reasons. First, of course, was a higher population, which simply put more hands in the fields and, therefore, allowed farmers to improve cultural practices that could increase yields. However, over the period of 1700 to 1850 when production increased so much, agricultural population only increased 14 percent. Therefore, some factors other than population were present to help boost farm production.

One factor was an increase in the total acreage under cultivation. The English observed the miraculous draining of land that the Dutch had accomplished and applied the same techniques to many of the swampy lands in England. Very difficult lands, not previously farmed, were brought into production because of the use of new plow designs and other farm implements. Increased incomes allowed the farmers to purchase this costly new equipment.

The use of nitrogen and phosphorous fertilizers significantly increased the yields. Previously, people had used no fertilizer or only natural fertilizer.

The discovery of America brought some new crops to Europe, and these proved to be very beneficial. Certain lands could be used for these new crops, especially potatoes, that were not suitable for any native European crops.

One other factor was the increase in meat and milk production through the use of improved breeding methods. The British were skilled at developing breeds of animals that were highly productive. For instance, the Jersey and Guernsey cows are both British breeds. Several horse breeds are also British, including the thoroughbred (which was not used in agricultural production but was a valuable product that could bring high returns to breeders).

Geography

It may seem strange that the geography of England would be a factor in promoting the acceleration of the Industrial Revolution, but it was. This island nation had, especially since Elizabethan times, looked to trade as a fundamental component of its economy. Therefore, much like ancient Greece, trade brought new concepts from faraway lands, and these were implemented in England or incorporated into English thinking so that lateral thinking, and therefore, creativity, could be improved.

England has many navigable rivers, which permitted the easy movement of goods to the sea. It is said that no one in England lived more than 20 miles from a navigable river. These rivers would still need to be supplemented by canals in order to ship the high volumes of goods created in the height of the Industrial Revolution, but the extensive river system made the canal system much easier to implement.

Whenever needed natural resources are present, technology is facilitated. Not only are costs lower, but the intuitive nature of technology is enhanced by constant exposure to the properties of these local natural resources. The most important natural resources in England at the time of the onset of the Industrial Revolution were coal and metals. Coal became the principal fuel that powered the steam engines that would drive the factories and trains. Coal would also become highly valuable in the production of iron and steel. The metals were important because most of the equipment that was used in the manufacturing facilities developed in the Industrial Revolution were metallic, chiefly iron and steel.

Water is another important resource, and England had water in abundance. Water is used in many manufacturing processes as a principle ingredient (such as the making of ceramics) and as a coolant for machines in other industries.

Successful Wars of Conquest and Exploration

Another factor that led to the birth of industrialization was the acquisition of colonies. Many European powers aggressively pursued the acquisition of foreign colonies, and England was one of the most active. Originally, European na-

tions wanted colonies so that they could extract the colonies' raw materials—chiefly precious metals, furs, and high-value agricultural products. However, as time passed, the nations of Europe realized that a colony was more lucrative if it was settled by people from the homeland. Raw material extraction could still be done, but the settlement colony also became a new market for goods manufactured in the homeland. This was the situation that England imposed on the American colonies (which angered the Americans, because they wanted to become manufacturers as well).

Some settlement colonies, unlike America, were begun as monopolies granted by the crown for settlement and trade purposes. The government would grant a group of investors the right to organize a company and settle a certain area. The government made money by charging a fee to grant the investment company permission to settle this area, by getting a percent of the profits of the company, and by increased taxes and trade with the residents of the colony should it be successful. All of this was done with very low risk to the crown, as the investors took the financial risk of settling the colony in hopes of making a profit through some means such as plantation farming, extraction of raw materials, or other endeavors. Thus, companies such as Sir Walter Raleigh's company in Virginia, the British East India Company, and the Hudson Bay Company were formed and served as pseudo-governments in place of the royal governments to their colonies. The Virginia company was not successful and soon disappeared, but other monopoly companies were immensely successful in other places.

The existence of settlement colonies caused a dramatic increase in the number and size of ships, especially from Great Britain and the Netherlands, who became intense trade and colonial rivals during this period. The increase in colonies and the expanded size of merchant navies led to continued economic growth, which helped contribute to the growing middle classes that would have excess money to spend and eventually help spur the Industrial Revolution.

Through a series of successful wars and foreign conquests, the British eventually became the dominant colonial power. During the 1600s, England and Holland fought three wars over colonies and trading dominance. They were initially nearly equal powers in the struggle for dominance, but as the years of warfare dragged on between them in the seventeenth century, the English were able to gain the upper hand and eventually drive the Dutch out of some of their most lucrative colonies.

During the 1700s, France became the main colonial rival of Great Britain (although the Dutch retained an important presence in trade with the East). However, as a result of the War of Spanish Succession, the French lost control of Newfoundland, Nova Scotia, the Hudson Bay Territory, and much of western Africa to the British. France remained Britain's key colonial rival until Great Britain was victorious in the Seven Years War and gained possession of the remainder of France's New World and Indian colonies. Britain's position as the dominant colonial power was never again threatened.

The greater number of colonies meant even more raw materials and more markets. The diversity of climate and soils was a tremendous advantage for the production of agricultural raw materials. If some difficulty arose in one colony that prevented a raw commodity from being delivered, some other area might be able to make up the difference. This occurred, for instance, during the American Civil War, when the supply of cotton from the southern states was cut off. England simply increased cotton production in India to make up the difference.

Economic Conditions

The domestic stability of the eighteenth and nineteenth centuries allowed the English government to focus on promoting trade and economic welfare—long-held objectives of this island nation, as we have mentioned. The government also established a strong and stable central bank to regulate the money supply and assist various credit institutions. These credit institutions financed much of the trade and thus assisted greatly in its increase. Later, these credit institutions were critical for supplying the capital for manufacturing. The government also created a patent system

which strongly encouraged inventions and helped companies raise investment capital.

The Act of Union in 1707 had joined Scotland to England and Wales to create the United Kingdom. In 1800, Ireland was added. These unions eliminated all internal tariffs, thus allowing goods to move freely between the various parts of the British Isles. Internal trade was thereby promoted. (Other countries of Europe, like France, Germany, and Italy had numerous internal tariffs into the nineteenth century.)

The successful economic policies pursued by the British government were increasing the power of the English economy and so the government adopted a policy of *laissez faire*—let the merchants do as they wish. This further created economic freedom and resulted in even more prosperity.

Increasing Importance of the Middle Class

In England, there was an attitude of praise and respect for the merchant class (except among the most haughty of nobles). The English merchant class grew in numbers and power throughout the eighteenth and nineteenth centuries. Younger sons left the farms and moved to the cities, where they became shopkeepers and trade merchants. The increased population increased the business of existing urban craftsmen, so these craftsmen expanded their businesses and thus created positions for peasants who might want to leave the farm and begin urban life. (There were many who wanted to make this change.) Soon this class of craftsmen and merchants had money in excess of that needed to simply buy food and survive. This excess money led them to seek for improved living and that usually meant more purchases of goods for home and recreation. It also led to the growth of funds available for capital investments.

The British merchant class developed an excellent reputation for dependability and forthrightness in business. Also, the credit institutions and the insurance companies added credibility and stability to the merchant class. Therefore, London became Europe's principle place to bank, get insurance, and market their goods. (For example, Portugal shipped $100,000 per week in

Brazilian gold through London during much of the seventeenth century.)

Home Manufacturing System

The need for manufactured goods to sell to the expanding merchant class and to the many foreign colonies led merchants to seek manufacturing capability outside the traditional craftsmen. (As we already mentioned, some of the craftsmen expanded, but that did not meet the demand.) Therefore, the already-existing home manufacturing system was greatly expanded.

In this system, raw materials were sent to the homes of the lower class, usually urban poor and rural peasants. These families, usually the wives and daughters, would convert the raw materials into goods according to the specifications of the merchant who supplied them with the work. During seasonal periods of slow farm work, the husbands and sons might also participate. That was especially true as the families got bigger (with population increases). Migrant farm workers might also be able to work for the merchants during slow seasons. The family would be paid according to the number of pieces successfully completed.

Most of the work done in the home manufacturing system was in textiles. The production of these products took advantage of the skills that most women developed as a matter of course in growing up. Also, the quality standards for textiles were relatively lax, so inspections were not important and the family could generally count on having all of their goods accepted by the merchant.

The men would often work on small metal items, again making use of the skills that most farming men developed as youths. These metal items might include products such as nails, pots, cooking utensils, and pins.

Weakness of Guild System

The guild system in Europe was initiated in the Middle Ages as a way to ensure quality and to restrict the number of people in the trade so that prices would remain high. In this system, the craftsmen making each type of product organized themselves into a guild (like a club) that met to decide on the quality standards for the product. For instance, in most cities there would be guilds for cobblers, coopers (barrel makers), wagon makers, and so on. The craftsmen of the guild would further control the quality by requiring that anyone who was a craftsman had to achieve that status by training as an apprentice. By limiting the number of apprentices that each craftsman trained, the total number of craftsmen was, therefore, controlled.

In England, the guild system was never particularly strong, and with the rapid increase in population, the demand for goods led to a breakdown in the ability of the guilds to insist that only goods made by guild members could be sold in a city. When craftsmen used some home manufacturing to make part of their products, that further eroded the system.

Therefore, when the time came to begin manufacturing using machines, England did not have to fight the natural resistance of the craft system. Joel Mokyr summarized the situation well in his book *The Gifts of Athena:*

> *In most of Europe, then, craft guilds eventually became responsible for a level of regulation that stifled competition and innovation. They did this by laying down meticulous rules about three elements of production that we might term "the three p's": prices, procedures, and participation. . . . The weak position of the guilds in Britain in the eighteenth century can go some way in explaining the series of technological successes we usually refer to as the British Industrial Revolution and why it occurred in Britain rather than on the European continent, although clearly this was only one of many variables at work.*

■ The Situation and the Concept

We have, therefore, considered the background that laid the foundation for the Industrial Revolution in Britain. All of the factors that we have discussed supported each other and worked synergistically to bring about the changes we call the

Industrial Revolution. These factors, and others, were summarized well by T. K. Derry and T. I. Williams in their book *A Short History of Technology*. We quote from their book:

> *What were the factors that already marked Britain, rather than any other European country, as the destined first home of the industrial revolution? The answer lies partly in things remote from technology, such as the religious freedom which brought in the Huguenots and other refugees with their numerous arts and encouraged the native Puritan capitalist. There was the confident attitude natural to an island people that had ceased . . . to reckon seriously with the prospect of invasion. The island possessed a valuable stimulus to trade in its long coastline and frequent navigable rivers. . . . Moreover, the Act of Union in 1707 had made Britain into a single economic unit long before any other area of comparable wealth and resources had ceased to be divided by numerous customs barriers. But even with the addition of the Scots, the smallness of the population as compared with the French gave at the same time an important incentive to the use of labor-saving devices. Lastly, there was the plentifulness and accessibility of coal in the island.*

The situation was appropriate, but a creative idea was needed to begin the actual Industrial Revolution. The idea was the following: *Machines could be used in a coordinated way to make goods.* When this concept came, the largely technology-based developments made up to that time were insufficient to take the needed step. Scientific knowledge was needed as well. Because of the developments of the Scientific Awakening, the scientific basis was already there or, at least, the means were available to gain it. We see, therefore, that left-brain and right-brain thinking combined to make the Industrial Revolution. Those creative individuals who had the idea of using machines in a coordinated way were able to implement their idea. The implementation seemed to have been first made in the textile industry.

▪ Textiles

The first steps in the development of textiles manufacturing were technology-based—that is, did not particularly require the involvement of the scientific method. Innovations were made because they seemed, intuitively, correct. The innovators did not need to know the scientific rules behind their inventions, other than the rudimentary concepts of "making it work." We will trace the first technology-based developments and then we can see when the idea of using machines in concert was the next step. From there, we will look at why science was required to join with technology to initiate the real Industrial Revolution.

Textile material (cloth) is made using a loom. By the beginning of the eighteenth century, the technology had evolved into a machine called a **hand loom** like that depicted in Figure 41.2. To understand the technology of weaving, think of a weaving machine as being like a harp. The threads are like the strings of the harp. These threads are called the warp. Weaving is done by interlacing other threads, called the weft or fill, over and under the warp threads. The interlacing process is facilitated by attaching the weft thread to a small torpedo-shaped piece of wood called the shuttle. After each weft thread is placed, it is tamped into place so that the weave is tight. Patterns were created by using warp and weft threads of different colors and by skipping some of the warp threads, for example, going over three or four and then going under one or two all the way across the face of the cloth.

Eventually, people realized that the interlacing process could be speeded up by running each warp thread through an eyelet so that these threads could be moved independently. Hence, if four warps were to be skipped, they could all be raised together and the weft passed beneath them. At this point, the loom was tipped flat so that the moving of the warp fibers could be simplified.

The next step was to improve the way the weft threads were moved across the loom. Rather than pass the shuttle by hand across the loom, a mechanical device was created to "throw" the shuttle from one side to the other. This was called the

Figure 41.2 ▪ *Weaver at hand loom.*

flying shuttle. All of these improvements led to a high output of cloth from a hand loom.

Throughout the Middle Ages and into the eighteenth century, the limiting factor to the amount of textiles that could be produced was getting enough thread for the weavers. Hand looms could use thread faster than six people could make it with the thread-spinning technology of the day (seventeenth century). That technology was the spinning wheel, which itself was a Renaissance improvement over the simple spindle and distaff of the Middle Ages. Therefore, many people, especially farm housewives and unmarried women (*spinsters*), supplemented their income by spinning thread. (This task became so associated with women that, today, a name for things associated with women is called *distaff* from the name of the staff used to hold the raw fibers that were spun onto the spindle.)

The next step in moving the textile industry into the Industrial Revolution was the development of cotton as a major fiber for textiles. Previously, wool and flax were the principal fibers, but

these were relatively weak and were less able to withstand the forces that would be required of the thread when the full Industrial Revolution was implemented. Therefore, without even knowing the future advantage, cotton became the dominant fiber. It was preferred simply because of cost. Great Britain had cotton-growing colonies in India and the Caribbean, and also retained close trade ties with the American south even after the American Revolution. Hence, the colonial connections of England were a key in this aspect of the story.

The next major improvement was an invention by **James Hargreaves** in 1767. When his daughter accidentally knocked over the family's spinning wheel while playing, Hargreaves noted that the wheel and the spindle kept turning. This accident caused him to think about the spinning process and led him to reason that a wheel might be used to feed more than one spindle. He then constructed the device that he named the *spinning jenny* after his daughter. (Different reports from the time indicate that another man in the same general area, Thomas Highs, may have previously made a similar machine, so the inventorship is in doubt, but Hargreaves is generally given credit.) The spinning jenny could initially make 8 threads simultaneously but was eventually improved to make up to 21 threads. A spinning jenny is pictured in Figure 41.3. While the total volume of threads was increased by the spinning jenny, the strength of the threads was still only suitable to be used as fill or weft (the threads that go across the cloth) and not the threads that go in the long direction, the warp.

At about this time, a wig maker, **Richard Arkwright,** who had to travel around the countryside to buy the hair he used for wigs, encountered Hargreaves and, separately, Highs, and was impressed with the machines. Arkwright was also impressed with a watchmaker, **John Kay,** who had been working with Highs. Arkwright hired Kay and other local craftsmen, and together the team invented an improved spinning machine that they called the *spinning frame.* It could make thread that was both finer and stronger than any previously made.

Figure 41.3 ■ *Spinning jenny.*

The team then expanded this machine to make more than a hundred spools of thread at a time. This machine, however, was too large to be powered by hand (as were all previous spinning machines), so the team had to find another method to power it. They initially tried horses but soon decided that water power would be more effective. They decided that one machine (a water wheel) could be used to drive another machine (the spinning frame). Arkwright then realized, and this is the key concept, *that if he had a power supply like a water wheel, several spinning machines could be driven from the same power source.* He went to a banker and secured the funds and built a spinning factory or, as it was called, a spinning mill. At this point, the Industrial Revolution was moved to a new level of intensity.

Note that this step was taken by a team of artisans. Some had knowledge of threadmaking, others of gears, others of water wheels, and still others employed other areas of expertise. Science was used because, first of all, the magnitude of everything was much larger than had ever been built before. For instance, consider the gears. Kay, the watchmaker, could not use just the gears of watches but, rather, needed to experiment with different and larger gearing systems. These experiments developed the knowledge that led to scientific principles on which the actual gears could be built. Another area that needed experimentation was the method of distributing the power. How could they get the water power to all the machines? They had to experiment with various belts and other mechanical linkages. Again, the scientific method became the basis for acquiring the knowledge they needed. They began an investigation into the nature of the spinning process itself, thus improving the quality of their products.

Arkwright's factory was a great success. After a few years, he realized that his production was limited because of the difficulty of carding the cotton—that is, smoothing it so that the spinning machines could use it as incoming material. Arkwright's team saw a carding machine that had been invented in 1748 and improved it and incorporated it into the factory. He soon ran out of people in the near vicinity who he could employ in his spinning factory and so he built a number of cottages close to the factory and hired people from all over Derbyshire to come and live in his cottages and work in his factory in Cromford.

With continued growth, Arkwright realized that he needed to expand beyond the town of Cromford, and so he replicated his factory in several towns from Manchester to Scotland. Eventually, several other businessmen heard of his success and they paid some of Arkwright's workers to reveal the systems that Arkwright employed to make the factory work. Soon, dozens of other textile factories were in operation all across England.

The skill of weavers was now in very high demand since the supply of thread was so abundant. Hence, weaver wages rose dramatically as many mills began to hire weavers to make their own cloth and keep up with the thread production. The high wages convinced many of the agricultural laborers to move to the cities and become weavers, thus adding to the number of workers in urban centers.

Edmund Cartwright visited one of Arkwright's factories and commented to his friends that what was needed was a mechanized weaving machine. His friends scoffed, but by 1785 Cartwright had invented a power loom, and by 1787 he had established a factory using power looms to make cloth. Such a factory is pictured in Figure 41.4. The power looms were usually made of metal, thus requiring knowledge of metallurgy, another contribution from science for the burgeoning textile industry.

Just a few years later, in 1801, the Jacquard loom was invented. The Jacquard loom used wooden slats in which holes were drilled to control the raising of the warps, thus controlling the pattern. To understand how this worked, remember that the warp threads ran through eyelets that moved each of the warp threads independently. In the Jacquard loom, each eyelet was attached to a rod that, when allowed to move, caused that particular warp thread to be lifted. The wooden slats were placed so that the rods were pressed against the face of the slats in a fixed array. The rods lined up with the holes in the wooden slats. They went through the slats and, therefore, caused the warps to be lifted. In this way, the holes on the slats controlled the weaving pattern. (This technology was later copied in IBM punch cards that were used early in the development of computers.)

Figure 41.4 ▪ *Power loom factory.*

Once the new looms were in place and both the spinning and weaving could be done quickly and efficiently, the textile industry really took off. By 1831, more than 22 percent of Britain's entire industrial production was due to textiles, proving the great economic benefits of industrialization.

■ General Manufacturing

Although textile production continued to be the largest single sector of English manufacturing, other types of industries were also growing. For example, an entire industry arose just to make the machines that were being used in the textile industry. Cartwright made more money from selling his power looms than he did by making the cloth. Other manufacturers soon joined in by selling components of machines, such as gears, drive shafts, mounting bases, and power take-off pulleys. Soon factories were located all over England, but mostly in cities as these were the places where housing and other infrastructure needs were available.

People who moved into the cities to work in the new factories earned higher wages than they had as agricultural laborers. However, there were other problems and drawbacks that came with working in the factories. Working conditions were very poor. Workers usually labored at least six days a week for at least 12 hours a day. Furthermore, the working conditions were monotonous, dirty, and dangerous. The workers had to be constantly careful—often a difficult task due to the extreme monotony of much of the work—or they could easily be maimed or killed. These harsh conditions led to sickness, injury, and death, and no compensation was given to those who missed too many days or could no longer work.

While the Industrial Revolution created jobs for some people, for others it had exactly the opposite effect. Many jobs were eliminated because machines could do the work better and more efficiently. In 1811, a group of these workers who had been displaced by industrialization formed an organization to try and stop the further spread of industrialization. They were called the **Luddites.** These men masked themselves and participated in nighttime raids to destroy the machines that were eliminating their jobs. However, the government could not allow such lawlessness, and the owners of the companies could not allow such a loss of profits. Thus, in 1813 a mass trial was held for all members of the Luddite organization. Several Luddites were hanged.

Many different people combined technology and science to create the factories. This was especially true because sites along the rivers were quickly being used up and sources of power other than water were needed. Soon steam engines were used to power the factories. When steam engines were introduced, that required different technologies and science, thus continuing the synergy between technology and science. We will discuss the development of power as the next phase in the Industrial Revolution.

■ Power

Up to the Industrial Revolution, most of the energy used in transportation, manufacturing, and agriculture was from animals. A few water wheels had been employed as early as the Roman period, but these were relatively rare. Windmills were used in some locations, like Spain and Holland, but they, too, were rare. Both wind and water energies were, of course, limited to areas of high wind or steep rivers. Therefore, animal power continued to be the most important way for Europe to gain power beyond what could be supplied by people themselves.

This difficulty in supplying cheap and reliable energy turned into a full-blown energy crisis for the iron industry, even before the textile production became industrialized. Iron production required lots of wood, both for burning, to supply energy, and to make charcoal, which was a critical component in the iron-making process. However, most of England's forests had been cut down for farmland years ago and so supplying the wood was expensive and required importation.

Fortunately, England was blest with a large supply of coal, which became the principle British energy source. Quite creatively, it was also converted into coke, which could take the place of charcoal in the iron-making process. The energy crisis for the iron industry seemed to be solved.

However, coal was also being used as the principal fuel for other industries and for personal use in heating homes. So much coal was being used that the coal mines continually were dug deeper and deeper. As these mines pushed deeper into the earth, they would fill up with water, making it difficult and dangerous to get at the coal. This created a new crisis—a mining crisis. All sorts of devices were developed to rid the mines of their water. Indeed, in the 100 years previous to the Industrial Revolution, 75 percent of the patents issued in England were connected in some way to the coal industry and 14 percent were devoted solely to the draining the mines. Eventually, pumps were installed to drain many of the mines, but they were driven by horses (sometimes as many as 500 at a single mine). These pumps, however, were not very efficient or cost-effective.

The first primitive steam engine pumps that could be used to drain the mines were developed in 1712 by Thomas Newcomen. His pumps used condensed steam to drive a piston that was attached to a pump submerged in the water at the bottom of the mine. Although Newcomen's steam engine pumps were not very efficient, they illustrated the concept of reliable steam power and were installed in many English mines.

In 1763, steam engines were dramatically improved by the skill and science of **James Watt.** As discussed in the quotation at the beginning of this chapter, he realized that by adding a separate condenser to Newcomen's system, the cylinder containing the drive piston would stay hot longer. This reduced the amount of steam used and therefore improved efficiency. Not only did James Watt design an effective steam pump, he secured financial backing and started a company that made steam engines. His design became the standard for many years. In recognition of his contribution to the world, the international unit of power, the *watt,* was named in his honor.

The steam engine was used extensively to provide power to both the textile industry and the iron works. The use of steam engines made the

acquisition of coal much easier than it had previously been and ushered in a new era in which the iron industry boomed. Between 1740 and 1844, England raised its production of iron from 17,000 tons to 3,000,000 tons.

Iron became not only a material for train tracks, it was also used as a construction material for bridges, buildings, and other structures. Figure 41.5 is a photo of the first iron bridge ever constructed. It is in a small valley not too far from Birmingham, England. The first integrated iron works is a mile up the valley from the bridge and that is where the iron for the bridge and the design were made.

The great success of the Industrial Revolution, combined with easier access to a cheap and stable power supply, encouraged industrialization in many industries. First, the industries related to textiles (such as dyeing and bleaching) and the making of soap were industrialized. Then, metalworking increased as the supply of iron improved. Eventually pottery factories sprung up in the regions where clay was especially plentiful and of good quality. Soon, industrialization had swept across the businesses and industries of the British Isles and Great Britain had become the industrial and financial center of the world.

■ Transportation

The large number of manufacturing facilities across Great Britain required a massive transportation system to move the raw materials and the finished goods. The rivers were the primary transportation route because roads in the eighteenth and nineteenth centuries were largely unpaved and, therefore, nearly impassable in wet weather for heavily laden carts. However, the rivers were often shallow during dry periods and, as the number of industrial mills increased, the rivers were being dammed to provide water for mill races to turn the water wheels.

Therefore, a system of canals was constructed to supplement the use of rivers. The canals gave a smooth and predictable waterway that could be used for larger barges than were able to travel on

Figure 41.5 ■ The Iron Bridge over the River Severn, England. © *2010 by Jean Frooms. Used under license of Shutterstock, Inc.*

most of the rivers. The building of the canals had an interesting side effect that greatly benefited science. One of the canal engineers, William Smith, noted the varied strata in the earth along the cuts for the canals, and it occurred to him that a geological map of England would be useful for other canal builders and for scientists in geology. He therefore created the map, and it still hangs on display in the British Geological Society building. Here is a case of technology assisting science.

The plethora of industrial sites meant that some factories were still not well serviced by water transport. To alleviate this problem, several creative people in England conceived of a system of metal rails (first iron and then steel) on which specially fitted carts could transport large amounts of goods. These inventors realized the need for efficient and transportable energy systems for these carriages and decided to use steam engines. These railroads were laid throughout England and were immediately profitable, as they provided flexibility to freight transportation and expanded the markets that could be served by a factory. They also provided easy transportation to and from work sites. This was especially important because now people could commute to and from work, and the

large urban centers of Great Britain began to develop. Figure 41.6 shows a steam engine train and also illustrates how engineering developed to support the trains by building bridges and other infrastructure improvements.

The industries that supplied the locomotives, cars, tracks, and other parts of the train system realized that other countries would benefit from a rail system. These companies worked hard to export their goods and, as a result, most of the early trains throughout Europe and the United States were of British manufacture.

■ The Spread of the Industrial Revolution

Great Britain was the first nation to industrialize, but industrialization was much too successful and profitable to remain strictly British for long. By 1860 England was producing 20 percent of the entire world's industrial goods and England's gross national product quadrupled between 1780 and 1851. Despite attempts by Great Britain to keep industrialization a British secret, the Industrial Revolution spread via both espionage and British

Figure 41.6 ■ The Rocket, an early steam locomotive. *Photo courtesy of the author.*

inventors who were willing to sell their knowledge to the highest bidder. These men were considered anti-British, but they often made so much money sharing their secrets and designing factories in foreign countries that they didn't care about any damage done to their reputation.

Belgium was the first continental country to adopt Britain's system of industrialization. Belgium was a new nation, created after the defeat of Napoleon, and was anxious to succeed on the world stage. Belgium was also rich in both coal and iron resources, thus it was a logical step to pattern themselves after the success of the British. Germany also focused on industrialization, especially in the Saxony and Silesia regions, where raw materials were plentiful, but was much slower in spreading industrialization throughout the country than England had been. Britain's biggest industrial rival was the United States, as it had an abundance of natural resources and a spirit of entrepreneurship. The United States was fairly successful at industrializing, especially in the northern states, but its location across the Atlantic Ocean (far from the biggest markets), the availability of cheap land, which encouraged many Americans to become farmers, and its struggling post-Revolutionary

economy kept the United States a distant second to the British through much of the nineteenth century.

The one notable exception to widespread industrialization was France. A variety of factors kept France from successfully implementing the Industrial Revolution. First, France had no tradition of paper money, which discouraged the formation of a middle class and investment in businesses, as most wealth was still tied up in land. Second, France was much larger than Britain, but had fewer navigable rivers and poorer roads. Third, France had fewer natural resources and was especially deficient in coal, which was used to power much of the industrial revolution. Finally, France was in political turmoil during much of the age of industrialization due to the French Revolution and its chaotic aftermath. This slowed progress and ate up much-needed capital.

Figure 41.7 shows the population centers that were created as a result of the Industrial Revolution. The greatest concentrations of urban centers are in England and Belgium, with Germany as a somewhat distant third.

Figure 41.8 shows the industrial output per capita of the major countries in the world from 1750 to 1913. A standard of 100 was chosen at the

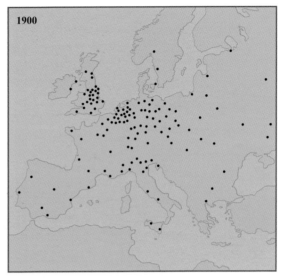

Figure 41.7 ■ *Population growth in the nineteenth century showing cities of 100,000 or more in 1900 and 1900.*

output of Great Britain in 1900. As you might expect, the output of Great Britain is higher than all other countries up to 1900, with Belgium and the United States trailing. (The United States output surpassed Great Britain's between 1900 and 1913.) Germany's industrialization was initially slow but then increased rapidly because of the unification of Germany. France was steady but slow.

■ Effects of the Industrial Revolution

The Industrial Revolution created the following changes in the world:

- National economies became rooted in industry and business rather than agriculture.
- The international balance of political and military power focused in Europe as the dominant culture of the world.
- Urbanization increased with an accompanying need for a large infrastructure (transportation, sewer, water, lights, etc.).
- Power shifted to the merchant middle class and improved their standard of living.

- A new social class was created—the urban poor.
- Use of natural resources was increased.
- The concept that technology could improve people's lives was established.

Some of these benefits were positive during the Industrial Revolution and have remained positive in the long view. However, others have now been seen to be a problem. We might ask, therefore, whether technology is, overall, good or bad. Joel Mokyr, in his book *The Gifts of Athena,* has suggested that the consequences of technology need to be viewed in short, medium, and long term to be properly understood:

1. **Short-term consequences:** Benefits are helpful and desirable (this is why we use it). Some dislocation is possible (such as loss of jobs). Overall, if proven to be a dud, it is discarded quickly.
2. **Medium-term consequences:** Negative consequences are noted and strong resistance often arises. Attempts are made in the medium term to stop the technology (Luddites, etc.); but these are rarely successful (except current efforts by environmental groups, who have the backing of

	1750	1800	1830	1860	1880	1900	1913
Great Britain	10	16	25	64	87	100	115
Belgium	9	10	14	28	43	56	88
United States	4	9	14	21	38	69	126
France	9	9	12	20	28	39	59
Germany	8	8	9	15	25	52	85
Austria-Hungary	7	7	8	11	15	23	32
Italy	8	8	8	10	12	17	26
Russia	6	6	7	8	10	15	20
China	8	6	6	4	4	3	3
India	7	6	6	3	2	1	2

Note: All entries are based on an index value of 100, equal to the per capita level of industrialization in Great Britain in 1900.

Source: P. Bairoch, "International Industrialization Levels from 1750 to 1980," *Journal of European Economic History* 11 (Fall 1982): 294. Data for Great Britain are actually for the United Kingdom, thereby including Ireland with England, Wales, and Scotland.

Figure 41.8 ■ *Per capita levels of Industrialization (1750–1913).*

politicians, courts, and many people). This resistance is outside market forces.

3. **Long-term consequences:** May require changes/evolution in the technology, but we rarely abandon the technology altogether because the benefits are great and the negatives are worked around. Over the long term, technology is self-correcting.

Sometimes the negatives of technology are associated with the complexity of the systems that began to be created during the Industrial Revolution. Robert Pool has suggested that complexity and not technology may be the culprit of our modern society.

Complexity creates unpredictability. The more complex a system, the more difficult it is to understand all the different ways the system may behave—and, in particular, to anticipate all the different ways it may fail. Interdependence among parts creates entirely new ways that things can go wrong, *ways that engineers often overlook or ignore. Thus many technological failures chalked up to mechanical breakdown or design flaws are more accurately described as the children of complexity.*

■ New Industrial Revolutions

We should pause in our story for just a moment to look at the Industrial Revolution in the long view and compare it to the situation in today's world and the future. At the beginning of the Industrial Revolution, England was the most powerful country in the world and had built a large domestic manufacturing sector. England had already created an empire with many colonies that helped with raw materials and became markets for finished goods.

Throughout the eighteenth and nineteenth centuries, the English remained committed to the policy of colonialism and restriction of manufacturing in their colonies (as they had attempted to do in America). This was accompanied with the imposition of taxes on the goods made in the colonies. The net result was, of course, a preferred price for English-produced goods. This policy is called **protectionism.**

The entire British Empire became, therefore, a preferred marketplace for English-produced goods. Over many decades, English protectionism led to a serious problem for the very manufacturers it sought to protect. These manufacturers enjoyed a profitable market without the need to improve. Therefore, they did not keep up with technology and create new technologies, as did the Americans and Germans. As a result, both America and Germany surpassed the British manufacturing output by the end of the nineteenth century. Outside of the British Empire, the Americans and Germans were higher in quality and lower in price. Eventually, the advantages of the American and German products became so great that even within the British Empire the non-English goods were preferred. The English manufacturers declined rapidly, accelerated by the First World War, and many are still struggling to recover.

Protectionism is not a policy that is unique to England. Labor unions have long endorsed this policy throughout the world. The unions want to force companies to retain their employees, and focus on other factors to reduce cost. In the mid-twentieth century, work rules imposed by labor union contracts resulted in higher costs for many American industries (and in other countries, too), so that these industries eventually became uncompetitive. Examples are the automobile industry, steelmaking, railroads, and coal mining. Today, all of these industries in America are struggling to compete on a worldwide basis.

The solution to the problem of jobs and local production seems to be this: creativity. Only by continuing to innovate with new products and new production methods can a local industry stay competitive on a worldwide basis. We must be prepared to change with the needs of the marketplace. As Alfred Toffler said in his book *Future Shock,* "The illiterate of the twenty-first century will not be those who cannot read or write, but, rather, those who cannot learn, unlearn, and relearn."

Some of the problems of society that came with the Industrial Revolution are the rise of poor working conditions and the pollution of the environment. These are the result of short-sighted manufacturing management. Not only are they bad for workers and for society in general, but they invite government regulations. The more intelligent long view sees the welfare of the workers and of the environment as important responsibilities of manufacturers. Avoiding responsibilities in these areas is, simply, a short-term response that is geared to immediate profits. It arises because management is not creative enough to find better solutions. In the next chapter we will explore the steps taken by governments and others to provide improved conditions for the workers of the world.

■ **Timeline—Important Dates**

Date	Event
1700	*Approximate beginning of the Industrial Revolution*
1712	*Newcomen invents his steam engine pump*
1763	*Watt patents an improved steam engine*
1767	*James Hargreaves invents the spinning jenny*
1771	*Richard Arkwright makes a spinning factory*
1787	*Edmund Cartwright starts first weaving factory*
1801	*Jacquard loom invented*
1811	*Formation of the Luddites*

■ **Suggested Readings**

Mokyr, Joel, *The Gifts of Athena,* Princeton University Press, 2002.

Pool, Robert, *Beyond Engineering,* Oxford University Press, 1997.

Toffler, Alvin, *Future Shock,* Bantam, 1984.

Winchester, Simon, *The Map that Changed the World,* Penguin Books, 2002.

Liberalism and Conservatism
Social Creativity

> For the next eight or ten months, Oliver was the victim of a systematic course of treachery and deception. He was brought up by hand.... [T]he parish authorities magnanimously and humanely resolved, that Oliver should be "farmed," or, in other words, that he should be dispatched to a branch-workhouse some three miles off, where twenty or thirty other juvenile offenders against the poor-laws, rolled about the floor all day, without the inconvenience of too much food or too much clothing, under the parental superintendence of an elderly female, who received the culprits at and for the consideration of sevenpence halfpenny per small head per week.
>
> —*Charles Dickens (from* Oliver Twist*)*

■ Tension

In the first chapter of this volume, we identified three general time periods that were distinguished by the issues of most importance during that time. We have already discussed the first two of those periods in which the nature of the First and Second Estates were redefined. We said that the third time period, 1790 to present, was dominated by the issue of social and economic equality, that is, redefinition of the Third Estate or the common people. This chapter is dedicated to that discussion.

The nineteenth century in Europe was a time of great social and political tension. The climate was established by two events: First, the final de-

feat of Napoleon and the repression of liberalism across continental Europe by the actions of the Congress of Vienna; second, the spread of industrialization and the resulting social upheaval that it caused.

The **Congress of Vienna** attempted to turn back the clock 100 years (at least) by restoring the monarchies to power all over continental Europe and pretending that the French Revolution and other liberal ideas had simply never happened. Of course, this task was impossible. The people did not forget their brief experience with liberty and better government. People were resentful of the monarchies as never before. No longer did they believe that having an absolute monarch was

God's way of ruling. They no longer saw themselves as links in the great chain of being and, therefore, locked into the social class and economic condition into which they were born. Those ideas were long dead, but the newly restored monarchical governments still operated on the old principles. The stability of the age was undercut by a gnawing desire for change and a strong feeling of betrayal and disillusionment.

This repression of political change was made more poignant because it was squarely at odds with the obvious socioeconomic changes that were taking place due to the effects of the Industrial Revolution. In continental Europe the people became aware of the changes in Britain, especially the initial feeling among the British poor that the Industrial Revolution was a chance to change their lives for the better. This caused the poor of continental Europe to yearn for similar opportunities.

In Britain, the bad living conditions that eventually accompanied the Industrial Revolution brought disappointment and disillusionment. The poor felt that they were being denied the basic rights that the Enlightenment had promised. The poor did not see how to solve the problem, but they were unhappy and restless. There were, however, some elements of society—liberal politicians, artists, writers, and social activists—who saw the deplorable conditions and resolved to take action. These forces were resisted by conservatives, who sought to maintain the basic principles of government and social policy that had led to Britain's dominant position in the world.

Throughout Europe, an ideological war began between those who believed creative and revolutionary change was needed to reshape Europe and those who believed a loss of the traditional values and structure would bring chaos and destruction. It was a conflict that shaped the nineteenth century and continues to the present.

▪ Personal Consequences of the Industrial Revolution

The success and spread of the Industrial Revolution brought with it sweeping changes. In the last chapter we discussed the political and economic changes that resulted in Britain's ascension to preeminence among the nations of the world through manufacturing. There were, however, changes that occurred at the personal level, especially for the working poor who moved from the farms of their fathers to seek a better life through honest hard labor.

The traditional family structure changed. Families had usually worked together farming small plots of land and producing cottage industry goods from their homes. The Industrial Revolution brought these families into cities and took people out of the home and into the factory, where they were divided off to their various tasks and often did not see each other for the whole day. The cohesion of families was much harder to maintain.

The schedule of daily life also changed. On the farm, work could be broken up into segments (milk the cows, feed the animals, mend the fence, plant the crop, plow the field, harvest the crop, etc.) and was sometimes even dictated by the seasons. Agricultural and cottage industry work also allowed people to work at their own pace as long as the work got done. Factory work was very monotonous. The pace of work was dictated by the speed of the machines.

The clock regulated the work day, with no allowances for disruptive problems or personal conditions. Workers received no breaks except briefly for supper. Sickness and family crises were given little or no consideration by ownership; the human workers were generally considered just another part of the industrial machine and could easily be replaced.

Working conditions were poor. The factories were often so loud that employees lost their hearing and were usually unbearably hot because of poor ventilation. Work was often dangerous; it was made worse by the very long working days, usually 12 to 14 hours for six days a week.

Child laborers were in demand because they could be paid less for their work and were needed for certain jobs that could only be done by their small fingers and bodies. Often, these jobs were some of the most dangerous. Children were forced to work the same hours as adults and were rarely able to withstand such a rigorous schedule. Therefore, death among working children was epidemic.

Eventually, the problem of child labor became so great and so obvious that some steps were taken to alleviate the situation. By 1802, forced child labor had been outlawed. In 1833 a law was passed requiring factory owners to establish schools for all children under the age of nine and set work hour limits for all children. However, these changes were not a sign of general improvement within the factories, and working conditions remained dangerous, harsh, unhealthy, and dehumanizing. A picture of typical working conditions for children is given in Figure 42.1.

The masses of people moving into the cities also caused a new series of urbanization problems that had never been dealt with before. Low-income housing was needed. This housing was often built by the companies, but the conditions were oppressive because the companies charged excessive rents in order to make the same high returns they were making in other aspects of their businesses. Private landlords were even worse,

since they often saw the working poor as easy prey for illegal or unethical schemes. One scheme was to entice a family to move into an apartment by offering initial low payments and then later raising the rent steeply. Because people were constantly moving into the city during this period, the demand for housing was usually greater than the number of apartments available. Thus, people stayed in their apartments despite the crushing rents because they had nowhere else to go. Another scheme was to offer homes for sale with mortgages that gave ownership (equity) to the occupants only when they had successfully completed all the payments, including a large balloon payment at the end. Many people spent 10 years making payments only to lose all when the final payment could not be made.

Another problem that most cities faced was that industrialization caused the cities to grow faster than the infrastructure could handle. Not only was housing overcrowded and poor, but transportation and roads were bad, sewer systems were often overwhelmed if they existed at all, and

Figure 42.1 ■ *Typical working conditions for children in the nineteenth century.* © *CORBIS.*

pollution was atrocious (much worse than what we see in even the worst modern cities). The poor sanitation and the overcrowding led to rampant disease. Figure 42.2 shows industrial pollution in a factory that would have been typical of the 19th Century.

There were few social amenities, and what existed was often poor. Hospitals were crowded and medical treatment was largely guesswork. There was no welfare program or social security to provide aid to those who could not find work, with the exception of a few underfunded charities. If people could not pay their bills, they were sent to the poorhouse. In reality these poorhouses were industrial work prisons, where conditions were even worse than in the real factories, and wages were so low that it was nearly impossible for these people to ever pay off their debts and regain their freedom.

Industrialization had several other negative consequences as well. Although industrialization did help create some positive changes in the economy, it also contributed to severe economic swings. Surges and depressions became common-

place, and when depressions occurred, up to half of all workers could find themselves out of work. Furthermore, while the onset of industrialization created many new jobs, it also caused the loss of other jobs. Skilled artisans were hardest hit as machines, operated by cheaper unskilled workers, began to be able to perform the artisans' tasks quicker and for less money. The Industrial Revolution spread because it made money for the factory owners. It also provided new opportunities for the poor to make money. However, industrialization brought many new problems that simply were not being addressed.

■ Universal Rights

Perhaps even more disturbing to the poor than the deplorable working and living conditions, at least in the long term, was their feeling that basic rights were being denied them. The principles of the Enlightenment were widely known and accepted but had been applied only to the upper and middle classes. In England, the middle class won inclusion

Figure 42.2 ■ Industrial pollution. © 2010 by Dudarev Mikhail. Used under license of Shutterstock, Inc.

into the franchised group (having protection of rights) in the English Civil War and the subsequent economic prosperity of the Industrial Revolution. In other countries, even the middle class was struggling to enjoy the basic rights of life, liberty, and the pursuit of happiness/property. The poor, both rural and urban, had never been included.

There was an attitude among businesses that they should act in a manner that was in their own self-interest (as discussed by Adam Smith in his book *Wealth of Nations*). In the nineteenth century, that generally meant businesses should seek short-term profits. Only rarely did a business consider long-term profits and, even more rarely, did a business consider the effects of its business practices on its employees, the environment, or other social considerations. Generally, business felt no responsibility for protecting the rights of individuals.

As a consequence of the Enlightenment, governments increasingly accepted their responsibility to ensure the rights of those who were franchised citizens (the upper and middle classes). Governments may have also felt the responsibility to guarantee the rights of the poor, but the governments were faced with a dilemma. They believed that economic success would come by following the British economic model (which had, after all, been immensely successful). That model was based on capitalism and governmental *laissez faire,* that is, the government would not interfere in business. If government attempted to guarantee the rights of the workers, it would interfere in business. Therefore, government had a conflict.

Groups within society tried to resolve the conflict in government and the issues of class differentiation with respect to rights in different ways. Some, especially business, just wanted the problems ignored. They believed that the natural forces of the marketplace would eventually solve the problems in some gradual way. They did not want governmental interference and hoped that the labor supply would continue to be compliant.

Other groups—political activists (conservatives and liberals), artists, writers, social activists—presented several highly creative solutions to the issues of class differences and the conflicts of governmental policy toward businesses and the poor.

We will discuss the class difference problems in more detail and then look at the solutions proposed by various groups.

■ The Rise of Class Conflicts

In spite of efforts by Europe's old aristocracy to pretend that all was as it had always been, the growth of the middle class over the seventeenth and eighteenth centuries had been changing the social fabric of Europe. Industrialization had been causing a change in the social hierarchy. A noble class that had gained its position by birth and ownership of land had long ruled Europe. The nobility were usually wealthy, but it was family name and not wealth that made one noble, and nobility gave power.

The growth of the middle class started to change this. By the time of the Industrial Revolution, wealth, not family, was the basis of power. This meant that some limited upward social mobility could be achieved. Thus, society was now divided into two groups: the wealthy (capitalists) and the poor (workers), rather than between nobility and commoners. The classes were identified by Karl Marx as the **bourgeoisie** (capitalists) and the **proletariat** (workers).

Many of the bourgeoisie were members of the old nobility that had understood the changes that were taking place and invested money into business ventures. However, other capitalists were from families that had been poor and/or previously discriminated against. In Britain the Scots and the Quakers became important parts of the bourgeoisie because they had invested early in industrial enterprises. (The Scots felt that they could gain prestige through manufacturing, and the Quakers looked to manufacturing because they were prohibited from owning land and so manufacturing was a good place for them to invest.) In France, Jews and Huguenots (Protestants) became important to industrialization for similar reasons.

Many of these newly rich had humble origins, but rather than feel empathy for the poor, they were more likely to feel proud of their accomplishments and disdainful of others' failures to similarly succeed. This attitude led to their separation from the working poor and a strong consciousness of class differences.

Class consciousness also grew because the growth of urbanization had drawn the working class together in a compact space for the first time. This gave the working class the opportunity to talk to each other and discuss what was happening. Although the proletariat had no real way to address their concerns with the owners, they did bond together in their afflictions. Later, other men would show these workers how to turn that bond, combined with frustration and anger, into political power.

■ Conservatives and Liberals

As has been discussed, the French Revolution, the reign of Napoleon, and the rise of industrialization were causing change across Europe. In an attempt to deal with these changes, two main political philosophies arose: conservatism and liberalism. Conservatives wanted to maintain the traditions of the past and allow changes to occur only gradually. Liberals wanted to bring about rapid political, social, and economic changes.

After the defeat of Napoleon, the conservatives were in control of all major governments in Europe. The Congress of Vienna, which shaped post-Napoleon Europe, reinstalled monarchies in all countries. Britain, Russia, Austria, and later France agreed to cooperate in the suppression of any new threats to the legitimate, existing monarchies. It seemed as though the conservatives would sweep aside any remnants of liberalism. After all, Austria was the political and cultural center of the world; Great Britain was Europe's greatest economic and naval power; Russia had such a vast population that it had been able to lose millions of men fighting Napoleon yet still turn him back; even France, the recent champion of liberalism, had joined the conservative alliance. Who could oppose such a force?

The authors of these conservative policies on continental Europe and the two great political leaders of the day were not kings, but the foreign ministers of Austria and France: **Klemens von Metternich** and **Charles de Tallyrand.** They understood that threats to the established governments would not come from other nations (whose monarchs had just as much to lose from liberal revolutions as did the Austrian emperor or the French king) but from internal threats. The internal threats in the future would come from two different internal factions: first, **ideological liberals,** who could stir up the discontent of the poor and would try to gain power at the expense of the upper classes; and second, **nationalists,** who would try to unite a religious or ethnic group within a larger empire in an effort to gain their independence.

Despite the overwhelming political and military might supporting the forces of conservatism, the nineteenth century was filled with revolutions throughout Europe. In 1821, Italian nationalists and liberals revolted against the Austrian Empire, which had been given control over northern Italy as part of the post-Napoleonic settlement. The Austrian army quickly crushed the Italian revolutionaries, thus keeping control of northern Italy.

Two years later, the French and Austrians assisted the Spanish government in defeating a liberal revolution. Spain had been in disarray for some time, as the nation's wealth and prestige diminished due to successful revolutions by many of Spain's American colonies. Spain had been prevented from regaining its colonies because of the Monroe Doctrine issued by the United States. The **Monroe Doctrine** stated that any foreign invasion anywhere in the Americas would be met with hostile resistance from the American military.

In 1825, the Greeks revolted against their Turkish rulers. Despite the fact that the Greeks were liberal revolutionaries, they were supported by Russia, which wanted to gain more influence in the region and drive out the Turks. The Russians felt justified in their support of this liberal revolution because the Ottoman Empire was not part of the European alliance. However, afraid that a successful liberal revolution in Greece would spread across Europe, England and France joined with the Ottoman Turks to put down the revolution.

German student agitations were suppressed in 1819, while a larger revolt had to be put down in Bavaria in 1830. Even the conservative Tory government in England had to put down liberal revolts within England when an economic slump caused unemployment to skyrocket.

In 1848, successful revolutions swept the traditional governments from power all across Europe. New governments came to power in Austria, Hungary, France, Prussia, Spain, and Italy. Liberals and commoners across Europe believed a new day had dawned. However, these new governments were not stable. They were governments headed by idealists who were generally unable to run the government operations and who failed to win the support of the traditional military units within the countries. These were costly mistakes. One by one, these new liberal and nationalistic governments fell. Within only six months, the revolutions in all countries but France were defeated and the governments returned to monarchies. (France returned to a republic under Louis Napoleon, nephew of Napoleon I.) 1848 became a year of lost hope.

Liberalism had won a chance, but it had been too weak and too unprepared for the burden of leadership. Many people across Europe began to believe what the conservatives had been saying all along: Liberal governments were weak at best and allowed for chaos and anarchy at worst. Government should be left to those who had the wealth, education, and time to run them properly.

Part of the problem that the liberals faced was that most of the champions of their cause were artists and political philosophers, not politicians. Thus, these were people who dealt with ideas and principles, but had no experience with the practicality, organization, and compromise that are required to run a government. These people generally wanted to help the poor and attempted to do so by making their plight known to the middle classes who controlled the power of government. Liberals did this in the hope that the middle and lower classes together could make real political and social changes.

Influence of Artists

Many Romantic artists and others who possessed a generally Romantic orientation felt that the rural or natural life was superior to the urban or industrialized life. These people yearned for a return to a more idyllic life of the past. When the Industrial Revolution resulted in great urban difficulties, many artists became activists and tried to change those conditions. Romantic artists saw themselves (and often were) starving and poor, thus adding to their identification with the urban masses.

Activist Romantic artists believed that wholesale change was needed and the concepts and restrictions of the day were no longer important, whether in art, politics, or society. Within the realm of politics, they felt that revolutions were acceptable any time the regime in power was restrictive of the rights of the people. Within society, they advocated the breaking down of the traditional class hierarchy. Within art, they ignored the forms, structures, and rules in favor of any expression of the artists' feelings.

Influence of Writers

Whereas the Romantic artists were calling for the return to the "more idyllic time" of rural Europe, many writers were trying to improve the conditions that faced the lower classes in industrialized Europe by vividly depicting the deplorable conditions and therefore pricking the consciences of the middle class. Several socially conscious writers who were not necessarily Romantics took sharp aim at the complacent middle class view of life. Among the most important of these was **Charles Dickens.**

English author Charles Dickens was immensely popular within his own lifetime, and many of his novels were direct attacks on the social problems faced by the poor of his day. Dickens attacked child orphanage problems and showed life in the London slums in his novel *Oliver Twist.* In *Hard Times* Dickens depicted the evils of industrialization and attacked the philosophy of utilitarianism. In *Bleak House* Dickens attacked the unhealthy London weather caused by industrialization. Several of his novels, including *David Copperfield, Great Expectations,* and *A Christmas Carol* attacked the single-minded pursuit of money and position.

Other important authors were **Jane Austen,** who criticized English manners and class consciousness in her books *Emma* and *Pride and Prejudice,* and sisters **Charlotte Bronte** (*Jane Eyre*) and **Emily Bronte** (*Wuthering Heights*), who both examined the roles of women in male-dominated Victorian society. Writing gave women a voice that they had previously not had in influencing attitudes and policy, especially within Great Britain.

Because of these British writers, there began to be real change, as the middle class began to feel sympathetic toward the plight of the poor. Despite the change in attitude, however, real change was slow in coming. The agents of this change, the middle class, were not well represented in Parliament, which was heavily weighted toward landholders. The ruling Tory party (conservatives) made a few token gestures toward change, but these feeble attempts were viewed as too little, too late by much of the middle class. Having misjudged the importance of reform to the middle class, the Tory government was toppled in 1830, and the more liberal reformed Whig party came to power. Once the Whigs were in power, some real steps were taken toward social reform.

■ Social Reformers: Utilitarianism

The rise of liberal politics and the Industrial Revolution led to several new philosophical theories. These new political philosophies were intended to give legitimacy and moral strength to the changes that were taking place. The philosophies were also designed to encourage further liberal progress within society. However, even within liberal circles, these new ideas were discussed, debated, and often disagreed with.

One of the first of these new political philosophies was the concept of utilitarianism. Developed by British philosopher **Jeremy Bentham,** utilitarianism states that every institution and every law must be measured according to its **social usefulness.** Social usefulness was defined as that which produces the greatest happiness for the greatest number of people. (In this basic belief Bentham's concepts were much like the ancient philosophy of the Epicureans.)

Bentham's underlying principle was that all people are basically self-interested—that is, they work for their own best good. He reasoned that people would support social issues that benefited the most people because they would be part of that group and would therefore also benefit. Bentham believed that governments that made decisions according to the principles of utilitarianism would be democratic because they would automatically support the concepts desired by the majority of the people. Utilitarianism, though based on self-interest, was harmonious with the liberal trends and political revolutions of the day because of its democratic orientation.

Utilitarianism also espoused the concept that science and technology (the products of the Enlightenment, scientific awakening, and the Industrial Revolution) should be used to solve the problems of society. Bentham's belief in science was so strong that he devised a science-based method for making utilitarian decisions. He called it the **calculus of felicity.** In this method decisions were rated according to the following set of criteria:

- Intensity—how intense is the effect from the decision?
- Duration—how long will the effect last?
- Certainty—how sure is the benefit if the decision is made?
- Propinquity—how soon will the benefit be seen?
- Fecundity—how many more benefits will follow?
- Purity—how free from pain is the decision?
- Extent—how many people will be affected?

One successful example of the application of the calculus of felicity was to the sewer systems within England. **Edwin Chadwick,** a skilled engineer and an adherent of the concept of utilitarianism, believed that disease contributed to poverty because sick people couldn't work. These sick and impoverished people might die and leave orphans, thus continuing the cycle of poverty, sickness, and death. Chadwick collected scientific evidence (researching Louis Pasteur, Robert Koch, and Joseph Lister) and proved that sanitation would reduce disease and improve the standard of living for everyone. He showed the numerical value of putting in sewers versus the money saved of not doing so. Chadwick then pushed for the installation of iron and ceramic sewers and showed that the cost of sewers was actually lower than the cost of hauling away sewage by hand from the outhouses. Thus, Chadwick's plan benefited everyone by providing better living conditions and by saving money. From this same method of reasoning, other strong public health laws were enacted. This is a good example of the principle of utilitarianism at its most successful.

Despite some of the obvious successes of utilitarianism, Bentham's philosophy had some drawbacks and concerns that many were quick to point out. First, utilitarianism assumes that science can actually determine what is of the most value. Science, however, has not been very successful in determining which alternative of several complex paths is the correct one. Second, utilitarianism provides no way to ensure that the leaders who decide what is of the most value for the most people will act correctly (or not act in their own self-interest if it conflicts with that of the majority). Third, utilitarianism ignores the idea that what is good for the most people might not always be the right (or moral) thing to do. Fourth, like democracy, utilitarianism requires a high level of education for all people so that the people can make informed choices and not be swayed easily by those with money or easy access to the media. Fifth, utilitarianism gives the majority absolute control (called the tyranny of the majority) and often ignores individual cases.

Charles Dickens openly attacked the philosophy of utilitarianism in his novel *Hard Times*. He showed how utilitarianism's pursuit of progress and the lack of empathy toward individual human situations and emotions brought about the ruin of a family.

Several of the other prominent philosophers of the time also were opposed to utilitarianism. The Scottish philosopher **Thomas Carlyle** felt that it merely justified the greed and acquisitiveness of the middle class. Carlyle supported the idea that progress in society came from great men, or heroes, who personally solved problems, not from majority rule decisions.

Modern governments (in the twenty-first century) are often utilitarian. They support concepts that benefit the most people. However, what would a utilitarian-based government decide if the majority of the people decided to choose a path that deviated from the pursuit of fundamentals such as life, liberty, and pursuit of happiness? This might occur in a situation where a radical group gained control over a country and convinced the majority that the radical policy would solve some major problem. (We are reminded of Germany during the Nazi regime.)

▪ Social Reformers: Marxism

Utilitarianism was not the most influential or controversial new political philosophy to arise out of liberal politics and the Industrial Revolution. That honor, at least in the impact in some countries, would go to a new socioeconomic political system known as **communism** and created by **Karl Marx.** He was born and raised in Germany and became involved in liberal politics while a university student. Marx was forced to leave Germany because of his politics and lived in a variety of other countries from which he also fled. Eventually, Marx moved to England, where he found two advantages. First, England had a strong constitutional monarchy and the individual rights of people were well protected, thus allowing Marx to work and write with less interference from the government. Second, Marx joined with **Friedrich Engels,** a wealthy German who was running a factory in England and who agreed with Marx's principles. Engles helped develop Marx's philosophy, and coauthored some of Marx's texts. Engles also helped to support Marx financially, allowing him to devote himself more to his writing.

Karl Marx and Friedrich Engles made a major impact in 1848 when their pamphlet *The Communist Manifesto* was published. This pamphlet was written for a meeting of the First International—an early workers group and precursor to labor unions. *The Communist Manifesto* outlined history as a struggle between classes: the nobility against the church, the middle class against the nobility, and so on. The underlying premise is that one class has always been exploited by another, and the oppressed class has attempted to assert itself and gain its freedom from or parity with the other class.

Marx and Engles argued that the nobility had triumphed over the church during the medieval age and the bourgeoisie had triumphed over the noble class in the eighteenth century. They argued that in their own time the middle class (bourgeoisie) was exploiting the worker class (proletariat), and that it was inevitable that eventually the proletariat would rise up and overthrow the bourgeoisie.

Marx and Engles advocated that the workers begin this uprising immediately and take political power into their own hands. *The Communist Manifesto* ends with the following call to action: "Let the ruling classes tremble at a Communist revolution. The proletarians have nothing to lose but their chains. They have a world to win. WORKING MEN OF ALL COUNTRIES, UNITE!" (Emphasis in the original.)

Having called for a communist revolution of workers, Karl Marx then gave his arguments a moral and philosophical support in his book *Das Kapital*. Where *The Communist Manifesto* had been brief, *Das Kapital* was more than a thousand pages long and laid out in detail Marx's theory of economics and political philosophy. The basic premise of *Das Kapital* is this: The value of a product is determined by the amount of labor it took to produce it. The fair wage for the laborer is the value of his work, which is the value of the product. However, in capitalism, the owner must sell the product for more than he pays the laborer so that he can make a profit himself. Marx points out that the lowest possible wage is the sustenance level (the wage needed just to sustain life), and

this wage can always be paid as long as there is a surplus of labor, and the pool of surplus labor can always be maintained by using machines to replace workers, who must then return to the surplus labor pool. Capitalism both artificially raises prices and lowers wages, thus robbing the worker twice—first, when he does his work for less than its value; and second, when he must buy the goods he produced for more than they are worth.

Marx asserts that this problem will ultimately lead to the five major inconsistencies of capitalism, which will lead to all means of production falling into the hands of the laborers and the elimination of the classes. These five major inconsistencies are as follows:

1. *Capitalism has an inconsistency because of competition between companies.* This leads one company to expand and hire more workers and therefore increases wages. In turn, that leads to the use of more machines to avoid the higher wages and thus to higher investment. But capitalism cannot increase profits from fixed investments, and so the labor must be further squeezed. However, there is ultimately a limit to how much this can be done, hence, an inconsistency.

2. *Capitalism inevitably leads to an increase in the concentration of economic power.* As firms compete, the biggest, most efficient firms will defeat the smaller, weaker ones and drive them out of business. This situation leads to monopolies, which only enhance the basic exploitation problem because a lack of competition means they can pay workers less and charge buyers more.

3. *Capitalism has economic swings, which include depression.* As firms compete and cause more unemployment and failures of small businesses, more and more people become unemployed. This reduces the ability of the people to buy products, thus leading to depression. This creates a downward spiral where companies have to lay off more workers in order to retain their profit margin, but in so doing they increase the number of people who can no longer purchase their product,

deepening the depression and causing the cycle to continue.

4. *The increasing number of people who are unemployed eventually will constitute an army of dissatisfied workers who will demand change.* But capitalism's inherent contradictions cannot be solved within the capitalist system and so the capitalists will be unable to deal with the situation and solve the crisis.

5. *Unable to find work and care for themselves and their families, the army of dissatisfied proletariat will rebel and assume power.* This will lead to a class-free society where the people control all means of production and each person contributes their labor in return for what they need. Because there will be no ownership that needs to earn a profit, each worker can be paid his actual value. Purchase prices will be less, as prices will not need to be inflated. Eventually, because the means of industry will be controlled by all (the community, thus, the title communism), all will be equal and nation-states will disappear, as all mankind will be united for the common good.

Marx's *Das Kapital* also outlines many radical changes to the political and economic system that will need to occur. Among these changes are the abolition of property in land and application of all rents of land to public purposes, a heavy progressive or graduated income tax, abolition of all rights of inheritance, confiscation of the property of all emigrants and rebels, free education for all children, and equal obligation of all to work. Another important aspect of communism is the centralization of the means of production in the state. This would include centralization of credit in the hands of the state by means of a national bank with state capital and an exclusive monopoly, centralization of the means of transportation and communication, and the centralization of control over industry and agriculture.

At first, this idea seems out of harmony with the idea that the state would dissolve. However, Marx believed that the state would have to exist to perform these functions for a time (possibly even generations) until the shared control of the means of production would be second nature and all would voluntarily contribute to the greater good. The state was supposed to be run by the workers themselves, however. It was only later, under Lenin and Stalin, that a political ruling class was added to the ideas of Marxism.

Many of Marx's concerns with capitalism seemed to have merit. The Great Depression that swept across the globe during the 1920s and 1930s seemed to prove what Marx had said regarding the inconsistencies of capitalism. However, communism was less practical in reality than it was in theory, and its implementation in several nations throughout the twentieth century revealed problems that Marx had not understood or anticipated. Some of those problems are:

■ *Communism largely ignores imagination, entrepreneurship, and creativity and gives no incentive for them.* As creativity is the driving force in the continual progress of man, Marx's oversight in this area meant that communism could easily fall prey to economic and cultural stagnation. Related to this is that communism attacks the natural self-interest of people (its prohibition of land ownership and inheritance, etc.) and assumes self-interest is a negative thing, when in reality, self-interest is amoral and can be focused as a positive or negative force.

■ *Communism does not effectively deal with the problem of improvement and change.* Communism preached that all technological improvements in capitalism are done to lower the wage of the worker and make a greater profit. However, some technological advances are simply more cost-effective and efficient, and thus lead to a better standard of living.

■ *Agriculture is generally not treated properly within the communist model.* Unlike in industry, in agriculture it is much more difficult to control the variables of production. Things like weather, soil conditions, and crop disease could not ever be totally controlled by the state. Furthermore, in agriculture there is a much stronger tendency to think of the land and the produce as "mine," as the entire process is generally done by the same worker or workers from start to finish, whereas a factory worker might do one small part of the assembly over and over again. Industrial workers think in terms of being paid for their time and skill, while agricultural workers think in terms of being paid for what they actually produce.

■ *Communism does not deal with several internal problems that arise from the human element.* It ignores human attributes such as education, experience, and talent, as well as human differences such as working at different rates and with varying amounts of effort. Communism fosters human corruption. This became one of communism's most glaring weaknesses, as leaders of communist nations in the twentieth century were unable to resist the temptation to live better than the workers, who were supposed to be their equals. Over and over again, party leaders in nations such as the Soviet Union, China, Cuba, and North Korea would live in opulent palaces, drive luxury cars, vacation and shop in the capitalist west, and take other perks unavailable to the workers.

■ *Marx did not anticipate capitalism being able or willing to adapt itself in order to survive and improve.* Democratic governments across the globe, to varying degrees, abandoned *laissez faire* policies in favor of more active roles and implemented some aspects of socialism/communism as a means of reining in the excesses of capitalism. Government regulation of certain industries became common, monopolies were outlawed, minimum incomes were set, maximum work days were fixed, and government-run welfare, workers' compensation, and other social programs were set up.

Social Reformers: Labor Unions

Laborers who were working in wretched conditions soon realized that they could unite together and positively influence their work environment. Formal organizations called **labor unions,** with leaders elected by the workers, sought to force businesses to create better conditions. The unions also worked to influence governments to mandate minimum acceptable conditions for work.

Initially, labor unions were illegal. They were viewed as being antibusiness and unpatriotic (since business helped nations become strong). However, in 1871 unions were declared legal in Great Britain and then also in most other countries within a few years.

Although often staffed with some radical elements, labor unions generally worked within the capitalist system rather than seeking to overthrow it. In this they were quite different from Marxist organizations. Their moderation gave unions access to conventional politicians and increased the unions' effectiveness. Many of the laws that alleviated the problems resulting from the Industrial Revolution were the result of union persuasion. In Great Britain, the labor union movement first joined with one of the major parties (the Liberals) and then broke away and formed its own party which, today, is one of the two major parties in Great Britain.

Social Change

Who is responsible for bringing about social change? We might look back at the nineteenth century and say that business was most culpable for the bad working conditions and therefore business executives should have made the changes. We might also have pointed to the traditional *laissez faire* policy of governments and said that they were delinquent in not acting sooner to protect the basic rights of their citizens. In today's world, both of those assertions are probably true. Back in the nineteenth century, manipulating social change was much more difficult, and people in all facets of society were reluctant to attempt to change what seemed to be such a natural system of existence. Remember that centuries of tradition were behind the separation of people according to class, and it just wasn't viewed as important for one class to help another. In this regard, Marx's thesis of class struggle was probably correct.

In the twenty-first century, many groups have stepped forward to try and cause social change. We live in an activist world. Just as in the past, some modern activists seek to make changes outside the system. They may even try to change through violence and terrorism. In general, these efforts are not successful. Eventually, good people will stop giving them support and they will cease to be able to influence policy. However, means should be found to offer such groups a legitimate way of voicing their objections and a way to effect change within the system.

Since creativity is associated with change, is conservatism anticreative? Blind and unchanging conservatism probably is anticreative. However, in today's world, conservatism is less against change than in favor of maintaining values. Therefore, to maintain values that have been proven in the past and also to enact change within those values is a task that requires great creativity. Such efforts usually result in gradual rather than rapid changes. Stability is often important for these creative people rather than chaotic change.

Romantic artists, writers, and some politicians took personal actions to change social conditions. They tried to affect the entire society. While admirable, most of the work of change is ultimately done by individuals—business leaders who accept responsibilities for improving working conditions in their factory, neighbors who assist others who are in need, church members who donate time or goods to help the poor. All of these are elements of social change on the individual level. Such efforts cumulatively can change the world.

▪ Timeline—Important Dates

Date	Event
1748–1832	Jeremy Bentham
1775–1817	Jane Austen
1802	Forced child labor law passed in England
1812–1870	Charles Dickens
1815	Congress of Vienna
1818–1883	Karl Marx
1830	Reformed Whig government
1833	Law limiting working hours for children passed
1848	Karl Marx and Friedrich Engles publish The Communist Manifesto
1848	Revolutions throughout Europe
1871	Trade unions became legal

▪ Suggested Readings

Bronte, Charlotte, *Jane Eyre,* Signet Classics, 1960.
Dickens, Charles, *Oliver Twist,* Bantam Books, 1982.

John Stuart Mill: Utilitarianism

John Stuart Mill (1806–1873) was born in London to the son of a philosopher and economist. Through his father's rigorous education, he learned Greek and Latin in his childhood, was a competent logician by age twelve, and a trained economist by age sixteen. He suffered a nervous breakdown in his twenties and realized that there was more to life than devotion to an analytical intellect. He then focused his energies on promoting the necessity of using the scientific approach to understand and effect social, political and economic change. He strongly supported individual freedom and advocated governmental intervention to guarantee those freedoms as opposed to the current governmental practices of *laissez faire.* He rejected the wage system and supported state ownership, thus laying the foundation for concepts of socialism and communism that followed closely behind him.

His book, *Utilitarianism,* became the fundamental defense of the philosophy carrying the same name. Utilitarianism was first developed by Jeremy Bentham, an English philosopher and social advocate, and is the doctrine that every institution or law should be measured by its social usefulness. Mill clarified this with his "Greatest Happiness Principle," which defines the usefulness of anything as that which produces the greatest happiness for the greatest number of people. The following passages from *Utilitarianism* illustrate this philosophy and Mill's basis for these conclusions.

■ **Chapter II**

What Utilitarianism Is

The creed which accepts as the foundation of morals, Utility, or the Greatest Happiness Principle, holds that actions are right in proportion as they tend to promote happiness, wrong as they tend to produce the reverse of happiness. By happiness is intended pleasure, and the absence of pain; by unhappiness, pain, and the privation of pleasure. To give a clear view of the moral standard set up by the theory, much more requires to be said; in particular, what things it includes in the ideas of pain and pleasure; and to what extent this is left an open question. But these supplementary explanations do not affect the theory of life on which this theory of morality is grounded— namely, that pleasure, and freedom from pain, are the only things desirable as ends; and that all desirable things (which are as numerous in the utilitarian as in any other scheme) are desirable either for the pleasure inherent in themselves, or as means to the promotion of pleasure and the prevention of pain.

Now, such a theory of life excites in many minds, and among them in some of the most estimable in feeling and purpose, inveterate dislike. To suppose that life has (as they express it) no higher end than pleasure—no better and nobler object of desire and pursuit—they designate as utterly mean and grovelling; as a doctrine worthy only of swine, to whom the followers of Epicurus were, at a very early period, contemptuously likened; and modern holders of the doctrine are occasionally made the subject of equally polite comparisons by its German, French, and English assailants.

When thus attacked, the Epicureans have always answered, that it is not they, but their accusers, who represent human nature in a degrading light; since the accusation supposes human beings to be capable of no pleasures except those of which swine are capable. If this supposition were true, the charge could not be gainsaid, but would then be no longer an imputation; for if the sources of pleasure were precisely the same to human beings and to swine, the rule of life which is good enough for the one would be good enough for the other. The comparison of the Epicurean life to that of beasts is felt as degrading, precisely because a beast's pleasures do not satisfy a human being's conceptions of happiness. Human beings have faculties more elevated than the animal appetites, and when once made conscious of them, do not regard anything as happiness which does not include their gratification. I do not, indeed, consider the Epicureans to have been by any means faultless in drawing out their scheme of consequences from the utilitarian principle. To do this in any sufficient manner, many Stoic as well as Christian elements require to be included. But there is no known Epicurean theory of life which does not assign to the pleasures of the intellect, of the feelings and imagination, and of the moral sentiments, a much higher value as pleasures than to those of mere sensation. It must be admitted,

Source: From *Utilitarianism* by John Stuart Mills (Middlesex: Penguin Books, Ltd., 1987).

however, that utilitarian writers in general have placed the superiority of mental over bodily pleasures chiefly in the greater permanency, safety, uncostliness, etc., of the former—that is, in their circumstantial advantages rather than in their intrinsic nature. And on all these points utilitarians have fully proved their case; but they might have taken the other, and, as it may be called; higher ground, with entire consistency. It is quite compatible with the principle of utility to recognize the fact, that some *kinds* of pleasure are more desirable and more valuable than others. It would be absurd that while, in estimating all other things, quality is considered as well as quantity, the estimation of pleasures should be supposed to depend on quantity alone.

If I am asked, what I mean by difference of quality in pleasures, or what makes one pleasure more valuable than another, merely as a pleasure, except its being greater in amount, there is but one possible answer. Of two pleasures, if there be one to which all or almost all who have experience of both give a decided preference, irrespective of any feeling of moral obligation to prefer it, that is the more desirable pleasure. If one of the two is, by those who are competently acquainted with both, placed so far above the other that they prefer it, even though knowing it to be attended with a greater amount of discontent, and would not resign it for any quantity of the other pleasure which their nature is capable of, we are justified in ascribing to the preferred enjoyment a superiority in quality, so far outweighing quantity as to render it, in comparison, of small account. . . .

What means are there of determining which is the acutest of two pains, or the intensest of two pleasurable sensations, except the general suffrage of those who are familiar with both? Neither pains nor pleasures are homogeneous, and pain is always heterogeneous with pleasure. What is there to decide whether a particular pleasure is worth purchasing at the cost of a particular pain, except the feelings and judgement of the experienced? When, therefore, those feelings and judgement declare the pleasures derived from the higher faculties to be preferable *in kind,* apart from the question of intensity, to those of which the animal nature, disjoined from the higher faculties, is susceptible, they are entitled on this subject to the same regard.

I have dwelt on this point, as being a necessary part of a perfectly just conception of Utility or Happiness, considered as the directive rule of human conduct. But it is by no means an indispensable condition to the acceptance of the utilitarian standard; for that standard is not the agent's own greatest happiness, but the greatest amount of happiness altogether; and if it may possibly be doubted whether a noble character is always the happier for its nobleness, there can be no doubt that it makes other people happier, and that the world in general is immensely a gainer by it. Utilitarianism, therefore, could only attain its end by the general cultivation of nobleness of character, even if each individual were only benefited by the nobleness of others, and his own, so far as happiness is concerned, were a sheer deduction from the benefit. But the bare enunciation of such an absurdity as this last, renders refutation superfluous.

According to the Greatest Happiness Principle, as above explained, the ultimate end, with reference to and for the sake of which all other things are desirable (whether we are considering our own good or that of other people), is an existence exempt as far as possible from pain, and as rich as possible in enjoyments, both in point of quantity and quality; the test of quality, and the rule for measuring it against quantity, being the preference felt by those who, in their opportunities of experience, to which must be added their habits of self-consciousness and self-observation, are best furnished with the means of comparison. This, being, according to the utilitarian opinion, the end of human action, is necessarily also the standard of morality; which may accordingly be defined, the rules and precepts for human conduct, by the observance of which an existence such as has been described might be, to the greatest extent possible, secured to all mankind; and not to them only, but, so far as the nature of things admits, to the whole sentient creation.

Meanwhile, let utilitarians never cease to claim the morality of self-devotion as a possession which belongs by as good a right to them, as either to the Stoic or to the Transcendentalist. The utilitarian morality does recognize in human beings the power of sacrificing their own greatest good for the good of others. It only refuses to admit that the sacrifice is itself a good. A sacrifice which does not increase, or tend to increase, the sum total of happiness, it considers as wasted. The only self-renunciation which it applauds, is devotion to the happiness, or to some of the means of happiness, of others; either of mankind collectively, or of individuals within the limits imposed by the collective interests of mankind.

I must again repeat, what the assailants of utilitarianism seldom have the justice to acknowledge, that the happiness which forms the utilitarian standard of what is right in conduct, is not the agent's own happiness, but that of all concerned. As between his own happiness and that of others, utilitarianism requires him to be as strictly impartial as a disinterested and benevolent spectator. In the golden rule of Jesus of Nazareth, we read the complete spirit of the ethics of utility. To do as one would be done by, and to love one's neighbour as oneself, constitute the ideal perfection of utilitarian morality. As the means of making the nearest approach to this ideal, utility would enjoin, first, that laws and social arrangements should place the happiness, or (as speaking practically it may be called) the interest, of every individual, as nearly as possible in harmony with the interest of the whole.

Karl Marx: Communist Manifesto

Karl Marx (1818–1883) was born in Germany and became involved in radical movements during college. He went to Paris, hoping to publish a radical newspaper, and there he met his lifelong friend, and co-author of *Communist Manifesto,* Friedrich Engels. Marx lived in Paris, Brussels, and Germany but eventually was exiled from these places because of his political activity, and he finally settled in London where he lived until his death. Unlike philosophers of the past, Marx believed that reality had an economic base. He wrote on the materialism and atheism of the Greek atomists, receiving his doctorate in 1841. He lived most of his life in poverty, seeking only to develop his ideas of economic and political theory.

Marx's *Communist Manifesto* was not a well-known document for many years after its publication, but has become one of the most widely read and discussed literary works of the twentieth century. The *Communist Manifesto* dictates that class struggles and the continual dominance of one class have driven the history of the world. It recounts how the aristocracy had dominated all other classes for so long, but was finally deposed by the rise of the middle class (bourgeoisie) in the eighteenth century. The working class (proletariat) was labeled as the new underprivileged class, and was exploited by the bourgeoisie. Marx and Engels advocate an uprising by the proletariat as the next step in the evolution of civilization. The proletariat was told they had the power to revolt, and if they did they would be able to adopt socialism to make the world a better place. Other writers had defended the principles of socialism before Marx, but no one had yet pushed for the real-world application of it, as did the *Communist Manifesto.*

These selections come from the dramatic end to the *Communist Manifesto.* After presenting the rationality for revolution, the famous call to arms was given in the final words: "Working Men of all Countries, Unite!"

▪ Proletarians and Communists

In what relation do the Communists stand to the proletarians as a whole?

The Communists do not form a separate party opposed to other working-class parties.

They have no interests separate and apart from those of the proletariat as a whole.

They do not set up any sectarian principles of their own, by which to shape and mould the proletarian movement.

The Communists are distinguished from the other working-class parties by this only: 1. In the national struggles of the proletarians of the different countries, they point out and bring to the front the common interests of the entire proletariat independently of all nationality. 2. In the various stages of development which the struggle of the working class against the bourgeoisie has to pass through, they always and everywhere represent the interests of the movement as a whole.

The Communists, therefore, are on the one hand, practically, the most advanced and resolute section of the working-class parties of every country, that section which pushes forward all others; on the other hand, theoretically, they have over the great mass of the proletariat the advantage of clearly understanding the line of march, the conditions, and the ultimate general results of the proletarian movement.

The immediate aim of the Communists is the same as that of all the other proletarian parties; formation of the proletariat into a class, overthrow of the bourgeois supremacy, conquest of political power by the proletariat.

The theoretical conclusions of the Communists are in no way based on ideas or principles that have been invented, or discovered, by this or that would-be universal reformer.

They merely express, in general terms, actual relations springing from an existing class struggle, from a historical movement going on under our very eyes. The abolition of existing property relations is not at all a distinctive feature of Communism.

All property relations in the past have continually been subject to historical change consequent upon the change in historical conditions.

The French Revolution, for example, abolished feudal property in favor of bourgeois property.

The distinguishing feature of Communism is not the abolition of property generally, but the abolition of bourgeois property. But modern bourgeois private property is the final and most complete expression of the system of producing and appropriating products, that is based on class antagonism, on the exploitation of the many by the few.

In this sense, the theory of the Communists may be summed up in the single sentence: Abolition of private property.

We Communists have been reproached with the desire of abolishing the right of personally acquiring property as the fruit of a man's own labor, which property is alleged to be the ground work of all personal freedom, activity and independence.

Source: From *The Communist Manifesto* by Karl Marx and Friedrich Engles.

Hard-won, self-acquired, self-earned property! Do you mean the property of the petty artisan and of the small peasant, a form of property that preceded the bourgeois form? There is no need to abolish that; the development of industry has to a great extent already destroyed it, and is still destroying it daily.

Or do you mean modern bourgeois private property?

But does wage-labor create any property for the laborer? Not a bit. It creates capital, i.e., that kind of property which exploits wage-labor, and which cannot increase except upon condition of getting a new supply of wage-labor for fresh exploitation. Property, in its present form, is based on the antagonism of capital and wage-labor. Let us examine both sides of this antagonism.

To be a capitalist, is to have not only a purely personal, but a social status in production. Capital is a collective product, and only by the united action of many members, nay, in the last resort, only by the united action of all members of society, can it be set in motion.

Capital is therefore not a personal, it is a social power.

When, therefore, capital is converted into common property, into the property of all members of society, personal property is not thereby transformed into social property. It is only the social character of the property that is changed. It loses its class-character. . . .

*   *   *

Abolition of the family! Even the most radical flare up at this infamous proposal of the Communists.

On what foundation is the present family, the bourgeois family, based? On capital, on private gain. In its completely developed form this family exists only among the bourgeoise. But this state of things finds its complement in the practical absence of the family among the proletarians, and in public prostitution.

The bourgeois family will vanish as a matter of course when its complement vanishes, and both will vanish with the vanishing of capital.

Do you charge us with wanting to stop the exploitation of children by their parents? To this crime we plead guilty.

But, you will say, we destroy the most hallowed of relations, when we replace home education by social.

And your education! Is not that also social, and determined by the social conditions under which you educate, by the intervention, direct or indirect, of society by means of schools, etc.? The Communists have not invented the intervention of society in education; they do but seek to alter the character of that intervention, and to rescue education from the influence of the ruling class.

The bourgeois clap-trap about the family and education, about the hallowed co-relation of parent and child, becomes all the more disgusting, the more, by the action of Modern Industry, all family ties among the proletarians are torn asunder, and their children transformed into simple articles of commerce and instruments of labor.

But you Communists would introduce community of women, screams the whole bourgeoisie in chorus.

The bourgeois sees in his wife a mere instrument of production. He hears that the instruments of production are to be exploited in common, and, naturally, can come to no other conclusion, than that the lot of being common to all will likewise fall to the women.

He has not even a suspicion that the real point aimed at is to do away with the status of women as mere instruments of production.

For the rest, nothing is more ridiculous than the virtuous indignation of our bourgeois at the community of women which, they pretend, is to be openly and officially established by the Communists. The Communists have no need to introduce community of women; it has existed almost from time immemorial.

Our bourgeois, not content with having the wives and daughters of their proletarians at their disposal, not to speak of common prostitutes, take the greatest pleasure in seducing each other's wives.

Bourgeois marriage is in reality a system of wives in common and thus, at the most, what the

Communists might possibly be reproached with, is that they desire to introduce, in substitution for a hypocritically concealed, an openly legalized community of women. For the rest, it is self-evident, that the abolition of the present system of production must bring with it the abolition of the community of women springing from that system, i.e., of prostitution both public and private.

The Communists are further reproached with desiring to abolish countries and nationalities.

The working men have no country. We cannot take from them what they have not got. Since the proletariat must first of all acquire political supremacy, must rise to be leading class of the nation, must constitute itself the nation, it is so far, itself national, though not in the bourgeois sense of the word.

National differences, and antagonisms between peoples, are daily more and more vanishing, owing to the development of the bourgeoisie, to freedom of commerce, to the world-market, to uniformity in the mode of production and in the conditions of life corresponding thereto.

The supremacy of the proletariat will cause them to vanish still faster. United action, of the leading civilized countries at least, is one of the first conditions for the emancipation of the proletariat.

In proportion as the exploitation of one individual by another is put an end to, the exploitation of one nation by another will also be put an end to. In proportion as the antagonism between classes within the nation vanishes, the hostility of one nation to another will come to an end.

The charges against Communism made from a religious, a philosophical, and generally, from an ideological standpoint, are not deserving of serious examination.

Does it require deep intuition to comprehend that man's ideas, views, and conceptions, in one word, man's consciousness, changes with every change in the conditions of his material existence, in his social relations and in his social life?

What else does the history of ideas prove, than that intellectual production changes in character in proportion as material production is changed? The ruling ideas of each age have ever been the ideas of its ruling class.

When people speak of ideas that revolutionize society, they do but express the fact that within the old society, the elements of a new one have been created, and that the dissolution of the old ideas keeps even pace with the dissolution of the old conditions of existence. . . .

The Communists turn their attention chiefly to Germany, because that country is on the eve of a bourgeois revolution, that is bound to be carried out under more advanced conditions of European civilization, and with a more developed proletariat, than that of England was in the seventeenth, and of France in the eighteenth century, and because the bourgeois revolution in Germany will be but the prelude to an immediately following proletarian revolution.

In short, the Communists everywhere support every revolutionary moment against the existing social and political order of things.

In all these movements they bring to the front, as the leading question in each, the property question, no matter what its degree of development at the time.

Finally, they labor everywhere for the union and agreement of the democratic parties of all countries.

The Communists disdain to conceal their views and aims. They openly declare that their ends can be attained only by the forcible overthrow of all existing social conditions. Let the ruling classes tremble at a Communistic revolution. The proletarians have nothing to lose but their chains. They have a world to win.

Working men of all countries, unite!

Charles Dickens: Oliver Twist

As a youth, Charles Dickens (1812–1870) was directly influenced by the dreadful conditions he sought to change when he wrote his great novels of social conscience that were so influential in Victorian England. In 1824, his father was imprisoned for debt and Dickens was placed in the factories, working to support his family. He spoke of his disturbing experiences in the factories to few, but began to write short stories attacking London's slums, the evils of industrialization, and the single-minded pursuit of money—clearly drawing on these bleak childhood experiences. Upon his father's release, Dickens attended school, worked as an office boy at an attorney's office, and studied shorthand at night. He was married in 1836, eventually had ten children, and continued to write and give public readings. His works became extremely popular during his lifetime, but he faced other challenges as he separated from his wife and faced health problems. Against his doctor's wishes, he continued to travel giving public readings until the day of his death.

Although Dickens was at first only practiced at short stories, the popularity of a few of them, based upon the life of young *Oliver Twist,* encouraged him to write a full-length novel. This novel is the account of the orphan Oliver and his flight from the workhouse into the criminal underground of London and finally into the wonderful life of English gentry. The conflict between childhood innocence and evil touches the reader's soul and has led to several successful theatre and screenplay adaptations. But it is Dickens' defense of the poor and otherwise underprivileged that makes this book so valuable to civilization. The poor had no champion or voice in government in 1830's England, just as in many other eras and locales. Dickens used his firsthand experiences of the horrors of oppression and governmental negligence in the life of the poor and exposed it to the world through this detailed narrative. Legislation to improve workhouse conditions was finally passed, largely as a result of Dickens' works. The success of *Oliver Twist* paved the way for a long line of other full-length works and extensive magazine serials, always brilliantly depicting the way of life in early nineteenth-century England.

Chapters 1 and 2 of *Oliver Twist* are included here. These passages were probably the original short stories that were later expanded into the novel we know today. They examine the birth of Oliver, his stay in an orphanage, and his transfer to a workhouse. It includes the "MORE?" dialogue that has become an unforgettable image of the oppression of the work-house orphanage.

Chapter the First

Treats of the Place Where Oliver Twist Was Born, and of the Circumstances Attending His Birth

Among other public buildings in the town of Mud-fog, it boasts of one which is common to most towns great or small, to wit, a workhouse; and in his workhouse there was born on a day and date which I need not trouble myself to repeat, inasmuch as it can be of no possible consequence to the reader, in this stage of the business at all events, the item of mortality whose name is prefixed to the head of this chapter. For a long time after he was ushered into this world of sorrow and trouble, by the parish surgeon, it remained a matter of considerable doubt whether the child would survive to bear any name at all; in which case it is somewhat more than probable that these memoirs would never have appeared, or, if they had, being comprised within a couple of pages, they would have possessed the inestimable merit of being the most concise and faithful specimen of biography extant in the literature of any age or country. Although I am not disposed to maintain that being born in a workhouse is in itself the most fortunate and enviable circumstance that can possibly befal a human being, I do mean to say that in this particular instance it was the best thing for Oliver Twist that could by possibility have occurred. The fact is, that there was considerable difficulty in inducing Oliver to take upon himself the office of respiration,—a troublesome practice, but one which custom has rendered necessary to our easy existence,—and for some time he lay gasping on a little flock mattress, rather unequally poised between this world and the next, the balance being decidedly in favour of the latter. Now, if during this brief period Oliver had been surrounded by careful grandmothers, anxious aunts, experienced nurses, and doctors of profound wisdom, he would most inevitably and indubitably have been killed in no time. There being nobody by, however, but a pauper old woman, who was rendered rather misty by an unwonted allowance of beer, and a parish surgeon who did such matters by contract, Oliver and nature fought out the point between them. The result was, that, after a few struggles, Oliver breathed, sneezed, and proceeded to advertise to the inmates of the workhouse the fact of a new burden having been imposed upon the parish, by setting up as loud a cry as could reasonably have been expected from a male infant who had not been possessed of that very useful appendage, a voice, for a much longer space of time than three minutes and a quarter.

As Oliver gave this first testimony of the free and proper action of his lungs, the patchwork coverlet, which was carelessly flung over the iron bedstead, rustled; the pale face of a young female was raised feebly from the pillow; and a faint voice imperfectly articulated the words, 'Let me see the child, and die.'

The surgeon had been sitting with his face turned towards the fire, giving the palms of his hands a warm, and a rub, alternately; but as the young woman spoke, he rose, and, advancing to

Source: From *Oliver Twist* by Charles Dickens (London: Penguin Books).

the bed's head, said with more kindness than might have been expected of him—'Oh, you must not talk about dying, yet.'

'Lor bless her dear heart, no!' interposed the nurse, hastily depositing in her pocket a green glass bottle, the contents of which she had been tasting in a corner with evident satisfaction. 'Lord bless her dear heart, when she has lived as long as I have, sir, and had thirteen children of her own, and all of 'em dead except two, and them in the wurkus with me, she'll know better than to take on in that way, bless her dear heart! Think what it is to be a mother, there's a dear young lamb, do.'

Apparently this consolatory perspective of a mother's prospects failed in producing its due effect. The patient shook her head, and stretched out her hand towards the child.

The surgeon deposited it in her arms. She imprinted her cold white lips passionately on its forehead, passed her hands over her face, gazed wildly round, shuddered, fell back—and died. They chafed her breast, hands, and temples; but the blood had frozen for ever. They talked of hope and comfort. They had been strangers too long.

'It's all over, Mrs Thingummy,' said the surgeon, at last.

'Ah, poor dear; so it is!' said the nurse, picking up the cork of the green bottle which had fallen out on the pillow as she stooped to take up the child. 'Poor dear!'

'You needn't mind sending up to me, if the child cries, nurse,' said the surgeon, putting on his gloves with great deliberation. 'It's very likely it will be troublesome. Give it a little gruel if it is.' He put on his hat, and, pausing by the bed-side on his way to the door, added, 'She was a good-looking girl too; where did she come from?'

'She was brought here last night,' replied the old woman, 'by the overseer's order. She was found lying in the street;—she had walked some distance, for her shoes were worn to pieces; but where she came from, or where she was going to, nobody knows.'

The surgeon leant over the body, and raised the left hand. 'The old story,' he said, shaking his head: 'no wedding-ring, I see. Ah! good night.'

The medical gentleman walked away to dinner; and the nurse, having once more applied herself to the green bottle, sat down on a low chair before the fire, and proceeded to dress the infant.

And what an excellent example of the power of dress young Oliver Twist was! Wrapped in the blanket which had hitherto formed his only covering, he might have been the child of a nobleman or a beggar;—it would have been hard for the haughtiest stranger to have fixed his station in society. But now he was enveloped in the old calico robes, that had grown yellow in the same service; he was badged and ticketed, and fell into his place at once—a parish child—the orphan of a workhouse—the humble, half-starved drudge—to be cuffed and buffeted through the world, despised by all, and pitied by none.

Oliver cried lustily. If he could have known that he was an orphan, left to the tender mercies of churchwardens and overseers, perhaps he would have cried the louder.

■ Chapter the Second

Treats of Oliver Twist's Growth, Education, and Board

For the next eight or ten months, Oliver was the victim of a systematic course of treachery and deception—he was brought up by hand. The hungry and destitute situations of the infant orphan was duly reported by the workhouse authorities to the parish authorities. The parish authorities inquired with dignity of the workhouse authorities, whether there was no female then domiciled in 'the house' who was in a situation to impart to Oliver Twist the consolation and nourishment of which he stood in need. The workhouse authorities replied with humility that there was not. Upon this, the parish authorities magnanimously and humanely resolved, that Oliver should be 'farmed,' or, in other words, that he should be despatched to a branch-workhouse some three miles off, where twenty or thirty other juvenile offenders against the poor-laws rolled about the floor all day, without the inconvenience of too much food, or too much clothing, under the parental superintendence of an elderly female who received the culprits at and for the consideration of sevenpence-halfpenny per small head per week. Sevenpence-halfpenny's worth per week is a good round diet for a child; a great deal may be got for sevenpence-halfpenny—quite enough to overload its stomach, and make it uncomfortable. The elderly female was a woman of wisdom and experience; she knew what was good for children, and she had a very accurate perception of what was good for herself. So, she appropriated the greater part of the weekly stipend to her own use, and consigned the rising parochial generation to even a shorter allowance than was originally provided for them; thereby finding in the lowest depth a deeper still, and proving herself a very great experimental philosopher.

Everybody knows the story of another experimental philosopher, who had a great theory about a horse being able to live without eating, and who demonstrated it so well, that he got his own horse down to a straw a day, and would most unquestionably have rendered him a very spirited and rampacious animal upon nothing at all, if he hadn't died, just four-and-twenty hours before he was to have had his first comfortable bait of air. Unfortunately for the experimental philosophy of the female to whose protecting care Oliver Twist was delivered over, a similar result usually attended the operation of *her* system; for just at the very moment when a child had contrived to exist upon the smallest possible portion of the weakest possible food, it did perversely happen in eight and a half cases out of ten, either that it sickened from want and cold, or fell into the fire from neglect, or got smothered by accident; in any one of which cases, the miserable little being was usually summoned into another world, and there gathered to the fathers which it had never known in this.

Occasionally, when there was some more than usually interesting inquest upon a parish child who had been overlooked in turning up a bedstead, or inadvertently scalded to death when there happened to be a washing, (though the latter accident was very scarce,—anything approaching to a washing being of rare occurrence in the farm,) the jury would take it into their heads to ask troublesome questions, or the parishioners would rebelliously affix their signatures to a remonstrance: but these impertinencies were speedily checked by the evidence of the surgeon, and the testimony of the beadle; the former of whom had always opened the body, and found nothing inside (which was very probably indeed), and the latter of whom invariably swore whatever the parish wanted, which was very self-devotional. Besides, the board made periodical pilgrimages to the farm, and always sent the beadle the day before, to say they were coming. The children were neat and clean to behold, when *they* went; and what more would the people have?

It cannot be expected that this system of farming would produce any very extraordinary or luxuriant crop. Oliver Twist's eighth birth-day found him a pale, thin child, somewhat diminutive in stature, and decidedly small in circumference. But nature or inheritance had implanted a good sturdy spirit in Oliver's breast: it had had plenty of room to expand, thanks to the spare diet of the establishment; and perhaps to this circumstance may be attributed his having any eighth birth-day at all. Be this as it may, however, it *was* his eighth birth-day; and he was keeping it in the coal-cellar with a select party of two other young gentlemen, who, after participating with him in a sound thrashing, had been locked up therein, for attrociously presuming to be hungry, when Mrs Mann, the good lady of the house, was unexpectedly startled by the apparition of Mr Bumble the beadle, striving to undo the wicket of the garden-gate.

'Goodness gracious! is that you, Mr Bumble, sir?' said Mrs Mann, thrusting her head out of the window in well-affected ecstasies of joy. '(Susan, take Oliver and them two brats up stairs, and wash 'em directly.)—My heart alive! Mr Bumble, how glad I am to see you, sure-ly!'

Now Mr Bumble was a fat man, and a choleric one; so, instead of responding to this open-hearted salutation in a kindred spirit, he gave the little wicket a tremendous shake, and then bestowed upon it a kick, which could have emanated from no leg but a beadle's.

'Lor, only think,' said Mrs Mann, running out,—for the three boys had been removed by this time,—'only think of that! That I should have forgotten that the gate was bolted on the inside, on account of them dear children! Walk in, sir; walk in, pray, Mr Bumble; do, sir.'

Although this invitation was accompanied with a curtsey that might have softened the heart of a churchwarden, it by no means mollified the beadle.

'Do you think this respectful or proper conduct, Mrs Mann,' inquired Mr Bumble, grasping his cane,—'to keep the parish officers a-waiting at your garden-gate, when they come here upon porochial business connected with the porochial orphans? Are you aware, Mrs Mann, that you are, as I may say, a porochial delegate, and a stipendiary?'

'I'm sure, Mr Bumble, that I was only a-telling one or two of the dear children as is so fond of you, that it was you a-coming,' replied Mrs Mann with great humility.

Mr Bumble had a great idea of his oratorical powers and his importance. He had displayed the one, and vindicated the other. He relaxed.

'Well, well, Mrs Mann,' he replied in a calmer tone; 'it may be as you say; it may be. Lead the way in, Mrs Mann; for I come on business, and have got something to say.'

Mrs Mann ushered the beadle into a small parlour with a brick floor, placed a seat for him, and officiously deposited his cocked hat and cane on the table before him. Mr Bumble wiped from his forehead the perspiration which his walk had engendered, glanced complacently at the cocked hat, and smiled. Yes, he smiled: beadles are but men, and Mr Bumble smiled.

'Now don't you be offended at what I'm a-going to say,' observed Mrs Mann with captivating sweetness. 'You've had a long walk, you know, or I wouldn't mention it. Now will you take a little drop of something, Mr Bumble?'

'Not a drop—not a drop,' said Mr Bumble, waving his right hand in a dignified, but still placid manner.

'I think you will,' said Mrs Mann, who had noticed the tone of the refusal, and the gesture that had accompanied it. 'Just a *leetle* drop, with a little cold water, and a lump of sugar.'

Mr Bumble coughed.

'Now, just a little drop,' said Mrs Mann persuasively.

'What is it?' inquired the beadle.

'Why it's what I'm obliged to keep a little of in the house, to put in the blessed infants' Daffy when they ain't well, Mr Bumble,' replied Mrs Mann as she opened a corner cupboard, and took down a bottle and glass. 'It's gin.'

'Do you give the children Daffy, Mrs Mann?' inquired Bumble, following with his eyes the interesting process of mixing.

'Ah, bless 'em, that I do, dear as it is,' replied the nurse. 'I couldn't see 'em suffer before my very eyes, you know, sir.'

'No,' said Mr Bumble approvingly; 'no, you could not. You are a humane woman, Mrs Mann.'—(Here she set down the glass.)—'I shall take an early opportunity of mentioning it to the board, Mrs Mann.'—(He drew it towards him.)—'You feel as a mother, Mrs Mann.'—(He stirred the gin and water.)—'I—I drink your health with cheerfulness, Mrs Mann;'—and he swallowed half of it.

'And now about business,' said the beadle, taking out a leathern pocket-book. 'The child that was half-baptised, Oliver Twist, is eight years old to-day.'

'Bless him!' interposed Mrs Mann, inflaming her left eye with the corner of her apron.

'And notwithstanding an offered reward of ten pound, which was afterwards increased to twenty pound,—notwithstanding the most superlative, and, I may say, supernat'ral exertions on the part of this parish,' said Bumble, 'we have never been able to discover who is his father, or what is his mother's settlement, name or condition.'

Mrs Mann raised her hands in astonishment; but added, after a moment's reflection, 'How comes he to have any name at all, then?'

The beadle drew himself up with great pride, and said, 'I invented it.'

'You, Mr Bumble!'

'I, Mrs Mann. We name our foundlin's in alphabetical order. The last was an S,—Swubble: I named him. This was a T—Twist: I named *him*. The next one as comes will be Unwin, and the next Vilkins. I have got names ready made to the end of the alphabet, and all the way through it again, when we come to Z.'

'Why, you're quite a literary character, sir!' said Mrs Mann.

'Well, well,' said the beadle, evidently gratified with the compliment; 'perhaps I may be; perhaps I may be, Mrs Mann.' He finished the gin and water, and added, 'Oliver being now too old to remain here, the Board have determined to have him back into the house; and I have come out myself to take him there,—so let me see him at once.'

'I'll fetch him directly,' said Mrs Mann, leaving the room for that purpose. And Oliver having by this time had as much of the outer coat of dirt which encrusted his face and hands removed as could be scrubbed off in one washing, was led into the room by his benevolent protectress.

'Make a bow to the gentleman, Oliver,' said Mrs Mann.

Oliver made a bow, which was divided between the beadle on the chair and the cocked hat on the table.

'Will you go along with me, Oliver?' said Mr Bumble in a majestic voice.

Oliver was about to say that he would go along with anybody with great readiness, when, glancing upwards, he caught sight of Mrs Mann, who had got behind the beadle's chair, and was shaking her fist at him with a furious countenance. He took the hint at once, for the fist had been too often impressed upon his body not to be deeply impressed upon his recollection.

'Will *she* go with me?' inquired poor Oliver.

'No, she can't,' replied Mr Bumble; 'but she'll come and see you, sometimes.'

This was no very great consolation to the child; but, young as he was, he had sense enough to make a feint of feeling great regret at going away. It was no very difficult matter for the boy to call the tears into his eyes. Hunger and recent ill-usage are great assistants if you want to cry; and Oliver cried very naturally indeed. Mrs. Mann gave him a thousand embraces, and, what Oliver wanted a great deal more, a piece of bread and

butter, lest he should seem too hungry when he got to the workhouse. With the slice of bread in his hand, and the little brown-cloth parish cap upon his head, Oliver was then led away by Mr Bumble from the wretched home where one kind word or look had never lighted the gloom of his infant years. And yet the burst into an agony of childish grief as the cottage-gate closed after him. Wretched as were the little companions in misery he was leaving behind, they were the only friends he had ever known; and a sense of his loneliness in the great wide world sank into the child's heart for the first time.

Mr. Bumble walked on with long strides; and little Oliver, firmly grasping his gold-laced cuff, trotted beside him, inquiring at the end of every quarter of a mile whether they were 'nearly there,' to which interrogations Mr Bumble returned very brief and snappish replies; for the temporary blandness which gin and water awakens in some bosoms had by this time evaporated, and he was once again a beadle.

Oliver had not been within the walls of the workhouse a quarter of an hour, and had scarcely completed the demolition of a second slice of bread, when Mr Bumble, who had handed him over to the care of an old woman, returned, and, telling him it was a board night, informed him that the board had said he was to appear before it forthwith.

Not having a very clearly defined notion of what a live board was, Oliver was rather astounded by this intelligence, and was not quite certain whether he ought to laugh or cry. He had no time to think about the matter, however; for Mr Bumble gave him a tap on the head with his cane to wake him up, and another on the back to make him lively, and, bidding him follow, conducted him into a large whitewashed room, where eight or ten fat gentlemen were sitting round a table, at the top of which, seated in an arm-chair rather higher than the rest, was a particularly fat gentleman with a very round, red face.

'Bow to the board,' said Bumble. Oliver brushed away two or three tears that were lingering in his eyes, and seeing no board but the table, fortunately bowed to that.

'What's your name, boy?' said the gentleman in the high chair.

Oliver was frightened at the sight of so many gentlemen, which made him tremble; and the beadle gave him another tap behind, which made him cry; and these two causes made him answer in a very low and hesitating voice; whereupon a gentleman in a white waistcoat said he was a fool, which was a capital way of raising his spirits, and putting him quite at his ease.

'Boy,' said the gentleman in the high chair; 'listen to me. You know you're an orphan, I suppose?'

'What's that, sir?' inquired poor Oliver.

'The boy *is* a fool—I thought he was,' said the gentleman in the white waistcoat, in a very decided tone. If one member of class be blessed with an intuitive perception of others of the same race, the gentleman in the white waistcoat was unquestionably well qualified to pronounce an opinion on the matter.

'Hush!' said the gentleman who had spoken first. 'You know you've got no father or mother, and that you are brought up by the parish, don't you?'

'Yes, sir,' replied Oliver, weeping bitterly.

'What are you crying for?' inquired the gentleman in the white waistcoat; and to be sure it was very extraordinary. What *could* he be crying for?

'I hope you say your prayers every night,' said another gentleman in a gruff voice, 'and pray for the people who feed you, and take care of you, like a Christian.'

'Yes, sir,' stammered the boy. The gentleman who spoke last was unconsciously right. It would have been very like a Christian, and a marvellously good Christian, too, if Oliver had prayed for the people who fed and took care of *him*. But he hadn't, because nobody had taught him.

'Well, you have come here to be educated, and taught a useful trade,' said the red-faced gentleman in the high chair.

'So you'll begin to pick oakum to-morrow morning at six o'clock,' added the surly one in the white waistcoat.

For the combination of both these blessings in the one simple process of picking oakum, Oliver bowed low by the direction of the beadle, and was then hurried away to a large ward, where, on a rough hard bed, he sobbed himself to sleep. What a noble illustration of the tender laws of his favoured country! they let the paupers go to sleep!

Poor Oliver! He little thought, as he lay sleeping in happy unconsciousness of all around him, that the board had that very day arrived at a decision which would exercise the most material influence over all his future fortunes. But they had. And this was it:—

The members of this board were very sage, deep, philosophical men; and when they came to turn their attention to the workhouse, they found out at once, what ordinary folks would never have discovered,—the poor people liked it! It was a regular place of public entertainment for the poorer classes,—a tavern where there was nothing to pay,—a public breakfast, dinner, tea, and supper, all the year round,—a brick and mortar elysium where it was all play and no work. 'Oho!' said the board, looking very knowing; 'we are the fellows to set this to rights; we'll stop it all in no time.' So they established the rule, that all poor people should have the alternative (for they would compel nobody, not they,) of being starved by a gradual process in the house, or by a quick one out of it. With this view, they contracted with the waterworks to lay on an unlimited supply of water, and with a corn-factor to supply periodically small quantities of oatmeal; and issued three meals of thin gruel a-day, with an onion twice a week, and half a roll on Sundays. They made a great many other wise and humane regulations having reference to the ladies, which it is not necessary to repeat; kindly undertook to divorce poor married people, in consequence to the great expense of a suit in Doctors' Commons; and, instead of compelling a man to support his family as they had theretofore done, took his family away from him, and made him a bachelor! There is no telling how many applicants for relief under these two heads would not have started up in all classes of society, if it had not been coupled with the workhouse. But they were long-headed men, and they had provided for this difficulty. The relief was inseparable from the workhouse and the gruel; and that frightened people.

For the first three months after Oliver Twist was removed, the system was in full operation. It was rather expensive at first, in consequence of the increase in the undertaker's bill, and the necessity of taking in the clothes of all the paupers, which fluttered loosely on their wasted, shrunken forms, after a week or two's gruel. But the number of workhouse inmates got thin, as well as the paupers; and the board were in ecstasies.

The room in which the boys were fed, was a large, stone hall, with a copper at one end, out of which the master, dressed in an apron for the purpose, and assisted by one or two women, ladled the gruel at meal-times; of which composition each boy had one porringer, and no more,—except on festive occasions, and then he had two ounces and a quarter of bread besides. The bowls never wanted washing—the boys polished them with their spoons, till they shone again; and when they had performed this operation (which never took very long, the spoons being nearly as large as the bowls), they would sit staring at the copper with such eager eyes as if they could devour the very bricks of which it was composed; employing themselves meanwhile in sucking their fingers most assiduously, with the view of catching up any stray splashes of gruel that might have been cast thereon. Boys have generally excellent appetites: Oliver Twist and his companions suffered the tortures of slow starvation for three months; at last they got so voracious and wild with hunger, that one boy, who was tall for his age, and hadn't been used to that sort of thing, (for his father had kept a small cook's shop), hinted darkly to his companions, that unless he had another basin of gruel *per diem,* he was afraid he should some night eat the boy who slept next to him, who happened to be a weakly youth of tender age. He had a wild, hungry eye, and they implicitly believed him. A council was held; lots were cast who should walk up to the master after supper that evening, and ask for more; and it fell to Oliver Twist.

The evening arrived: the boys took their places; the master in his cook's uniform stationed himself at the copper; his pauper assistants ranged themselves behind him; the gruel was served out, and a long grace was said over the short commons. The gruel disappeared, and the boys whispered each other and winked at Oliver, while his next neighbours nudged him. Child as he was, he was desperate with hunger and reckless with misery. He rose from the table, and advancing, basin and spoon in hand, to the master, said, somewhat alarmed at his own temerity—

'Please, sir, I want some more.'

The master was a fat, healthy man, but he turned very pale. He gazed in stupified astonishment on the small rebel for some seconds, and then clung for support to the copper. The assistants were paralysed with wonder, and the boys with fear.

'What!' said the master at length, in a faint voice.

'Please, sir,' replied Oliver, 'I want some more.'

The master aimed a blow at Oliver's head with the ladle, pinioned him in his arms, and shrieked aloud for the beadle.

The board were sitting in solemn conclave when Mr Bumble rushed into the room in great excitement, and addressing the gentleman in the high chair, said,—

'Mr Limbkins, I beg your pardon, sir,—Oliver Twist has asked for more.' There was a general start. Horror was depicted on every countenance.

'For more!' said Mr Limbkins. 'Compose yourself, Bumble, and answer me distinctly. Do I understand that he asked for more, after he had eaten the supper allotted by the dietary?'

'He did, sir,' replied Bumble.

'That boy will be hung,' said the gentleman in the white waistcoat; 'I know that boy will be hung.'

Nobody controverted the prophetic gentleman's opinion. An animated discussion took place. Oliver was ordered into instant confinement; and a bill was next morning pasted on the outside of the gate offering a reward of five pounds to anybody who would take Oliver Twist off the hands of the parish: in other words, five pounds and Oliver Twist were offered to any man or woman who wanted an apprentice to any trade, business, or calling.

'I never was more convinced of anything in my life,' said the gentleman in the white waistcoat, as he knocked at the gate and read the bill next morning,—'I never was more convinced of any-thing in my life, than I am that that boy will come to be hung.'

As I propose to show in the sequel whether the white-waistcoated gentleman was right or not, I should perhaps mar the interest of this narrative, (supposing it to possess any at all,) if I ventured to hint just yet, whether the life of Oliver Twist will be a long or a short piece of biography.

Empires and Inventions
Expanding Frontiers of Creativity

Chapter 43

> Success usually comes to those who are too busy to be looking for it.
>
> —*Henry David Thoreau*

Throughout the nineteenth century, in addition to dealing with the adverse social conditions that had arisen in most of the countries of Europe, all the major European nations and the United States embarked on various types of empire building. In some cases, like Great Britain, the empire was built across the world. In other cases, like the United States, Germany and Italy, the empire was built at home.

Building these empires required great creativity. In the British case, for example, the explorers who discovered the new lands claimed by England were creative in their methods of exploration. The military leaders who conquered some parts of the British Empire were creative in their military tactics. Some administrators of the various territories were creative in settling local problems and continuing the relationship of the country with the British Empire.

In other places, such as America, creativity in conquering the empire came from the inventions and culture that led to overcoming the wilderness and uniting all parts of the continent. In Germany and Italy, leaders were highly creative in resolving the issues of competing local interests and traditions of separateness descended from medieval times.

Despite the turbulent times in Europe, which we have discussed in the previous chapters, the nineteenth century was one of optimism and expansion for the European powers and America. A combination of economics (both for the extraction of raw materials and as a market for finished goods); scientific exploration, national pride, and a feeling of moral superiority (mixed with a dose of racism) caused Western nations to colonize "less-civilized" locations. This period of colonization became known as imperialism. By the end of the nineteenth century, most of the Earth had been colonized by one Western power or another. The extent of empire building is shown in Figure 43.1.

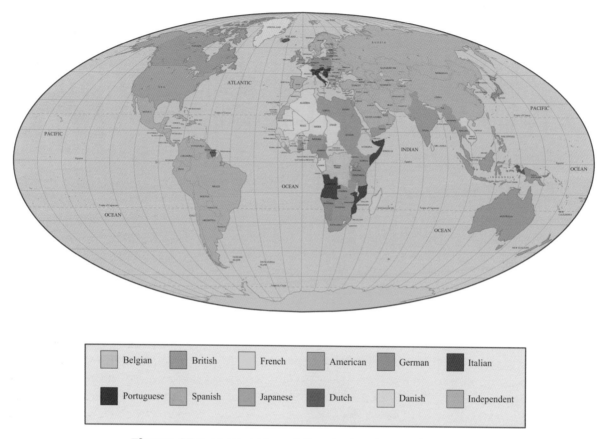

Figure 43.1 ■ *World imperialism in the nineteenth century.*

■ The British Empire

The largest and most powerful colonial power and the author of the imperial model was Great Britain. England had embraced the idea of expansion very early in its history—attempting to control Wales, Scotland, and Ireland from medieval days. Scotland and Wales were officially unified with England in 1707, and Ireland followed in 1800. Furthermore, during the Stuart era of the 1600s, England had actively pursued colonization in North America. This colonization served as the blueprint for later English colonization and proved financially lucrative, as the English were able to both extract raw materials and trade English goods with the American colonists. Even after the revolt of the American colonies and the creation of the United States, Great Britain still con-

trolled the northern part of the continent (modern day Canada) and retained a lucrative relationship with those colonies.

Great Britain had also begun expanding into India during the 1600s. England's main naval rival in those days, the Portuguese, had established trading posts in Asia during the 1500s. Not wanting to lose ground to the Portuguese, the British formed a rival trading company (it had private ownership, but with special governmental privileges) called the **British East India Company** and began establishing trade centers in India. Both the Dutch and the Danes quickly created rival trading companies to compete with the British and Portuguese within India. Each nation made trade agreements with local governments to secure favored trading positions. However, when the Mughal (Indian) Empire began to break up in the

1700s, all the European nations began to take sides in local disputes and became increasingly involved in the internal politics of India. Soon the European trading companies began exerting direct political power in the areas where they dominated trade.

Over the next hundred years, the Portuguese influence was reduced to just the single trading port of Goa. The Dutch and the Danish companies became mired in debt due to poor management, and by the early 1800s both had been disbanded in India, leaving control over trade within India to the British. With the removal of the Dutch and Danes, the British East India Company gradually took political control of all of India until, in 1857, a rebellion of Indian army troops led to intervention of the British army, and that led to a transfer of official sovereignty of all of India to the British crown. To formalize the acquisition of India into the British Empire, Queen Victoria was crowned Empress of India. With this act, India became a possession of Great Britain and was governed from London, half a world away.

Many other parts of the British Empire were added through exploration and claims by the explorers who found the territories. Even though Europeans had begun extensive explorations in the late 1400s, much of the Earth was still unexplored as late as the 1700s. Exploration became a matter of national pride among many nations, especially the British. Furthermore, the intellectual climate of the era was still largely shaped by the thoughts and writings of the Enlightenment and the Scientific Awakening. The belief was held that science was the key to progress and that all of humankind's ills would eventually be resolved through the application of science. Thus, many of these ships of exploration also had a secondary purpose of scientific discovery and research.

Possibly the foremost naval explorer to ever live was the British sailor, **Captain James Cook** (1728–1779). In his career Captain Cook journeyed to Newfoundland and to the South Pacific (three voyages). Cook's trips to the South Pacific were primarily to claim territories for the British crown and to search for the great southern continent. Many in Europe believed such a continent must exist in the vast expanse of the Pacific Ocean

because, they reasoned, the total landmass in the northern and southern hemispheres must be roughly equal. Cook hoped to find this final continent and claim its land and treasures for Great Britain. Of course, no great southern continent exists (which made it extremely difficult for Captain Cook to find it). Nevertheless, Cook did discover many other lands, including Australia, Tahiti, Samoa, and Hawaii. Cook also likely was the first European to see Antarctica, although he never set foot on the continent. Many of Cook's discoveries became British colonies and a part of the vast British Empire.

Captain Cook also played an important role in naval history and in making the British navy the best in the world. Cook developed the model for a thoughtful, effective sea captain. He was willing to experiment in order to improve life aboard ship and lessen its many dangers. One of Cook's great discoveries was taking limes on a voyage and making his sailors eat them, thus ridding his crews of scurvy, a dreaded disease caused by a lack of vitamin C that had plagued sailors for centuries. Discoveries like this kept the British sailors more healthy and vigorous and gave their navy an edge until other countries picked up on this. (It also was the origin of the nickname of *limey* for a British sailor.) Cook made extensive and accurate maps of the places he visited. He also studied scientific phenomena such as eclipses. Cook was killed in Hawaii when he became involved in a local dispute.

Other British explorers and scientists also made lasting impacts. The British navy desperately needed an accurate method to determine longitude and therefore offered a prize to the first person who could develop a system to do it accurately. The problem was that, in contrast to determining latitude, which could be done with sightings of the sun and stars, longitude had to be determined by referencing the ship's position to a home base (chosen as the observatory in Greenwich, England). This required a very accurate clock. Many years were spent in developing a clock that would withstand the salty and damp environment of a ship, including the inevitable rough seas and other disturbances. Finally, a craftsman, **John Harrison,** was able to make several working models. After many years of fighting with the naval bureaucracy (because the British admiralty did not think that a commoner could invent such a clever device), he was awarded the prize.

Another famous explorer was **David Living-stone** (1813–1873), a British missionary and explorer in Africa. Livingstone, a devout Christian who abhorred the typically abusive treatment of the natives by the Europeans, became famous by mapping the Zambezi River (in the process, discovering Victoria Falls) and searching for the source of the Nile. Later, on another journey into the heart of Africa, Livingstone became the subject of much media attention when he mysteriously vanished and an American reporter, **Henry Morton Stanley,** set out to find him. Stanley sent back newspaper reports of his travels and adventures in Africa. The popular series had the perfect ending when Stanley found Livingstone alive and the two spent four months exploring Lake Tanganyika together.

British colonization continued, and the British Empire expanded into Africa and the Far East. As in India, Great Britain often began by establishing a trading outpost. However, in order to protect their economic interests when local instabilities occurred, the British would often step in and take control of an area politically. This pattern was followed in South Africa as the British defended their economic interests against other European colonists in the Boer Wars, and later against African natives in the Zulu wars. The British also established a protectorate over Egypt in order to protect the recently built Suez Canal. Great Britain slowly extended its rule in Africa from Egypt to the Sudan. By the end of Queen Victoria's reign in 1901, the British controlled over one-third of Africa.

The British followed a similar pattern in the Far East. China had long been a prize in the eyes of European traders. However, the Chinese had a strict policy of isolationism and a strong enough military to mostly keep out the Europeans and their culture. China was self-sufficient and did not need (or particularly want) European trade or the cultural influences it brought. However, China did have several products, such as silk and tea, which Europeans wanted. Because of extreme European pressure to have access to these items, China allowed a limited amount of trade under very strict restrictions. European merchants, regardless of nationality, were all required to live in Guangzhou (Canton) and trade only with the local merchants. By following this policy, the Chinese government tried to limit the amount of trade and the influence of Western culture. This plan was satisfactory for a time, but the European powers each wanted an advantage in Chinese trade and looked for ways to gain control of the trade in China and have greater (or sole) access to the massive Chinese market.

Great Britain was particularly desirous to achieve a preferred position in Chinese trade. Great Britain had begun to sell opium, grown legally in India, and had found a large market for the opium in China. However, the sale of opium in China was illegal. Despite warnings from the Chinese government, British merchants continued to conduct this illegal selling. The British refusal to comply with Chinese laws forced the Chinese to act, and they threw out all British merchants and confiscated all British warehouses and goods. Outraged (and afraid of losing the Chinese trade), Britain declared war on China. The **Opium Wars** between Great Britain and China lasted from 1839 to 1860, but eventually the British won the wars and forced the Chinese to cede to them the island of Hong Kong to serve as a British trading center and military base. Great Britain retained control of Hong Kong until 1997.

The British and French also worked together to force open several other key Chinese ports and cities, including Beijing and Shanghai, to European merchants. After the Chinese defeat in the Opium Wars, China took no further official action to drive out the Europeans, but the Chinese empress did quietly support the anti-European resistance groups fighting the Europeans in the Boxer Rebellion in 1900. After the death of several hundred Europeans, and the threat of invasion, the rebellion was suppressed and the European governments were all given additional access to Chinese markets. The tensions of the Chinese situation and the continuing competition for trade advantages led to the Great War.

By the mid-nineteenth century, Great Britain had a vast empire and had become the world's great economic and military power. Great Britain controlled territory on all six inhabitable continents and many islands. The famous expression, "The sun never sets on the British Empire," was literally true. At the height of British colonial domination, over one quarter of the Earth's total population lived within the empire.

In some instances, Great Britain used this vast economic and military power to force compliance with values that the British people and government held to be absolute. For instance, from 1850 to 1851, Great Britain blockaded Brazil to force the country to stop the slave trade. Again in 1873, Britain sent ships to threaten Zanzibar to stop its slave trading. These were the last countries to openly trade slaves, and Great Britain believed that it had a moral duty to end what the British considered to be a morally repugnant practice. In both cases, Britain was successful.

On the one hand, we might wonder whether any nation has the right to interfere in the internal practices of another country. On the other hand, can a country with the ability to make a difference look aside while some practice continues that is morally wrong (in the eyes of the dominant country)? This issue is, of course, pertinent in the twenty-first century for the United States. Some countries criticize the war launched in Iraq in 2003, while others (like Great Britain) support the action of the United States. One opposing view is that given by the French president, Jacques Chirac: "Any community with only one dominant power is always a dangerous one. That's why I favor a multi-polar world, in which Europe obviously has its place." Chirac's view is, of course, that all countries, regardless of their power, must consult before any major international decision. If that is not done, he would imply that the dominant country is simply a bully. Alternately, the question could be asked, should a country with strong moral convictions be bound by the feelings of a majority of other countries? The answers to these questions are certainly critical to our current world.

The prestige and economic strength of Great Britain's empire encouraged many of Europe's nations to want to be colonial powers as well, and much of the nineteenth century was a race between the nations of Europe to colonize the areas that Great Britain did not already control.

■ Post-Napoleonic France

A series of largely inept Bourbon kings ruled France between the fall of Napoleon and 1848, when the last Bourbon was toppled in the revolution of that year. These kings made some efforts at industrialization and empire building. For example, in 1834 France occupied northern Africa. France dominated the region militarily and treated it as a French colony until post-World War II. France continues in an advisory role for several North African nations.

With the removal of the Bourbons in 1848, the second French Republic was declared and **Louis Napoleon Bonaparte,** a nephew of Napoleon I, was elected president of France. The elections had resulted in a split government, with republicans controlling the presidency (Louis Napoleon) but monarchists controlling the Assembly. This led to a government that had great difficulty in governing effectively, and a series of minor riots ensued. After three years of stagnant government, Louis Napoleon won a *coup d'etat* in 1851, and declared the start of the Second Empire and named himself Emperor Napoleon III. (Napoleon II was Napoleon's son who had died).

Napoleon III then made efforts to create a new colonial empire for France. He tried to exercise control over Mexico by installing Maximilian (a member of the Austrian ruling family) as emperor of Mexico in 1863 under French control. At first the United States, deeply involved in the American Civil War, could do little to stop a French takeover of Mexico. Once the war ended, however, the United States put pressure on the French to withdraw support of Maximilian, who was soon overthrown by Benito Juarez in a Mexican revolution.

In 1870 Napoleon III was overthrown as a result of France's defeat in the Franco-Prussian War. A year later, the third republic was declared and a series of weak governments ran France until World War I.

■ Spain

Spain was Europe's first colonial power, but by the nineteenth century, the Spanish colonial empire was in serious decline. Spain initially sparked Europe's interest in colonization with its success in acquiring territory and extracting treasures from the New World. However, the Spanish colonies were grossly mismanaged and plagued by corruption. Furthermore, Spain had always placed its colonial emphasis on extraction of raw materials rather than settlement. As time passed, the gold and other raw materials became more difficult to find and Spain's wealth and power waned. In the early 1800s, Spain's heavy-handed treatment of its colonies, combined with the rampant corruption and high taxes, led to revolutions in many of Spain's American territories.

In the northern half of South America, **Simon Bolivar** (1783–1830) led these revolutions. He was educated in his native Venezuela and then in Europe, where he studied the philosophies of the Enlightenment. Upon his return to Venezuela, he became the leader of a group of patriots who were already fighting for Venezuelan independence from Spanish rule. Eventually Bolivar's struggle for independence spread to other Spanish colonies, and before long all of northern South America was in open revolt against Spanish control. One by one, Spain's northern South American colonies gained their freedom. The modern-day nations of Venezuela, Colombia, Ecuador, Peru, Panama, and Bolivia (named for him) can all attribute their independence to Simon Bolivar.

Spain faced a similar situation in the southern part of South America, where another revolutionary named **José San Martín** was pushing for freedom from Spanish rule. Like Bolivar, San Martín was born in the New World and educated in Spain. San Martín even fought for Spain against Napoleon. However, San Martín was a liberal and disliked the monarchy and the colonial system. While in London, San Martín met some re-

volutionary Spanish Americans and joined their cause. With his extensive military experience, San Martín was a valuable asset, and rose quickly through the ranks to become their leader after returning to Argentina. José San Martín helped Argentina, Chile, and Peru gain their independence from Spain (at approximately the same time as Bolivar was doing so in the north).

Further north, Spain had trouble in Mexico, as well. An initial attempt at independence in 1810 under the leadership of Father Miguel Hidalgo was unsuccessful. However, the Mexican people did not give up their desire to be free, and in 1821 Augustin de Iturbide was able to achieve Mexican independence. Iturbide forced the Mexican congress to appoint him emperor but he was deposed two years later because of his extreme harshness. Mexico was then declared a republic based on the model of the United States. **General Santa Anna** was elected president of Mexico and was in charge when Texas and other Mexican territories north of the Rio Grande were lost to the United States. A coalition government led by Benito Juárez followed Santa Ana's presidency. Juárez's government was weakened by internal dissent and spent much of its time fighting off political and military efforts by conservatives within the government to limit reform. This war between the liberals and conservatives invited the invasion by France under Napoleon III, when the French installed Maximilian as Mexico's emperor (and a French puppet). After Maximilian was overthrown, a dictatorship under Porfirio Díaz was established in 1877. It lasted for over 30 years. A political party known as the Partido Revolucionario Institucional (PRI) overthrew Díaz and set up a new republican government based on the American model. This model persists to the present.

Back in Spain, the political climate was not much better than it was in the Spanish colonies, as both liberal and conservative forces struggled to gain power. Queen Maria Christina allied herself with the liberals in order to gain the throne for her daughter, Isabella II, and in 1833 the liberals successfully installed Isabella as a constitutional monarch. Queen Isabella II was an inept ruler and was eventually overthrown. A tumultuous period in Spanish government followed, but after several abortive attempts, a stable constitutional monarchy was installed in 1876. During the 1890s the Spanish government became unstable again and another revolution ensued. This time, the revolutionaries were supported by the United States, which led to the Spanish American War. Eventually a liberal government was installed, but it was largely unstable, even though it persisted until after World War I.

Belgium

At the Congress of Vienna, the Dutch Republic and the Hapsburgian Netherlands (the forerunners to modern Holland and Belgium) had been united into a single political entity. Tired of being dominated by the Dutch, the southern parts of the Netherlands revolted in 1831 and withdrew from their union with the Dutch, creating the new nation of Belgium. Belgium was established as a constitutional monarchy and the uncle of Queen Victoria of England, Leopold, was made king. However, the creation of the new nation did not solve all of the old problems. Tensions between the French-speaking Walloons and the Dutch-speaking Flemish portions of the Belgium population continued throughout the 1800s, until finally both languages were officially recognized in 1888.

King Leopold II was a typical constitutional monarch, with mostly ceremonial duties and little actual influence on policy. However, he was an ambitious man and was constantly trying to convince the Belgian parliament to try and acquire colonies. Leopold attempted to buy an Argentine province, rent the Philippines from Spain, and establish colonies in China, Japan, and Vietnam. None of these schemes came anywhere near fruition. The Belgian government simply refused all of Leopold's suggestions, seeing the acquisition of a colony as a good way to spend large amounts of money for little or no return.

When his own government would not grant his wishes, Leopold II devised a new plan. In 1878, Leopold II had creatively formed the International Association of the Congo with one shareholder—

Leopold himself. In essence, Leopold had bought himself his own private kingdom, which was officially established in 1885 and named the Congo Free State. Leopold basically could rule as he wanted in the Congo, and he took advantage of this power. In an effort to enforce his control and to extract precious raw materials, Leopold committed atrocities on a breathtaking scale. The Congo became a scene of native heartbreak and the worst example of European brutality, greed, and genocide. The Belgians were like slave overlords. But, because of the poor communication and transportation out of Africa, general European racism, and the lack of any oversight of Leopold's actions, the conditions within the Congo remained largely unknown. Finally, in 1908, Leopold's actions were revealed in the Western press, and the government of the Congo Free State was taken over by Belgium. The Congo Free State became an orthodox colony of the nation of Belgium and was renamed the Belgian Congo.

Russia

Russia had visions of grandeur and empire. Ruled by the Romanoff family, the longest, continuous ruling dynasty in Europe, Russia considered itself the successor of the Roman Empire (the word *czar* is a Russian rendering of the word *caesar*) and as such wanted to establish their political, military, and territorial dominance. Russia's ambitions were largely limited, however, by their slowness to modernize and the never-ending political intrigues of the Russian court.

In spite of these limitations, Russia continued to pursue a policy of expansion. Much like the United States, considerable Russian effort was spent simply exploring and conquering its vast frontier. Although Russia already claimed central Asia, Siberia, and Alaska as its territories, much of that land was unexplored and Russian in name only. During the eighteenth and nineteenth centuries, Russia began to take a greater interest in establishing administrative control over their territories and taking advantage of any resources there.

Russia also wanted to play a larger role within Europe and on the world stage. However, in order to do this, Russia understood that it needed to expand westward into Europe and to have access to a warm-water seaport. These goals were accomplished by defeating Sweden in the Great Northern War. As part of the spoils of war, Russia acquired the territory where the port city of St. Petersburg was built and the Baltic nations of Estonia and Latvia in 1721. Later, in 1795, Russia acquired the third Baltic nation, Lithuania, as part of the partition of Poland. The acquisition of the Baltic nations served its intended purpose by making Russia more prominent in the affairs and politics of Europe.

Russia's further attempts to gain access to warm-water seaports were less successful. Russia had long desired control of the Crimea, a region along the shores of the Black Sea that would give its ships ice-free access to the Mediterranean Sea through the Bosporous area then controlled by the Ottoman Turks. Russia fought the Ottomans in the Crimean War (1853) but was defeated by the combined forces of Turkey, England, and France who all wanted to limit Russia's expansion. This was a war in which many poor military decisions were made on both sides. For example, the British blundered and sent hundreds of men to their deaths, as related in the poem "The Charge of the Light Brigade" by Alfred Lord Tennyson.

In light of Russia's defeat, **Czar Alexander II** had to admit that the country had fallen behind the rest of Europe in military capabilities. This realization caused Alexander II to begin a series of reforms designed to modernize Russia. However, Russian industrialization was slow and largely unsuccessful. As part of his reform policy (and in hopes of providing more workers to improve industrialization), Czar Alexander II freed the serfs in 1861. Alexander also implemented some mild democratic reforms, including limited local self-government and trial by jury. In spite of his efforts to reform Russia, in 1881 a student who was a member of a radical revolutionary organization called **The National Will** mortally wounded Czar Alexander II with a bomb. (A wonderful medieval-style Russian Orthodox Church called the Church on Spilled Blood is built on the spot in St. Petersburg where the czar was killed.) Upon

his death, Alexander III succeeded to the Russian throne. Czar Alexander III was reactionary and stopped most of his father's reforms. Russia would remain backward with only minor improvements until the revolutions of 1917 that led, ultimately, to a communist government.

◼ Germany

Although a strong German identity existed due to Luther's German Bible and a vigorous German cultural heritage (Bach, Mozart, Beethoven, Brahms, Goethe, Kant, etc.), there had never been a unified German nation. Since the Middle Ages, Germany had been divided into small kingdoms and principalities. The first step toward a unified Germany came following the Napoleonic Wars. The Congress of Vienna (ironically, following the lead of Napoleon) combined several German kingdoms and formed a German Confederation to replace the Holy Roman Empire. In doing so, it reduced the number of German states from more than 300 to 39. The Vienna settlements also created a congress, or *Bundestag,* with representatives from all of the German states that met in Frankfurt. This loose German confederation was further strengthened by the establishment of a German trading union in the 1830s.

The confederation/union was dominated by Prussia, which viewed it as a precursor to German political unity. Austria, which had not been included in the original German confederation or union, had its own plan for German unity under the Austrian emperor. The Prussian position was further strengthened in the revolution of 1848 when the liberal group that had seized control over the German Confederation wrote a constitution for a united country under a limited monarchy and asked William of Prussia to be the king. Because he disagreed with many of the liberal elements of the constitution, William refused to become the unified king. Unable to find strong leadership and direction, the new unified Germany soon collapsed, and the German Confederation was reestablished. The rivalry between Prussia and Austria for German leadership continued.

In 1862 King Wilhelm of Prussia appointed **Otto von Bismarck** as prime minister. Bismarck initiated a strong policy of Prussian military expansion. In 1866 Bismarck took the German-speaking duchies of Schleswig and Holstein from Denmark in a short war. Bismarck followed that by declaring war on Austria in 1867. The war lasted only seven weeks and resulted in a general recognition of Prussia as the leading German state. Prussia's leadership position was further enhanced when Prussia then went to war with France in 1870. The Prussians humiliated the French, causing the French government of Napoleon III to fall and resulting in the formation of a unified German nation with the King of Prussia, **Wilhelm I,** as kaiser (caesar or emperor) and Bismarck as chancellor. Modern Germany had been formed.

Germany, like Belgium, was very late to acquire colonies. Germany quickly snatched up unclaimed areas of eastern Africa and the islands of Samoa. However, the Germans felt (probably rightly so) that all of the good colonies had already been claimed by other European nations. German industry was forced to buy raw materials from Great Britain or other European countries that had colonies that could supply these raw materials. Because of this (and very creatively), the Germans invested much of their efforts into science in hopes of developing synthetic materials to replace some of the raw materials obtained in colonies (such as dyes to replace indigo, synthetic rubber, and drugs such as aspirin).

■ Italy

Like Germany, Italy was a patchwork of small states left over from the Middle Ages and was one of the last nations of Europe to unify into a modern nation-state. In the liberal revolutions of 1848, Italian nationalists revolted against the Austrians, who controlled large parts of northern Italy. Liberal politics swept across the more important kingdoms of the Italian peninsula. The kings of both Sardinia and Naples granted constitutions to their people, and republics were declared in Venice, Tuscany, and Rome. Italian victory was to

be short-lived though. The counter-revolution of 1849 restored all of Austria's holdings, eliminated the republics, and toppled the throne in Sardinia where the king's son, **Victor Emmanuel II,** had been made a constitutional monarch (being more liberal than his father).

Over the next decade, a revolutionary movement grew within Italy and the Italian people expressed their desire for a united Italian kingdom under Victor Emmanuel II. In 1859 Austria began a war in Italy to suppress the revolutionaries and strengthen its holdings, but the French intervened on the side of Victor Emmanuel II and defeated the Austrians. With the French and Italian victory, the Kingdom of Italy was declared, which covered all of northern Italy and Sardinia.

A year later, southern Italy was brought into the Italian kingdom when **Giuseppe Garibaldi** and his red shirt army freed Sicily from the control of the ruling Bourbon family and marched northward and captured Naples, where the people of the city were already in revolt against their government. Garibaldi then united his territories with those of Victor Emmanuel II in the north.

Now all of Italy was united with the exception of the Papal States: the city of Rome and the surrounding area that belonged to the Catholic Church. Ten years later, in 1870, Rome and the Papal States were also acquired with only Vatican City, within the city of Rome, being given to the Church as its territory.

■ United States

During the nineteenth century the United States of America was, in many ways, the model of a creative society. The young nation faced many challenges to its survival and development. At the same time, it was still trying to earn respect and legitimacy in the eyes of the nations of Europe. These obstacles to the young nation, combined with a strong sense of individualism and practicality, helped to make the United States a nation. The American experiment seemed to be working, and the freedom that was protected by the government, along with cheap land and ease of opportunity, provided conditions that allowed the United States to enjoy a true creative explosion and to forge a unique national identity. This creativity paved the way for an American rise to preeminence in the twentieth century.

Two concepts drove many highly creative people in several different cultural areas to define America and conquer the American frontier during the nineteenth century. The first concept was a feeling of **manifest destiny,** that all of the American continent, from Atlantic to Pacific, should be part of the United States. This feeling was similar to the feelings in Russia, Germany, and Italy about creating their national empires. The concept was even present in Britain as it formed their worldwide empire, in part, to spread British culture.

Although limited in comparison to European countries, the United States did embark on some empire building, particularly with respect to trade. Japan also enjoyed its isolation from Europe. Japan had allowed some limited access to the Dutch in the 1600s, but the Japanese had viewed the experience with the Dutch traders as a negative one because the Dutch had broken promises regarding sending Christian missionaries into the country. Japan had not allowed any trade with Europe since that time. Therefore, the Japanese were isolated from the rest of the world. However, the United States had recently granted California statehood (1850) and now the country stretched across the American continent from the Atlantic to the Pacific. The United States looked to dominate the Pacific trade from their west coast ports and the Americans felt the Japanese refusal to trade was *uncivilized.*

In 1853, the United States sent Commodore Perry to Japan with the instructions to open up Japan to foreign (specifically American) trade. Commodore Perry steamed into Tokyo Bay and demanded diplomatic negotiations with the emperor. Although Japan's long isolation had protected and preserved Japanese culture, it had also served to isolate Japan creatively, and the Japanese were astonished at the obvious power of the American warships. Realizing that they had no technology that even remotely rivaled what the United States had, and fearing a naval bombard-

ment of Tokyo, the Japanese relented and opened up Japan to trade with the United States. The United States later increased pressure on Japan to comply with American wishes and to shore up its dominance in the Pacific by going to war with Spain in 1898. The American victory in the Spanish-American War gave the United States control of the Philippines, which gave the United States a trade center and military port near Japan.

The second concept driving American creativity was not present anywhere in Europe because of the stifling class separations that were encountered there. The uniquely American concept was that all Americans could achieve whatever success they were willing to work for. These two concepts were expressed by American authors and philosophers, supported by governmental policies, and implemented by highly creative inventors and entrepreneurs. These will be the subjects of the remainder of this chapter.

American Literature

The first American artists that gained some international respect and forged a unique identity separate from their European counterparts were American authors. Many early American authors tried to capture the unique American spirit by writing tales that told of "rugged American individualism," the American frontier (including the American Indian), and the glories of the American wilderness. All of these themes were in harmony with the ideals of Romanticism that were popular in Europe at the time, yet were also uniquely American. Thus, many American authors gained popularity not only at home, but abroad, and played an important role in raising the legitimacy of the young United States in Europe.

Probably the first American author to gain international notice was **Washington Irving** (1783–1859). As a young man Irving entered the hardware business and was sent to Europe to represent his company there. While in Great Britain, Irving became acquainted with Sir Walter Scott, the British author with a strong interest in folklore and the inventor of the historical novel. Scott's interests led Washington Irving to study American folklore, and Irving later wrote many of his stories based on

American folk tales and legends. Among Irving's most popular tales were *The Legend of Sleepy Hollow* and *Rip Van Winkle*. Both stories recall the popular Romantic themes of European literature of the time, but also are uniquely American in setting (on the frontier of early New York) and in origin (American fables and myths). Washington Irving's stories found moderate success in Europe (more so than in America), and he spent much of his life traveling Europe promoting his stories and America itself.

The first American author to have his works fully embraced by Europe was **James Fenimore Cooper.** Cooper's novels of the American frontier and the American Indian, such as *Leatherstocking Tales, The Deerslayer,* and *The Last of the Mohicans,* were bestsellers across Europe and then in America. (During this phase in history, Americans generally looked to Europe for cultural trends and accepted works only after the Europeans had done so.)

Cooper's works created an image of the typical Romantic hero within an American setting. The hero of many Cooper books was Natty Bumppo (also called Hawkeye), who was a blueprint for the stereotypical American hero. It is easy to find the American hero based on the ideal of Natty Bumppo: The rugged individual in touch with his surroundings who has a casual disregard for the rules of "civilized" society. Such characters as Indiana Jones, Dirty Harry, and most heroes of American westerns all fit into this tradition.

Cooper also started another American tradition with tales of sailors and the sea. Like his frontier stories, the hero of these sea stories was also a rugged, independent man firmly in the Romantic tradition.

Cooper's works cast Native American Indians as both good and bad. Near the same time, **Henry W. Longfellow** wrote *The Song of Hiawatha,* a poem that romanticized the Indians. This work was highly successful even in Longfellow's life (selling over a million copies) and further solidified the prestige of American writing. Longfellow continued to create an American literary style in his work *The Courtship of Miles Standish,* which was about the early American settlers. Longfellow's literary works

also include a translation of Dante's *Divine Comedy* in which he conveyed Dante's works to an American audience.

Another key early American writer was **Nathaniel Hawthorne.** Hawthorne spent his life in Massachusetts and became obsessed with America's Puritan history, the contradictions within that history, and the influence those roots had on the American experience. (Hawthorne was a direct descendent of one of the judges of the Salem Witch Trials.) Hawthorne had written a few novels without much critical or popular success but then, in 1850, Hawthorne published his masterpiece, *The Scarlet Letter.* It dealt with the moral contradictions of early Puritan society and cast as its main protagonist Hester Prynne, a woman straight from the mold of the traditional American hero. The novel was an instant success among both critics and the general public.

Hawthorne followed that success with another classic novel, *The House of Seven Gables,* which dealt with a curse from the Salem Witch Trials. Hawthorne went on to write several other successful novels that dealt with American issues. Among these other novels was *The Blithedale Romance,* a novel about a religious community that was attempting to live in a communal society. Groups such as these were becoming increasingly common in America at the time and had some similarities to the growing socialist/communist movements that were then occurring in Europe.

Following in the tradition of Cooper's seafaring novels were the novels of **Herman Melville.** Born in New York, Melville moved to Massachusetts and became a sailor. Using his own experiences aboard ships and traditional sailors' tales as a basis for his novels, Melville wrote about life at sea. His works were psychological novels, where much of the story is symbolic. Melville was unpopular with critics during his lifetime and had to supplement his writing income by working as a customs agent. Melville's popularity increased in the early twentieth century (about 20 years after his death) when his novels came to be seen as symbolic of the American experience. Today Melville's novel *Moby Dick* is considered to be one of the greatest novels in American literature.

Another important American author was **Edgar Allan Poe.** He survived a rough and tragic childhood and a failed military career before finding success as a writer. While Poe was serving in the military, he also worked on his writing. He published his first book of poetry, *Tamerlane and Other Poems,* at his own expense.

It was after his discharge from the military that Poe first found any real success as a writer when a story he wrote won a $50 prize from a Baltimore paper. Poe was then able to get a job as a journalist and editor. He was able to occasionally get his poetry and short stories published with a modest degree of success.

Although Poe always wrote poetry, he is most famous as the inventor of the mystery story and as the master of the horror story. His classic short story *The Murder in the Rue Morgue* is generally believed to be the first mystery, while his dark horror stories, such as *The Fall of the House of Usher, The Tell-Tale Heart, The Cask of Amontillado,* and *The Pit and the Pendulum* are still considered classics of the horror genre.

The great American poet of the age was **Walt Whitman.** Fiercely independent, brave, and close to nature, in many ways Whitman embodied the American persona. He was a volunteer nurse during the American Civil War. He wrote his poetry in a radical free verse style that was so unusual that no book company would agree to publish it. Undaunted, Whitman financed the publication himself. This collection of poetry is titled *Leaves of Grass* and all the poems are about life in America. The poems range in topic from nature, God, politics, and love, to the Civil War, and baseball. All the poems are written in Whitman's free verse style that seems to symbolically represent the freedom of America. *Leaves of Grass* is now considered one of the greatest literary works in the world, and many critics consider it the high-water mark of American literature.

Transcendentalism

Based on the philosophy of the German Immanuel Kant, **transcendentalism** was a belief that some knowledge could be gained beyond what we get from the five senses. Among the basic premises of transcendentalism are that intuitive truths are absolute and transcend empirical knowledge, and that the ability to trust one's own insight is the secret to truth. (For example, the concept of learning through sensory experimentation is like a man trying to buy property one inch at a time, while the use of intuition allows the entire property to be acquired.) Transcendentalism states that nature is a source of joy and learning and should be revered. Transcendentalists also believe that materialist goals conflict with spiritual learning, and therefore man must set high standards of behavior that reject materialism. Also, there is a natural order in the universe that man does not impose, but follows. Finally, followers of transcendentalism believe that poets are the voice of the soul because they work from intuition.

Transcendentalism became a powerful influence in early nineteenth-century New England among members of the Unitarian church. It seemed to represent the American prototype. Transcendentalism spread across the country, primarily among the intellectual community. The movement had strong religious overtones but was not part of, nor did it ever form, any official church. The center of transcendentalism was in Concord, Massachusetts, and several literary figures were drawn to the movement and formed a community there. Among the most famous members of this group and its sympathizers were Ralph Waldo Emerson, Henry David Thoreau, Louisa May Alcott, and Emily Dickinson.

Ralph Waldo Emerson was the leader of the transcendental movement in the United States. Born in Boston, Emerson was educated as a Unitarian minister at Harvard and served as a minister for a time. Eventually Emerson resigned his ministerial position because he no longer believed that the ordinances of his church had real value. After traveling Europe for a year, Emerson returned to Concord, where he became a writer and lecturer. Emerson's essay Nature came to be the defining work of the transcendentalist movement in America. In this essay Emerson argues that nature represents the true order and design of the universe, that man's basic nature can be understood by studying nature, that a man's soul existed pre-birth, that the spirit world is more important than the physical world, that there is a basic morality in nature, and that when humans align themselves with nature they align themselves with truth.

Another key essay, both for its lasting impact and for its influence within transcendentalism, was Emerson's treatise *Self Reliance.* In *Self Reliance* Emerson states that people should trust themselves, their own thoughts, feelings, and intuition, when making the decisions in their lives. Humans should learn to rely on their own thoughts and not have them validated by someone else. In order to do this with confidence and comfort, a person's self-reliance must rely on their soul's affinity with God. Emerson says that each person must be individual, original, and creative.

Emerson's great disciple was **Henry David Thoreau,** who became convinced of the correctness of the transcendentalist philosophy when Emerson spoke at Harvard graduation the year Thoreau graduated. Thoreau was so enamored with Emerson's ideas that after graduation he moved in with Emerson and helped write some of his books. However, after a time, Thoreau wanted to experience transcendentalism, not just be academic about it. In order to do this, Thoreau went to live at Walden Pond to be alone with nature, and to think, write, and live the simple life. Thoreau lived at Walden for two years. Upon his return, Thoreau wrote about his experiences living close to nature in his book *Walden.* Walden Pond, near Concord, Massachusetts is shown in Figure 43.2.

Thoreau also took Emerson's belief in self-reliance to a new level and discussed his ideas in his essay *On Civil Disobedience.* Thoreau believed that basic laws transcend the laws of the land and that people must be free to act according to their own idea of right and wrong without interference from the government. (These were strongly Enlightenment principles.) Thoreau was unafraid to act on his convictions, choosing, at one point, to go to prison rather than pay his taxes because he opposed America's war with Mexico and refused to help finance it. The principle of civil disobedience presented in *On Civil Disobedience* had a lasting effect on later leaders such as Gandhi and Martin Luther King.

Transcendentalism was also one of the driving forces behind America's premier poetess, **Emily Dickinson.** She was uncomfortable with the outside world and lived most of her life in near seclusion in her Amherst, Massachusetts, home. There Emily Dickinson found in transcendentalism a philosophy she could embrace (at least to a degree), and most of her poems deal with the interaction between the inner self and the outside world, a strongly transcendentalist theme. In her isolation, Dickinson wrote over 1,700 poems, only 7 of which were published during her own lifetime.

Figure 43.2 ■ Walden Pond in Massachusetts. © *2010 by Nelson Sirlin. Used under license of Shutterstock, Inc.*

Besides Emerson, Thoreau, Dickinson, and Whitman, many of the other leading American intellectuals of the day were transcendentalists, including writer Nathaniel Hawthorne, Unitarian pastor Ellery Channing, author and doctor Oliver Wendell Holmes (father of the Supreme Court justice of the same name), and renowned educator Bronson Alcott (father of Louisa May Alcott, author of *Little Women*). These men and women, and like-minded others, helped give a philosophical backing to the image of the American which contributed to Americans' desires to conquer the frontiers and become what they envisioned.

Manifest Destiny

One of the great driving forces behind the growth and development of America as a nation and the American character was western expansion. The availability of cheap and available land had several desirable effects on the United States. First, it allowed (relatively) easy opportunity for upward social mobility and the acquisition of wealth and a better life through the acquisition of land. Second, it encouraged continual immigration from other countries. Third, it inspired the American imagination, in both technology and the arts. These factors created the idea of America as a land of hope and opportunity, as well as a land of extraordinary individuality and creativity. Thus, westward expansion impacted nearly all aspects of American history and the American experience.

Although Americans had been pushing westward since colonial times, the purchase of the Louisiana Territory in 1803 opened up the western frontier to a new level of expansion. The Louisiana Purchase doubled the size of American territory and sparked an immediate interest in exploration and increased settlement. Figure 43.3 shows the size of the Louisiana Purchase. Remember that when it was purchased, the United States was entirely east of the Mississippi River. The availability of so much land made land prices cheap. Many people saw this as an opportunity for individual economic improvement and decided a better life waited for them in the west. Furthermore, many people believed it was America's manifest destiny to one day extend across the continent.

Although the Louisiana Territory had been purchased from France, some of that territory was also claimed by other European nations, such as Great Britain and Spain. Great Britain wanted to claim land in the northwest part of Louisiana to add to Canada. Many in Great Britain wanted to retake the United States, and saw acquisition of this territory as the first step in the reconquest.

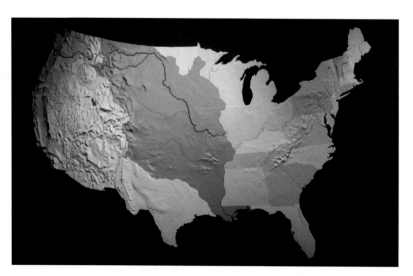

Figure 43.3 ■ The Louisiana Purchase. © *2010 by Jose Gil. Used under license of Shutterstock, Inc.*

The British desire to control the west (and possibly retake their lost colonies) combined with continual harassment of American ships and interference with American trade led to the War of 1812.

Much of the War of 1812 ended in stalemate. A series of battles were fought between the Americans and British along the American-Canadian border with neither side able to claim any strategic victories. The United States failed in three separate attempts to invade Canada, while the British were unable to gain any meaningful victories over the Americans, suffering defeat in attempts to capture both Baltimore and New Orleans. Eventually, the British were able to capture Washington, D.C., and burn down the White House. This narrow victory was somewhat hollow for the British, as it did little to aid the British war effort, while it convinced Americans that the survival of the country was at stake, and volunteers swarmed into the army. The British then lost several key battles and eventually the two sides agreed to peace.

While the War of 1812 ended in a military stalemate, for the United States the war had two positive outcomes. First, it ended any legitimate British claims to the Louisiana Territory. Second, it served as a second war of independence for the United States and solidified its survival as an independent and autonomous country.

With control of the Louisiana Territory now firmly in American hands, the United States had to deal with a different obstacle to western expansion—how to get there. Separated from the eastern seaboard by the Appalachian Mountains and with most navigable rivers running north-south, rather than east-west, travel and trade between the original 13 states and the new western territories was difficult and expensive.

American politicians, engineers, and frontiersmen set to work to solve this problem and extend the nation. The constant push west over the next century repeatedly served as a spur to American engineering, technology, and creativity (similar to the effect the space program had in the latter half of the twentieth century). The national road, connecting Cumberland, Maryland with Vandalia, Illinois, was completed in 1811, providing settlers and traders with easy and quick access over the Appalachians. In 1825 the Erie Canal was completed, providing a navigable waterway from the eastern seaboard to the Great Lakes. Several other canals were finished shortly thereafter. In 1830, the Baltimore and Ohio Railroad connected the east and west by rail, and the Tom Thumb steam locomotive became the first American-built steam locomotive to be operated on a common-carrier railroad.

As the Ohio Valley and the other regions just west of the Appalachian Mountains began to be heavily populated, Americans pushed into the American prairie and further west. As the pioneers moved west, they first blazed, and then followed, a series of trails that became the highways between the regions east of the Mississippi River, across the plains, and to the Rocky Mountains and Pacific coast. The three most important of these trails west were the Santa Fe, Oregon, and Mormon trails.

The Santa Fe Trail went from Franklin, Missouri, to Santa Fe, New Mexico, and was used primarily (at least initially) as a trade route between the United States and the Spanish territories in the west. It also served as a transportation trail for the army in its effort to control and suppress the Native Americans of the southwest. The Oregon Trail began at Independence, Missouri, and extended west to the rich and fertile farmlands of the Pacific Northwest. Later, after gold was discovered, another branch led south into the agricultural lands and gold fields of California. The Mormon Trail wound from Nauvoo, Illinois (a predominately Mormon city that was larger than Chicago in its heyday), to the Great Basin in the Rocky Mountains. The Mormons had been persecuted by their neighbors and driven from Missouri to Illinois, where they built the city of Nauvoo. However, the intense persecution followed them to Illinois, leading to the eventual murder of **Joseph Smith,** founder of Mormonism (The Church of Jesus Christ of Latter-day Saints). Tired of the persecution and feeling that neither the state nor federal government was protecting their religious rights, the Mormons began a massive migration west, led by their new leader, **Brigham Young.** The Mormons eventually settled near the Great Salt Lake in the Rocky Mountains because they believed that the inhospitable location would be unwanted by others and they would be left alone to worship in peace.

A series of wars and treaties resulted in the eventual completion of the concept of manifest destiny. Texas successfully fought for its independence from Mexico in 1836. Briefly becoming an independent nation, it was annexed into the United States approximately a year later. Ten years later, in 1846, the United States fought a war with Mexico over control of western territories. This war was won by the United States, which then acquired California (also briefly an independent country) and the modern southwestern United States. Finally, in that same year, 1846, a treaty with Great Britain gave America official control over the Oregon Territory in exchange for the end to any American claims on British Columbia. The United States now stretched from coast to coast.

The American Civil War

Sadly, political and regional tensions escalated to a breaking point in the United States over the issues of states rights and slavery in 1861. At the core of this debate was the fundamental difference in lifestyle and political philosophy between the industrial northern states and the agricultural southern ones. Slavery was the economic basis for southern life and strongly backed by the large plantation owners, the traditional center of southern political might and financial wealth. However, in the north slavery had been virtually abolished, and was strongly opposed by many politicians and intellectuals who saw the inherent conflict of the practice of slavery in a nation built on the principle "that all men are created equal."

While this dichotomy had existed between the northern and southern states since the birth of the nation, even threatening to derail the Constitutional Convention before a compromise could eventually be achieved, it reached a new peak at this time due to western expansion. Up until this time the delicate political balance between northern and southern interests had been maintained by nearly equal representation in Congress. However, expansion west and the eventual desire of many of the territories to become states led to difficult decisions about whether slavery should be allowed in the territories. A majority of the new states decided to ban slavery.

As the balance of power began to shift in favor of the northern states, the South began to grow increasingly concerned. This concern turned to fear with the election of the Republican candidate, **Abraham Lincoln,** to the presidency because of his dislike of slavery. Shortly after Lincoln's election, the southern states, beginning with South Carolina, began to secede from the United States. These states claimed that the states had voluntarily agreed to join the union and that it was therefore within their rights to withdraw from that union. The northern states argued that once the states had joined the union, they gave up their sovereignty permanently and no longer had the right to withdraw. This conflict led to war.

The **American Civil War** began officially with the Confederate (Southern) army's attack on Fort Sumter, a Union (Northern) fort located in South Carolina, in 1861. President Lincoln's plan to gain quick and decisive victories in the early battles did not work, and over the next four years the United States was torn apart in civil war.

Both sides had distinct advantages that they tried to use to bring the war to an end. The northern union armies had a technological and industrial advantage, with access to far more railroads, canals, and factories to produce equipment. Furthermore, the population of the North was considerably larger, giving the union armies more men to draw upon. However, the South had advantages too. Southerners had a greater enthusiasm for the war. The southern states were fighting for their way of life and defending their homes, as most of the fighting occurred in the south. The South also felt justification for the war in that the union armies had attacked first and had invaded their territory. Furthermore, another southern advantage was that many northern generals were in favor of a negotiated settlement and therefore were reluctant to push aggressively to win battles and capture southern territory. Finally, the southerners did not have to really win the war, they just had to harass the northern forces until the northern people and politicians tired of war and gave up. Thus, in effect, to gain victory the South only needed to reach a stalemate, whereas the North would have to conquer.

The war was long and bloody and the technology had advanced quicker than the military strategy, leading to mass killing on both sides. The war was further prolonged because both sides lacked the key ingredient needed to finish off the other. The South was initially more successful, but the lack of industry, manpower, and good transportation constantly hampered them. At the same time, most of the early northern defeats and heavy casualties were due to the hesitation of the northern generals, who were unwilling to take advantage of their superior firepower and manpower.

To give the North a reason to fight beyond just the preservation of the union, in 1863 Lincoln emancipated the slaves. Despite all of the early southern victories, the North just kept sending more men and firepower to the war. The South simply didn't have the resources to win a war of attrition and decided to take decisive action by staging a major battle at Gettysburg, Pennsylvania. The southern hope in doing this was to crush northern resolve and make a final attempt at a decisive victory to end the war. The battle was the longest and bloodiest of the American Civil War, with heavy casualties on both sides. In the end, the northern forces proved victorious.

President Lincoln finally found a competent general with the will to win the war. He appointed Ulysses S. Grant commander of all union forces. Grant won major victories at Vicksburg and in Tennessee, thus dividing the South. He also sent Generals Sherman and Sheridan to devastate southern morale through marches in Georgia and Virginia. In April 1865 General Lee, head of the southern armies, surrendered at Appomattox Courthouse, Virginia, bringing an end to the war.

The northern victory brought about the end of the traditional southern lifestyle and economic ruin to the South. And while the South was allowed back into the union without serious penalty, the region was forced to submit to a period of northern economic and political domination known as "reconstruction." The Constitution was amended to protect the newly won freedom and rights of American blacks. Although slavery

was ended, the union was preserved, and the question of states rights versus federal power was resolved in favor of the national government, the North did not win complete victory. Despite the efforts of reconstruction, the South still felt the racial divide deeply and a new set of local laws and traditions continued discrimination against black Americans. This discrimination eventually evolved into legally protected segregation of the races that was not ended until the American civil rights movement of the 1960s. Only a few days after the end of the Civil War, a southern sympathizer assassinated President Abraham Lincoln.

American Technology and Entrepreneurship

During the nineteenth century the United States experienced a technological renaissance driven by three main factors: American opportunity for social advancement, the desire to conquer and tame the frontier, and the needs of the military to fight its various wars and to subdue the Native Americans. Many of these new inventions and technologies gave the United States an edge against other nations and helped to create American economic and military power in the twentieth century.

The true Renaissance Man of American invention, as well as the starting point of the American tradition of innovation and ingenuity that would dominate the 1800s was actually a product of the 1700s. Like an American Leonardo da Vinci, **Benjamin Franklin** dabbled in nearly all of the important fields of the time and was a master of many. Benjamin Franklin made his fortune as a printer and author and was so successful in these endeavors that he was able to retire from active business pursuits and devote himself to other areas of interest by his mid-forties. Franklin became famous for his publication of *Poor Richard's Almanac* and for his own sage sayings that it included. Many of these sayings are well known today and have become part of American culture. Examples of sayings written by Benjamin Franklin include, "A penny saved is a penny earned," "Early to bed, early to rise, make's a man healthy, wealthy, and wise," "Fish and visitors smell in three days," and "He who falls in love with himself has no rivals."

Besides being a successful printer and writer, Franklin was also an accomplished scientist and inventor. As a scientist he studied and wrote about comets and hurricanes. He also conducted (or proposed) a series of famous experiments with electricity, in which by using a kite and key he discovered that lightning is electricity. Franklin also invented many practical items such as bifocals, a step ladder, a rocking chair with a fan to keep flies away, a device to remove books from the top shelf in his library, a system that allowed him to lock his door at night without getting out of bed, and the Franklin stove.

Benjamin Franklin was also an important politician and statesman and one of the founding fathers of the United States. Among his accomplishments as a leader in the city of Philadelphia was the organization of a fire department, the establishment of a means of lighting the city's streets at night, the development of a system to dispose of the city's garbage, and the development of a postal system that cut the mail time between Philadelphia and Boston from six weeks to six days. Franklin also set up the academy that became Pennsylvania University and established Philadelphia's major hospital. Franklin served his country effectively, as well. He was ambassador to France during the Revolutionary War and convinced the French to support the Americans. Later, he was the ambassador to Great Britain who worked out the terms of the peace treaty that ended the Revolutionary War. He advised Thomas Jefferson in the writing of the Declaration of Independence and he was an active participant at the Constitutional Convention in 1787. Franklin proved to be the first in a series of inventors and scientists that would make a lasting impact on America and the world over the next century.

Possibly the most important technological breakthrough of the era was accomplished by **Eli Whitney** when he invented the concept of interchangeable parts in order to save the military money and effort. Prior to interchangeable parts, every rifle was made individually and was unique. If a gun broke, a part had to be specifically made to fit that particular weapon. This proved costly and resulted in many failed weapons.

Whitney's concept was to make gun parts by machine so that they would be replicated over and over again in exact size. Thus, replacing parts became quick, cheap, and easy because all the guns were the same and used the exact same parts. The concept of interchangeable parts laid the groundwork for American industrial strength and was a key to many later inventions, such as Elias Howe's sewing machine in 1846. Interchangeable parts also brought immediate improvement in quality and production efficiency. (To demonstrate the principle of interchangeable parts, Whitney took boxes of parts for 10 rifles to the war department and dumped them onto the table in a meeting with several department officials and instructed them to put the rifles together. When they succeeded, they were convinced of the value of his new system of manufacture.)

Eli Whitney also played a key role in agriculture production with the invention of the cotton gin in 1793. The cotton gin helped make the young United States an important trading partner with Great Britain during the height of the Industrial Revolution when cotton was so critical to the textile industry. Another important innovation in agriculture was Cyrus McCormick's invention of the reaper in 1834. The reaper gave an economic advantage to farmers in the Midwest and allowed the rapidly growing American population to be adequately fed.

There were also several key American innovations in the area of transportation during this time. In 1807 Robert Fulton made a practical steamboat, thus freeing ships from the unpredictability of wind patterns and water currents. The steamboat gave the United States a shipping advantage and helped to ease America's isolationism. (Later inventions such as the clipper ships further reduced American isolation and made American shipping a power in the world.) Finally, the transcontinental railroad was completed in 1869, connecting the west with the east.

The vast size of the United States also served as a creative spur to innovation in the field of communication. While the improvements in transportation helped, it was the invention of the telegraph first, and later the telephone, that united the nation through quick communication. In 1838 Samuel Morse invented the telegraph and Morse code as a means of sending messages. (see Figure 43.4). The telegraph facilitated the mass migration of people west. The telegraph was a crude method of transmitting information but its strong effect on the growth of the nation illustrated the importance of communications. Communication over long distances was made even easier in 1876 with Alexander Graham Bell's invention of the telephone. Not only did the telephone help unite the vast American nation, but it also captured the imagination of the world and helped to improve America's status on the world stage.

The vulcanization of rubber was discovered by Charles Goodyear in 1839. Goodyear was trying to improve the properties of rubber and discovered that by heating and mixing sulphur with natural rubber he could obtain the properties he desired. He built a great industrial empire.

However, the master of American invention, with over 1,000 registered patents, was the "Wizard of Menlo Park," **Thomas Edison.** Among Edison's many inventions were a vote recorder, a stock ticker tape machine, the phonograph, the electric light, motion pictures, a storage battery, a cement mixer, the Dictaphone, and a duplicating machine. Edison also improved many already existing products such as the typewriter and the telephone. Most importantly, Thomas Edison developed a complete electrical use and distribution system, including, of course, the light bulb, and oversaw the organization of Edison Electric (later to become General Electric). To this day Thomas Edison has more patents than any other American.

During the 1900s, United States manufacturing followed the model of Great Britain. The Industrial Revolution was sweeping across the nation, bringing with it many changes and innovations. And, as in Europe, the spread of industrialization caused poor economic conditions for the urban workers. Americans had developed a two-party system that helped overcome the problems of the poor workers and ultimately led to higher efficiencies. Furthermore, within America the concept of upward mobility and the opportunity to move westward helped to relieve the tensions of the cities, at least for some. (In Europe, those who wanted to escape the drudgery of the urban situation came to America.)

Entrepreneurship in America was very strong. Many of the inventors became leaders of industry

Figure 43.4 ■ The telegraph transmitter. © *2010 by Anyka. Used under license of Shutterstock, Inc.*

to capitalize on their inventions. Other entrepreneurs arose who saw opportunities in the rapid expansion of the American economy. Some of these entrepreneurs included John D. Rockefeller (oil), Joseph Pulitzer (newspapers), William Randolph Hearst (newspapers), Cornelius Vanderbilt (railroads), Edward H. Harriman (railroads), E. I. DuPont (chemicals), Henry Ford (automobiles), Alfred P. Sloane (automobiles), Andrew Carnegie (steel), James Fisk (finance), Jay Gould (finance), and J. P. Morgan (finance).

Some of the inventors and entrepreneurs (such as Carnegie, Bell, and DuPont) immigrated to America to improve their lives. From the beginning of this country, the "American dream" of a chance to improve your status in life was a driving force for creativity.

◼ Timeline—Important Dates

Date	Event
1728–1779	Captain James Cook
1783–1830	Simon Bolivar
1783–1859	Washington Irving
1789–1851	James Fennimore Cooper
1793	Eli Whitney's cotton gin invented
1803	Thomas Jefferson completes the Louisiana Purchase
1803–1882	Ralph Waldo Emerson
1804–1864	Nathaniel Hawthorne
1807	Fulton's steamboat
1807–1882	Henry W. Longfellow
1809–1849	Edgar Allen Poe
1813–1873	David Livingstone
1817–1862	Henry David Thoreau
1819–1891	Herman Melville
1819–1892	Walt Whitman
1830	Belgium formed
1830–1881	Emily Dickenson
1832–1888	Louisa May Alcott
1834	Cyrus McCormick's reaper invented
1838	Samuel Morse invents the telegraph
1839	Goodyear vulcanizes rubber
1839-1860	Opium Wars
1846	Elias Howe's sewing machine invented
1847–1931	Thomas Alva Edison
1848	Liberal revolutions throughout Europe
1853	Crimean War
1853	Japan opened for trade by United States pressure
1859	Kingdom of Italy declared (Sardinia and northern Italy)
1859	Drake drills first oil well
1861–1865	American Civil War
1862	Otto von Bismarck named prime minister of Prussia
1870	Franco-Prussian War; Napoleon III overthrown
1870	Italy united under Victor Emmanuel II
1871	German Empire declared
1876	Alexander Graham Bell invents the telephone
1885	Congo Free State established under Leopold II
1900	The Boxer Rebellion in China
1908	Belgian Congo formed

◼ Suggested Readings

Achebe, Chinua, *Things Fall Apart,* Anchor Books, 1959.

Alger, Horatio, Jr., *Ragged Dick,* Signet Classic, 1990.

Ambrose, Stephen E., *Undaunted Courage,* Touchstone, 1996.

Buck, Pearl S., *The Good Earth,* Pocket Books, 1931.

Franklin, Benjamin, *Autobiography,* Penguin, 1961.

Hawthorne, Nathaniel, *The Scarlet Letter,* Penguin Classics, 1986.

Irving, Washington, *Tales of the Alhambra,* Sleepy Hollow Press, 1982.

Michener, James, *The Covenant,* Random House, 1980.

Mitchell, Margaret, *Gone With the Wind,* Avon Books, 1964.

Sinclair, Upton, *The Jungle,* Bantam Books, 1981.

Sobel, Dava, *Longitude,* Penguin Books, 1996.

Stowe, Harriet Beecher, *Uncle Tom's Cabin,* Bantam Books, 1981.

Twain, Mark, *Huckleberry Finn,* Charles L. Webster and Co., 1895.

Alfred, Lord Tennyson: The Charge of the Light Brigade

Alfred, Lord Tennyson (1809–1892) began writing poetry when he was eight years old and wrote his first blank verse when he was fourteen. He was tutored from his home after several unsuccessful years at school and attended Trinity College in Cambridge where he joined a literary club. In 1833, he published a book of poetry that received poor reviews. Because of this criticism and the sudden death of his best friend, Tennyson vowed to not publish again for ten years so that he could spend his time in reading and contemplation. He did, however, continue to write during this period. At the end of his self-imposed silence, Tennyson published a book of poetry that received strong critical support. This collection contained works such as "Mort d'Arthur," "Locksley Hall," and "Ulysses."

Tennyson became immensely popular and was appointed poet laureate, succeeding William Wordsworth. As part of his duties as poet laureate, he was asked to write poems celebrating great accomplishments of the English people. *The Charge of the Light Brigade* is one such poem. He wrote it in a few minutes in response to reading an article in the newspaper about a battle in the Crimean War. The article mentioned that some leader had blundered leaving the Light Brigade Cavalry surrounded. This mistake resulted in a courageous last stand where all Brigade members were killed. The poem was very popular in its day, perhaps due to its exoneration of the uneducated soldiers' willingness to stand for a cause, regardless of the difficulties. It also expressed the dedication to duty that is inherent in the English mentality. It typifies the spirit present in Britain during the period of empire. For these reasons, and because of its wonderful rhythms and rhymes, it is included here.

Toward the end of his life, Tennyson returned to some of the themes of his earlier work completing "Idylls of the King." Most of his later works were created in his head and then transcribed by his wife because Tennyson had lost much of his sight. He is considered one of the most famous poets of the Victorian age and is widely acclaimed even today because of his mastery of so many poetic genres.

Alfred, Lord Tennyson: The Charge of the Light Brigade

1

Half a league, half a league,
Half a league onward,
All in the valley of Death
    Rode the six hundred.
"Forward the Light Brigade!   5
Charge for the guns!" he said.
Into the valley of Death
    Rode the six hundred.

2

"Forward, the Light Brigade!"
Was there a man dismay'd?   10
Not tho' the soldier knew
    Some one had blunder'd.
    Theirs not to make reply,
    Theirs not to reason why,
    Theirs but to do and die.   15
Into the valley of Death
Rode the six hundred.

3

Cannon to right of them,
Cannon to left of them,
Cannon in front of them   20
    Volley'd and thunder'd;

Storm'd at with shot and shell,
Boldly they rode and well,
Into the jaws of Death,
Into the mouth of hell   25
    Rode the six hundred.

4

Flash'd all their sabres bare,
Slash'd as they turn'd in air
Sabring the gunners there,
Charging an army, while   30
    All the world wonder'd.
Plunged in the battery-smoke
Right thro' the line they broke;
Cossack and Russian
Reel'd from the sabre-stroke
    Shatter'd and sunder'd.   35
Then they rode back, but not,
    Not the six hundred.

5

Cannon to right of them,
Cannon to left of them,
Cannon behind them   40
    Volley'd and thunder'd;
Storm'd at with shot and shell,
While horse and hero fell,

Source: From *Tennyson's Poetry,* edited by Robert W. Hill, Jr. (New York: W. W. Norton, 1999).

They that had fought so well
Came thro' the jaws of Death,   45
Back from the mouth of hell,
All that was left of them,
    Left of six hundred.

▪ **6**

When can their glory fade?
O the wild charge they made!   50
    All the world wonder'd.
Honor the charge they made!
Honor the Light Brigade,
    Noble six hundred!   55

Ralph Waldo Emerson: Self-Reliance

Ralph Waldo Emerson (1803–1882) was born in Boston, Massachusetts into a family where many had been clergymen. He attended Harvard University, receiving an education as a Unitarian minister, and became the pastor at the Second Unitarian Church of Boston. When his first wife died of consumption, his faith in Unitarianism faltered and he resigned from his position as pastor. He traveled to Europe where he became acquainted with several members of the English literary elite and developed friendships with them that lasted a lifetime.

Upon his return to America, he settled in Concord, Massachusetts where he led a group of intellectuals who sought to live in accordance with nature with a strong emphasis on individual responsibility for actions. Some of those in the group included Henry David Thoreau and the Branson Alcott family, which included Louisa Mae Alcott, the author of *Little Women.* The philosophy of this group became known as Transcendentalism because of their belief that knowledge could transcend information gained through the senses. They believed that people had innate knowledge that directed them to a simple and yet abundant life. They rejected organized religion and viewed nature in an almost religious way. Emerson published a collection of essays entitled *Nature* that became the defining work of Transcendentalism. In the years just prior to the Civil War, the group became strongly abolitionist.

Emerson's most read work, *Self-Reliance,* was the result of his lifelong advocacy of individualism. *Self-Reliance* declares trust in one's self to be all-important and to be superior to trust in traditional authority. Society is decried as a conspiracy against the individual because it imposes conformity. Similar to Descartes' *Discourse on Method,* it urges man to disregard everything taught him by society and to find the truth himself. Happiness does not come from travel or possessions, but from a quiet life centered in the present time and on inner truth. The following selections from *Self-Reliance* include the discussion of these principles.

I read the other day some verses written by an eminent painter which were original and not conventional. The soul always hears an admonition in such lines, let the subject be what it may. The sentiment they instil is of more value than any thought they may contain. To believe your own thought, to believe that what is true for you in your private heart is true for all men,—that is genius. Speak your latent conviction, and it shall be the universal sense; for the inmost in due time becomes the outmost, and our first thought is rendered back to us by the trumpets of the Last Judgment. Familiar as the voice of the mind is to each, the highest merit we ascribe to Moses, Plato and Milton is that they set at naught books and traditions, and spoke not what men, but what *they* thought. A man should learn to detect and watch that gleam of light which flashes across his mind from within, more than the lustre of the firmament of bards and sages. Yet he dismisses without notice his thought, because it is his. In every work of genius we recognize our own rejected thoughts; they come back to us with a certain alienated majesty. Great works of art have no more affecting lesson for us than this. They teach us to abide by our spontaneous impression with good-humored inflexibility then most when the whole cry of voices is on the other side. Else to-morrow a stranger will say with masterly good sense precisely what we have thought and felt all the time, and we shall be forced to take with shame our own opinion from another.

There is a time in every man's education when he arrives at the conviction that envy is ignorance; that imitation is suicide; that he must take himself for better for worse as his portion; that though the wide universe is full of good, no kernel of nourishing corn can come to him but through his toil bestowed on that plot of ground which is given to him to till. The power which resides in him is new in nature, and none but he knows what that is which he can do, nor does he know until he has tried. Not for nothing one face, one character, one fact, makes much impression on him, and another none. This sculpture in the memory is not without preëstablished harmony. The eye was placed where one ray should fall, that it might testify of that particular ray. We but half express ourselves, and are ashamed of that divine idea which each of us represents. It may be safely trusted as proportionate and of good issues, so it be faithfully imparted, but God will not have his work made manifest by cowards. A man is relieved and gay when he has put his heart into his work and done his best; but what he has said or done otherwise shall give him no peace. It is a deliverance which does not deliver. In the attempt his genius deserts him; no muse befriends; no invention, no hope.

Trust thyself: every heart vibrates to that iron string. Accept the place the divine providence has

---

Source: From *The Spiritual Emerson: Essential Writings* by Ralph Waldo Emerson (Boston: Beacon Press, 2003).

found for you, the society of your contemporaries, the connection of events. Great men have always done so, and confided themselves childlike to the genius of their age, betraying their perception that the absolutely trustworthy was seated at their heart, working through their hands, predominating in all their being. And we are now men, and must accept in the highest mind the same transcendent destiny; and not minors and invalids in a protected corner, not cowards fleeing before a revolution, but guides, redeemers and benefactors, obeying the Almighty effort and advancing on Chaos and the Dark.

* * *

Society everywhere is in conspiracy against the manhood of every one of its members. Society is a joint-stock company, in which the members agree, for the better securing of his bread to each shareholder, to surrender the liberty and culture of the eater. The virtue in most request is conformity. Self-reliance is its aversion. It loves not realities and creators, but names and customs.

Whoso would be a man, must be a nonconformist. He who would gather immortal palms must not be hindered by the name of goodness, but must explore if it be goodness. Nothing is at last sacred but the integrity of your own mind. Absolve you to yourself, and you shall have the suffrage of the world. I remember an answer which when quite young I was prompted to make to a valued adviser who was wont to importune me with the dear old doctrines of the church. On my saying, "What have I to do with the sacredness of traditions, if I live wholly from within?" my friend suggested,—"But these impulses may be from below, not from above." I replied, "They do not seem to me to be such; but if I am the Devil's child, I will live then from the Devil." No law can be sa-

cred to me but that of my nature. Good and bad are but names very readily transferable to that or this; the only right is what is after my constitution; the only wrong what is against it. A man is to carry himself in the presence of all opposition as if every thing were titular and ephemeral but he. I am ashamed to think how easily we capitulate to badges and names, to large societies and dead institutions. Every decent and well-spoken individual affects and sways me more than is right.

* * *

Then again, do not tell me, as a good man did today, of my obligation to put all poor men in good situations. Are they *my* poor? I tell thee, thou foolish philanthropist, that I grudge the dollar, the dime, the cent I give to such men as do not belong to me and to whom I do not belong. There is a class of persons to whom by all spiritual affinity I am bought and sold; for them I will go to prison if need be; but your miscellaneous popular charities; the education at college of fools; the building of meeting-houses to the vain end to which many now stand; alms to sots, and the thousand-fold Relief Societies;—though I confess with shame I sometimes succumb and give the dollar, it is a wicked dollar, which by and by I shall have the manhood to withhold. . . .

What I must do is all that concerns me, not what the people think. This rule, equally arduous in actual and in intellectual life, may serve for the whole distinction between greatness and meanness. It is the harder because you will always find those who think they know what is your duty better than you know it. It is easy in the world to live after the world's opinion; it is easy in solitude to live after our own; but the great man is he who in the midst of the crowd keeps with perfect sweetness the independence of solitude.

Henry David Thoreau: Walden

Henry David Thoreau (1817–1862) was born in Concord, Massachusetts and became known as a serious, but unconventional, scholar. He was a member of the 1837 graduating class at Harvard where he heard Emerson's speech in which Emerson outlined the principles of Transcendentalism. Because of Thoreau's strong interest in Transcendentalism, Emerson invited Thoreau to live at his home where Emerson became Thoreau's mentor and friend. Thoreau worked for Emerson as a handy man and helped to edit and contribute to the transcendentalist magazine. Thoreau became a strong voice for the transcendental movement and expanded on Emerson's ideas from *Self-Reliance* by asserting that the basic laws of nature transcend the laws of the land. His essay *On Civil Disobedience* explained that people must be free according to their own idea of right and wrong and not be bound by governments. Thoreau chose to go to jail rather than pay a tax that was associated with the Mexican War, which he opposed. Friends paid his fine so that Thoreau did not have to spend extended time in jail. Thoreau advocated passive resistance to governmental demands that were, in the view of the individual, illegal or immoral—a philosophy later adopted by Mohandas Gandhi.

In many ways, Thoreau's thoughts closely mirrored those of Jean Jacques Rousseau—believing in the right to overthrow (in this case, ignore) governments that did not respect the rights of individuals. He also believed in the concept of the noble savage. In hopes of applying Emerson's and Rousseau's teachings, Thoreau moved to Walden Pond and wrote of his experiences in the woods. His writings show his disparaging view of materialism. Included here are two passages from *Walden*. The first contains Thoreau's reflections on our reasons for existence and the proper reasoning for waking up in the morning. The second passage is his powerful concluding discussion of his experiences and what he learned at Walden Pond.

Morning is when I am awake and there is a dawn in me. Moral reform is the effort to throw off sleep. Why is it that men give so poor an account of their day if they have not been slumbering? They are not such poor calculators. If they had not been overcome with drowsiness they would have performed something. The millions are awake enough for physical labor; but only one in a million is awake enough for effective intellectual exertion, only one in a hundred millions to a poetic or divine life. To be awake is to be alive. I have never yet met a man who was quite awake. How could I have looked him in the face?

We must learn to reawaken and keep ourselves awake, not by mechanical aids, but by an infinite expectation of the dawn, which does not forsake us in our soundest sleep. I know of no more encouraging fact than the unquestionable ability of man to elevate his life by a conscious endeavor. It is something to be able to paint a particular picture, or to carve a statue, and so to make a few objects beautiful; but it is far more glorious to carve and paint the very atmosphere and medium through which we look, which morally we can do. To affect the quality of the day, that is the highest of arts. Every man is tasked to make his life, even in its details, worthy of the contemplation of his most elevated and critical hour. If we refused, or rather used up, such paltry information as we get, the oracles would distinctly inform us how this might be done.

I went to the woods because I wished to live deliberately, to front only the essential facts of life, and see if I could not learn what it had to teach, and not, when I came to die, discover that I had not lived. I did not wish to live what was not life, living is so dear; nor did I wish to practise resignation, unless it was quite necessary. I wanted to live deep and suck out all the marrow of life, to live so sturdily and Spartan-like as to put to rout all that was not life, to cut a broad swath and shave close, to drive life into a corner, and reduce it to its lowest terms, and, if it proved to be mean, why then to get the whole and genuine meanness of it, and publish its meanness to the world; or if it were sublime, to know it by experience, and be able to give a true account of it in my next excursion. For most men, it appears to me, are in a strange uncertainty about it, whether it is of the devil or of God, and have *somewhat hastily* concluded that it is the chief end of man here to "glorify God and enjoy him forever."

*   *   *

I left the woods for as good a reason as I went there. Perhaps it seemed to me that I had several more lives to live, and could not spare any more time for that one. It is remarkable how easily and insensibly we fall into a particular route, and make a beaten track for ourselves. I had not lived there a week before my feet wore a path from my door to the pond-side; and though it is five or six years since I trod it, it is still quite distinct. It is true, I fear that others may have fallen into it, and so helped to keep it open. The surface of the earth is

---

Source: From *Walden and Civil Disobedience* by Henry David Thoreau (Boston: Houghton Mifflin Company, 2000).

soft and impressible by the feet of men; and so with the paths which the mind travels. How worn and dusty, then, must be the highways of the world, how deep the ruts of tradition and conformity! I did not wish to take a cabin passage, but rather to go before the mast and on the deck of the world, for there I could best see the moonlight amid the mountains. I do not wish to go below now.

I learned this, at least, by my experiment; that if one advances confidently in the direction of his dreams, and endeavors to live the life he has imagined, he will meet with a success unexpected in common hours. He will put some things behind, will pass an invisible boundary; new, universal, and more liberal laws will begin to establish themselves around and within him; or the old laws be expanded, and interpreted in his favor in a more liberal sense, and he will live with the license of a higher order of beings. In proportion as he simplifies his life, the laws of the universe will appear less complex, and solitude will not be solitude, nor poverty poverty, nor weakness weakness. If you have built castles in the air, your work need not be lost; that is where they should be. Now put the foundations under them.

Walt Whitman: Leaves of Grass

Walt Whitman (1819–1892) was a well-known poet who was born in Long Island, New York and grew up with his family of eleven in Brooklyn. At the age of twelve, he learned about the printing trade and became enthralled with the words of great writers of the past. He started teaching school when he was seventeen, but returned to journalism and founded a local newspaper and began editing several others. He worked for a short time in New Orleans where he saw the effects of slavery first-hand, and then returned to the North and began developing his unique style of poetry. At the outbreak of the Civil War, he began working in a Washington hospital caring for the sick until he suffered a stroke and was no longer able to do it. He was never a wealthy man and occasionally received donations from other writers in America and Europe so that he could survive. He published all of his books at his own expense because he couldn't find a publisher willing to publish his unusual and unique style.

That style is best illustrated in Whitman's *Leaves of Grass,* a compilation of poems about life in America. His open verse is highly rhetorical, leaving a dreamy and misty feel. The constant use of the first person makes each poem a journal entry through Whitman's soul and personal reflections. He maintains a mood of almost stoical reserved optimism throughout the poems, even when contemplating his death or the tragedy of the Civil War.

The following poems are from the "Songs of Parting" in *Leaves of Grass* and are selected for their illustration of many of characteristics of Whitman's poetry.

Walt Whitman: Leaves of Grass

▪ Songs of Parting

As the Time Draws Nigh
As the time draws nigh glooming a cloud,
A dread beyond of I know not what darkens me.

I shall go forth,
I shall traverse the States awhile, but I cannot tell
    whither or how long,
Perhaps soon some day or night while I am
    singing my voice will suddenly cease.

O book, O chants! must all then amount to but
    this?
Must we barely arrive at this beginning of us?—
    and yet it is enough, O soul;
O soul, we have positively appear'd—that is
    enough.

Ashes of Soldiers
Ashes of soldiers South or North,
As I muse retrospective murmuring a chant in
    thought,
The war resumes, again to my sense your shapes,
And again the advance of the armies.

Noiseless as mists and vapors,
From their graves in the trenches ascending,
From cemeteries all through Virginia and Ten-
    nessee,
From every point of the compass out of the
    countless graves,

In wafted clouds, in myriads large, or squads of
    twos or threes or single ones they come,
And silently gather round me.

Now sound no note O trumpeters,
Not at the head of my cavalry parading on spir-
    ited horses,
With sabres drawn and glistening, and carbines
    by their thighs, (ah my brave horsemen!
My handsome tan-faced horsemen! what life,
    what joy and pride,
With all the perils were yours.)

Nor you drummers, neither at reveillé at dawn,
Nor the long roll alarming the camp, nor even the
    muffled beat for a burial,
Nothing from you this time O drummers bearing
    my war-like drums.

But aside from these and the marts of wealth and
    the crowded promenade,
Admitting around me comrades close unseen by
    the rest and voiceless,
The slain elate and alive again, the dust and de-
    bris alive,
I chant this chant of my silent soul in the name of
    all dead soldiers.

Faces so pale with wondrous eyes, very dear,
    gather closer yet,
Draw close, but speak not.
Phantoms of countless lost,

Source: From *Leaves of Grass* by Walt Whitman (New York: Modern Library, 2001).

Invisible to the rest henceforth become my companions,
Follow me ever—desert me not while I live.

Sweet are the blooming cheeks of the living—
  sweet are the musical voices sounding,
But sweet, ah sweet, are the dead with their silent
  eyes.

Dearest comrades, all is over and long gone,
But love is not over—and what love, O comrades!
Perfume from battle-fields rising, up from the fœtor* arising.

Perfume therefore my chant, O love, immortal
  love,
Give me to bathe the memories of all dead sol-
  diers,
Shroud them, embalm them, cover them all over
  with tender pride.
Perfume all—make all wholesome,
Make these ashes to nourish and blossom,
O love, solve all, fructify all with the last chem-
  istry.

Give me exhaustless, make me a fountain,
That I exhale love from me wherever I go like a
  moist perennial dew,
For the ashes of all dead soldiers South or North.

Thoughts
1
Of these years I sing,
How they pass and have pass'd through convuls'd
  pains, as through parturitions,
How America illustrates birth, muscular youth,
  the promise, the sure fulfilment the absolute
  success, despite of people—illustrates evil as
  well as good,
The vehement struggle so fierce for unity in
  one's-self;
How many hold despairingly yet to the models
  departed, caste, myths, obedience, compul-
  sion, and to infidelity,

How few see the arrived models, the athletes, the
  Western States, or see freedom or spirituality,
  or hold any faith in results,
(But I see the athletes, and I see the results of the
  war glorious and inevitable and they again
  leading to other results.)

How the great cities appear—how the Democratic masses, turbulent, wilful, as I love
  them,
How the whirl, the contest, the wrestle of evil
  with good, the sounding and resounding keep
  on and on,
How society waits unform'd, and is for a while
  between things ended and things begun,
How America is the continent of glories, and of
  the triumph of freedom and of the Democracies, and of the fruits of society, and of all
  that is begun,

And how the States are complete in themselves—
  and how all triumphs and glories are complete in themselves, to lead onward,
And how these of mine and of the States will in
  their turn be convuls'd, and serve other parturitions and transitions,
And how all people, sights, combinations, the
  democratic masses too, serve—and how
  every fact, and war itself, with all its horrors,
  serves,
And how now or at any time each serves the exquisite transition of death.

2
Of seeds dropping into the ground, of births,
Of the steady concentration of America, inland,
  upward, to impregnable and swarming places,
Of what Indiana, Kentucky, Arkansas, and the
  rest, are to be,
Of what a few years will show there in Nebraska,
  Colorado, Nevada, and the rest,
(Or afar, mounting the Northern Pacific to Sitka
  or Aliaska.)
Of what the feuillage of America is the prepara-
  tion for—and of what all sights, North,
  South, East and West, are,

---

*Fœtor = stench

Of this Union welded in blood, of the solemn
   price paid, of the unnamed lost every present
   in my mind;
Of the temporary use of materials for identity's
   sake,
Of the present, passing, departing—of the growth
   of completer men than any yet,
Of all sloping down there where the fresh free
   giver the mother, the Mississippi flows,
Of might inland cities yet unsurvey'd and unsus-
   pected,
Of the new and good names, of the modern developments, of inalienable homesteads,

Of a free and original life there, of simple diet
   and clean and sweet blood,
Of litheness, majestic faces, clear eyes, and per-
   fect physique there,
Of immense spiritual results future years far
   West, each side of the Anahuacs,
Of these songs, well understood there, (being
   made for that area,)
Of the native scorn of grossness and gain there,
(O it lurks in me night and day—what is gain af-
   ter all to savageness and freedom?)

Upton Sinclair: The Jungle

Upton Sinclair (1878–1968) was born in Baltimore, Maryland to a poor family that had once belonged to the ruined southern aristocracy. He began writing short stories as a teenager to help finance his education. He learned of socialism while in college and became an avid supporter of its principles for the rest of his life. Exposing the evils of capitalism became a common theme of his literature and this developed in him a flare for the shocking and controversial. He got an assignment in 1904 from the socialist newspaper, *Appeal to Reason* to travel to Chicago to document the dismal life of the city's meatpacking plant workers. *The Jungle* was based upon this research, a work so controversial that Sinclair tried numerous publishers before finding one willing to put their name on it.

The Jungle is the tale of a Lithuanian immigrant, Jurgis Rudkus, and his family who move to the United States hoping to live "the American Dream," but they end up being ruined by the "everyman for himself" environment in an Industrial Revolution city. The steady streams of social injustices they suffer are meant by Sinclair to show the evils of capitalism in America. Jurgis conveniently walks almost accidentally into a Socialist meeting and finally finds happiness in a socialist commune with the surviving remnants of his family.

The Jungle is not most remembered for its condemnation of capitalism, however. Sinclair included a stinging account of the working conditions and harrowing images of unhealthy standards in the meatpacking industry of early twentieth-century Chicago. This account provoked a national uproar over the quality of meat being consumed across the country. Sinclair was so effective in his aim to disturb his audience that the resulting public outcry led to passage of The Pure Food and Drug Act within the same year of its publication. Sinclair intended this book to promote Socialism, but instead it made him into an unintended champion of food standards. As Sinclair puts it, "I aimed for America's heart and hit it in the stomach."

The first passage here recounts how Jurgis' family is deceived into putting money down for a house without being told of a stipulation in the contract that keeps them from ever owning any interest in the house. The second passage presented is the infamous, stinging descriptions of the meat processing methods that aroused ire in an entire nation.

Chapter 4

Their good luck, they felt, had given them the right to think about a home; and sitting out on the doorstep that summer evening, they held consultation about it, and Jurgis took occasion to broach a weighty subject. Passing down the avenue to work that morning he had seen two boys leaving an advertisement from house to house; and seeing that there were pictures upon it, Jurgis had asked for one, and had rolled it up and tucked it into his shirt. At noontime a man with whom he had been talking had read it to him and told him a little about it, with the result that Jurgis had conceived a wild idea.

He brought out the placard, which was quite a work of art. It was nearly two feet long, printed on calendered paper, with a selection of colors so bright that they shone even in the moonlight. The center of the placard was occupied by a house, brilliantly painted, new, and dazzling. The roof of it was of a purple hue, and trimmed with gold; the house itself was silvery, and the doors and windows red. It was a two-story building, with a porch in front, and a very fancy scrollwork around the edges; it was complete in every tiniest detail, even the doorknob, and there was a hammock on the porch and white lace curtains in the windows. Underneath this, in one corner, was a picture of a husband and wife in loving embrace; in the opposite corner was a cradle, with fluffy curtains drawn over it, and a smiling cherub hovering upon silver-colored wings. For fear that the significance of all this should be lost, there was a label, in Polish, Lithuanian, and German—*"Dom. Namai. Heim."* "Why pay rent?" the linguistic circular went on to demand. "Why not own your own home." Do you know that you can buy one for less than your rent? We have built thousands of homes which are now occupied by happy families."—So it became eloquent, picturing the blissfulness of married life in a house with nothing to pay. It even quoted "Home, Sweet Home," and made bold to translate it into Polish—though for some reason it omitted the Lithuanian of this. Perhaps the translator found it a difficult matter to be sentimental in a language in which a sob is known as a *gukcziojimas* and a smile as a *nusiszypsojimas.*

Over this document the family pored long, while Ona spelled out its contents. It appeared that this house contained four rooms, besides a basement, and that it might be bought for fifteen hundred dollars, the lot and all. Of this, only three hundred dollars had to be paid down, the balance being paid at the rate of twelve dollars a month. These were frightful sums, but then they were in America, where people talked about such without fear. They had learned that they would have to pay a rent of nine dollars a month for a flat, and there was no way of doing better, unless the family of twelve was to exist in one or two rooms, as at present. If they paid rent, of course, they might pay forever, and be no better off; whereas, if they could only meet the extra expense in the beginning, there would at last come a time when they would not have any rent to pay for the rest of their lives. . . .

Source: From *The Jungle* by Upton Sinclair.

An hour before the time on Sunday morning the entire party set out. They had the address written on a piece of paper, which they showed to someone now and then. It proved to be a long mile and a half, but they walked it, and half an hour or so later the agent put in an appearance. He was a smooth and florid personage, elegantly dressed, and he spoke their language freely, which gave him a great advantage in dealing with them. He escorted them to the house, which was one of a long row of the typical frame dwellings of the neighborhood, where architecture is a luxury that it's dispensed with. Ona's heart sank, for the house was not as it was shown in the picture; the color-scheme was different, for one thing, and then it did not seem quite so big. Still, it was freshly painted, and made a considerable show. It was all brand-new, so the agent told them, but he talked so incessantly that they were quite confused, and did not have time to ask many questions. There were all sorts of things they had made up their minds to inquire about, but when the time came, they either forgot them or lacked the courage. The other houses in the row did not seem to be new, and few of them seemed to be occupied. When they ventured to hint at this, the agent's reply was that the purchasers would be moving in shortly. To press the matter would have seemed to be doubting his word, and never in their lives had any one of them ever spoken to a person of the class called "gentleman" except with deference and humility.

The house had a basement, about two feet below the street line, and a single story, about six feet above it, reached by a flight of steps. In addition there was an attic, made by the peak of the roof, and having one small window in each end. The street in front of the house was unpaved and unlighted, and the view from it consisted of a few exactly similar houses, scattered here and there upon lots grown up with dingy brown weeds. The house inside contained four rooms, plastered white; the basement was but a frame, the walls being unplastered and the floor not laid. The agent explained that the houses were built that way, as the purchasers generally preferred to finish the basements to suit their own taste. The attic was also unfinished—the family had been figuring that in case of an emergency they could rent this attic, but they found that there was not even a floor, nothing but joists, and beneath them the lath and plaster of the ceiling below. All of this, however, did not chill their ardor as much as might have been expected, because of the volubility of the agent. There was no end to the advantages of the house, as he set them forth, and he was not silent for an instant; he showed them everything, down to the locks on the doors and the catches on the windows, and how to work them. He showed them the sink in the kitchen, with running water and a faucet, something which Teta Elzbieta had never in her wildest dreams hoped to possess. After a discovery such as that it would have seemed ungrateful to find any fault, and so they tried to shut their eyes to other defects. . . .

They had talked about looking at more houses before they made the purchase; but then they did not know where any more were, and they did not know any way of finding out. The one they had seen held the sway in their thoughts; whenever they thought of themselves in a house, it was this house that they thought of. And so they went and told the agent that they were ready to make the agreement. They knew, as an abstract proposition, that in matters of business all men are to be accounted liars, but they could not but have been influenced by all they had heard from the eloquent agent, and were quite persuaded that the house was something they had run a risk of losing by their delay. They drew a deep breath when he told them that they were still in time.

They were to come on the morrow, and he would have the papers all drawn up. This matter of papers was one in which Jurgis understood to the full the need of caution; yet he could not go himself—every one told him that he could not get a holiday, and that he might lose his job by asking. So there was nothing to be done but to trust it to the women, with Szedvilas, who promised to go with them. Jurgis spent a whole evening impressing upon them the seriousness of the occasion—and then finally, out of innumerable hiding places about their persons and in their baggage, came forth the precious wads of money, to be done up tightly in a little bag and sewed fast in the lining of Teta Elzbieta's dress. . . .

Early in the morning they sailed forth. . . . The agent had the deed ready, and invited them to sit down and read it. This was not a deed of sale at all, so far as he could see—it provided only for renting of the property! It was hard to tell, with all the strange legal jargon, words he had never heard before. . . . The agent was most polite and explained that this was the usual formula. . . . Elzbieta had firmly fixed in her mind the last solemn warning of Jurgis: "If there is anything wrong, do not give him the money, but go out and get a lawyer." . . . They went a long way, on purpose to find a man who would not be a confederate. Then, let anyone imagine their dismay, when, after a half hour, they came in with a lawyer, and heard him greet the agent by his first name!

They felt that all was lost; they sat like prisoners summoned to hear the reading of their death warrant. There was nothing more that they could do—they were trapped! The lawyer read over the deed, and when he had read it he informed Szedvilas that it was all perfectly regular, that the deed was a blank deed such as was often used in these sales. And was the price as agreed? the old man asked—three hundred dollars down, and the balance at twelve dollars a month, till the total of fifteen hundred dollars had been paid?

Yes, that was correct. . . .

The lawyer explained that the rental was a form—the property was said to be merely rented until the last payment had been made, the purpose being to make it easier to turn the party out if he did not make the payments. So long as they paid, however, they had nothing to fear, the house was all theirs.

■ Chapter 14

With one member trimming beef in a cannery, and another working in a sausage factory, the family had a first-hand knowledge of the great majority of Packingtown swindles. For it was the custom, as they found, whenever meat was so spoiled that it could not be used for anything else, either to can it or else to chop it up into sausage. With what had been told them by Jonas, who had worked in the

pickle rooms, they could now study the whole of the spoiled-meat industry on the inside, and read a new and grim meaning into that old Packingtown jest—that they use everything of the pig except the squeal.

Jonas had told them how the meat that was taken out of pickle would often be found sour, and how they would rub it up with soda to take away the smell, and sell it to be eaten on free-lunch counters; also of all the miracles of chemistry which they performed, giving to any sort of meat, fresh or salted, whole or chopped, any color and any flavor and any odor they chose. In the pickling of hams they had an ingenious apparatus, by which they saved time and increased the capacity of the plant—a machine consisting of a hollow needle attached to a pump; by plunging this needle into the meat and working with his foot a man could fill a ham with pickle in a few seconds. And yet, in spite of this, there would be hams found spoiled, some of them with an odor so bad that a man could hardly bear to be in the room with them. To pump into these the packers had a second and much stronger pickle which destroyed the odor—a process known to the workers as "giving them thirty per cent." Also, after the hams had been smoked, there would be found some that had gone to the bad. Formerly these had been sold as "Number Three Grade," but later on some ingenious person had hit upon a new device, and now they would extract the bone, about which the bad part generally lay, and insert in the hole a white-hot iron. After this invention there was no longer Number One, Two, and Three Grade—there was only Number One Grade. The packers were always originating such schemes—they had what they called "boneless hams," which were all the odds and ends of pork stuffed into casings; and "California hams," which were the shoulders, with big knuckle joints, and nearly all the meat cut out; and fancy "skinned hams," which were made of the oldest hogs, whose skins were so heavy and coarse that no one would buy them, that is, until they had been cooked and chopped fine and labelled "head cheese"!

It was only when the whole ham was spoiled that it came into the department of Elzbieta. Cut up by the two-thousand-revolutions-a-minute fly-ers, and mixed with half a ton of other meat, no odor that ever was in a ham could make any difference. There was never the least attention paid to what was cut up for sausage; there would come all the way back from Europe old sausage that had been rejected, and that was mouldy and white—it would be dosed with borax and glycerine, and dumped into the hoppers, and made over again for home consumption. There would be meat that had tumbled out on the floor, in the dirt and sawdust, where the workers had tramped and spit uncounted billions of consumption germs. There would be meat stored in great piles in rooms; and the water from leaky roofs would drip over it, and thousands of rats would race about on it. It was too dark in these storage places to see well, but a man could run his hand over these piles of meat and sweep off handfuls of the dried dung of rats. These rats were nuisances, and the packers would put poisoned bread out for them, they would die, and then rats, bread, and meat would go into the hoppers together. This is no fairy story and no joke; the meat would be shovelled into carts, and the man who did the shoveling would not trouble to lift out a rat even when he saw one—there were things that went into the sausage in comparison with which a poisoned rat was a tidbit. There was no place for the men to wash their hands before they ate their dinner, and so they made a practice of washing them in the water that was to be ladled into the sausage. There were the butt-ends of smoked meat, and the scraps of corned beef, and all the odds and ends of the waste of the plants, that would be dumped into old barrels in the cellar and left there. Under the system of rigid economy which the packers enforced, there were some jobs that it only paid to do once in a long time, and among these was the cleaning out of the waste barrels. Every spring they did it; and in the barrels would be dirt and rust and old nails and stale water—and cart load after cart load of it would be taken up and dumped into the hoppers with fresh meat, and sent out to the public's breakfast. Some of it they would make into "smoked" sausage—but as the smoking took time, and was therefore expensive, they would call upon their chemistry department, and preserve it with borax and color it with gelatine to make it brown. All of their sausage came out of the same bowl, but when they came to wrap it they would stamp some of it "special," and for this they would charge two cents more a pound. . . .

The "Union Stockyards" were never a pleasant place; but now they were not only a collection of slaughter houses, but also the camping place of an army of fifteen or twenty thousand human beasts. All day long the blazing midsummer sun beat down upon that square mile of abominations: upon tens of thousands of cattle crowded into pens whose wooden floors stank and steamed contagion; upon bare, blistering, cinder-strewn railroad tracks, and huge blocks of dingy meat factories, whose labyrinthine passages defied a breath of fresh air to penetrate them; and there were not merely rivers of hot blood and carloads of moist flesh, and rendering vats and soap caldrons, glue factories and fertilizer tanks, that smelt like the craters of hell—there were also tons of garbage festering in the sun, and the greasy laundry of the workers hung out to dry, and dining rooms littered with food and black with flies, and toilet rooms that were open sewers.

Determinism and Uncertainty
What Is, Isn't

> Chance favors the prepared mind.
>
> —*Louis Pasteur*

Scientific Progress

The engine that drove the wheels of progress throughout the seventeenth, eighteenth, and nineteenth centuries was science. Initially, the new scientific method helped investigators satisfy their yearnings for a way to understand nature, and nature began to yield her secrets to them.

When the method was applied to human interactions and government, all humans became enlightened and the concepts of government changed. The knowledge about nature gained from science was combined with the innovativeness of technology to change the methods of producing goods, and the Industrial Revolution resulted. People's lives changed.

Many believed that science would solve all of humankind's problems and answer all of humankind's questions. For them, it was just a matter of time and asking the right questions; eventually, all would fall into place. In the process of all that change, the ultimate reliability of science grew to

be irrefutable. If an answer was based on science, it was taken as truth. Courts of law, politicians, manufacturers, and everyone else gave credence to scientific knowledge.

A few minor questions about the absolute power of science lurked in the shadows of civilization. One was the potential conflict between science and religion that had troubled Galileo and a few others. However, nineteenth-century scientists generally believed that science was simply discovering the handiwork of God, and they saw no real conflicts. Religious knowledge was assumed to be of a different type.

Another slightly differing view of the supremacy of science came from transcendentalism—the belief that some knowledge was not gained through the senses, but came through intuition. Romantics also believed in non-sensory knowledge and associated it with feelings. However, most transcendentalists and Romantics simply assumed that this non-sensory knowledge was used for purposes other than investigating nature and was not, therefore, in conflict with scientific knowledge. Therefore, even for those who had reservations, science, at least in its realm, was absolute. People who were ardent supporters of empiricism (knowledge only through the senses and therefore strong supporters of science) rejected the transcendentalists, Romantics, and religionists as having knowledge that was unreliable. These empiricists asserted that science was absolutely true. Few people or groups really challenged this empiricist view. This was the situation midway through the nineteenth century.

Initially, most early science was done as a hobby by members of the gentry The principle forum for scientific discussion was still in the publications and meetings, which included hobbyist reports. In the nineteenth century, science was becoming a professional discipline. The hobbyist nature of scientific societies was decreasing and the professional scientist was emerging, especially in connection with the universities.

Occasional breakthroughs in technology stimulated theoretical (scientific) investigations, which, in turn, led to additional technological breakthroughs. A good example of this process was the development of the science of thermodynamics, which arose from technologies of steam power developed during the Industrial Revolution. Then, once the science of thermodynamics was understood, better, more efficient machines could be built.

The major foundations for physics, mathematics, and chemistry had been established using the scientific methods—a method in which the underlying principles of its operation had become so ingrained in the human mind that there was no doubt of their validity. Those underlying principles were cause and effect, determinism, reductionism, and objectivity. Each of these deserves some brief discussion.

Cause and Effect

Nothing in science is more fundamental than cause and effect. This means, simply, that when something is observed in an experiment in which all but one variable are controlled, the one changing variable must be the cause of the change. From the beginning of the Scientific Awakening,

Francis Bacon proposed experimentation (and, therefore, cause and effect) as the way to discover knowledge. Generations of scientists after him followed in his experimental footsteps. Antoine Lavoisier carefully replicated experiments and showed that the cause and the effect could be linked quantitatively. Cause and effect had a strong philosophical basis as well as a scientific basis.

Determinism

Isaac Newton's laws of motion suggested that nature's actions are determined by strict laws. Therefore, when science has properly understood the laws, the actions of nature can be predicted. The analogy often used was of the world as a giant clock (built by God). Once it was started in motion, all subsequent actions were determined by the laws of motion that governed the turning of the gears inside the clock. The mathematical basis of science strengthened the concept of determinism.

Reductionism

The method of Descartes in solving a highly complex problem was to reduce the complexity by dividing the problem into smaller segments and attempting to solve those. If a segment of the problem was still too complex to solve, further reductions in the size and complexity should be taken until, finally, the problem was simple enough that it could be solved. Then, when that small problem is solved, its solution will lead to solutions of more complex problems from which it was taken. Continuing the process of repeated solutions will eventually lead back to the original highly complex problem, which can then finally be solved.

Objectivity

Science insists on objectivity, that is, the complete separation of the researcher's personal opinions from the gathering and interpretation of the data. One way that science assures that this is done is by requiring that the experiments be repeatable, not only by the original scientist, but by any other scientist. Also, science requires peer review to ensure that, at least from a distance, the methods followed and the data gathered seem reasonable in light of all other scientific data. In some cases, experimental protocols require that neither the scientist supervising the experiment nor the people involved in the experiment know some critical elements of the experiment, thus preserving their "blindness" or complete objectivity to the final results.

Scientific Lighthouses

In the mid-nineteenth century a multitude of scientists were illuminating the laws of nature and categorizing the knowledge of humankind into logical disciplines, each one confident that with investigation of the world through experimentation and exploration, all knowledge would eventually be obtained. It was an exciting time in which scientists were attacking the great problems of civilization, such as disease, and winning. It was a time when ships and explorers were traversing the world to seek out knowledge in the most remote places. It was a time of great optimism and confidence in the power of humans and their ability to understand and control nature.

Two mid-nineteenth century scientists made tremendous creative contributions. One, **Louis Pasteur,** revolutionized our understanding of the nature of disease, made discoveries that saved several industries, and became a French national hero. Each milk container still honors him with the word *pasteurized.* Another scientist also made a tremendous impact but, unlike Pasteur, he did not receive universal praise. While some hailed him as a genius, others criticized his work with great vehemence. The second scientist was **Charles Darwin.** They both demonstrated how creativity could be used to work on problems and achieve new insights. Pasteur made some discoveries as if by accident. When some suggested that his work was just luck, Pasteur replied with the quotation found at the beginning of this chapter. He certainly had a prepared mind and was able to interpret strange occurrences in highly creative ways. Darwin demonstrated creativity by bringing together concepts from many diverse fields to solve a nagging problem in biology. Both thought laterally and then linearly to achieve their breakthroughs.

Louis Pasteur

Pasteur (1822–1895) was born in France and educated at the Sorbonne in Paris. He later became a professor of science at the university in Strasbourg, France. Pasteur's area of technical expertise was the field of crystal chemistry, and he was already well recognized in that field by the age of 26.

As a young professor, he was investigating an interesting anomaly exhibited by the crystals of tartaric acid. When polarized light was shone through a solution of tartaric acid crystals that were derived exclusively from natural sources, the plane of the light was rotated. However, when polarized light was shown through a solution of tartaric acid crystals that were synthetically derived, no such rotation was seen. Pasteur carefully examined the tartaric acid crystals and found that two types could be distinguished in the synthetic material but only one type in the natural material. He painstakingly separated the two types from the synthetic batch and confirmed that one of those was the same as the natural. He then reasoned that the molecular structures of the two tartaric acids were arranged differently around one of the carbons in the acid, and that the two possible arrangements were responsible for the two crystal types. For Pasteur, this finding also confirmed his belief that natural processes and synthetic processes are inherently different.

Pasteur was promoted to become the dean of the College of Science in Lille, France, and then, only three years later, became the director of scientific studies at the *École Normal Supérieure,* thus becoming one of the chief scientists in France.

His position of scientific leadership and his reputation as an innovative researcher led to his involvement in solving a problem with the French brewing industry. The fermentation process was not understood, thus leading to unacceptable variations in the quality of French beer. Pasteur demonstrated that fermentation was caused by the growth of microorganisms. Some suggested that these microbes (and even more complex species) were generated spontaneously by the decay of organic matter. (For instance, some said that mice grew from the decay of wheat, since mice were often found in wheat storage facilities.) Pasteur proved that this spontaneous generation did not happen. Rather, he showed that the microorganisms came from contaminations of the liquid to be fermented.

Pasteur demonstrated that these microorganisms could be killed by heating the contaminated liquid to a high temperature. He then showed that similar microorganisms grew in milk, and that milk could be improved by a similar heating process. That process is still practiced today, and is called pasteurization.

Beverage contamination led Pasteur to believe that infections in humans came from contamination of microorganisms. Others had already proposed the germ theory, but Pasteur's work confirmed it, and led to Joseph Lister's development of antiseptic surgery.

Pasteur's success with understanding of fermentation then led to a request that he solve a problem in the French silk industry. Silkworms were dying mysteriously and, of course, decreasing the amount of silk that could be produced and threatening the future of the industry. Pasteur discovered that a microbe was attacking the silkworm eggs, thus causing a disease that was killing the worms. He suggested ways to eliminate this microbe from silkworm nurseries (including isolation and sterilization techniques) and thereby saved the industry.

The French chicken industry then approached Pasteur for help. Chickens were being ravished by a disease known as chicken cholera. Pasteur began a study in which he injected healthy chickens with the live bacteria and then investigated several possible methods of curing the chickens. During the course of these experiments, a hypodermic of the virulent solution was left on the laboratory bench during a vacation. When the researchers returned, they injected some healthy chickens with this material. These chickens did not get as sick as others had done, and so the researchers injected this anomalous batch of chickens and some previously uninjected chickens with new virulent solution. The previously uninjected chickens got sick in the same way as had been seen many times before, but the twice-injected chickens did not get sick.

Pasteur did not just ignore these results. He reasoned that something that happened over the holiday had somehow attenuated the potency of the virulent solution. Then, when it was used on healthy chickens, they contracted only a light case of the disease. When the chickens were subsequently given the full-strength solution, they were somehow able to resist the disease. He believed that the heat of the room during the vacation had done the attenuation. His reasoning was completely confirmed. He developed the concepts behind inoculations. Applying these concepts to another disease, he personally developed inoculations for sheep anthrax.

Pasteur later proved that vaccinations could work in humans as well. In his day there was no way to treat rabies. If a rabid animal bit a person, death would almost certainly occur. Pasteur was working toward developing human vaccinations, but still felt there was much to understand before he felt confident in testing them on people. However, Pasteur was forced into early action when a rabid dog bit a neighbor boy. The boy's mother, knowing the boy would almost certainly die, begged Pasteur to try and save him. Pasteur decided to act and try and save the boy, even though he feared that human vaccines were not ready. He treated the boy, and he lived.

Pasteur's work made him an important figure in the creation of the modern world. Today, inoculations for many diseases have their roots in the work done by Pasteur. He has been called "the father of modern medicine." He was given many honors in his lifetime and has been remembered in many ways even until today, including being voted "the Frenchman of the Millennium" in the year 2000 by the French people. That honor is certainly impressive in light of other famous Frenchmen of the millennium, such as Napoleon and Louis XIV.

At the same time as Pasteur, the latter part of the nineteenth century, advances were made in many other areas and important and lasting theories were proposed. In physics the basic equations of electromagnetic theory were developed. In chemistry the atomic model was proposed and the periodic table was developed. In biology it was theorized that all living things are made up of cells, and the rules for genetics were established. Science also continued to improve the lives of people. Electricity was better understood and harnessed for easier use, while amazing advances were made in the medical field, including the discovery of penicillin. Most of these contributions came from the same two pathways that Pasteur had used—careful experimentations coupled with hard work, and determination to creatively investigate results that might be anomalous or accidental.

■ Charles Darwin

Charles Darwin (1809–1882) was born in England to a well-respected family of scientists, clergymen, and industrialists. He was trained in the clergy but was mentored in the university by a biologist who noted Darwin's love of science and his excellent scientific skills. Darwin was active in the collection of beetles and also became interested in geology and botany. His mentor recommended Darwin for a position as ship's scientist on a voyage of the *HMS Beagle,* which was departing on a planned two-year voyage to map the coast of South America. (This journey was typical of the scientific and exploratory excitement of the nineteenth century.) Darwin was accepted for the position.

The voyage of the *Beagle* was full of scientific wonderment for Darwin, which he carefully

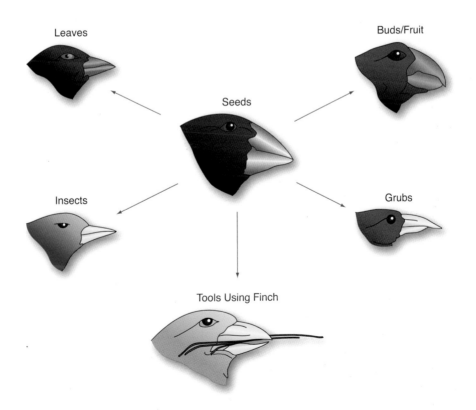

Figure 44.1 ■ Darwin's finches showing adaptation. © *Kendall Hunt Publishing Company.*

reported. He experienced an earthquake, studied natives in Patagonia, saw seashells high in the Andes, found fossils of gigantic extinct animals, and identified several new species of plants and animals. The trip included stops at the Galápagos Islands, off the coast of Ecuador, where he noted, among other things, interesting distinctions between the finch types on the various islands. He found that finches on one island seemed to have physical characteristics that were unique to just their island and were particularly well suited to getting food on their island. Finches on other islands had different physical characteristics that were similarly well suited for their unique islands. These finches are shown in Figure 44.1.

When Darwin returned from the voyage, he found that much of his work from college and his findings on various projects had been published by his college mentor. Darwin was, therefore, already respected as a scientist. In light of that acclaim, Darwin's father was convinced that Charles would make a fine scientist. He established an allowance on which Charles would live for the rest of his life.

The young Darwin was immediately involved in the British scientific community. He gave a paper on the geology of South America and presented his biology samples to the Zoological Society. Other presentations followed, but Darwin became sick and withdrew from London society for a season. For the next several years Darwin worked on various projects of biology (such as the classification of barnacles), but began to form a theory of how species might originate and change. In this theory, Darwin drew upon concepts from geology, population growth theory, botany, and biology. (He used a high degree of lateral thinking, which he combined with linear thinking in biology.)

Finally, at the urging of friends, he presented a paper on his theory, along with another friend who was proposing a similar theory. Darwin then published the book, *On the Origin of Species by Means of Natural Selection* in which he described the theory in detail. The book quickly sold out the first printing. He later published *The Descent of Man.*

Much has been said about Darwin's theory and it has been given several interpretations. One of those we have found useful was given by Stephen Toulmin and June Goodfield in their book, *The Discovery of Time.* They said,

Organic evolution, as Darwin conceived it, involved at least three distinct propositions: first, that more complex forms of life appeared on the earth later than simpler ones (the doctrine of progression); second, that these later forms of life were descended from the earlier ones (the doctrine of transformation); and third—Darwin's essential contribution—that the descent of these later species from the earlier was a consequence of variation and natural selection.

Although many people hailed Charles Darwin's theories on the evolution of species and the origin of man as great scientific breakthroughs, many others felt that Darwin had gone too far and that his theories were full of argumentation and theoretical assertions. Debates were held in which supporters and detractors argued vehemently over his theories. Darwin was often ill and did not participate directly in any of the public debates.

Much of the criticism came from people who believed that Darwin's theory was inconsistent with the Bible and also suggested that God did not exist. This anti-Darwinian fervor reached its apex in the United States with the **Scopes Trial** in Tennessee. In that trial the two opposing opinions of man's origin were debated by two of America's great orators. Defending Darwin's theories on evolution was Clarence Darrow, one of the premier attorneys in the United States; defending the biblical view was a senator, former presidential candidate, and Bible scholar, William Jennings Bryan. This trial is depicted in the movie *Inherit the Wind.* The debate between evolution and creationism continues today.

In the latter twentieth century, a group of scientists have noted that evolution is really divided into two separate concepts—micro-evolution and macro-evolution. Micro-evolution concerns the adaptations that species make in response to environmental forces or mutations. Macro-evolution concerns the origins of species and of life itself. These twentieth-century scientists suggest that micro-evolution is probably true and accept much of the evidence that has been gathered in support of evolution. However, these scientists say that no evidence exists for macro-evolution. They state that macro-evolution is simply an extrapolation based on unsupported assumptions. These scientists who are critical of macro-evolution usually go to great lengths to insist that they are not creationists (that is, supporters of the biblical account of the creation), but many of them suggest that the complexity of the world and its creatures could not have been achieved randomly. Many of these people therefore support the idea now called **Intelligent Design.** Today, supporters of Intelligent Design and supporters of Darwinian Evolution seemed poised for a confrontation.

Other critics, perhaps not as vocal, suggested that Darwin's theories dealt a serious blow to determinism because the theory of evolution seemed to rely on quite random mutations and adaptations. Some people even dared to question the underlying concepts and traditional models of science and to wonder aloud if they were even correct. Thus, just as many people believed science was about to deliver mankind from darkness and transform the Earth into a utopia, science itself took a sharp detour, and the late nineteenth and early twentieth century became an era of scientific questioning which ultimately redefined what science was and what it could do.

■ Twentieth-Century Science

Even though Darwin's work had brought the concept of determinism into question, most people and most scientists believed that traditional science was still on a firm foundation. However, some scientific questions soon led to a sequence of events that would shake the foundations of science itself.

In 1900, Max Planck, a German physicist, gave a powerful mathematical backing to the concept that light traveled in small packets of energy,

which Planck called quanta. However, Planck's concept of the nature of light was in opposition to the mathematical formulations proposed in the late 1800s by James Clerk Maxwell, which showed that light traveled as a wave. Maxwell's equations were very compelling as they neatly and completely described and linked light, electricity, and magnetism. However, Planck's work was also compelling and was backed by Sir Isaac Newton's proposal many years before that light was discrete particles, which he (Newton) called corpuscles. Scientists, including Planck, didn't know what to think. They were bewildered by two powerful doctrines which described light in two apparently conflicting ways.

In 1905, **Albert Einstein,** then an obscure patent clerk in Switzerland, explained what is now called the photoelectric effect, and his explanation gave support to the concept of light as particles. Einstein's explanation also supported the idea, which followed from Planck's theory, that energy was not continuous but was also in discrete states of existence.

In 1913 Neils Bohr, a Danish scientist, applied the concepts of Planck, now called the **quantum theory,** to calculate the energy states of a hydrogen atom and found excellent correlation with experimental data. Bohr found that electrons exist only in discrete shells surrounding the nucleus as illustrated in Figure 44.2. At this point, the nature of the electron became related to the nature of light. It seemed as though those who supported particulate light and analogous electrons were about to win the argument.

However, in 1924, Louis de Broglie suggested some new concepts that strengthened the wave theory of light, and then in 1926 Erwin Schrödinger developed wave equations that gave a good theoretical backing to the wave theory. However, Schrödinger's equations, under some conditions, also allowed for light to be a particle. Perhaps the solution to the light wave/particle problem was at hand.

In 1932 Werner Heisenberg added one more concept to the situation. He suggested that the position of an electron and the momentum (or speed) of an electron could not be simultaneously

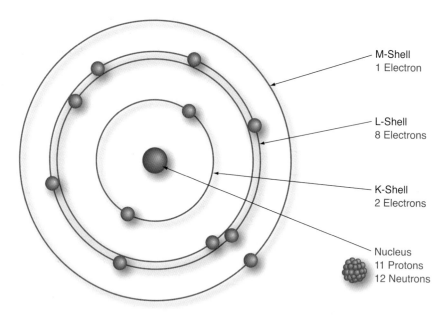

The Bohr Picture of the Sodium (Na 11) Atom

Figure 44.2 ■ The Bohr model of the sodium atom. © *Kendall Hunt Publishing Company.*

determined. This suggestion directly contradicted classical physics (based on the laws of Newton) which said that speed and position were always determinable. Heisenberg's suggestion became known as the **Uncertainty Principle.** In essence, Heisenberg's principle said that electrons and light could not be described exactly (quantitatively) but could be described generally by statistics. The Uncertainty Principle also says that some phenomena are changed when any experiment is performed on them.

The Uncertainty Principle causes us to ponder about the ancient idea of the Form as described by Plato. The Form of something was the real essence of it. However, Forms do not exist in the physical world and can only be understood through philosophical contemplation. We cannot, therefore, ever detect the real Form through our senses. In a similar way of thinking, we cannot detect the real electron or photon by experimentation. Perhaps the problem is that we are trying to describe a physical entity that can only be described philosophically—the way that Plato insisted we must describe the Form of things.

In a similar way, we are reminded of Plato's love for small whole numbers (which he learned from another Greek philosopher—Pythagoras). In the world of Pythagoras, small whole numbers and their ratios were the fundamental building blocks of the world. In the quantum theory, we find that energy states and other characteristics of electrons and light are described by specific states, which are denoted by small whole numbers. An electron must be in energy shell 1 or 2 or 3 but cannot be in some energy state between them. (Much of the larger world has states like this also. For instance, you have trains at platforms 8 or 9 or 10 but not at 9–3/4 unless you are magic, like Harry Potter.) We wonder, therefore, whether the absoluteness of the small whole numbers of the Pythagoreans should be reconsidered in a modern context.

The implications of all these experiments are profound. People wondered why science could not come to a definite conclusion about things as fundamental as the true nature of light and of electrons. Evidence, both theory and experiment, seemed to support conflicting views. Could it be that science could not resolve this problem?

Equally disturbing was the implication that some experiments might be changing reality just by being performed. This struck at the basis of science—the validity of experimentation.

The frustrations of the public were expressed by Fritjof Capra who described them in *The Turning Point.*

> *While it [an electron] acts like a particle, it is capable of developing its wave nature at the expense of its particle nature, and vice versa, thus undergoing continual transformations from particle to wave and from wave to particle. This means that neither the electron nor any other atomic "object" has any intrinsic properties independent of its environment. The properties it shows— particle-like or wave-like—will depend on the experimental situation, that is, on the apparatus it is forced to interact with.*

However, the problems of the nature of light and electrons were only one of the areas that were highly disturbing to scientists and to the general public. In 1905, the same year he explained the photoelectric effect, Albert Einstein published his **Theory of Relativity.** This theory suggests that the size, mass, and even time associated with an object are not constants and that, depending on the speed of the object, the relative natures will change. A *thought* experiment suggested, for example, that if twin brothers were to be on trains traveling at different speeds, one would age faster than the other. They would also have different masses and be different sizes although when at rest, their masses and sizes were the same. Most people, including leading scientists, were highly disturbed by these nonintuitive assertions.

Some of the concepts of the theory of relativity have been explained well by Howard Gardner in *Creating Minds,* as follows:

> *A clock attached to a system that is in relative motion will be observed to run more slowly than one that is stationary with respect to us. Rods appear to contract in the direction of their motion when they are observed to move*

> *from rest into uniform motion. . . . The mass of a moving body increases with the body's velocity relative to its observer.*

These concepts were not only highly counterintuitive, they directly contradicted Newton's formulations, which said that mass was a constant and accelerated uniformly with the force applied to the mass. (Einstein's formulation is given as $e = mc^2$ where c is a constant and e and m are variables. Newton's formulation is given as $f = ma$ where m is a constant and f and a are variables.)

Scientists realized that Newton's laws were based on Euclidean geometry, which stated, for instance, that two parallel lines never cross and that the shortest distance between two points is a straight line. They also saw that Einstein's laws were based on another kind of geometry, one developed by a German mathematician, Bernhard Riemann, that stated the shortest distance between two points is a curve and that parallel lines will cross at infinity. (Euclid's world assumed flat surfaces, whereas Riemann saw space as curved.) Euclid and Riemann looked at the world in different ways and, as a result, so did Newton and Einstein. But, which was right?

■ Challenges to Traditional Science Itself

We have already noted that determinism was challenged by Darwin's theories and by the development of the quantum theory, especially the culmination of that work by the Uncertainty Principle. Nature was no longer ruled by set laws but, rather, by probability. This conclusion was highly disturbing, even to many scientists. In reaction to the probabilistic view, Einstein himself said, "God does not play dice with the universe."

The quantum debate and the Theory of Relativity both bring another fundamental of science into question. How can meaningful experiments be conducted if time, mass, and space are no longer well defined?

The fundamental nature of experimentation received another challenge in the 1960s when meteorologist **Edward Lorenz** was simulating the weather on his computer. On one occasion, the simulation was interrupted by a power outage. Rather than begin that simulation again, Lorenz decided to enter the data from the run at the midpoint. When the program commenced again, Lorenz discovered that the simulation was giving very strange results—not like any he had seen before. He then reran the simulation from the beginning and got results that were much more normal. He wondered why the truncated and restarted results were so strange. After much investigation, he discovered that the data he entered to restart the simulation were entered with 8 significant figures, whereas the computer actually stored the data to 12 significant figures. The implication was that very small changes (perhaps only as much as a pressure difference of 0.00000001) were affecting the results. Lorenz likened this small change to the pressure difference that the flapping of a butterfly's wings in South America might cause a tornado in New York. This phenomenon has been called the **butterfly effect.**

The butterfly effect can be easily imagined by considering a sharply pointed cone. If it is stood on its pointed end, the least disturbance will cause it to tip over. If stood on its point again, a disturbance will likely cause it to tip over again, but the second time (and all subsequent times) the direction of the tipping will be different. This occurs because the causes of the tipping are so subtle that they cannot be identified.

The most important implication of the butterfly effect is that the cause and effect relationship might not be reliable. In other words, we might not really be able to link a particular cause to an effect. Before a recognition of the butterfly effect, most scientists would see deviations in their data and just say that they were small and unimportant. Essentially, they ignored them, often by averaging the data. However, the butterfly effect suggests that those deviations might be from real and very important different causes, which should not be ignored.

Work with the butterfly effect led to the science of **chaos theory.** Science previously had almost exclusively dealt with linear systems and overlooked dynamical systems as random and un-

predictable. The problem with that approach is that humans live in a dynamic, not a linear, world. Chaos theory examines how seemingly random and unrelated events in nonlinear systems can still lead to patterns.

A metaphor that explains chaos theory more easily is the process of human history. In an examination of human history, broad patterns in the rise and fall of civilizations may be observed; however, no events ever repeat *exactly*. Chaos theory says a similar process happens in nature. A specific rule (or law) is given, but then there is a random or independent implementation of the rule. For example, when a river reaches a cliff we can accurately predict that the water will obey gravity and fall downward to the Earth. Similarly, we can predict a single drop of water in the river will also obey the law. However, we cannot predict the exact course a single drop of water will take as it plunges over the edge and falls.

A comment about these minute events was given many years ago by the French mathematician Poincaré and has been related by Peter Bernstein in *Against the Gods:*

> Poincaré [1854–1912] also points out that some events that appear to be fortuitous are not; instead, their causes stem from minute disturbances. A cone perfectly balanced on its apex will topple over if there is the least defect in symmetry; and even if there is no defect, the cone will topple in response to "a very slight tremor, a breath of air." That is why, Poincaré explained, meteorologists have such limited success in predicting the weather. . . . Chaos theory, a more recent development, is based on a similar premise. According to this theory, much of what looks like chaos is in truth the product of an underlying order, in which insignificant perturbations are often the cause of [events].

Another concept that calls into question traditional cause and effect (and the accuracy of science) is synchronicity. **Synchronicity** is the awareness that some events, which should not be related, occur in a related way. An example of this would be getting a parking space by setting your mind to it or influencing a TV show by some action that you do. Despite the intuitive feeling most people have that this is not possible, there is some scientific evidence that it does make a difference. Religious thinkers will recognize that God can intervene to give synchronicities to our lives. In Rudy Rucker's book *The Fourth Dimension*, Rucker describes the world like this:

This, finally, is the essence of synchronicity: the world we live in is filled with harmonies and coincidences that have no explanation in terms of cause and effect. It is fruitless to seek after hidden forces and occult powers. The world is a given—it is just as it is, full of cause and effect, full of synchronicity.

We have seen challenges to determinism and to cause and effect. What about the concepts of reductionism and objectivity? Those, too, have been questioned in the twentieth century. Reductionism was questioned by, among others, Fritjof Capra as follows:

Like human-made machines, the cosmic machine was thought to consist of elementary parts. Consequently it was believed that complex phenomena could always be understood by reducing them to their basic building blocks and by looking for the mechanisms through which these interacted. This attitude, known as reductionism, has become so deeply ingrained in our culture that it has often been identified with the scientific method.

A movie made in the latter part of the twentieth century explores the difficulties of reductionism. That movie is *Mindwalk.* It suggests that the world is a great harmonious, indivisible whole and that some problems, especially problems that concern people or their environment, are so complex that if reductionism is applied, the interactions that are critical to solving the problems are missed. Hence, reductionism cannot work on these problems.

Objectivity has also been questioned in the twentieth century. The work of Thomas Kuhn is especially important in this regard. In his book, *The Structure of Scientific Revolutions,* Kuhn says:

Observation and experience can and must drastically restrict the range of admissible scientific belief, else there would be no science. But they cannot alone determine a particular body of such belief. An apparently arbitrary element, compounded of personal and historical accident, is always a formative ingredient of the beliefs espoused by a given scientific community at a given time.

Here Kuhn says that a person's background is important in interpreting the data obtained in an experiment. For instance, if we believe in the atomic theory of matter and do a chemistry experiment, we will interpret the results in light of the atomic theory. Others who may read our work will similarly interpret it within the atomic theory because that theory is so widely held to be true. However, what if someone finds data that just cannot agree with the atomic theory? That may require a change in thinking; as Kuhn says, a change in paradigm. But, such a change is very difficult.

The transfer of allegiance from paradigm to paradigm is a conversion experience that cannot be forced. Lifelong resistance, particularly from those whose productive careers have committed them to an older tradition of normal science, is not a violation of scientific standards but an index to the nature of scientific research itself.

Two philosophies grew out of the perceived emptiness of science: nihilism and existentialism. **Nihilism** is a philosophical movement that strongly echoes the general feeling within the scientific community of the time. It questions whether anything is real or true. Although there were nihilists all across Europe, and even in America, nihilism was especially strong among the intelligentsia of Russia. The philosophy of nihilism led to a repudiation of all religions and, eventually, all social norms. A second philosophical movement of the era was existentialism. **Existentialism** emphasizes individual existence, freedom, and choice. According to the principles of existentialism, subjectivity, freedom, and personal choice are more important (more real) than objective, universal norms. In fact, a corollary of existentialism is that there may be no truth that is universal to everybody, but that people decide what is individually true for themselves.

As we think about science and technology in the past, we encounter an interesting contradiction. Most scientists would agree that the new science of the twentieth century (relativity, uncertainty, Einstein, etc.) is more correct than the science of the traditional past (determinism, reductionism, Newton, etc.), but the old science gave us the Industrial Revolution and still forms the foundation for many modern innovations. Although it is true that several modern inventions depend on concepts of the new science (such as the laser, atomic energy, and transistors), the new era of scientific uncertainty does not seem to inspire or encourage the same levels of creative endeavor. This is not to suggest that the rate of new product development is slowing (for it certainly is not), but only to observe that most of these new products and inventions are based more on the old concepts of the world rather than the new.

Does creativity require some certainty or, perhaps, some anchor to provide a basis for launching into new areas? The study of highly creative people done by Mihaly Csikszentmihalyi, which we have previously discussed, suggests that these creative people can adjust their thinking to be creative both when they are uncertain and when they are confident. But, maybe the person who is not so highly creative needs more security and stability from which to launch into a new field.

We might also observe that much good was achieved using flawed concepts. That tells us that somehow our brains can create new products and advance our general knowledge even when our basic concepts are not completely correct. Perhaps this capability attests to the inherent creativity of the human brain. Synthesis of data to fill in the gaps or to correct the errors or to proceed in spite

of the errors seems to occur. We should worry that maybe our brains inherently overlook the errors and simply smooth the discontinuities of the data. This is, of course, the point made by Kuhn, as we discussed earlier.

We might also ask the related question, Can creativity be benefited by rules even if the rules are wrong? If something as quantitative as science can benefit even when the concepts are not fully correct, what about the study of creativity that is much less quantitative?

■ Where Is Science in the Twenty-First Century?

Scientists should be justly proud of the progress of the world that has been due to the combination of science and technology. People are better off in the twentieth century than ever before, by almost any measure. However, because science (and not technology) is a method for discovering and classifying new knowledge, many scientists and those who trust science, believe that science is a way of discovering "truth." That view of science, if pursued, will likely lead to continued questioning and philosophical battles.

Isaac Asimov, a renowned chemist and author has said that

A theory is a set of basic rules, supported by a great many confirmed observations by many scientists, that explains and makes sensible a large number of facts that, without the theory, would seem to be unconnected. . . . Theories are not necessarily correct in every detail, to begin with, and might never be entirely correct in every detail, but they are sufficiently correct (if they are good theories) to guide scientists in understanding the subject the theory deals with, in exploring further observations, and, eventually, in improving the theory. No scientific theory is instantly accepted by scientists. There are always those scientists who are suspicious of anything new—and this is perhaps a good thing. Theories should not slide into acceptance too easily; they should be questioned and tested vigorously. In this way, weak spots in the theory will be uncovered and, perhaps, strengthened.

David Bohm, in *the Special Theory of Relativity,* says that

The purpose of science was not the "accumulation of knowledge [truth]" (since, after all, all scientific theories are eventually proved false) but rather the creation of "mental maps" that guide and shape our perception and action, bringing about a constant "mutual participation between nature and consciousness.

Therefore, science is useful as a way to get information and arrange that information to help us think about the world. John Hatton and Paul Plouffe in their book *Science and Its Ways of Knowing* confirm this view when they said, "In science, 'fact' can only mean 'confirmed to such a degree that it would be perverse to withhold provisional assent.'"

In spite of these underlying uncertainties in science, most scientists tend to view their findings as "truth." Perhaps they might want to consider them as "knowledge" or "information" rather than the more absolute "truth." If science is the gatherer of knowledge, what method can be used to affirm truth? This question has been the basis of many philosophical discussions and is, of course, the subject of much religious writing. In the modern world, many people look to religion for truth (as do the authors), but our secular society seems to continue to rely on science as the basis for truth (such as in courts of law and among secular scientists).

To establish a more complete picture of the world, another step which scientists might take is to accept that some concepts in the world might not lend themselves to scientific inquiry. The facts might, for instance, be chaotic. Perhaps they are not definable by empirical means. Scientists might just accept the situation as suggested by Fritjof Capra:

The quantum effect is a feature of the subatomic world which has no analogy in macroscopic physics: the more a particle is confined, the faster it moves. . . . Modern physics thus pictures matter not at all as passive and inert but as being in a continuous dancing and vibrating motion whose rhythmic patterns are determined by the molecular, atomic, and nuclear configurations. We have come to realize that there are not static structures in nature. There is stability, but this stability is one of dynamic balance, and the further we penetrate into matter the more we need to understand its dynamic nature to understand its patterns.

Jokingly, Nobel prize winner William Bragg may have captured the spirit of the problem best when he said,

God runs electromagnetics by wave theory on Monday, Wednesday, and Friday. The Devil runs them by quantum theory on Tuesday, Thursday, and Saturday.

We can appreciate some of the strangeness of the quantum world by considering something as simple as a wall. The actual mass of the atoms that make up the wall is very small. In fact, if all the atoms that compose the bodies of all the people in the world were to be gathered together without any forces to keep them apart, they would easily fit into a thimble. Therefore, the wall we are considering is mostly empty space. Why, then, can't we just walk through it? Obviously, it's because of the forces. However, we know how to overcome most forces we encounter; can't we overcome those atomic forces also?

We may find that science's tools of experimentation and observation are inherently limited by the three-dimensional world in which we live. Scientists have proposed the existence of other dimensions. Some of these ideas include the proposal that light may be a separate dimension (explaining why light has both wave and particle properties), as may electrons; and that complex laws become very simple in the tenth dimension.

There has been an attempt at reconciliation between science and religion with a hypothesis that God may exist in a dimension outside of the dimensions that exist on Earth (thus explaining divine exemption from time and space and gravity, etc.).

Edwin Abbott has described the dimensionality of existence well in his little book, *Flatland*. He describes a creature that lives in a two-dimensional world. That creature would not be able to see any height. Therefore, if we draw a pencil line around the creature, it is imprisoned by the line. We can poke our finger inside the line and, magically to the creature, the tip of our finger will appear. Abbott suggested that God might exist in a higher dimension and appear or not appear to us in a similar way. Perhaps in God's existence the forces of the atoms are understood and overcome, thus explaining the way Christ could pass through walls to meet with His disciples.

Scientists might also consider that nonempirical knowledge is both valuable and at least as reliable as scientific data which, as we have seen, is always questionable. Hatton and Plouffe have said,

> *But our understanding of nature does not proceed simply by means of scientific method, however understood. It frequently involves the kind of discovery that turns on less predictable (and less definable) factors such as accident and luck, as well as such personal traits as intuition, empathy, passion, openness to surprise, etc. that have to do with the personality of the individual scientist.*

They also said,

> *But where evidence is sparse or absent—as it is for a growing number of questions in physics—other criteria, including aesthetic ones, come into play in an essential way, both for formulating a theory and for evaluating it. In view of this fact, it is imperative that physicists know what they mean when they make appeals to such standards as elegance, coherence, and inner beauty. Many professional scientists use these terms to re-*

> *fer to their work, but few take the trouble to define them. What, then, is meant by elegance? By coherence? And, What is beauty, in the context of mathematical formulas and physical theories? ... All science is the search for unity in hidden likenesses. ... The equality of ratios is to physics what rhythm is to poetry, and balance to painting.*

Peter Dirac, a Nobel prize winner, once rejected data obtained by his students that seemed to contradict a mathematical equation he had developed. He stood by the equation because it had beauty. This "feeling" for science might be termed *intuition*. Science looks for hidden patterns, and these might only be seen by intuition and analogy. That is to say, the traditional scientist who seems to always think logically (linearly) might find that greater creativity and better science can come from also thinking intuitively (laterally).

Even religion and science might find that they are on the same ground. Faith can be defined as trusting that you understand the cause of some effect. In science, you trust that the cause is proximate—that is, nearby in time and space. In religion, you trust that the cause is known to God. Both methods require trust, which is just another way of expressing faith.

Science needs to consider the extreme circumstances that occur when science is overpoweringly accepted. Vaclav Havel, a powerful force for freedom within his country and the first prime minister of Czechoslovakia after the fall of communism, said the following:

> *The modern era has been dominated by the culminating belief, expressed in different forms, that the world—and Being as such—is a wholly knowable system governed by a finite number of universal laws that man can grasp and rationally direct for his own benefit. This era, beginning in the Renaissance and developing from the Enlightenment to socialism, from positivism to scientism, from the Industrial Revolution to the information revolution, was characterized by rapid advances in rational, cognitive thinking. This,*

in turn, gave rise to the proud belief that man, as a pinnacle of everything that exists, was capable of objectively describing, explaining and controlling everything that exists, and of possessing the one and only truth about the world. It was an era in which there was a cult of depersonalized objectivity, an era in which objective knowledge was amassed and technologically exploited, an era of systems, institutions, mechanisms and statistical averages. It was an era of freely transferable, existentially ungrounded information. It was an era of ideologies, doctrines, interpretations of reality, an era in which the goal was to find a universal theory of the world, and thus a universal key to unlock its prosperity.

Communism was the perverse extreme of this trend. . . . The fall of communism can be regarded as a sign that modern thought—based on the premise that the world is objectively knowable, and that knowledge so obtained can be absolutely generalized—has come to a final crisis. This era has created the first global, or planetary, technical civilization, but it has reached the limit of its potential, the point beyond which the abyss begins.

Traditional science, with its usual coolness, can describe the different ways we might destroy ourselves, but it cannot offer truly effective and practicable instructions on how to avert them.

■ Timeline—Important Dates

Date	Event
1809–1882	*Charles Darwin*
1822–1985	*Louis Pasteur*
1900	*Max Planck develops quantum theory concept*
1905	*Albert Einstein proposes solution to photoelectric effect*
1905	*Albert Einstein proposes the Theory of Relativity*
1913	*Neils Bohr describes the energy of a hydrogen atom*
1926	*Erwin Schrödinger proposes wave equations*
1932	*Werner Heisenberg proposes the Uncertainty Principle*

■ Suggested Readings

Abbott, Edwin A., *Flatland,* Dover, First published 1884.

Asimov, Isaac, *Atom,* Truman Talley Books/Plume, 1992.

Bernstein, Peter L., *Against the Gods,* Wiley, 1996.

Capra, Fritjof, *The Turning Point,* Bantam Books, 1983.

Carroll, Lewis, *Alice's Adventures in Wonderland and Through the Looking-Glass,* Signet Classics, 1960.

Gardner, Howard, *Creating Minds,* Basic Books, 1993.

Hatton, John and Paul Plouffe, *Science and its Ways of Knowing,* Prentice Hall, 1997.

Hawking, Stephen W., *A Brief History of Time,* Bantam Books, 1988.

Kuhn, Thomas, *The Structure of Scientific Revolutions,* University of Chicago Press, 1962.

Rucker, Rudy, *The Fourth Dimension,* Houghton Mifflin, 1984.

Silver, Brian L., *The Ascent of Science,* Oxford University Press, 1998.

Strathern, Paul, *Mendeleyev's Dream,* The Berkley Publishing Group, 2000.

Taylor, Frank J., *The Physics of Immortality,* Doubleday, 1994.

Toulmin, Stephen and June Goodfield, *The Discovery of Time,* University of Chicago Press, 1965.

Watson, James, *The Double Helix,* Mentor Books, 1968.

Winchester, Simon, *The Professor and the Madman,* Harper Perennial, 1998.

Woodward, Thomas, *Doubts about Darwin,* Baker Books, 2003.

Charles Darwin: The Origin of Species by Means of Natural Selection, The Descent of Man

Charles Darwin (1809–1882) was born into a prominent English family—his paternal grandfather was a famous physician, Erasmus Darwin, and his maternal grandfather was the famous pottery entrepreneur, Josiah Wedgwood. Charles Darwin initially studied medicine at college but then changed to theology in anticipation of becoming a clergyman. While at college, he came under the influence of a renowned naturalist and a respected geologist. Upon graduation, he accepted a position aboard the HMS Beagle as an unpaid naturalist, largely upon the recommendation of his naturalist and geologist mentors. It was on the voyage of the HMS Beagle that he made his life-altering discoveries.

Darwin will forever be known as the father of the theory of evolution. Theorists had hinted at evolution since the days of ancient Greece, but Darwin was the first to give the theory a credible explanation through detailed experimentation and observation. Darwin first came to this theory during the sea voyage aboard the Beagle during which he spent many days off the west coast of South America and observed some surprising animal and plant species on the Galápagos Islands. He noted that each island supported its own distinctive varieties of tortoise, finch, and mockingbird which were all related but differed in eating habits and structure. Upon returning to England, he spent years contemplating the meaning of his observations and eventually came to the conclusion that the animals had adapted to their local surroundings and therefore changed their habits and physical characteristics. Darwin named this process of adaptation Natural Selection.

One key element of Natural Selection that had to be explained was the reason for the adaptation. He theorized that animals would become modified because of chance genetic occurrences that proved to be advantageous to the survival of the animal. These superior animals would then pass that superior trait on to their offspring and, eventually, the entire group of this particular species would possess the desired characteristic. This method of adaptation became known as "survival of the fittest."

Another key element of Natural Selection that Darwin needed to explain was the time frame in which these adaptations occurred. He realized that the commonly-accepted timeframe, in which the age of the earth was approximately 6000 years, would not give sufficient time to allow for the gradual changes if the process were adaptation by Natural Selection. Because of his geological training, he linked the very long time demands of geological processes, which were then being proposed, with these biological events and theorized that the world was not, in fact, about 6000 years old but actually much older.

He eventually published his theory in the book *Origin of Species by Means of Natural Selection.* The religious implications of the book were immediately apparent and many church leaders and other religious people stridently condemned the book. Just as quickly, many others rose to defend the book or, at least, defended Darwin's right to publish it. Debates and lawsuits were held with much anger on both sides.

The furor over Darwin's writings became even more severe when he published *The Descent of Man,* a book describing how mankind developed from a prehistoric ancestor who was common to both man and apes.

Gradually, however, main elements of the concepts of Darwin have been largely accepted by science. Details remain troublesome to many people, especially with respect to the accuracy of the time frame proposed by many later scientists and the ability of species to form a new species. Many religious people have come to an acceptance of major parts of Darwin's concepts and have reconciled those concepts with their belief in God and His scriptures. The readings presented here are typical of the carefully written arguments of Darwin and allow a sampling of his works.

Charles Darwin: The Origin of Species by Means of Natural Selection

Chapter III

Struggle for Existence

Nothing is easier than to admit in words the truth of the universal struggle for life, or more difficult—at least I have found it so—than constantly to bear this conclusion in mind. Yet unless it be thoroughly engrained in the mind, the whole economy of nature, with every fact on distribution, rarity, abundance, extinction, and variation, will be dimly seen or quite misunderstood. We behold the face of nature bright with gladness, we often see super-abundance of food; we do not see or we forget, that the birds which are idly singing round us mostly live on insects or seeds, and are thus constantly destroying life; or we forget how largely these songsters, and their eggs, and their nestlings, are destroyed by birds and beasts of prey; we do not always bear in mind, that, though food may be now superabundant, it is not so at all seasons of each recurring year.

*   *   *

A struggle for existence inevitably follows from the high rate at which all organic beings tend to increase. Every being, which during its natural lifetime produces several eggs or seeds, must suffer destruction during some period of its life, and during some season or occasional year, otherwise, on the principle of geometrical increase, its numbers would quickly become so inordinately great that no country could support the product. Hence, as more individuals are produced than can possibly survive, there must in every case be a struggle for existence, either one individual with another of the same species, or with the individuals of distinct species, or with the physical conditions of life. It is the doctrine of Malthus applied with manifold force to the whole animal and vegetable kingdoms; for in this case there can be no artificial increase of food, and no prudential restraint from marriage. Although some species may be now increasing, more or less rapidly, in numbers, all cannot do so, for the world would not hold them.

There is no exception to the rule that every organic being naturally increases at so high a rate, that, if not destroyed, the earth would soon be covered by the progeny of a single pair. Even slow-breeding man has doubled in twenty-five years, and at this rate, in less than a thousand years, there would literally not be standing-room for his progeny. Linnæus has calculated that if an annual plant produced only two seeds—and there is no plant so unproductive as this—and their seedlings next year produced two, and so on, then in twenty years there would be a million plants. The elephant is reckoned the slowest breeder of all known

Source: From *The Origin of Species* by Charles Darwin (Amherst: Prometheus Books, 1991).

animals, and I have taken some pains to estimate its probable minimum rate of natural increase; it will be safest to assume that it begins breeding when thirty years old, and goes on breeding till ninety years old, bringing forth six young in the interval, and surviving till one hundred years old; if this be so, after a period of from 740 to 750 years there would be nearly nineteen million elephants alive, descended from the first pair.

*   *   *

As the species of the same genus usually have, though by no means invariably, much similarity in habits and constitution, and always in structure, the struggle will generally be more severe between them, if they come into competition with each other, than between the species of distinct genera. We see this in the recent extension over parts of the United States of one species of swallow having caused the decrease of another species. The recent increase of the missel-thrush in parts of Scotland has caused the decrease of the song-thrush. How frequently we hear of one species of rat taking the place of another species under the most different climates! In Russia the small Asiatic cockroach has everywhere driven before it its great congener. In Australia the imported hive-bee is rapidly exterminating the small, stingless native bee. One species of charlock has been known to supplant another species; and so in other cases. We can dimly see why the competition should be most severe between allied forms, which fill nearly the same place in the economy of nature; but probably in no one case could we precisely say why one species has been victorious over another in the great battle of life.

A corollary of the highest importance may be deduced from the foregoing remarks, namely, that the structure of every organic being is related, in the most essential yet often hidden manner, to that of all the other organic beings, with which it comes into competition for food or residence, or from which it has to escape, or on which it preys. This is obvious in the structure of the teeth and talons of the tiger; and in that of the legs and claws of the parasite which clings to the hair on the tiger's body. But in the beautifully plumed seed of the dandelion, and in the flattened and fringed legs of the water-beetle, the relation seems at first confined to the elements of air and water. Yet the advantage of plumed seeds no doubt stands in the closest relation to the land being already thickly clothed with other plants; so that the seeds may be widely distributed and fall on unoccupied ground. In the water-beetle, the structure of its legs, so well adapted for diving, allows it to compete with other aquatic insects, to hunt for its own prey, and to escape serving as prey to other animals.

■ Chapter IV

Natural Selection; or the Survival of the Fittest

How will the struggle for existence, briefly discussed in the last chapter, act in regard to variation? Can the principle of selection, which we have seen is so potent in the hands of man, apply under nature? I think we shall see that it can act most efficiently. Let the endless number of slight variations and individual differences occurring in our domestic productions, and, in a lesser degree, in those under nature, be borne in mind; as well as the strength of the hereditary tendency. . . . Let it also be borne in mind how infinitely complex and close-fitting are the mutual relations of all organic beings to each other and to their physical conditions of life; and consequently what infinitely varied diversities of structure might be of use to each being under changing conditions of life. Can it, then, be thought improbable, seeing that variations useful to man have undoubtedly occurred, that other variations useful in some way to each being in the great and complex battle of life, should occur in the course of many successive generations? If such do occur, can we doubt (remembering that many more individuals are born than can possibly survive) that individuals having any advantage, however slight, over others, would have the best chance of surviving and of procreating their kind? On the other hand, we may feel sure that any variation in the least degree injurious would be rigidly destroyed. This preservation of favourable individual differences and variations, and the destruction of those which are injurious, I have called Natural Selection, or the Survival of the Fittest. Variations neither useful nor injurious would not be affected by natural selection, and would be left either a fluctuating element, as perhaps we see in certain polymorphic species, or would ultimately become fixed, owing to the nature of the organism and the nature of the conditions.

Several writers have misapprehended or objected to the term Natural Selection. Some have even imagined that natural selection induces variability, whereas it implies only the preservation of such variations as arise and are beneficial to the being under its conditions of life. No one objects to agriculturists speaking of the potent effects of man's selection: and in this case the individual differences given by nature, which man for some object selects, must of necessity first occur. Others have objected that the term selection implies conscious choice in the animals which become modified; and it has even been urged that, as plants have no volition, natural selection is not applicable to them! In the literal sense of the word, no doubt, natural selection is a false term; but who ever objected to chemists speaking of the elective affinities of the various elements?—and yet an acid cannot strictly be said to elect the base with which it in preference combines. It has been said that I speak of natural selection as an active power or Deity; but who objects to an author speaking of the attraction of gravity as ruling the movements of the planets? Every one knows what is meant and is implied by such metaphorical expressions; and they are almost necessary for brevity. So again it is difficult to avoid personifying the word Nature; but I mean by Nature, only the aggregate action and product of many natural laws, and by laws the sequence of events as ascertained by us. With a little familiarity such superficial objections will be forgotten.

*   *   *

As man can produce, and certainly has produced, a great result by his methodical and unconscious means of selection, what may not natural selection effect? Man can act only on external and visible characters: Nature, if I may be allowed to personify the natural preservation or survival of the fittest, cares nothing for appearance, except in so far as they are useful to any being. She can act on every internal organ, on every shade of constitutional difference, on the whole machinery of life. Man selects only for his own good: Nature only for that of the being which she tends. Every selected character is fully exercised by her, as is implied by the fact of their selection. Man keeps the native of many climates in the same country; he seldom exercises each selected character in some peculiar and fitting manner; he feeds a long- and a short-beaked pigeon on the same food; he does not exercise a long-backed or long-legged quadruped in any peculiar manner; he exposes sheep with long and short wool to the same climate. He does not allow the most vigorous males to struggle for the females. He does not rigidly destroy all inferior animals, but protects during each varying season, as far as lies in his power, all his productions. He often begins his selection by some half-monstrous form; or at least by some modification prominent enough to catch the eye or to be plainly useful to him. Under nature, the slightest differences of structure or constitution may well turn the nicely-balanced scale in the struggle for life, and so be preserved. How fleeting are the wishes and efforts of man! how short his time! and consequently how poor will be his results, compared with those accumulated by Nature during whole geological periods! Can we wonder, then, that Nature's productions should be far "truer" in character than man's productions; that they should be infinitely better adapted to the most complex conditions of life, and should plainly bear the stamp of far higher workmanship?

*   *   *

That natural selection generally acts with extreme slowness I fully admit. It can act only when there are places in the natural polity of a district which can be better occupied by the modification of some of its existing inhabitants. The occurrence of such places will often depend on physical changes, which generally take place very slowly, and on the immigration of better adapted forms being prevented. As some few of the old inhabitants become modified, the mutual relations of others will often be disturbed; and this will create new places, ready to be filled up by better adapted forms; but all this will take place very slowly. Although all the individuals of the same species differ in some slight degree from each other, it would often be long before differences of the right nature in various parts of the organisation might occur. The result would often be greatly retarded by free intercrossing. Many will exclaim that these several causes are amply sufficient to neutralise the power of natural selection. I do not believe so. But I do believe that natural selection will generally act very slowly, only at long intervals of time, and only on a few of the inhabitants of the same region. I further believe that these slow, intermittent results accord well with what geology tells us of the rate and manner at which the inhabitants of the world have changed.

*　　*　　*

Natural selection acts solely through the preservation of variations in some way advantageous, which consequently endure. Owing to the high geometrical rate of increase of all organic beings, each area is already fully stocked with inhabitants; and it follows from this, that as the favoured forms increase in number, so, generally, will the less favoured decrease and become rare. Rarity, as geology tells us, is the precursor to extinction. We can see that any form which is represented by few individuals will run a good chance of utter extinction, during great fluctuations in the nature of the seasons, or from a temporary increase in the number of its enemies. But we may go further than this; for, as new forms are produced, unless we admit that specific forms can go on indefinitely increasing in number, many old forms must become extinct. That the number of specific forms has not indefinitely increased, geology plainly tells us; and we shall presently attempt to show why it is that the number of species throughout the world has not become immeasurably great.

We have seen that the species which are most numerous in individuals have the best chance of producing favourable variations within any given period. We have evidence of this, in the facts stated in the second chapter, showing that it is the common and diffused or dominant species which offer the greatest number of recorded varieties. hence, rare species will be less quickly modified or improved within any given period; they will consequently be beaten in the race for life by the modified and improved descendants of the commoner species.

From these several considerations I think it inevitably follows, that as new species in the course of time are formed through natural selection, others will become rarer and rarer, and finally extinct. The forms which stand in closest competition with those undergoing modification and improvement, will naturally suffer most. And we have seen in the chapter on the Struggle for Existence that it is the most closely-allied forms,—varieties of the same species, and species of the same genus or of related genera,—which, from having nearly the same structure, constitution, and habits, generally come into the severest competition with each other; consequently, each new variety or species, during the progress of its formation, will generally press hardest on its nearest kindred, and tend to exterminate them. We see the same process of extermination amongst our domesticated productions, through the selection of improved forms by man. Many curious instances could be given showing how quickly new breeds of cattle, sheep, and other animals, and varieties of flowers, take the place of older and inferior kinds. In Yorkshire, it is historically known that the ancient black cattle were displaced by the long-horns, and that these were "swept away by the short-horns" (I quote the words of an agricultural writer) "as if by some murderous pestilence."

■ Chapter XV

Recapitulation and Conclusion

It can hardly be supposed that a false theory would explain, in so satisfactory a manner as does the theory of natural selection, the several large classes of facts above specified. It has recently been objected that this is an unsafe method of arguing; but it is a method used in judging of the common events of life, and has often been used by the greatest natural philosophers. The undulatory theory of light has thus been arrived at; and the belief in the revolution of the earth on its own axis was until lately supported by hardly any direct evidence. It is no valid objection that science as yet throws no light on the far higher problem of the essence or origin of life. Who can explain what is the essence of the attraction of gravity? No one now objects to following out the results consequent on this unknown element of attraction; notwithstanding that Leibnitz formerly accused Newton of introducing "occult qualities and miracles into philosophy."

I see no good reason why the views given in this volume should shock the religious feelings of anyone. It is satisfactory, as showing how transient such impressions are, to remember that the greatest discovery ever made by man—namely, the law of the attraction of gravity—was also attacked by Leibnitz, "as subversive of natural and inferentially of revealed, religion." A celebrated author and divine has written to me that "he has gradually learnt to see that it "is just as noble a conception of the Deity to believe that He created "a few original forms capable of self-development into other and "needful forms, as to believe that He required a fresh act of creation "to supply the voids caused by the action of His Laws."

Why, it may be asked, until recently did nearly all the most eminent living naturalist and geologists disbelieve in the mutability of species. It cannot be asserted that organic beings in a state of nature are subject to no variation; it cannot be proved that the amount of variation in the course of long ages is a limited quantity; no clear distinction has been, or can be, drawn between species and well-marked varieties. It cannot be maintained that species when intercrossed are invariably sterile, and varieties invariably fertile; or that sterility is a special endowment and sign of creation. The belief that species were immutable productions was almost unavoidable as long as the history of the world was thought to be of short duration; and now that we have acquired some idea of the lapse of time, we are too apt to assume, without proof, that the geological record is so perfect that it would have afforded us plain evidence of the mutation of species, if they had undergone mutation.

But the chief cause of our natural unwillingness to admit that one species has given birth to other and distinct species, is that we are always slow in admitting great changes of which we do not see the steps. The difficulty is the same as that felt by so many geologists, when Lyell first insisted that long lines of inland cliffs had been formed, and great valleys excavated, by the agencies which we see still at work. The mind cannot possibly grasp the full meaning of the term of even a million years; it cannot add up and perceive the full effects of many slight variations, accumulated during an almost infinite number of generations.

* * *

Analogy would lead me one step farther; namely, to the belief that all animals and plants are descended from some one prototype. But analogy may be a deceitful guide. Nevertheless all living things have much in common, in their chemical composition, their cellular structure, their laws of growth, and their liability to injurious influences. We see this even in so trifling a fact as that the same poison often similarly affects plants and animals; or that the poison secreted by the gall-fly produces monstrous growths on the wild rose or oak-tree. With all organic beings, excepting perhaps some of the very lowest, sexual reproduction seems to be essentially similar. With all, as far as is at present known, the germinal vesicle is the same; so that all organisms start from a common origin. If we look even to the two main divisions—namely, to the animal and vegetable kingdoms—certain low forms are so far intermediate in character that naturalists have disputed to which kingdom they should be referred. As Professor Asa Gray has remarked, "the spores and other reproductive bodies of many of the lower algæ may claim to have first a characteristically animal, and then an unequivocally vegetable existence." Therefore, on the principle of natural selection with divergence of character, it does not seem incredible that, from some such low and intermediate form, both animals and plants may have been developed; and, if we admit this, we must likewise admit that all the organic beings which have ever lived on this earth may be descended from some one primordial form. But this inference is chiefly grounded on analogy, and it is immaterial whether or not it be accepted. No doubt it is possible, as Mr. G. H. Lewes has urged, that at the first commencement of life many different forms were evolved; but if so, we may conclude that only a very few have left modified descendants. For, as I have recently remarked in regard to the members of each great kingdom, such as the Vertebrata, Articulata, &c., we have distinct evidence in their embryological, homologous, and rudimentary structures, that within each kingdom all the members are descended from a single progenitor.

Charles Darwin: The Descent of Man

▪ Chapter xxi

The main conclusion here arrived at, and now held by many naturalists who are well competent to form a sound judgment, is that man is descended from some less highly organized form. The grounds upon which this conclusion rests will never be shaken, for the close similarity between man and the lower animals in embryonic development, as well as in innumerable points of structure and constitution, both of high and of the most trifling importance,—the rudiments which he retains, and the abnormal reversions to which he is occasionally liable,—are facts which cannot be disputed. They have long been known, but until recently they told us nothing with respect to the origin of man. Now when viewed by the light of our knowledge of the whole organic world, their meaning is unmistakable. The great principle of evolution stands up clear and firm, when these groups or facts are considered in connection with others, such as the mutual affinities of the members of the same group, their geographical distribution in past and present times, and their geological succession. It is incredible that all these facts should speak falsely. He who is not content to look, like a savage, at the phenomena of nature as disconnected, cannot any longer believe that many is the work of a separate act of creation. He will be forced to admit that the close resemblance of the embryo of man to that, for instance, of a dog—the construction of his skull, limbs and whole frame on the same plan with that of other mammals, independently of the uses to which the parts may be put—the occasional re-appearance of various structures, for instance of several muscles, which man does not normally possess, but which are common to the Quadrumana—and a crowd of analogous facts, all point in the plainest manner to the conclusion that man is the co-descendant with other mammals of a common progenitor.

*   *   *

The main conclusion arrived at in this work, namely that man is descended from some lowly organized form, will, I regret to think, be highly distasteful to many. But there can hardly be a doubt that we are descended from barbarians. The astonishment which I felt on first seeing a party of Fuegians on a wild and broken shore will never be forgotten by me, for the reflection at once rushed into my mind—such were our ancestors. These men were absolutely naked and bedaubed with paint, their long hair was tangled, their mouths frothed with excitement, and their expression was wild, startled, and distrustful. They possessed hardly any arts, and like wild animals lived on what they could catch; they had no government, and were merciless to every one not of their own

Source: From *The Descent of Man* by Charles Darwin (Amherst: Prometheus Books, 1998).

small tribe. He who has seen a savage in his native land will not feel much shame, if forced to acknowledge that the blood of some more humble creature flows in his veins. For my own part I would as soon be descended from that heroic little monkey, who braved his dreaded enemy in order to save the life of his keeper, or from that old baboon, who descended from the mountains, carried away in triumph his young comrade from a crowd of astonished dogs—as from a savage who delights to torture his enemies, offers up bloody sacrifices, practises infanticide without remorse, treats his wives like slaves, knows no decency, and is haunted by the grossest superstitions.

Man may be excused for feeling some pride at having risen, though not through his own exertions, to the very summit of the organic scale; and the fact of his having thus risen, instead of having been aboriginally placed there, may give him hope for a still higher destiny in the distant future. But we are not here concerned with hopes or fears, only with the truth as far as our reason permits us to discover it; and I have given the evidence to the best of my ability. We must, however, acknowledge, as it seems to me, that man with all his noble qualities, with sympathy which feels for the most debased, with benevolence which extends not only to other men but to the humblest living creature, with his god-like intellect which has penetrated into the movements and constitution of the solar system—with all these exalted powers—Man still bears in his bodily frame the indelible stamp of his lowly origin.

Thomas Kuhn: The Structure of Scientific Revolutions

Thomas Kuhn (1922–1996) was an American scientist and philosopher who startled the scientific world with his assertions regarding the nature of the scientific process and the reliability of scientific data. His Ph. D. in theoretical physics from Harvard prepared him for a career in scientific research, but his interest shifted to the field of the history and philosophy of science. He taught in that discipline at Harvard, the University of California at Berkeley, Princeton, and the Massachusetts Institute of Technology (MIT). These excellent scientific credentials gave his assertions credibility and major elements of his concepts have been widely accepted, although many others vigorously dispute his theories.

The most important of Kuhn's works is *The Structure of Scientific Revolutions* in which he describes the process of scientific discovery. According to Kuhn, most scientific work is conducted within a framework of belief that he calls a paradigm. The paradigm provides a set of beliefs within which the scientists operate and interpret data. For instance, a widely held paradigm is the atomic theory of matter. Another is the Newtonian equations of motion. In general, scientists expand human knowledge by relating new data to old data by using the framework of the paradigm. Kuhn points out that scientists are conditioned by the paradigm so that, in reality, their observations are not independent and objective. Kuhn also asserts that because of this paradigm bias, much data that does not agree with the paradigm is suppressed as being experimentally erroneous—that is, in error because of experimental error. These assertions have angered many scientists because they have always believed that their work is valuable because of its objectivity. In this respect, Kuhn's work has yet to be fully explored and resolved.

Kuhn also notes that within the history of science we can see times when the accumulation of data tends to contradict a particular paradigm. An example of this is the data of celestial motion taken in the sixteenth century that contradicted the theory of Ptolemy and the ancient Greeks that the earth was the center of the universe. Kuhn said that the old theory, on which most of the scientists of that day had based their knowledge, could not be immediately discarded because of the difficulty those scientists had in changing their paradigm. Perhaps change would come only with a new generation.

Kuhn explored the details of the change of paradigms during this transition period and noted that the shift from one paradigm to another was not logical. Instead, the shift required a creative leap to a new concept. Creativity theory would agree.

Thomas S. Kuhn: The Structure of Scientific Revolutions

■ Preface

The essay that follows is the first full published report on a project originally conceived almost fifteen years ago. At that time I was a graduate student in theoretical physics already within sight of the end of my dissertation. A fortunate involvement with an experimental college course treating physical science for the non-scientist provided my first exposure to the history of science. To my complete surprise, that exposure to out-of-date scientific theory and practice radically undermined some of my basic conceptions about the nature of science and the reasons for its special success. . . .

I was struck by the number and extent of the overt disagreements between social scientists about the nature of legitimate scientific problems and methods. Both history and acquaintance made me doubt that practitioners of the natural sciences possess firmer or more permanent answers to such questions than their colleagues in social science. Yet, somehow, the practice of astronomy, physics, chemistry, or biology normally fails to evoke the controversies over fundamentals that today often seem endemic among, say, psychologists or sociologists. Attempting to discover the source of that difference led me to recognize the role in scientific research of what I have since called "paradigms." These I take to be universally recognized scientific achievements that for a time provide model problems and solutions to a community of practitioners. Once that piece of my puzzle fell into place, a draft of this essay emerged rapidly.

*　　*　　*

. . . [T]he early developmental stages of most sciences have been characterized by continual competition between a number of distinct views of nature, each partially derived from, and all roughly compatible with, the dictates of scientific observation and method. What differentiated these various schools was not one or another failure of method—they were all "scientific"—but what we shall come to call their incommensurable ways of seeing the world and of practicing science in it. Observation and experience can and must drastically restrict the range of admissible scientific belief, else there would be no science. But they cannot alone determine a particular body of such belief. An apparently arbitrary element, compounded of personal and historical accident, is always a formative ingredient of the beliefs espoused by a given scientific community at a given time.

*　　*　　*

Normal science, the activity in which most scientists inevitably spend almost all their time, is predicated on the assumption that the scientific

Source: From *The Structure of Scientific Revolutions* by Thomas S. Kuhn. Copyright © 1970 by Thomas Kuhn. Reprinted by permission of The University of Chicago Press.

community knows what the world is like. Much of the success of the enterprise derives from the community's willingness to defend that assumption, if necessary at considerable cost. Normal science, for example, often suppresses fundamental novelties because they are necessarily subversive of its basic commitments. Nevertheless, so long as those commitments retain an element of the arbitrary, the very nature of normal research ensures that novelty shall not be suppressed for very long. . . .

*   *   *

In this essay, 'normal science' means research firmly based upon one or more past scientific achievements, achievements that some particular scientific community acknowledges for a time as supplying the foundation for its further practice. Today such achievements are recounted, though seldom in their original form, by science textbooks, elementary and advanced. These textbooks expound the body of accepted theory, illustrate many or all of its successful applications, and compare these applications with exemplary observations and experiments. Before such books became popular early in the nineteenth century (and until even more recently in the newly matured sciences), many of the famous classics of science fulfilled a similar function. Aristotle's *Physica*, Ptolemy's *Almagest*, Newton's *Principia* and *Opticks* Franklin's *Electricity*, Lavoisier's *Chemistry*, and Lyell's *Geology*—these and many other works served for a time implicitly to define the legitimate problems and methods of a research field for succeeding generations of practitioners. They were able to do so because they shared two essential characteristics. Their achievement was sufficiently unprecedented to attract an enduring group of adherents away from competing modes of scientific activity. Simultaneously, it was sufficiently open-ended to leave all sorts of problems for the redefined group of practitioners to resolve.

Achievements that share these two characteristics I shall henceforth refer to as 'paradigms,' a term that relates closely to 'normal science.' By choosing it, I mean to suggest that some accepted examples of actual scientific practice—examples which include law, theory, application, and instrumentation together—provide models from which spring particular coherent traditions of scientific research. . . .

The study of paradigms, including many that are far more specialized than those named illustratively above, is what mainly prepares the student for membership in the particular scientific community with which he will later practice. Because he there joins men who learned the bases of their field from the same concrete models, his subsequent practice will seldom evoke overt disagreement over fundamentals. Men whose research is based on shared paradigms are committed to the same rules and standards for scientific practice. That commitment and the apparent consensus it produces are prerequisites for normal science, i.e., for the genesis and continuation of a particular research tradition. . . .

Acquisition of a paradigm and of the more esoteric type of research it permits is a sign of maturity in the development of any given scientific field. . . .

*   *   *

Paradigms gain their status because they are more successful than their competitors in solving a few problems that the group of practitioners has come to recognize as acute. To be more successful is not, however, to be either completely successful with a single problem or notably successful with any large number. . . .

*   *   *

The best-known and the strongest case for this restricted conception of a scientific theory emerges in discussions of the relation between contemporary Einsteinian dynamics and the older dynamical equations that descend from Newton's *Principia*. From the viewpoint of this essay these two theories are fundamentally incompatible in the sense illustrated by the relation of Copernican to Ptolemaic astronomy: Einstein's theory can be accepted only with the recognition that Newton's was wrong. Today this remains a minority view.

We must therefore examine the most prevalent objections to it.

The gist of these objections can be developed as follows. Relativistic dynamics cannot have shown Newtonian dynamics to be wrong, for Newtonian dynamics is still used with great success by most engineers and, in selected applications, by many physicists. Furthermore, the propriety of this use of the older theory can be proved from the very theory that has, in other applications, replaced it. Einstein's theory can be used to show that predictions from Newton's equations will be as good as our measuring instruments in all applications that satisfy a small number of restrictive conditions. For example, if Newtonian theory is to provide a good approximate solution, the relative velocities of the bodies considered must be small compared with the velocity of light. Subject to this condition and a few others, Newtonian theory seems to be derivable from Einsteinian, of which it is therefore a special case.

But, the objection continues, no theory can possibly conflict with one of its special cases. If Einsteinian science seems to make Newtonian dynamics wrong, that is only because some Newtonians were so incautious as to claim that Newtonian theory yielded entirely precise results or that it was valid at very high relative velocities. Since they could not have had any evidence for such claims, they betrayed the standards of science when they made them. In so far as Newtonian theory was ever a truly scientific theory supported by valid evidence, it still is. Only extravagant claims for the theory—claims that were never properly parts of science—can have been shown by Einstein to be wrong. Purged of these merely human extravagances, Newtonian theory has never been challenged and cannot be.

Some variant of this argument is quite sufficient to make any theory ever used by a significant group of competent scientists immune to attack. . . .

But to save theories in this way, their range of application must be restricted to those phenomena and to that precision of observation with which the experimental evidence in hand already deals. Carried just a step further (and the step can scarcely be avoided once the first is taken), such a

limitation prohibits the scientist from claiming to speak "scientifically" about any phenomenon not already observed. Even in its present form the restriction forbids the scientist to rely upon a theory in his own research whenever that research enters an area or seeks a degree of precision for which past practice with the theory offers no precedent. These prohibitions are logically unexceptionable. But the result of accepting them would be the end of the research through which science may develop further. . . .

But the argument has still not done what it purported to do. It has not, that is, shown Newton's Laws to be a limiting case of Einstein's. For in the passage to the limit it is not only the forms of the laws that have changed. Simultaneously we have had to alter the fundamental structural elements of which the universe to which they apply is composed.

This need to change the meaning of established and familiar concepts is central to the revolutionary impact of Einstein's theory. Though subtler than the changes from geocentrism to heliocentrism, from phlogiston to oxygen, or from corpuscles to waves, the resulting conceptual transformation is no less decisively destructive of a previously established paradigm. We may even come to see it as a prototype for revolutionary reorientations in the sciences. Just because it did not involve the introduction of additional objects or concepts, the transition from Newtonian to Einsteinian mechanics illustrates with particular clarity the scientific revolution as a displacement of the conceptual network through which scientists view the world.

These remarks should suffice to show what might, in another philosophical climate, have been taken for granted. At least for scientists, most of the apparent differences between a discarded scientific theory and its successor are real. Though an out-of-date theory can always be viewed as a special case of its up-to-date successor, it must be transformed for the purpose. And the transformation is one that can be undertaken only with the advantages of hindsight, the explicit guidance of the more recent theory. Furthermore, even if that transformation were a legitimate device to employ in interpreting the older theory, the result of its application would be a theory so restricted that it could only restate what was already known. Because of its economy, that restatement would have utility, but it could not suffice for the guidance of research.

Let us, therefore, now take it for granted that the differences between successive paradigms are both necessary and irreconcilable.

* * *

What a man sees depends both upon what he looks at and also upon what his previous visual-conceptual experience has taught him to see.

* * *

Given a paradigm, interpretation of data is central to the enterprise that explores it.

But that interpretive enterprise—and this was the burden of the paragraph before last—can only articulate a paradigm, not correct it. Paradigms are not corrigible by normal science at all. Instead, as we have already seen, normal science ultimately leads only to the recognition of anomalies and to crises. And these are terminated, not be deliberation and interpretation, but by a relatively sudden and unstructured event like the gestalt switch. Scientists then often speak of the "scales falling from the eyes" or of the "lightning flash" that "inundates" a previously obscure puzzle, enabling its components to be seen in a new way that for the first time permits its solution. On other occasions the relevant illumination comes in sleep. No ordinary sense of the term 'interpretation' fits these flashes of intuition through which a new paradigm is born. Though such intuitions depend upon the experience, both anomalous and congruent, gained with the old paradigm, they are not logically or piecemeal linked to particular items of that experience as an interpretation would be. Instead, they gather up large portions of that experience and transform them to the rather different bundle of experience that will thereafter be linked piecemeal to the new paradigm but not to the old.

* * *

But is sensory experience fixed and neutral? Are theories simply man-made interpretations of given data? The epistemological viewpoint that has most often guided Western philosophy for three centuries dictates an immediate and unequivocal, Yes! In the absence of a developed alternative, I find it impossible to relinquish entirely that viewpoint. Yet it no longer functions effectively, and the attempts to make it do so through the introduction of a neutral language of observations now seem to me hopeless.

The operations and measurements that a scientist undertakes in the laboratory are not "the given" of experience but rather "the collected with difficulty." They are not what the scientist sees—at least not before his research is well advanced and his attention focused. Rather, they are concrete indices to the content of more elementary perceptions, and as such they are selected for the close scrutiny of normal research only because they promise opportunity for the fruitful elaboration of an accepted paradigm. Far more clearly than the immediate experience from which they in part derive, operations and measurements are paradigm-determined. Science does not deal in all possible laboratory manipulations. Instead, it selects those relevant to the juxtaposition of a paradigm with the immediate experience that that paradigm has partially determined. As a result, scientists with different paradigms engage in different concrete laboratory manipulations. The measurements to be performed on a pendulum are not the ones relevant to a case of constrained fall. Nor are the operations relevant for the elucidation of oxygen's properties uniformly the same as those required when investigating the characteristics of dephlogisticated air.

As for a pure observation-language, perhaps one will yet be devised. But three centuries after Descartes our hope for such an eventuality still depends exclusively upon a theory of perception and of the mind. . . .

* * *

[T]he transition between competing paradigms cannot be made a step at a time, forced by logic and neutral experience. Like the gestalt switch, it must occur all at once (though not necessarily in an instant) or not at all. . . .

These facts and others like them are too commonly known to need further emphasis. But they do need re-evaluation. In the past they have most often been taken to indicate that scientists, being only human, cannot always admit their errors, even when confronted with strict proof. I would argue, rather, that in these matters neither proof nor error is at issue. The transfer of allegiance from paradigm to paradigm is a conversion experience that cannot be forced. Lifelong resistance, particularly from those whose productive careers have committed them to an older tradition of normal science, is not a violation of scientific standards but an index to the nature of scientific research itself. . . .

Still, to say that resistance is inevitable and legitimate, that paradigm change cannot be justified by proof, is not to say that no arguments are relevant or that scientists cannot be persuaded to change their minds. Though a generation is sometimes required to effect the change, scientific communities have again and again been converted to new paradigms. Furthermore, these conversions occur not despite the fact that scientists are human but because they are. Though some scientists, particularly the older and more experienced ones, may resist indefinitely, most of them can be reached in one way or another. Conversions will occur a few at a time until, after the last holdouts have died, the whole profession will again be practicing under a single, but now a different, paradigm. We must therefore ask how conversion is induced and how resisted. . . .

Probably the single most prevalent claim advanced by the proponents of a new paradigm is that they can solve the problems that have led the old one to a crisis. When it can legitimately be made, this claim is often the most effective one possible. In the area for which it is advanced the paradigm is known to be in trouble. That trouble has repeatedly been explored, and attempts to remove it have again and again proved vain. . . .

The claim to have solved the crisis-provoking problems is, however, rarely sufficient by itself. Nor can it always legitimately be made. . . .

All the arguments for a new paradigm discussed so far have been based upon the competitors' comparative ability to solve problems. To scientists those arguments are ordinarily the most significant and persuasive. The preceding examples should leave no doubt about the source of their immense appeal. But, for reasons to which we shall shortly revert, they are neither individually nor collectively compelling. Fortunately, there is also another sort of consideration that can lead scientists to reject an old paradigm in favor of a new. Theses are the arguments, rarely made entirely explicit, that appeal to the individual's sense of the appropriate or the aesthetic—the new theory is said to be "neater," "more suitable," or "simpler" than the old. . . .

The man who embraces a new paradigm at an early stage must often do so in defiance of the evidence provided by problem-solving. He must, that is, have faith that the new paradigm will succeed with the many large problems that confront it, knowing only that the older paradigm has failed with a few. A decision of that kind can only be made on faith.

That is one of the reasons why prior crisis proves so important. Scientists who have not experienced it will seldom renounce the hard evidence of problem-solving to follow what may easily prove and will be widely regarded as a will-o'-the-wisp. But crisis alone is not enough. There must also be a basis, though it need be neither rational nor ultimately correct, for faith in the particular candidate chosen. Something must make at least a few scientists feel that the new proposal is on the right track, and sometimes it is only personal and inarticulate aesthetic considerations that can do that. Men have been converted by them at times when most of the articulable technical arguments pointed the other way. When first introduced, neither Copernicus' astronomical theory nor De Broglie's theory of matter had many other significant grounds of appeal. Even today Einstein's general theory attracts men principally on aesthetic grounds, an appeal that few people outside of mathematics have been able to feel.

This is not to suggest that new paradigms triumph ultimately through some mystical aesthetic. On the contrary, very few men desert a tradition for these reasons alone. Often those who do turn out to have been misled. But if a paradigm is ever to triumph it must gain some first supporters, men who will develop it to the point where hardheaded arguments can be produced and multiplied. And even those arguments, when they come, are not individually decisive. Because scientists are reasonable men, one or another argument will ultimately persuade many of them. But there is no single argument that can or should persuade them all. Rather than a single group conversion, what occurs is an increasing shift in the distribution of professional allegiances.

Impressionism to Cubism
Creative Techniques

Chapter 45

> I dream of painting and then I paint my dream.
>
> —*Vincent Van Gogh*

Art and Technology

The relationship between art and technology is interesting and complex. In its origins, art was considered to be technology (art was called *teche*) and therefore has a strong component of practicality. Artists and craftsmen were both artisans. This linkage reflected the emphasis of early art on the execution of the art—it was not to be a reflection of something "inside" the artist but, rather, a representation of something desired by the patron. The artist's work might have been, for example, a statue of Pharaoh Ramses II or a depiction of Minoan youths exercising by jumping over a bull, which should be represented as seen or as the sponsor wished. Even into the Middle Ages, we see standard representations of things and little of the artist's personality. In most cases, we know nothing of artists who created great works such as, for example, the rose windows of Notre Dame.

Today we see two components in art—the craft and the inspiration. A young composer, Mary Gautier, said, "Song writing is both an art and a craft: If you've got the craft without the art, it's boring, if you've got the art without the craft, people don't know what you're talking about." She then added, "Conceive it, believe it, achieve it!" which implies that the craft and the inspiration should be combined to make the work happen.

Much time for many artists is spent in developing their abilities in the craft. This is very important. If not so, all of us could compose a symphony and play it, if we did nothing more than get the inspiration for one. Obviously, much skill and talent are used for the craft. High skills in craft may be inborn in some people (such as Mozart), but even in those people excellence must be developed through long hours of practice.

Craft is developed through practice, which impresses patterns on the brain and is controlled principally by the left side of the brain. Inspiration, however, relates different stored information, and this function is controlled by the right side of the brain. Therefore, art combines both the left and right sides of the brain. Creativity comes best when both craft and inspiration, left and right brains, are combined.

The Renaissance and the Baroque emphasized the craft component of art. Michelangelo's *David* shows wonderful execution. Bernini's works like *David* or *Daphne and Apollo* move us emotionally because of their superb technique. (Note, by the way, the linkage between *technique* and *technical*.)

In the Romantic period, the inspiration was moved to the dominant position in art. The focus of the artist was to "put himself" into the art. Artists wanted to tell their story and convey their emotions. To do this, they often shifted the focus from the technique to the idea conveyed through the art.

In the midst of the Romantic era, about 1870, a group of artists, mostly painters, were living in Paris and talking about the relationships between the two parts of painting—the craft or technique and the inspiration or emotions. They felt that the Romantic artists had placed so much focus on inspiration and emotion that it was time to focus back on the craft. Moreover, technology had just given them a new tool—oil paints in individual little tubes. Previously, each painter would have to mix pigments with the oil to make his or her own paints. This was messy and time consuming. It also meant that as soon as the paint was mixed, the oil began to evaporate and dry. The nature of these freshly mixed oil paints changed very rapidly, soon becoming too hard to use. After a few hours, perhaps even several minutes, new batches had to be made.

However, with the new tubes of oil paints, those problems were eliminated. The artist could mix paints from several tubes on a palette and use the mix for a painting. If more was needed, it could be squeezed fresh from the tubes.

The group of Parisian artists saw this technology as a way to free them from the necessity of working mostly in the studio. Now they could go outside and work within nature. (The importance of nature in this era gave special impetus to their plan.) Therefore, they started to paint in many different places, trying to capture the mood of a place by being there.

As they worked outside, they found something else that fascinated them. That was the changes in light. They became obsessed with capturing the moment. Some even painted the same scene many times, at different times of day, to capture the light. Others experimented with dappling the paints to show light diffusing through trees. Therefore, new concepts in art were directly related to concepts in technology.

This group had great difficulty exhibiting their works because they were so different from the normal Romantic paintings of the day. Therefore, they decided to rent a showroom and put on their own exhibition. They did this in 1874. Many critics expressed dismay and distaste. But the public seemed to enjoy the works, and they began to sell.

The entire exhibition seemed to be characterized by one painting, shown in Figure 45.1. It features light reflected off a shimmering sea, capturing a moment in time. The figures are shown indistinctly so that their instantaneous nature is emphasized. The artist, Claude Monet, called the work *Impression, Sunrise.* The writers covering the exhibition seized upon this painting's title and called the entire group **Impressionists.** The name stuck and became the name of their movement.

In Paris, the last decades of the nineteenth century were known as the fin de siècle (French for "end of the century") or la belle époque ("the beautiful age"). Europeans everywhere seemed satisfied with life in general (these were the days of empire and world dominance), but especially in Paris there was an emphasis on culture (art, architecture, food, and music) and pleasurable living. Many of the loveliest buildings in Paris were built during this era. A typical example is shown in Figure 45.2. Other cities around the world copied the style of the Parisian buildings during this age.

However, the happiness and gaiety of the age were largely forced. Under the glossy surface lurked some serious social problems, such as continued class separation due to industrialization, economic exploitation, colonial tension, and a general loss of standards. France was recovering from a disastrous war with Prussia and seemed shocked that the Germans had grown so strong

Figure 45.1 ■ Impression: Sunrise *by Claude Monet. Erich Lessing/
Art Resource, NY.*

Figure 45.2 ■ **A)** *Exterior of the Ritz Hotel, Paris.* **B)** *Interior of the Ritz Hotel, Paris (examples of buildings in la belle époque). A) © Corel. B) © Corel.*

militarily and industrially. Among the intellectuals
and artists, it was a time of questioning what was
real and what was true; a time of breaking away
from the traditions and standards of the past.

The Romantic art of the period grew more intense and exotic. Painters wanted to reflect some of
the disturbances they felt in the undercurrent of society. Some paintings were quite grotesque, while
others were intentionally shocking.

One of those Romantic protest painters was
Édouard Manet (1832–1883). His famous work
Le Déjeuner sur l'Herbe (Luncheon on the Grass)
caused an outrage in Paris upon its release. The
painting (Figure 45.3) was of a picnic in the park.

Figure 45.3 ■ Le Déjeuner sur l'Herbe (Luncheon on the Grass) *by Édouard Manet.* Reunion des Musees Nationaux/Art Resource, NY.

It included a nude female with two males and another woman in the background. However, it was not the nude figure that caused the controversy, but the casualness of her nudity and direct gaze at the viewer. This created an impression that she may be a woman of ill repute. This feeling is heightened because the two men in the painting are fully clothed. The sensation and tone are heightened even further because Manet used a traditional Romantic setting—a woods—thus mixing traditional expectations with shocking surprises.

In addition to the obvious creativity of the subject matter of this painting, Manet's technique was also original. The human figures are very flat and stark, but the background is light and airy. By doing this, Manet strongly brings the human figures to the foreground of the picture and to the consciousness of the viewer. The somber colors and the shocking features give the painting a sadness, in spite of the smiles of the individuals in the painting and the pastoral setting.

Another painting by Manet, *A Bar at the Folies-Bergère,* similarly has a deep sadness. As with the luncheon painting, the setting is one in which the viewer would expect happiness, but the forlorn expression of the waitress belies that initial expectation. Again, Manet uses stark and flat colors for the foreground figure and an indistinct rendering of the background to make the foreground stand out strongly.

Manet's painting *The Fifer* is very flat and exhibits very few characteristics of reality. In this painting the background is eliminated completely, thus forcing the viewer to see only the figure (see Figure 45.4). Manet's desire was to concentrate on the technique and not the subject, which becomes merely the vehicle of the message. By doing this, the painting becomes less a window on the world and more a screen on which the world is depicted. Manet was one of the first artists who could be said to create art for art's sake; to really believe it was the process and not the product that was the art.

Manet was an inspiration for the small group of Impressionists. They copied many of the concepts Manet used (such as the indistinct backgrounds). Manet was a bridge between traditional Romantic paintings and the new Impressionism, but he rejected the label "Impressionist" and

Figure 45.4 ■ The Fifer *by Édouard Manet.*
© *Corel.*

asserted that it was the prerogative of the artist to combine whatever elements he pleased for aesthetic feeling alone. (In fact, he used Impressionistic style in the background of the *Luncheon* and *Bar* paintings.) To put it another way, the painter's first loyalty is to the canvas and not to the outside world; brush strokes and color patches themselves, not what they stand for, are the artist's primary reality. It is up to the viewer to make the brush strokes and color into a whole and give it meaning. This became the basis for most art in the late nineteenth century, and has continued to be so today.

■ Impressionism

The Parisian setting for the young artists who began the Impressionist movement was ideal. The public's emphasis on art and culture and the questioning of past norms gave the artists an opportunity to join with others in discussions of art, to experiment, and, perhaps, even to be successful.

As previously mentioned, these young artists

wanted to focus on how to actually put the paint on the canvas. Part of their technique was to use short brush strokes and not blend the strokes completely, thus forcing the viewer's eye to connect the color segments into a coherent image. Thus, the viewer and the artist create the final product together.

These ideas, and the art that such a philosophy creates, were radical; the Parisian art critics generally disdained their works. Over time, however, Impressionism began to be respected within the art world, and numerous other movements were based in the Impressionistic challenge to the classical model of painting. (A few died respected and wealthy.) Furthermore, nearly all of the movements in art since Impressionism are based in the Impressionistic idea that the art is not the final work, but the process of mental assimilation and human emotion that occurs within the viewer is the actual "art."

The leader of the Impressionist movement was **Claude Monet** (1840–1926). His focus, and the focus of much of Impressionism, was on light and color, rather than the traditional emphasis on realism of shape. Monet was very interested in painting outdoors at the actual site so that he could capture the light and feeling of the moment. In his attempts to capture the changing light, Monet would often paint the same subject over and over again, but do it at different times of day and under different lights to capture those subtle (or not-so-subtle) changes. Monet's most famous example of this process is his series of paintings of the Rouen Cathedral. He painted more than 20 renditions of the Rouen Cathedral in different lights. Two of them are shown in Figure 45.5.

Monet also focused on the study of color. Many of his most famous works are landscapes. Monet left Paris and moved to a home in a small village of Giverny, in the countryside northwest of Paris. His home had a lovely traditional garden and a water garden, where he had lilies and several other aquatic plants in the ponds. Many of his most famous works such as *Water Lilies* and also *Japanese Bridge,* shown in Figure 45.6, use scenes from the gardens as subjects. Claude Monet lived many years and epitomized Impres-

Figure 45.5 ■ *Two paintings of Cathedral at Rouen by Laude Monet in different lighting.* © Art Resources, NY.

sionism throughout his life.

Another key figure of the Impressionist movement was **Pierre Auguste Renoir** (1841–1919). Renoir's style and techniques shared Monet's concept of using patches of color placed side by side to let the eye blend them. However, whereas Monet worked mostly with landscapes and architecture, Renoir painted people. Renoir's masterpiece is his *Le Moulin de la Galette* (Figure 45.7). This picture of happy customers at a Parisian café captures the animation and joy of life in Paris at the *fin de siècle* as he saw it. Renoir, who had a happy and fulfilled life himself, did not portray the undercurrents of pessimism of the era, but instead focused on the *joie de vivre* (joy of life). His use of the Impressionistic style is masterfully done. Notice not only how the people are painted convincingly using the Impressionistic style, but also how the light is filtering down through the trees above the patrons in the painting, mottling

everything in an interplay of light and shadow.

Edgar Degas (1834–1917) participated in the Impressionist exhibitions (which the artists held regularly) but focused on the nature of the moving body. He used many mediums (pastel, oils, even bronze) and focused on ballerinas and race horses as his subjects. The painting of the *Rehearsal of a Ballet on Stage* (Figure 45.8) shows the fluid motion that characterizes many of Degas's works. He has strong realism elements but also uses elements of Impressionism. There is neither happiness nor sadness, but, perhaps because we expect happiness in a setting like the ballet, the absence of happiness is a telling commentary on the times.

Georges Seurat (1859–1891) lived somewhat after the first Impressionists but admired their focus on technique and wanted to reinvigorate their concepts. Seurat took the Impressionistic idea of not blending colors to a new level and invented a painting style known as **Pointillism.** In Pointil-

Figure 45.6 ■ Japanese Bridge *by Claude Monet.* © *Geoffrey Clements/CORBIS.*

Figure 45.7 ■ Le Moulin de la Galette *by Pierre Auguste Renoir. Scala/Art Resource, NY.*

Figure 45.8 ■ Rehearsal of a Ballet on Stage *by Edgar Degas.* © *Edimédia/CORBIS.*

lism Seurat used thousands of tiny dots of paint applied according to strict theories of color (which he studied scientifically throughout his life). The colored dots are visible separately when viewed up close, but as the viewer pulls backs and looks at the picture from a distance, the dots converge and form a picture. A good example of both Pointillism and Seurat's work is *A Sunday on La Grande Jatte* (Figure 45.9).

Figure 45.9 ▪ A Sunday on La Crande Jatte *by Georges Seurat.*
© *The Gallery Collection/Corbis*

Post-Impressionism

Impressionism was followed by a new, even more radical movement in art called **Post-Impressionism.** Post-Impressionism was not an art school in the normal sense that the artists share a common technique or painting characteristic. In fact, the Post-Impressionists have been grouped together mostly as a matter of historical convenience. However, most of the Post-Impressionists do have a few things in common. First, all of these artists rejected Impressionism, although not in the same way. Second, each of these painters had an Impressionist phase but later moved on to other techniques. Third, most considered Impressionism to be *passé* and they wanted to be on the cutting edge of painting concepts (known as the *avant-garde*).

The first artist who could correctly be labeled a Post-Impressionist is **Paul Cézanne** (1839–1906). As a young man, Cézanne left his home in southern France and went to Paris to become an artist. Initially, Cézanne loved Romanticism and idolized Delacroix, but upon arriving in Paris, Cézanne began to study with Manet. Through him, Cézanne learned the principles and techniques of Impressionism. He worked in the Impressionistic style

briefly, but soon expanded the ideals of Impressionism into his own style. Cézanne believed that all forms in nature are based on the cone, sphere, and cylinder, and he tried to suggest their presence in whatever he painted. Cézanne did not try to reproduce nature. He looked for natural order rather than trying to impose order in his work. Cézanne said that he wanted to give Impressionism solidness.

Cézanne's style began the concept of abstract painting. After spending some time in Paris on the fringes of the Impressionist scene, Cézanne decided to return to his childhood home in Aix-en-Provence in the south of France and apply his technique to landscape painting. These features can be seen clearly in Cézanne's *View over Mont Sainte-Victoire* (Figure 45.10). Cézanne loved the mountain, painting it over 60 times. Because of his interest in the basic shapes of the features of the mountain and surrounding area, he painted the scene from many different angles. This would be the geometric variation equivalent of Monet's painting the Rouen Cathedral at many different times to achieve variations in light.

Cézanne's influence was profound. He was an example to Van Gogh and Gaugin, who also moved to the south of France after periods in

Figure 45.10 ■ View over Mont Sainte-Victoire *by Paul Cézanne.* *Scala/Art Resource, NY.*

Paris, and was cited by Picasso as his inspiration for Cubism (which we will examine later). Some have called Cézanne the "father of modern painting."

Perhaps the most famous of the Post-Impressionist painters is **Vincent Van Gogh** (1853–1890). Van Gogh believed that Impressionism was too rigid and did not give the artist enough emotional freedom. Van Gogh's style is sometimes known as **Expressionism,** and it emphasized the dream-like nature of the artist's work. This concept is reflected in Van Gogh's statement that is quoted at the beginning of this chapter.

Van Gogh, who was born in Holland, had early interests in literature and religion, and he even served as a lay preacher for a time to impoverished coal miners, but he went to work for his uncle, a renowned painter in the Netherlands. In his uncle's shop he fell in love with painting. Many of his early paintings were emotionally intense, but drab and dark, and seemed to reflect the mood and tone of his life and the lives of the poor and desperate people he was serving as a preacher.

Van Gogh later gave up the preacher's life and moved to Paris, where his brother Theo owned an art gallery. While in Paris, Van Gogh became acquainted with the Impressionists and incorporated some of their ideas into his work. Van Gogh was never really accepted by the Impressionists and eventually fled to the south of France, like Cézanne, to find peace and paint nature. Van Gogh's time in Paris was a difficult period for him. He found no commercial success as an artist, selling only one painting to his brother. He began to suffer from severe emotional extremes and possible mental illness, which would continue to get worse throughout his life.

Despite the difficulties he faced both personally and professionally while in Paris, Van Gogh's time there had a dramatic effect on his art. His post-Paris work left behind the drab themes and colors of his early work and embraced a unique and colorful style. After Paris, Van Gogh's paintings were alive with color and featured strong, obvious, brush strokes that often had a swirling pattern. In this regard, he was focusing on technique, conceptually like the Impressionists, but very different in execution. His work *Starry Night* (Figure 45.11) illustrates the dream-like quality, strong colors, and the bold brush strokes that characterize his latter period. Similar qualities can be seen

Figure 45.11 ▪ Starry Night *by Vincent Van Gogh.* © *Corel.*

in Van Gogh's other paintings from this period such as the famous *Sunflowers, The Night Café,* and his self-portraits.

These works seemed to show the emotional turmoil and mental struggle that Van Gogh constantly dealt with. He even cut off one of his own ears. Van Gogh consulted physicians to seek a cure for his mental disturbances and even checked himself into an asylum. He worked in a near frantic pace during his entire time in the south of France, even when in the asylum. When his brother married, Van Gogh moved to be near him. He continued his frantic pace (creating 70 paintings in 70 days). However, the mental problems overwhelmed him, and he took his own life.

Although Van Gogh's works were not popular or successful during his lifetime, they are among the most respected, beloved, and expensive paintings today.

Paul Gauguin (1848–1903) lived a relatively normal upper-middle-class life and spent the first half of his life as a stockbroker in Paris. Gauguin was successful and became quite wealthy, using much of his wealth to collect art, including pieces by Cézanne. Through his art collecting, Gauguin became acquainted with the Impressionists and even did a few paintings in the Impressionist style himself.

Gauguin grew unhappy with his life, and at age 35 abandoned his family and occupation to devote himself completely to painting. Gauguin seemed to be well accepted by the Impressionists but was uncomfortable in Paris and moved to Brittany in western France. Gauguin later spent a brief time with Van Gogh in Arles (the south of France), but the two men could not get along and Gauguin soon left. (The book and movie *Lust for Life* are excellent depictions of the interactions of these two great artists.) Gauguin then moved to Tahiti, where he attempted to learn about real living and find the inner peace that had eluded him.

Gauguin's paintings strive to achieve primitive emotions by painting primitive peoples. Most of his works are of either the peasants of Brittany or the natives of Tahiti. Gauguin also used strong colors and flat backgrounds to emphasize the emotional content of the piece over the literal picture. His paintings speak of the South Seas and the Tahitian people tending toward acceptance and peace with life, the qualities that Gauguin was personally seeking. Figure 45.12 shows Gauguin's *La Orana Maria,* which is typical of his Tahitian works.

Another development of Post-Impressionism was **Fauvism,** a new movement led by **Henri Matisse** (1869–1954). The term *Fauvism* comes

Figure 45.12 ■ La Orana Maria *by Paul Gauguin.* © *Francis G. Mayer/CORBIS.*

Figure 45.13 ■ The Red Room *by Henri Matisse.* © *2010 Succession H. Matisse/Artists Rights Society (ARS), New York. Photo: Archives Matisse.*

Figure 45.14 ■ The Scream *by Edvard Munch. Erich Lessing/Art Resource, NY.* © *2010 The Munch Museum/The Munch-Ellingsen Group/Artists Rights Society (ARS), NY.*

from the French word for "wild beasts," which referred to the artists and their attitudes. The intent of the Fauvist movement was to depart even more sharply from traditional painting. The emotions of the artist were to be the most important part of their work, and this emotion was shown in color and other techniques, as well as subject matter. The Fauvists were strongly inspired by the bold colors and emotional content of Post-Impressionist painters such as Van Gogh and Gauguin. However, it took these elements to greater extremes.

The works of Henri Matisse are filled with bold accents and brilliant colors, as can be seen in *The Red Room,* which is depicted in Figure 45.13. Such works call to mind the sheer joy of painting and of life, more than they result in a beautiful final product. An unusual quality about Matisse's work is that most of his paintings have a positive and optimistic feel about them that was quite unusual for his era.

Another outgrowth of Post-Impressionism was a fascination by some artists with the new science of psychology. These painters, such as the Norwegian **Edvard Munch** (1863–1944) and the German **Erich Heckel** (1883–1970), were using the elements of Expressionism and Fauvism, but using them to analyze the insecurity, sadness, and pessimism of the time. Munch's works are filled with paranoia and insecurity, as can be seen in his painting *The Scream* (Figure 45.14), while Heckel even went so far as to dedicate his most famous painting, *Two Men at a Table,* to the Russian master of the psychological novel, Feodor Dostoevsky.

Cubism

Art continued in its path away from the traditional models and away from realism. The next major art movement was **Cubism,** developed by the painters Pablo Picasso and Georges Braque. They argued that it was more faithful to not try to imitate three-dimensional figures with a two-dimensional art, thus rejecting realism. They were inspired by Cézanne's efforts to reduce all figures to basic forms. These concepts led to a radical reduction of the forms in the painting to basic shapes. Sometimes the object in the painting was even depicted showing all of the sides simultaneously on separate planes. These innovations forced the viewer to either reconstruct the original form or to appreciate the art without regard to the original form.

Pablo Picasso (1881–1973) was born in Spain but lived most of his life on the French Riviera. He was highly prolific over his long life and became very popular. He was, therefore, quite wealthy and lived a life of ease. He became a prototype of the modern artist.

Picasso's painting *Three Musicians* (Figure 45.15) shows the concepts of cubism in the way the musicians are segmented and represented by basic geometric shapes. Later in his life, Picasso used his Cubist style to make social commentary. Picasso's masterpiece in this area is *Guernica* (Figure 45.16). This painting was both an excellent example of Cubist art and a social statement against the Fascist bombing of the city of Guernica, Spain, during the Spanish Revolution.

Figure 45.15 ▪ Three Musicians *by Pablo Picasso. The Philadelphia Museum of Art/Art Resource, NY. © 2010 Estate of Pablo Picasso/Artists Rights Society (ARS), New York.*

Figure 45.16 ▪ Guernica *by Pablo Picasso. John Bigelow Taylor/Art Resource, NY. © 2010 Estate of Pablo Picasso/Artists Rights Society (ARS), New York.*

It shows the effects of the bombing in sadness and carnage.

Not everyone could appreciate Cubism. One day, while Picasso was painting, a tourist sought him out in order to buy a painting as a souvenir. The artist approached Picasso and, seeing that he was working on a painting, asked how much the painting would cost. When Picasso answered with what the tourist considered to be an outrageous price, the tourist replied that he thought his six-year-old daughter could paint something that was just as good. Picasso then replied, "Congratulations, sir, your daughter is a genius."

■ Sculpture

The greatest sculptor of the nineteenth century was **Auguste Rodin** (1840–1918). His works were classical in concept but impressionistic in execution. Some of his pieces, like the famous *The Thinker,* could have been done in the neoclassical period, as evidenced by their fine attention to body structure and form. However, even in these pieces, there is a feeling of impressionistic styling. In other pieces, such as *The Burghers of Calais* (shown in Figure 45.17), Rodin has achieved a remarkable lifelike appearance with an impression of reality. This piece was especially challenging because it depicts six figures and yet spatially ties them together. He does this by grouping them in pairs and then animating their actions to move between the pairs.

The story behind *The Burghers of Calais* is interesting. In the fourteenth century, Calais was under siege from the English King Edward III. After nearly a year, with the population nearly at starvation, the citizens of Calais asked terms of surrender. King Edward demanded that the keys of the city be brought to him by six of the most eminent burghers of Calais. They are to be barefoot and linked together with a rope around their necks. The king then added, "I shall do with them as I please." Six leading citizens volunteered to be those who would surely give their lives to spare the lives of their follow-citizens. Rodin's sculpture captures these six burghers in their most agonizing moment. However, the story ends happily.

Figure 45.17 ■ The Burghers *of Calais* by Auguste Rodin. *Vanni/Art Resource, NY.*

King Edward's wife, Queen Phillipa de Hainaut, was pregnant at the time and did not want her child to be born into such violence. She prevailed upon her husband to spare the lives of the burghers, and he did.

■ Impressionism in Music

The influence of Impressionism was not limited to painting. Like Impressionistic painting, Impressionism in other art forms focused on involving the viewer, had an emphasis on technique (including the interplay of light and shadow), emphasized emotional content, and evoked an "impression" of something without actually realistically recreating it.

Impressionism had a strong influence in music, and many of the great composers of the era chose to compose Impressionistic pieces rather than more traditional Romantic music. Among these composers were Richard Strauss, Gustav Mahler, Claude Debussy, and Maurice Ravel. These composers experimented with different tonalities and harmonies and tried to either use tone poems to tell stories (Strauss), capture the feeling of human emotions such as anxiety, fear, happiness, and sexual passion (Mahler and Ravel), or tried to recreate the feelings of nature (Debussy and Ravel).

Of particular note in illustrating the Impressionist style in music are the works of **Claude Debussy** (1862–1918). His *Prelude to the Afternoon of a Faun* beautifully represents a scene, as if in a garden, where the listener seems to gaze around to see the wonders and beauty of the surroundings. There are few long melodies but, rather, impressions of melodies. There is no progression in the music—that is, no feeling of movement toward a logical conclusion. Rather, it is an experience to be enjoyed at the moment without thought of moving on. To give a feeling of comfort during the piece, the tonic key is asserted repeatedly, but the contrasts of traditional progressive styles are not present. Other famous works by Debussy that similarly show the Impressionist style are *Claire de Lune* and *Le Mer.*

Maurice Ravel (1875–1937) was equally masterful in composing in the Impressionist style. In some of his works, like *Pavanne for a Dead Princess,* the tones are soft and serene, much like those of Debussy. However, in Ravel's *Bolero* a totally different concept is explored. It is highly progressive, building gradually from the simplicity of a single instrument to a highly complex orchestration with many instruments. All the while the same theme is repeated with a strong rhythmic accompaniment. When the finale is reached, the orchestration climaxes into a cacophony of dissonance. The impression is overwhelming.

As in painting, a Post-Impressionistic school developed with music as well. It has also been called, simply, Twentieth Century music or Modern music. It included composers such as Arnold Schoenberg and Igor Stravinsky. These composers experimented with atonal compositions that completely avoided traditional tones and harmonies and gave a feeling of instability. These composers also were looking to find the fundamentals of music. They utilized folk music and other simple forms to try and discover music's core elements.

■ Literature

The pessimism and questioning of the era, as well as the development of psychology, led to the development of the psychological novel, which is at least loosely connected with Post-Impressionism and Fauvism in that these novels try to create certain emotional tones and are attempting to involve the reader emotionally and mentally in the story. **Feodor Dostoevsky** (1821–1881) was the master of the psychological novel and wrote powerfully about the meaning of life and death. Dostoevsky's two masterpieces are *Crime and Punishment* and *The Brothers Karamazov. Crime and Punishment* is about a man who believes he is of the class that is superior to all others and can, therefore, do what he wants. Believing this, he kills a woman, essentially just to see what killing is like, but then must live his life through terrible phases of regret and remorse. *The Brothers Karamazov* is about a disjointed family. It follows the lives of the brothers in the family as they search for meaning in their lives. The theme of the novel is closely connected to the sense of questioning and lack of purpose that was underlying society at this time.

The Norwegian playwright **Henrik Ibsen** (1828–1906) also employed psychological themes in his plays. Ibsen used ordinary life as the setting of his plays but examined this life in a new and deeper way, especially looking at human aspirations and limitations. Ibsen also exposed themes that were considered controversial and even taboo, such as divorce (from a favorable view), venereal disease, incest, and insanity. Ibsen became world-famous within his lifetime as the leader of this new psychological movement in the theater and strongly influenced later dramatists.

Ibsen's most famous and best work is his play *A Doll's House,* which strongly supports women's independent place in life, a topic well ahead of its time. The play examines the actions of Nora, a married woman who initially seems satisfied with her life of wife and mother. However, when she tries to take some initiative, she is reprimanded and realizes that her husband, Torvald, sees her as a child and as a possession (like a doll). Nora then feels stifled and isolated. When Nora tries to express her concerns, Torvald can't even understand what those concerns are, and refuses to deal with the issue. Torvald's refusal to attempt to understand her or consider any change forces Nora to act and make changes herself. She decides to leave her disbelieving and perplexed husband. The play is psychologically complex and thematically controversial and was among the first of its kind.

Another writer of the era, **Friedrich Nietzsche** (1844–1900), wrote philosophy, not fiction. In harmony with the pessimism of the age and the disillusionment of science, Nietz_sche challenged the belief in progress. Nietzsche also rejected religion, especially Christianity, and claimed that "God is dead" (meaning that mankind had moved past its need to believe in a controlling supernatural power that Nietzsche believed did not exist). Nietzsche stated that mankind should instead rely on basic animal passions and reject intellectuality, which gave undue power to the weak and robbed

the strong of body and of will from having power and freedom. A corollary of this idea was that Nietzsche advocated the superiority of certain groups, especially those few who could free themselves from the bondage of civilization. Twentieth-century dictators like Adolph Hitler later twisted Nietzsche's ideas to justify the superiority of the German race and the extermination of the Jews.

▪ Technique

It is not coincidence that Impressionism (both painting and music) was centered in France. French culture is concerned about technique—which is, of course, a critical feature of Impressionism. To illustrate the French concern about technique, consider cooking. The classical cooking methods (techniques) used today by most of the great chefs of the world were developed in France. The French are justifiably proud of their cooking tradition and can point out how their methods have promoted good eating for generations. Even today, when some chefs are fusing different cooking traditions together, the French classical methods are the basis of the new fused forms.

We see creativity among these great chefs when they use the classical form to present unique eating experiences. Sometimes they also emphasize technique and win the hearts of their customers with excellence in preparation (as with a superb crème brulee). At other times they deviate from the classical repertoire by creating a dish featuring a non-French origin, but they do it with recognition of the basics of the French style. Hence, like Impressionism in painting, the most creative chefs use classical concepts but are willing to experiment with some changes in techniques and with some changes in tastes to give the impression of classical ingredients but with new concepts.

Another facet of Impressionism is the expression of forms without depicting them clearly. In art this is done by suggesting the form with daubs of paint that the eye of the viewer brings into a coherent picture. In music it is done by suggesting melodies and movement without actually giving the listener either. The French perceive their language in much the same way. For the French, how you say something is just (or more) important than what you say. (That is certainly not the case in English or German.) Hence, the language of the French supported the concepts of Impressionism. Undoubtedly, those early discussions by the young Impressionist artists were facilitated by their native French language.

We find it interesting that the Japanese are similar to the French in these two areas. Japanese cooking is highly formalized and is classic in its preparation. Likewise, the Japanese language is highly concerned about how things are said. We are told that in Japanese, the connections between reading, writing, and speaking are not one-to-one as they are in Western languages. There are few connections in Japanese between the communication forms. Whereas Western languages have alphabets that reflect speaking, Japanese is written in pictographs but spoken linearly. Also, the pronunciation and meaning of any particular Kanji (Japanese writing) is a function of context. Further, Japanese has many homophones, and so the only distinguishing feature is the Kanji. We would, therefore, expect to see and hear Impressionistic forms in painting and music in Japan. This is, indeed, the case. Japanese art asks the viewer to blend artistic representations that are conveyed quite simply but with deep suggested meanings.

The Impressionists were highly creative in combining their native culture with new concepts in art. This is an example of lateral thinking, and its effects are very important and pleasurable. The Impressionist style in art is one of the most popular and has given us great insights into artistic thinking and execution.

■ Timeline—Important Dates

Date	Event
1863	Manet's *Le Déjuneur Sur l'Herbe* is exhibited
1866	Dostoevsky's *Crime and Punishment* written
1874	Exhibition in which *Impression Sunrise* is exhibited
1875	Degas's *Rehearsal of a Ballet on Stage* painted
1876	Renoir's *Le Moulin de la Galette* painted
1879	Ibsen's *A Doll's House* performed
1884	Seurat's *A Sunday on La Grande Jatte* painted
1885–1887	Cezanne's *View over Mont Sainte-Victoire* painted
1886	Rodin's *The Burghers of Calais* completed
1888	Van Gogh's *Starry Night* painted
1891	Gauguin's *La Orana Maria* painted
1894	Debussy's *Prelude to the Afternoon of a Faun* performed
1895	Munch's *The Scream* painted
1911	Matisse's *The Red Room* painted
1921	Picasso's *Three Musicians* painted
1928	Ravel's *Bolero* premieres
1937	Picasso's *Guernica* painted

■ Suggested Readings

Dostoevsky, Feodor, *The Brothers Karamazov,* Signet Classic, 1957.

Ibsen, Henrik, *Four Major Plays,* Oxford University Press, 1998.

Henrik Ibsen: A Doll's House

Henrik Ibsen (1828–1906) shocked people with *A Doll's House*. The play portrays a woman who is living a normal and standard life in the late 19th Century. She decides to leave her husband and, in essence, strike out into a new life on her own. The reasons for her decision are quite subtle and are not fully explained in the play. However, in the last scene of the play, which is presented here, she confronts her husband and, in response to his questions and accusations, gives some reasons for her actions. The power of the play is that these reasons revolve around the awakening that she has of her position in her husband's life. She realizes that he views her as nothing more than a possession and that her individuality is ignored. She sees that her existence is as shallow as a doll.

The message is made more powerful because of the ordinariness of the characters. The husband, Helmer Torvald, is not a bad man. He doesn't abuse his wife or commit bad acts. He simply acts in the way a man of his age would act when he is unaware of his wife's emotional needs. Nora, the wife, is not vindictive or mean. She remains a kind and gentle person throughout the play. Thus, her actions are made powerful because she is very likeable. The husband brings up arguments based on traditional roles for women, on religion, on duty, and other common factors that the wife simply deflects. She does not have a crusade to follow. She merely wants to find her true self. In doing that, the play lays the foundation for the awakening of women's rights and position that became so powerful in the 20th Century.

Act III—Final Scene

[The following action takes place in the Helmers' living room in the evening and Nora has changed into street clothes rather than her bed clothes.]

HELMER *[standing at the open door]*. Yes, do. Try and calm yourself, and make your mind easy again, my frightened little singing-bird. Be at rest, and feel secure; I have broad wings to shelter you under. *[Walks up and down by the door.]* How warm and cosy our home is, Nora. Here is shelter for you; here I will protect you like a hunted dove that I have saved from a hawk's claws; I will bring peace to your poor beating heart. It will come, little by little, Nora, believe me. Tomorrow morning you will look upon it all quite differently; soon everything will be just as it was before. Very soon you won't need me to assure you that I have forgiven you; you will yourself feel the certainty that I have done so. Can you suppose I should ever think of such a thing as repudiating you, or even reproaching you? You have no idea what a true man's heart is like, Nora. There is something so indescribably sweet and satisfying, to a man, in the knowledge that he has forgiven his wife—forgiven her freely, and with all his heart. It seems as if that had made her, as it were, doubly his own; he has given her a new life, so to speak; and she has in a way become both wife and child to him. So you

shall be for me after this, my little scared, helpless darling. Have no anxiety about anything, Nora; only be frank and open with me, and I will serve as will and conscience both to you—. What is this? Not gone to bed? Have you changed your things?

NORA *[in everyday dress]*. Yes, Torvald, I have changed my things now.

HELMER. But what for?—so late as this.

NORA. I shall not sleep tonight.

HELMER. But, my dear Nora—

NORA *[looking at her watch]*. It is not so very late. Sit down here, Torvald. You and I have much to say to one another. *[She sits down at one side of the table.]*

HELMER. Nora—what is this?—this cold, set face?

NORA. Sit down. It will take some time; I have a lot to talk over with you.

HELMER *[sits down at the opposite side of the table]*. You alarm me, Nora!—and I don't understand you.

NORA. No, that is just it. You don't understand me, and I have never understood you either—before tonight. No, you mustn't interrupt me. You must simply listen to what I say. Torvald, this is a settling of accounts.

HELMER. What do you mean by that?

NORA *[after a short silence]*. Isn't there one thing that strikes you as strange in our sitting here like this?

HELMER. What is that?

NORA. We have been married now eight years.

A Doll's House by Henrik Ibsen, translated by William Archer 1879.

Does it not occur to you that this is the first time we two, you and I, husband and wife, have had a serious conversation?

HELMER. What do you mean by serious?

NORA. In all these eight years—longer than that—from the very beginning of our acquaintance, we have never exchanged a word on any serious subject.

HELMER. Was it likely that I would be continually and forever telling you about worries that you could not help me to bear?

NORA. I am not speaking about business matters. I say that we have never sat down in earnest together to try and get at the bottom of anything.

HELMER. But, dearest Nora, would it have been any good to you?

NORA. That is just it; you have never understood me. I have been greatly wronged, Torvald—first by papa and then by you.

HELMER. What! By us two—by us two, who have loved you better than anyone else in the world?

NORA [shaking her head]. You have never loved me. You have only thought it pleasant to be in love with me.

HELMER. Nora, what do I hear you saying?

NORA. It is perfectly true, Torvald. When I was at home with papa, he told me his opinion about everything, and so I had the same opinions; and if I differed from him I concealed the fact, because he would not have liked it. He called me his doll-child, and he played with me just as I used to play with my dolls. And when I came to live with you—

HELMER. What sort of an expression is that to use about our marriage?

NORA [undisturbed]. I mean that I was simply transferred from papa's hands into yours. You arranged everything according to your own taste, and so I got the same tastes as your else I pretended to, I am really not quite sure which—I think sometimes the one and sometimes the other. When I look back on it, it seems to me as if I had been living here like a poor woman—just from hand to mouth. I have existed merely to perform tricks for

you, Torvald. But you would have it so. You and papa have committed a great sin against me. It is your fault that I have made nothing of my life.

HELMER. How unreasonable and how ungrateful you are, Nora! Have you not been happy here?

NORA. No, I have never been happy. I thought I was, but it has never really been so.

HELMER. Not—not happy!

NORA. No, only merry. And you have always been so kind to me. But our home has been nothing but a playroom. I have been your doll-wife, just as at home I was papa's doll-child; and here the children have been my dolls. I thought it great fun when you played with me, just as they thought it great fun when I played with them. That is what our marriage has been, Torvald.

HELMER. There is some truth in what you say—exaggerated and strained as your view of it is. But for the future it shall be different. Playtime shall be over, and lesson-time shall begin.

NORA. Whose lessons? Mine, or the children's?

HELMER. Both yours and the children's, my darling Nora.

NORA. Alas, Torvald, you are not the man to educate me into being a proper wife for you.

HELMER. And you can say that!

NORA. And I—how am I fitted to bring up the children?

HELMER. Nora!

NORA. Didn't you say so yourself a little while ago—that you dare not trust me to bring them up?

HELMER. In a moment of anger! Why do you pay any heed to that?

NORA. Indeed, you were perfectly right. I am not fit for the task. There is another task I must undertake first. I must try and educate myself—you are not the man to help me in that. I must do that for myself. And that is why I am going to leave you now.

HELMER [springing up]. What do you say?

NORA. I must stand quite alone, if I am to understand myself and everything about me. It is for that reason that I cannot remain with you any longer.

HELMER. Nora, Nora!

NORA. I am going away from here now, at once. I am sure Christine will take me in for the night—

HELMER. You are out of your mind! I won't allow it! I forbid you!

NORA. It is no use forbidding me anything any longer. I will take with me what belongs to myself. I will take nothing from you, either now or later.

HELMER. What sort of madness is this!

NORA. Tomorrow I shall go home—I mean, to my old home. It will be easiest for me to find something to do there.

HELMER. You blind, foolish woman!

NORA. I must try and get some sense, Torvald.

HELMER. To desert your home, your husband and your children! And you don't consider what people will say!

NORA. I cannot consider that at all. I only know that it is necessary for me.

HELMER. It's shocking. This is how you would neglect your most sacred duties.

NORA. What do you consider my most sacred duties?

HELMER. Do I need to tell you that? Are they not your duties to your husband and your children?

NORA. I have other duties just as sacred.

HELMER. That you have not. What duties could those be?

NORA. Duties to myself.

HELMER. Before all else, you are a wife and a mother.

NORA. I don't believe that any longer. I believe that before all else I am a reasonable human being, just as you are—or, at all events, that I must try and become one. I know quite well, Torvald, that most people would think you right, and that views of that kind are to be found in books; but I can no longer content myself with what most people say, or with what is found in books. I must think over things for myself and get to understand them.

HELMER. Can you not understand your place in your own home? Have you not a reliable guide in such matters as that?—have you no religion?

NORA. I am afraid, Torvald, I do not exactly know what religion is.

HELMER. What are you saying?

NORA. I know nothing but what the clergyman said, when I went to be confirmed. He told us that religion was this, and that, and the other. When I am away from all this, and am alone, I will look into that matter too. I will see if what the clergyman said is true, or at all events if it is true for me.

HELMER. This is unheard of in a girl of your age! But if religion cannot lead you aright, let me try and awaken your conscience. I suppose you have some moral sense? Or—answer me—am I to think you have none?

NORA. I assure you, Torvald, that is not an easy question to answer. I really don't know. The thing perplexes me altogether. I only know that you and I look at it in quite a different light. I am learning, too, that the law is quite another thing from what I supposed; but I find it impossible to convince myself that the law is right. According to it a woman has no right to spare her old dying father, or to save her husband's life. I can't believe that.

HELMER. You talk like a child. You don't understand the conditions of the world in which you live.

NORA. No, I don't. But now I am going to try. I am going to see if I can make out who is right, the world or I.

HELMER. You are ill, Nora; you are delirious; I almost think you are out of your mind.

NORA. I have never felt my mind so clear and certain as tonight.

HELMER. And is it with a clear and certain mind that you forsake your husband and your children?

NORA. Yes, it is.

HELMER. Then there is only one possible explanation.

NORA. What is that?

HELMER. You do not love me anymore.

NORA. No, that is just it.

HELMER. Nora!—and you can say that?

NORA. It gives me great pain, Torvald, for you have always been so kind to me, but I cannot help it. I do not love you any more.

HELMER *[regaining his composure].* Is that a clear and certain conviction too?

NORA. Yes, absolutely clear and certain. That is the reason why I will not stay here any longer.

HELMER. And can you tell me what I have done to forfeit your love?

NORA. Yes, indeed I can. It was tonight, when the wonderful thing did not happen; then I saw you were not the man I had thought you were.

HELMER. Explain yourself better. I don't understand you.

NORA. I have waited so patiently for eight years; for, goodness knows, I knew very well that wonderful things don't happen every day. Then this horrible misfortune came upon me; and then I felt quite certain that the wonderful thing was going to happen at last. When Krogstad's letter was lying out there, never for a moment did I imagine that you would consent to accept this man's conditions. I was so absolutely certain that you would say to him: Publish the thing to the whole world. And when that was done—

HELMER. Yes, what then?—when I had exposed my wife to shame and disgrace?

NORA. When that was done, I was so absolutely certain, you would come forward and take everything upon yourself, and say: I am the guilty one.

HELMER. Nora—!

NORA. You mean that I would never have accepted such a sacrifice on your part? No, of course not. But what would my assurances have been worth against yours? That was the wonderful thing which I hoped for and feared; and it was to prevent that, that I wanted to kill myself.

HELMER. I would gladly work night and day for you, Nora—bear sorrow and want for your sake. But no man would sacrifice his honour for the one he loves.

NORA. It is a thing hundreds of thousands of women have done.

HELMER. Oh, you think and talk like a heedless child.

NORA. Maybe. But you neither think nor talk like the man I could bind myself to. As soon as your fear was over—and it was not fear for what threatened me, but for what might happen to you—when the whole thing was past, as far as you were concerned it was exactly as if nothing at all had happened. Exactly as before, I was your little skylark, your doll, which you would in future treat with doubly gentle care, because it was so brittle and fragile. *[Getting up].* Torvald—it was then it dawned upon me that for eight years I had been living here with a strange man, and had borne him three children—. Oh, I can't bear to think of it! I could tear myself into little bits!

HELMER *[sadly].* I see, I see. An abyss has opened between us—there is no denying it. But, Nora, would it not be possible to fill it up?

NORA. As I am now, I am no wife for you.

HELMER. I have it in me to become a different man.

NORA. Perhaps—if your doll is taken away from you.

HELMER. But to part!—to part from you! No, no, Nora, I can't understand that idea.

NORA *[going out to the right].* That makes it all the more certain that it must be done. *[She comes back with her cloak and hat and a small bag which she puts on a chair by the table.]*

HELMER. Nora, Nora, not now! Wait until tomorrow.

NORA *[putting on her cloak].* I cannot spend the night in a strange man's room.

HELMER. But can't we live here like brother and sister—?

NORA *[putting on her hat].* You know very well that would not last long. *[Puts the shawl round her.]* Goodbye, Torvald. I won't see the little ones. I know they are in better hands than mine. As I am now, I can be of no use to them.

HELMER. But some day, Nora—some day?

NORA. How can I tell? I have no idea what is going to become of me.

HELMER. But you are my wife, whatever becomes of you.

NORA. Listen, Torvald. I have heard that when a wife deserts her husband's house, as I am doing now, he is legally freed from all obligations towards her. In any case, I set you free from all your obligations. You are not to feel yourself bound in the slightest way, any more than I shall. There must be perfect freedom on both sides. See, here is your ring back. Give me mine.

HELMER. That too?

NORA. That too.

HELMER. Here it is.

NORA. That's right. Now it is all over. I have put the keys here. The maids know all about everything in the house—better than I do. Tomorrow, after I have left her, Christine will come here and pack up my own things that I brought with me from home. I will have them sent after me.

HELMER. All over! All over!—Nora, shall you never think of me again?

NORA. I know I shall often think of you, the children, and this house.

HELMER. May I write to you, Nora?

NORA. No—never. You must not do that.

HELMER. But at least let me send you—

NORA. Nothing—nothing—

HELMER. Let me help you if you are in want.

NORA. No. I can receive nothing from a stranger.

HELMER. Nora—can I never be anything more than a stranger to you?

NORA *[taking her bag]*. Ah, Torvald, the most wonderful thing of all would have to happen.

HELMER. Tell me what that would be!

NORA. Both you and I would have to be so changed that—. Oh, Torvald, I don't believe any longer in wonderful things happening.

HELMER. But I will believe in it. Tell me! So changed that—?

NORA. That our life together would be a real wedlock. Goodbye. *[She goes out through the hall.]*

HELMER *[sinks down on a chair at the door and buries his face in his hands].* Nora! Nora! *[Looks round, and rises.]* Empty. She is gone. *[A hope flashes across his mind.]* The most wonderful thing of all—?

[The sound of a door shutting is heard from below.]

World War I
Creativity Gone Awry

> We see men living with their skulls blown open; we see soldiers run with their two feet cut off. . . .
> Still the little piece of convulsed earth in which we lie is held. We have yielded no more than a few
> hundred yards of it as a prize to the enemy. But on every yard there lies a dead man.
>
> —*Erich Remarque (from* All Quiet on the Western Front*)*

■ Optimism and Pessimism

From some points of view, the dawn of the twentieth century seemed to be a time of great promise for Europe in particular, and Western culture in general. Most governments had implemented at least some liberal, democratic reforms to include more people in the process of government and give them a greater say. Industrialization was largely transforming society from a rural world to an urban one and laying the foundations for the modern world. European economies were generally strong due to Europe's vast colonial holdings. With the formations of Germany and Italy, nearly all of Europe had finally been organized into modern nation-states. And science, despite being in an era of deep questioning and doubt about its meaning and capabilities, was transforming society with an array of new discoveries and the development of new technologies. Many looked forward to the new twentieth century as a time when most of the problems of the world would be eliminated; the most optimistic even saw this new century as an era when the perennial dream of utopia may be neared. Yet, somehow all of the promise and hope of this new era quickly evaporated.

Less than two decades into the twentieth century, most of the world found itself involved in the largest and most destructive war that the Earth had ever known—World War I. They called it "the war to end all wars," but really, it was just the beginning of a century that was dominated by nearly constant warfare on a scale that had never been seen before. The results of World War I led directly to World War II, which, in turn, led directly to the Cold War and its series of proxy wars in Korea, Vietnam, and elsewhere.

Part of the reason that the promise of the twentieth century faded so quickly was that much of it was false to begin with. As we discussed in the last chapter, the spirit of the *fin de siècle,* had an underlying pessimism about the modern world. Some problems, such as social conditions, were obvious. There were other problems of a more subtle nature, and people understood that these problems would eventually have to be dealt with. This knowledge lent a feeling of unease to life that many tried to ignore but had difficulty in doing. Many of these underlying tensions were the problems that eventually led to the war that devastated Europe.

The Causes of World War I

The emergence of Germany as a nation greatly disturbed the other nations of Europe. German military might, long respected even when only the Prussians were powerful, had proven to be overpowering in the Franco-Prussian war of 1870–1871 when several German principalities united under Prussian leadership against France. France had previously believed that it was the greatest and most powerful nation in continental Europe, superceded only by the offshore power—Great Britain. The humiliation of the loss to the Germans was temporarily difficult, causing a change in the government of France from the Second Empire to the Third Republic. This new government was very weak, having emerged only over the continued efforts of monarchists to create a constitutional monarchy. France saw a series of governments that collapsed often and were barely able to continue with some semblance of control. This governmental weakness was a cause of the great war.

Great Britain was also concerned about Germany. Although there had been no military confrontations between Great Britain and Germany (in fact, the queen of England, Victoria, was the grandmother of the German kaiser), German militarism worried the British, as they wanted Europe to be balanced and relatively weak. To further alarm the British, they saw some limited colonialism interest in Germany (Samoa and Tanganyika) and knew that Germany would seek more colonies, given any opportunity. However, of greatest concern to the British was the rise in German manufacturing. As we saw in Chapter 41 on the Industrial Revolution, Britain had long dominated world manufacturing, but at the end of the nineteenth century, a combination of British laxity and German (and American) creativity had resulted in both Germany and America moving ahead of England in per-capita manufacturing output. Moreover, Germany and America had done this without colonial empires but based their gains on science and technology. Britain's move to contain German manufacturing and military advances was a cause of the war.

The largest area where the European colonial presence had remained extremely limited was Asia, where both China and Japan were tempting prizes that had remained largely untapped. Both China and Japan were too weak, both technologically and militarily, to keep from being forced to open the ports to Western trade and culture. Furthermore, both nations resented the blatant disregard for their wishes and sovereignty that the United States and the European powers exhibited. However, realizing they had no choice, China and Japan took advantage of their new access to Western products and technology and used it to modernize quickly. Both China and Japan remembered the embarrassment they felt from the superior technology of the West, and the West's aggressive position toward the Orient and this lingering resentment spilled over to the conflicts of the twentieth century. Thus, in effect, European and American imperialism in the nineteenth century was a contributing factor to the wars of the twentieth century.

The Japanese resolved to become a manufacturing power and, to the chagrin of the British and Americans, chose Germany as the proper model. This decision was not surprising because Germany was already the second greatest manufacturing nation (behind the United States) and had little resources and no colonies—a situation that Japan saw in its own country. This colonial competition, in Asia and around the world, was one of the direct causes of World War I, and the poor treatment of China and Japan would contribute directly to the Japanese attack on Pearl Harbor and the Chinese adoption of Communism and alignment with the Soviet Union later in the twentieth century.

By 1900, most of the areas of the world had been colonialized. However, two of the world's largest empires were in obvious decline, and that caused a continuing competition among the stronger European nations to influence and, perhaps, benefit directly from the decline of the Ottoman and Austrian empires.

The Ottoman Empire had existed since the fifteenth century. During the sixteenth century it had threatened major areas of Europe and had proceeded literally to the walls of Vienna. The Ottomans had conquered many areas of the Balkans, including Greece, and most of North Africa and the Middle East. However, by the latter part of the nineteenth century, the Ottoman Sultans became disinterested in the work required to keep the empire together, thus the empire fell into decay. A group of liberals known as the **Young Turks** eventually forced change. The Young Turks led a revolt in 1908 and forced the Sultans to establish a constitution and an elected parliament. Still, the Ottoman Empire was held together only by the weakest of administrative threads. It was called the "sick man of Europe."

Austria had long been a significant player on the European political scene and the dominant force in southeastern Europe. Austria was the descendant of the Holy Roman Empire (along with parts of Germany) and still possessed much of the prestige associated with that medieval empire. However, it was an empire of varied nationalities with no real cohesion other than the might of the Austrian army and some minor traditions.

Within the Austrian Empire, the largest minority group, the Hungarians (Magyars), revolted against their Austrian rulers and forced the government in Vienna to grant them semi-independence. In 1867 the empire was renamed Austria-Hungary and the Austrians and Hungarians shared a monarch, as well as the ministers of finance, defense, and foreign affairs, but the rest of the government was split into separate Austrian and Hungarian entities.

Another serious blow to the Austrians was the loss of northern Italy. This portion of their empire, which they had possessed from the eleventh century, gained its independence in the mid-1800s.

The success of the Hungarians and the Italians inspired many of the other nationalities that were under Austrian control. Soon the Czechs, Poles, Slavs, Romanians, Bulgarians, and other groups were all agitating for more freedom, and a greater degree of self-government. This caused a great deal of resentment within the German-Austrian majority, which worried about both a loss of prestige and lack of control over their possessions. There also arose a strong feeling of anti-Semitism, as all of the parties involved took out their frustrations on the Jews.

The decline of these two empires led to war in at least two ways. First, the many oppressed nationalities in the two dying empires threw the whole region into chaos and disarray with their repeated attempts at more self-government. Second, as these two powerful empires began to disintegrate, it created a power vacuum that the other powers of Europe each wanted to fill so as to increase their own influence. This added an outside pressure to a region already falling apart from within because of the many ethnic revolts. Combined, these pressures created an environment that was just waiting to explode into violence.

■ Alliances

Throughout the latter decades of the nineteenth century and the first years of the twentieth century, European nations formed several diplomatic alliances. Some of the nations sought to maintain the status quo and keep any one nation from gaining too much power and control. Others sought to manipulate the weak nations and thereby gain a strategic advantage.

Beginning in the mid-nineteenth century, Prussia, under the guidance of then-Prime Minister Otto von Bismarck, gained preeminence among the German principalities through the skillful use of alliances coupled with carefully chosen wars of expansion. His first goal was to unite the German principalities under Prussian leadership. He then wanted to join the Austrian Empire with the new Germany so that all German-speaking people were under Prussian control. The King of Prussia gave

Bismarck great latitude in accomplishing these goals. We are reminded of the absolute kings of France, who had great vision for their country and the power to accomplish their plan.

As the need would arise, Bismarck would cleverly dissolve one alliance and form another. For example, he took advantage of the problems of the Austrian Empire to challenge Austria for leadership among the German-speaking world. After gathering some of the German states under his control, he fought a war against Austria to force Austria to stay out of German involvement, thus freeing him to acquire other German states without competition. He later united with Austria in an alliance to thwart the attempts by the French to limit the power of Germany. He then consolidated his hold on the German states by instituting reforms within Germany, such as a system of social security that offered workers insurance against loss of job, hospitalization, and guaranteed them an income in retirement. He also unified the monetary system and eliminated tariffs between German states.

Bismarck kept all of Europe off balance through these diplomatic manipulations. He attempted to spread the power of Prussia by installing a relative of the Prussian king on the throne of Spain. (This would effectively surround France, the great rival of Prussia at that time.) France's objection to this attempt eventually led to the Franco-Prussian War. Because of Bismarck's creative alliances, the German states all joined with Prussia in the war and then, realizing the power of having a common enemy, Bismarck orchestrated the formal unification of the German states into a single country under Prussian leadership. The Prussian king was declared to be an emperor or *kaiser* (German rendering of caesar), and Bismarck was named chancellor of all Germany. He accomplished one of his key goals by implementing his plan. He also precipitated the fall of the Second (French) Empire and the establishment of the weak Third Republic. Germany was now in a stronger position than France. This all followed Bismarck's plan and was certainly creative.

After the Franco-Prussian War, Bismarck worked to keep a careful balance of power. He sought to consolidate his country and then to gradually move to unite Germany with Austria in a grand German alliance. He did not want to be aggressive at this time because he thought that much internal work was needed. To maintain the status quo, Bismarck continued to make and break alliances as powerful leaders rose and declined and as the fortunes of countries changed because of ethnic revolts and other disturbances. In the midst of this effort, the Prussian kaiser died and was succeeded by his young son, Wilhelm II. After only two years, the new German Emperor became tired of the shifting alliances and complex diplomacy and dismissed Bismarck in 1890. The kaiser was also unwilling to be patient with Bismarck's gradual approach to acquiring an overseas empire for Germany. When Bismarck was dismissed, the kaiser immediately began attempts to acquire overseas colonies.

Germany entered an alliance with Austria and then expanded the alliance in 1882 when Italy joined them. This became known as the **Triple Alliance.** Because of this growing threat from Germany and the Triple Alliance, the other major powers of Europe formed their own alliance. The new **Triple Entente,** an alliance between Russia, France, and Great Britain, was intended to serve as the counterweight to the growing power of Germany and its allies. The two alliances are shown in Figure 46.1. While at first these alliances kept a balance of power, they also created a situation that allowed a small, isolated conflict in southern Europe to evolve into a world war.

We can gain insight into the situation in Europe on the eve of World War I by considering the goals of each of the major powers of Europe:

■ Germany: Solidify the German-speaking world and build an empire.
■ Austria: Hold together the weakening empire.
■ Italy: Consolidate its new country and resist foreign aggression.
■ Great Britain: Maintain a balance on the continent and sea superiority for itself.
■ France: Confine Germany, regain some prestige, and revenge losses of the Franco-Prussian War.

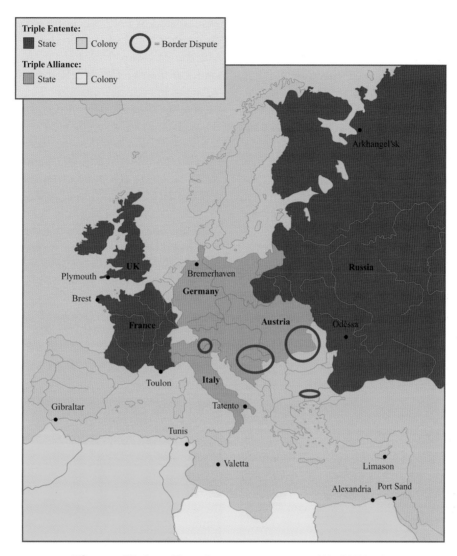

Figure 46.1 ■ *The alliances just prior to World War I.*

- Russia: Expand if possible, especially into the disintegrating Ottoman Empire.
- Ottoman Empire: Survive.

Another key to our understanding of the alliances just prior to the beginning of the war is the strategy of Germany. The German military strategists realized that they were confronted by enemies on both their western and eastern borders. They also realized that Germany would be at a great disadvantage if required to fight a two-front war. Therefore, if war were to break out, the German plan was to concentrate their forces on the western front and

attack France as quickly and forcefully as possible. They hoped to overcome France and conclude the western-front portion of the war before Russia had time to mobilize. This strategy assumed that the Russians would be slow to move, as had always been the case in the past because of Russia's relatively poor preparedness and general backwardness in industrialization and infrastructures (like roads and communications). Germany hoped to keep Great Britain out of the war by using diplomacy to convince the British that Germany posed no threat to Great Britain or its empire because of the lack of a German naval threat.

■ World War I

World War I began as a small revolt in the Austrian Empire. As discussed, the Austrian and Ottoman empires were both in serious decay, and by 1900 several of the larger ethnic groups in these two empires had gained some measure of self-rule. However, the success of these larger ethnic groups and the capitulation of the Austrian and Ottoman governments to their demands only served to encourage further revolts. Thus, in 1905, the Serbs, with Russian support, began a revolt against their Austrian rulers. The Russians backed the Serbs in their revolt because both are Slavic peoples and Russia wanted to increase its power in the Balkan region, possibly obtaining some territory from the disintegrating Ottoman Empire. The tensions between Serbia and Austria were further

exacerbated in 1912 when the Serbs, Greeks, and Bulgarians fought together and took Albania and Macedonia away from the Ottoman Empire. As spoils of their victory, the Serbs gained control of Albania, but Austria intervened and forced Serbia to give up Albania (which then became independent). This led to a heightened sense of hatred by the Serbs for the Austrians and gave new energy to the Serbian effort to gain independence from Austria. The changing situation in the Balkans from 1911 to 1914 is shown in Figure 46.2.

All of these factors and tensions came to a head on June 28, 1914. On that day the heir to the Austro-Hungarian throne, Archduke Ferdinand, was touring the Austrian possession of Bosnia, when a Serbian revolutionary assassinated him.

Austria decided that the Serbian government was involved in the assassination and needed to be

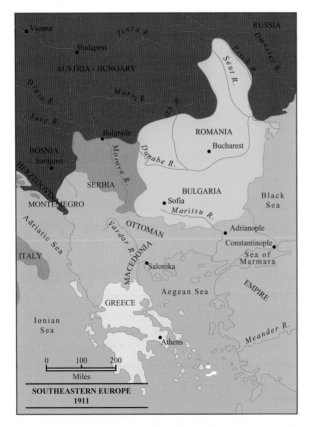

Figure 46.2 ■ *The changing situation in the Balkans just prior to World War I.*

punished. Austria made demands that would have subjected Serbia to full Austrian control. Serbia responded evasively to Austria's ultimatum, and this led Austria to declare war on Serbia. Soon after, Austria began a heavy bombardment of Serbia, thus initiating armed conflict and marking the official start of World War I.

Austria-Hungary precipitated the war in an effort to save its dying empire and exert influence over those countries that would try to take some of its possessions. The Austrians wanted to limit the conflict to a small war in just the Balkans, where they envisioned they could gain some lost territory and bolster public spirit. However, the conflict between Serbia and Austria would soon expand beyond the Balkan region. Russia quickly joined the conflict on the side of Serbia, declared war on Austria, and began a troop mobilization to the front.

The war had now spread to include Austria, Serbia, and Russia. The Austrians sought assistance from the Germans on the basis of their mutual alliance. The Germans agreed to enter the war, but for more reasons than just their alliance with Austria.

The Germans realized that the French were angry over the settlement of the Franco-Prussian war and sought revenge, thus suggesting that the French would use their alliance with Russia as a pretext to attack Germany. The Germans knew that the French believed their military improvements, made by their new government since their loss in the Franco-Prussian War, would allow them to defeat the Germans and regain the territory they had been forced to cede to the Germans. Hence, the Germans anticipated that they would be at war with France, regardless of their action.

Because of their alliance with Austria, Germany also anticipated that they would be involved in the Russian offensive. This involvement would force Germany to fight a two-front war, and that possibility was against the overall German war strategy.

Furthermore, Germany felt frustrated in its efforts to acquire an international empire. Germany was still a relatively new nation and had not been well accepted in the sisterhood of nations, especially since the dismissal of Bismarck. Germany also felt isolated against the real powers of the world (Great Britain, France, and the United States) and left out in the quest for colonies. Thus, Germany was looking for a fight to gain territories and respect, and Austria's war with Serbia opened the door for that to happen.

The German peoples had not yet fully accepted their unity. The rapid industrialization of Germany had also created some social problems (similar to those in Britain and the United States), and the social reforms initiated by Bismarck were not fully adequate to calm the social unrest. The German leadership realized that a war would unite the people against their common enemy, as it had in the Franco-Prussian War, and solve some of these domestic problems.

In light of all these reasons, Germany declared war on the side of Austria on August 1, 1914. The Germans then immediately initiated their strategic plan to defeat the French on the western front before the Russians could mobilize. Germany invaded neutral Belgium—the shortest pathway to Paris and a route that avoided the massing of the French army along the French-German border.

From the beginning, things did not go as the Germans had hoped. The Belgians gave stronger resistance than the Germans planned, thus slowing the German advance. This provided time for the French to move their troops north and join with the Belgian forces. The combined French and Belgians gave the Germans stiff resistance, but in the end the Germans still pushed into France.

Things went contrary to the German plan again, though, when Great Britain decided to send troops to France. The British felt compelled not only because of their alliance with the French, but also because of Germany's invasion of Belgium, with whom the British had a mutual protection treaty. Perhaps equally important, however, was Britain's unease with the efforts of Germany to create an international empire. As part of this effort, the Germans began to build a navy with many commercial ships and with several large warships. The British felt that this navy was beginning to threaten British dominance of the seas and they were anxious to prevent further German power thrusts.

English armies landed in France very quickly and joined the Belgians and French, thus slowing the German advance toward Paris even more and spreading the attack out over a wide front. German plans were foiled further when the Russians were able to mobilize much more quickly than expected and forced Germany to also establish an eastern front, occupying valuable troops and supplies that Germany had intended to use against France.

In September of 1914, a month after Germany's declaration of war, the French counterattacked at the Marne River in France. The French sensed that there might be a gap in the German forces at this location and threw everything they had into the battle of the Marne. The French government even went so far as to requisition Paris taxi cabs and used them to shuttle reinforcements to the front. The ferocity of the French attack forced the Germans to stall in their march toward Paris. Both sides quickly dug long trenches from which they could defend themselves against further attacks. The war entered a long period of stalemate, where neither side gained or lost much territory despite extremely heavy loss of life.

By November 1914 continuous trenches extended from the Belgian ports to the Swiss border, and the horrors of trench warfare had begun. Initially, the trenches were dug to protect the soldiers from machine gun fire. Machine guns were a new technology of World War I and had inflicted extremely high casualty rates early in the war as the armament technology had advanced quicker than military strategy. At first, both sides used the traditional manner of fighting, where armies lined up and marched toward one another, even though the invention of the machine gun made this tactic a foolhardy bloodbath. Trench warfare was developed as a means of limiting the effectiveness of the machine gun, but it caused other new horrors.

War from the trenches was brutal. Both sides launched nearly endless barrages of artillery on the other side in an effort to "soften up" the enemy. Furthermore, the trenches made it very difficult to gain territory, so both sides developed other new weapons to flush the enemy out of the trenches. World War I saw the first use of poison gas. The Germans used these poison gases initially in 1915 as an experiment, and many French died without warning. The French soon began using them as well. Neither side had much skill in

their use, and both sides caused heavy casualties to not only the enemy, but to themselves as well. A sudden change in wind direction or a miscommunication about troop location in the midst of the heat of battle could result in the gassing of your own forces, and often did.

Quite creatively, tractors made by the Holt tractor company (later to be Caterpillar) which were used to haul the large artillery pieces, were shrouded with armor to protect the drivers and gunners from machine gun fire. This was the first instance of an armored vehicle and was the precursor of the tank.

Airplanes were also used in warfare for the first time during World War I. Initially, aircraft were used for reconnaissance, but quickly both sides began to drop handheld bombs from airplanes into the trenches. Eventually machine guns were added to planes as well, adding to the death toll.

The trenches were death traps not only because of new technology, but because of disease as well. Living conditions in the trenches were unsanitary, and men lived close together. There was no good system for the removal of human waste and nowhere for it to go on its own. The trenches nearly always had water in them, so the men were usually wet and often cold. Furthermore, rats were everywhere, living off food scraps, human feces, and dead bodies. These rats grew to be unafraid of people, often chewing on soldiers while they slept, and usually grew to be quite large, sometimes even as big as cats. Under these conditions, it is easy to see how disease became rampant and spread fast, especially since men had to sit close together, share water bottles and food, and sleep in puddles of dirty water. The spread of disease was only made worse by the omnipresent rats.

In a sad and ironic twist, trench warfare was begun to limit the slaughter caused by machine guns, only to have other more horrible weapons developed to kill men in their trenches. Sadder still is the fact that in order to gain ground, soldiers still had to leave the trenches (going over the top) and run across *no man's land* (the area between the trenches) where they were still exposed to the withering machine gun fire that the trenches had been built to protect against. All of these conditions led to an extremely high cost in lives for miniscule gains in territory. For example, the battle of the Somme gained 125 square miles at a cost of 600,000 allied dead and 500,000 German dead. The battle of Verdun resulted in the loss of 700,000 lives on both sides, with no gain in territory by either. Eventually, the slaughter was limited somewhat by the German construction of the Siegfried Line, a group of forts along the German-French border that provided improvements over the trenches. The French built their own series of forts, the Maginot Line, to run parallel to that of the Germans and provide protection. The quotation at the beginning of the chapter reflects the nature of trench warfare. A picture of the trenches is shown in Figure 46.3.

The eastern front of the war was more successful for the Germans. Despite the quick Russian mobilization that had forced Germany to fight a two-front war, the Germans were able to stop the Russian forces short of the Vistula River in September of 1914. Then the combined military forces of Germany and Austria-Hungary began to slowly push the Russians back until, by mid-1915,

the Russians had been pushed back into Russian territory.

Things only got worse for the Russian army as basic supplies such as artillery shells and rifles ran out. The lack of supplies got so bad that the Russians began to have to find weapons among the dead in order to continue defending their homeland. The lack of supplies, among other factors, led to massive Russian casualties, and by the time the war ended more than 2.5 million Russians had been killed. The Russian Czar, Nicholas II, was so alarmed that he personally went to the front to lead the Russian armies. This move proved to be a costly mistake. His presence did not significantly change the situation and he then became a scapegoat for blame of the Russian failures. This led directly to the Russian revolution that was soon to occur.

As World War I went on, it continued to spread to more countries and became an increasingly pan-European affair. Italy had been a member of the Triple Alliance with Austria-Hungary and Germany, but had refused to aid Austria in 1914 because it viewed Austria as the aggressor. Then, in 1915, Italy was convinced by the Allies (Great Britain, France, and Russia) to join the

Figure 46.3 ■ Trench warfare. © *Bettmann/CORBIS.*

war on their side in return for possession of some Austrian territory in the Balkans. (The war was not successful for Austria-Hungary in the Balkans, as the Serbians were able to repel the initial Austrian attack and force a stalemate.)

Italy's defection to the Allies was somewhat balanced, however, when the Ottoman Empire joined with the Central Powers (Germany and Austria) in an attempt to gain more territory in Russia and the Balkans. Turkey then proceeded to kill more than one million Armenians in an attempt to get their land. The Bulgarians, wanting to protect themselves from Turkish aggression, then joined with the Allies. The war situation in Europe is reflected in the map shown in Figure 46.4.

The joining of the Ottoman Turks with the Central Powers helped to spread the war outside of Europe. Great Britain sought to undercut the Ottoman Empire by initiating nationalistic wars among various Arab tribes against their Turkish overlords. Britain gave promises of independence to Arab groups who would aid the Allied cause by revolting against the Turks. The famous Lawrence of Arabia was made the liaison to these Arab tribes.

The war also spread to the various colonies of the European powers. German colonies fought against French and English colonies all around the world; fighting was especially fierce between German Samoa and the British-backed New

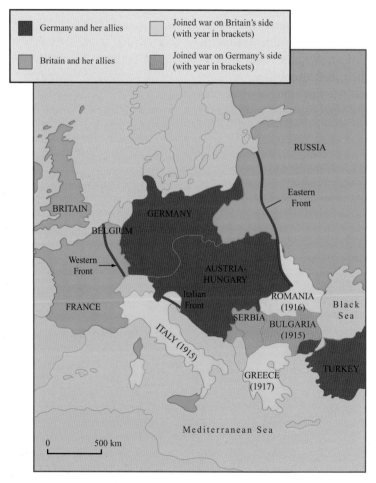

Figure 46.4 ■ *Alliances in Europe at the height of World War I.*

Zealanders. Warfare occurred in Africa, where the Germans attempted to control Lake Tanganyika (as wonderfully shown in the movie *The African Queen*). The seeds of Japanese aggression that would blossom prior to World War II were even laid when Japan seized German colonies in China. Warfare even spread to within Great Britain, as Ireland saw this as their chance to gain their long desired independence from England and revolted on Easter Sunday 1916. However, the British quickly crushed Ireland's Easter Rebellion and the rebel leaders were executed.

▪ Russian Revolution

Ireland was not the only nation to use the chaos of World War I as a springboard to revolution. As the war dragged on, political turmoil within Russia continually threatened to undermine the eastern front that the Allied forces were relying on to keep Germany from using all of its power to break the stalemate on the western front in France. The extremely heavy Russian casualties turned the Russian people against the war and the war became closely associated with the unpopular reign of **Czar Nicholas II.** A progressive, democratic political block within Russia used the unpopularity of the war and the czar to its advantage and called for a new government with a stronger Duma (Russia's elected body).

Already a political conservative who still clung to the idea of absolute rule, Czar Nicholas was further blinded to the need for real political change within Russia by the great dual burdens of running the massive war campaign and dealing with the hemophilia of his only son, Alexis. This disease left the heir sickly, fragile, and only a minor cut away from death at any moment. The Czar's task was made much more difficult because the royal family refused to make the Russian people aware of Alexis's condition. Thus, not understanding the deep desire of the people for change, Czar Nicholas gave in to pressure from his wife and her spiritual adviser, Rasputin, and adjourned the Duma in 1915. This act only lent more strength to the reformers.

Nicholas's burdens were increased further by the presence of Rasputin at court. Rasputin had come to the royal court as an unknown mystic from the Russian wilderness and almost immediately fell into disfavor with the Russian people. However, just as quickly, Rasputin gained a mystical hold over the czarina, Alexandra, and seemed to have a strange control over Alexis's hemophilia and was able to stop the bleeding, at one point even saving the boy's life when death seemed sure. Thus, the czar quickly found himself in a position where he could not win. The people and most of the nobility hated Rasputin and viewed his presence at court as a sign of Nicholas's weakness and backwardness. Meanwhile, his wife, and to a certain extent Nicholas himself, were convinced that if Rasputin were to be sent away, their son would die.

This belief was only reinforced when Nicholas's secret police overheard a drunken Rasputin bragging about his control over the czar and his sexual relationships with czarina Alexandra and all four of the czar's young daughters. These rumors, which had already been circulating around St. Petersburg, were almost certainly untrue (the czarina was a devoutly religious woman); however, they were given a degree of credence by the public because of the royal couples' strange reliance on Rasputin (remember that Alexis's hemophilia was a carefully guarded secret). Nevertheless, when Nicholas heard what Rasputin had said, he punished him by banishing him from the capital and sending him back to the provinces. However, no sooner had Rasputin left than another bleeding crisis nearly killed Alexis. Rasputin was quickly invited back, and the czar never again challenged his position within the court. Rasputin's saving of Alexis did not win him any new friends. In fact, the Russian nobility, including several members of the czar's family, were increasingly concerned about Rasputin's influence on the royal family and saw to it that he was murdered in 1916.

The situation in Russia continued to deteriorate quickly. Three months after Rasputin's murder, in March 1917, bread riots swept across St. Petersburg. Czar Nicholas, unable to restore order to the city and feed his people and unwilling to pull Russia out of the war, saw his unpopularity increase even more. The Duma, sensing the czar's vulnerability, reassembled itself in March 1917 and declared a provisional government, with power being shared between the elected Duma and the Petrograd Soviet, a council of workers and soldiers. Nicholas was unwilling to condone this arrangement, so he abdicated the throne. Despite stepping aside, the czar and his family would be murdered a short time later.

However, the fragile, new, semi-democratic government was to be short-lived. The Bolsheviks (Russian communists) soon came to power. Germany saw in Russia's severe internal problems an opportunity to get the Russians to pull out of the war and eliminate the need for Germany to maintain an eastern front. In order to help facilitate this, the Germans found Vladimir Lenin, the Bolshevik leader in exile in Switzerland, and helped him get back into Russia. (The Germans transported Lenin across Germany and into Russia in a closed railroad car—a rather creative endeavor in light of Germany's traditional hatred toward socialist concepts.) Lenin immediately began to denounce the new Russian democratic government and was able to convince the Petrograd Soviet to issue Army Order No. 1, which stripped officers of their authority and placed power in the hands of elected committees of common soldiers. The Bolsheviks were then able to become selected as leaders of the Soviets, and they used that power to take control of the government via a military coup, in October 1917, eventually converting it to a communist system. Despite coming to power without being elected and without any clear mandate from the Russian people, Lenin and the Bolsheviks quickly gained popularity by seeking peace terms with the Germans and pulling Russia out of World War I. The Soviet Union would formally be declared in 1922.

■ Ending the War

The Russian withdrawal from World War I was a serious setback for the Allies. The Germans were

now finally able to put all of their energies into the invasion of France, and the tide of the war seemed to be shifting in favor of the Central Powers. The Allies had long hoped the Americans would come into the war on the Allied side but the United States had been unwilling to get involved in what they considered a "European war" and had initially remained neutral. However, American neutrality began to wane in favor of open support of the Allies due to German naval warfare.

England and France had established a naval blockade of the Central Powers in 1914. The Germans then established a counter-blockade and used their submarines (another new technology of World War I) to sink Allied supply ships. The Germans then attacked the British passenger liner *Lusitania,* killing over 1,000 people (139 Americans). The British objected to the German attack on a passenger ship, but the Germans claimed that the *Lusitania* was carrying war supplies and munitions and was therefore a fair target. The sinking of the *Lusitania* and the death of the Americans angered the American public, and the Allies were able to use a successful propaganda campaign that convinced America to become the main supplier of the Allied armies (despite continued official neutrality).

The Germans were aware of the United States' fairly open support of the Allied cause and warned the United States that continued support of the Allies would lead to German attacks on American ships. The American government continued to claim that they were neutral even while they were supplying England and France. Eventually, German submarines began to sink American ships suspected of carrying supplies. The repeated attacks on American ships caused the United States to enter the war on the Allied side in 1917.

The arrival of American troops came just in time for the Allies. Once Russia had withdrawn from the war, Germany closed down the eastern front and rushed its forces to the west. Germany assembled its troops in northern France's Argonne Forest as quickly as it could with plans to make a fast, hard push in an attempt to make some major gains in territory. The German naval attacks on American ships brought the United States into the war within a few months of the Russian withdrawal, and American forces arrived at the Battle of Argonne Forest just in time to help repel the German advance. The arrival of the United States tipped the scale of trench warfare in favor of the Allies and was the turning point in the war.

Stopping the massive German attack in the Argonne Forest broke the German morale; while Germany remained militarily strong, the other Central Powers were falling apart. The Ottoman Empire was disintegrating from rebellions in Turkey and from successful Arab attacks, and essentially was forced to withdraw from the war. Austria-Hungary was also losing badly in the Balkans. Tiny Serbia had fought Austria to a stalemate, and the arrival of British and Greek support for Serbia and other oppressed Balkan peoples turned the tide of the war firmly against Austria. With German morale so low and Germany's allies facing total collapse, Germany's Kaiser Wilhelm II formed a new government with instructions to seek peace terms with the Allies.

■ The Treaty of Versailles

With all sides tired of the war, a conference was held in Versailles, France, to discuss the terms of peace. Over 70 nations attended the Versailles conference, and there was great hope for long-lasting peace and a new order of living based on self-determination of peoples. President **Woodrow Wilson** of the United States insisted on the creation of a permanent international organization (the League of Nations). The **League of Nations** was such a popular idea that it became the first item of business, even over the objections of both Germany and France. The League of Nations was approved by the delegates of the Versailles conference but was almost immediately doomed to ineffectiveness when the United States Congress refused to ratify the treaty, thus keeping America from ever becoming a member despite President Wilson's ardent support of the idea. The League of Nations was formed but could not last without American involvement and quickly proved ineffective. It eventually crumbled. Wilson's idea out-

lasted the failed League, however, and was also the blueprint for the modern United Nations.

While the formation of the League of Nations was successful and nearly universally accepted (with the exception of the United States Congress), at least initially, the remainder of the Versailles conference was divisive and bitter. Great Britain and France insisted that Germany had to pay for the war. Their desire was eventually granted, and Germany was forced to pay exorbitant sums of money to the Allied nations. However, the effort to try and pay this massive debt eventually drove Germany into financial collapse and brought about the rise of Hitler.

French demands included the creation of a buffer state between France and Germany and punishment of Germany, Austria, and Turkey (the nation that emerged from the chaos of the old Ottoman Empire). Both Great Britain and the United States felt that rather than have a separate state between France and Germany, a better solution would be to give France possession of Alsace and Lorraine (which were ceded to Germany at the end of the Franco-Prussian War) and to disarm Germany in the Rhineland (the German region near the French border) and severely limit the size of the German army elsewhere. The Allies also guaranteed France support if Germany ever attacked again.

Other actions taken as part of the **Treaty of Versailles** included stripping Germany of its colonies and giving them to Allied nations as colonies or protectorates. The loss of Germany's colonies hurt Germany's economy and also contributed to the conditions that allowed Hitler to achieve power.

One of the most significant results of the treaty, although not fully understood at the time, was the awarding of former Ottoman territories to England and France as protectorates (such as Syria and Lebanon to France; Palestine and Iraq to Britain). Many of the Arab groups that had fought at the urging of the Allies (mostly Great Britain) attended the Versailles conference in hopes of being given the freedom and independence that had been promised. The Arabs left very disappointed, finding themselves colonies of new leaders rather than being granted their own nations. For many, this arrangement was worse than rule by the Ottomans, who at least were Muslim.

The reasons for Great Britain reneging on promises made to the Arabs are complex, but may include the belief that Britain had a responsibility to assist the Jews to return to their homeland in order to accelerate the second coming of Christ. (This concept is proposed by Barbara Tuchman in her book *Bible and Sword.*) Therefore, the British foreign minister, Lord Balfour, issued a proclamation in the midst of World War I that guaranteed the right of the Jews to return to the Holy Land. This declaration, which is presented in Figure 46.5, was cited by the Jews following World War I as a mandate to enter the Holy Land and, later, to create the state of Israel.

Arabs have pointed to the perfidy of the British at the end of World War I and the subsequent support of the British and Americans for Israel as causes of the relatively poor state of Arabs in the world today. These are issues that are used in recruiting terrorists. They probably have some justification for their feelings, but, as Lewis Bernard has observed in his book *What Went Wrong?,* the Arabs must see beyond just these issues for the real cause of their troubles and consider their own lack of creativity as a potential cause. Bernard suggests that some other causes might be the Ottomans, who held the Arabs under their thumb for several hundred years, the Germans, who persecuted the Jews and created the desperate situation that followed World War II, and even the Arabs themselves, who continue in a largely tribal society and have, so far, been unable to reach a consensus on how to unite and become a single political entity. The Arabs have a difficult situation. They look to the glories of the past as their inspiration. However, that perspective may tend to limit their creativity, just as happened with the ancient Egyptians who were always trying to recapture the glory of the Old Kingdom. The Arab situation is further complicated because of their belief in the timelessness of Islam. This belief can be stifling to creativity unless they find a way to be

---

Balfour Declaration

November 2nd, 1917

Dear Lord Rothschild,

I have much pleasure in conveying to you, on behalf of His Majesty's Government, the following declaration of sympathy with Jewish Zionist aspirations which has been submitted to, and approved by, the Cabinet.

"His Majesty's Government view with favour the establishment in Palestine of a national home for the Jewish people, and will use their best endeavours to facilitate the achievement of this object, it being clearly understood that nothing shall be done which may prejudice the civil and religious rights of existing non-Jewish communities in Palestine, or the rights and political status enjoyed by Jews in any other country."

I should be grateful if you would bring this declaration to the knowledge of the Zionist Federation.

Yours sincerely,

Arthur James Balfour [Foreign Secretary]

Figure 46.5 ■ *The Balfour Declaration.*

creative within the rules and concepts of the past. However, just as Mozart was creative within rules, the Arabs can also, but no one has yet led the way in developing that combination that brings past and present together in a creative way.

For the German people, the conditions of the Treaty of Versailles were viewed as unfair and extremely harsh. Germans felt justified in the war because of the system of alliances that existed and, from the German point of view, Germany was merely fighting the enemies of their ally, Austria. Thus, Germans felt little regret for the war even after the war was over. Furthermore, the war was not fought on German soil, so the German people didn't feel the deprivations of war, except hunger caused by the blockades. Finally, Germans felt that Germany had not lost the war, but that it had ended in stalemate. After all, there had been no decisive final battle, no invasion of German territory, no surrender; only an agreement by all sides that the fighting should stop. For these reasons, the German people did not understand why Germany was being treated like a vanquished enemy. Thus, the terms of the Treaty of Versailles were both an embarrassment and caused great resentment among the German public. In effect, the treaty that ended World War I also laid the groundwork for World War II by burdening the German people with crushing debt and robbing Germany of its pride. Furthermore, the Treaty of Versailles continued European colonialism and caused increased resentment and mistrust of Europe in much of the rest of the world.

■ Creativity and the War

Since the days of Richelieu in the seventeenth century, France had used creative diplomacy to build its nation and control the growth of other nations. That tradition of diplomatic creative work was continued through the aftermath of Napoleon's reign, when Metternich of Austria and Talleyrand of France attempted to recreate the supposed stability of the old monarchies of Europe. Bismarck's highly creative diplomatic work united Germany and laid the foundation for Germany as a powerful state. However, just before World War I, the diplomats of Europe seemed to not understand the implications of their various diplomatic alliances. They worked hard at diplomatic thrust and counterthrust but without making any real contribution other than to erect a set of dependencies that, like dominoes, would all tumble if only one fell. We think that the diplomats stopped being creative and merely reacted to initiatives that were, themselves, merely reactions.

Germany's strategy for fighting the war was creative, but its ability to react to changing circumstances seemed somewhat limited. The lack of responsiveness may have been due to Germany's lack of resources compared with the combined power of France, Great Britain, Russia, Belgium, and their allies and not from Germany's lack of strategic creativity. We certainly see some creativity later in the war, when Germany supported the Russian Revolution in order to get the Russians out of the war.

Technological creativity was a factor throughout the war. The invention of the machine gun in the decades preceding the war had changed warfare, but the generals who led the war didn't realize its full implications. As a result, the war settled into trench warfare and millions of lives were lost due to the devastating effect of the machine gun against traditional tactics.

Some creativity was seen in the adaptation of airplanes to warfare, although the technology of flight did not develop fast enough to make the airplane an effective tool during the First World War. That is also true of the tank. It was a good idea, but its real value was in the future. The creativity of poisonous gas was shortsighted. Its use killed many of the enemy, but also killed many on the side of those who released the gas, both from poor handling of the gas and from the retaliations.

This use of poisonous gas brings up a key issue with technology. Creative development of new technologies can often be used for good or ill. Too often, those who employ technology for their own ends fail to look beyond the immediate results and consider the long-term effects. The control of technology needs to be just as creative as the invention of the technology itself. Sometimes the control is to limit the technology, but that does not seem to be very creative. Wouldn't it be better to find a way to use the technology for the benefits that it can provide and then limit its use for non-beneficial purposes? The task of doing that is much harder than merely restriction of its use, but in the long run, overall progress will likely be better if the effort to use the work properly is creatively made.

◼ Timeline—Important Dates

Date	Event
1882	*Triple Alliance created*
1907	*Triple Entente created*
1908	*Young Turks force change in the Ottoman Empire*
1914	*Assassination of the Grand Duke of Austria*
1914	*War declared between Austria and Serbia*
1914	*Russia declares war on Austria*
1914	*Germany declares war and invades Belgium*
1914	*France and England declare war*
1915	*Use of poison gas*
1917	*Balfour Declaration*
1917	*Russian Revolution*
1917	*United States enters the war*
1919	*Treaty of Versailles ends the war*

◼ Suggested Readings

Lawrence, T. E., *Seven Pillars of Wisdom,* Anchor Books, 1991.

Remarque, Erich Maria, *All Quiet on the Western Front,* Fawcett Crest, 1958.

Tuchman, Barbara, *Bible and Sword,* New York University Press, 1956.

Between the Wars
Good and Bad Creativity

> Nonviolence is the law of our species as violence is the law of the brute. The spirit lies dormant in the brute and he knew no law but that of physical might. The dignity of man requires obedience to a higher law—to the strength of the spirit.
>
> —*Gandhi*

Effects of World War I

Perhaps more than any war since the fourteenth century, World War I changed the nature of society. Ancient and medieval societies were characterized by a series of empires—Babylonian, Persian, Hellenistic, Roman, Byzantine, Carolingian, Umayyad, Abbasid, Mongolian, Chinese, Mughal, and others. These empires seemed to follow each other and their interactions determined the political course of history. After the Renaissance, two empires grew by assimilation and conquest—the Holy Roman Empire (which later became the Austro-Hungarian Empire) and the Ottoman Empire. Another route to empire-building was acquiring new territories that had not previously been claimed by Europeans. The Portuguese and Spanish were the first to assemble great overseas empires. They were soon followed by the Dutch, English, and French.

After World War I, two great empires, the Austro-Hungarian and the Ottoman, ceased to exist. The formation of the German Empire was aborted. The seeds of destruction for the French and British Empires were sown. Generally, then, the major effects of World War I were to destroy empires. Peoples in every part of the world sought self-determination, and this caused the empires to crumble.

One nation was an exception to the general pattern. That nation was Russia. The leaders of Russia, newly installed during World War I and filled with the zeal of communism, were anxious to spread their doctrine over the whole world. They proclaimed the first empire of ideology. Realistically, they were also anxious to control territories for the same reasons that other empires had been built—economic benefit and political power.

This chapter discusses these political changes that were wrought by the First World War and then also looks at the societal and cultural changes that occurred. In some cases the politics directly affected the changes in society and culture, but in other locales, especially where a country like the United States sought isolation, the societal and cultural changes seemed to be independent of politics.

Creativity was exhibited (or not) in several different ways during this time. Some political leaders were reactive rather than creative, and their nations suffered. Others were highly creative and their nations flourished. In our view from today's perspective, some of the most creative of leaders—Stalin and Hitler, for example—brutally ignored the rights of people under their control. Other leaders were at least as creative—like Gandhi—but they set new, higher standards of ethical behavior. We see, therefore, that creativity can be good or bad.

Creativity in the arts was affected by a culture in which many traditional values had eroded. Therefore, artists in all fields experimented with new forms. Some were readily accepted and pronounced good, but others were rejected as foolishly bad. We will look at both types.

■ Political Changes

Austro-Hungarian Empire

As a consequence of World War I, Austria and Hungary split apart and formed two separate nations. Nationalistic wars against the Austrian government brought about several new nations, such as Czechoslovakia, Yugoslavia, and Albania. Furthermore, several other countries, including Romania, Poland, Italy, and Greece, were enlarged at Austria's expense. As a partner with Germany on the "losing" side of the war, Austria could do little else but accept these impositions.

Some of the nations created from the Austro-Hungarian Empire were formed according to ethnic populations (such as Albania), but others seemed cobbled together without much thought. (Perhaps they were the work of compromise and committees.) Examples of the latter include Yugoslavia and Czechoslovakia. These latter nations

have not survived into the twenty-first century and, in the case of Yugoslavia, have been the site for continuing wars of self-determination based on ethnic separation.

Ottoman Empire

A similar dismantling of the Ottoman Empire was included in the Treaty of Versailles. Out of the old Ottoman Empire came the new countries of Armenia, Palestine, Transjordan, Mesopotamia, Syria, Iraq, Lebanon, and several countries in northern Africa. Furthermore, after World War I, Greece, assisted by Great Britain, invaded and took control of parts of Turkey (the new name of what was left of the Ottoman Empire).

Turkey itself had a successful democratic revolution against the sultan and the Greek invaders led by Mustafa Kemal (Ataturk) in 1923. Ataturk was declared the president of Turkey, and the capital was moved from Constantinople to Ankara. Constantinople was renamed Istanbul. The new government also announced several social reforms along the Western pattern, transforming Turkey from a religiously controlled state to a modern, secular state with constitutional protections of freedoms of speech, religion, and other human rights.

As was the case in Europe, many of the new countries in the Middle East seemed to be formed irrationally. Iraq, for example, was a collection of Shiite Arabs, Sunni Arabs, and Kurds who were thrown together without any consideration for their ethnicity or religious feelings. To add further to the difficulties in the Middle East, as we briefly discussed in the previous chapter, these new nations became **protectorates** of Britain and France, which effectively gave the European nations control over these new states.

Britain and France were reluctant to allow the Arabs to form a unified ethnic kingdom. The natural leader of the Arabs was Hussein, the Emir (ruler) of Mecca and a direct descendent of the **Prophet Mohammed.** He and his sons cooperated with the European powers during World War I in what the Arabs call the Great Arab Revolt against the Ottoman Turks. However, as we have already discussed, the British and French decided to create several states in the Middle East and to assume protective care over them. After a few years, Great Britain installed two of the sons of Hussein, Abdullah and Faisal, as kings in Transjordan and Iraq, respectively. Great Britain facilitated the conquering of most of the Arabian peninsula by the Saudi tribe, thus dividing the Arab strength, and also retained British control over the coastal area of the Levant known as Palestine. A series of uprisings in Iraq and Syria, as well as pressure for autonomy in Syria and Lebanon, eventually led to the creation of independent countries in all of these Middle East territories. Some of these countries experienced revolutions and installed republican governments or dictatorships. That was the situation at the beginning of World War II.

Russia and the Soviet Union

Vladimir Lenin led the Bolsheviks in Russia through a tempestuous establishment of the communist government. Soon after World War I, the Russian monarchists mounted three armies to attack the communists. Each of those armies was independently controlled and supported by other European nations that were frightened of the communists and otherwise anxious for the return of "normalcy" in Russia. But, the outgunned and outmanned communists had four great advantages that led them to victory. First, the opposing armies were not able to coordinate their activities, thus allowing the communists to deal with them quite independent of each other. Second, the communists were in control of the center of the country, and that included the large cities and, therefore, the population and manufacturing. Also, they could move their troops by train from one battlefront to another as the need arose. Third, they immediately began to make reforms like land and wealth redistribution, thus winning the hearts of the majority of the poor. Fourth, they were in control of the government, and that meant that, nominally, the apparatus of government and the army were loyal to them. The use of these advantages was highly effective, and the communists were able to declare the establishment of the Soviet Union in 1922 with four member republics—Russia, Ukraine, Bylorussia, and Trans-Caucasia.

The leader of the communists, Vladimir Lenin, died in 1924. After a period of some instability, **Josef Stalin** defeated Lenin's chosen successor, Leon Trotsky, in a takeover dispute. Stalin ruled the Soviet Union until his own death 30 years later. As ruler of the Soviet Union, Stalin expanded the communist model beyond the Marxist concept of an industrial system to include agriculture. This was done in spite of the reluctance of the peasants to give up direct control of the land they had been able to possess as part of the land reforms immediately following the communist takeover following World War I. However, Stalin's commitment to rural communism was complete, and he forced the people to comply with his wishes, killing millions of dissenters in the process.

Stalin's government was highly expansionist. The Soviet Union annexed several independent states that surrounded its original core states. The new states included several in Central Asia, several in the Caucasus, and several along the Baltic.

Stalin also actively sought to spread communist revolution around the world in hopes of speeding up the process of achieving a global socialist utopia. Stalin's attempt to do this ran in direct opposition to the ideas of Karl Marx, who taught that communist revolutions would occur naturally when a society has reached a certain point of industrial development. Stalin's aggressive brand of communism played a large part in starting the Cold War between the United States and Soviet Union that would dominate the latter half of the twentieth century.

Germany

The 1920s and 1930s were an extremely difficult period nearly everywhere in the world, but conditions in Germany during this time were among the very worst. The cost of fighting World War I, combined with the ruinous terms of the Treaty of Versailles, left the German economy in shambles and gave little hope of allowing it to recover. These economic problems led to a terrible depression in Germany in which inflation was so high that, literally, a wheelbarrow of money was needed to buy a loaf of bread.

Political instability only added to Germany's problems. At the end of World War I, German citizens elected a new government, known as the **Weimar Republic.** The Weimar Republic was weak, fractious, and poorly equipped to deal with the staggering problems that faced Germany.

Furthermore, Germany suffered from a negative collective psychology. No major battles of World War I were fought on German soil, and the German army had lost no major decisive battle at the end of the war that would guarantee that they were the losing side. Thus, the terms of the Treaty of Versailles, which treated Germany like the losers in the conflict, seemed unfair and vindictive to the majority of the German people. Therefore, to much of the German population, the Treaty of Versailles was not seen as a peace accord, but as punishment and penance owed to countries that had not beaten them on the field of battle, but simply outnumbered them in the diplomatic meetings held to end the war. These conditions led directly to the rise of Adolph Hitler and Nazism in Germany. Thus, the seeds of World War II were sown in the treaty that ended World War I.

Adolph Hitler was born in Branau-am-Inn, Linz, Austria, in 1889. As a young man, Hitler wished to be an artist, and he moved to Vienna with the intention of pursuing a career in painting. These plans were frustrated when young Hitler was not accepted into art school. Hitler's time in Vienna did have a major effect on his life, however, as he came under the influence of the population's general feeling of hatred toward the minorities living in Austria, who were blamed for weakening of the Austro-Hungarian Empire. Hitler embraced this hatred of minorities and allowed it to guide his opinions and actions for much of his life.

At the beginning of World War I, Hitler moved from Vienna to Munich, Germany. He fought in the German army and earned the Iron Cross for bravery. After the war, the horrible conditions in Germany caused Hitler to become involved in politics, where he quickly assumed control of the small Workers' Party. Hitler renamed his party the National Socialist German Workers' Party (which was abbreviated in German to the

acronym NAZI), and his hatred of minorities and communists quickly became a central part of his rhetoric and policy, as German minorities (particularly Jews and communists) became Hitler's scapegoats for Germany's problems.

Despite still being a tiny, radical political party on the fringe of German politics, the Nazis were gaining in membership and influence as Hitler outlined his plan to restore Germany to its economic and military greatness. Dissatisfied with the direction of the elected German government, Hitler and his supporters tried to overthrow the government in 1923. His party was still a small group and lacked support from the German army, however, so Hitler and the Nazis were defeated. As a result of this failed revolution, the Nazi party was outlawed and Hitler was tried for treason and thrown into prison. While in prison, Hitler wrote his autobiography, *Mein Kampf (My Struggle),* in which he outlined his political ideas and foreshadowed the drastic steps he would take during World War II. Hitler was released from prison after serving only 13 months of his sentence.

Upon his release from prison, Hitler found that conditions within Germany were worse than ever. Inflation was skyrocketing out of control due to Germany's paying of war reparations and the other onerous requirements of the Versailles Treaty. Therefore, despite its illegal status, Hitler began again the meetings of the Nazi party and began to gain members and influence throughout the 1920s. In 1928, Hitler was elected to the German Reichstag (parliament), along with 11 other Nazis. Their announced intent was to overthrow the Weimar Republic government and establish a government based on nationalism and suppression of disruptive forces (minorities).

The stock market crash of 1929 was especially devastating to the already weak German economy. Under these extreme conditions, the German chancellor, Heinrich Bruning, asked the German president, Paul von Hindenburg, to grant him (Bruning) emergency power to rule by decree until the economic crisis could be ended. Hindenburg agreed, and this opened the door for Hitler's eventual assumption of power. Bruning's policies failed to correct the economy, thus leading to further attacks from Hitler and the Nazis. Soon Bruning's government failed, and a new coalition was formed in which Hitler was appointed chancellor, even though the Nazis were still a minority party in the Reichstag.

Hitler's strategy to become chancellor was highly creative. He used propaganda against the current government to instill a sense of dissatisfaction in the public. The public did not yet accept Hitler, but they were ready for change. Then, in private negotiations, he threatened to stop all legislation by any means possible if he were not named chancellor, thus further crippling the new government. In the end, his use of propaganda and power combined to give him what he wanted.

As chancellor, Hitler immediately called for a new election in which he hoped that the Nazis might gain a majority of seats in the Reichstag. In the middle of the campaign, the Reichstag building was burned (probably secretly by the Nazis). As the current chancellor (at least until the election), Hitler asked President Hindenburg to grant him emergency powers, similar to those that had been given to Bruning, in order to deal with the emergency situation. The president felt compelled to oblige Hitler. Then, with the emergency powers in hand, Hitler manipulated the election to ensure his party's victory.

When the Nazis won 44 percent of the vote in the new election, Hitler took that as a mandate and formed a new government. He used his position as head of the government to outlaw the Communist Party and arrest their Reichstag deputies. Hitler then pushed through an act that granted him total control for four years. With this new power Hitler outlawed all other political parties and took control of the media. By 1936 Hitler and the Nazis were in complete control of Germany.

He wasted no time using his new powers to try and improve the situation in Germany and in unifying the German people behind his policies. Hitler promised business leaders that he would restore their depression-shattered profits by breaking Germany's labor movement (headed largely by Bolshevik communists). He instituted fascism, a system of government-sponsored monopolies that Hitler had seen implemented with great success in

Italy by its fascist dictator, **Benito Mussolini.** The fascist system, coupled with other policies of military expansion and rearmament, helped to restore the German economy and helped bring down unemployment, as German industry could afford to employ people once again.

Hitler also assured top military leaders that he would overturn the parts of the Treaty of Versailles that demilitarized parts of Germany. He then backed up those promises by pulling out of a disarmament conference of the League of Nations in 1933, building up the German army once again (which was also popular with the people, as it also reduced the severe unemployment), and placing German troops back in the demilitarized areas, including the Rhineland along the border with France. By doing this, Hitler ensured himself the support of the army.

Hitler established several new organizations that fell under the direct control of the Nazi party that he used to help maintain his control of the country. The largest of these groups was the Hitler Youth, a paramilitary group that taught the young men and women of Germany what their roles were to be in the **Third Reich,** or 1,000 years of German rule that Hitler believed the Earth was about to embark upon. The young men learned military skills so that they could defend the Fatherland, while young women learned homemaking and child-rearing skills so that they could rear the next generation of Germans. Of course, both boys and girls were also firmly indoctrinated in Nazi ideas and propaganda. The Hitler Youth was extremely popular, and nearly all young Germans joined willingly. However, membership was eventually made mandatory, and obedience to Hitler Youth leaders was required, even over obedience to the youths' parents.

Hitler formed his own elite military unit/bodyguard corps called the SS, whose job was to protect Hitler and ensure loyalty and obedience in both the military and the Nazi party. A similar group, the Gestapo, was established as a civilian secret police and was assigned to keep the general public in line.

Once Hitler had assured himself of control and established his own Nazi infrastructure, he began to persecute and suppress many of the minority groups within Germany. Hitler did this for two reasons. First, Hitler largely blamed these groups for the difficult times that Germany had experienced during the 1920s and 1930s, and felt they were not loyal to Germany or the Nazi party. Second, Hitler envisioned a Germany that was "pure." He believed that Germany was a land for Germans and even favored Germans who had an Aryan or Teutonic look (blonde hair and blue eyes). He believed that these people were the strong and true ancestors of the German race. Thus, German minorities, especially Jews, Gypsies, Jehovah's Witnesses, Slavs, communists, and homosexuals, were Nazi targets and eventually fell victim to the evils of the Holocaust.

After Hitler had a firm grip on Germany, he began to solidify Germany's position in Europe. Hitler quickly made an alliance with Mussolini in Italy. Then Hitler and Mussolini both openly supported the Spanish fascist Francisco Franco in his struggle to take control of Spain in the Spanish Civil War against the elected Republicans (communists). Hitler, however, envisioned more than just political alliances with like-minded European dictators. He foresaw a future where Europe was under German control. Hitler wanted a massive German empire with a greater-Germany that encompassed all German-speaking peoples at its heart.

It was Hitler's imperial desires that eventually caused problems with his European neighbors and sparked the beginning of World War II. In 1938 Hitler threatened Austria with invasion if Austria did not agree to become a part of the greater Germany. Believing that the threats of invasion were real, the Austrian Prime Minister capitulated and merged Austria with Germany. Austria was able to retain some local autonomy, but was controlled by Germany in all military, economic, and foreign affairs.

After his successful and easy annexation of Austria, Hitler demanded that the Sudetenland, the German-speaking portion of Czechoslovakia, be given to Germany as well. British Prime Minister Neville Chamberlain and French Premier Edouard Daladier went to Munich to meet with Hitler and discuss the matter. Hitler was able to convince Chamberlain and Daladier that he only wanted to unite all German people who had been arbitrarily separated from each other by various treaties of the past. He assured them that he had no other aggressive desires. Thus, the French and British appeased Hitler and allowed him to take the Sudetenland, declaring that with this agreement they had achieved "peace in our time." One year later, World War II had begun with Germany's invasion of Poland.

The events of Munich in 1938 deserve some discussion from the standpoint of creativity. Throughout the 1930s, Hitler had formulated a creative plan and then aggressively acted to implement it. He satisfied all of the requirements of creativity. Because of his positive actions, Germany prospered. In contrast, France and Great Britain were first passive and then merely reactive to Hitler's actions. They exhibited a lack of creativity and, as a result, their countries eventually suffered. The conclusion seems obvious: Creative work with strong implementation will lead to positive results (for the creative person) and noncreative and reactive actions will lead to grief.

We will, of course, discuss Germany further in the next chapter when World War II is analyzed. We note here, however, that Hitler's creativity was overcome only when equal (or greater) creativity was arrayed against him.

Ireland

The question of Irish independence had troubled England for centuries. In some views, Ireland was the first of the English colonies but had always remained apart. During the sixteenth and seventeenth centuries when England, Scotland, and Wales became Protestant, Ireland remained Catholic. In part because of this religious difference, but also because of many other cultural and economic differences, England continued to treat the Irish as second-class citizens. This led to a continual undercurrent of Irish discontent that only became worse with the occasional attempts by Irish-backed leaders to overthrow English domination and England's retaliations to suppress further Irish dissent.

The movement for Irish self-determination became very strong during the nineteenth century, especially during and after the great potato famine of the mid-nineteenth century when the Irish felt that the English government did not give sufficient help during this catastrophe. The prime minister during many of these years, Gladstone, was a supporter of limited Irish autonomy. He submitted to Parliament several bills to create an Irish state, but they were all defeated. Then, during World War I, when the British army was occupied in Europe, the Irish rebelled on Easter Day of 1916. The British were shocked at the apparent betrayal of loyalty and rushed to suppress the rebellion.

Although the British had reacted harshly and quickly to put down the Irish Easter Rebellion, the British did not enact any real, lasting punishment on Ireland. Ireland continued as a part of the United Kingdom with full representation in Parliament. Following World War I, Irish Republicans (those who wanted an independent Ireland) won a majority of the Irish seats in Parliament and decided to meet together in Dublin, rather than London. In 1919 they declared Ireland an independent nation. At first the English acted with alarm but eventually agreed to hold an election in Ireland on the issue of separation from the United Kingdom. Most of Ireland voted in favor of separation and independence, but the northern six counties, the mostly Protestant region of Ireland known as Ulster, voted to stay with England. Thus, in 1920 Ireland was declared to be independent (the Irish Free State) except for Ulster, which would remain part of the United Kingdom. According to the terms granted by England, both the Irish Free State and Ulster were to remain part of the British Commonwealth.

The northern counties accepted the British arrangement, but the southern counties rejected the act and continued to fight for both total independence (out of the Commonwealth) and Irish unity. In 1922, the southern counties made a treaty with Great Britain in which The Irish Free State was granted the status of a dominion, like Canada. However, many people in the Irish Free State continued to work for complete independence and

they formed a political party opposed to those who supported the treaty. In 1932, those who wanted more independence gained control of the government. This new government severed most of the ties with Great Britain, and support was officially given to guerilla efforts to unite northern and southern Ireland.

In 1948, Ireland declared itself to be the Republic of Ireland and became totally independent of Great Britain. Continued political fighting (under the guise of religious conflict) continued between the Irish Republican Army (IRA) and the Ulster Provisional Militia (Provos) throughout the remainder of the twentieth century. The IRA supports union of the north and south under the control of the Republic of Ireland, while the Provos want continued association of the north with Great Britain. The conflict has taken on a religious dimension because most people in favor of total Irish union are Catholic, while those who want Ulster to remain British are generally Protestant. However, some reasonable solution might be yet reached, as both sides have begun meaningful talks and a certain additional independence has been granted to the parliament of Northern Ireland.

India

Besides conflict with Ireland, Great Britain also spent much of the period between the two World Wars dealing with a growing independence movement in India. India had supported its British overlords during World War I in the hope that the British would grant Indians more control over their own affairs. In 1916, the Hindus and Muslims, longtime rivals within India, formed an alliance in an effort to make the British hear the voice of a united Indian people. It was at this time that **Mohandas (Mahatma) Gandhi** assumed leadership of the nationalist groups. Following World War I, British rule in India was inconsistent, with the British both granting additional freedoms and committing horrible atrocities.

Mohandas Gandhi was an Indian citizen born into British-controlled, colonial India. Taking advantage of Great Britain's colonial policies of relative freedom of movement within the British

Empire, Gandhi went to London to receive a higher education and then moved to South Africa (another British colony), where he became a practicing lawyer. While living in South Africa, Gandhi encountered great racial discrimination. This discrimination led him to an unsuccessful attempt to change the "colored laws" of South Africa. He based his actions on the concept of nonviolent resistance that he called *Satyagraha,* which loosely translates as "soul force." The basis of Gandhi's vision of nonviolence is given in the quotation at the beginning of this chapter.

Gandhi was familiar with the writings of the American transcendentalist philosophers Ralph Waldo Emerson and Henry David Thoreau, and his idea of *Satyagraha* was adapted from their ideas on civil disobedience. He stated the following about civil disobedience:

> *Civil disobedience is the inherent right of a citizen. He dare not give it up without ceasing to be a man. Civil disobedience is never followed by anarchy. Criminal disobedience [, however,] can lead to it. Every state puts down criminal disobedience by force. It perishes, if it does not. But to put down civil disobedience is to attempt to imprison conscience. . . . Disobedience to be civil must be sincere, respectful, restrained, never defiant, must be based upon some well-understood principle, must not be capricious and, above all, must have no ill will or hatred behind it.*

In 1915, he returned to his homeland of India and began a national campaign of nonviolent resistance to injustices in British rule with a long-term objective of Indian independence. Obviously, Gandhi's encouragement of civil disobedience made him an unpopular figure with the British, and when some Indians resisted with violence (against Gandhi's rules), Gandhi was put into jail.

Upon being released from prison, Gandhi put a special emphasis on resisting the British salt law (which he saw as especially onerous). This law stated that all salt sold in India had to be imported from Great Britain. This guaranteed a tremendous market for British salt manufacturers. For Gandhi,

this law was ridiculous. India could make its own salt just as easily as could the British. Gandhi organized a massive, peaceful demonstration against the law. This demonstration was a march to the sea, where the participants dipped a cup into the ocean so that the water would evaporate and leave the salt. This simple act was prohibited by the salt law. Following Gandhi, 50,000 peaceful resistors marched to the sea and there many were beaten senseless by Indian units of the British army. This violence coalesced public opinion around the world in Gandhi's favor and led to the British granting India a new constitution in 1935 that allowed India much more autonomy, but not full independence. A United Press news service report of the event said the following:

> *Suddenly at a word of command, scores of native policemen rushed upon the advancing marchers and rained blows on their heads with their steel-shod latha. Not one of the marchers even raised an arm to fend off the blows. They went down like ten pins. From where I stood I heard the sickening whack of the clubs on unprotected skulls. The waiting crowd of marchers groaned and sucked in their breath in sympathetic pain at every blow. . . . They marched steadily, with heads up, without the encouragement of music or cheering or any possibility that they might escape serious injury or death. The police rushed out and methodically and mechanically beat down the second column. There was no fight, no struggle; the marchers simply walked forward till struck down. The police commenced to savagely kick the seated men in the abdomen and testicles and then dragged them by their arms and feet and threw them into the ditches. . . . Hour after hour stretcher-bearers carried back a stream of inert bleeding bodies. . . . By 11 A.M. the heat had reached 116 degrees and the assault subsided.*

A short time later World War II broke out. Gandhi encouraged Indians to support Great Britain in the war and to not disturb the peace while the war was going. This proved to be a sound policy, as shortly after the close of World War II, in 1947, India was granted its independence by Great Britain, although the nation was split into two countries: India, which is predominately Hindu, and Pakistan, which is mostly Muslim. Gandhi was assassinated a year later, in 1948.

Gandhi's creativity was as powerful as Hitler's. Both took strong initiatives against a passive and reactive foe. Both men were successful. However, whereas Hitler's creativity was oriented toward goals of power and dominance, Gandhi's goals were freedom and justice. Their personal lives reflected their different goals. Hitler was a megalomaniac and Gandhi was a meek and gentle person who believed that personal integrity was paramount in his life. Gandhi once said, "A man cannot do right in one department of life whilst he is occupied in doing wrong in any other department. Life is one indivisible whole." Later, when asked what his message would be for the world, he replied, "My life is my message."

China

India's Asian neighbor, China, also underwent a series of changes during and following World War I that would cause both economic and military tension in the region that would spill over to the conflicts of World War II. In 1894, a war broke out between Japan and China that demonstrated the ineffectiveness of the Manchu Dynasty, China's ruling family. This led to a gradual weakening of Manchu power, until the dynasty was finally overthrown in 1912 by a military dictator named Yüan Shi-kai. However, upon the death of Yüan Shi-kai in 1916, all central authority vanished in China and control of the country fell into the hands of various local warlords.

In 1923, the country was reunited under **Sun Yat-sen** and his Nationalist (Kuomintang) Party, which was also supported (temporarily) by the Chinese Communist Party. Following the death of Sun Yat-sen, the Nationalist (Kuomintang) Party continued to rule China under Sun's successor, **Chiang Kai-shek.** However, under Chiang Kai-shek the Nationalist Party lost the support of the Communists and the two factions went to war.

Things went poorly for the Communists and they were on the verge of being completely destroyed by the Nationalists when the Communists suddenly broke off the battle and marched 6,000 miles to a place of refuge. (This event is called "the long march.") The Nationalists were prevented from pursuing the Communists and completing their destruction because of a new flare-up in the hostilities between China and Japan.

After World War II, the Nationalists and Communists renewed their war and, this time, the Communists were successful. The Nationalists fled from the mainland to the nearby island, Taiwan, where they are governed separately under the name of the Republic of China.

Japan

Unlike China, which continued to try and keep Western influences out of its culture and country, Japan embraced Westernization and made every attempt to modernize quickly. Japan copied Western governments, particularly Germany, and worked hard to industrialize and acquire colonies. The acquisition of a colonial empire was especially vital to Japan's efforts to industrialize, because Japan lacked natural resources.

The imitation of Western culture and industry also brought imitation of Western thought. Japan soon felt that it had a special position as the leader of Asia and therefore had a right to colonies (much like the Europeans felt that their culture was superior to the culture of their colonies). Japan then launched a series of imperial wars in efforts to gain more territory and the prestige and resources that came with them. Japan fought and won wars against China, to gain Korea, and Russia, to gain Port Arthur and other Russian territories in Asia. Japan also seized the German holdings within China during World War I and then moved aggressively into Manchuria. Japan was then able to install a member of the old Manchu family to serve as a puppet emperor in Manchuria and continued its attacks against China in order to gain more territory.

This warlike situation was occurring as part of the background of World War II, which we will shortly discuss.

■ Roaring Twenties and the Great Depression

In Versailles at the end of World War I, President Woodrow Wilson was the architect and strongest supporter of the creation of the League of Nations as a means of dealing with international problems. President Wilson was successful in convincing the nations of Europe to form a League of Nations, only to then have the American congress refuse to allow the United States to join because of public reluctance to become too involved in international affairs and a fear of giving up any American sovereignty to an international body. Thus, despite the efforts of President Wilson, the United States never joined the League of Nations. This inability to get Wilson's own country into the organization robbed the League of Nations of any legitimacy or credibility from the start.

Despite Wilson's belief that the surest way to avoid future conflict was by becoming more involved in world affairs, the predominant mood in the United States was to return to the longstanding American tradition of isolationism. In fact, following World War I the United States became more isolated than it had been before the war. America wanted to avoid war, and so it intentionally disarmed to a minimum level. Many Americans felt that the European nations would be more cautious if the United States was not prepared to come to their aid.

The United States also enacted a new set of protective tariffs. The new tariffs, the strongest ever, were designed to aid American business and reduce trade between the United States and Europe. However, the protective tariffs ended up hindering Europe's recovery after the war because of the difficulty and expense of trading with the United States. (These same tariffs also eventually made it difficult for the United States to pull itself out of the Great Depression.)

The American public was elated at the successful conclusion of World War I. This feeling contributed to an overall euphoria about the basic strength of the United States and its position in the world. Americans became a consumer society and

were anxious to acquire the luxuries of the upper middle class.

With this spending, the entire U.S. economy prospered. Companies had record profits and people's salaries rose sharply. Millions invested in the stock market in what seemed to be a perpetual bull market.

The United States also underwent a period of moral revival during this time that was spurred by the desire to uphold the values recognized as being American. This strong sense of morality led to a desire to solve America's social problems. Social problems such as poor job safety and working conditions were addressed in legislation. Labor unions were legitimized and strengthened. The socialist and communist movements gained popularity in the United States as a means of helping out their fellow man. The abuses of some companies were curtailed by creating anti-monopoly legislation. Women were given the vote.

In this period of increased moral fervor, Prohibition (the outlawing of alcohol) was enacted and initially supported on a large scale. However, by the late 1920s much of this renewed morality had fallen by the wayside and the United States had embraced the loose morality and disregard for law (particularly Prohibition) that marked the **Jazz Age.** It seems as though prosperity brought a decrease in spirituality.

The Jazz Age was characterized by consumerism and frivolity. In a rush to live the lifestyle of the rich, people bought up the new inventions created by the Industrial Revolution. If they could not afford the inventions, they bought them on credit, for the first time paying for purchases on the installment plan. Because of this, many people had a lot of debt and little or no savings. If this bothered them, they did not show it outwardly. Men and women gathered at speakeasies (clubs that sold illegal alcohol). Often, these clubs entertained patrons with jazz music, good food, and dance floors. The decade became known as the **Roaring Twenties** for its booming economy and party atmosphere.

The carefree spirit of the Jazz Age was to be short-lived, however, as the severe economic depression that had gripped much of the world since shortly after World War I finally struck the United

States in 1929. Many of the European nations, particularly Germany, were slow in rebuilding their infrastructure and economies after World War I, thus depressing the world economy. Nearly every nation faced difficulty because of America's isolationism and high tariffs, and many faced difficulty because of severe political instability at home as well. The Treaty of Versailles itself made life extremely difficult, for Germany in particular, as they were forced to pay England and France war reparations, but had no means to do so because of political turmoil and a severely weakened economy due to the loss of their colonies and ruined infrastructure. Germany's economic woes slowly spread across much of Europe (and indeed, the world, due to the continuation of European colonialism).

America, due to its extreme economic isolation and abundance of natural resources, was able to largely avoid the effects of this worldwide depression for nearly a decade. However, large amounts of speculation in the stock market, combined with the continually worsening conditions around the world, finally caused the stock market to crash on Friday, October 28, 1929. This day became known as **Black Friday** and marked the beginning of nearly ten years of extreme economic depression in the United States. The collapse of the American stock market caused the collapse of European stock markets and this, in turn, caused the American stock market to fall even more, creating a vicious, downward spiral.

The stock market collapse was the initial trigger of the depression in the United States, but the Depression continued because companies didn't have the money to expand and improve because the Federal Reserve kept interest rates high to help foreign sales. It was also difficult for companies to increase revenue because of the high protective tariffs, which limited foreign trade, and because the government tried to increase its own revenue by raising taxes. People did not have money to spend, so companies had to lay people off, which meant fewer people had money to spend, which led to more layoffs. Mass unemployment swept across the country, and the soup line was a common sight.

Furthermore, a severe drought struck the Midwest and South causing widespread crop failure and forcing many to sell their farms to large corporations that could employ fewer people because they could afford mechanized farm tools. Thus, the Depression spread from industry to agriculture. The loss of family farms forced many to migrate to other parts of the country to look for the work. American author John Steinbeck illustrated the hopelessness of the Great Depression and the difficulties faced by one of these migrating families in his novel *The Grapes of Wrath*. The downward cycle of the economy continued when widespread rumors about the instability of the banks caused a run on the banks, thus resulting in the failure of many banks.

The president of the United States, Herbert Hoover, could not gain the confidence of the people and his own political ideology of *laissez faire* kept him from taking more drastic actions to improve the situation. He did not believe that the government should take an active role in the lives of people, particularly in regards to the economy. This idea made him popular and electable during the Roaring Twenties when the economy was strong and people wanted to be left alone to live out the excesses of the Jazz Age. However, these same tendencies and beliefs left President Hoover completely unable to deal with the problems caused by the Great Depression.

Hoover finally attempted a modest response with a *trickle-down* approach. This means that the government gives assistance to the companies in the form of lower taxes and other incentives and the companies, in turn, pass that extra money down via higher wages or by creating new jobs. The companies, struggling to survive themselves, could not and/or would not allow this extra money to trickle down, and Hoover's efforts failed completely. Thus, the shantytowns that popped up everywhere to house the unemployed and homeless became known as "Hoovervilles," a poignant reminder of failure for this quiet man who was elected during the good times of the Jazz Age.

Hoover's inability to solve the problems of the Great Depression led to the election of **Franklin Delano Roosevelt** to the presidency in

1932. Roosevelt wasted no time in attacking the problems of the Great Depression and his plan, called the **New Deal,** took drastic steps to find a way to end the Depression. The New Deal created many government-funded public works projects that would employ people and created the idea that the government would take care of them.

This was a drastic shift in the tone and nature of U.S. government. Some people felt that some of Roosevelt's ideas were unconstitutional and/or illegal. The Supreme Court agreed with some of the arguments and its action led Roosevelt to attempt to add several New Deal-friendly judges to the Supreme Court. The scheme, which was called *packing the court* was not allowed.

Roosevelt's New Deal was only partially successful in alleviating the conditions of the Great Depression. Some of the problems were reduced but recovery was a slow, painful process that took most of the decade and was not finalized until World War II returned American industry to full capacity. However, what Roosevelt did accomplish was return a sense of hope and confidence to the American people. Under Roosevelt the American people believed that things would eventually be better and that something was being done—things that the American populace could never claim when Hoover was in office.

The contrast between Roosevelt and Hoover again illustrates the differences between creativity and reactivity. Roosevelt developed a creative plan and then strongly implemented it. As a result, the people prospered. This was good creativity. Hoover, although highly intelligent, either had no creativity or had bad creativity. He largely reacted to events and did not attempt to control events. As a result, the people suffered.

■ Modern Art

Artists that gained fame and notoriety during the era between the two world wars were Marcel Duchamp, Piet Mondrian, and Salvador Dali. Duchamp and Mondrian worked in abstract visual art, but in very different ways. Dali was the leader of the Surrealist movement.

Marcel Duchamp became known as the "bad boy" of art in that he aimed to aggravate people. Some of his early art, like *Nude Descending A Staircase* (Figure 47.1) seemed to be an extension (possibly a lampoon) of Cubism. The work gives the impression of a woman walking down stairs, but some critics felt it was totally absurd. One called it "an explosion in a shingle factory."

Duchamp gained great notoriety as the leader of **Dadaism**—a movement in abstract art that was meant to show the meaninglessness and randomness of art. The point of Dada can be seen in how the movement got its name. The word *dada* (French for "hobbyhorse") was the first word the originators of the movement arbitrarily selected from a French dictionary. The art of Duchamp and Dadaists was meant to be (or at least appear) meaningless and random, so that all meaning or conclusions had to come completely from the viewer without any guidance from the artist. This is the ultimate extension of the Impressionistic idea of viewer involvement with the work.

One example of Duchamp's Dada work is *Fountain* (shown in Figure 47.2). This work, which

Figure 47.1 ■ Nude Descending a Staircase *by Marcel Duchamp. The Philadelphia Museum of Art/ Art Resource, NY. © 2010 Artists Rights Society (ARS). New York ADAGP, Paris/Succession Marcel Duchamp.*

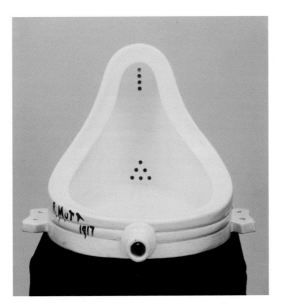

Figure 47.2 ■ Fountain *by Marcel Duchamp.* CNAC/MNAM/Dist. *Réunion des Musées Nationaux/Art Resource, NY. © 2010 Artists Rights Society (ARS), New York, ADAGP, Paris/Succession Marcel Duchamp.*

Figure 47.3 ■ "Relativity" by M.C. Escher

M.C. Escher's "Relativity" © 2010 The M.C. Escher Company-Holland. All rights reserved. www.mcescher.com

is merely a signed urinal, tries to be provocative and, generally, succeeds. Most people hate it. For Duchamp, that is exactly the reaction desired. He wants to engage the mind of the viewer and, thereby, make a statement about the uselessness of art in solving the problems of the world.

M.C. Escher also wanted to explore the mind of the viewer through his art. He focused on optical illusions and merging patterns as ways to engage and delight the viewing mind. See Figure 47.3 as an example.

The development of psychology helped to spawn a new movement in art called **Surrealism.** Surrealist paintings were meant to represent the world of the subconscious and the world of dreams. Several accomplished and successful artists such as Paul Klee and Jean Arp pioneered the movement. However, it was a latecomer to Surrealism, the Spanish painter **Salvador Dali,** who has become synonymous with the movement. Dali's paintings such as *The Persistence of Memory* (Figure 47.4) and *Inventions of the Monsters* both overtly deal with the Freudian unconscious and have references to repressed terror, violence, apathy, and sexuality.

Figure 47.4 ■ Persistence of Memory *by Salvador Dali.* Digital Image © *The Museum of Modern Art/Licensed by SCALA/Art Resource, NY. © 2010 by Salvador Dali. Fundacio Gala-Salvador Dali/Artists Rights Society (ARS) New York.*

■ Architecture

Architecture also underwent vast changes during the early twentieth century. Advances in architectural technology allowed for many of these changes. **Louis Sullivan** and the Chicago school used frame-steel construction to push the height of buildings further and further upward, thus giving birth to the towering modern-day skyscraper and reshaping the skylines of most of the world's great cities. Other architects then began to experiment with the skyscraper even more. For example, Ludwig Mies Van Der Rohe designed the first box skyscraper. Their work eventually resulted in a style of skyscraper that was a steel and glass box. These structures became known as the International Style.

American architect **Frank Lloyd Wright** began the architectural concept of "organic design" where the structure is designed both on the inside and out to match the occupants of the building and the geographic location where it was built. Although Frank Lloyd Wright designed a wide variety of unique and interesting buildings including New York City's Guggenheim Museum (where the inside eliminates nearly all corners and harsh angles, thus guiding patrons along their journey and prompting Wright to say "democracy needs something better than a box"), he is most famous for the houses he designed. Among these unique and "or-

ganic" homes is Wright's most famous work, the "Falling Water" house in Bear Run, Pennsylvania, that incorporates the surrounding woods and waterfall into the design of the home (Figure 47.5). However, some engineering problems with the house, point out the architect's responsibility to incorporate good engineering with good design.

However, not all of the great twentieth-century architects followed the lead of Frank Lloyd Wright. The talented French architect Le Corbusier disagreed with Wright's concept of blending architecture and the environment. Le Corbusier felt that architecture should highlight human achievement over nature. Over the span of his career, Le Corbusier oversaw the design and building of individual buildings, but also of entire apartment complexes and whole cities. A notable example of the work of Le Corbusier is *L'Unité d'Habitation*. These are large apartment complexes in Marseilles and Nantes, France, which attempted to make large housing units very livable by including recreation, shopping, and walking areas and highlight his style by purposefully eschewing soft lines and any concession to a natu-

Figure 47.5 ■ Falling Water House *by Frank Lloyd Wright. Art Resources, NY. © 2010 Frank Lloyd Wright Foundation, Scottsdale, AZ/Artists Rights Society (ARS), NY.*

ral feel. While *L'Unité d'Habitation* has a certain style, history has been less kind to Le Corbusier as his works served as the basis for lesser architects to design much of the public housing used in low income inner cities throughout the world.

■ Literary Modernism

The dramatic changes of the early twentieth century led to new directions being explored in literature. Similar to what was occurring in the art world, many of the traditional boundaries and rules of literature were being experimented with or abandoned altogether. Among these literary pioneers were authors such as **James Joyce, Franz Kafka, Aldous Huxley,** and **George Orwell.**

Born and raised in Ireland, but living in Paris for most of his adult life, James Joyce was among the first to experiment with new techniques that abandoned the traditional narrative style of a novel. Joyce invented the **stream-of-consciousness** technique instead of the narrative style that had heretofore been used. His new technique attempts to trace the restlessly shifting consciousness of the literary character and thus tells the story from the rapidly changing point of view of the character's internal thoughts and motivations. Because of this, the narrative is disconnected and lacks the order and linear story of the traditional novel.

Joyce also invented the concept of an epiphany in a novel in which the protagonist gains a sudden insight of meaning into the turbulence of life. Often, these sudden mental insights serve as the climax and purpose of the novel. Both *Ulysses* and *Finnegan's Wake,* James Joyce's two most heralded novels, use these new techniques.

Another important author of the period was Franz Kafka. Possibly more than any other author, Kafka was able to capture the upheaval, paranoia, and hopelessness of the era. Franz Kafka was born in Prague (in the modern Czech Republic) and earned his Ph.D. from the University of Prague. Kafka worked in the accident claims department of a large insurance company, but his true love was writing.

In Kafka's novels the typical protagonist undergoes disorienting life changes. These changes and problems are often perpetuated by persons who claim to represent a faceless bureaucracy that holds sovereign sway over the life of the protagonist. The protagonist then becomes absorbed in efforts to contact and reason with the bureaucracy. These general ideas can be seen in Kafka's two most acclaimed novels, *The Trial* and *The Metamorphosis.*

Interpretation of Kafka's meaning and themes is open because Kafka gave few insights into his own thoughts, but the faceless bureaucracies that inhabited his writings eerily foreshadow the bureaucracy-laden political ideologies of totalitarianism and communism that would come to dominate much of Europe shortly after his death.

Englishman George Orwell more directly attacked the philosophies of big government, totalitarianism, and communism in his novels *Animal Farm* and *1984.* In *Animal Farm* Orwell uses barnyard characters to illustrate the weaknesses and corruption that he believed were inherent in a communist society. The novel is a scathing attack on the loss of individual freedoms and choice and the easy abuse of power in such a system of government.

In *1984* Orwell invented the concept of "Big Brother"—an invasive, dictatorial government that was always watching and controlled the lives of its citizens. Orwell was personally concerned about the future of humanity and feared the growing power of communism and totalitarianism. In one famous quote Orwell said: "If you want a picture of the future, imagine a boot stamping on a human face—forever." Orwell hoped his novels would help to dissuade people from giving up too much freedom to their governments in return for security.

Another English author, Aldous Huxley, also feared that humans might give up too much freedom and individualism to their government. Huxley, however, feared that the loss of freedom would not be for security, as Orwell said, but for ease. In Huxley's classic novel, *Brave New World,* he parodied the future by showing how the world might be if scientists took over and their only goal was efficiency. In this society people are genetically bred into different classes and have exchanged art, culture, and religion in return for a life of ease and pleasure.

◼ Modern Music

Music between the World Wars was the era of jazz and of big band/swing music. Jazz evolved from the traditional music of American blacks and their improvised, loose style of playing instruments (often done out of necessity because black musicians had no formal music training and sometimes could not read music). Jazz was among the first avenues granted to black Americans that allowed them to gain recognition in white America and the world.

Although jazz was initially a genre for American blacks, white artists soon joined them. Artists like Billie Holliday, Ella Fitzgerald, Benny Goodman, Dave Brubeck, and Louis Armstrong successfully brought jazz to a national and international audience. **Louis Armstrong,** in particular, became an ambassador of jazz, taking it to many countries (occasionally officially sponsored by the U.S. government). Armstrong was a master of the Dixieland style and developed scat singing, an important component of jazz music. Furthermore, he became well known for appearing in many movies.

Another jazz music pioneer and ambassador was **Duke Ellington.** Ellington gained attention by being a regular player at the Cotton Club in Harlem. The Cotton Club was a nightclub owned by blacks, where blacks entertained but the clientele was mostly white. Ellington turned harmony upside-down in his *Mood Indigo,* where he had the trombones play high and the clarinets play low, with trumpets in the middle. Ellington composed more than 2,000 works. His signature song, *Take the "A" Train,* became a classic hit that helped to move jazz further toward the American mainstream.

Jazz gained critical approval and a more lofty status as "serious music" thanks to the efforts of American composer **George Gershwin,** who wrote jazz in classical form or, alternately, wrote in the classical form but included jazz themes, rhythms, and other characteristics. Gershwin wrote many jazz-influenced classical pieces that were critical and popular successes worldwide. Among Gerswin's compositions were *Rhapsody In Blue, American in Paris, Concerto in F,* and his jazz opera *Porgy and Bess.* Jazz gained a strong cultural acceptance from these works. Gershwin also wrote many Broadway shows and was as equally successful in the world of popular music as he was within the classical audience.

An outgrowth of jazz was the **Big Band era.** Bandleaders like Benny Goodman (who combined jazz and popular music into a sound he called "swing," Glenn Miller, Tommy Dorsey, and Artie Shaw, became stars, as did singers such as Frank Sinatra, Tex Beneke, and Helen O'Connell.

New inventions like radio took the big band sound across the country. The jukebox allowed music to be available on demand. (An amazing statistic highlights the popularity of this big band music. It is estimated that over one-third of all money spent in jukeboxes during this era played a Glenn Miller song). Everyone loved to dance, and the bands went on concert tours across the country to play live for their fans. During the period between the two World Wars, both jazz and big band were successful worldwide, and while jazz has retained a measure of popularity, the heyday of big band was short lived, as the popularity of the music largely died out after World War II.

◼ Disillusionment and Values

The nineteenth and early part of the twentieth centuries were times of great disillusionment, unrest, and questioning. In both the sciences and the arts there was a movement away from traditional structures and ideas and a questioning of purpose, meaning, and direction. Many began to feel that science and art (and, as an extension, life) had no meaning and that there were no rules or truths except those that each individual ascribes to. People began to wonder if everything was subjective, if there really were any objective ideals or truths. These worries can be seen in the science and art of the time.

These feelings and ideas only seemed to be reinforced by the carnality and brutality of World War I. A brief time of hope and positivism occurred immediately following World War I (at least in America) and may help to account for the international appeal of jazz and big band, both of which were American styles of music that were generally upbeat and fun. (America was the one Western nation not seriously afflicted by the pessimism and disillusionment of post-World War I). However, this brief window of happiness was to quickly vanish with the rise of fascist regimes across Europe, the onset of the Great Depression, and the start of World War II.

Some people fought hard for the retention of values or the creation of higher values. One example of this effort is Gandhi. He creatively made a plan, backed by a strong ethical standard, and then set about to implement the plan. Others, sensing the strength of his personality and the righteousness of his methods, joined him. Eventually, the British government could not resist his persuasive campaign. His ultimate success gives us hope that good creativity can ultimately triumph over apathy (reactivity) and bad creativity.

▪ Timeline—Important Dates

Date	Event
1872–1944	*Piet Mondrian*
1882–1941	*James Joyce*
1883–1924	*Franz Kafka*
1887–1968	*Marcel Duchamp*
1894–1963	*Aldous Huxley*
1898–1937	*George Gershwin*
1899–1974	*Duke Ellington*
1901–1971	*Louis Armstrong*
1903–1950	*George Orwell*
1904–1989	*Salvador Dali*
1916	*Indian independence movement under Gandhi*
1919	*End of World War I*
1920	*Irish Free State declared*
1921	*Formation of Iraq and Transjordan*
1922	*Soviet Union formed*
1923	*Sun Yat-sen unites the new China*
1923	*Ataturk creates modern Turkey*
1929	*Stock market crash*
1933	*Hitler becomes chancellor of Germany*
1948	*Republic of Ireland declared*
1948	*India given freedom; Gandhi assassinated*

▪ Suggested Readings

Gardner, Howard, *Creating Minds,* Basic Books, 1993.

Huxley, Aldous, *Brave New World,* MCA Publishing, 1978.

Orwell, George, *Animal Farm,* Signet Classic, 1946.

Orwell, George, *1984,* Signet Classic, 1949.

Rand, Ayn, *The Fountainhead,* Signet Books, 1952.

Steinbeck, John, *The Grapes of Wrath,* Garden City Publishers, 1940.

Aldous Huxley: Brave New World

Aldous Huxley (1894–1963) was born in England to a family that included many distinguished intellectuals. Huxley probably felt the weight of expectation from such a heritage and dreamed from an early age of future personal scientific achievement, but an eye illness when he was sixteen left him nearly blind for the remainder of his life and squelched his ability to excel in the scientific community. He devoted much attention in his later literary works to visual images showing his appreciation for vision. His skill at imagery led to an even later career as a screenwriter.

Huxley wrote *Brave New World* in four months in 1931. This was a time when totalitarian powers were growing across Europe. *Brave New World* pioneered the blending of science and fiction to show how dark the world might be under a totalitarian society with the only goal of efficiency. *Brave New World* discusses a future world where all sperm and ova are removed from the body and selectively matched to create people with specific traits. This results in a separation of classes. The most healthy and intelligent were called Alphas and Betas. Gammas and Deltas had to suffer from oxygen depletion during development, causing intentional brain defects, and Epsilons were stunted enough to not have mental capacity. This was done to maintain the peace in society, so that some would be great leaders and some would not mind employment in menial jobs.

Totalitarianism is undermined by art because it poses new ways of thinking to the reader, viewer, or listener. Huxley certainly struck a blow against totalitarianism with this artistic literary work. Chapters 16 and 17 of *Brave New World* are presented here for their treatment of this conflict. The value of art for the soul is argued against the value of societal stability. The references to Shakespeare show Huxley's deep love for the classics and their value to civilization.

16

The room into which the three were ushered was the Controller's study.

"His fordship will be down in a moment." The Gamma butler left them to themselves.

Helmholtz laughed aloud.

"It's more like a caffeine-solution party than a trial," he said, and let himself fall into the most luxurious of the pneumatic arm-chairs. "Cheer up, Bernard," he added, catching sight of his friend's green unhappy face. But Bernard would not be cheered; without answering, without even looking at Helmholtz, he went and sat down on the most uncomfortable chair in the room, carefully chosen in the obscure hope of somehow deprecating the wrath of the higher powers.

The Savage meanwhile wandered restlessly round the room, peering with a vague superficial inquisitiveness at the books in the shelves, at the sound-track rolls and reading machine bobbins in their numbered pigeon-holes. On the table under the window lay a massive volume bound in limp black leather-surrogate, and stamped with large golden T's. He picked it up and opened it. MY LIFE AND WORK, BY OUR FORD. The book had been published at Detroit by the Society for the Propagation of Fordian Knowledge. Idly he turned the pages, read a sentence here, a paragraph there, and had just come to the conclusion that the book didn't interest him, when the door opened, and the Resident World Controller for Western Europe walked briskly into the room.

Mustapha Mond shook hands with all three of them; but it was to the Savage that he addressed himself. "So you don't much like civilization, Mr. Savage," he said.

The Savage looked at him. He had been prepared to lie, to bluster, to remain sullenly unresponsive; but, reassured by the good-humoured intelligence of the Controller's face, he decided to tell the truth, straightforwardly. "No." He shook his head.

Bernard started and looked horrified. What would the Controller think? To be labelled as the friend of a man who said that he didn't like civilization—said it openly and, of all people, to the Controller—it was terrible. "But, John," he began. A look from Mustapha Mond reduced him to an abject silence.

"Of course," the Savage went on to admit, "there are some very nice things. All that music in the air, for instance . . ."

"Sometimes a thousand twangling instruments will hum about my ears and sometimes voices."

The Savage's face lit up with a sudden pleasure. "Have you read it too?" he asked. "I thought nobody knew about that book here, in England."

"Almost nobody. I'm one of the very few. It's prohibited, you see. but as I make the laws here, I can also break them. With impunity, Mr. Marx,"

Source: Pages 217–240 from *Brave New World* by Adlous Huxley. Copyright © 1932, 1960 by Adlous Huxley. Reprinted by permission of HarperCollins Publishers, Inc.

he added, turning to Bernard. "Which I'm afraid you *can't* do."

Bernard sank into a yet more hopeless misery.

"But why is it prohibited?" asked the Savage. In the excitement of meeting a man who had read Shakespeare he had momentarily forgotten everything else.

The Controller shrugged his shoulders. "Because it's old; that's the chief reason. We haven't any use for old things here."

"Even when they're beautiful?"

"Particularly when they're beautiful. Beauty's attractive, and we don't want people to be attracted by old things. We want them to like the new ones."

"But the new ones are so stupid and horrible. Those plays, where there's nothing but helicopters flying about and you *feel* the people kissing." He made a grimace. "Goats and monkeys!" Only in Othello's words could he find an adequate vehicle for his contempt and hatred.

"Nice tame animals, anyhow," the Controller murmured parenthetically.

"Why don't you let them see *Othello* instead?"

"I've told you; it's old. Besides, they couldn't understand it."

Yes, that was true. He remembered how Helmholtz had laughed at *Romeo and Juliet*. "Well then," he said, after a pause, "something new that's like *Othello*, and that they could understand."

"That's what we've all been wanting to write," said Helmholtz, breaking a long silence.

"And it's what you never will write," said the Controller. "Because, if it were really like *Othello* nobody could understand it, however new it might be. And if it were new, it couldn't possibly be like *Othello*."

"Why not?"

"Yes, why not?" Helmholtz repeated. He too was forgetting the unpleasant realities of the situation. Green with anxiety and apprehension, only Bernard remembered them; the others ignored him. "Why not?"

"Because our world is not the same as Othello's world. You can't make flivvers without steel—and you can't make tragedies without social instability. The world's stable now. People are happy; they get what they want, and they never want what they can't get. They're well off; they're safe; they're never ill; they're not afraid of death; they're blissfully ignorant of passion and old age; they're plagued with no mothers or fathers; they've got no wives, or children, or lovers to feel strongly about; they're so conditioned that they practically can't help behaving as they ought to behave. And if anything should go wrong, there's *soma*. Which you go and chuck out of the window in the name of liberty, Mr. Savage. *Liberty!*" He laughed. "Expecting Deltas to know what liberty is! And now expecting them to understand *Othello!* My good boy!"

The Savage was silent for a little. "All the same," he insisted obstinately, "*Othello's* good, *Othello's* better than those feelies."

"Of course it is," the Controller agreed. "But that's the price we have to pay for stability. You've got to choose between happiness and what people used to call high art. We've sacrificed the high art. We have the feelies and the scent organ instead."

"But they don't mean anything."

"They mean themselves; they mean a lot of agreeable sensations to the audience."

"But they're . . . they're told by an idiot."

The Controller laughed. "You're not being very polite to your friend, Mr. Watson. One of our most distinguished Emotional Engineers . . ."

"But he's right," said Helmholtz gloomily. "Because it *is* idiotic. Writing when there's nothing to say . . ."

"Precisely. But that requires the most enormous ingenuity. You're making flivvers out of the absolute minimum of steel—works of art out of practically nothing but pure sensation."

The Savage shook his head. "It all seems to me quite horrible."

"Of course it does. Actual happiness always looks pretty squalid in comparison with the overcompensations for misery. And, or course, stability isn't nearly so spectacular as instability. And being contended has none of the glamour of a good fight against misfortune, none of the picturesqueness of a struggle with temptation, or a fatal overthrow by passion or doubt. Happiness is never grand."

"I suppose not," said the Savage after a silence. "But need it be quite so bad as those twins?"

He passed his hand over his eyes as though he were trying to wipe away the remembered image of those long rows of identical midgets at the assembling tables, those queued-up twin-herds at the entrance to the Brentford monorail station, those human maggots swarming round Linda's bed of death, the endlessly repeated face of his assailants. He looked at his bandaged left hand and shuddered. "Horrible!"

"But how useful! I see you don't like our Bokanovsky Groups; but, I assure you, they're the foundation on which everything else is built. They're the gyroscope that stabilizes the rocket plane of state on its unswerving course." The deep voice thrillingly vibrated; the gesticulating hand implied all space and the onrush of the irresistible machine. Mustapha Mond's oratory was almost up to synthetic standards.

"I was wondering," said the Savage, "why you had them at all—seeing that you can get whatever you want out of those bottles. Why don't you make everybody an Alpha Double Plus while you're about it?"

Mustapha Mond laughed. "Because we have no wish to have our throats cut," he answered. "We believe in happiness and stability. A society of Alphas couldn't fail to be unstable and miserable. Imagine a factory staffed by Alphas—that is to say by separate and unrelated individuals of good heredity and conditioned so as to be capable (within limits) of making a free choice and assuming responsibilities. Imagine it!" he repeated.

The Savage tried to imagine it, not very successfully.

"It's an absurdity. An Alpha-decanted, Alpha-conditioned man would go mad if he had to do Epsilon Semi-Moron work—go mad, or start smashing things up. Alphas can be completely socialized—but only on condition that you make them do Alpha work. Only an Epsilon can be expected to make Epsilon sacrifices, for the good reason that for him they aren't sacrifices; they're the line of least resistance. His conditioning has laid down rails along which he's got to run. He can't help himself; he's foredoomed. Even after decanting, he's still inside a bottle—an invisible bottle of infantile and embryonic fixations. Each

one of us, of course," the Controller meditatively continued, "goes through life inside a bottle. But if we happen to be Alphas, our bottles are, relatively speaking, enormous. We should suffer acutely if we were confined in a narrower space. You cannot pour upper-caste champagne-surrogate into lower-caste bottles. It's obvious theoretically. But it has also been proved in actual practice. The result of the Cyprus experiment was convincing."

"What was that?" asked the Savage.

Mustapha Mond smiled. "Well, you can call it an experiment in rebottling if you like. It began in A.F. 473. The Controllers had the island of Cyprus cleared of all its existing inhabitants and re-colonized with a specially prepared batch of twenty-two thousand Alphas. All agricultural and industrial equipment was handed over to them and they were left to manage their own affairs. The result exactly fulfilled all the theoretical predictions. The land wasn't properly worked; there were strikes in all the factories; the laws were set at naught, orders disobeyed; all the people detailed for a spell of low-grade work were perpetually intriguing for high-grade jobs, and all the people with high-grade jobs were counter-intriguing at all costs to stay where they were. Within six years they were having a first-class civil war. When nineteen out of the twenty-two thousand had been killed, the survivors unanimously petitioned the World Controllers to resume the government of the island. Which they did. And that was the end of the only society of Alphas that the world has ever seen."

The Savage sighed, profoundly.

"The optimum population," said Mustapha Mond, "is modelled on the iceberg—eight-ninths below the water line, one-ninth above."

"And they're happy below the water line?"

"Happier than above it. Happier than your friend here, for example." He pointed.

"In spite of that awful work?"

"Awful? *They* don't find it so. On the contrary, they like it. It's light, it's childishly simple. No strain on the mind or the muscles. Seven and a half hours of mild, unexhausting labour, and then the *soma* ration and games and unrestricted copulation and the feelies. What more can they ask for? True," he added, "they might ask for shorter hours. And of course we could give them shorter hours. Technically, it would be perfectly simple to reduce all lower-caste working hours to three or four a day. But would they be any the happier for that? No, they wouldn't. The experiment was tried, more than a century and a half ago. The whole of Ireland was put on to the four-hour day. What was the result? Unrest and a large increase in the consumption of *soma;* that was all. Those three and a half hours of extra leisure were so far from being a source of happiness, that people felt constrained to take a holiday from them. The Inventions Office is stuffed with plans for labour-saving processes. Thousands of them." Mustapha Mond made a lavish gesture. "And why don't we put them into execution? For the sake of the labourers; it would be sheer cruelty to afflict them with excessive leisure. It's the same with agriculture. We could synthesize every morsel of food, if we wanted to. But we don't. We prefer to keep a third of the population on the land. For their own sakes—because it takes *longer* to get food out of the land than out of a factory. Besides, we have our stability to think of. We don't want to change. Every change is a menace to stability. That's another reason why we're so chary of applying new inventions. Every discovery in pure science is potentially subversive; even science must sometimes be treated as a possible enemy. Yes, even science."

Science? The Savage frowned. He knew the word. But what it exactly signified he could not say. Shakespeare and the old men of the pueblo had never mentioned science, and from Linda he had only gathered the vaguest hints: science was something you made helicopters with, something that caused you to laugh at the Corn Dances, something that prevented you from being wrinkled and losing your teeth. He made a desperate effort to take the Controller's meaning.

"Yes," Mustapha Mond was saying, "that's another item in the cost of stability. It isn't only art that's incompatible with happiness; it's also science. Science is dangerous; we have to keep it most carefully chained and muzzled."

"What?" said Helmholtz, in astonishment. "But we're always saying that science is everything. It's a hypnopædic platitude."

"Three times a week between thirteen and seventeen," put in Bernard.

"And all the science propaganda we do at the College . . ."

"Yes; but what sort of science?" asked Mustapha Mond sarcastically. "You've had no scientific training, so you can't judge. I was a pretty good physicist in my time. Too good—good enough to realize that all our science is just a cookery book, with an orthodox theory of cooking that nobody's allowed to question, and a list of recipes that mustn't be added to except by special permission from the head cook. I'm the head cook now, but I was an inquisitive young scullion once. I started doing a bit of cooking on my own. Unorthodox cooking, illicit cooking. A bit of real science, in fact." He was silent.

"What happened?" asked Helmholtz Watson.

The Controller Sighed. "Very nearly what's going to happen to you young men. I was on the point of being sent to an island."

The words galvanized Bernard into violent and unseemly activity. "Send *me* to an island?" He jumped up, ran across the room, and stood gesticulating in front of the Controller. "You can't send *me*. I haven't done anything. It was the others. I swear it was the others." He pointed accusingly to Helmholtz and the Savage. "Oh, please don't send me to Iceland. I promise I'll do what I ought to do. Give me another chance. Please give me another chance." The tears began to flow. "I tell you, it's their fault," he sobbed. "And not to Iceland. Oh please, your fordship, please . . ." And in a paroxysm of abjection he threw himself on his knees before the Controller. Mustapha Mond tried to make him get up; but Bernard persisted in his grovelling; the stream of words poured out inexhaustibly. In the end the Controller had to ring for his fourth secretary.

"Bring three men," he ordered, "and take Mr. Marx into a bedroom. Give him a good *soma* vaporization and then put him to bed and leave him."

The fourth secretary went out and returned with three green-uniformed twin footmen. Still shouting and sobbing, Bernard was carried out.

"One would think he was going to have his throat cut," said the Controller, as the door closed.

"Whereas, if he had the smallest sense, he'd understand that his punishment is really a reward. He's being sent to an island. That's to say, he's being sent to a place where he'll meet the most interesting set of men and women to be found anywhere in the world. All the people who, for one reason or another, have got too self-consciously individual to fit into community-life. All the people who aren't satisfied with orthodoxy, who've got independent ideas of their own. Every one, in a word, who's any one. I almost envy you, Mr. Watson."

Helmholtz laughed. "Then why aren't you on an island yourself?"

"Because, finally, I preferred this," the Controller answered. "I was given the choice; to be sent to an island, where I could have got on with my pure science, or to be taken on to the Controllers' Council with the prospect of succeeding in due course to an actual Controllership. I chose this and let the science go." After a little silence, "Sometimes," he added, "I rather regret the science. Happiness is a hard master—particularly other people's happiness. A much harder master, if one isn't conditioned to accept it unquestioningly, than truth." He sighed, fell silent again, then continued in a brisker tone, "Well, duty's duty. One can't consult one's own preference. I'm interested in truth, I like science. But truth's a menace, science is a public danger. As dangerous as it's been beneficent. It has given us the stablest equilibrium in history. China's was hopelessly insecure by comparison; even the primitive matriarchies weren't steadier than we are. Thanks, I repeat, to science. But we can't allow science to undo its own good work. That's why we so carefully limit the scope of its researches—that's why I almost got sent to an island. We don't allow it to deal with any but the most immediate problems of the moment. All other enquiries are most sedulously discouraged. It's curious," he went on after a little pause, "to read what people in the time of Our Ford used to write about scientific progress. They seemed to have imagined that it could be allowed to go on indefinitely, regardless of everything else. Knowledge was the highest good, truth the supreme value; and the rest was secondary and subordinate. True, ideas were beginning to change even then. Our Ford himself did a great deal to shift the emphasis from truth and beauty to comfort and happiness. Mass production demanded the shift. Universal happiness keeps the wheels steadily turning; truth and beauty can't. And, of course, whenever the masses seized political power, then it was happiness rather than truth and beauty that mattered. Still, in spite of everything, unrestricted scientific research was still permitted. People still went on talking about truth and beauty as though they were the sovereign goods. Right up to the time of the Nine Years' War. *That* made them change their tune all right. What's the point of truth or beauty or knowledge when the anthrax bombs are popping all around you? That was when science first began to be controlled—after the Nine Years' War. People were ready to have even their appetites controlled then. Anything for a quiet life. We've gone on controlling ever since. It hasn't been very good for truth, of course. But it's been very good for happiness. One can't have something for nothing. Happiness has got to be paid for. You're paying for it, Mr. Watson—paying because you happen to be too much interested in beauty. I was too much interested in truth; I paid too."

"But *you* didn't go to an island," said the Savage, breaking a long silence.

The Controller smiled. "That's how I paid. By choosing to serve happiness. Other people's—not mine. It's lucky," he added, after a pause, "that there are such a lot of islands in the world. I don't know what we should do without them. Put you all in the lethal chamber, I suppose. By the way, Mr. Watson, would you like a tropical climate? The Marquesas, for example; or Samoa? Or something rather more bracing?"

Helmholtz rose from his pneumatic chair. "I should like a thoroughly bad climate," he answered. "I believe one would write better if the climate were bad. If there were a lot of wind and storms, for example . . ."

The Controller nodded his approbation. "I like your spirit, Mr. Watson. I like it very much indeed. As much as I officially disapprove of it." He smiled. "What about the Falkland Islands?"

"Yes, I think that will do," Helmholtz answered. "And now, if you don't mind, I'll go and see how poor Bernard's getting on."

■ 17

"Art, science—you seem to have paid a fairly high price for your happiness," said the Savage, when they were alone. "Anything else?"

"Well, religion, of course," replied the Controller. "There used to be something called God—before the Nine Years' War. But I was forgetting; you know all about God, I suppose."

"Well . . ." The Savage hesitated. He would have liked to say something about solitude, about night, about the mesa lying pale under the moon, about the precipice, the plunge into shadowy darkness, about death. He would have liked to speak; but there were not words. Not even in Shakespeare.

The Controller, meanwhile, had crossed to the other side of the room and was unlocking a large safe set into the wall between the bookshelves. The heavy door swung open. Rummaging in the darkness within, "It's a subject," he said, "that has always had a great interest for me." He pulled out a thick black volume. "You've never read this, for example."

The Savage took it. *"The Holy Bible, containing the Old and New Testaments,"* he read aloud from the title-page.

"Nor this." It was a small book and had lost its cover.

"The Imitation of Christ."

"Nor this." He handed out another volume.

"The Varieties of Religious Experience. By William James."

"And I've got plenty more," Mustapha Mond continued, resuming his seat. "A whole collection of pornographic old books. God in the safe and Ford on the shelves." He pointed with a laugh to his avowed library—to the shelves of books, the rack full of reading-machine bobbins and sound-track rolls.

"But if you know about God, why don't you tell them?" asked the Savage indignantly. "Why don't you give them these books about God?"

"For the same reason as we don't give them *Othello:* they're old; they're about God hundreds of years ago. Not about God now."

"But God doesn't change."

"Men do, though."

"What difference does that make?"

"All the difference in the world," said Mustapha Mond. He got up again and walked to the safe. "There was a man called Cardinal Newman," he said. "A cardinal," he exclaimed parenthetically, "was a king of Arch-Community-Songster."

"'I Pandulph, of fair Milan, cardinal.' I've read about them in Shakespeare."

"Of course you have. Well, as I was saying, there was a man called Cardinal Newman. Ah, here's the book." He pulled it out. "And while I'm about it I'll take this one too. It's by a man called Maine de Biran. He was a philosopher, if you know what that was."

"A man who dreams of fewer things than there are in heaven and earth," said the Savage promptly.

"Quite so. I'll read you one of the things he *did* dream of in a moment. Meanwhile, listen to what this old Arch-Community-Songster said." He opened the book at the place marked by a slip of paper and began to read. "'We are not our own any more than what we possess is our own. We did not make ourselves, we cannot be supreme over ourselves. We are not our own masters. We are God's property. Is it not our happiness thus to view the matter? Is it any happiness or any comfort, to consider that we *are* our own? It may be thought so by the young and prosperous. These may think it a great thing to have everything, as they suppose, their own way—to depend on no one—to have to think of nothing out of sight, to be without the irksomeness of continual acknowledgment, continual prayer, continual reference of what they do to the will of another. But as time goes on, they, as all men, will find that independence was not made for man—that it is an unnatural state—will do for a while, but will not carry us on safely to the end . . ." Mustapha Mond paused, put down the first book and, picking up the other, turned over the pages. "Take this, for example," he said, and in his deep voice once more began to read: "'A man grows old; he feels in himself that radical sense of weakness, of listlessness, of discomfort, which accompanies the advance of age; and, feeling thus, imagines himself merely sick, lulling his fears with the notion that this distressing condition is due to some particular cause, from which, as from an illness, he hopes to recover. Vain imaginings! That sickness is old age; and a horrible disease it is. They say that it is the fear of death and of what comes after death that makes men turn to religion as they advance in years. But my own experience has given me the conviction that, quite apart from any such terrors or imaginings, the religious sentiment tends to develop as we grow older; to develop because, as the passions grew calm, as the fancy and sensibilities are less excited and less excitable, our reason becomes less troubled in its working, less obscured by the images, desires and distractions, in which it used to be absorbed; whereupon God emerges as from behind a cloud; our soul feels, sees, turns towards the source of all light; turns naturally and inevitably; for now that all that gave to the world of sensations its life and charms has begun to leak away from us, now that phenomenal existence is no more bolstered up by impressions from within or from without, we feel the need to lean on something that abides, something that will never play us false—a reality, an absolute and everlasting truth. Yes, we inevitably turn to God; for this religious sentiment is of its nature so pure, so delightful to the soul that experiences it, that it makes up to us for all our other losses.'" Mustapha Mond shut the book and leaned back in his chair. "One of the numerous things in heaven and earth that these philosophers didn't dream about was this" (he waved his hand), "us, the modern world. 'You can only be independent of God while you've got youth and prosperity; independence won't take you safely to the end.' Well, we've now got youth and prosperity right up to the end. What follows? Evidently, that we can be independent of God. 'The religious sentiment will compensate us for all our losses.' But there aren't any losses for us to compensate; religious sentiment is superfluous. And why should we go hunting for a substitute for youthful desires, when youthful desires never fail?

A substitute for distractions, when we go on enjoying all the old fooleries to the very last? What need have we of repose when our minds and bodies continue to delight in activity? of consolation, when we have *soma?* of something immovable, when there is the social order?"

"Then you think there is no God?"

"No, I think there quite probably is one."

"Then why? . . ."

Mustapha Mond checked him. "But he manifests himself in different ways to different men. In premodern times he manifested himself as the being that's described in these books. Now . . ."

"How does he manifest himself now?" asked the Savage.

"Well, he manifests himself as an absence; as though he weren't there at all."

"That's your fault."

"Call it the fault of civilization. God isn't compatible with machinery and scientific medicine and universal happiness. You must make your choice. Our civilization has chosen machinery and medicine and happiness. That's why I have to keep these books locked up in the safe. They're smut. People would be shocked if . . ."

The Savage interrupted him. "But isn't it *natural* to feel there's a God?"

"You might as well ask if it's natural to do up one's trousers with zippers," said the Controller sarcastically. "You remind me of another of those old fellows called Bradley. He defined philosophy as the finding of bad reason for what one believes by instinct. As if one believed anything by instinct! One believes things because one has been conditioned to believe them. Finding bad reasons for what one believes for other bad reasons—that's philosophy. People believe in God because they've been conditioned to believe in God."

"But all the same," insisted the Savage, "it is natural to believe in God when you're alone—quite alone, in the night, thinking about death . . ."

"But people never are alone now," said Mustapha Mond. "We make them hate solitude; and we arrange their lives so that it's almost impossible for them ever to have it."

The Savage nodded gloomily. At Malpais he had suffered because they had shut him out from the communal activities of the pueblo, in civilized London he was suffering because he could never escape from those communal activities, never be quietly alone.

"Do you remember that bit in *King Lear?*" said the Savage at last. "'The gods are just and of our pleasant vices make instruments to plague us; the dark and vicious place where thee he got cost him his eyes,' and Edmund answers—you remember, he's wounded, he's dying—'Thou hast spoken right; 'tis true. The wheel has come full circle; I am here.' What about that now? Doesn't there seem to be a God managing things, punishing, rewarding?"

"Well, does there?" questioned the Controller in his turn. "You can indulge in any number of pleasant vices with a freemartin and run no risks of having your eyes put out by your son's mistress. 'The wheel has come full circle; I am here.' But where would Edmund be nowadays? Sitting in a pneumatic chair, with his arm round a girl's waist, sucking away at his sex-hormone chewing-gum and looking at the feelies. The gods are just. No doubt. But their code of law is dictated, in the last resort, by the people who organize society; Providence takes its cue from men."

"Are you sure?" asked the Savage. "Are you quite sure that the Edmund in that pneumatic chair hasn't been just as heavily punished as the Edmund who's wounded and bleeding to death? The gods are just. Haven't they used his pleasant vices as an instrument to degrade him?"

"Degrade him from what position? As a happy, hard-working, goods-consuming citizen he's perfect. Of course, if you choose some other standard than ours, then perhaps you might say he was degraded. But you've got to stick to one set of postulates. You can't play Electro-magnetic Golf according to the rules of Centrifugal Bumble-puppy."

"But value dwells not in particular will," said the Savage. "It holds his estimate and dignity as well wherein 'tis precious of itself as in the prizer.'"

"Come, come," protested Mustapha Mond, "that's going rather far, isn't it?"

"If you allowed yourselves to think of God, you wouldn't allow yourselves to be degraded by pleasant vices. You'd have a reason for bearing

things patiently, for doing things with courage. I've seen it with the Indians."

"I'm sure you have," said Mustapha Mond. "But then we aren't Indians. There isn't any need for a civilized man to bear anything that's seriously unpleasant. And as for doing things—Ford forbid that he should get the idea into his head. It would upset the whole social order if men started doing things on their own."

"What about self-denial, then?" If you had a God, you'd have a reason for self-denial."

"But industrial civilization is only possible when there's no self-denial. Self-indulgence up to the very limits imposed by hygiene and economics. Otherwise the wheels stop turning."

"You'd have a reason for chastity!" said the Savage, blushing a little as he spoke the words.

"But chastity means passion, chastity means neurasthenia. And passion and neurasthenia mean instability. And instability means the end of civilization. You can't have a lasting civilization without plenty of pleasant vices."

"But God's the reason for everything noble and fine and heroic. If you had a God . . ."

"My dear young friend," said Mustapha Mond, "civilization has absolutely no need of nobility or heroism. These things are symptoms of political inefficiency. In a properly organized society like ours, nobody has any opportunities for being noble or heroic. Conditions have got to be thoroughly unstable before the occasion can arise. Where there are wars, where there are divided allegiances, where there are temptations to be resisted, objects of love to be fought for or defended—there, obviously, nobility and heroism have some sense. But there aren't any wars nowadays. The greatest care is taken to prevent you from loving any one too much. There's no such thing as a divided allegiance; you're so conditioned that you can't help doing what you ought to do. And what you ought to do is on the whole so pleasant, so many of the natural impulses are allowed free play, that there really aren't any temptations to resist. And if ever, by some unlucky chance, anything unpleasant should somehow happen, why, there's always *soma* to give you a holiday from the facts. And there's always *soma* to calm your anger, to reconcile you to your enemies, to make you patient and long-suffering. In the past you could only accomplish these things by making a great effort and after years of hard moral training. Now, you swallow two or three half-gramme tablets, and there you are. Anybody can be virtuous now. You can carry at least half your morality about in a bottle. Christianity without tears—that's what *soma* is."

"But the tears are necessary. Don't you remember what Othello said? 'If after every tempest came such calms, may the winds blow till they have wakened death.' There's a story one of the old Indians used to tell us, about the Girl of Mátaski. The young men who wanted to marry her had to do a morning's hoeing in her garden. It seemed easy; but there were flies and mosquitoes, magic ones. Most of the young men simply couldn't stand the biting and stinging. But the one that could—he got the girl."

"Charming! But in civilized countries," said the Controller, "you can have girls without hoeing for them; and there aren't any flies or mosquitoes to sting you. We got rid of them all centuries ago."

The Savage nodded, frowning. "You got rid of them. Yes, that's just like you. Getting rid of everything unpleasant instead of learning to put up with it. Whether 'tis better in the mind to suffer the slings and arrows of outrageous fortune, or to take arms against a sea of troubles and by opposing them . . . But you don't do either. Neither suffer nor oppose. You just abolish the slings and arrows. It's too easy."

He was suddenly silent, thinking of his mother. In her room on the thirty-seventh floor, Linda had floated in a sea of singing lights and perfumed caresses—floated away, out of space, out of time, out of the prison of her memories, her habits, her aged and bloated body. And Tomakin, ex-Director of Hatcheries and Conditioning, Tomakin was still on holiday—on holiday from humiliation and pain, in a world where he could not hear those words, that derisive laughter, could not see that hideous face, feel those moist and flabby arms round his neck, in a beautiful world . . .

"What you need," the Savage went on, "is something *with* tears for a change. Nothing costs enough here."

("Twelve and a half million dollars," Henry Foster had protested when the Savage told him that. "Twelve and a half million—that's what the new Conditioning Centre cost. Not a cent less.")

"Exposing what is mortal and unsure to all that fortune, death and danger dare, even for an eggshell. Isn't there something in that?" he asked, looking up at Mustapha Mond. "Quite apart from God—though of course God would be a reason for it. Isn't there something in living dangerously?"

"There's a great deal in it," the Controller replied. "Men and women must have their adrenals stimulated from time to time."

"What?" questioned the Savage, uncomprehending.

"It's one of the conditions of perfect health. That's why we've made the V.P.S. treatments compulsory."

"V.P.S.?"

"Violent Passion Surrogate. Regularly once a month. We flood the whole system with adrenin. It's the complete physiological equivalent of fear and rage. All the tonic effects of murdering Desdemona and being murdered by Othello, without any of the inconveniences."

"But I like the inconveniences."

"We don't," said the Controller. "We prefer to do things comfortably."

"But I don't want comfort. I want God, I want poetry, I want real danger, I want freedom, I want goodness. I want sin."

"In fact," said Mustapha Mond, "you're claiming the right to be unhappy."

"All right then," said the Savage defiantly, "I'm claiming the right to be unhappy."

"Not to mention the right to grow old and ugly and impotent; the right to have syphilis and cancer; the right to have too little to eat; the right to be lousy; the right to live in constant apprehension of what may happen tomorrow; the right to catch typhoid; the right to be tortured by unspeakable pains of every king." There was a long silence.

"I claim them all," said the Savage at last.

Mustapha Mond shrugged his shoulders. "You're welcome," he said.

World War II
Linear and Lateral Creativity

> We shall not flag or fail. We shall go on to the end. . . . We shall fight in the seas and oceans. . . . We shall fight on the beaches, we shall fight on the landing-grounds, we shall fight in the fields and in the streets, we shall fight in the hills; we shall never surrender.
>
> —*Winston Churchill*

■ Right-Brain and Left-Brain Thinking about War

There are many ways to think about war. Alexander the Great saw it as a pathway to immortal glory. Some, like Julius Caesar, used it as a political tool. Still others, like William the Conqueror, corrected perceived wrongs using war. For Genghis Khan, war was a way of life. General William Tecumseh Sherman, whose devastating march through Georgia in the American Civil War brought the South to its knees, said, "I am tired and sick of war. Its glory is all moonshine. . . . War is hell."

In the Second World War, we would see an equivalent array of thinking on the subject of war. However, because it is so close to us in time and communications were so prevalent, a somewhat different view was also seen. For example, General George S. Patton, a tank division commander

for the American army said, "If a man does his best, what else is there?" This is a decidedly personal view of war. Also personal was the comment of General **Douglas MacArthur,** when he was forced to abandon much of his army to almost certain death in the Philippines. He said, "I shall return." In a similar vein, Winston Churchill, the prime minister of Britain during World War II, said, "Let us therefore brace ourselves to our duties, and so bear ourselves that, if the British Empire and its Commonwealth last for a thousand years, men will say, 'This was their finest hour'."

The many ways of thinking about war reflect some right-brain thinking and some left-brain thinking. In general, however, war is a left-brain activity. Armies and navies try to consider every contingency in their battle plans and then logically try to meet all the challenges so that, in the actual battle, they would have already thought about and prepared for what might happen. General Dwight

Eisenhower, overall commander of Allied troops in Europe, was a fanatic for planning. He insisted on months of planning before every major battle. He forced the soldiers to train by repeating their battle tactics over and over again. He knew that uncertainty always exists, but he would have agreed with Louis Pasteur: "Chance favors the prepared mind."

Undoubtedly, therefore, success in war depends on logical, linear, left-brain thinking and planning. However, we believe that World War II was won because of lateral thinking. Not that the winners neglected or diminished right-brain thinking, but they added to it left-brain, lateral, intuitive thinking. It was this added component that, at certain moments in the war, gave the Allies an advantage. The combination of right- and left-brain thinking is, of course, the essence of creativity. That was a winning factor.

The Axis powers, especially Germany and Japan, had the greatest military machines in the world. Surely these machines would be invincible. However, at some very critical moments in the war, the Allies did the unexpected. They surprised the enemy and, therefore, took away the advantage of the machine. We will attempt to point out those creative moments in our discussion and show why they were so critical to success.

▪ German Supremacy

Despite Hitler's 1938 assurances to Britain and France that German expansion was over, on September 1, 1939, Germany invaded Poland. Poland fell to the Nazis in four weeks.

Several factors led to the quick domination of Poland. First, Poland's allies, Britain and France, were not ready for war and had trusted Hitler's promises of peace. Thus, Poland would receive no help from its allies. Second, Germany struck using a new technique called *blitzkrieg* (lightning war) where fast-moving and well-armored tanks swept in quickly and overwhelmed enemy positions and then followed up rapidly with motor-mounted infantry to secure the areas taken. Third, Poland itself was militarily weak and had fallen behind the times. Germany invaded using the most advanced military technology of the time, while the Poles

fought back as they had a hundred years earlier— horseback cavalry and foot soldiers trying to advance on muddy roads. Finally, potential invaders of Poland had long worried about angering Russia if they were to invade Poland, as Russia felt Poland fell under its sphere of influence. Germany, however, did not have that worry because Hitler had already struck a secret deal with Stalin where the two countries agreed to not interfere with one another concerning Poland (and to give Russia part of Poland for this consideration).

The German occupation of Poland was especially brutal. The city of Warsaw was surrounded and bombed repeatedly, until only a minor fraction of the population survived. The devastation was particularly bad in the Jewish ghetto. Other cities in Poland were also destroyed. The large Jewish population was systematically violated— first with forced labor and then with concentration camps and holocaust. However, even in the midst of this evil, some creativity was seen. Scott Thorpe tells the story of Polish Jews' creative resistance in his book *How to Think Like Einstein:*

> *The Nazi occupation of Poland was horrific. Twenty percent of the Polish people died in forced labor, of hunger, or from fighting. Resistance was impossible. Even the feeblest opposition brought devastating, over-whelming reprisals. Drs. Lazowski and Matulewicz decided to resist anyway, and their solution was brilliant. They knew that the Germans were terrified of a typhus outbreak. So they injected dead typhus bacteria into various patients, then sent blood samples to the German authorities. The blood tested positive for typhus. The Germans conducted more tests, and most were also positive. The occupation authorities quarantined the area. The people were not deported for slave labor and German troops stayed away. Drs. Lazowski and Matulewiczs spared their neighbors the worst of World War II, because even impossible problems have solutions.*

Immediately after the Polish invasion, Hitler contacted the British government in an attempt to

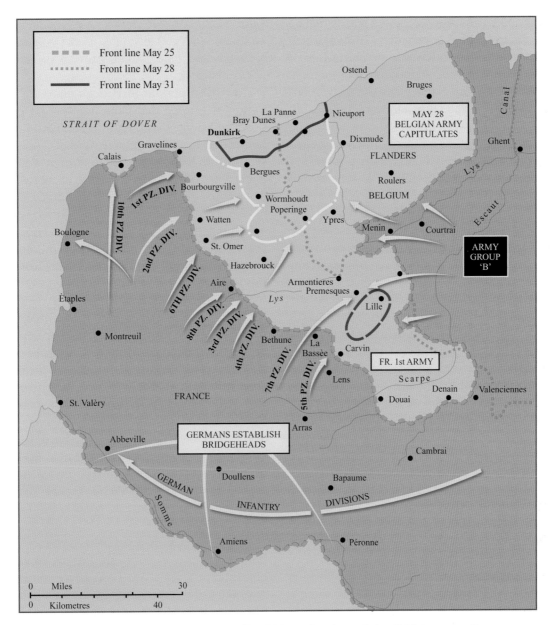

Figure 48.1 ■ *Situation near Dunkirk at the time of the British evacuation.*

convince them that Poland was the last area that Germany would try to conquer. (In compliance with their treaty of protection for Poland, Britain and France had declared war two days after the German invasion.) This claim of limited aggression was, of course, the same refrain that Hitler sang when he conquered the Sudetenland only months previously. During the period of his negotiations with Britain, there were a few minor skir-

mishes with France and a few isolated naval battles, but nothing significant. However, Britain would not back away this time.

When Hitler realized that he would not succeed in his attempt to keep Britain out of the war, Germany attacked Denmark and Norway in April 1940. Denmark was quickly occupied. As soon as Norway was invaded, Vidkun Abraham Lauritz Quisling, the head of a Norwegian party that was copied after the Nazis, announced that he was in control of the government. Although few Norwegians liked or followed him, the concept of a Norwegian supporting an invading foreign force was confusing to the Norwegians and disheartening, especially as the Germans were highly successful. (To this day, a person who is inside one government and assists a foreign invader is called a *Quisling*.) Sweden, which declared neutrality and supplied Germany with steel, was spared from invasion.

The British gave some assistance to the Norwegians, but when the Germans attacked the Low Countries in May 1940, Britain had to withdraw its support of all continental European countries. This occurred because of a brilliant German tactic. Rather than move southward through the Low Countries toward Paris, the Germans struck toward the North Sea along the Belgium-French border. This effectively isolated the British army north of the German line and, with Germany occupying Denmark, the British army was trapped between enemy forces. The Germans moved quickly to close the circle around the British. The British retreated to the beach city of Dunkirk, where they hoped to be evacuated back to England. The map given in Figure 48.1 shows the situation near Dunkirk.

This evacuation was one of the most heroic events of the war. The French troops who were in the area were asked to hold off the advancing German army as best they could while the British army was evacuated. In spite of their heroic defense, the French soldiers were overwhelmed. The time for evacuation was, therefore, very short. The British government asked all British citizens who had boats to assist in the evacuation. Hundreds of little boats made repeated crossings of the English Channel to evacuate the army. Today, a marker on the shore at Dunkirk remembers these brave boaters and also the valiant French troops who gave their lives trying to delay the German onslaught.

Germany then turned its sights to France. The French government had not been idle since the end of World War I, especially since Germany had violated the terms of the Versailles Treaty and had placed troops back in the Rhineland, near the French border. France had reinforced the Maginot

Line, a series of defensive forts along the French-German border. Thus, any direct attack from Germany to France would prove a difficult and costly endeavor.

It was important to Hitler's plans for domination of Europe that Germany not get bogged down in a long battle with France. Hitler knew he needed to strike quickly against France and remove the French threat. He did not want a reoccurrence of the trench warfare of World War I. Therefore, instead of attacking France directly at the French-German border, Hitler and his commanders decided to avoid the French defenses altogether and invade from the north by sweeping through Belgium first and then entering France.

The plan was extremely effective. As we have already discussed, the drive of the Germans westward cut off the British near Dunkirk, but it also created a front along France's northern border from which the Germans could launch their attack against France. Northern France, including Paris, was occupied by the German army in a matter of a few weeks and was ruled directly from Germany. Southern France was controlled by a German-puppet government under the nominal leadership of aging marshal Henri-Philippe Pétain, with its capital in the city of Vichy. France remained completely under German control for the next four years.

The Germans had reached agreements with Italy and Japan to form an axis of strength in both Europe and the Far East. These were, therefore, called the **Axis countries.** Opposing the Axis powers were the **Allies**—Great Britain and France, which had a small force in exile in Great Britain, and other countries of the world such as the British Commonwealth countries and, eventually, the United States.

■ The Battle of Britain

With France defeated and the eastern front safe because of Germany's treaty with the Soviet Union, Hitler felt confident enough to turn his attention toward Great Britain. As Great Britain was an island nation, Hitler knew a successful invasion would be extremely difficult. After all, England had not been successfully invaded since the Normans did so in 1066. However, following the debacle of Dunkirk for the British, Hitler saw invasion as likely being successful. The British also saw an imminent German invasion as likely and were worried because the British army was very discouraged and poorly equipped. (Like most of the European nations other than Germany, Britain had not kept its army up to date and had not developed new military technologies.)

Winston Churchill, the new prime minister of Great Britain, took strong and creative action to forestall the possible German invasion. Churchill publicly reasoned, so that the British people would take heart and the Germans would be forced to think deeply about the invasion, that the evacuation from Dunkirk was actually good for the British army because it concentrated the entire army in the British homeland rather than having it spread all across Europe trying to help defend other countries. Moreover, and most importantly, Churchill gave a speech in which he rallied the British people and, in very clever terms, let Hitler know that a German invasion would be met with the strongest resistance. A portion of that speech is quoted at the beginning of this chapter. The words of the speech were well chosen. All of the words in the quotation are of Anglo-Saxon origin except the last word, *surrender.* This choice of words was very powerful and moving for the British people and, of course, the German origin of these words could be understood clearly by other Germans, especially Hitler.

(Churchill understood that English is basically a Germanic language with French overlaid. However, when the combination of the Germanic and French languages was made, the common people were those who spoke the Germanic-based tongue. Therefore, when simple and powerful concepts are to be conveyed, using Germanic-based words is more effective than using French-based words, which are usually more refined and vague.)

The speech and other comments had their desired effect. Churchill's determination convinced Hitler to not invade immediately. Instead, Hitler

had a new technology that he felt could shift the odds in Germany's favor—an air force. Hitler decided to destroy Great Britain's own fledgling air force and then Britain's industrial and military base. This, he reasoned, would destroy the British morale and cripple the British military capability so that the German army could later invade successfully. Thus, the **Battle of Britain** was an air war.

Initially, the German air raids were quite successful. However, things quickly became more difficult than Hitler had imagined. The British invented a new fighter plane, the Spitfire, that was quicker and more maneuverable than the larger German bombers. The Spitfires made it much more difficult for the German bombers to successfully reach their targets.

The British also invented radar, which allowed its fighters the advantage of knowing where the Germans were and therefore maximized the effectiveness of the few Spitfires that Britain was able to produce in the midst of having its manufacturing facilities constantly under attack. This also allowed British pilots to conserve fuel.

Hitler grew increasingly anxious that things were not going as planned and began to bomb British nonmilitary sites, such as cities, in hopes of destroying the morale of the British people by attacking civilians. In what was called the **Blitz of London,** the British people would go to work and then, if an attack came, would leave their offices and go into the British subway (Underground) stations to wait out the attack.

The German plan backfired, as the attacks on civilians only firmed up British resolve to not give in to Germany, and the morale of the people was kept high by the inspirational and creative speeches given by Winston Churchill. Britain kept resisting the German bombing and, with a tremendous increase in airplane manufacturing, eventually took control of the skies. This victory caused the eloquent Churchill to praise the Royal Air Force by saying: "Never in the field of human conflict was so much owed by so many to so few."

While Germany's air force was focused on Great Britain, Hitler's army turned eastward towards the Balkans. Nazi Germany quickly forced Hungary, Romania, and Bulgaria into alliances with the Third Reich, while assisting Italy in attacking Greece and Yugoslavia. The Nazis also looked south to Switzerland and Liechtenstein, both nations with cultural and language ties to Germany, but both had declared themselves neutral. The Germans decided to not bother immediately with the Swiss, as it is difficult to invade Switzerland due to the massive mountains on nearly all of its borders. Germany did send an SS column to the border with the intention of taking control of tiny Liechtenstein. Liechtenstein had no army, but in a brave stand, a priest and the local Boy Scout troop went to the border to defend the independence of tiny Liechtenstein. For unknown reasons, the SS troop never invaded Liechtenstein and the small nation remained independent and neutral throughout the duration of World War II.

Italy and Germany attacked and conquered much of North Africa and, essentially, cut off trade between Europe and Asia. The German navy was very active in the Atlantic, attempting to reduce the amount of assistance that Great Britain was receiving from the United States and other countries. Germany's domination of Europe and most of the surrounding territory (except Great Britain) was essentially complete.

■ The Great Mistake in Russia

German war strategy has always been to avoid fighting a two-front war. As you might remember from our discussion of World War I, the German plan was to throw all of their might against the French and other western-front targets so that they could conquer the west before the Russians had time to mobilize. Hitler was even more clever than the World War I strategists. He signed the nonaggression pact with the Russians, and this gave him time to completely dominate the western front without fear of a Russian invasion.

In retrospect, we can see that Hitler made a serious mistake in June of 1941 when he broke the nonaggression pact that Germany had signed with the Soviet Union and attacked Russia. The German army made slow, but steady, progress into the Russian interior, but then got bogged down at several

key Russian cities. One of these cities, Leningrad (now called St. Petersburg), was especially difficult, and so the Germans put the city under siege. Unbelievably, the people of Leningrad withstood the German bombardment for almost three years (900 days from 1941 to 1944). People ate rats, dogs, cats, and almost anything else that was even partially edible. All public transportation stopped. Homes ran out of heating fuel. In the winter when the land was frozen, thousands of bodies were stacked in the streets awaiting burial. In the end, perhaps as many as 800,000 people died, but the city did not give in and the siege was finally lifted.

While some contingents of the German army surrounded Leningrad, others pushed past Leningrad and on to Moscow, where they were stopped just outside the city when the brutal Russian winter struck. The Germans were not able to capture Moscow, and Hitler's plan of spending the winter in Moscow was foiled. The German army was forced to remain in the fields, exposed to the Russian winter.

Another disaster was encountered by the German armies that thrust toward the Caucasus region. The Germans were able to advance successfully until they reached the city of **Stalingrad** (present-day Volgograd). They were again stopped and forced to put the city under siege. Massive bombardments were not successful in forcing Stalingrad to surrender.

While the Germans were advancing across Russia, the Russian army was fighting a delaying tactic and burning the crops before the German army, thus forcing the Germans to maintain very long supply lines. (The Russians had used this same tactic against Napoleon.) Furthermore, the Russians disassembled factories that were in the path of the German advance and then transported them to the Ural Mountains, far to the east, where the factories were reassembled and began production of supplies for the war.

Eventually, with the German advance stopped at Moscow and Stalingrad, and with Leningrad still resisting the German siege, the Russian army had gained sufficient materials and manpower that they could begin a counterattack. We will discuss the success of that counterattack later.

In the United States, isolationism was the popular political ideology of the day. America was still wary of becoming entangled in what many considered to be another "European war," especially since American involvement in World War I seemed to have done little to change long-term conditions in Europe. Furthermore, the United States was finally escaping the horrors of the Great Depression, although recovery was not yet complete. Thus, the United States remained officially neutral in the war, in spite of the aggressive and nondemocratic actions of Nazi Germany. President Roosevelt realized, however, that the long-term interests of the United States favored the Allies, and eventually a deal was struck between the United States and the Allies called the lend-lease program. The lend-lease program allowed the Allies to buy American goods on credit (which became, in essence, free). Thus, the United States eventually began to favor the Allies but refused to become militarily involved in the European conflict.

■ Japan Attacks

The United States may have remained militarily uninvolved for the duration of the war if not for the actions of the Japanese. Like Germany, Japan had been late to modernize politically and economically. Also like Germany, Japan looked to the acquisition of an empire as a means of showing Japanese prestige and strength and of improving its economy. Furthermore, a colonial empire was especially important to the Japanese because the islands of Japan itself had few natural resources. Thus, Japan began to expand throughout Asia and the Pacific and declared that region to fall under the Japanese sphere of influence.

Japan began its attempt at empire building by invading Korea early in the twentieth century and by precipitating the Russo-Japanese War near the same time. Then, in 1937, the Japanese invaded China. Despite China's geographic size and massive population, internal problems and a refusal to modernize left the Chinese vulnerable to the Japanese invasion. Japan had an even greater technological advantage over the Chinese because the

United States had provided the Japanese with airplanes. Large portions of China fell under Japanese domination.

The United States recognized their error in China and initiated a policy of assistance to the Chinese. They supplied the Nationalist Chinese government with a squadron of airplanes under the command of American General Chennault. These were the Flying Tigers, and they proved to be very effective in slowing the Japanese advance, at least within the flying range of the airplanes.

The conflicting interests of the United States and Japan were increased further when Japan signed a treaty with Germany and became one of the Axis powers. While the United States was not at open war with Germany, it was clear that the United States favored the Allied side of the conflict. Finally, the Japanese were a very proud and honor-bound people, and that pride and honor had been severely wounded when the United States had steamed into Tokyo harbor in the 1850s and forced Japan to open itself to the modern era.

Japan felt it was the rightful power to dominate the Pacific and its many islands. This belief, however, put the Japanese in direct conflict with the United States, which viewed itself as the dominant power in the Pacific Ocean since the days of clipper ship trading in the late nineteenth century. In accord with its stated intentions, Japan initiated a conquest of Burma but was thwarted in that effort, at least initially, by a combination of United States and British forces. Also, the Japanese indicated that they intended to pursue colonization throughout the Pacific area. The United States threatened counteractions such as a blockade of Japanese ports. This threat greatly alarmed the Japanese, who saw such a move as a threat to their national existence since Japan depended so heavily on imports of food and raw manufacturing materials.

In the midst of negotiations with the United States over their conflicting interests in the Pacific, the Japanese decided that a show of strength against the United States would convince the Americans that Japan's intentions were strongly held and that any move to blockade Japan would be futile. Therefore, the Japanese decided to attack Pearl Harbor. This had the added benefit for the Japanese that they would be able to sink much of the U.S. naval power in the Pacific and therefore further discourage the Americans from any aggressive actions. The well-known reluctance of the United States to enter foreign wars was another factor that emboldened the Japanese.

Pearl Harbor, a naval base in the islands of Hawaii, was the hub of American military power in the Pacific. The Japanese attack on December 7, 1941, sunk nearly the entire American Pacific fleet and killed hundreds of American soldiers and citizens. However, the Japanese underestimated America's response to their actions; the attack on Pearl Harbor woke up a sleeping giant. The Japanese did not believe the United States would be able to immediately respond (because of the decimation of their fleet) or have the willpower to react strongly (because of the strong feeling of isolationism in the United States) leaving Japan free to exert their influence throughout the Pacific.

The United States, however, had not been attacked on its own soil since the War of 1812, and the American people were outraged by what they felt was a sneak attack and the high casualty rate. Following a stirring address by President Franklin Roosevelt the next day, the United States of America declared war on Japan. Three days later, Japan's allies, Germany and Italy, declared war on the United States, thus bringing the USA into the conflict in Europe as well.

Following the attack on Pearl Harbor, the Japanese moved quickly to take advantage of America's inability to respond. Japanese troops spread southeastward through China and occupied most of Southeast Asia. The Japanese also pushed into the Pacific Ocean and occupied as many of the islands as they could, including the Philippines, which was an American territory, and had many American soldiers stationed there.

The American soldiers, under General Douglas MacArthur, became trapped on the small island of Corregidor and the nearby Bataan peninsula. MacArthur led the troops in their defense, but eventually had to withdraw to Australia to avoid capture as the Japanese overran the American positions. Upon leaving the Philippines, General MacArthur vowed that he would personally return to reclaim the territory for the United States. While General MacArthur was able to get away, most of the American soldiers were not. They became Japanese prisoners, forced to go on the brutal and long death marches to Japanese prison camps.

Late 1941 and early 1942 was the high point for the Axis powers. Nearly all of Europe was under German and Italian control or influence, and the German army was just outside of Moscow. The maximum German occupation of Europe is shown in Figure 48.2. The Japanese had nearly uncontested control of eastern and southeastern Asia, as well possession of most of the islands of the Pacific. The maximum control area of Japan is shown in Figure 48.3.

■ Some Allied Victories

Beginning in 1942, the tide of the war would slowly begin to shift toward the Allied powers, which now consisted principally of Great Britain and its commonwealth (especially including Australia, New Zealand, Canada, and India), France, the United States, and the Soviet Union. The extent of countries participating in the war truly created a world conflict. The various attacks are shown in Figure 48.4.

In the Soviet Union the Russian army counterattacked in 1942 and trapped 300,000 German troops, eventually inflicting a devastating defeat. From this point on the Soviets began a slow, long push toward Germany.

Meanwhile, in northern Africa where the Germans, under General Rommel (called the Desert Fox) had dominated up to this point, the Allies began to gain victories as well. British armor units under General Montgomery defeated the combined German and Italian forces in Egypt in 1943. At the same time the Americans, under General Patton, attacked from Morocco in the west. Caught between two advancing armies, the Germans and Italians were squeezed out of Africa and had to abandon it to the Allies.

With control of North Africa, the Allies decided to push into Europe from the south. Later in

Figure 48.2 ■ *Map of Europe at the point of maximum control by the Axis nations.*

1943 American and British troops landed in Sicily and then onto the Italian mainland. After a few tenuous days following the invasion, the Allies were securely positioned on the Italian mainland and began a slow but successful push northward. Tired of the war, the Italian people executed Mussolini and installed a new government that surrendered to the Allies on September 8, 1943. However, Germany occupied the northern half of Italy, so the war in Italy continued for two more years as the Allied forces battled with the Germans.

The invasion in Italy was never intended by the Allies to be the main push into Germany. This main attack was to be made in France. Therefore, on June 6, 1944, **D-Day,** Allied forces under the command of American General Dwight Eisenhower, landed on the beaches of Normandy in northern France. The D-Day landing was the largest invasion ever made in the history of mankind. Despite horrific casualty rates suffered by the Allies as they stormed the long, open beaches and parachuted behind enemy lines, they made significant advances into German-controlled territory because the Germans continued to look elsewhere for the real invasion.

The befuddlement of the Germans and the timing of the D-Day attack were both highly creative maneuvers by the Allies. Hitler knew that an invasion of Europe was being planned and that the attack would be based from the British Isles. The Allies created several diversions to confuse the Germans. One of the most innovative was the creation of an entirely fictitious division, complete with an organization chart (in which one of

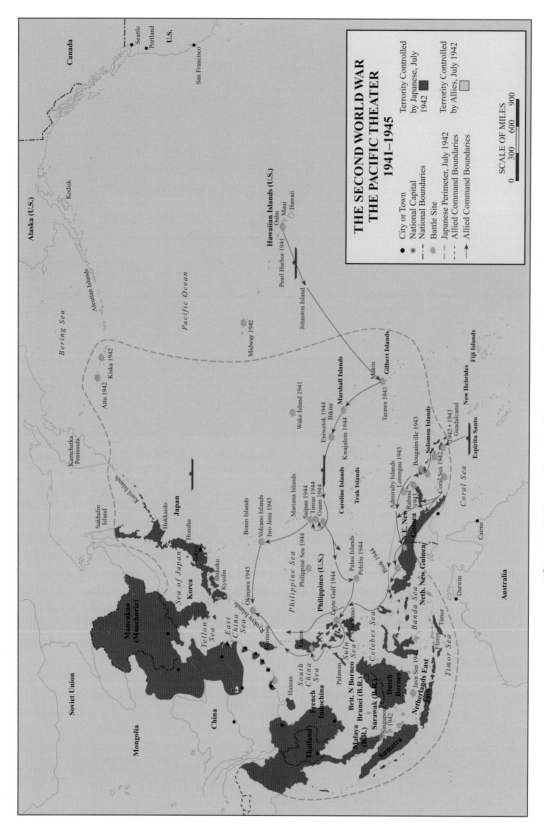

Figure 48.3 ■ *Allies Pacific strategy (island hopping).*

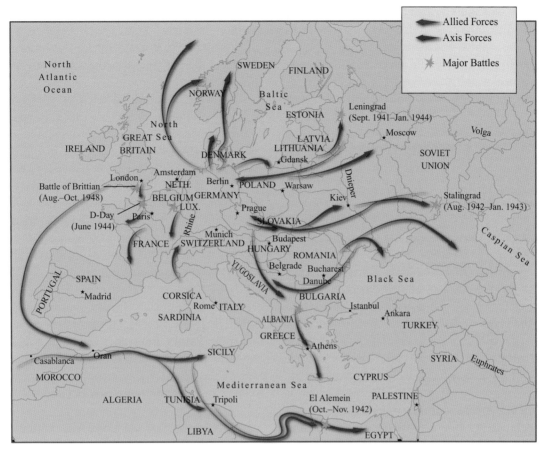

Figure 48.4 ■ *Map of the European Theater showing Axis and Allied attacks.*

the best allied generals was shown as the commander), an extensive list of supplies, transfers of personnel between units, and requisition of many items that would be needed for an invasion. This unit was placed among other real units (thereby increasing the total strength of the troops) in the area that would be ideal for an invasion toward the French port of Calais. This port was over a hundred miles from the actual invasion location. The Allies also released several false reports to places that they believed the Germans had stationed spies, thus further convincing the Germans that Calais was the target. On the day of the actual invasion, great activity was commenced within this fictitious division, thus suggesting that they were about to invade. The German commanders, espe-

cially Hitler, believed the subterfuge and delayed sending any support to Normandy because of their belief that Normandy was merely a diversion and that the real invasion would come at Calais. (What a tremendously creative effort by the Allies!)

The success of the D-Day invasion left the Germans in the perilous position of having to fight a war on two fronts because of Hitler's decision to invade the Soviet Union. Furthermore, the surrender of the Italians meant that the Germans were fighting alone in Italy as well, and had to divert men, arms, and supplies there as well. (So the war was actually on three fronts.) With German resources so scattered, the Allies successfully advanced across France, Belgium, and the Netherlands and reclaimed those countries from the Nazis.

Hitler and the Germans were not yet at the point of panic, however, and another massive push against the Allies was planned. Hitler believed that one strong drive could push the Allies back into the ocean and then Germany could turn its attention to the Russians unhindered. This last push by the Germans became known as the **Battle of the Bulge.**

It was deep in the winter of 1944 (one of the coldest and most bitter winters in European history) and Allied troops were nearing the borders of Germany when the Germans launched a massive attack through the Ardennes forest of Belgium and eastern France. The Germans surrounded the American troops near the city of Bastogne and hoped to crush them. In a bold stand, the Americans held out despite constant bombardment, a lack of supplies, no reinforcements, and brutal cold. At one point, the Germans offered the trapped Americans a surrender with honorable internment in prisoner of war camps. The American commander sent back a single-word response, "Nuts." Using nearly unbelievable troop movements, General Patton arrived with reinforcements to lift the siege.

Unable to crush or capture the Americans, the Germans pushed past Bastogne and strove to cut off other Allied units. However, lack of resources eventually proved to be the great German problem in their attack. The Germans eventually ran out of fuel and were forced to leave their tanks in the field and retreat. At about this same time, the winter weather cleared, thus allowing the American and British airplanes to give support to the Allied ground troops and further deny the Germans the ability to move forward.

Soon after the Battle of the Bulge, the Allies were able to capture the bridges over the Rhine River into Germany. This signaled to the Germans that the end was near. Hitler, knowing defeat was imminent, now began to act even more erratically and dangerously. Among other things, Hitler ordered the killing of as many Jews and other "undesirables" as possible in the concentration camps, just so they could not be rescued. Furthermore, Hitler ordered Hitler Youth groups (boys 12 to 16 years old) to hold positions against the Allied advances that even experienced soldiers

could not have held. Refusal, or failure, to do so resulted in death. Some boys were even given quick training as pilots to make up for the dwindling number of pilots in the German *Luftwaffe* (air force).

Knowing that Allied victory was coming, Winston Churchill, Franklin Roosevelt, and Josef Stalin, the leaders of Great Britain, the United States, and the Soviet Union, met in the city of Yalta to discuss the German surrender and what course to take following the war. The three leaders agreed that the German surrender would have to be total. They also agreed to divide up Germany into four parts with Great Britain, France, the United States, and the USSR, each being responsible for rebuilding and monitoring its section of Germany following the war. It was also agreed that the governments of the newly freed countries of Europe should be freely elected. However, it became obvious at the **Yalta Conference** that there was a deep and growing division between democratic and capitalist Allies (France, Great Britain, and the United States) and the communist Soviet Union.

In fact, the decisions made at Yalta led directly to the start of the Cold War, following the defeat of the Germans in World War II. The decision to divide Germany led to the eventual creation of two German nations: A democratic nation known as West Germany and a communist nation known as East Germany. Furthermore, despite the decision that the nations of Europe should be allowed to have free elections, Stalin was also promised that the Soviet Union could have a sphere of influence over the nations of Eastern Europe and use them as a buffer between Germany and the Soviet Union. This promise allowed Stalin to deny free elections in these eastern European countries and place communist governments in nearly all of the nations of Eastern Europe, turning them into puppets of the Soviet Union following the war.

Following Yalta, the Allies made the final push into Germany. Two months later, Hitler committed suicide during a bombing raid while Russian troops entered Berlin. Eight days later Germany surrendered to the Allies unconditionally and war in Europe ended.

The Allies immediately began to enact the plan agreed upon in Yalta. Germany was divided into four zones of control. Furthermore, in order to avoid the severe economic problems that had followed World War I and led to many of the conditions that caused World War II, the United States enacted the Marshall Plan. The **Marshall Plan,** in essence, gave grants and loans to the nations of Western Europe so that their economies and infrastructure could be quickly rebuilt following the war. The same offer was given to the nations of Eastern Europe, but under pressure from the Soviet Union, those nations rejected the offer. War in Europe was over, but the United States was still at war in the Pacific with Japan, and soon after the European victory most of the American soldiers were given orders to prepare to deploy to fight in the Pacific.

▪ The Unexpected Strategy

Using the lull in America's ability to respond following the attack on Pearl Harbor and the decimation of the American fleet, the Japanese had occupied most of the islands of the Pacific. Furthermore, the Japanese navy still controlled most of the ocean. However, while patrolling near Midway Island, American aircraft carriers came upon several Japanese carriers and were able to sink the Japanese carriers just as the fuel-starved Japanese fighters were returning. The loss of the Japanese carriers and aircraft served as a major blow. **Midway** turned out to be a major turning point in the war because the Japanese navy no longer had total control of the Pacific.

Many of the Japanese-occupied islands were strongly fortified and deeply entrenched, and the American commanders realized that the push toward Japan was going to be extremely difficult and was going to cost many American lives. General MacArthur and Admiral Nimitz decided that the Americans would not even try to liberate all of the occupied islands but would **island hop** from key island to key island until the Americans were within striking distance of the Japanese mainland (see Figure 48.3).

This strategy was totally unexpected by the Japanese. They anticipated the gradual and methodical recapturing of the islands, which seemed to fit their logical approach to warfare. It is, after all, what a war machine should do. In that scenario, the Japanese were confident that the Americans would lose their willingness to continue the war and therefore the Japanese would be able to retain many of the islands as colonies and, even more importantly, retain the countries of southeast Asia that were vital as supply points for raw materials.

However, the American island-hopping approach had some unexpected benefits. For example, the Japanese were not able to anticipate the place of attack, since almost any island was a potential target. Also, the strategy allowed the Americans to establish air bases on many forward islands and then use those bases to later acquire islands in their rear and also to use the island air bases to help attack islands in their front. The island-hopping strategy also meant that many of the Japanese troops, forced to stay in place and occupy an island that was not attacked, would be unavailable for support of the islands that were actually attacked.

To further complicate the position of the Japanese, the Americans attacked in multiple thrusts. One was led by General MacArthur from his base in Australia (where he had fled when he had to abandon the Philippines) against the Japanese positions in the Solomon Islands and Indonesia. Another thrust was toward the islands of the South Pacific. This thrust later split into two as it attacked both the Philippines (coordinated with MacArthur) and northward to islands that were gateways to Japan. There were also attacks by the Allies in the far north Pacific region and in southeast Asia (based from India). Japan still had to fight the continuing battle in China.

Progress was slow and difficult for the American army. The Japanese were firmly entrenched and had more experience fighting in the tropical climates and jungle terrain found in most of the islands. The Americans went through the Solomon Islands and then leapfrogged through several of the islands of Indonesia. MacArthur eventually got back to the Philippines as he had promised, saying, "I have returned." The American military continued to push toward the outlying Japanese-owned islands of Iwo Jima and Okinawa. The Japanese defense became even fiercer.

The Americans were now close enough that they began to bomb cities in Japan itself. As the Americans approached, the Japanese became increasingly desperate and began to use **kamikaze pilots,** suicide planes in which the pilots intentionally fly into American ships and military installations. (The term *kamikaze* means "divine wind" and recalls the time in the fourteenth century when a typhoon sunk an invading Chinese fleet and saved Japan. The suicide planes were to be the new divine wind that would save Japan.)

■ The Atomic Bomb

President **Harry Truman** had become president when President Roosevelt died in early 1945. Seeing the fierce nature of the Japanese defense and the use of kamikazes and other extreme tactics, he began to realize that an invasion of Japan could take years and cost potentially millions of American lives. Truman realized that the honor-bound Japanese would never surrender until they were utterly and totally defeated. He thus began to consider using a new weapon the United States had been developing throughout the war—atomic bombs.

Truman grappled with whether to use the bombs. On the one hand, he knew that they caused massive devastation (although nobody really understood the long-term effects of using nuclear weapons), and that using them would kill many Japanese civilians. On the other hand, President Truman thought that use of the bombs might convince the Japanese to surrender without requiring an American invasion of Japan, which would cost countless American and Japanese lives.

President Truman made the decision to use the atomic bombs. The United States only had two of the nuclear bombs, so Truman was gambling that two displays of their awesome destructive power would convince the Japanese that they had no chance of victory and that they had to surrender. Truman gave the order, and on the morning of August 6, 1945, the first of the two bombs was dropped on the Japanese industrial city of Hiroshima. Immediately following the bombing, the United States requested that the Japanese unconditionally surrender. When the Japanese refused to do so, Truman ordered the second atomic bomb to be used. Three days later, on August 9, the second bomb was dropped on the city of Nagasaki. Once again, the United States requested Japan to surrender. Many of Japan's leaders wanted to continue to fight, but in a bold move to protect his people, the Japanese emperor ordered the unconditional Japanese surrender.

The formal surrender took place shortly thereafter on the deck of the USS Missouri in Tokyo Bay, where General MacArthur and Admiral Nimitz accepted the Japanese surrender, officially ending World War II.

■ Creativity Saved the Free World

The ability of the Allies to use both right- and left-brain thinking resulted in creativity that eventually won the war. People can be creative with just left-brain thinking, and they can also be creative with just right-brain thinking, but creativity is best when the two sides of the brain think together. Some examples of unusually creative moments in the war were when Churchill convinced Hitler that an invasion of Britain should be postponed, when the Allies orchestrated many diversions to mask the real D-Day invasion, and the strategy of island-hopping that maximized Allied forces against the deployable Japanese forces.

We believe, without any real supporting evidence, that the underlying cause of an action can also be a factor in creativity. We believe that the Allies' actions were based on a desire to save freedom. This cause was more noble than the cause of Germany, Italy, and Japan. It led to a clearer purpose and, we believe, to a better ability to think. These led to that greater creativity.

■ Timeline—Important Dates

Date	Event
1939	*Germany invades Poland, starting WWII*
1940	*Invasions of Denmark, Norway, Low Countries, France*
1940	*Battle of Britain begins*
1941	*Axis powers invade Russia*
1941	*Japanese attack Pearl Harbor*
1942	*Battle of Midway turns the tide of war in the Pacific*
1943	*Italy surrenders; Mussolini executed*
1944	*D-Day invasion by Allies*
1945	*German surrender; Hitler commits suicide*
1945	*Atomic bombs dropped on Hiroshima and Nagasaki*
1945	*Japanese surrender*

■ Suggested Readings

Ayer, Eleanor, Helen Waterford, and Alfons Heck, *Parallel Journeys,* Aladdin Paperbacks, 1995.

Brokaw, Tom, *The Greatest Generation,* Random House, 1998.

Dupuy, Trevor Nevitt, *The Military History of World War II,* Franklin Watts, Inc., 1965.

Frankl, Victor, *Man's Search for Meaning,* Pocket Books, 1962.

Hanson, Victor Davis, *Carnage and Culture,* Anchor Books, 2002.

Manchester, William, *American Caesar,* Dell Publishing Company, 1978.

Perret, Geoffrey, *A Country Made by War,* Vintage, 1990.

Thorpe, Scott, *How to Think Like Einstein,* Barnes & Noble Books, Inc., 2000.

Viktor Frankl: Man's Search for Meaning

Austria was under Nazi occupation in 1942. Viktor Frankl (1902–1997) married in that year and was already an acclaimed neurologist in Vienna. He had been granted a visa to the United States, but never used it out of concern for his parents and his patients. The Nazis had a policy of treating mental illness with euthanasia (medical killing), which Frankl tried to get around by making many false diagnoses of his patients. In the fall of that year, he, his new bride, his brother, and his parents were all arrested by the Nazis and sent to a concentration camp. Like all other camp prisoners, he was separated from his family and would not see them for the rest of his three-year internment. He spent many secret moments in prison working on a manuscript (*The Doctor and His Soul*) describing his reflections as a doctor in such an environment, but the manuscript was discovered during a transfer and destroyed.

Frankl survived the Holocaust when his camp was liberated in 1945. He soon learned of the deaths of each of his family members who had been arrested with him. Frankl immediately resumed his work as a neurologist and finally published *The Doctor and His Soul* based on the small scraps of stolen paper he had used to record his memory of the original text while still in prison. He had not yet quenched his desire to be understood, however, so he dictated over the course of nine days another book, entitled *Man's Search for Meaning*. This work recounts many of his vivid experiences in the concentration camps and has sold over 9 million copies. Frankl remarried, earned a Ph.D. in philosophy, and received countless awards, professorships, and honorary doctorates in medicine, philosophy, and psychiatry. In addition, Frankl was a proficient mountain climber, earned his pilot's license at the age of sixty-seven, and continued teaching at the University of Vienna until 1990 when he was eighty-five. Frankl's life story of courage, honor, service, love, and dedication is as inspiring as any of the great literary works known to our civilization.

In *Man's Search for Meaning,* Frankl develops the psychological theory of "logotherapy"—where a consciousness of meaning is used as the root of all human motivation. He recounts how those who ended up surviving the camps were those who had a reason to survive. For Frankl, wanting to finish his book, *The Doctor and His Soul,* as well as the enduring hope to be reunited with his loved ones, served to give him enough meaning to keep him alive. Frankl suggests that these sources of meaning—a mission to accomplish, the hope of being reunited with loved ones, or great faith in a divine purpose—were the most common reasons for survival in the Nazi death camps. *Man's Search for Meaning* is thus not only meant to be an exposal of the Jewish plight under the Nazi occupation but to be a philosophical treatise on the will to survive. It urges the reader to find meaning in his or her life no matter what the circumstances are and to find satisfaction in existence from that meaning.

In attempting this psychological presentation and a psychopathological explanation of the typical characteristics of a concentration camp inmate, I may give the impression that the human being is completely and unavoidably influenced by his surroundings. (In this case the surroundings being the unique structure of camp life, which forced the prisoner to conform his conduct to a certain set pattern.) But what about human liberty? Is there no spiritual freedom in regard to behavior and reaction to any given surroundings? Is that theory true which would have us believe that man is no more than a product of many conditional and environmental factors—be they of a biological, psychological or sociological nature? Is man but an accidental product of these? Most important, do the prisoners' reactions to the singular world of the concentration camp prove that man cannot escape the influences of his surroundings? Does man have no choice of action in the face of such circumstances?

We can answer these questions from experience as well as on principle. The experiences of camp life show that man does have a choice of action. There were enough examples, often of a heroic nature, which proved that apathy could be overcome, irritability suppressed. Man can preserve a vestige of spiritual freedom, of independence of mind, even in such terrible conditions of psychic and physical stress.

We who lived in concentration camps can remember the men who walked through the huts comforting others, giving away their last piece of bread. They may have been few in number, but they offer sufficient proof that everything can be taken from a man but one thing: the last of the human freedoms—to choose one's attitude in any given set of circumstances, to choose one's own way.

And there were always choices to make. Every day, every hour, offered the opportunity to make a decision, a decision which determined whether you would or would not submit to those powers which threatened to rob you of your very self, your inner freedom; which determined whether or not you would become the plaything of circumstance, renouncing freedom and dignity to become molded into the form of the typical inmate.

Seen from this point of view, the mental reactions of the inmates of a concentration camp must seem more to us than the mere expression of certain physical and sociological conditions. Even though conditions such as lack of sleep, insufficient food and various mental stresses may suggest that the inmates were bound to react in certain ways, in the final analysis it becomes clear that the sort of person the prisoner became was the result of an inner decision, and not the result of camp influences alone. Fundamentally, therefore, any man can, even under such circumstances, decide what shall become of him—mentally and spiritually. He

Source: From *Man's Search for Meaning* by Viktor Frankl. Reprinted by permission of Beacon Press, Boston.

may retain his human dignity even in a concentration camp. Dostoevski said once, "There is only one thing that I dread: not to be worthy of my sufferings." These words frequently came to my mind after I became acquainted with those martyrs whose behavior in camp, whose suffering and death, bore witness to the fact that the last inner freedom cannot be lost. It can be said that they were worthy of their sufferings; the way they bore their suffering was a genuine inner achievement. It is this spiritual freedom—which cannot be taken away—that makes life meaningful and purposeful.

An active life serves the purpose of giving man the opportunity to realize values in creative work, while a passive life of enjoyment affords him the opportunity to obtain fulfillment in experiencing beauty, art, or nature. But there is also purpose in that life which is almost barren of both creation and enjoyment and which admits of but one possibility of high moral behavior: namely, in man's attitude to his existence, an existence restricted by external forces. A creative life and a life of enjoyment are banned to him. But not only creativeness and enjoyment are meaningful. If there is a meaning in life at all, then there must be a meaning in suffering. Suffering is an ineradicable part of life, even as fate and death. Without suffering and death human life cannot be complete.

The way in which a man accepts his fate and all the suffering it entails, the way in which he takes up his cross, gives him ample opportunity—even under the most difficult circumstances—to add a deeper meaning to his life. It may remain brave, dignified and unselfish. Or in the bitter fight for self-preservation he may forget his human dignity and become no more than an animal. Here lies the chance for a man either to make use of or to forgo the opportunities of attaining the moral values that a difficult situation may afford him. And this decides whether he is worthy of his sufferings or not.

Do not think that these considerations are unworldly and too far removed from real life. It is true that only a few people are capable of reaching such high moral standards. Of the prisoners only a few kept their full inner liberty and obtained those values which their suffering afforded, but even

one such example is sufficient proof that man's inner strength may raise him above his outward fate. Such men are not only in concentration camps. Everywhere man is confronted with fate, with the change of achieving something through his own suffering.

Take the fate of the sick—especially those who are incurable. I once read a letter written by a young invalid, in which he told a friend that he had just found out he would not live for long, that even an operation would be of no help. He wrote further that he remembered a film he had seen in which a man was portrayed who waited for death in a courageous and dignified way. The boy had thought it a great accomplishment to meet death so well. Now—he wrote—fate was offering him a similar chance.

Those of us who saw the film called *Resurrection*—taken from a book by Tolstoy—years ago, may have had similar thoughts. Here were great destinies and great men. For us, at that time, there was no great fate; there was no chance to achieve such greatness. After the picture we went to the nearest café, and over a cup of coffee and a sandwich we forgot the strange metaphysical thoughts which for one moment had crossed our minds. But when we ourselves were confronted with a great destiny and faced with the decision of meeting it with equal spiritual greatness, by then we had forgotten our youthful resolutions of long ago, and we failed.

Perhaps there came a day for some of us when we saw the same film again, or a similar one. But by then other pictures may have simultaneously unrolled before one's inner eye; pictures of people who attained much more in their lives than a sentimental film could show. Some details of a particular man's inner greatness may have come to one's mind, like the story of the young woman whose death I witnessed in a concentration camp. It is a simple story. There is little to tell and it may sound as if I had invented it; but to me it seems like a poem.

This young woman knew that she would die in the next few days. But when I talked to her she was cheerful in spite of this knowledge. "I am grateful that fate has hit me so hard," she told me.

"In my former life I was spoiled and did not take spiritual accomplishments seriously." Pointing through the window of the hut, she said, "This tree here is the only friend I have in my loneliness." Through that window she could see just one branch of a chestnut tree, and on the branch were two blossoms. "I often talk to this tree," she said to me. I was startled and didn't quite know how to take her words. Was she delirious? Did she have occasional hallucinations? Anxiously I asked her if the tree replied. "Yes." What did it say to her? She answered, "It said to me, 'I am here—I am here—I am life, eternal life.'"

We have stated that that which was ultimately responsible for the state of the prisoner's inner self was not so much the enumerated psychophysical causes as it was the result of a free decision. Psychological observations of the prisoners have shown that only the men who allowed their inner hold on their moral and spiritual selves to subside eventually fell victim to the camp's degenerating influences. The question now arises, what could, or should, have constituted this "inner hold"?

Former prisoners, when writing or relating their experiences, agree that the most depressing influence of all was that a prisoner could not know how long his term of imprisonment would be. He had been given no date for his release. (In our camp it was pointless even to talk about it.) Actually a prison term was not only uncertain but unlimited. A well-known research psychologist has pointed out that life in a concentration camp could be called a "provisional existence." We can add to this by defining it as a "provisional existence of unknown limit."

New arrivals usually knew nothing about the conditions at a camp. Those who had come back from other camps were obliged to keep silent, and from some camps no one had returned. On entering camp a change took place in the minds of the men. With the end of uncertainty there came the uncertainty of the end. It was impossible to foresee whether or when, if at all, this form of existence would end.

The latin word *finis* has two meanings: the end or the finish, and a goal to reach. A man who could not see the end of his "provisional existence" was not able to aim at an ultimate goal in life. He ceased living for the future, in contrast to a man in normal life. Therefore the whole structure of his inner life changed; signs of decay set in which we know from other areas of life. The unemployed worker, for example, is in a similar position. His existence has become provisional and in a certain sense he cannot live for the future or aim at a goal. Research work done on unemployed miners has shown that they suffer from a peculiar sort of deformed time—inner time—which is a result of their unemployed state. Prisoners, too, suffered from this strange "time-experience." In camp, a small time unit, a day, for example, filled with hourly tortures and fatigue, appeared endless. A larger time unit, perhaps a week, seemed to pass very quickly. My comrades agreed when I said that in camp a day lasted longer than a week. How paradoxical was our time-experience! In this connection we are reminded of Thomas Mann's *The Magic Mountain,* which contains some very pointed psychological remarks. Mann studies the spiritual development of people who are in an analogous psychological position, i.e., tuberculosis patients in a sanatorium who also know no date for their release. They experience a similar existence—without a future and without a goal.

One of the prisoners, who on his arrival marched with a long column of new inmates from the station to the camp, told me later that he had felt as though he were marching at his own funeral. His life had seemed to him absolutely without future. He regarded it as over and done, as if he had already died. This feeling of lifelessness was intensified by other causes: in time, it was the limitlessness of the term of imprisonment which was most acutely felt; in space, the narrow limits of the prison. Anything outside the barbed wire became remote—out of reach and, in a way, unreal. The events and the people outside, all the normal life there, had a ghostly aspect for the prisoner. The outside life, that is, as much as he could see of it, appeared to him almost as it might have to a dead man who looked at it from another world.

A man who let himself decline because he could not see any future goal found himself occupied with retrospective thoughts. In a different connection, we have already spoken of the tendency there was to look into the past, to help make the present, with all its horrors, less real. But in robbing the present of its reality there lay a certain danger. It became easy to overlook the opportunities to make something positive of camp life, opportunities which really did exist. Regarding our "provisional existence" as unreal was in itself an important factor in causing the prisoners to lose their hold on life; everything in a way became pointless. Such people forget that often it is just such an exceptionally difficult external situation which gives man the opportunity to grow spiritually beyond himself. Instead of taking the camp's difficulties as a test of their inner strength, they did not take their life seriously and despised it as something of no consequence. They preferred to close their eyes and to live in the past. Life for such people became meaningless.

Naturally only a few people were capable of reaching great spiritual heights. But a few were given the chance to attain human greatness even through their apparent worldly failure and death, an accomplishment which in ordinary circumstances they would never have achieved. To their others of us, the mediocre and the half-hearted, the words of Bismarck could be applied: "Life is like being at the dentist. You always think that the worst is still to come, and yet it is over already." Varying this, we could say that most men in a concentration camp believed that the real opportunities of life had passed. Yet, in reality, there was an opportunity and a challenge. One could make a victory of those experiences turning life into an inner triumph, or one could ignore the challenge and simply vegetate, as did a majority of the prisoners.

The Contemporary World
Creativity and Value

Chapter 49

> There can be no art without discipline.
>
> —*Igor Stravinsky (quoted in Greenberg,* How to Listen to and Understand Great Music, *The Teaching Company)*

Changing Values

Immediately following World War II, and for the next sixty-plus years, many political and social difficulties resulted in a worldwide atmosphere of nearly continuous tension. We will discuss these difficulties and explore what creative actions were taken (or not taken) to resolve them.

As we indicated in the opening chapter of this book and have additionally discussed in several chapters, the period from 1790 has been dominated by the issue of social and economic equality. The background of tension following World War II gave even greater emphasis to the issue of equality and has led to an avalanche of changes in all aspects of civilization. The general trend throughout all these changes has been toward greater individual freedom and less recognition of existing societal structures and values. Some of the structures and values that have changed include the follow-

ing: educational patterns, definitions of citizenship, role of police authority, roles of men and women, sexual mores, concepts of the family, religious attitudes, political philosophy, role of government, and many others.

These astonishing changes have also brought changes in the arts. The standards by which art was judged have now largely been abandoned, at least by some. There is a feeling that an artist can do absolutely anything and declare that it is art—and some will agree. These artists and their supporters equate what they have done with creativity and point to the uniqueness of their work. However, our definition of creativity includes both uniqueness and value. This begs the question, What constitutes value? We will examine the changes that have occurred, along with discussions of the problems that gave rise to the tensions. Then, when we have seen the trends in context, we will attempt to answer the question of values.

■ The Cold War

Peace was to be short-lived following World War II. The United States was not able to retreat back into isolation following World War II the way it had after the First World War. The problem was that the Soviet Union immediately broke its promise given at Yalta and disallowed free elections in Eastern Europe. Poland, Czechoslovakia, Romania, Bulgaria, Hungary, all fell to wars of communist national determinism, and they all became communist satellite states of the Soviet Union. Seeing the state of postwar Europe, British Prime Minister Winston Churchill ominously warned that an **Iron Curtain** had fallen across Europe. In some of the countries in Eastern Europe, the Iron Curtain was an actual armed barrier. In Berlin and along the separation between the Soviet-controlled portion of Germany (called East Germany), a massive wall was built to discourage people from escaping into the West. Other countries, such as the Baltic republics of Lithuania, Latvia, and Estonia were in the Soviet sphere, as were numerous areas in the Caucasus region and central Asia.

Only the United States was militarily and economically strong enough to stand against the Soviet Union, and the two nations quickly emerged from World War II as the world's two superpowers: The USSR was the champion of communism, working to spread its influence throughout the world, while the United States worked to contain (or eliminate) communism and spread the principles of democracy and capitalism.

This struggle between the two superpowers became known as the **Cold War.** The Cold War was given that name because both superpowers had nuclear weapons and were, therefore, hesitant to begin open warfare (a "hot" war) against each other lest it lead to a nuclear holocaust. However, despite the reluctance on both sides to fight openly and directly, the Cold War was tense and suspicious. The entire world lived in fear of complete and total nuclear annihilation should the two superpowers ever go to war. The United States and the Soviet Union never did go to war directly with one another, but the Cold War between them lasted for 45 years, including three full-blown proxy wars, many smaller skirmishes, and several close calls.

To strengthen their positions, the United States and Soviet Union both formed military alliances. The alliance of countries arrayed against communism was called the **North Atlantic Treaty Organization (NATO).** The opposing side, led by the Soviet Union, was called the **Warsaw Pact.** The European members of these two blocks are shown in Figure 49.1.

With Europe politically divided and both sides firmly entrenched, the Soviet Union turned its attentions elsewhere, fomenting communist revolutions in other parts of the world. The USSR was successful in gaining an ally when the Chinese communists defeated the Nationalists in 1949, leading to the formation of the Communist People's Republic of China, while the Nationalists fled to the island of Taiwan and set up a government there. The communists then worked to encourage the spread of communism throughout Asia. Concerned that other Asian nations might embrace communism, the United States and its allies promised to contain communism. This led to two hot wars in Asia that pitted U.S. forces against local forces supported militarily and economically by the People's Republic of China and the Soviet Union.

The first of these hot wars took place in **Korea,** beginning in 1949 when the freely elected government in the south of Korea was attacked by communist forces from northern Korea. The **United Nations** (a multinational organization similar to the failed League of Nations that was formed following WWII, this time with American participation) condemned the actions of the communists and sent troops to Korea to reinstate the freely elected Korean government. The United States led the UN forces in the fight against the communist North Koreans. The Soviets did not become directly involved in the fighting, but did supply the communist North Koreans with money, supplies, arms, leadership, and small numbers of elite forces. In July 1953 the United States, China (which had fought with the Koreans), and North Korea, signed an armistice, which ended the war

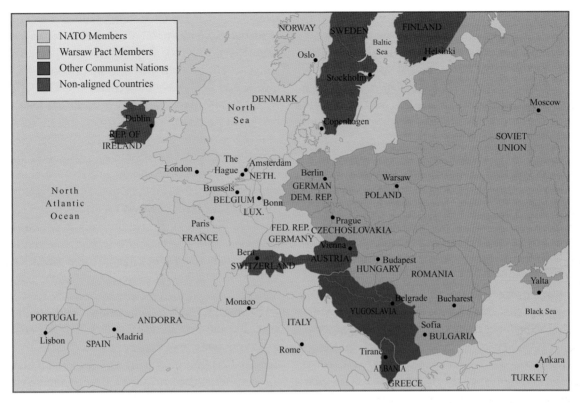

Figure 49.1 ■ *Division of Europe along Cold War lines.*

but failed to bring about a permanent peace. Korea was divided at the 38th parallel, with the communist nation of North Korea on the northern side and the democratic nation of South Korea on the southern side. North and South Korea have not signed a peace treaty with one another to this day, and the border between the two nations is the most heavily fortified border in the world. For the two superpowers, Korea was a draw of sorts, with neither side gaining the upper hand.

The second hot war within the Cold War also took place in Asia, in the small country of **Vietnam.** Conditions were similar to the Korean War. Once again, the United States was attempting to contain the spread of communism throughout Asia. This time, however, the United States was working largely alone (although several allies sent some troops to support the American effort), without the support of the United Nations. Once again the United States sent troops to fight, while the Soviets and Chinese supported the Vietnamese communists with supplies, weapons, leadership,

and small numbers of elite forces. Vietnam turned into a quagmire for the American military.

Despite much greater numbers and few defeats in open battle, the war in Vietnam went poorly. The American soldiers, especially at first, were not well trained for jungle warfare. Second, the enemy was elusive and unpredictable. When major battles took place, the United States almost always won. However, the Vietnamese rarely fought open battles, preferring instead to take advantage of their knowledge of the jungles and to fight using guerilla hit-and-run tactics. Third, the South Vietnamese government was hopelessly corrupt, and unpopular with its own people. Fourth, the war quickly became unpopular at home in the United States, where it had been politicized and its goals poorly communicated. Eventually, after nearly a decade in Vietnam, the United States pulled its troops out. Shortly after the American evacuation, Vietnam fell to the communists.

The scenario of the Vietnam War is much like the American War of Independence, with the sides changed: the North Vietnamese were like the Americans of the Revolution and the modern-day Americans were like the British of 1776. In both wars the creative tactics of the smaller armies were able to defeat the larger, in large part because of guerilla tactics and extended warfare during which the larger country lost public support and the will to continue fighting.

The third and final hot war within the Cold War was similar to Vietnam in many ways, but involved the Soviet Union as the major army and a small nation as the minor army. In the late 1970s the Soviet Union made attempts to expand its influence in the Muslim world of central Asia and in 1979 invaded the nation of **Afghanistan.** This time, it was the Soviets who sent their armies and the United States and its allies that sent supplies, weaponry, and leadership. Afghanistan became the USSR's quagmire. Despite overwhelming numbers and better technology, the Soviets could not suppress the Afghan rebels, who refused to accept communism. The war became unpopular back in the Soviet Union, and after 10 years the USSR finally withdrew its forces.

Although the threat of complete nuclear annihilation kept the two superpowers from going to war with one another, in 1962 the United States and the Soviet Union came very close to direct war as the events surrounding the **Cuban missile crisis** unfolded. Earlier that year the United States had placed several nuclear warheads in the nation of Turkey, one of its allies. This posed a severe threat to the USSR because the missiles in Turkey could reach the heavily populated western half of Russia, including the capital city of Moscow. In order to retain parity with the United States, the Soviet Union decided to place its own missiles on the island of Cuba, a small nation in the Caribbean Sea, about 70 miles from Florida, ruled by the communist dictator Fidel Castro. From Cuba, Soviet missiles could hit most of the eastern United States, including Washington, D.C.

Despite warnings from the CIA that the Soviets would likely try to put missiles in Cuba, President Kennedy did not believe that they would be so bold. Only when a U-2 spy plane showed that a few missiles had already been delivered and that mis-

sile silos for more were being built did Kennedy realize the seriousness of the situation and act. Kennedy warned the Soviets that any attack from Cuba would be considered a direct attack by the USSR and that the United States would retaliate. Kennedy also gave the order to blockade Cuba so that no more missiles could arrive.

The standoff continued as the Soviets, determined to call the American bluff, sent another fleet of ships toward Cuba with the intent of running the blockade. For 13 days, the situation was extremely tense and the world braced for nuclear Armageddon. The Soviet ships kept advancing as Kennedy struggled with the situation. Under international law, the American blockade of Cuba was illegal; furthermore, although it was a threat to the United States, it was legal for Cuba to have the missiles. The United States was on dubious legal ground at best, and the Soviets were still declaring publicly that there were no missiles in Cuba and that they had no intention of placing any there. The tide of the conflict shifted in favor of the United States, however, at an emergency meeting of the United Nations when the Soviet UN ambassador, Valerian Zorin, declared again that there were no nuclear missiles in Cuba, only to then have the American UN ambassador, Adlai Stevenson, produce the pictures proving that the missiles were there. Embarrassed, Soviet Premier Nikita Khrushchev then agreed to pull the missiles out of Cuba if the United States would remove their missiles from Turkey and promise to not invade Cuba and overthrow Castro. Kennedy agreed to the terms, and war was avoided.

The Cold War came to an end in the late 1980s when the economic basis for the communist world proved unable to compete with capitalism, leading to the political collapse of the Soviet Empire and its satellites. For a variety of reasons, the economies of the USSR and the other communist nations were not as productive as their capitalist foes. In order to keep military parity with the United States and its Western allies, the Soviet Union and its allies had to pour increasingly large percentages of money into the military. Doing this caused the standard of living between the east and west to increasingly divide. As life in Western capitalist nations became easier and more luxurious, life in communist nations became increasingly difficult and burdensome.

Realizing that some changes were needed to keep pace with the West, the soviet premier in the mid- to late-1980s, Mikhail Gorbachev, began to improve relations with the United States and loosen Soviet controls on the economy slightly. The American president, Ronald Reagan, encouraged Gorbachev to continue these reforms, all the while spending more and more money on the American military, forcing the Soviets to do the same to try and keep up. Eventually, so much of the Soviet Union's resources were being used for military developments that the economy of the Soviet Union teetered on collapse.

Under these difficult conditions, citizens of the many Soviet satellites in Eastern Europe found places along the border where the guards were lax, and people began to sneak across the barrier separating these states from Western Europe. These repeated and well-publicized defections were highly embarrassing for the Soviets and were motivating for the anti-Soviet movements in all of the satellite states. Within a few months, the satellite nations were able to break free of Soviet domination through a series of revolutions overthrowing their communist governments. The most strident of the communist puppet states was East Germany, and there the guards were diligent in protecting their border against defections. The border in Berlin was a massive, fortified wall. It had become a symbol of Soviet tyranny in Europe. In 1990, the **Berlin wall** was breached and the East German government overthrown, and then the wall was completely torn down.

The Soviet Union itself disintegrated in 1991, with many of its republics declaring themselves independent and the Communist Party losing power. In open elections Boris Yeltsin was named the first president of a democratic Russia.

■ European Union

Europe since the end of the Cold War has pursued a policy of both nationalism and unification. With only a few exceptions (such as the Basques in Spain and the Chechens of Russia), the many ethnicities, nationalities, languages, and religious groups of Europe have been able to increase their own self-rule. What was formerly Czechoslovakia has been split into the countries of the Czech Republic (ethnic Czechs) and Slovakia (ethnic Slovaks). The former Soviet Union split into its different ethnic parts, and what was formerly the Soviet Union is now Russia, Lithuania, Latvia, Estonia, Ukraine, Belarus, Georgia, Kazakhstan, and several other nations that are made up of one predominate ethnic, language, or religious group. Similar trends are even occurring in the more stable nations of Western Europe. For example, the United Kingdom has recently granted both Scotland and Northern Ireland a large measure of self-rule over local matters, allowing separate ruling bodies for local matters to exist in Edinburgh and Belfast rather than having the English rule from London.

This fracturing of larger nations was done quite peacefully in the former Czechoslovakia and Soviet Union because the different groups already lived largely in separate geographic regions, thus making the division relatively easy. However, in places where all of the groups have intermixed and moved around extensively, such as in the former nation of Yugoslavia, the break-up of the larger nation has led to bloody wars and ethnic and religious cleansing. Thus, after wars and much movement of people, the Balkans now consist of the less ethnically diverse nations of Slovenia, Croatia, Bosnia, Serbia, Macedonia, Albania, and Montenegro.

However, at the same time that Europe has been dividing itself into smaller, less diverse nations, the continent as a whole is undergoing a process of unification. Realizing that in the increasingly global world market, the small nations of Europe are not very competitive, they have increasingly banded together, especially economically, so as to be able to compete with the United States and the Asian powers. In doing this, Europe first formed the European Common Market, a loose economic union of European nations. Recently Europe has moved increasingly toward unification in other ways as well, such as the formation of the

European Union, which had worked to break down political barriers between the various nations of Europe.

Some of the changes that have been made include the adoption of a single currency, the euro, across much of Europe; the weakening of borders so that travel between different European nations is easier (more like going from state to state in the United States, although not quite that transparent); and attempting to bring the differing laws of Europe's many nations into greater harmony.

This process, although infinitely more difficult because of language barriers and longstanding individual nationalities, is somewhat analogous to what the United States went through in the transition from a nation based on the Articles of Confederation to the formation of a single, unified nation under the Constitution. The states had to give up some of their individual autonomy and powers, and people had to give up some of their home-state loyalties, to form a larger, stronger, nation. We should also remember that the United States was not finally defined until after the Civil War, which was fought, at least in part, over the issue of states' rights.

Europe is finding it must undergo a process of very gradual forward movement, with many delays and some reverses. However, as major Asian economies, such as India and China, emerge as world manufacturing powers, Europe is increasingly aware that if it wants to remain competitive on the global market, more unification is required. The interesting fact is that Europe is doing this while individual groups are seeking greater control over local, more nationalist affairs.

■ The Middle East

The region that suffered the most strife following the Second World War was the Middle East. The area around the city of Jerusalem proved to be an especially difficult problem to solve; indeed, the problems have yet to be resolved. The city of Jerusalem and the region around it, known at the time as Palestine, presented a series of old and new problems that both the local inhabitants and the

former colonial powers had to deal with. First, the city of Jerusalem was considered a holy city to all of the peoples living in the region: Jews, Muslims, and Christians and all claimed it as theirs (Christians claiming it as a way to settle the dispute). Second, Jerusalem and the Palestine area had been the home of the Arabs for nearly 2,000 years; however, the Jews claimed Jerusalem and Palestine as their ancestral homeland from an even earlier time, and also claim that God granted them the land. Third, while Palestine had been under British colonial control, the Balfour Declaration had invited the Jews to return to Palestine and make it a homeland. Fourth, the world had great compassion for the Jews following the atrocities of World War II. However, the Balfour document also promised the Arabs already living in Palestine that the arrival of the Jews would not affect them, thus rendering the document entirely inconsistent.

In 1946 the British granted independence to Transjordan (which changed its name to Jordan a few years later). However, in 1948 the United Nations created the new nation of Israel as a permanent homeland for the Jews. The boundaries of the proposed 1948 Jewish state and the Palestinian state are shown in Figure 49.2.

Immediately upon the creation of the nation of Israel, war broke out between the Israelis and Palestinians. The Israelis, with U.S. backing, were militarily much stronger than their Arab neighbors, and when a truce was agreed to, Israel was in possession of a large amount of land in Palestine and many Palestinian refugees. Many Palestinians living in the area given to Israel fled to the neighboring area of the western bank of the Jordan River (an area under Jordanian supervision). Tensions between Israel and its Arab nations continued until, in 1967, war again broke out between them. Israel was once again victorious, and this time occupied all of the land between the Jordan River and the Mediterranean Sea.

While many radical Arabs still insist that the nation of Israel exists on land stolen from them and that the only solution to the problem is the eradication of Israel as a nation and the return of all Palestinian lands to the Arabs, a larger, more moderate element now accepts the existence of

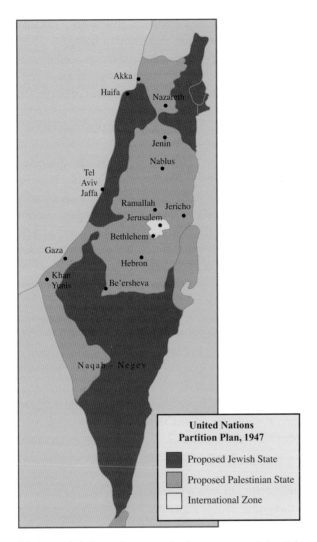

**United Nations
Partition Plan, 1947**

■ Proposed Jewish State

■ Proposed Palestinian State

□ International Zone

Figure 49.2 ■ *A map of the proposed Jewish and Palestinian states.*

The fractured nature of the Israeli Knesset (parliament) has resulted in disproportionate power for the radical parties within Israel. This has complicated the peace process. Further problems have occurred because of the establishment of Jewish settlements within the Palestinian areas taken by Israel in 1967. These Jewish settlers are especially radical in their demands for no transfer of land back to Palestinian control.

The Palestinians are likewise afflicted by disproportionate power for radical elements. The many abuses of the Jewish government toward Palestinians have resulted in the formation of several extremist Palestinian groups who will take any action, regardless of its long-term consequences, to protest and disrupt the peace process.

Therefore, it has been difficult to achieve any compromise or lasting peace when the more extreme groups have such power. These groups refuse to compromise or honor past agreements, and they make inflammatory demands on one another. Furthermore, when the moderates are in control and headway is made, the radicals on both sides engage in acts of terrorism and oppression to anger the other side and resort to violence and assassinations to keep trust from being gained and compromise from being achieved. Tensions have thus continued into current times, although recently the Palestinians have been granted some partial sovereignty and self-government in return for suppression of violence against Jewish targets. Both sides must show restraint and good will. Long-held beliefs may need to be changed. Some people may need to move. Others may need to accept inconveniences. Change can be difficult. Creativity is needed!

■ The United States of America

Following World War II, the United States had a decade of prosperity and domestic tranquility at home, even though the public was also focused on the Soviet Union and the spread of communism. The Soviets had developed atomic weapons shortly following World War II and as tension between the USA and USSR increased, a fear of communism spreading to the United States grew

Israel as a nation, but would like to see Israel give back the land it occupied in the 1967 war that was not within the original boundaries granted Israel by the UN. On the Israeli side, the moderates understand that to achieve peace in the region, some compromise and sacrifice is going to have to be made by Israel, including a return of the land won in 1967. However, the Israeli radicals (both political and religious) do not want to turn back any land to the Palestinians, either for security reasons or because they believe that God promised this land to the Jews.

until a full-blown **red scare** swept across the country. It was headed by Senator Joseph McCarthy and his hunt for communists in both Hollywood and Washington, D.C. McCarthy accused many of being communists, and while most were not, both movie stars and politicians found it difficult to recover their careers once such accusations were made. McCarthy was eventually censored by the Senate for these attacks.

Despite the red scare, the 1950s were relatively calm compared to the turbulent and violent 1960s in the United States. The 1960s saw the rise of the Civil Rights movement, the Women's Liberation movement, the establishment of the hippie counterculture, the height of the unpopular Vietnam War, and the assassination of several popular figures, including President John F. Kennedy, his brother and presidential candidate Robert F. Kennedy, and civil rights leader Dr. Martin Luther King Jr. America was in turmoil, and seemed to be falling apart.

These turbulent times would pass. By the middle of the 1970s, many corrections had been made to American society to help alleviate the pressures that had built up during the 1960s. After a time, when the United States seemed to be falling behind the USSR technologically, America met the challenge of President Kennedy and put a man on the moon ahead of the Russians in 1969. The Civil Rights movement also had been extremely difficult (indeed, things were still far from perfect), but by the mid-1970s tensions had eased considerably, thanks to the Supreme Court striking down the concept of "separate, but equal" based on race. The integration of schools and other public facilities was also accomplished and accepted by the vast majority of America by this time. Finally, several laws and constitutional amendments now protected the voting rights of African Americans and removed many of the barriers that had kept African Americans from becoming fully involved in politics.

Furthermore, by the mid-1970s, President Richard Nixon was finally pulling American troops out of Vietnam. The development of the birth control pill and the Supreme Court's protection of a woman's right to an abortion in *Roe v. Wade* served as the finale to the strident women's liberation movement. Continued work for women's equality proceeds, but with less anger and militancy.

The hippie movement and drug counterculture still existed, but where it seemed a great danger to the moral fabric of America during the 1960s, it seemed little more than quaint and removed from the mainstream of American culture by the 1980s.

Many issues continued to divide America even after the 1980s. Examples would be abortion rights and economic parity. However, a certain calm seemed to be descending on America, especially after the fall of communism in 1989. The waning of the twentieth century looked to herald the dawning of a better age for mankind. Science and technology had taken amazing leaps over the previous century, particularly in the fields of medicine and computer technology, making life on Earth both longer and easier. The twenty-first century looked to possibly be an era of relative peace and prosperity.

However, only a few years into this new century, many other problems have arrived and, in many ways, the world is more unpredictable and chaotic than before. The attacks on New York City and Washington, D.C. on September 11, 2001, made the United States and the world aware that terrorism was a constant threat anywhere and at anytime. Bombings have also occurred in many locations, including Spain and England. It seems, at least early in this new century, that a worldwide struggle between legitimate governments and terrorist groups may be the defining struggle of the twenty-first century.

Another difficulty is the role of the United States as the world's lone superpower. The United States is currently walking a difficult road where much of the underdeveloped world looks to the United States for trade, military assistance, and humanitarian aid, while America's traditional allies in Europe think America has become too unilaterally involved in world affairs and should rely more heavily on Europe for advice. Thus, the United States feels it must defend its role as a unilateral power, while still working to build multilateral goodwill and cooperation. Underlying all of these concerns is the ever-increasing economic and lifestyle gap between the developed and the developing world that causes the underdeveloped world to resent the United States and Europe, even as they request their assistance.

The twenty-first century, just like all other centuries in human history, will have its own set of problems for humankind to struggle with and solve, whether it be the ones listed here or others that now we can't currently even conceive. Yet, if the history of the world has taught us anything, we can rely on humanity to use its creativity to find solutions to the problems and push us into the future.

■ Literature in the Modern Era

The near-constant warfare and other serious problems that engulfed the twentieth century led to a general pessimism in much of the literature of the era. Inspired by earlier authors such as Dostoevsky, Kierkegaard, and Nietzsche, many new authors adopted a philosophy known as **existentialism.** Many existentialists do not believe in God, and feel that humans only exist by mere chance. Existentialism teaches that the only reality is what the individual believes to be true. In existentialism, all standards are discarded and reality is individualized. Therefore, absolute truth does not exist, but each person decides what is true for him or her. Existentialists believe that humans can only find meaning in life by becoming engaged in full awareness of their responsibility for their own actions. In essence, what is true or right for one person may not be true for another. Everything is subjective—based on the individual experience, situation, and beliefs.

Two of the leading existentialist authors were **Jean-Paul Sartre** and **Albert Camus.** Sartre's most famous novel, *Nausea,* is a Kafka-esque story about a researcher who becomes convinced that inanimate objects and daily situations are encroaching upon his ability to define himself. Sartre's philosophical treatise *Being and Nothingness* serves as the foundation and blueprint for modern existentialism. Albert Camus's most important novels are *The Stranger* and *The Myth of Sisyphus.* In *The Stranger* (whose title is better translated into English as *The Foreigner* or *The Outsider*), Camus tells the story of a lonely and isolated French colonial living in Algeria, who needlessly murders a local Arab. Then, as the Frenchman goes through his trial and his imprisonment while awaiting execution, he begins to understand the value and meaning of life. Camus also uses the novel to explore the theme that humans, and not God, are responsible for their own actions and the consequences. In *The Myth of Sisyphus,* Camus introduces the philosophy of the absurd, which holds that our lives are meaningless and have no values other than those we create. It is a bleak and pessimistic essay/novel in which Camus wonders aloud that if the world is so pointless, what is a better alternative than suicide?

Not all literature of the twentieth century is so bleak. New genres, notably **fantasy** and **science fiction,** were created or vastly expanded and seemed to fight the literary pessimism of the age. Fantasy, pioneered by English professors **J. R. R. Tolkien** and **C. S. Lewis,** used escapism to tell stories of mankind's ability to do noble and heroic things and overcome daunting, even impossible, tasks. Written during and after the two world wars (both men fought in World War I), Tolkien's *Lord of the Rings* and Lewis's *Chronicles of Narnia* both dealt with the theme of accomplishment over darkness and hope in dark and strange circumstances. A recent series that is wonderfully fun and has the same sense of virtue winning over darkness is J. K. Rowling's *Harry Potter* novels.

Meanwhile, authors such as Aldous Huxley, **Isaac Asimov, Arthur C. Clarke,** and Ray Bradbury helped develop the modern genre of science fiction. Science fiction was created in the late 1800s by authors such as H. G. Wells and Jules Verne. However, these early sci-fi authors used science more as a backdrop for their action and adventure stories. This genre was expanded by Aldous Huxley and George Orwell, who we discussed in Chapter 47. Following the lead of these early authors, Asimov, Clarke, and others used science fiction as a means of showing the heights that humans could attain, and to highlight the dangers of man's possible future if certain trends were not changed. Among the classics of this genre are Asimov's *Foundation* and *I, Robot;* Clarke's *2001:*

Figure 49.3 ■ *Number 1 by Jackson Pollack. Digital Image © The Museum of Modern Art/Licensed by SCALA/Art Resources, NY. © 2010 The Pollock-Krasner Foundation/Artists Rights Society (ARS), NY.*

A Space Odyssey; and Ray Bradbury's *The Martian Chronicles* and *Fahrenheit 451.*

The visual arts from World War II onward had a similar underlying theme as existentialism in literature did: The individual artist and his or her own vision were all-important. All of the rules and forms were thrown out (if they hadn't been already by cubism and dadaism), and what could be considered art became completely subjective.

Jackson Pollack took art to the next level of individualism by completely abandoning form. Pollack made his paintings by pouring or splattering the paint onto the canvas. Pollack's painting *Number 1* is a good example of his work and is shown in Figure 49.3.

Andy Warhol developed the concept of pop art. Warhol took everyday items or iconic celebrity figures and gave the pictures of them strange twists to make them into art. His "portraits" of Mick Jagger and Marilyn Monroe and his Campbell's soup cans are good examples of his work. Figure 49.4 shows an example of Warhol's work.

Sculpture followed a similar pattern to the other arts of the time as well in that it broke away from the traditional manner and delved into the abstract and formless. Sculptors such as Constantin Brancusi and Henry Moore began to explore

Figure 49.4 ■ *Pop art by Andy Warhol. © Andy Warhol Foundation/CORBIS.*

the abstract side of sculpture, where shape and form suggested objects or concepts to the viewer's mind rather than trying to recreate them, such as Brancusi's *Bird in Space* (see Figure 49.5) and Moore's *Recumbent Figure.* Meanwhile, sculptor Alexander Calder invented the mobile and began experimenting with the different things that could

Figure 49.6 ■ *A mobile* by Alexander Calder.
*"Crinkly" by Alexander Calder, Calder Foundation, New York/
Art Resources, NY. © 2010 Calder Foundation/Artists Rights
Society (ARS), New York.*

Figure 49.5 ■ Bird in Flight *by Brancusi.* Digital
Image *© The Museum of Modern Art/Licensed by SCALA/
Art Resource, NY. © 2010 Artists Rights Society (ARS), New
York/ADAGP, Paris.*

be explored in that medium. One of his mobiles is
seen in Figure 49.6.

■ Values

The combination of rapid changes in society toward greater individualism and a literary under-
pinning of existentialism has led to elimination of
many social structures and the rule of individual
freedom. This situation is demonstrated most dramatically in art. Recent examples of art in which
all structure has been lost include a piece made by
attaching paint brushes to elephants' trunks and
then letting the elephants daub paint on a canvas.
Similarly, a painting was made by dipping a dog's
feet in paint and having the dog walk on a canvas.
These "artworks" lack the basic elements of
value and skill. They are, simply, a unique idea
and nothing more. However, some "art experts"
today are willing to recognize such works as art
and may even buy them, or at least exhibit them in
their galleries. (Exhibiting such art is probably

within the definition of freedom of expression, but
buying them seems to reward the ridiculous.)

Some artists gain their value by being deliberately provocative. There was a painting of a
Madonna made, in part, of cow dung. When it
was exhibited in Brooklyn and there was a great
outrage from religious people, the artist said that
the purpose of the art had been accomplished. It
existed, therefore, only to engage the mind of
the viewer. To that extent, this art is probably the
logical extension of the trend in art that we have
seen since the Romantic period—the increasing
prevalence of emotion and exoticism in art. The
Impressionists asked the viewer to complete the
picture, thus carrying the Romantic concept even
further. These provocative modern works ask the
viewer to both complete the art and to be offended by it.

The completion of art by the viewer, or for
music, the listener, has also been demonstrated in
the work by **John Cage** called *4'33"(Four Minutes, Thirty-three Seconds).* The piece is silent for
the entire length of time indicated in the title.
Some see Cage's work as ridiculous, whereas others think that Cage is tapping into a zone of new
meaning in which, perhaps, the random sounds of
the concert hall are the essence of the music.
Maybe the thoughts of a person are the concept to
be learned from the piece. Whatever the concept

may be, the skill of execution is lacking and, therefore, implementation is doubtful. We do not believe that the work is creative and doubt that it qualifies as music. It is, again, a clever idea and nothing more.

What is art? Are there values? We are reminded of the Greeks and their ideas of symmetry, beauty, proportion. In some views, we appear to have lost all values of the past and are redefining art in light of what the artist wants to say and not in terms of whether anyone is participating in the conversation. Just as the Romantic composers gave their listeners methods of understanding their message, modern artists must communicate a message to us. Most of us also believe that the values of the past, whether Greek or Romantic, are important. The complete ignoring of these values seems to neglect that key element of creativity.

We realize that creativity is different for different people. Bach was not immediately accepted as great. Therefore, the test of time will say whether these totally individualistic works will be remembered and valued as anything beyond mere curiosities that represent an age where values were being questioned or ignored. For us, at least for the moment, they might be creative to some, and they might have value to some, but they need to have more value to us.

Hegel, a German philosopher, said that somewhere or somehow the natural juices from which organisms were created must have "inclined toward the Greek." By this he meant that there was some tendency that led humans to seek perfection in spirit, beauty, and behavior. We think that Douglas Hofstadter, author of the book *Gödel, Escher, Bach* expressed this same concept when he said, "Perhaps what differentiates highly creative ideas from ordinary ones is some combined sense of beauty, simplicity, and harmony."

This seeking for aesthetical perfection could not be explained by science. We believe that something in humans strives for this beauty that is beyond empirical knowledge. It has always been present in humans and has given us some special reasons to belong to a civilization. We should not ignore these values.

■ Timeline—Important Dates

Date	Event
1945–1949	Eastern European countries become Soviet satellites
1949–1953	Korean War
1959	Cuba becomes communist
1962	Cuban missile crisis
1965–1973	Vietnam War
1979–1989	Soviet War in Afghanistan
1989	Destruction of the Berlin wall
1991	Breakup of the Soviet Union

■ Suggested Readings

Asimov, Isaac, *Foundation* (set), Spectra, 2001.

Hofstadter, Douglas R., *Gödel, Escher, Bach,* Basic Books, 1999.

Lewis, C. S., *The Chronicles of Narnia,* HarperTrophy, 1994.

Roberts, J. M., *A Short History of the World,* Oxford University Press, 1993.

Rowling, J. K., *Harry Potter* (set), Scholastic, 2004.

Strickland, Carol, *The Annotated Mona Lisa,* Andrews and McMeel, 1992.

Tolkien, J. R. R., *The Lord of the Rings,* Del Rey Books, 2001.

Epilogue
Personal Creativity

> I have no special gift. I am only passionately curious.
>
> —*Albert Einstein*

What Has Been Learned?

The full title of this book is *The History of Creativity in the Arts, Science, and Technology.* It seems reasonable that we might discuss each of the elements of the title and assess what we have learned about each one. Let's begin with history.

For most people, other than historians, history is a peripheral subject. It is something that we all have studied, but its study is not in the mainstream of our daily lives. If you think about your mind as a filing cabinet with each drawer as a major subject area, you have opened the history drawer and put some information in it. This is logical and analytical thinking, illustrated in Figure 50.1. For many, the history drawer may have been seldom used previously. For some, it might be opened only infrequently again, at least as an area of study. That is a shame.

History has some important lessons for us, and not just as an academic pursuit. The lessons can help us with whatever our area of major focus might be. What we need to do is think about history in an interconnected way. That is, we should try to think of how history relates to our lives. Referring to the analogy of a filing cabinet again, you should try to make a leap to connect the information in one drawer (that is, in one subject) with the material in another drawer (some other subject where, perhaps, you have a new interest or a new problem to solve). In this way, you develop analogies and unique thinking. This type of thinking is critically important in creativity. The situation we are describing is illustrated in Figure 50.2.

We have looked at changes in history as moments when creativity was critical. As Mihaly Csikszentmihalyi (one of the world's leading experts on creativity) has said, "Creativity is the engine that drives cultural evolution." When considered in the light of creativity, history then becomes a way to learn about change. It is, therefore, helpful in all areas of human endeavor.

The value of the creativity viewpoint of history might best be reinforced with several examples of

How Our Brains File Information
Logical Thinking

Figure 50.1 ■ *File cabinet drawers are like subjects. Learning about a subject is like filing material into the drawer. This thinking is logical and linear.*

creative people who lived during the time period covered by this volume—1500 to the present. With each person, we will identify one aspect of their creativity. Hopefully you will be able to see applications of these various traits in your life.

■ Creative People in History

■ **Lorenzo de Medici**—He saw value in sponsoring art and learning for his own personal growth and the improvement of his city. Like Pericles of ancient Athens, Lorenzo saw the big picture of what it takes to be great and he made it happen. He improved his city and himself. Following the lead of his father and grandfather, he laid the foundation for much creative work that was to follow. Having a vision is a key element of creativity.

How Our Brains File Information
Intuitive Thinking

Figure 50.2 ■ *Leaping from one drawer to another is like making connections between subjects. These connections are like intuitive or analogy thinking.*

■ **Leonardo da Vinci**—No one else in history has been able to integrate so many areas of expertise at such a high level of accomplishment. Leonardo was an artist, scientist, technologist, engineer, and writer. He was able to think linearly in many fields but was superb because he could also think laterally. He was the prototype of a Renaissance Man because he could combine all of the elements of creativity better than anyone else.

■ **Niccolò Machiavelli**—If anyone had a purpose in his work, it was Machiavelli. He catered to the favors of the Medici court in Florence and sought to return to their service. It was not to be. However, the motivation he felt was a key part of his creativity. We might also look to our motivations and, if insufficient for the task at hand, strive to find new ways to be motivated. Machiavelli would have enjoyed our efforts to control our thinking in that way.

- **Michelangelo**—Perhaps even better than the ancient Greeks, Michelangelo was able to see the Form of the figure he wanted to sculpt or paint. This vision of the Form allowed him to execute his works with a majesty and power that no other artists could capture. His creativity was, therefore, in the unique vision and the superb execution which, especially in his case, were linked.

- **Elizabeth I**—History has rarely seen a person so adept at solving problems. She was inundated with them when she became queen, but her intuitive understanding of the way through the complexities of these problems allowed her to both solve them and to grow, personally and nationally. Her time was named for her, and justly so. She dominated the Elizabethan Age.

- **William Shakespeare**—It was not the plots that were creative, at least not always so, but rather, it was the way the plots were executed. His command of the language was wonderfully rich, both in vocabulary (some invented by him) but also in meter and rhyme. However, the language was only a means to express his understanding of humans and their trials and joys. His creativity was in putting language and understanding together in unique and powerful ways. All the world looks to Shakespeare's works as insightful and motivating explorations of the nature of human beings.

- **Artemisia Gentileschi**—She was very brave to pursue her career as an artist even though she was the only woman in the studio or, it seems, the only woman in any artist studio anywhere up to that time. She was assaulted (perhaps several times), but she endured, even though she received no comfort from her father or from the others in the studio. Her bravery in the face of overwhelming difficulties is an example for all creative people who, usually to a lesser degree, still need to be courageous to push their unique ideas through to realization in spite of dissent and, occasionally, ridicule.

- **Lorenzo Bernini**—Born with wonderful natural ability in sculpting, Bernini was still forced to work in the shadow of the great Michelangelo. How does an artist cope with such a burden? Bernini met the issue straightforwardly; he simply felt that he was better than the best sculptor that had ever lived. Bernini saw a fluidity and realism in his own work that even Michelangelo did not have. Therefore, Bernini accepted commissions for works that were so technically challenging that they would have daunted anyone else. His unique ideas of motion and realism in sculpting were executed to perfection. He demonstrated belief in his own talent and that gave him the confidence to succeed.

- **John Locke**—Locke, like his approximate contemporary René Descartes, was able to get to the basics of a concept. For Locke, the basics were the fundamental reasons that humans had for entering into civilization. He showed that governments, ideally, existed to protect these fundamental rights. The world changed because of his creative concepts.

- **Louis XIV**—When creative people implement their ideas, they must have power. Sometimes it is power over self and sometimes it is power over those who would do the work for us. No one demonstrated the use of power better than Louis XIV. He had a vision for his country and then he made it happen by making others do what he wanted. The courtiers sought even the smallest recognition and favor from him, thus giving him the ability to choose those who could best accomplish what he wanted. He moved the court from Paris to Versailles to isolate the courtiers and to gain more direct influence over them. We can also use vision and then strong execution to accomplish our goals.

- **Isaac Newton**—His mind was undoubtedly very sharp, but another trait may have been just as important to his success as the world's greatest scientist. That trait was concentration. He could be so absorbed in a problem that he was oblivious to others who might be present in the room, even friends who came for dinner. His focus was not only deep, it could extend over a long period of time. Newton was also interested in many areas of inquiry, so his focus was also wide. What better combination for creativity?

■ **Johann Sebastian Bach**—Hard work was the trait that set Bach apart from others. He was highly talented as both a composer and an organist—as were many others of his time and later. But, how could anyone measure up to the immense body of work that he accomplished? For very little pay and almost no personal honor, Bach wrote cantatas for his church weekly for more than eight years. He supervised the performances, including the rehearsals. He found time to teach music performance to his own family and to others in the city. His highly organized mind loved the beauty of music, but it must have also given him the ability to work on many things simultaneously. He had mind control to go with his work ethic.

■ **George Frederick Handel**—Inspiration is the creative trait that Handel represents. His work on *Messiah* was so rapidly accomplished that we remain amazed at the thought of it, especially when we consider the short length of time (about 30 days) and the newness of the genre of oratorio for him. He borrowed some of the themes from works that he had previously written, but that only emphasizes his creativity in seeing multiple ways in which a theme can be set. He was open to inspiration and allowed it to flow throughout his being so that great works could be accomplished.

■ **Benjamin Franklin**—Being wise and being clever are not the same. Wisdom comes with experience and with understanding of the situation. Cleverness comes with unique associations and quick thinking. Franklin was both wise and clever. His wisdom helped to shape America. His cleverness, especially in the foreign courts of Europe where he was highly respected, helped give America the breath of life. Both wisdom and cleverness contribute to creativity.

■ **Wolfgang Mozart**—His natural talent was only part of his creativity. Many people have natural talent and don't become great. Mozart was able to maximize his native abilities. One way that he did this was practice, especially as a youth. Of course, when you are a child

prodigy, practice is probably quite fun, but still, hard work is required. Mozart's work improved as he became more adept in music. He pushed himself to be great.

■ **Napoleon Bonaparte**—Napoleon could see the big picture. During a battle, this ability led him to know the right moment and the right place to attack. In politics, he saw the pathway for France to stability and glory. He knew when to compromise (as with the Catholic Church) and when to remain firm (as with dissenters from the revolution). His creativity was just as broad as his view.

■ **Ludwig Beethoven**—Few people have handicaps so devastating as deafness would be to a composer. When Beethoven realized that he was becoming deaf, he was devastated. However, he gradually changed his thinking so that he resolved to overcome his deafness and succeed in spite of it. The emotions that he used to force himself in this task spilled out into his music, but his discipline was also evident. The combination was highly creative.

■ **Charles Darwin**—The idea of evolution was not entirely unique when it was proposed by Darwin. He had the ability to synthesize from many different sources. He studied biology, geology, population theory, and other disciplines and then drew from them for his own work. This ability uses both lateral thinking and some linear thinking in analyzing how to fit all the ideas together.

■ **Giuseppe Verdi**—Like his contemporary, Richard Wagner, Verdi was determined to create the type of opera he envisioned without regard to the critics of the day. Both Verdi and Wagner, independently and in quite different ways, sought to make opera a richer experience by enhancing all the parts of the opera. Up to then, opera was largely a showcase for talented singers. They made opera a wonderful theatrical and musical experience. The improvement of opera as an art form was not an easy task, but the success of Verdi and Wagner, even in their own time, confirmed that their determination to push past early critics was the right thing to do.

■ **Louis Pasteur**—This great scientist was twice blessed in creativity traits. He was astute enough to see the implications of errors and mistakes. This ability was related to his preparedness in the field in which he worked. He trained himself to be aware and then to capture the information, even when it seemed to be an anomaly. The other blessing, perhaps related, was Pasteur's ability to relate his findings to the world around him. He simply made the world a better place to live.

■ **Thomas Edison**—The trait of perseverance was demonstrated by Edison as well as by anyone else in history. He pursued his inventive concepts with great vigor and determination. He also had a vision of entire systems and what was needed to make the various parts work together.

■ **Mohandas Gandhi**—The ability to break with normal methods and pursue creative new ideas was exemplified in Gandhi's concept of peaceful disobedience. He changed an empire through his quiet pursuit of freedom.

■ **Winston Churchill**—Sometimes others will see our creative works and trumpet them to the world. At other times, the creative person may have to sell the ideas. In the case of Churchill, the selling of the ideas was the creative gift. He understood language and also understood timing. By combining these, he was able to convince the world of the rightness of his position. He rallied people when they were down and praised them when they were up. His manner of doing it was creative in both ideas and implementation.

■ **Albert Einstein**—If we refer to the quotation at the beginning of this chapter, we can see what Einstein thought his own special gift was—curiosity. We also believe that Einstein possessed other creative talents, such as concentration, the ability to conceive powerful analogies, and, of course, intelligence.

■ **Pablo Picasso**—Picasso's art went through many stages. That is a reflection of his intense effort to master the art of the past. He felt that only by mastering what had gone on before could he change it meaningfully. Then, when he wanted to create a totally new way of painting, he was able to do it with depth of understanding and obvious professionalism. Others, copycats, rarely could duplicate the depth and meaning because they rarely perfected their skills first.

■ **Adolf Hitler**—Bad people can be creative. In Hitler's case, his creativity was enhanced by his single-visioned determination. He justly titled his autobiography *Mein Kampf (My Struggle)* because he understood his own determination to accomplish the goal he had set. However, Hitler lacked the ability to change his goal and determination when the situation changed. He was too fanatical. Hence, even good traits, if taken to the extreme, can be negative.

■ **Frank Lloyd Wright**—An architect who understood the need to integrate buildings with their environment. In many ways, this concept has led to the strong integration of environmental concerns in our lives.

■ **George Gershwin**—A great composer who showed how to combine different genres of music, in his case, jazz and classical. This type of combination is often the essence of creativity.

You will undoubtedly have a different set of creative people and, perhaps, some different creative trait for the ones that we have chosen. The purpose of the list is not just to link these people to creative traits, but to demonstrate how history can give us insights into so many aspects of life and, especially, creativity.

■ Creativity in the Arts

We can also discuss the next facet of this book—the arts. Just as history is off the mainstream for most people, arts are seen as enrichment in life but rarely mainstream. However, where history would give us lessons to learn, art's function in our lives is different. It gives us aesthetic enjoyment. (We agree that a good history book can also give us this aesthetic enjoyment, but that is the literature speaking and not the history.) We have, therefore, studied the various art forms to give us a background whereby we would be able to more richly enjoy life because we know more about what we are experiencing in the art. It is also a pattern of creativity that we might emulate, with greater or lesser talent.

However, art is also academic. It is a skill to be learned and a subject to be studied. Even in this academic realm, we learn much about creativity. For instance, consider the following artistic features and their development: perspective, realism, color, light and dark, landscape, technique, emotion, and communication. We have not only traced the history of art's development, we have expanded out understanding of creativity if we will apply these same features to our creative efforts.

Most artists see themselves as uniquely creative, not only as artists in comparison to nonartists, but also in comparison to other artists. Although their creativity is often admirable, they should look for the creativity in other fields and learn from it. DaVinci investigated the science of light, in part to be a better artist. Picasso studied about science's view of time. Those who would do art could similarly study the world around them and the creative techniques of others.

We who are not directly involved in artistic creativity can, of course, learn about creativity from artists. That has been one of the reasons we studied the artists of the past. Lessons learned from artists in the preceding list are examples that can be applied to other artists. We can also learn about creativity by studying great artworks themselves. Technique changes can be creative, as with the Impressionists. We can also learn about the essence of what art is, or is not, by studying the many forms of expression that have been called art in the twentieth century. Perhaps art has new meaning as it seeks to involve both the artist and the beholder.

Creativity in Science

We hope you have been impressed with the importance of science in shaping our modern world.

Understanding the natural world has, of course, been the basic purpose of science, but the development of political theory and social standards has also depended on the scientific method.

Science is mostly a linear way of thinking. It takes data under well-defined circumstances and then analyzes the data to find the correlations that help to build generalized theories. Science's objective and dispassionate approach to inquiry seems logical and linear, but recent studies of the nature of the scientific method have revealed a surprising subjectivity and love of beauty that even most scientists are not aware of. We can also see the inspirational side of scientific inquiry as, for example, when Pasteur recognized the importance of attenuated serum in developing the concepts of inoculations. In general, while most scientists are linear and logical, truly great science, especially when breakthroughs of knowledge occur, happen with lateral thinking and insight beyond the narrow field of investigation.

Scientists have a tendency to believe that their method is the only pathway to truth. We have shown that science has limitations as a method of discovering truth. Moreover, science does not even possess all the attributes normally assumed to exist within science (like objectivity). Hence, we have noted that most great scientists are able to think both linearly and laterally. Many have a healthy respect for knowledge that is not science-based.

Creativity and Technology

Our world is better because of technology. This is, after all, technology's purpose. We may not be able to completely control all of the technology we have, but that is not the fault of the technology. Rather, it is the fault of people who would use the technology for bad or inappropriate purposes. We should not try to control technology by preventing its development. Doing so would be to stop an important component of progress. We might as well put our heads in the sand.

However, as Rodney Custer has said in his discussion in *Technology and the Quality of Life,*

In a real sense, technology is one of the defining dimensions of our time. It is woven seamlessly into the very fabric of our culture. At times, its presence is obvious, stark, and even harsh. More often, it simply hums along under the hood, behind the screen, or within our bodies.

He goes on to say,

Technology does not simply impact culture. . . . The mix is inherently interactive, complex, and dynamic and should be explored in that way. . . . [C]hanges in technology were followed by cultural and social adaptations. Technology is viewed as an innovative, and often singular, force on culture and cultural values and social change lags behind its leadership.

This suggests that technology is the basic agent for change.

If that is the case, then the linkage between technology and creativity (also a basic agent for change) should be intimate. In fact, technology may be the most fundamental of creative areas because of its basic nature. We have, for instance, noted that much of art depends on technology (from the methods of brush strokes to the tools of art like brushes, paint tubes, and musical instruments). Therefore, we can probably get a deeper understanding of creativity by examining how it is done in technology than in any other field.

How is technology done? First, a need is recognized or an interesting occurrence is noted. That is, there is a motivation for taking some action. Then, usually after considerable pondering, the thought that sparks technology innovation occurs. That may be a new way of doing things or an old concept that is applied to a new area. Usually it is an association from one area to another. Then, the value of the technology is assessed. If there is no value, then technology stops. After all, the definition of technology is mastering the environment for human benefit. After the value is judged to be worthwhile, the idea is implemented. Note that

the direction of the implementation is known—toward the idea that has been defined. Then, persistence is required because, inevitably, difficulties arise and must be overcome. We see, therefore, that all of the elements of creativity are present in technological development.

■ Creativity and You

We hope that the exploration of creativity throughout history given in this book has been interesting for you. However, that discussion was only a portion of our purpose. We also wanted to encourage the development of your (the reader's) personal creativity. Perhaps the summary of creative individuals in history will serve as a reminder of some of the personal creative lessons that can be gained from history.

After reading this book, what steps could you take to continue to improve creativity? We suggest that you think about these steps in two categories—steps to improve linear creativity and steps to improve lateral creativity. Linear and lateral thinking are associated with the left-brain and right-brain thinking, respectively. Scott Thorpe has commented in his book, *How to Think Like Einstein,* on the subject of the two sides of the brain:

Could the answers you've been seeking be on the other side of your head? Your brain is really two brains. You use one of them more, but the other brain is just as clever in a different way. It too has been diligently gathering information on your problem, and may have a solution for you. However, because of your dominant brain, the other brain has had trouble making its opinions known. Give your other brain an avenue to express its ideas. To divine a solution from your other brain, switch hands and techniques.

The chart in Figure 50.3 illustrates some of the basics of these thinking patterns. In our opinion, both types of thinking, linear and lateral, are required for abundant creativity. We give, therefore, some

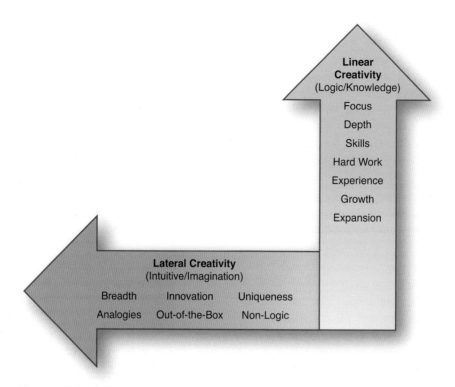

Figure 50.3 ■ *Linear and lateral thinking (Derived from* Lateral Thinking *by Edward de Bono, Harper and Row, 1970).*

ideas that have proven to be useful in increasing and maintaining linear and lateral thinking.

■ Improving Linear Thinking

Linear thinking usually depends on an accumulation of knowledge in a single field. Therefore, to improve linear thinking, the first step is to continue to acquire knowledge in that field. Usually that is done by reading the literature of the field, performing experiments or analyses, and by attending conferences in the field. The conferences assist by providing a venue to hear current work and to network with others who are in the field. Both of these activities help in learning about the domain and gaining more knowledge in the field.

There is great value in being at the edge of knowledge in a particular field. It allows you to understand just how deep a subject can get and to

gauge the depth of your knowledge in that field and in other fields in comparison to the total depth that is possible. This is, usually, very humbling. Without that gauge of depth, a person who has shallow knowledge in many fields might assume (incorrectly) that they also have depth. Only by getting depth in at least one field can we really gauge our depth in other fields.

There is, however, more to linear thinking than just the accumulation of knowledge in a field. We should also understand that knowledge and its relevance. In other words, we should not just ask "what" but also ask "why." The question of "why" has fallen in importance since the seventeenth century when Bacon laid down the rules for the modern scientific method. Because "why" questions cannot readily be investigated with experiments, science has stopped asking that type of question. We can take the example of a watch to understand this concept better. A scientist would be able to observe the watch working and see that it could (or could not) keep accurate time. The scientist could take it apart and observe the gears and timing mechanisms to understand the nature of its workings. A technologist might be able to make a similar or improved watch. However, neither would really be able to answer the question, "Why does the watch exist?" They might answer, "To tell the time," but that would be a supposition. If the watch were very expensive, the user might wear it simply to gain prestige. Alternately, it might exist because the watchmaker needed the money, or might have wanted to demonstrate a particular skill.

An even more interesting example is about the human body. We might ask, "Why do we have bodies?" A scientist might say, "Because evolution made it." We don't think that is really an answer and, even if it were, we then have the question, "Why does evolution make it?" The answer to that might be, "It is just the way it is," to which we ask again, "Why?" Perhaps the answer lies outside of modern science.

Aristotle understood the need for a "why" question and included it in his ancient scientific method. We think that Aristotle might have been right—not in the scientific sense, but in the true knowledge sense. We encourage you to ask the "why" question.

We have found that people are able to better understand the field in which they have depth when they explain their knowledge to someone else. That explanation is increased even further if the explanation is in writing rather than given verbally. Hence, write about your in-depth knowledge and explain it to someone else. If you want a real test of your ability to explain your knowledge, explain it to someone outside your field.

We think that part of left-brain thinking and accumulation of knowledge in a particular field is associated with being focused. This mental discipline is also important in being creative. Benjamin Franklin said in this regard, "Genius is the ability to hold one's vision steady until it becomes a reality." The focus of at least one genius is instructive in this regard. Scott Thorpe reports the following about Einstein:

Once Einstein and an assistant needed a paper clip. All they could find was a single bent paper clip. Einstein proceeded to try and straighten it, but he needed a tool. He and the assistant searched the office again. This time they found a box of paper clips. Einstein took a paper clip from the box and bent it into a tool to straighten the first paper clip. The assistant asked why Einstein was bothering to repair the paper clip now that they had a whole box. Einstein responded, "Once I am set upon a goal it becomes difficult to deflect me."

We don't think that this intense focus is all that is needed to be a genius, but it is an important component.

A few comments about linear knowledge are important in general. In the long run, of far greater importance than the facts you have learned is your ability to learn *how* to learn. We believe that Alvin Toffler was correct in his book *Future Shock* when he said:

The illiterate of the 21st century will not be those who cannot read or write, but those who cannot learn, unlearn, and relearn.

Toffler realized that much of what we learn will shortly be obsolete. Your ability to unlearn and relearn comes from the way you think about learning and not from the specifics. Knowledge is not the answer to the problem you are trying to solve; it is the method used to get the answer.

■ Improving Lateral Thinking

Lateral thinking is not logical. We have said that lateral thinking is *intuitive*, but that term should be taken to include several nonlogical processes such as aesthetic perception, analogous thinking, and dreaming. Learning about and participating in art is one key way to improve our lateral thinking. Inherently, good art is an aesthetic experience. We have seen paintings that seemed to draw us into them with their aesthetic force. We have heard music that moved us to tears. We have been lost in a good book. All of these reflect the nonlogical experience of art.

Another method of enhancing lateral thinking is to travel extensively. This not only gives an appreciation of new forms of art that might be observed in the distant location, but it also helps you experience a new culture that can only be approximated by a description. When you travel with someone else who is also attuned to the experience, the sensations are heightened as you share what you are seeing and feeling with that other person.

Another important method of improving lateral thinking can be understood from a study conducted at a research laboratory. The researcher was asked to investigate the output of the scientists who worked in the lab. He found that some scientists were highly productive in conceiving patents, innovating research directions, developing new products, and leading others. He called these people the *Innovators*. The researcher also found that some scientists were highly productive in pushing forward an area of research, expanding knowledge about a phenomenon, moving ideas forward, and working on teams to accomplish tasks. He called them the *Implementers*. The researcher found a third group of scientists that didn't do much of anything. They neither innovated nor implemented. He called them the *Slugs*.

The directors of the laboratory then asked the researcher to find out what were the personal characteristics that led to the three behavior types he identified. The researcher searched for correlations in the personality types, educational backgrounds, age, sex, race, and many other qualities that were suggested or imagined. Only one personal characteristic was seen to correlate. That characteristic was personal reading habits. Those who were Innovators read avidly and widely, across many fields and subjects. Those who were Implementers also read avidly but almost exclusively in their narrow field. Those who were Slugs hardly read at all.

We think that the Implementers were strengthening their linear thinking. They give a noble and valuable service to humankind. These people

move the world forward. Innovators are lateral thinkers. They read widely, and from that knowledge, make analogies that result in the new concepts and directions. They think out of the box.

■ Putting the Thinking Processes Together

Specialists in creativity have developed several methods that help anyone think more creatively. Sometimes they help with linear thinking and sometimes with lateral thinking. One of the best examples is the concept developed by Edward de Bono in his book *Six Thinking Hats*. He suggests that when a problem is to be solved, the people working on the problem focus their thinking patterns in particular ways at different times. Sometimes, for example, they would be innovative, sometimes critical, and sometimes emotional. He suggests six different thinking patterns and identifies each with a different colored hat so that, when you are thinking in one mode, you would be wearing a different hat (figuratively, unless you want to emphasize the system by wearing a real colored hat). Some of the thinking modes encourage linear thinking and some encourage lateral thinking. Therefore, de Bono's methods are designed to force us to think with both sides of our brain, but to use one side at a time.

Another powerful method for helping us integrate our left-brain and right-brain thinking is **brainstorming.** This method has been well-described by Rick Crandall in his book *Break-out Creativity.* When done properly, brainstorming can lead to amazing results. Perhaps the best practitioners of brainstorming are the folks at IDEO, an industrial design firm. Their method of brainstorming and other corporate creative techniques have been described in the book *The Art of Innovation* by Tom Kelley.

Still other methods that have been recommended are role playing, seeking illogical solutions, game playing, puzzle solving, and using humor. All are valuable.

Psychologist Mihaly Csikszentmihalyi surveyed 100 highly creative people (Nobel prize winners, Pulitzer prize winners, successful artists, renowned scientists, etc.) about the conditions under which they were most creative. Were they, for instance, more likely to be creative when alone or with other people? Did they enjoy thinking about themselves as ignorant (thus getting drive to acquire more knowledge) or intelligent (thus gaining confidence that they could solve the problem)? Did they think of themselves as realistic or imaginative? There were 10 such contrasting conditions.

The study found that, generally, the 100 highly creative people were able to be creative under both extremes of all of the conditions. Sometimes they liked to be alone to increase focus, but at other times they enjoyed the stimulation derived from other people.

We believe that the two extremes of each condition represent right-brain and left-brain thinking. These 100 creative people simply said that they could choose to think with their right brain or their left brain as the situation required. Therefore, one of the secrets of creativity is brain control. We gain an insight into that brain control capability from Napoleon:

> *Different subjects and different affairs are arranged in my head as in a cupboard. When I wish to interrupt one train of thought, I shut that drawer and open another. Do I wish to sleep? I simply close all the drawers and there I am—asleep.*

Most of us can readily practice mind control. Scott Thorpe has said,

> *If you have multiple problems you want solved, record them even if you can't consciously work on all of them. Just reviewing a problem list regularly will inspire interesting ideas. Most problems suffer from a lack of attention. We don't give difficult problems enough attention to spark a solution. But our brains can work on problems around the clock, regardless of whatever else we might be doing. The mind just needs to know that you want a solution. When you think about a*

> *problem regularly, even if it is only a brief review, your brain is reminded that the solution is needed. Your neurons will fire away until eventually you find some answers.*

Brain control can actually be quite fun. If you are conscious of working on brain control, your ability to do it will improve greatly and you will be more creative.

■ The Benefits of Being Creative

Some benefits are obvious, like making more money and being a better leader. A benefit that we would like to mention is that society itself will be better if we have more people who are creative. Because of their ability to think with both left and right sides of the brain, creative people are more likely to have knowledge of many different aspects of life. They will, therefore, be able to communicate better between the two cultures of society—science and humanities. These two cultures and the problems of not communicating between them were discussed by C. P. Snow:

> *In our society (that is, advanced western society) we have lost even the pretence of a common culture. Persons educated with the greatest intensity we know can no longer communicate with each other on the plane of their creative, intellectual and, above all, our normal life. It is leading us to interpret the past wrongly, to misjudge the present and to deny our hopes of the future. It is making it difficult or impossible for us to take good action.*

We need to integrate the thinking of the sciences with that of the humanities. Such an integration has been, of course, one purpose of this course. The authors have tried to discuss art, science, and technology seamlessly. We believe that people can be well versed in all of these areas and, therefore, can provide insights for society because they can make connections from the otherwise disparate domains.

Another personal and societal advantage of creativity is related to inner motivation and fulfillment. Abraham Maslow has described the levels of human needs. The lower levels, such as physical needs and safety needs, must be satisfied and, if not, are highly motivating. (For example, we must have food and air and will do whatever is necessary to get them.) The higher Maslow needs are less urgent but ultimately more satisfying. The highest of these needs is self-actualization. We believe that one way, perhaps the best way, to fill that need is by being creative. It will be personally fulfilling and also has the potential of contributing to society. It is from such creative activities that civilization has advanced. The desire for this type of fulfillment might have been the principal motivator that led humans out of their primitive existence and into a cooperative society that we call civilization.

We hope that this book will have contributed to your understanding of civilization and also to making *you* more creative and more personally fulfilled.

■ Suggested Readings

Crandall, Rick (editor), *Break-out Creativity,* Select Press for the Association for Innovation in Management, 1998.

Csikszentmihalyi, Mihaly, *Creativity,* HarperCollins, 1996.

Custer, Rodney, and A. Emerson Wiens, *Technology and the Quality of Life,* Council on Technology Teacher Education, 1996.

De Bono, Edward, *Six Thinking Hats,* Back Bay Books, 1999.

Kelley, Tom, *The Art of Innovation,* Doubleday, 2001.

Snow, C. P., *The Two Cultures,* Cambridge University Press, 1998.

Thorpe, Scott, *How to Think Like Einstein,* Barnes & Noble Books, Inc., 2000.

Toffler, Alvin, *Future Shock,* Bantam, 1984.

Index

A

A Discussion of Free Will (Erasmus), 103, 105–6
A Man for All Seasons (More), 81
Abbott, Edwin, 642
Abdullah, 705
Absolute monarchs, 217–45. *See also* Enlightened despots
  Austria, 239–40
  England, 235–39
  France, 222–29
  Germany and the Thirty Years War, 220–23
  Netherlands, 231–34
  Russia, 240–42
  seventeenth century, 217–20
  Spain, 229–31
  timeline, 245
Address at the Diet of Worms (Luther), 66, 75–76
Adoration of the Magi, The (Botticelli), 23
Aerial perspective, 20
Afghanistan, Soviet Union invasion of, 758
Africa
  British Empire in, 588
  French imperialism in, 589
  northern countries, 704
Against the Gods (Bernstein), 638
Age of Louis XIV (Voltaire), 369
Age of Reason, 355. *See also* Enlightenment
Agriculture, Industrial Revolution and, 533
Aida (Verdi), 511
Airplanes, in WWI, 694
Albania, 704, 759
Albert of Mainz, 54
Alcott, Bronson, 598

Alighieri, Dante, Divine Comedy, 11
All Quiet on the Western Front (film), 687
Alliances, in World War I, 689–91, 696–97
Allied countries (WWII), 736
Allied Powers (Triple Entente-WWI), 690
Amati, 261
American Civil War, 600–601
"American Dream," 604
American in Paris (Gershwin), 718
American Revolution, 438, 461–73
  Bill of Rights, 470, 472
  Boston Massacre, 464
  Boston Tea Party, 464–65
  causes
    British military interference, 463–64
    George III, 463
    Intolerable Acts, 465
    Stamp Act, 463
    Townsend Acts, 464
  compared to French Revolution, 499
  continuance and, 468–71, 472
  Declaration of Independence, 467
  Enlightenment and, 462–63, 483–84
  intent and, 466–67, 472
  leading to war, 465–67
  timeline, 473
  value and, 471–72
  war and peace, 468–71
An Essay Concerning Human Understanding (Locke), 358
Ana, Santa, 590
Anabaptists, 58
Analytical geometry (Descartes), 314–16, 333
Anarchists, 355
Ancient empires, 703

Ancient Greece and Rome (classical period), 450
Ancient Greeks, 502–3
Animal Farm (Orwell), 717
Anna Karenina (Tolstoy), 505
Anne of Cleves, 63
Anthems, 101
Anti-Machiavelli treatise (Frederick II), 427
Anti-Semitism, 689
Antiseptic surgery, 632
Antoinette, Marie, 485
Aquinas, Thomas, 11, 27
Arab nations, post-World War I, 704–5
Arabs, end of WWI and, 699–700
Archduke Ferdinand, 692
Architecture
  Baroque, 251–54
  linkage to Classical music, 459–60
  modern, 715–17
  Neoclassical, 449
  Rococo, 446–47
Aria, 260
Aristotle, 302–3
  Bacon, Francis and, 327
Arkwright, Richard, 538–40
Armenia, 704
Armstrong, Louis, 718
Arnold, Benedict, 468
Arouet, Francois Marie. *See Voltaire* (Francis Marie Arouet)
Arp, Jean, 715
Art
  in early Renaissance, 18–22
  modern, 714–15
  neoclassical, 447–49
  of Northern Renaissance, 97–101
  Rococo, 444–46
  technology and, 663–67
Art of Innovation (Kelley), 776

Articles of Confederation, 469–70
Artists, industrialization and, 555
Arts, creativity in, 771–72
Asia, British Empire in, 588
Asimov, Isaac, 640–41, 763–64
Astronomy
   Copernicus's heliocentric universe,
     307–8
   Jupiter's moons, fig, 310
   Ptolemaic model of the universe,
     306–7
Ataturk (Mustafa Kenal), 704
Atmospheric perspective, 20
Atomic attacks on Japan, 746
Augustulus, Romulus, 9
Austen, Jane, 556
Austria
   Joseph II, 436–37
   Maria Theresa, 435–37
   monarchies in, 239–40
   Triple Alliance, 690
Austro-Hungarian Empire. *See also*
   World War I
   post-World War I, 704
   pre World War I, 689
Authority of science, 317
Avant-garde, 670
Axis countries (WWII), 736

B

Bacchus and Ariadne (Titian), 45
   fig, 46
Bach, Johann Sebastian, 263, 450
   compared to George Handel,
     270–73
   creativity and, 770
   life and works of, 266–67
Bacon, Francis, 299, 312–14, 630
   Aristotle and, 327
   life of, 327
   New Organon, The, 327, 329–32
Balfour Declaration, 700, 760
Balkans, pre World War I, 692
Bar at the Folies-Bergére
   (Manet), 666
Baroque Period, 247–74, 664
   architecture, 251–54
   characteristics of, 248–51
   literature, 267–70
   music, 259–67
   origins of, 247–48
   painting, 254–59
   timeline, 273–74
   vs. Renaissance scientific thinking,
     299–301

   vs. Renaissance style of painting,
     251
Barzun, Jacques
   on the decline of Spain throughout
     the centuries, 5
   on *Hamlet,* 129
   on Romantic era painting, 514
   on the Romantic period, 502
Bastard Queen (Elizabeth I), 119
Bastille, 488
Battle of Britain, 736–38
Battle of the Bulge, 744
Battle of Trenton, 468
Beauharnais, Josephine de, 493, 497
Beethoven, Ludwig von
   Bonaparte, Napoleon and,
     495, 501
   bridge between Classical and
     Romantic, 506–7
   creativity and, 770
   life and works of, 456–58
Being and Nothingness (Sartre), 763
Bel-canto style, 511
Belgian Congo, 591
Belgium, imperialism and, 591
Bell, Alexander Graham, 603
Bentham, Jeremy, 556
Berlin wall, 759
Berlioz, Hector, 507
Bernard, Lewis, 700
Bernini, Gianlorenzo, 252–53, 769
Bernstein, Peter, 638
Beyond Engineering (Pool), 531
Bible
   English, 138–39
   Erasmus' translation, 95–96
   King James version, 118, 139
   literal interpretation of, 58
   Tyndale, 61
Bible and Sword (Tuchman), 700
Big Band era, 718
Big "C" Creativity, 3
Bill of Rights, 472
Bird in Flight (Brancusi), fig, 765
Bird in Space (Brancusi), 764
Birth of Venus (Botticelli), 22
   fig, 23
Bismarck, Otto von, 593, 689–90
Black Death, 10
Black Friday, 713
Bleak House (Dickens), 555
Blithedale Romance, The
   (Hawthorne), 595
Blitz of London, 737
Blitzkrieg, 734

Bloody Mary, 63, 119. *See also* Tudor,
   Mary
Blue Boy, The (Gainsborough),
   445–46
Boer Wars, 588
Bohemia, 221–22
Bohm, David, 641
Bohr, Neils, 635
   model of sodium atom, fig, 636
Bolero (Ravel), 676
Boleyn, Anne, 63
Bolivar, Simon, 589
Bolsheviks, 698
Bonaparte, Louis Napoleon, 589
Bonaparte, Napoleon, 777
   creativity and, 770
   demise of, 497–98
   as Emperor, 495–97
   Enlightenment and, 449
   exile of, 498
   as First Consul, 494–95
   French revolution and, 484
   Hundred Days, 498
   life of, 492–98
   Napoleonic Code, 494
   rise to power, 492–94
   Waterloo, 495, 498
Bonnie Prince Charlie, 438
Bono, Edward de, 774
Book of Common Prayer, 119
Borgia, Cesare, 25
   Machiavelli and, 29
Bosch Hieronymus, 100
Boston Massacre, 464
Boston Tea Party, 464–65
Botticelli, Alessandro, 22, 23, 27
Boucher, Francis, 444
Bourbons, 60, 240, 498
Bourgeoisie, 553
Boxer Rebellion, 588
Bradbury, Ray, 764
Bragg, William, 641
Brain, right and left sides of, 663–64,
   733–34
Brain control, 777
Brainstorming, 776
Brancacci Chapel, 19
Brancusi, Constantin, 764
Brandenburg Concertos (Bach), 267
Brave New World (Huxley), 717, 721,
   723–31
British Columbia, 600
British East India Company, 586–87
British Empire, 586–89. *See also*
   England

British explorers, 587–88
British navy, 587–88
Bronte, Charlotte, 556
Bronte, Emily, 556
Brothers Karamazov, The
　　(Dostoevsky), 676
Brubeck, Dave, 718
Bruegel, Pieter, 100
Brunelleschi, Filippo, 14, 27
　dome of, fig, 17
Bruning, Heinrich, 706
Bryan, William Jennings, 634
Bubonic Plague, 10
Bundestag, 592
Bunyan, John, 270
Buonarroti, Michelangelo. *See*
　　Michelangelo
Burghers of Calais (Rodin), 675
Burial of the Count of Orgaz (El
　　Greco), 256
Butterfly effect, 638
Byron, Lord George Gordon, 506
Byronic hero, 506
Byzantine Empire, 3, 9–10
　collapse of, 12
Byzantine scholars, 12

C
Cage, John, 765
Cahill, Thomas, 95
Calculus, Newton, Isaac and, 339
Calculus of felicity, 556
Calder, Alexander, 764–65
California, 594
Calling of Saint Matthew, The
　　(Caravaggio), 255
Calvin, John, 59
　church and, 77
　Institutes of the Christian Religion,
　　77, 79
Calvinist Protestantism, 59, 357
Camerata scholars, 260
Camille (Dumas), 509
Camus, Albert, 763
Canals, 542–43
Candide (Voltaire), 368–69
Cantatas, 261
Cantons, 58
Capitalism, 366, 558–60
　inconsistencies of (Marx), 558–59
Capra, Fritjof
　on declining societies, 5
　on reductionism, 639
　on scientific uncertainties,
　　637, 641

Caravaggio (Michelangelo Merisi),
　　254–55
Cardinal Richelieu, 224–26
Carding machine, 539
Carlyle, Thomas, 557
Carnegie, Andrew, 604
Cartesian coordinate system
　　(Descartes), 315, 333
Cartwright, Edmund, 540
Cask of Amontillado, The (Poe), 596
Categorical imperative (Kant), 372
Cathedral construction, 15–18
Catherine of Aragon, 62–63, 118,
　　124–25
Catherine the Great, 425
Catholic Church, 4, 10, 51–52
　Baroque music and, 259–60
　Copernicus and, 308
　Descartes, René and, 333
　Eramus and, 103
　French Revolution and, 483, 486,
　　488–89
　Galileo and, 310–11
　Inquisition and, 58
Cause and effect, 365, 630
Celtic Christian church, 60–61
Central Powers (Triple Alliance), 690
Cervantes, Miguel de, 268–69,
　　275, 360
　Don Quixote de la Mancha,
　　275–76, 277–83
Cézanne, Paul, 670–71
Chadwick, Edwin, 556–57
Chamberlain, Neville, 708
Channing, Ellery, 598
Chanson masses, 46
Chansons, 47
Chaos theory, 638
Charge of the Light Brigade, The
　　(Tennyson), 605, 607–8
Charles I, 236–38
Charles II, 231, 238
　Milton, John and, 285
Charles III, 434–35
Charles IX, 224
Charles V, 62, 239
　Florentine Republic and, 25
　French reformation and, 60
　Luther, Martin and, 65
Charles VI, 435
Chefs, 677
Chiang Kai-shek, 711
Chiaroscuro (light and dark), 37, 49,
　　254–58
Child labor, 550–51

Childe Harold (Byron), 506
China
　British Empire in, 588
　Opium Wars, 588
　post-World War I, 711
　pre World War I, 688
　trade and, 588
Chinese, 3
Chirac, Jacques, 589
Chopin, Frederic, 508
Christian IV, 221
Christianity, 12
　Medieval science and, 303
Christmas Carol, A (Dickens), 556
Chronicles of Narnia (Lewis), 763
Church of England, 63
Church of Scotland (Presbyterian
　　Church), 124, 232
Churchill, Winston, 467, 733, 737
　creativity and, 771
Circle of fifths, 262
Civil disobedience, 597
Civil Rights movement, 762
Civil War (American), 600–601
Claire de Lune (Debussy), 676
Clarke, Arthur C., 763–64
Class conflicts, 553–54
Classical, use of term, 449–50
Classical allusions, 97
Classical period, 444, 502–3. *See also*
　　Neoclassical period
　Beethoven, Ludwig von and,
　　456–58
　form and movement, 452–54
　Haydn, Franz Joseph and, 454–55
　linkage of music to architecture,
　　459–60
　Mozart, Wolfgang Gottlieb and,
　　455–56
　music/literary analogy, 452
　music of, 449–58
　sonata-allegro form, 453
　timeline, 460
　Viennese Classical style, 450–52
Classical science, 301–3
Clothed Maja, The (Francisco), 512
Coal, 541–42
Coda, 453
Code of Napoleon, 449
"Cogito, ergo sum" (Descartes),
　　315, 333
Cold War, 756–59, 762
Coleridge, Samuel Taylor, 506
Collina (Reynolds), 445
　fig, 446

Colonialism. *See also* Imperialism
Industrial Revolution and, 534–35
pre World War I, 688–89
Combustion theory, 323
Comedies, William Shakespeare, 134–35
Committee for Public Safety (France), 490
Commodore Perry, 594
Common Sense (Paine), 466
Commoners, 4, 10
Commune (France), 490
Communism, 557. *See also* Marx, Karl; Marxism
establishment in China, 711
fall of, 642–43
problems with, 559–60
Soviet Union, 705
Communist Manifesto, The (Marx and Engels), 558, 569, 571–73
Concerto, 261
Concerto in F (Gershwin), 718
Concord Bridge, 465
Congo
Belgium imperialism in, 591
Free State, 591
Congress of Vienna, 498–99, 549, 554, 591, 592
Conservatives, industrialization and, 554–55
Constable, John, 514
Constantine, 52
Constitution of the United States of America, 381, 469
Constitutional Convention, 469–70, 602
Continental Army, 468
Continuance, 1–2
American Revolution and, 468–71, 472
Continuous improvement, 305
Cook, James (Captain Cook), 587
Cooper, James Fenimore, 595
Copernicus, Nicolas, 305–8
Coronation of Napoleon (David), 449
fig, 495
Coronation of Poppea, The (Monteverdi), 264
Cotton Club, 718
Council of Trent, 220
Count of Monte Cristo, The (Dumas), 504
Counter-Reformation, 57–58, 248, 252
Counterpoint musical style, 260

Courage, 57
Courtship of Miles Standish, The (Longfellow), 595
Craft, 663–64
Craft system, Industrial Revolution and, 536
Creating Minds (Gardner), 637
Creative People at Work (Wallace and Gruber), 1
Creativity
in the arts, 771–72
defined, 1–3
in science, 772
technology and, 772–73
Creativity and Beyond (Weiner), 35
Crime and Punishment (Dostoevsky), 676
Critique of Pure Reason (Kant), 372
Cromwell, Oliver, 237–38, 357
Milton, John and, 285
Csikszentmihalyi, Mihaly, 640, 767
creativity and, 776
Cuban Missile Crisis, 758
Cubism, 674–75
Cultural stagnation, 5
Custer, Rodney, 772–73
Cyrillic alphabet, 241
Czar Alexander II, 592
Czar Alexander III, 592
Czar Peter I, the Great, 241–42
Czechoslovakia, 704

D
D-Day, 741
Da Vinci, Leonardo. *See* Vinci, Leonardo da
Dadaism, 714–15
Daladier, Edouard, 708
Dali, Salvador, 715
Damnation of Faust (Berlioz), 507
Dante, 11, 270
Danton, Georges, 490–91
Daphne and Apollo (Bernini), 253
Dark Ages, 9, 11
Darrow, Clarence, 634
Darwin, Charles, 631, 633–35, 770
Descent of Man, The, 645–46, 653–654
life and works of, 645
Origin of Species by Means of Natural Selection, The, 645, 647–52
Das Kapital (Marx), 558
David (Bernini), 252–53, 664
fig, 249

David (Donatello), 21–22
David (Michelangelo), 41–42
fig, 249
David, Jacques Louis, 448–49
David Copperfield (Dickens), 556
De Medici. *See* Medici
De revolutionibus (Book of Revolutions) (Copernicus), 308
Death of Socrates (David), 448
Debussy, Claude, 676
Declaration of Independence, 381, 467, 602
Declining societies, 4–5
Deductive reasoning, 312
Deerslayer, The (Cooper), 595
Defacing, 488
Defoe, Daniel, 270, 360–61
Degas, Edgar, 668
Deism, 367, 369, 373
Delacroix, Eugene, 514
Democracy in America (Tocqueville), 475, 477–82
Democritus, 301
Derry, T.K., 537
Descartes, René, 367, 484, 630
Discourse on Method, 333, 335–38
life of, 333
Descent of Man, The (Darwin), 634, 645–46, 653–54
Despots. *See* Absolute monarchs
Destruction of Privilege, The, 488
Determinism (Descartes), 315–16, 630
Deutschland Uber Alles (Haydn), 455
Development, 453
Diagonal perspective, 20
Dialogue Concerning the Two Chief World Systems (Galileo), 310
Diaz, Porfirio, 590
Dickens, Charles, 549, 555–56, 557
life of, 575
Oliver Twist, 575, 577–84
Dickinson, Emily, 597
Diderot, Denis, 371–72, 373
Diet of Worms, 51, 55
Diminution, 20
Dirac, Peter, 642
Directory (France), 492, 493–94
Discourse on Method (Descartes), 315, 333, 335–38, 367
Discrimination, 601
Dispensations, 51
Divergent perspective, 20
Divine Comedy (Dante), 11, 270
Divine right of kings, 219

Doctor and His Soul, The
    (Frankl), 749
Doll's House, A (Ibsen), 677, 679,
    681–85
Domain of knowledge, 3
Domination periods, 3–5
Don Quixote de la Mancha
    (Cervantes), 268–69, 275–76,
    277–83, 360
Donatello, 21–22
Dostoevsky, Feodor, 674, 676–77
Dr. Faust (Goethe), 504
Drake, Sir Francis, 122, 126
Duchamp, Marcel, 714–15
Dufay, Guillaume, 46
Duke Sforza, 38
Duma (Russia), 697–98
Dumas, Alexandre, 224, 504, 509
    life of, 525
    Three Musketeers, The, 525,
        527–30
Dunkirk, 736
DuPont, E.I., 604
Dürer, Albrecht, 98–100
Dutch painters, 100, 258

E
Early Medieval Period, 1
Early Renaissance, 9–28
    art and sculpture, 18–22
    creativity and, 26–27
    humanism in, 11–13
    Medici family, 22–25
    Niccolò Machiavelli, 25–26
    sponsors, 13–18
    timeline, 27–28
Easter Rebellion (Ireland),
    697, 709
Eastern Orthodox churches, 12
Eastern Roman Empire, 9
Economic conditions, Industrial
    Revolution and, 535
Economic equality (Third Estate), 4
Ecstasy of St. Teresa (Bernini), 253
Edict of Nantes, 60, 224
Edison, Thomas, 603
    creativity and, 771
Edward VI, 63, 118–19, 124
Egalitarianism, 369, 419
Egyptians, 3
Einstein, Albert, 57
    creativity and, 767, 771
    photoelectric effect and, 635
    Theory of Relativity and, 637
El Greco, 256

Electromagnetic theory, 633
Electrons, 635–37
Elements (earth, air, fire, wind), 302–3
Elements of Chemistry
    (Lavoisier), 322
Elizabeth I, 63, 235–36
    creativity and, 769
Elizabethan England, 115–40
    acceptance of Elizabeth I, 119–22
    Christopher Marlowe, 127
    Elizabeth I, ascension to the throne,
        118–19
    English Bible, 138–39
    France and, 123
    language in, 117–18
    merchant class, 116–17
    money in, 122
    religion in, 117, 122
    Scotland and, 437
    Shakespeare, 127–38, 141–42
        comedies and, 134–35
        historical plays and, 135
        sonnets and, 138
        tragedies and, 135–38
        use of language and, 130–34
    Spain and, 124–26
    timeline, 140
Elizabethan Golden Age, 119
Emerson, Ralph Waldo, 596–97,
    609, 710
    Self Reliance, 609, 611–12
    Thoreau, Henry and, 613
Emile (Rousseau), 371
Empire-building. *See* Imperialism
Empiricism, 314
*Encyclopedia: The Rational
    Dictionary of the Sciences,
    the Arts, and the Crafts*
    (Diderot), 371
Engels, Friedrich, 557–58, 569
England. *See also* British Empire;
    Elizabethan England
    Enlightenment in, 355–67
    George II, 437–38
    George III, 438–39
    Locke, John and, 381
    monarchies in, 235–39
    Protestant Reformation and, 60–63
English
    Bill of Rights, 239
    Civil War, 237, 360
    language, 117–18
    period, 4
    rulers, seventeenth century,
        chart, 235

    succession, Tudor and early Stuart
        times, chart, 120
Enlightened despots, 425–41
    Catherine the Great of Russia,
        429–35
    Charles III of Spain, 434–35
    Frederick II of Prussia, 426–29
    George II of England, 437–38
    George III of England, 438–39
    Gustavus III of Sweden, 434
    Joseph II of Austria, 436–37
    Maria Theresa of Austria, 435–37
    royal dilemmas and creativity,
        439–41
    timeline, 441
Enlightenment, 353–74. *See also* Age
    of Reason
    American Revolution and, 462–63,
        483–84
    in England, 355–67
        Adam Smith, 366
        Alexander Pope, 361–62
        David Hume, 365–66
        Edward Gibbon, 366–67
        John Locke, 357–60
        Jonathan Swift, 362–65
        Thomas Hobbes, 355–57
    in France, 367–72
        Denis Diderot, 371–72
        Jean-Jacques Rousseau, 369–71
        Voltaire (François Marie Arouet),
            368–69
    French Revolution and, 483–84
    in Germany, 372–73
        Immanuel Kant, 372–73
    Locke, John and, 381
    premises of, 354–55
    review of, 373–74
    Scientific Method and social
        problems, 353–54
    timeline, 374
    Voltaire and, 409–10
Entrepreneurship, American, 601–4
Epistle of James, 56
Erasmus, Desiderius, 94–96
    church and, 103
    A Discussion of Free Will, 103, 105–6
    Hyperaspistes, 103, 106–8
    In Praise of Folly, 96
Erie Canal, 599
Erlkönig, The (Schubert), 507
Escher, Maurits Cornelis, 715
*Essay Concerning Human
    Understanding* (Locke),
    381, 383

Essay on Man (Pope), 361–62, 389,
    391–93
Essays from *The Complete Works*
    (Montaigne), 111–13
Essays on the Law of Nature
    (Locke), 358
Estates General, 487
Esteemed creativity, 3
Ettal church, 447
Euclidean geometry, 637
European Union, 759–60
Evolution of species, 634–35
*Execution of the Madrilenos on
    May 3,* 1808 (Goya), 513
Existentialism, 640, 763
Exposition, 453
Expressionism, 671
Expulsion from Paradise
    (Masaccio), 18

F
Faerie Queen, The (Spenser), 127
Faisal, 705
Fall of the House of Usher, The
    (Poe), 596
"Falling Water" (Wright), 716
Family, Industrial Revolution and, 550
Fantasy, 763
Fascism, 707–8
Fauvism, 672–73
Ferdinand and Isabella, 62
Feudal societies, 116
Fielding, Henry, 361
Fifer, The (Manet), 666–67
Fifth Symphony (Beethoven), 458, 506
Fighting Temparaire, The (Turner),
    515, 516
Fin de Si`e cle (end of the century),
    664, 668, 687–88, 719
Finnegan's Wake (Joyce), 717
First Consul (Napoleon), 494–95
First Continental Congress, 465
First Estate, 3, 4, 218, 486–88
First Folio (Shakespeare), 127–28
First Treatise of Civil Government
    (Locke), 359
Fisk, James, 604
Fitzgerald, Ella, 718
Flatland (Abbott), 642
Florence, Italy, 10–11, 35–36
Florentine Artists Guild, 37
Florentine Republic, 22–25
    Machiavelli and, 29
Flying Dutchman, The (Byron), 506
Folk music, 508

Ford, Henry, 604
Foreshortening, 37
Form, 302, 451–53, 636. *See also*
    Logos
Fort Sumter, 600
40th Symphony (Mozart), 459
Foundation (Asimov), 763
Fountain (Duchamp), 714
    fig, 715
Four Horsemen of the Apocalypse
    (Dürer), 99
Four Minutes, Thirty-three Seconds
    (Cage), 765
Four Rivers, The (Bernini), 253
Four Seasons (Vivaldi), 264
Fourth Dimension, The (Rucker), 639
Fourth European Coalition, 498
Fragonard, Jean-Honoré, 444–45
France
    Elizabethan England and, 123
    Enlightenment in, 367–72
    imperialism and, 589
    impressionism and, 677–78
    monarchies and, 222–29
    Protestant Reformation and, 59–60
    Triple Entente, 690
Francis I, 59–60
Franco, Francisco, 708
Franco-Prussian War, 690, 693
Frankenstein (Shelley), 505
Frankl, Viktor, 749, 751–54
Franklin, Benjamin, 3
    American revolution and, 468–69
    creativity and, 770
    Declaration of Independence
        and, 467
    entrepreneurship and, 601–2
Frederick II (Frederick the Great),
    426–29
    palace of, fig, 428
Frederick the Wise, 53
Frederick Wilhelm I
    (Soldier-King), 222
Freemasonry, 373
French and Indian War (Seven Years
    War), 427, 462, 463
French period, 4–5
French Revolution
    causes, 484–86
        American Revolution
            influence, 485
        Anglophile feelings, 485
        aristocracy, 486
        class resentment, 486
        economic crisis, 486

    Enlightenment principles, 484
    French monarchy, 485–86
    Roman Catholic Church, 486
    compared to American
        Revolution, 499
    Congress of Vienna, 498–99
    Declaration of the Rights of Man
        and the Citizen, 488
    Destruction of Privilege, 488
    the Directory, 492, 493–94
    Enlightenment and, 483–84
    groups: moderates, radicals,
        peasants, 484–85
    Jacobins, 490–92
    Napoleon and, 492–98
    National Convention, 490–91
    National/Legislative Assembly,
        487–89
    Reign of Terror, 490
    stage 1: control by the moderates,
        488–89
    stage 2: control by the radicals,
        489–91
    stage 3: return to moderate control,
        491–92
    Thermidorian Reaction, 491–92
    timeline, 499–500
French-speaking Switzerland,
        Protestant Reformation and, 59
From Dawn to Decadence (Barzun), 5,
    129, 502, 514
Fructiferous experiments (Bacon), 313
Fugues, 261
Future Shock (Toffler), 547

G
Gainsborough, Thomas, 445–46
Galileo, 308–11
Galileo, Science, and the Church
    (Langford), 311
Gandhi, Mohandas (Mahatma), 703,
    709–11
    creativity and, 771
Garden of Earthly Delights (Bosch),
    100
Gardner, Howard, 637
Garibaldi, Giusppe, 593
Gauguin, Paul, 672
Gautier, Mary, 663
General Cornwallis, 469
Genius, 2–3
Gentileschi, Artemisia, 255–56
    creativity and, 769
Geography, Industrial Revolution
    and, 534

Geometric arrangements, 22
George I, 437–38
George II, 437–38
George III, 438–39, 463–65, 467
German Confederation, 592
German Mathematical Society, 267
German period, 4
German-speaking Switzerland,
    Protestant Reformation and, 58
Germanic languages, 117
Germany
    Axis country (WWII), 736
    imperialism and, 592–93
    post-World War I, 705–8
    pre World War I, 688
    resentment about the Treaty of
        Versailles, 701, 705–6
    stock market crash of 1929 impact,
        706–7
    Thirty Years War, 220–23
    Triple Alliance, 690
Gershwin, George, 718
    creativity and, 771
Gestapo, 707
Ghiberti, Lorenzo, 14–18
Gibbon, Edward, 366–67
Giovanni, Bertoldo di, 41
Girondists, 489
Globe Theatre, 130
    fig, 131
Glorious Revolution, 238, 359, 360
Gödel, Escher, Bach (Hofstadter), 766
Goethe, Johann Wolfgang von, 503–4
Gogh, Vincent Van, 663, 671–72
Goldberg Variations (Bach), 267
Good King Henry (Henry IV), 224
Goodman, Benny, 718
Goodyear, Charles, 603
Gorbachev, Mikhail, 759
Gould, Jay, 604
Government (Second Estate), 4
Goya, Francisco, 512–13
Grand Master, 426
Grant, Ulysses S., 601
Grapes of Wrath (Steinbeck), 713
Gravity, 318, 321–22
    Newton, Isaac and, 339
Great Arab Revolt, 704–5
Great Britain
    Ally country (WWII), 736
    Triple Entente, 690
Great Depression, 713–14
Great Expectations (Dickens), 556
Great War, 588
Greek Golden Mean, 267

Greeks, 3
Guarneri, 261
Guernica (Picasso), 674
Guidi, Tomasso (Masaccio), 18–19
Guild of Cloth Merchants, 13
Guillotine, 490
Gulliver's Travels (Swift), 362–65,
    395, 397–401
Gustavus III, 434
Gutenberg, Johannes, 12

H
Hagia Sophia, 16
Hall of Mirrors, 226
    fig, 228
Hals, Frans, 259
Hamlet (Shakespeare), 141, 143–201
    Act I, 143–56
    Act II, 156–66
    Act III, 166–80
    Act IV, 180–90
    Act V, 190–201
Hand loom, 537
Handel, George Frederick, 264–66,
    270–71, 455, 770
Hanseatic League, 426
Hapsburg family (Netherlands), 4, 591
Hapsburgs, 232, 239–40
    coat of arms, fig, 240
Hard Times (Dickens), 555, 557
Hargreaves, James, 538
Harpsichords, 262
Harriman, Edward H., 604
Harrison, John, 587–88
Harry Potter novels (Rowling), 763
Hatton, John, 641, 642
Havel, Vaclav, 642–43
Hawthorne, Nathaniel, 595, 598
Hay Wain (Constable), 514
    fig, 515
Haydn, Josef, 264, 443, 454–55
Hearst, William Randolph, 604
Heckel, Erich, 673
Heisenberg, Werner, 635–36
Heliocentric universe (Copernicus),
    307–8
Henry II, 60
Henry III, 60
Henry IV, 60, 224
Henry of Navarre, 60
Henry VII, 62
Henry VIII, 95–96, 117, 118–19
    Protestant Reformation and, 62–63
Hidalgo, Miguel, 590
High Renaissance, 35–50

Buonarroti, Michelangelo and,
    41–43
creative ideas and, 48–49
Raphael, 43–45
Renaissance man, 47–48
Renaissance music, 45–47
timeline, 49–50
Titian and the Venetian School, 45
Vinci, Leonardo da and, 36–41
Highs, Thomas, 538
Hindenburg, Paul von, 706–7
Hiroshima, Japan, 746
Historical plays, Shakespeare, 135
History of the Decline and Fall of the
    Roman Empire, The (Gibbon),
    366–67
Hitler, Adolf, 677, 706–8, 771
Hitler Youth, 707
Hobbes, Thomas, 355–57, 360
    Leviathan, 375, 377–80
    purpose of existence and, 375
Hofstadter, Douglas, 766
Hohenzollerns, 426
Holliday, Billie, 718
Holmes, Oliver Wendell, 598
Holocaust, 708
Holt tractor company, 694
Holy Roman Emperor, 426
Holy Roman Empire, 222, 239, 426
Holy Trinity, The (Masaccio), 19, 21
    fig, 20
Home manufacturing, 536
Homophony musical texture,
    260, 451
Hong Kong, 588
Hooke, Robert, 319
Hoover, Herbert, 713
Hoovervilles, 713
House of Orange, 233, 498
House of Seven Gables, The
    (Hawthorne), 595
How the Irish Saved Civilization
    (Cahill), 95
How to Think Like Einstein (Thorpe),
    734, 773, 775, 777
Howard, Catherine, 63
Howe, Elias, 602
Hugo, Victor, 504–5
Huguenots, 60
Humanism, 51
    in early Renaissance, 11–13, 27
    Eramus and, 103
    Montaigne, Michel de, 109
    More, Thomas and, 81
Hume, David, 365–66, 371

Hunchback of Notre Dame, The
    (Hugo), 504
Hundred Days, 498
Hundred Years War, 123
Hungarian Rhapsody 2 (Liszt), 509
Hussein, 705
Huxley, Aldous, 717, 721, 723–31
Hydrogen atom, 635
Hymns, 261, 271
Hyperaspistes (Erasmus), 103, 106–8

I
I, Robot (Asimov), 763
"I think, therefore I am" (Descartes),
    315, 333
Ibsen, Henrik, 677, 679, 681–85
Ideological liberals, 54
Idols of the cave (Bacon), 313
Idols of the marketplace (Bacon), 314
Idols of the theatre (Bacon), 314
Idols of the tribe (Bacon), 313
*"If God Did Not Exist He Would Have
    to Be Invented"* (Voltaire),
    409, 415
Il Trovatore (Verdi), 511
Imperialism, 585–604. *See also*
    Colonialism
    Belgium, 591
    British Empire, 586–89
    Germany, 592–93
    Italy, 593
    post-Napoleonic France, 589
    Russia, 591–92
    Spain, 590
    United States, 593–94
    world in 19th century, 586
Implementers, 776
Impression, Sunrise (Monet), 664
    fig, 665
Impressionism, 664–69. *See also*
    Post-Impressionism
    in music, 676
    technique, 677–78
    timeline, 678
In Praise of Folly (Erasmus), 96
India
    as part of British Empire, 586–87
    post-World War I, 709–11
Indians, 3
Inductive reasoning, 313
    Bacon, Francis and, 327
Indulgences, 51, 53–54, 58
Industrial Revolution, 5, 531–47
    accelerated growth curve of
        technology over time, 532

causes, 533–37
    agricultural improvements, 533
    economic conditions, 535
    geography, 534
    home manufacturing system, 536
    increasing population, 533
    middle class, 535–36
    successful wars of conquest and
        exploration, 534–35
    weakness of craft system, 536
consequences of
    artists, 555
    changing daily life, 550
    changing family structure, 550
    changing working conditions,
        550–52
    child labor, 550–51
    class conflicts, 553–54
    conservative and liberal reaction,
        554–55
    economic cycles, 552
    inadequate infrastructure, 551–52
    inadequate social amenities, 552
    labor unions, 560
    Marxism, 558–60
    social change, 560–61
    timeline, 561
    urbanization, 551
    utilitarianism, 556–57
    writers, 555–56
effects of, 545–46
general manufacturing, 541
new, 546–47
per capita levels of industrialization
    (1750-1913), chart, 546
power, 541–42
science defined, 531
spread of, 543–45
technology defined, 531
textiles, 537–40
timeline, 547
transportation, 542–43
Inherit the Wind, 634
Innovators, 776
Inquisition, 57–58
    Galileo and, 311
Inspiration, 663–64
Institutes of the Christian Religion
    (Calvin), 77, 79
Intelligent Design, 635
Intent, 1–2
Interchangeable parts, 602
Intervention of the Sabine Woman, The
    (David), 448
Intolerable Acts, 465

Intuition, 642, 775–76
Intuitive perspective, 20–21
Inventions
    of Americans, 602–3
    of Newton, Isaac, 339
    of Pascal, Blaise, 347
Inventions of the Monsters (Dali), 715
Iraq, 704
Ireland, post-World War I, 708–9
Irish Republican Army (IRA), 709
Iron, 542
Iron Curtain, 756
Irving, Washington, 594–95
Isabella II, 590
Isacoff, Stuart, 253, 263
Islamic Empire, 3
Island hopping (WWII), 745
Isolationism, 712
Israel, 760–61
Italian city-states, 10, 35–36, 45
Italian period, 4–5
Italy
    Axis country, 736
    imperialism and, 593
    Triple Alliance, 690
Ivan IV, the Terrible, 242
Ivanhoe (Scott), 504, 519, 521–24

J
Jacobins, 323, 490–92
Jacobites, 438
Jacquard loom, 540
James I, 124, 139, 236
    Bacon, Francis and, 327
James II, 238–39
James V, 123
James VI, 124, 235–36
Jan Hus of Bohemia, 52–53
Jane Eyre (Bronte), 556
Japan
    atomic bombing of, 746
    Axis country, 736
    Dutch and, 594
    impressionism and, 678
    post-World-War I, 711
    pre-World War I, 688
    Spain and, 594
    United States and, 594
    in World War II, 739–40
Japanese Bridge (Monet), 667
    fig, 669
Jazz, 718
Jazz Age, 712–13
Jefferson, Thomas, 467, 496, 602
Jennens, Charles, 265

Jesuits, 57–58
Jews, Balfour Declaration and, 700
John of Gaunt, 52
John the Baptist, 13
Joie de vivre (joy of living), 668
Joseph II, 436–37
Josephine. *See* Beauharnais, Josephine de
Joyce, James, 717
Juarez, Benito, 589, 590
Judith and Holofernes (Gentileschi), 255–56
Jukebox, 718
Jungle, The (Sinclair), 623, 625–28

K
Kafka, Franz, 717
Kaiser, 690
Kamikaze pilots, 746
Kanji (Japanese writing), 678
Kant, Immanuel, 372–73, 596
Karnaim (horns), 42
Kay, John, 538
Kelley, Tom, 776
Kenal, Mustafa (Ataturk), 704
Kennedy, John F., 762
Kennings, 118
Kepler, Johannes, 311
   laws of planetary motion, fig, 312
Kiev (Kyiv), 241
King, Jr., Martin Luther, 762
King James version of the Bible, 118
Klee, Paul, 715
Knight, Death and the Devil, The (Dürer), 99
Knox, John, 124, 232
Koestler, Arthur, 308
Korean War, 756–57
Koren (light), 42
Kroeber, Alfred, 2–3
Kuhn, Thomas, 639, 640, 655, 657–62
Kuomintang Party (China), 711
Kyiv (Kiev), 241

L
La belle öpoque (the beautiful age), 664
La Orana Maria (Gauguin), 672
   fig, 673
La Tour, George de, 259
La Traviata (Verdi), 511
Labor unions, 560
Lady Jane Grey, 63, 119

Laissez-faire la nature (let nature take its course), 366, 553, 560, 563, 713
Langford, Jerome J., 311
Language
   in Elizabethan England, 117–18
   Shakespeare's use of, 130–34
Las Meninas (Velazquez), 257
Last Judgment (Michelangelo), 43
Last of the Mohicans, The (Cooper), 595
Last Supper (Riemenschneider), 98 fig, 99
Last Supper, The (da Vinci), 37–38
Lateral thinking, 773–74
   improving, 775–76
Lateral Thinking (de Bono), 774
Latin-based languages, 117
Lavoisier, Antoine, 322–23, 630
Le Corbusier, 716–17
Le Déeuner sur l'Herbe (Manet), 665–66
Le Mer (Debussy), 676
Le Monde (Descartes), 316
Le Moulin de la Galette (Renoir), 668
   fig, 669
League of Nations, 699, 712
Leatherstocking Tales (Cooper), 595
Leaves of Grass (Whitman), 596, 617, 619–21
Lebanon, 704, 705
Left wing (liberals), origin of term, 488
Legend of Sleepy Hollow, The (Irving), 595
Lenin, Vladimir, 698, 705
Leopold II, 437, 591
Les Miserables (Hugo), 504–5
Les Muses Galantes (Rousseau), 371
Letter of Majesty, 221
Letters on England (Voltaire), 410, 417–18
Leviathan (Hobbes), 356, 375, 377–80
Lexington Green, 465
"*L'homme arme*" mass (Dufay), 46
Liberals, industrialization and, 554–55
Liberty Leading the People (Delacroix), 514
Libretto, 265
Lieder, 507
Light waves/particle problem, 635–37
Limey, 587
Lincoln, Abraham, 600, 601
Linear perspective, 20–21

Linear thinking, 773–74
   improving, 774–75
Lister, Joseph, 632
Liszt, Franz, 509
Literary genres, 452
Literary modernism, 717
Literature
   American, 594–96
   Baroque, 267–70
   of Enlightenment, 360–67
   modern, 717, 763–64
   nineteenth century, 676–77
   Romantic Period, 503–6
Little Dutch art, 257–58
Little Women (Alcott), 598
Livingstone, David, 588
Locke, John, 353, 357–60, 373
   creativity and, 769
   Essay Concerning Human Understanding, 381, 383
   philosophy and, 381
   Two Treatises of Government, 381, 385–87
Logical thinking, 768
Logos, 303. *See also* Form
Lollards, 52
Long Parliament, 237
Longfellow, Henry W., 595
Lord of the Rings (Tolkien), 763
Lorenz, Edward, 637–38
Los Trabajos de Persiles y Sigismunda (Cervantes), 268
Louis XII, 40
Louis XIII, 224–25
Louis XIV, 4
   Baroque style and, 248
   creativity and, 769
   divine right of kings and, 219
   quotes of, 217
   reign of, 226–29
   statue, fig, 227
   Versailles Palace and, 253–54
Louis XVI, 485, 487, 489
Louis XVIII, 498
Louisiana Purchase, 496, 598
Loyalists, 466
Loyola, Ignacio, 57
Luciferous experiments (Bacon), 313
Luddites, 541
L'Unité d'Habitation, (Le Corbusier), 716–17
Lusitania, 698
Lust for Life (Gauguin), 672
Luther, Martin, 51–57, 95, 117, 307

Address at the Diet of Worms, 66, 75–76
To the Christian Nobility of the German Nation, 65, 71–74
church and, 65–66
On the Enslaved Will, 103
95 Theses, 65, 69–70
Salvation Through Faith Alone, 65, 67
Lyrical ballads, 506

M
MacArthur, Douglas, 740
Machiavelli, Niccolò, 25–26, 225, 372
creativity and, 768
life of, 29
Prince, The, 29, 31–33
"The end justifies the means," concept of, 29
Machine gun, in WWI, 694
Madonna of the Rocks (da Vinci), 37
Madrigals, 47, 101
Magna Carta, 117, 235
Mahler, Gustav, 676
Man in the Iron Mask, The (Dumas), 504
Manchu Dynasty, 711
Manet, Édouard, 665–67
Manifest destiny, 594, 598–600
Man's Searching for Meaning (Frankl), 749, 751–54
Manufacturing, Industrial Revolution, 541
Marat, Jean-Paul, 323, 490–91
Marie Louise, 497
Marlowe, Christopher, 127
Marquette, 58
Marriage of Figaro (Mozart), 506
Marshall Plan, 745
Martian Chronicles (Bradbury), 764
Martin, Jose San, 590
Martyrdom of Saint Matthew, The (Caravaggio), 255
Marx, Karl, 553, 558–60, 705
Communist Manifesto, 569, 571–73
life of, 569
Marxism, 558–60. *See also* Marx, Karl
Mary, Queen of Scots, 437
Mary Magdalene (Donatello), 22
Mary of Guise, 123–24
Masaccio (Tomasso Guidi), 18–19
Mass in Honor of Pope Marcellus (Palestrina), 47
Matisse, Henri, 672–73
Maximilian, 589–90

Maxwell, James Clerk, 635
Mazarin, Jules, 225–26
M.C. Escher, 715
McCormick, Cyrus, 602
McGrath, Alister, 11
Medici, Cosimo de, 22–23
Medici, Lorenzo de, 23–24, 41, 768
Medici, Marie de, 258
Medici, Piero de, 23
Medici family, 22–25
Machiavelli and, 29
Medieval Period, 2, 3–4, 11
Medieval science, 303
Mein Kampf (Hitler), 706, 771
Melodies, 272
Melville, Herman, 595
Mendeleyev's Dream (Strathern), 323
Mendelssohn, Felix, 267, 512
Mercantilism, 4, 366
Merchant class, in Elizabethan England, 116–17
Merchant fleet, 122
Merchant rich, 13
Mesopotamia, 3, 704
Messiah (Handel), 265–66, 455
Metamorphosis, The (Kafka), 717
Metaphoric tendency of language, 118
Metternich, Klemens von, 554
Mexico
French imperialism in, 589
Spanish imperialism in, 590
wars with U.S., 600
Michelangelo, 41–43, 664, 769
Middle Ages, 3, 10
Middle class, Industrial Revolution and, 535–36
Middle East, contemporary, 760–61
Middle English, 118
Midsummer Night's Dream (Mendelssohn), 512
Midway, 745
Mighty Fortress is Our God, A (Bach), 266
Military Polonaise (Chopin), 508
Mill, John Stuart, 563, 565–67
Milton, John
life of, 285
Paradise Lost, 247, 269, 271, 285, 287–97
Mindwalk, 639
Moby Dick (Melville), 595
Modeling, 317
Modern architecture, 715–17
Modern art, 714–15
Modern English, 118

Modern music, 718
Modern World, 301
Modest Proposal, A (Swift), 362, 365, 395, 403–7
Moll Flanders (Defoe), 361
Mona Lisa (da Vinci), 39–40
fig, 39
Monarchs. *See* Absolute monarchs; Enlightened despots
Mondrian, Piet, 714
Monet, Claude, 664, 667
Money, Elizabethan England and, 122
Mongols (Tartars), 241
Monophony musical texture, 260
Monroe Doctrine, 554
Montaigne, Michel de, 97
essays, invention of genre, 109
Essays from *The Complete Works,* 111–13
humanism and, 109
Montenegro, 759
Monteverdi, Claudio, 263–64
Mood Indigo (Ellington), 718
Moore, Henry, 764
More, Thomas, 61–62, 95–96
humanism and, 81
A Man for All Seasons, 81
Utopia, 81, 83–91
Morgan, J.P., 604
Mormon Trail, 599
Mormons, 599
Morse, Samuel, 603
Moses (Michelangelo), 42
Motets, 101
Motifs, 506
Motion, 321–22
Movable printing type, 12
Movement
classical music form and, 452–54
Romantic music and, 506–7
Mozart, Wolfgang Gottlieb (Amadeus), 455–56
creativity and, 770
Munch Edvard, 673
Murder in the Rue Morgue, The (Poe), 596
Music
Baroque, 259–67
Classical, 449–58
impressionism in, 676
modern, 718
of Northern Renaissance, 101
Post-Impressionistic, 676
Romantic Period, 506–12
Music drama, 509

Music/literary analogy, 452
Musical scale, 261–63
Muslims, 12
Mussolini, Benito, 707–8
Myth of Sisyphus, The (Camus), 763

N

Nabucco (Verdi), 511
Nagasaki, Japan, 746
Napoleon. *See* Bonaparte, Napoleon
Napoleon Crossing the Alps
    (David), 449
Napoleon II, 497
Napoleon III, 589
Napoleon in his Study (David), 448
    fig, 449
Napoleonic Code, 494
National Convention (France), 490–91
National/Legislative Assembly
    (France), 487–89, 494
National Will, The (Russia), 592
Nationalism, 554, 704
Nationalist (Kuomintang) Party
    (China), 711
Natural man, 354
Natural selection, 634, 645
    adaption, fig, 633
Nature (Emerson), 596, 609
Nausea (Sartre), 763
Nazis (National Socialist German
    Workers' Party), 706–8
Neoclassical period, 444, 503. *See
    also* Classical period
    architecture, 449
    art, 447–49
Netherlands
    imperialism and, 586–87
    monarchies in, 231–34
Neuschwanstein castle, 510
New Organon, The (Bacon), 327,
    329–32
Newcomen, Thomas, 542
Newton, Isaac, 635, 637
    creativity and, 769
    laws of motion, 630
    life and works of, 316–22,
        339–40, 630
        mathematical equation and
            gravity, fig, 319
        third law of, 318
        non-Trinitarian belief and, 322
    Principia Mathematica, 339–40,
        341–46
        third law of, 321
        three laws of motion, fig, 320

Nicholas II, 695, 697–98
Nietzsche, Friedrich, 677
Night Cafe, The (Van Gogh), 672
Night Watch, The (Rembrandt),
    234, 258
Nihilism, 639–40
1984 (Orwell), 717
95 Theses (Luther), 54, 56, 65,
    69–70, 300
Nixon, Richard, 762
No man's land, 694
Nobility, 3–4, 10
    medieval, 116
Noble savages, 369, 419
Nobles of the robe, 486
Nobles of the sword, 486
North Atlantic Treaty Organization
    (NATO), 756
Northern Ireland, 709
Northern Renaissance, 93–102
    creativity and, 101–2
    Erasmus, 94–96
    migration northward, 93–94
    Montaigne, Michel de and, 97
    music of, 101
    timeline, 102
    visual art, 97–101
Novelty, 1–2
Novum Organum (Bacon), 313
Nude Descending a Staircase
    (Duchamp), 714
Number 1 (Pollack), 764
Nutcracker Suite (Tchaikovsky), 512

O

Oath of the Horatii, The (David), 448
Objectivity, 630–31
Octave, 262
Old English, 117–18
Oliver Twist (Dickens), 549, 555, 575,
    577–84
On Civil Disobedience (Thoreau),
    597, 613
On the Enslaved Will (Luther), 103
*On the Origin of Species by Means
    of Natural Selection*
    (Darwin), 634
Opera, 260–61
Ophelia Syndrome, 137
Opium Wars, 588
Oration on the Dignity of Man
    (Mirandola), 24
Oratorio, 261, 265
Oregon Territory, 599
Orfeo (Monteverdi), 263

Organon, 327
*Origin of Species by Means of Natural
    Selection, The* (Darwin), 645,
    647–52
Orwell, George, 717
Ottoman Empire, 690. *See also* World
    War I
    post-World War I, 704–5
    pre World War I, 689
Overlapping, 20

P

Packing the court, 714
Paganini, Nicolo, 512
Paine, Thomas, 461, 466
Painting
    Baroque, 254–59
    Baroque vs. Renaissance styles, 251
    Romantic Period, 512–15
Palace of Versailles
    fig, 227
    gardens of, fig, 228
Palestine, 704, 760–61
Palestrina, Giovanni, 47
Papal States, 593
Paradigm, 655
Paradise Lost (Milton), 247, 269, 271,
    285, 287–97
    Book I, 287–90
    Book IX, 290–95
    Book X, 295–97
Parlement (France), 487
Parr, Catherine, 63
Partido Revolucionario Institucional
    (PRI-Mexico), 590
Pascal, Blaise, 347, 349–52
Pascal's Law, 347
Pasteur, Louis, 629, 631–33
    creativity and, 771
Pasteurization, 631, 632
Pastoral Symphony (Sixth Symphony)
    (Beethoven), 507
Patriots, 466
Pavanne for a Dead Princess
    (Ravel), 676
Pazzi Chapel, 18
Peace of Augsburg, 220
Peace of Westphalia, 4, 222
Pearl Harbor, 740
Peasant farmers, 4
Peasant Wedding Feast (Bruegel), 100
    fig, 101
Penicillin, 633
Pensées (Pascal), 347, 349–52
Periodic table, 633

Persistence of Memory, The
(Dali), 715
Perspective, 20–21, 49
types of, 21
Perugino, 43
Peter III, 425, 430–31
Peter the Great, 241–42
Petrarch, Francesco, 11–12
Petrograd Soviet, 698
Phillip II, 125–26, 224, 230–33, 239
Phillip V, 231
Phlogiston theory, 323
Pianoforte (soft-loud), 456
Picasso, Pablo, 674–75, 771
Pietà (Michelangelo), 41
Pilgrimage (Wateau), 444
fig, 445
Pilgrim's Progress (Bunyan), 270
Pit and the Pendulum, The (Poe), 596
Plagues, 9–10, 13
Planck, Max, 635
Plato, 302, 303, 636
Plessey, Marie de, 509
Plouffe, Paul, 641, 642
Plutarch's Lives, 449
Poe, Edgar Allan, 596
Poincarö, 638
Pointillism, 669
Poison gas, in WWI, 694
Poland, Germany's invasion of
(WWII), 708
Pollack, Jackson, 764
Polyphony, 259–61
Pool, Robert, 531
Poor Richard's Almanac
(Franklin), 601
Pope, Alexander, 322, 361–62
Essay on Man, 389, 391–93
life of, 389
Pope Clement VII, 24
Pope Gregory I, 60
Pope Leo X, 24
Pope Paul III, 43
Population, Industrial Revolution
and, 533
Porgy and Bess (Gershwin), 718
Portugal, imperialism and, 586
Post-Impressionism, 670–74
music, 676
Post-World War I, 703–14. *See also*
World War I
Great Depression, 713–14
political changes
Austro-Hungarian Empire, 704
China, 711

Germany, 706–8
India, 709–11
Ireland, 708–9
Japan, 711
Ottoman Empire, 704–5
Russia and the Soviet Union, 705
Roaring Twenties, 712–13
timeline, 719
Power, in Industrial Revolution, 541–42
Power loom factory, fig, 540
Pragmatic Sanction, 435
Prelude to the Afternoon of a Faun
(Debussy), 676
Presbyterian Church (Church of
Scotland), 124, 232
Pride and Prejudice (Austen), 556
Prince, The (Machiavelli), 25–26, 29,
31–33
Prince and the Pauper, The
(Twain), 119
Principia Mathematica (Newton),
318, 319, 339–40, 341–46
Privateers, 122
Program music, 507
Proletariat, 553, 558
Prophet Mohammed, 704
Protectionism, 547
Protectorate, 237–38
Protectorates, 704
Protestant Reformation, 4, 51–64
Calvin, John and, 77
counter reformation, 57–58, 248
creativity and, 63–64
England and, 60–63
Eramus and, 103
France and, 59–60
French-speaking Switzerland and
John Calvin, 59
German-speaking Switzerland and
Ulrich Zwingli, 58
Henry VIII and, 62–63
Luther, Martin and, 65–66
Martin Luther, 51–57
music and, 261
timeline, 64
Prussia
Franco-Prussian War, 690
Frederick II, 426–29
pre World War I, 689–90
Ptolemaic model of the universe,
306–7
Ptolemy, 306
Pulitzer, Joseph, 604
Pursuit of Love, The (Fragonard), 445
Pythagoras, 262–63, 301–2, 636

Q
Quantitative rigor (Lavoisier), 322
Quantum theory, 635, 637–38
Queen Christina, 316, 590
Queen Victoria, 587
Quintessence, 302

R
Railroads, 543
Rape of Proserpina (Persephone)
(Bernini), 253
Raphael, 43–45
Rasputin, 697
Ravel, Maurice, 676
Realism, 49
Recapitulation, 453
Reconstruction, 601
Recumbent Figure (Moore), 764
Red Room, The (Matisse), 673
Red scare, 762
Reductionism (Descartes), 315,
630, 639
Rehearsal of a Ballet on Stage
(Degas), 668
fig, 669
Reichstag (German parliament), 707
Reign of Terror, 490
Religion. *See also* Protestant
Reformation
in Elizabethan England, 117, 122
Religion (First Estate), 4
Rembrandt, 234, 258–59
Renaissance, 664. *See also* Early
Renaissance; Elizabethan
England; Northern
Renaissance
Machiavelli and, 29
vs. Baroque scientific thinking,
299–301
vs. Baroque style of painting, 251
Renaissance art, principal
characteristics of, 49
Renaissance man, 36, 47–48
Renaissance music, 45–47
Renoir, Pierre Auguste, 668
Requiem (Berlioz), 507
Restoration, 238
Revolutionaries, 355
Reynolds, Joshua, 445–46, 501, 503
Rhapsody in Blue (Gershwin), 718
Richard II (Shakespeare), 115
Riemann, Bernhard, 637
Riemenschneider, Tilman, 98
Right wing (conservatives), origin
of term, 488

Rights
  individual vs. group, 4
  universal, 552–53
Rigoletto (Verdi), 511
Rime of the Ancient Mariner
  (Coleridge), 506
Ring Cycle (Wagner), 509
Rip Van Winkle (Irving), 595
River societies, 3
Roaring Twenties, 712–13
Robespierre, Maximilien, 490–91
Robinson Crusoe (Defoe), 360
Rockefeller, John D., 604
Rococo, 443–47
  architecture, 446–47
  art, 444–46
  timeline, 460
Rodin, Auguste, 675
Rohe, Ludwig Mies Van Der, 716
Roman Empire, 9
Romance languages, 117
Romanoff family, 241
Romans, 3
Romantic Period. *See* Romanticism
Romanticism, 501–17, 664
  defined, 502–3
  feelings about, 515–17
  literature
    Alexandre Dumas, 504
    Dumas, Alexadre, 525, 527–30
    Johann Wolfgang von Goethe,
      503–4
    Leo Tolstoy, 505
    Lord George Gordon Byron, 506
    Mary Wollstonecraft Shelley, 505
    Percy Bysshe Shelley, 505
    Samuel Taylor Coleridge, 506
    Scott, Sir Walter, 519, 521–24
    Sir Walter Scott, 504
    Victor Hugo, 504–5
    William Wordsworth, 506
  music, 506–12
    Beethoven's bridge between the
      Classical and Romantic
      periods, 506–7
    Franz Liszt, 509
    Franz Schubert, 507
    Frederic Chopin, 508
    Giuseppe Verdi, 510–12
    Hector Berlioz, 507
    Peter Ilych Tchaikovsky, 512
    Richard Wagner, 509–10
  painting, 512–15
    Eugene Delacroix, 514
    Francisco Goya, 512–13

    John Constable, 514
    Joseph Mallord William
      Turner, 515
    timeline, 517
Romeo and Juliet (Shakespeare), 141,
  203–13
  Act I, 203–5
  Act II, 205–8
  Act V, 208–13
Romeo and Juliet (Tchaikovsky), 512
Roosevelt, Franklin Delano, 713–14
Rosetta Stone, 493
Rouen Cathedral paintings
  (Monet), 667
  fig, 668
Rough wooing, 123
Rousseau, Jean Jacques, 369–71
  life of, 419
  Social Contract, The, 419, 421–23
  Thoreau, Henry and, 613
Rowling, J.K., 763
Rubens, Peter Paul, 258
Rucker, Rudy, 639
Rules, in Classical period, 458–60
Rump Parliament, 237
Russia
  Catherine the Great, 429–35
  imperialism and, 591–92
  monarchies in, 240–42
  post-World War I, 705
  territory added by Peter the Great,
    map, 243
  Triple Entente, 690
  war with Napoleon, 497–98
  in World War II, 738–39
Russian Revolution, 697–98

S
St. Augustine, 11, 27, 60
St. Bartholomew's Day Massacre, 60
St. Crispin's Day speech, 135
St. George (Donatello), 21
St. Mary Magdalene, 22
St. Peter's Basilica, 252
St. Peter's Square, fig, 252
Salvation Through Faith Alone
  (Luther), 65, 67
Santa Fe Trail, 599
Santa Maria Novella, 19
Sanzio, Raffaello, 43–45
Sartre, Jean-Paul, 763
Saturn Devouring One of His Sons
  (Goya), 513
Satyagraha (Gandhi), 710
Saudis, 705

Savonarola, 24–25, 36
Scarlet Letter, The (Hawthorne), 595
Schoenberg, Arnold, 676
School of Athens (Raphael),
  43–44, 98
Schrödinger, Erwin, 635
Schubert, Franz, 507
Science
  cause and effect, 630
  challenges to traditional science,
    637–40
  Charles Darwin, 631, 633–35
  classical (Greece and Rome), 301–3
  creativity in, 772
  determinism, 630
  Louis Pasteur, 631–33
  Medieval, 303
  objectivity, 630–31
  quantum theory, 635
  reductionism, 630
  scientific progress, 629–30
  theory of relativity, 637
  timeline, 643
  twentieth-century, 635–37
  twenty-first century, 640–43
  uncertainty principle, 636
  vs technology, 304
Science and Its Ways of Knowing
  (Hatton and Plouffe), 641, 642
Science fiction, 763
Scientific Awakening, 299–325
  Bacon, Francis and, 312–14
  Baroque vs. Renaissance, 300–301
  Copernicus, Nicolas and, 305–8
  Descartes, René and, 314–16
  Galilei, Galileo and, 308–11
  Kepler, Johannes and, 311
  Lavoisier, Antoine and, 322–23
  Newton, Isaac and, 316–22
  science, technology, and theory,
    303–5
  summary of contributions to
    scientific method, 323–25
  summary of intellectual situation in
    17th century, 324
  timeline, 325
  worldly analysis, chart, 324
Scientific Method, 314
  contributions by scientists,
    chart, 325
  social problems and, 353–54
Scopes Trial, 634
Scotland, Elizabethan England and,
  123–24
Scott, Sir Walter, 504

Ivanhoe, 519, 521–24
   life of, 519
Scream, The (Munch), 673
Sculpture, 675–76
   in early Renaissance, 18–22
Second Continental Congress,
   466–67, 469
Second Estate, 3–4, 218, 487–88
Second Treatise of Civil Government
   (Locke), 359
Secularism, 4
Segregation, 601
Self Reliance (Emerson), 597, 609,
   611–12, 613
Serbia, World War I and, 692–93
Seurat, Georges, 668–69
Seven Years War (French and Indian
   War), 427, 462, 463
Seventeenth century, monarchs in,
   217–20
Seymour, Jane, 63
Sfumato (smoky), 40, 49
Shakespeare, William, 127–38
   comedies of, 134–35
   creativity and, 769
   Globe Theatre, 130
   Hamlet, 143–201
   historical plays of, 135
   list of plays and major
      poems, 129
   Romeo & Juliet, 141, 203–13
   sonnets of, 138, 142, 215–16
   tragedies of, 135–38
   use of language of, 130–34
   works of, 141–42
Shelley, Mary Wollstonecraft, 505
Shelley, Percy Bysshe, 505
Short History of Technology, A (Derry
   and Williams), 537
Sigismund, 53
Simonton, Keith, 2–3
Simony, 51
Sinclair, Upton, 623, 625–28
Sistine Chapel, 42–43
Sixth Symphony (Pastoral Symphony)
   (Beethoven), 507
Slavery, in United States, 600
Sleeping Beauty (Tchaikovsky), 512
Sleepwalkers, The (Koestler), 308
Sloane, Alfred P., 604
Small "c" creativity, 3
Smith, Adam, 366, 553
Smith, Joseph, 599
Smith, William, 543
Snow, C.P., 777

Social Contract, The (Rousseau),
   369–70, 371, 419, 421–23
Social usefulness, 556
Society of Jesus (Jesuits), 57–58
Sonata-allegro form, 453–54
Sonatas, 261, 452–54
Song of Hiawatha, The
   (Longfellow), 595
Sonnets, Shakespeare, 138, 142,
   215–16
Sons of Liberty, 464
Sophoclean defeat, 136
South America, Spanish imperialism
   in, 590
Soviet Union, post-World War I, 705
Spain
   Charles III, 434–35
   Elizabethan England and, 124–26
   imperialism and, 590
Spanish-American War, 594
Spanish Armada, 126
Spanish period, 4
Special Theory of Relativity
   (Bohm), 641
Spenser, Edmund, 127
Spinning frame, 539
Spinning jenny, 538–39
Spinsters, 538
Sponsors, in Renaissance, 13–18
SS, 707
Stadtholder (Dutch province),
   233, 238
Stalin, Josef, 705
Stalingrad, 738
Stanley, Henry Morton, 588
Starry Night (Van Gogh), 671
   fig, 672
Steam engines, 542
Steam-of-consciousness, 717
Stock market crash of 1929, 713
   impact on Germany, 706–7
Story of English, The (McCrum, Cran,
   and MacNeil), 131–32
Stradivari, 261
Stranger, The (Camus), 763
Strathern, Paul, 323
Strauss, Richard, 676
Stravinsky, Igor, 676, 755
Structure of Scientific Revolutions, The
   (Kuhn), 639, 655, 657–62
Stuart, James, 124
Stuart, Mary, 238–39
Sturm and Drang (Goerthe), 503
Sufferings of Young Werther (Goerthe),
   503–4

Suffrage, 712
Sullivan, Louis, 715–16
Sun King. *See* Louis XIV
Sun Yat-sen, 711
Sunday on La Grande Jatte, A
   (Seurat), 669
   fig, 670
Sunflowers (Van Gogh), 672
Supper at Emmaus (Caravaggio), 255
Surprise Symphony (Haydn), 454
Surrealism, 715
Surrender of Breda, The (Velazquez),
   232, 257
Sweden, Gustavus III, 434
Swift, Jonathan, 361, 362–65
   Gulliver's Travels, 395, 397–401
   life of, 395
   Modest Proposal, A, 395, 403–7
Switzerland
   French-speaking Protestant
      Reformation, 59
   German-speaking Protestant
      Reformation, 58
Symphonie Fantastique (Berlioz), 507
Symphonies, 506–7
Symphony No. 6 (Pathétique), 512
Synchronicity, 638–39
Syria, 704, 705

T
Tabula rasa, 461
Taiwan, 711
Take the "A" Train (Ellington), 718
Tallyrand, Charles de, 554
Tamerlane and Other Poems (Poe),
   596
Tariffs, 712
Tartars (Mongols), 241
Tchaikovsky, Peter Ilych, 512
Technology, 304–5
   American, 601–4
   art and, 663–67
   creativity in, 772–73
   vs. science, 304
Technology and the Quality of Life
   (Custer), 772–73
Telegraph, 603
Tell-Tale Heart, The (Poe), 596
Temperament (Isacoff), 253, 263
Tempering, 261, 263
Tennis Court Oath (France), 487
Tennyson, Lord Alfred, 605,
   607–8
Terrorists, recruiting, 700
Teutonic Knights, 426

Texas, 590
  independence from Mexico, 600
Textiles, Industrial Revolution,
  537–40
Thales, 301–2
Theory, 303–4
Theory of evolution, 645
Theory of relativity, 637–38
Theotokopoulos, Domenikos, 256
Theresa, Maria, 435–37
Thermidorian Reaction (France),
  491–92
Thinker, The (Rodin), 675
Third Estate, 3–4, 218, 486–88, 549
Third Reich, 707
Third Symphony (Beethoven), 458,
  495, 501
Thirty Years War, 4, 57, 220–23
  population losses in Germany,
  map, 223
Thoreau, Henry David, 585,
  597, 710
  life of, 613
  Walden, 613, 615–16
Thorpe, Scott, 734, 773, 775, 777
Three Musicians (Picasso), 674
Three Musketeers, The (Dumas), 224,
  504, 525, 527–30
Timelines
  absolute monarchies, 245
  American Revolution, 473
  Baroque, 273–74
  consequences of Industrial
  Revolution, 561
  contemporary, 766
  early Renaissance, 27–28
  Elizabethan England, 140
  enlightened despots, 441
  Enlightenment, 374
  French Revolution and Napoleon,
  499–500
  high Renaissance, 49–50
  Impressionism, 678
  Industrial Revolution, 547
  Northern Renaissance, 102
  post-World War I, 719
  Protestant Reformation, 64
  Romantic Period, 517
  science, 643
  Scientific Awakening, 325
  United States, 604
  World War I, 702
  World War II, 749
Titian (Vecillio Tiziano), 45
Tiziano, Vecellio, 45

*To the Christian Nobility of the
  German Nation* (Luther), 65,
  71–74
Tocqueville, Alexis de, 471–72
  Democracy in America, 475,
  477–82
  life of, 475
Toffler, Alvin, 5, 547
Tolkien, J.R.R., 301
Tolstoy, Leo, 505
Tom Jones (Fielding), 361
Townsend Acts, 464
Tragedies, Shakespeare, 135–38
Trans-Caucasia, 705
Transcendentalism, 372
  Emerson, Ralph and, 609
  in United States, 596–98
Transjordan, 704
Transportation, Industrial Revolution,
  542–43
Travel, in Renaissance, 12–13
Treatise on Tolerance (Voltaire), 409,
  411–14
Treaty of Paris, 469
Treaty of Utrecht, 231
Treaty of Versailles, 699–701, 707, 713
Trench warfare, 694–95
Trial, The (Kafka), 717
Tribute Money, The (Masaccio), 19, 21
Trickle-down approach, 713
Triple Alliance (Germany, Austria,
  Italy), 690
Triple Entente (Russia, France, Great
  Britain), 690
Trotsky, Leon, 705
Truman, Harry, 746
Tuchman, Barbara, 700
Tudor, Mary, 62–63, 119, 123–24,
  125. *See also* Bloody Mary
Turkey, 704
Turner, Joseph Mallord William, 515
Turning Point, The (Capra), 637
Two Men at a Table (Heckel), 674
2001: A Space Odyssey (Clarke), 764
Two Treatises of Government (Locke),
  353, 381, 385–87
Tyndale, William, 61, 139
Tyndale Bible, 61, 139

U
Ukraine, 705
Ulster Provisional Militia
  (Provos), 709
Ulysses (Joyce), 717
Uncertainty Principle, 636

United States
  Civil War, 600–601
  contemporary, 761–63
  entrepreneurs, 604
  extending the nation, 598–600
  imperialism in, 593–94
  inventions, 602–3
  Japan and, 594
  literature, 594–96
  manifest destiny, 594, 598–600
  Mexico and, 590
  technology and entrepreneurship,
  601–4
  timeline, 604
  transcendentalism, 596–98
United States period, 5
Universal rights, 55–553
Universities, growth of, 12
Urban VIII, 311
Urbanization, 551
Utilitarianism, 556–57
Utilitarianism (Mill), 563, 565–67
Utopia (More), 61–62, 81, 83–91
Utopian society, 61

V
Vaccinations, 632
Valley Forge, 468
Valois dynasty, 59–60
Value, 1–2
Value American independence and,
  471–72
Values, contemporary, 765–66
Van Dyke, Anthony, 259
Vanderbilt, Cornelius, 604
Velazquez, Diego, 232, 256–57
Venetian School, 45
Verdi, Giuseppe, 510–12, 770
Vermeer, Jan, 259
Verrocchio, Andrea, 36–37
Versailles Palace, 253–54
Vertical perspective, 20
Victor Emmanuel II, 593
Vienna
  Congress of Vienna, 498–99
  Germany, Italy and, map, 451
Viennese Classical style, 450–52
Vietnam War, 757–58·
View over Mont Sainte-Victoire
  (Cezanne), 670
  fig, 671
Vikings, 241
Vinci, Leonardo da, 36–41, 59
  creativity and, 768
  inventions of, fig, 39

VINE, 2, 18
Violin, invention of, 261
Visual art, of Northern Renaissance, 97–101
Vivaldi, Antonio, 264
Vocal music, 101
Voltaire (Francis Marie Arouet), 368–69
   "If God Did Not Exist He Would Have to Be Invented," 409, 415
   Letters on England, 410, 417–18
   life of, 409
   Treatise on Tolerance, 409, 411–14

W

Wagner, Richard, 509–10
Walden (Thoreau), 597, 614, 615–16
Walpole, Robert, 437–38
Wandering Jew, The (Byron), 506
War and Peace (Tolstoy), 505
War of 1812, 599
War of Spanish Succession, 231, 240
Warhol, Andy, 764
Warsaw Pact, 756
Washington, George, 468, 471, 484
Wateau, Jean Antoine, 444
Water Lilies (Monet), 667
Waterloo, 495, 498
Watermusic (Handel), 265
Watt, James, 542
Wealth, in Renaissance, 13
Wealth of Nations (Smith), 366, 553
Weimar Republic (Germany), 706
Well Tempered Clavier (Bach), 263, 266–67
"Wellington's Victory" (Beethoven), 495
Wenceslas, 52
Western Roman Empire, 3
What Went Wrong? (Bernard), 700
When in the Hour of Utmost Need, 271

Whitman, Walt, 596
   Leaves of Grass, 617, 619–21
   life of, 617
Whitney, Eli, 602
Wies church, 447
William, Frederic, 234
William and Mary, 238–39
William I of Orange, 232
William III of Orange, 238–39
William of Prussia, 592
William Pitt the Younger, 438–39
William the Silent, 233
Williams, T.I., 537
Wilson, Woodrow, 712
Wordsworth, William, 506
Working conditions, Industrial Revolution, 550–52
World War I, 687–702. *See also* Post-World War I
   alliances, 689–91, 696–97
   causes
      anti-Semitism, 689
      Austro-Hungarian empire, 689
      China, 688
      Germany's emergence as a nation, 688
      Japan, 688
      Ottoman empire, 689
   creativity and, 701–2
   ending, 698–99
   goals of each of the major powers on the eve of, 690
   Russian Revolution, 697–98
   timeline, 702
   Treaty of Versailles, 699–701
   trench warfare, 694–95
World War II, 733–46
   Allied victories, 740–44
   atomic bomb attacks on Japan, 746
   Battle of Britain, 736–38
   Battle of the Bulge, 744

   Blitz of London, 737
   D-Day, 741
   Dunkirk, 736
   Europe, Axis and Allied attacks of, map, 743
   German supremacy, 734–36
   Germany's invasion of Poland, 708, 734
   island hopping, 745
   island hopping, map, 742
   Japan and, 739–40
   kamikaze pilots, 746
   map of Axis control of Europe, 741
   Marshall Plan, 745
   Midway, 745
   Pacific Theater, map, 742
   Pearl Harbor, 740
   Russia and, 738–39
   timeline, 749
   Yalta Conference, 744
Wright, Frank Lloyd, 716
   creativity and, 771
Writers, industrialization and, 555–56
Wuthering Heights (Bronte), 556
Wycliffe, John, 52
Wycliffe Bible, 61

X

Xavier, Francis, 57

Y

Yalta Conference, 744
Young, Brigham, 599
Young Turks, 689
Yüan Shi-kai, 711
Yugoslavia, 704

Z

Zulu wars, 588
Zurich Protestants, 58
Zwingli, Ulrich, 58